COTINGAS
AND
MANAKINS

COTINGAS AND MANAKINS

Guy M. Kirwan and Graeme Green

Illustrated by Eustace Barnes

With a photographic contribution by Hadoram Shirihai
from the collection of the
Photographic Handbook to Birds of the World (Jornvall & Shirihai)

CHRISTOPHER HELM
LONDON

For the late David Snow – unparalleled expert on cotingas and
manakins, without whose groundwork this book
would be far poorer

For Richard O. Prum – devoted student of manakins for more
than two decades, whose many keynote contributions have
undoubtedly inspired many others to work with Pipridae

For Ercilia Veronica Nogueira Gama – *Quando me chamou, eu vim;
quando dei por mim, tava aqui; quando me achei, me perdi; quando vi
você, me apaixonei.* GMK

Published in 2011 by Christopher Helm, an imprint of Bloomsbury Publishing Plc
49–51 Bedford Square, London, WC1B 3DP

ISBN (print) 978-0-7136-6025-8
ISBN (e-pub) 978-1-4081-5674-2
ISBN (e-pdf) 978-1-4081-5673-5

A CIP catalogue record for this book is available from the British Library

Commissioning Editor: Nigel Redman
Project Editor: Jim Martin

Design by Julie Dando at Fluke Art

Printed and bound in China by C&C Offset Printing Co Ltd

10 9 8 7 6 5 4 3 2 1

Cover illustration: Guianan Cocks-of-the-Rock at lek *by Eustace Barnes*

Visit www.acblack.com/naturalhistory to find out more about our authors and their books. You will
find extracts, author interviews and our blog, and you can sign up for newsletters to be the first to
hear about our latest releases and special offers.

CONTENTS

PREFACE

A flash of red as a 'thunderbolt' male Andean Cock-of-the-Rock *Rupicola peruvianus* crosses a forest trail unannounced ahead of you. The stunning turquoise-blue of a Spangled Cotinga *Cotinga cayana* perched high in the canopy against a still latent yet steamy blueness of an early Amazonian morning. The cacophony of sound and vision that represents a Long-tailed Manakin's *Chiroxiphia linearis* lek in a Middle American rainforest. What birdwatcher could not thrill to such experiences? Experiences that are still available to us at the end of the first decade of the 21st century, despite the ever-worsening state of the Earth's biodiversity in our world seemingly so irreversibly dedicated to consumption and 'development'.

The suboscine passerines of South and Central America comprise one of the most diverse assemblages of birds in the world. Furthermore, they probably epitomise the birds of the Neotropical region as much as, or more than, any other group, and due to a combination of rarity and beauty they number some of the major 'prizes' for visiting or resident birdwatchers alike. Indeed, the song of the Screaming Piha *Lipaugus vociferans*, now known to be the 'loudest' bird on Earth, is used by moviemakers to epitomise jungle sounds the world over, not just in its native South America! Within this enormous assemblage of over 1,000 species, there is a particularly large grouping of suboscine passerines loosely referred to as the tyrannids, i.e. the flycatcher-like birds (becards, tityras, etc.), including the cotingas and manakins. Hardly anyone who has studied the plates in any of the standard Neotropical field guides can have failed to be stirred by these exciting-looking birds.

Cotingas and manakins are considered families in their own right, but instead of the two families that we had originally imagined covering here, this work now treats species belonging to at least five families (for a full discussion see 'Systematics' and the taxonomy and nomenclature section in 'How to use this book'). Many of the higher-level systematic changes have been wrought by the increasing application of molecular techniques. Cotingidae and Pipridae, and their allies as included here, contain some of the most extravagant and bizarre birds found in the Neotropics, as well as others that vie with the birds-of-paradise of the Australian–Papuan region for both their immense beauty and great interest to biologists. Although they do not possess quite the same mystique to the keenest observers as those denizens of the forest floor such as the antpittas, they do exhibit a much wider range of forms and colours than most other suboscine groups. They range in size from the large fruitcrows to the diminutive Kinglet Calyptura *Calyptura cristata* and some equally tiny manakins, and in colour from some of the most stunningly beautiful of all Neotropical birds, such as the cocks-of-the-rock (*Rupicola*), to amongst the plainest, for example the two *Tyranneutes* tyrant-manakins. They occur in most habitats from the tall forests of the Amazonian lowlands right up to the Andean treeline, and it is generally only in a few far-flung points of the Neotropical compass that the dedicated birder or field worker would fail to register at least some cotingas or manakins. Their abundance is such that they include some of the commonest members of local avifaunas (especially some Pipridae such as Golden-headed Manakin *Pipra erythrocephala* or Blue Manakin *Chiroxiphia caudata*), as well as some of the rarest; the southeast Brazilian endemic Kinglet Calyptura was considered possibly extinct until its rediscovery in 1996, but since then has slunk back into obscurity. The two groups also contain species that are especially difficult to observe due to their relatively secretive habits, rather than their rarity, as well other, more arboreal, species that regularly perch out in the open within the canopy of emergent trees. Despite this latter propensity, particularly marked in several members of the Cotingidae, our knowledge of their life histories remains no better than those of more skulking species. Nonetheless, with the increasing use of canopy towers, especially in Amazonia, modern-day observers are fortunate in having many more opportunities than their forebears to increase their knowledge of these and other birds. One common feature that, to some extent, 'binds' the two groups are their lekking strategies, which behaviour often offers much the best insight into the lives of these fascinating birds. Indeed, leks of many species have been intensively studied for some time, aided by their great lek site fidelity. Nonetheless, it should be made explicit that not all species covered herein use leks, indeed many do not, but it is the case that cotingas and manakins include some of the best-studied lek species in the Neotropics.

The aim of the book is simple: to summarise all of the available information on cotingas and manakins in such a way that readers are enthused to discover more about the birds themselves. What qualifies us to engage in this task? Put simply, our extensive recent experience in the region, entailing a well-marked field-oriented approach to the book, although museum-based research has not been ignored. Most of the latter load eventually fell to GMK, who worked at a number of institutions detailed in the Acknowledgements, but EB too made many visits to the Natural History Museum at Tring while preparing the plates and GG also worked at the same institution. Between us, we have field experience of all but a relative handful of the species (e.g. Golden-crowned Manakin *Lepidothrix vilasboasi*) covered herein, with far-western Amazonian Brazil virtually the only area where we lack relevant field time. The book's illustrator, EB, and first author,

GMK, are both tour leaders with extensive field experience throughout South America, in particular, whilst GG has held a deep interest in the birds of the entire region since the late 1980s. Both authors were initially involved in the administration of the relatively recently founded Neotropical Bird Club, and GMK still edits the Club's respected journal *Cotinga*.

Although this book leans as much as possible on our personal field experience, the publications of ornithological pioneers such as Alexander Skutch, Helmut Sick and Ted Parker, and now those of a new generation of men and women have provided the cornerstone for much of the information contained in these pages. The tour de force about cotingas was the late David Snow's marvellous book *Cotingas*, illustrated by Martin Woodcock, published as long ago as 1982. David also prepared the texts on both cotingas and manakins for the relevant volume of the highly regarded *Handbook of the Birds of the World*. His was a rare genius; a respected museum worker also steeped in fieldcraft, he studied cotingas and manakins throughout many parts of the Neotropics, from southeast Brazil to Trinidad & Tobago, Colombia and Costa Rica. It has been our privilege to walk some of the same trails and share his conversation. Many of his publications, and those of his wife Barbara, remain classics within their field. Our knowledge of the natural history of several species of Cotingidae and Pipridae studied by the Snows has not been substantially advanced since their pioneering work. We trust that what is contained in these pages is relevant, contemporary and of interest to anyone fascinated by tropical birds, particularly those from the 'bird continent', and that David would have approved of our efforts.

ACKNOWLEDGEMENTS

We are grateful to the following museum personnel for permitting us (principally GMK) to examine specimens of Cotingidae and Pipridae in their care, and for access to library facilities at the same institutions: Robert Prŷs-Jones, Mark Adams and Alison Harding (The Natural History Museum, Tring, UK); Michael Brooke (Cambridge University Museum of Zoology, Cambridge, UK); Hein van Grouw and René Dekker (Naturalis, Leiden, The Netherlands); Kees Roselaar and Tineke Prins (Zoological Museum, University of Amsterdam, The Netherlands); John Bates, David Willard and Mary Hennen (Field Museum of Natural History, Chicago, USA); Ghisselle Alvarado and Silvia Elena Bolaños (Museo Nacional de Costa Rica, San José, Costa Rica); Mauricio Vargas (Museo Ecuatoriano de Ciencias Naturales, Quito, Ecuador); Mario Cohn-Haft and Ingrid Torres de Macedo (Instituto Nacional de Pesquisas da Amazônia, Manaus, Brazil); Marcos Raposo, Renata Stopiglia and Jorge Nacinovic (Museu Nacional, Rio de Janeiro, Brazil); Luís Fábio Silveira (Museu de Zoologia da Universidade de São Paulo, Brazil); Miguel Lentino and Robin Restall (Phelps Collection, Caracas, Venezuela); and Vladimir Loskot (Zoological Institute, Russian Academy of Sciences, St Petersburg, Russia). At these institutions, I must make special mention of Marcos Raposo and all the 'gang' at MNRJ, who have made that museum very much a 'home from home', John Bates and Shannon Hackett, who twice made me a welcome guest in Chicago, and all of the staff at NHM for their constant good-natured assistance with this and many other projects. GMK also thanks John & Effie Warr, Roy & Moira Hargreaves, William Price, Ron Demey and Rita Swinnen, who proffered accommodation during some of his many museum visits. Marcelo Vasconcelos kindly provided data on specimens held in the ornithological collection of the Departamento de Zoologia, at the Universidade Federal de Minas Gerais, Belo Horizonte, Brazil. In addition to Alison Harding, we thank Travis Rosenberry of the Peregrine Fund library for providing copies of many items of vital literature. The ever-vivacious Amy Chernasky at Lynx Edicions gave us a head start with our bibliography by providing a copy of David Snow's working list of literature for the cotinga and manakin texts for the *Handbook of the Birds of the World*. A great many other ornithologists, too numerous to name individually here, have assisted by providing copies of specific papers, usually but not exclusively their own. Each one has been of value.

Ornithologists and birdwatchers who have assisted our endeavours by providing unpublished information, or clarifications to published data, include the following: Adrian Azpiroz, David Capper, Chris Collins, Thomas Donegan (for many unpublished mensural data from Colombia), Daniel Firme, David Fisher, Jeremy Flanagan, Juan Freile, Arthur Grosset, Renato Gaban-Lima, Ron Hoff, Jon Hornbuckle (mensural data from Bolivia, Ecuador and Peru), Fernando D'Horta, Peter Hosner, Niels Krabbe, Daniel F. Lane, Jeremy Minns, Fábio Olmos, José Fernando Pacheco, Thomas S. Schulenberg, the late David Snow, Thomas Stuart, Joseph Tobias, Andrew Whittaker and Kevin J. Zimmer.

Kevin Easley of Costa Rica Gateway organised and planned, and Jason Horn and Ernesto Carman guided, a special and most successful trip to Costa Rica that enabled GMK to study several species of cotingas and manakins in the field. Rod McCann and Jonathan Price helped share his costs. Furthermore, Jonathan and William Price joined several other recent trips to various parts of the Neotropics, during which Cotingidae and Pipridae were special foci. Most recently, Alejandro Solano-Ugalde introduced GMK to the Mashpi road area of northwest Ecuador and its superb birdlife. Numerous local guides and lodge owners, from far-flung reaches of the Neotropics and over the course of many years, went out of the way to share their hard-won expertise or to make us unusually welcome guests on their property. All have contributed in some measure to the success of this project.

Particular gratitude is due to Lina Marcela for making available mensural and other data for Colombian cotingas and manakins held in the ProAves database, as well as all of the observers who contributed their information (who are mentioned in the relevant species accounts) and Thomas Donegan, once again, for initiating access to this fantastic data source. For reviews of the advancing texts, we thank Thomas Donegan (Colombian species), Jeremy Flanagan (Peruvian Plantcutter *Phytotoma raimondii*), Harold Greeney (Ecuadorian breeding data), Johan Ingels (Guianan species), Alexander Lees (Amazonian Brazil and mass data), Huw Lloyd (Peruvian species), José Fernando Pacheco (Brazilian species), Steven Sevillano (*Zaratornis*) and Joe Tobias (selected Bolivian species) for their many critical and useful comments. Needless to say, any errors of omission or commission remain ours.

Graeme and I take this last opportunity to salute the late Barbara and David Snow, outstanding fieldworkers both, whose many published contributions on cotingas and manakins, and frugivory, were not only singularly invaluable in the production of this book, but in many instances remain unsurpassed as single-species studies of their subjects. David, in particular, with his gentlemanly manner, will be much missed by both of us, and a great many others, for his patient, wise, kind and forever modest words of advice and assistance.

GMK is especially grateful to Hadoram Shirihai who has funded much of his fieldwork in Brazil and elsewhere in South and Middle America since 2006, enabling valuable field experience of many poorly known birds that feature in this book. Furthermore, Hadoram also made an enormous contribution to the photographic collection for the present work, all of which images were taken as part of his work for the forthcoming *Photographic Handbook to Birds of the World* (Jornvall and Shirihai, A&C Black). The talented bird artist and observer Dave Beadle, who has joined me on many trips to the 'bird continent' over the past two decades, has always been a critical and much-valued field companion and friend. With time and age, we spend much less time chasing down owls and nightjars than we did formerly, but we do know a little more about those infuriating Tyrannidae than in the early days! Dave also provided more 'material' assistance to the project by measuring some Cotingidae and Pipridae held in the Royal Ontario Museum, Toronto, Canada.

It is a special pleasure to pay tribute to the skill and sheer hard work of Julie Dando who, as she has done countless times before with other bird books, has transformed our texts, photographs and plates into a unitary whole which we could take much greater pride in.

I have enjoyed an especially close relationship with Brazil for the last 16 years: it is always a special feeling to return there, whether I have been away a few weeks, or a few months (fortunately never longer). For a little under half of that period there has been another special 'draw', apart from all the amazing birds, and the great food and attitude to life of my adopted 'povo', the Cariocas. And, therefore, my most heartfelt and tender acknowledgement is reserved for my very own 'cotinga', the most lovely of them all, who although she does not share my love of birds in wild places, travels everywhere and always with me in spirit – Veronica Nogueira Gama.

Guy M. Kirwan

My first full day's birding in the Neotropics started around a hotel in Caracas, Venezuela, and ended in Guatopo National Park, where virtually the first bird I saw was a stunning male Wire-tailed Manakin *Pipra filicauda*, resplendent yet immobile, which permitted protracted views. Thereafter, cotingas and manakins became the 'stars' of many further visits to the 'bird continent'. A Scaled Fruiteater *Ampelioides tschudii* lit by the rising sun along the 'Old' Mindo Road in Ecuador, male Banded Cotingas *Cotinga maculata* in eastern Brazil, along with many others, ultimately led to a proposal being made to the late Christopher Helm, and Nigel Redman, then of Pica Press, with a view to publishing this book in two years!

However, *Cotingas and Manakins* has experienced a much-protracted gestation since the initial discussions among the original authors, leading to the book you finally hold in your hands 16 years later. I accept major responsibility for this, but my tardiness has resulted in a finer (and much more complete) tome than would have been the case if the original schedule had been kept. Advances in publishing and photography have permitted the inclusion of a fine selection of photographs, many of which simply could not have been taken two decades ago. Our thanks go to all of the photographers who submitted their work for publication; they are named on page 14. The artwork of my close friend, Eustace Barnes, has also been made more contemporary by him repainting virtually all of the plates, a decision entirely his own, but which demands commendation. The intervening years have provided Eustace with much relevant field experience, along with the concomitant rise in available images, enabling new interpretations of these wonderful birds. Work on the plates would have been immeasurably harder without the excellent facilities provided by the staff at the Natural History Museum in Tring, and Eustace and I express thanks to all of them for their assistance over the years.

I thank all those birders who responded to the original request for information and photographs in the journal *Cotinga*. Many gave freely of their data. Mark Pearman and David Willis were excellent repositories of knowledge, grounded in many trips to the Neotropics, and both were of considerable assistance. Some correspondents replied with lengthy contributions, such as Peter Boesman, who is, of course, well known for his CD-ROM guides to Neotropical birds. David and John Cooper sent copious notes on several species, as did Andrew Moon and Tony Smith. Other notable contributions came from Jan Zwaaneveld, Lyann Cormack, Barry Wright, Alice M. Geffen, Charles Davies, the late Bruce Forrester and Ottavio Janni. If I have neglected to mention anyone, please accept my apologies.

I also sincerely thank those companions who have joined me on field trips to the Neotropics. In no particular order, they are: Colin Bushell, John Mason, Simon Fogg, Cris Baker, Pete Naylor, Andrew Moon, Richard Bosanquet, Pete Colston, Paul Higson, Chris & Barbara Kightley, and Philip Whittington. They have endured my foibles with good grace, in particular my affinity to a certain football team. I have occasionally joined larger groups, and I also thank all the birders on those trips for their company; to the Manu Road in November 2000, the expedition organised by Barry Walker to see Scarlet-banded Barbet *Capito wallacei* in

2002, a trip to eastern Brazil in 2004 and to northern Peru in 2005 (organised by Eustace Barnes). I express my thanks to Mercedes Ribandeira of the Neblina Forest tour company in Ecuador, who helped me visit the excellent Sacha Lodge. I have had the pleasure of meeting many fieldworkers based in Latin America, alas too many to be named, many of whom provided anecdotal information.

Major thanks go to my wife, Carole, and daughters, Louise and Julianna, for 'accommodating' my lengthy absences over the years, although some would say it might have been a blessing for them! My late parents, Fred and Sheila, always encouraged my interest in natural history and birds in particular; without their encouragement this interest may have waned. Their passing in 1997 left a big hole in my life, and to a significant extent 'put the brakes' on my contribution to this book. For reapplying momentum to the project, I have Nigel Redman and Jim Martin at A&C Black to thank for suggesting Guy Kirwan as a collaborator, and to Guy himself huge praise for ensuring the work's completion, so that these fantastic birds receive the treatment they undoubtedly deserve.

Graeme Green

This project would hardly have been possible without the encouragement, knowledge and dedication of a great many people, both professionals based in museums or universities, and amateurs whose field observations contribute so greatly to our knowledge. Much of my work has been undertaken at the Natural History Museum, Tring, and I am particularly indebted to Mark Adams, Dr Robert Prŷs-Jones and Michael Walters for their tireless enthusiasm for the project and for facilitating access to the specimen collection.

For a great deal of field assistance and encouragement during the lengthy gestation of this project, I also thank the late David Snow, Barry Walker, David Willis, the late Paul Coopmans, Gunnar Engblom, John Cox, Clifford & Dawn Frith, Lester Short and the late Jennifer Horne, Dr Charlotte Cook-Fuller, Nigel Lawson, Huw Lloyd, Jon Hornbuckle, János Oláh, Richard Webster, Rose-Ann Rowlett, John Rowlett, Robert Ridgely, Nigel Simpson, Geoff Kingery, Richard Schofield, Joseph Tobias, Alfredo Begazo, Sebastian Herzog, Bennett Hennessey and Howie Nielsen. Also, sincere thanks are due to all the many people I have travelled with throughout South America and without whom my knowledge of the continent's birds would be poorer. Special thanks are extended to my mother Joanna and wife Diana, without whose support I would not have been able to undertake either the fieldwork or prepare the plates.

Finally, I am indebted to the late Christopher Helm and Nigel Redman for their patience and encouragement during the many years that this book has been in preparation.

Eustace Barnes

HOW TO USE THIS BOOK

As should be expected, this book generally conforms to the generic nature of other titles in the Christopher Helm bird family series. One of the main differences compared with at least some of the other titles lies in the more 'artistic' style employed for the plates; the reasons for this change in emphasis are outlined below. Many of the books in the series have certainly been more identification oriented; however, to some extent, identification issues are of only peripheral concern with these groups of tropical, often extremely colourful birds. Nonetheless, wherever there is scope for potential confusion between species, this will be analysed as fully as possible or necessary.

The plates

Eustace Barnes has painted the 34 magnificent plates to illustrate this volume. From the start, we discussed our preferences with respect to the format of the plates, and we reached the conclusion that less 'stilted', more 'artistic' plates with some emphasis on background detail would be more attractive and aesthetically pleasing. In several cases, Eustace has attempted to portray the birds within their natural surroundings, for instance at lekking arenas. Although these are artistic impressions, we trust that they still convey scientific accuracy. The plates usually illustrate a male and female of the nominate race, where applicable. As a norm, juveniles and immatures are not illustrated, mainly because immature males resemble adult females, with the addition of 'splashes' of colour, and immature females are basically identical to adult females.

The photographs

We are delighted to augment Eustace's plates with a series of photographs illustrating as many species and obviously different plumages (including sexes and subspecies) as possible. These have been selected, where possible, to illustrate aspects of the identification and life history of the species concerned. The emphasis has been on field photographs, rather than in-the-hand images. Regrettably, there are a few instances where it proved impossible to source a usable image of the species in question. Arguably the most notable example is that of the near-mythical Kinglet Calyptura, where we are all too aware that no photograph of a live bird, published or otherwise, exists. All of us await the moment when this situation changes with more than a considerable degree of anticipation. We remain indebted to the following photographers who submitted their images for possible publication: Daniel Alarcón, Ciro Albano, Göran Altstedt, Nick Athanas, Juan Bahamon, Rafael Bessa, Dušan Brinkhuizen, Sávio Freire Bruno, Diego Calderón-Franco, César Cestari, Robin Chittenden, Marc Chrétien, Bernardo Clausi, Maxime Dechelle, Mark Dennis, Harvey van Diek, Lee Dingain, Steven Easley, Kevin Easley, Stuart Elsom, David Fisher, Roberto Gallardo, Steve Garvie, Philippe Geraut, Chris Gooddie, Arthur Grosset, Marc Guyt, Roy de Haas, Ron Hoff, Stefan Hohnwald, Jason Horn, Jon Hornbuckle, J. Jackson, Andrew Kratter, Manfred Kusch, Daniel Lebbin, Alexander C. Lees, Gabriel Leite, José Silverio Lemos, Huw Lloyd, James C. Lowen, Alexander More, Pete Morris, Paul Noakes, János Oláh, Fábio Olmos, Scott Olmstead, Leonardo Patrial, Otte Plantema, William Price, Alonso Quevedo (ProAves), Juan David Ramirez, Jaqueline Rizzi Fortuna, Hadoram Shirihai, David Southall, David Spelt, Pascal Studer, Alejandro Tabini, Johann Tasconn, Frederico Tavares, Moss Taylor, Joseph Tobias, Andrew Walker, Emilio White and Andrew Whittaker.

Taxonomy and nomenclature

Each species is introduced in a short paragraph outlining some aspect of interest unique to it, although any complex taxonomic discussion will be found in the main species text. Nonetheless, a significant number of species are part of well-defined superspecies groupings, and many are monotypic. In consequence, species-level taxonomy of many of the species covered herein, with a relative handful of notable exceptions, is comparatively lacking in controversy. The same, however, cannot be said for generic and family-level relationships. A full discussion of generic and family relationships appears in the review of Systematics (pp. 38–47) that immediately precedes the species accounts. Nonetheless, the current struggle for 'supremacy' between advocates of the Phylogenetic and Biological Species Concepts will doubtless lead to some revisions, but such upheaval is likely to produce fewer changes at lower taxonomic levels than in other groups such as tyrant flycatchers (Tyrannidae) or woodcreepers (Dendrocolaptidae).

The systematics of the cotingas and manakins have undergone considerable flux in the past two decades, especially during the last ten years, particularly with the advent and relatively widespread use of molecular methods to resolve taxonomic conundrums, although several papers by Rick Prum, in particular, prior to this were already bringing substantial clarification to long-standing errors in classification. The taxonomy employed herein for the majority of species initially followed that in Ridgely and Tudor (1994), with information and taxonomic decisions extrapolated from this reference work, and related publications, for Middle American species. In consequence, the plantcutters were included, but the tityras and becards (which were traditionally included within the Tyrannidae) were excluded. Enigmatic species such as Sharpbill *Oxyruncus cristatus* and Broad-billed Sapayoa *Sapayoa aenigma* were also included, if only to highlight the potential for confusion with sympatric, closely related species. Subsequently, various molecular studies have postulated numerous changes to the generic and family-level classifications employed in Ridgely and Tudor (1994). For example, both *Oxyruncus* and *Sapayoa* should probably be classified in different families, the former in its own family and *Sapayoa* with the otherwise exclusively Old World family Eurylaimidae. Both these recommendations are followed herein. Equally, a number of other genera have been found to lie outwith the Cotingidae and Pipridae, and to be better placed with the tityras and becards in a newly erected family, Tityridae. Examples include *Schiffornis*, *Piprites* and *Iodopleura*. Most recently, the genus *Calyptura* has been found to belong within the Tyrannidae (Ohlson *et al.* 2010). Despite this, we have persisted in including these 'traditional' cotingas and manakins, but have excluded tityras and becards. In contrast, because of the close relationship revealed between *Laniisoma* and *Laniocera* by some molecular studies, we made an 'eleventh-hour' decision to include the latter genus herein. Still other genera, for example *Phibalura*, are still not classified with certainty and might yet be proven to lie outwith Cotingidae, Tityridae or Tyrannidae; for now, we are content to maintain them within the first-named family. From this, it will be clear to even the most unobservant reader that this book covers species belonging to a mix of families and that we have failed to include all of those taxa in each of these families. Despite this rather haphazard end result, in large part the product of the relatively fast pace of new discoveries and our own slowness, we can at least report that all those species long considered cotingas and manakins have been included.

Many of the superspecies in the cotingas were formerly considered to comprise a single polytypic species, so the modern theme of 'splitting' has already occurred with many taxa, and this indeed was how many superspecies were treated by Snow (1982). There may still be 'cryptic' species to be 'found', such as the case with the recent splitting of *Neopelma aurifrons* into its two constituent taxa: Serra do Mar *N. chrysolophum* and Wied's Tyrant-Manakins *N. aurifrons* (Whitney *et al.* 1995). The polytypic Thrush-like Schiffornis *Schiffornis turdina* probably will be diagnosable into several phylogenetic, if not biological, species (see Nyári 2007). Much of the driving force behind these and other taxonomic revisions is being led by improved knowledge of vocalisations; indeed, some recently described species in other Neotropical families have been discovered purely by voice alone (e.g. Schulenberg and Parker 1997). Relatively speaking, many cotingas are not particularly vocal, so some historical taxonomic decisions have been based on less easily quantifiable morphological differences (i.e. it looks different, therefore it is different!). Where these taxa are not sympatric, as is the case with the *Carpodectes* 'white' cotingas for example, judgements on whether taxa have reached biological species level have been made arbitrarily, although they would surely be diagnosable as phylogenetic species, or as subspecies (*sensu* Remsen 2010). Here is unquestionably not the place to discuss the relative merits of the Biological Species Concept (BSC) in relation to any one of the several variations of the Phylogenetic Species Concept currently in use. Because the BSC remains in stronger currency among ornithologists, we are content to continue to discuss 'subspecies' herein. In this respect we welcome the timely contribution by Remsen (2010) to this ongoing debate and consider his riposte to comments, for example by Zink (2004), concerning species concepts and conservation to be especially persuasive. We also consider it worthwhile to draw interested readers' attention to the paper by Tobias *et al.* (2010) concerning robust application of the BSC to revising species limits.

The vexed question of universally agreed vernacular English names for all of the world's birds remains 'live'. However, with the relatively recent publication of the list of the International Ornithological Congress (Gill and Wright 2006), which is frequently updated online (see Acronyms used in the text), and a degree of overlap in personnel involved in the IOC committee and the production of other lists, for instance 'Howard & Moore' (Dickinson 2003), there is probably a greater level of homogeneity than might have been expected a couple of decades ago. Again, the basis for the vernacular names used here has been Ridgely and Tudor (1994, 2009), whilst Middle American species names by and large follow those used in Gill and Wright (2006).

Identification

This section provides a guide to the identification of similar, not necessarily closely related species. It commences with the bird's overall length, expressed in centimetres. These measurements are generally taken from the published literature, but supplemented by specimen label data where indicated as having been taken prior to death, i.e. total length was not measured by the authors. Where there are significant and obvious differences in the relative sizes of males and females, perhaps because of the presence of modified tail feathers, this is usually mentioned here. The text then goes on to discuss the identification of both sexes compared with similar species, including those in other groups, perhaps most especially tyrant flycatchers.

For males of many species, there are relatively few identification difficulties, given reasonable views, because a great many closely related taxa occur parapatrically or allopatrically. Knowledge of relative ranges is therefore important and often key to identifying, for instance, which species of red-headed and black-bodied *Pipra* manakin an observer is watching. Non-morphological clues, such as these, are always emphasised within the Identification section. Females of some cotingas, e.g. those of the genera *Carpodectes*, *Cotinga* and *Xipholena*, and a great many manakins are generally rather more challenging, especially given brief views and because of the often poor light in the forest. Again, however, range and altitude (as well as habitat) can be extremely important clues in the identification process, while overall size, bill size, tail length, bare-parts coloration and jizz can be especially instructive when attempting to separate what at first appear very similar females of many manakin species. At many localities, even comparatively species-rich sites in the subtropical Andes or the Amazon basin, it will generally be the case that only one, more occasionally two, species of a given genus of manakin occurs, making the identification process usually rather more straightforward than might initially seem likely. Nonetheless, separating female manakins still requires some practice and familiarity with the basic characters and jizz of the different genera, and initially will necessitate some exposure to them to gain a degree of familiarity. Following such groundwork, and coupled with a knowledge of range (both geographical and altitudinal), identification of these initially confusing basically yellow-and-green birds will often become relatively automatic, even if views are comparatively brief. Consequently, identification issues are often afforded less space than in some previous titles in this series.

Distribution

It is important to use this section in conjunction with the range map presented for each species. Some maps also indicate subspecies' ranges, particularly for those species in which specific limits are still under discussion. The distributional section usually commences with a general statement concerning the species' overall range; for example, if it is restricted to a certain part of South America – e.g. the Guianan Shield, the Atlantic Forest biome, or is endemic to a specific country – this will be stated at the outset. Thereafter, a more or less detailed statement of the species' range (usually, however, without reference to subspecies) will be outlined, largely based on and with regular reference to the published literature. As always in this book, specific facts are reasonably closely referenced, while simultaneously attempting to maintain readability. While the range map provides an at-a-glance 'overview' of a given species' range, the text enables the reader to fine-tune his or her understanding. Especially at the range limits, specific localities are frequently mentioned, in conjunction with the appropriate reference(s), enabling readers to more easily identify extensions to the range of a species as currently understood. This section closes with a résumé of each species' altitudinal range, usually illustrated with examples from various range states for those species of particularly broad geographical distribution. Several points should be borne in mind, when reviewing both the text and the maps, as follows. The maps, like those of most previous reliable sources on which they are based, employ a 'broad-brush' approach, whereby unless gaps in a species' range are obvious or well documented, for instance due to a known lack of suitable habitat, then the area between known sites for a species is mapped as if the species is indeed present. At the small scale necessary for mapping most species with relatively large ranges, it is not possible to take account of the finest-scale distributional information, even where known. However, especially within Amazonia, adequate (and published) avian inventories are frequently still lacking over large areas (see reviews in Oren and Albuquerque 1991, J. M. C. Silva 1995, Isler 1997). This means that the precise ranges of many species are, to some extent, still based as much on educated guesswork as on definitive data. Furthermore, because of the difficulties in mapping bird ranges at a fine scale, species with particularly well-known preferences for specialised habitats (e.g. white-sand forests) or even microhabitats (e.g. bamboo) pose special problems. For instance, Black Manakin *Xenopipo atronitens*, a species everywhere confined to *campinaranas* (see Glossary) or similar habitats, and therefore of naturally localised distribution, is, across its main range, of necessity mapped using a 'broad brush', even though areas of suitable habitat might be widely separated. Other species may be frequently confined to river-edge habitats, for example Flame-crested Manakin *Heterocercus linteatus*, while still others may be subject to shifts in habitat preference (sometimes dramatically so) across their broad ranges. For this reason, it is important to read the distributional data and view the maps with one eye also on the Habitat section. In addition to the great many 'traditional' data sources, ranging from the standard field guides and other keynote texts such as the *Handbook of the Birds of the World* to a veritable barrage of papers in journals both well known and obscure, several electronic sources of distributional data must be mentioned. First are the digital maps for the birds of the Western Hemisphere published on CD by NatureServe (Ridgely *et al.* 2003). Various internet sites are also useful sources of information on the distributions of Neotropical birds, of which we should give special recognition to that devoted to the birds of Surinam administered and updated by Jan-Hein Ribot (http://www1.nhl.nl/~ribot/english/). A particularly exciting new initiative, not yet online at the time of writing, is the forthcoming 'automatic ornithologist' website, which will aim both to map and to predict the ranges of birds in Amazonian Brazil, and enable the user to produce predictive species lists for any area within the basin (Cohn-Haft *et al.* 2009).

Movements

Most species of cotingas and manakins are generally considered resident or sedentary. Nonetheless, given that by far the majority of species treated in this book are primarily frugivorous, to some extent they must follow the availability of fruiting trees. Relatively few species are regular migrants, either elevational (e.g. Three-wattled Bellbird *Procnias tricarunculatus* or some populations of White-ruffed Manakin *Corapipo leucorrhoa altera*) or otherwise (e.g. White-tipped Plantcutter *Phytotoma rutila* is, to some extent, an austral migrant). However, a greater number of cotingas and some manakins may to a greater or lesser extent almost certainly wander quite extensively during their foraging, perhaps especially in the non-breeding season and/or in response to exceptional climatic events. At least in some species, the degree to which a species moves around may differ in males and females. For instance, some cotingas, especially the red cotingas (genus *Phoenicircus*) and blue cotingas (genus *Cotinga*), seem to possess 'mobile' leks, meaning that the males are much less sedentary than females, at least when the latter are occupied with nesting. In contrast, radio-tracking studies in French Guiana have revealed that in many manakins, the males, which are highly faithful to their lek sites, are far less 'mobile' and occupy smaller territories on average than the females, even during the nesting season. Unfortunately, data on movements, either regular or not, are still very few and frequently weak, meaning that the Movements section is often based more on assumption than definite information. Any instances of vagrancy are also discussed under this section.

Habitat

The favoured habitats of each species are usually discussed in rather general terms, and only in rather special or particularly well-understood instances do we provide more detailed descriptions of habitat physiognomy. Several standard habitat types are frequently mentioned in these texts, more information on which can be found in the Glossary and we also recommend the early chapters in Stotz *et al.* (1996) for descriptions of these. Attention is also paid to any seasonal differences in habitat use or spatial changes in preferences, one example of the latter being Wire-tailed Manakin (see also Distribution).

Description

This section opens with a brief statement concerning the species' overall impression in the field (jizz), sometimes focusing on a few key features that serve to discriminate it from most or all other similar taxa, but in most cases merely those that identify it to genus. Any peculiarities of the species in question not covered within the remainder of the section are covered early on; for instance, any modifications to the wing and tail feathers, the singular characters associated with the soft parts (but not their colours) and any differences between the sexes are briefly noted. Thereafter follow the individual age/sex descriptions commencing with the adult, and including separate subsections for males and females, where appropriate, and briefly mentioning descriptions of nestlings in the literature. Plumage descriptions are detailed but are not intended to be absolutely exhaustive, and usually refer to the nominate race (the taxon involved is always stated, unless the species is monotypic). We note some instances of plumage variation, particularly examples of female manakins exhibiting partial male plumage (cf. Graves 1981), and also some aberrant individuals from either the field or museum. It should be noted that a great many juvenile plumages are apparently identical to those of adult females, at least in the field, although recent moult studies of some manakins have unsurprisingly revealed that ageing (and possibly sexing) such individuals will be possible in the hand, with mist-netted birds (see, for instance, Ryder and Durães 2005, Wolfe *et al.* 2009). When possible, information on plumage maturation and moult is provided within a separate subsection, but note that most data, especially for the cotingas, are confined to generalities, and all such recent studies that have elucidated the moult regimes of taxa covered here are for members of the Pipridae. In some cases we have suggested potential extrapolation from better-studied but closely related species. Well-documented cases of hybridisation, both inter- and intra-generic, are reported in detail, with references to any published images of such individuals wherever possible. The Description section closes with a résumé of data concerning bare-parts coloration (i.e. irides, bill, legs and feet). Only rarely are these based exclusively on general sources, such as field guides or Snow (2004a, 2004b). In the majority of cases we have relied on personal data (based on field observations and photographs), more detailed handbooks and information in specialist papers, and, in many cases, recently collected data-rich museum specimens. These specimens have been particularly useful in documenting the range of variation in bare-part coloration in many species. However, it should be noted that any perceived differences in this respect between adults or young birds, for example, are typically mentioned in the detailed descriptions of the sexes/ages rather than here.

Measurements

A variety of sources has been used to compile this section. Especially for species of Pipridae, but also for the majority of cotingas, measurements were taken by GMK at a number of museums in North and South America, and Europe. These institutions are referred to by their acronyms (see Abbreviations below) and the broad geographical range from which specimens were analysed is stated in parentheses (unless the species has a well-proscribed overall range). Data are generally presented separately for males and females, but means have not been calculated. Only for a handful of species are data not segregated according to sex. Wing and tail measurements were made to 0.5mm accuracy, using a metal wing-rule with a perpendicular stop at zero, while bill (culmen) and tarsus measurements were generally made using digital callipers, accurate to 0.01mm. Wing was measured as maximum chord, culmen from the tip to the base (rather than the feathers) and tarsus from the notch at the back of the inter-tarsal joint to the lower side of the last complete tarsal scale above the point where the toes diverge. Published sources have also been used for mensural data, especially to give a more complete range for those species represented by many subspecies, or alternatively because the sample size of our own specimen pool was not large. In addition to a great many papers, particularly important sources of mensural data have been Hellmayr (1929b), Zimmer (1936a, 1936b, 1936c, for some Peruvian Pipridae), Wetmore (1972, for Central American species) and Snow (1982, for cotingas). It should be noted that, in general, where these alternative sources have been utilised, wing and tail data have been rounded up or down to the same 0.5mm accuracy, and that bill (and tarsus) measurements are usually much less accurate being either to 0.5 or 0.1mm accuracy, and bill is usually taken to represent the culmen from the tip to the feathers. In some cases, because the data presented in these (and other) publications are sufficiently difficult to compare with our own, published data for bill and tarsus measurements are ignored. A final source of mensural data has been unpublished measurements of live birds by field workers employed or volunteering for ProAves in Colombia (see Acknowledgements), and data collected in Bolivia, Ecuador and Peru by Jon Hornbuckle. We are also grateful to Weber Girão and his colleagues for specifically supplying unpublished mensural data for Araripe Manakin *Antilophia bokermanni*. For both published and unpublished sources of data, sample sizes and geographical representation are always given wherever these are known. Weight (mass) data are also given for nearly every species, based on both published sources and specimen label data. These data are usually (but not always) segregated by sex, but except in a handful of cases we do not list mass data for each subspecies. Sample sizes are also rarely given, simply because many published data do not indicate this information. Nonetheless, where we are aware of the data being based on particularly small sample sizes we have endeavoured to state this. Readers should be mindful that mass data for birds can vary strongly with season, activity (e.g. a female with eggs in the ovaries will naturally weigh more) and even time of day. In a great many cases our collective data are still too 'raw' (i.e. lacking in background information) and insufficiently calibrated to draw many, if indeed any, conclusions. For an overview of this issue, in relation to Neotropical birds in general, interested readers are referred to Vuilleumier (1999).

Geographical variation

This section principally discusses any named (or, in a relative handful of cases, undescribed) geographical variation, commencing with a brief statement as to whether the species is monotypic or polytypic (see Glossary). Thereafter, in the case of polytypic species, each subspecies is described, usually commencing with the nominate, or following a natural geographical progression (e.g. from north to south), its range is given (with country names in bold type) and its distinguishing characters are discussed, and in a tiny handful of cases rejected based on our own museum and field work. However, for those species that exhibit geographical variation in their vocalisations, such information is generally reserved for the following section. For species exhibiting particularly complex racial variation, we endeavour to provide an overview of the nature of the plumage differences (e.g. whether they are merely clinal) prior to the details concerning each subspecies. Complete citations for subspecies are generally not given, but the authors and dates are given for all recognised here or in other recent and important works (e.g. Dickinson 2003, Snow 2004a, 2004b). Subspecies not generally accorded recognition in the modern-day literature are generally discussed more briefly. Throughout this section, we have attempted to pay particularly close attention to the comments of earlier museum and field ornithologists. In many cases, perhaps surprisingly, some of the most detailed commentaries remain those by C. E. Hellmayr and J. T. Zimmer, made in the first half of the last century. Any other taxonomic comments, e.g. concerning the diagnosability of certain subspecies (based on our own work or that of others), the advisability of recognising more than one species, or the information contained within recent molecular studies, are also made here. It should be emphasised that we have only very rarely attempted to revise subspecific limits as maintained in standard works such as Dickinson (2003), although we concur strongly with Remsen (2010) that critical and quantifiable revision, so rarely attempted for many species, is definitely warranted. Instead, we have been content to note those cases where variation seems clinal or otherwise might be unworthy of named recognition based on the earlier proposals of Barrowclough

(1982) and Haffer (2003) in respect to subspecies delimitation. Formal revision of taxonomy should be argued in the technical literature.

Voice

Voice is an extremely important component in fieldcraft in the Neotropics (and in any other tropical region of the world), and a good sound-recorder and microphone, or at least playback device, are of virtually equal importance to a pair of binoculars. Indeed, knowledge of vocalisations will help more acute observers to pinpoint a species' presence well before any successful observations. This is particularly the case with some of the more vocal, but sluggish, cotingas and manakins, many individuals of which will perch in one position for many minutes at a time, with only constant vocalisation providing any clue to their presence. The main described vocalisations for each species are treated in this book, although it should be noted that, especially for some cotingas, the social function of a given vocalisation is often incompletely or almost wholly unknown. We have endeavoured to correctly label the function of a given vocalisation where possible, but we suspect that many voices will be subject to future clarification of their context. For those manakin species subject to (recent) intensive study, albeit still by a relative handful of particularly dedicated researchers, we have been able to provide extensive details of the vocal repertoire: see, for example, White-crowned Manakin *Dixiphia pipra*, Band-tailed Manakin *Pipra fasciicauda* and Yellow-crested Manakin *Heterocercus flavivertex*. For such well-studied species, it will swiftly become apparent that there is extensive cross-referencing between the vocal and display sections, and we recommend that interested readers should study them in conjunction. Any geographical variation in voice is also fully discussed within this section, rather than the previous one. The availability of any published sonograms is usually mentioned, wherever known to us. A list of published recordings on readily available commercial compilations is also provided (for northern South American species this is heavily based on the compilation in Restall *et al.* 2006), as well as some information concerning the material available freely online at http://www.xeno-canto.org. Although this to some extent ignores the extremely important and arguably more permanent sound-recording archives, e.g. at the British Library (London, UK) and Macauley Library of Natural Sounds, Cornell (Ithaca, NY, USA), we consider that the easy accessibility of the xeno-canto archive argues for its special consideration herein.

Natural history

Because of the large quantities of data now available for certain manakins, in particular, our original plan to treat the natural history of each species in a single section was eventually discarded, and instead the data have been 'broken down' into four sections: Natural History, Food and Feeding, Display, and Breeding. For some species, especially amongst the Cotingidae, the extreme brevity of just about all four sections has perhaps served to emphasise just how poorly known some of the birds covered by this book remain. Thus, despite our initial minor reservations as to how well the system eventually adopted might work, we believe the twofold advantages of (a) affording the accounts for better-studied species greater structure and (b) emphasising how little known some species are, and the importance of even amateur observers publishing novel observations on, for instance, nesting behaviour, far outweigh any cosmetic disadvantages. Consequently, the first of these behavioural sections, entitled simply Natural History, serves as something of a catch-all for data inappropriate to the following three sections, and as an overview of our knowledge of each species' biology.

Food and feeding

Most manakins and many cotingas are to some extent omnivorous, although probably largely frugivorous. Although we do not attempt to provide exhaustive lists of known foodstuffs for each species, the major constituent fruits (species or families) are given, wherever known, including any potential regional variation, and a résumé of any non-fruit diet is also presented (data for the latter are typically much sparser). We also describe the manoeuvres used by the birds for securing food, often including any flocking behaviour (for particularly poorly known species listing any published or unpublished associations of which we are aware) or at least its relative prevalence for a given species.

Display

For many species of manakins this is one of the longest sections within an account. Although we have observed a great many of the manakin and cotinga species with highly structured displays at their lek sites, our observations have, of necessity, often been made within the context of other fieldwork, either general avifaunal research or leading bird tours. As such, this section is very heavily based on the published work of a handful of particularly devoted researchers who have conducted long-term studies of a single species or group of species. These have included pioneers such as Frank Chapman, Alexander Skutch and more latterly David & Barbara Snow and Alan Lill, while present-day workers such as Rick Prum, Mark Robbins and José Tello have, through classic studies of the taxa concerned, significantly increased our knowledge of a handful of different species between them, and others such as the team surrounding John Blake, Bette Loiselle and Renata Durães have greatly augmented our understanding of the lives of manakins in Costa Rica and Amazonian Ecuador. As mentioned above, interested readers will frequently find it highly advantageous, if not almost imperative, to read this section in conjunction with that on Voice. For the best-studied species, the Display section describes the general characteristics of the arena at which birds display and any special factors that might influence or control their behaviour. Data on the number of individuals attending regular lek sites, spatial distances between displaying individuals, favoured display perches, seasonality or periodicity of display, etc., are all given, wherever known. Thereafter, all of the different known display behaviours are described, usually following closely the terminology employed by those works cited. Quotes, sometimes extensive, are used wherever we have felt it to be appropriate. In some cases, again where known, we have commented on the similarity between different species' displays, the mechanisms operating on any hierarchical system and the inter-relatedness of birds displaying at individual leks. Such topics are increasingly the focus of specialist work as more researchers discover the model applicability of manakins for investigating the evolution of tropical birds in general. Nonetheless, while we have attempted to keep abreast of the near-stream of highly technical research now being conducted on some Pipridae, we have considered it beyond our remit to discuss all of this work extensively, especially when much of it is designed to answer more general biological and evolutionary questions, and does not of itself further our knowledge of the basic biology of the study species.

Breeding

The fourth of the biology sections summarises our knowledge of each species' reproductive behaviour. Again, in many cases, it will become apparent to even the rather cursory reader that very much more published information is available for some of the commoner manakin species especially, compared with even some of the more numerous Cotingidae. Many of the latter beg serious study, but the low densities at which many cotingas occur presumably continues to act as a significant deterrent to university students and other academics to 'tackle' them, unlike many manakins, which in stark contrast often appear to serve as 'models' for investigation. Each account discusses, where known, nest architecture, including materials, height above the ground, substrate, etc., with any described variation, the number and colour of the eggs (measurements of nests and eggs are not given, but sources for such data are explicitly mentioned), seasonality of breeding behaviour (usually by country), and any information concerning incubation and fledging periods, nestling care and provision, and predation rates. These five last-named topics are particularly poorly studied to date, although robust data are increasingly being published, especially for some of the western Amazonian manakin species. For those taxa (usually cotingas) whose nesting behaviour is especially poorly known, information from museum specimens, our own observations and other observers (some of it unpublished), as well as in the more general literature has been freely used to augment our knowledge as far as possible, although such data were usually collected opportunistically. It merits noting that, despite the marvellous standard set by the soon-to-be-completed *Handbook of the Birds of the World* series, we have noted many examples of 'missed' literature pertaining to both cotingas and manakins, especially in relation to reproduction. Sometimes this comment extends to other relevant works. Doubtless we will be proven guilty of the same failing, but we have 'dug as deep' as we have been able.

Status

The Status paragraph typically commences with the IUCN threat category afforded the species by BirdLife International. Any changes in that status since the major baseline review provided by Collar *et al.* (1992) are subject to discussion. Those species considered Vulnerable, Endangered or Critically Endangered are generally accorded most attention, with a discussion of threats (known or suspected to be relevant), as well as any ongoing conservation measures proposed or implemented (sadly, usually very few). The species' overall range (as estimated by BirdLife International) may be mentioned and the degree to which this perhaps 'insulates' a species from current threats is discussed. Nonetheless, it should be stated that the plausible effects of predicted levels of climate change on the habitat available to many manakins was the subject of a recent paper (Anciães and Peterson 2006), and these findings are usually also mentioned. It is unquestionable that many Amazonian species, until quite recently considered practically invulnerable, must increasingly be viewed as at risk, initially through ongoing forest destruction, particularly at the eastern and southern margins of the basin (in the so-called 'Arc of Deforestation'), but also as a result of the massive climate change predicted if the rampant logging does not cease soon (see, for example, Fearnside 2005, 2009, Soares-Filho *et al.* 2006). The extent to which a given species might be 'safe' within currently proposed protected areas, either privately or publicly owned, is also dealt with in this section, with particularly important or representative sites frequently mentioned, especially for those species of greater conservation concern. We also frequently take the opportunity to discuss the degree of dependence of a species on Important Bird

Areas or Endemic Bird Areas identified by BirdLife International. For some species (usually less common or rare taxa), we also mention other sites, not necessarily protected areas, which we consider to be particularly good places to visit to find the bird in question. In many (but not all) instances, the major protected areas mentioned represent the most convenient or best places to observe the species.

Acronyms used in the text

Throughout this book personal observations by the authors and artist are denoted by their initials, i.e. GMK = Guy Kirwan, GG = Graeme Green and EB = Eustace Barnes. Acronyms used in the text principally pertain to museums in which we worked or which provided data, as follows:

AOU = American Ornithologists' Union (specifically its checklist of North American birds, which covers all of Central America within its remit)

BMNH = The Natural History Museum (Tring, UK), formerly the British Museum (Natural History)

COP = Phelps Collection (Caracas, Venezuela)

CUMZ = Cambridge University Museum of Zoology (Cambridge, UK)

DZUFMG = Departamento de Zoologia, Universidade Federal de Minas Gerais (Belo Horizonte, Brazil)

FMNH = Field Museum of Natural History (Chicago, USA)

INPA = Instituto Nacional de Pesquisas da Amazônia (Manaus, Brazil)

IOC = International Ornithological Congress (refers to the list of recommended English names, originally published in book format (Gill and Wright 2006) and subsequently updated regularly on the internet, at http://www.worldbirdnames.org)

MECN = Museo Ecuatoriano de Ciencias Naturales (Quito, Ecuador)

MNCR = Museo Nacional de Costa Rica (San José, Costa Rica)

MNRJ = Museu Nacional Rio de Janeiro (Rio de Janeiro, Brazil)

MPEG = Museu Paraense Emílio Goeldi (Belém, Brazil)

MVZ = Museum of Vertebrate Zoology, Harvard University (Cambridge, MA, USA)

MZUSP = Museu de Zoologia da Universidade de São Paulo (São Paulo, Brazil)

RMNH = Naturalis (Leiden, The Netherlands)

SACC = South American Checklist Committee, founded by the American Ornithologists' Union (AOU; see above)

ZISP = Zoological Institute, Russian Academy of Sciences (St Petersburg, Russia)

ZMA = Zoological Museum, University of Amsterdam (Amsterdam, The Netherlands)

Glossary

The following elucidates the basic meanings of some of the technical terms employed in the species texts. More expansive definitions of some of these terms can be found in other texts; for instance, for habitat descriptions, we thoroughly recommend the relevant chapters in Stotz *et al.* (1996) to all those with more than a cursory interest in Neotropical birds.

Allopatric: Refers to two or more taxa that are geographical replacements of each other, i.e. without any overlap in their ranges (see also **sympatric** and **parapatric**).

Bare parts: The non-feathered parts of a bird, namely the eyes (irides), eye-ring, bill, legs and feet. Also sometimes referred to as 'soft parts'.

Caatinga: A biogeographical domain and vegetation type confined to the interior of northeast Brazil, south as far as northern Minas Gerais. The vegetation of this very dry region (annual rainfall ranges from 300 to 800mm) is generally low in stature and wholly deciduous, with many drought-resistant features. Cacti and terrestrial bromeliads are common features.

Canga: A Brazilian term employed for a vegetation type (scrubby grassland) associated with iron ore deposits, especially in rocky areas. The water table is often close to the surface, and small lakes often characterise such regions. *Canga* swiftly grades into adjacent vegetation types, even tall *terra firme* forest in Amazonia.

Cerrado: The biogeographical domain that covers much of central Brazil, adjacent eastern Bolivia and northeast Paraguay, but also used (when italicised herein, *cerrado*) to refer to the non-forest vegetation types that cover much of the Brazilian shield. These range from open grasslands (*campo sujo*) to relatively dense woodland (*cerradão*).

Chocó: This well-known biodiversity hotspot stretches from southeast Panama along the Pacific coast of Colombia to northwest Ecuador. The forests of this region are super-wet and harbour many endemic taxa, but are steadily declining due to ongoing urbanization, deforestation and agricultural expansion.

21

Cline: Any change involving one or more characters across a species' range in a gradient, often gradual, of variation. 'Stepping stones' along the cline might be the subject of some debate as to their validity, but those taxa at their geographical extremities are often reasonably distinctive from one another.

Cloud forest: A popular albeit somewhat ambiguous term that refers to montane forest that is frequently cloud-covered, with trees festooned with many lichens, bromeliads, etc. Such forests are damp and mossy.

Congeneric: Belonging to the same genus, but usually referring to different species.

Conspecific: Belonging to the same species.

Dimorphic: Used in this book usually to refer to sexual dimorphism, whereby males and females of the same species show differences in plumage.

Elfin forest: The higher regions of **cloud forest** (q.v.) close to the limits of the treeline, where the trees are stunted, gnarled and twisted, wrought not only by wind action but also due to the stresses of drought and/or fire.

Endemic: Restricted to a defined area and most usually used in reference to countries, although geopolitical units rarely coincide with biogeographical divisions. Thus, we might describe a species (or subspecies) as being endemic to Brazil or the Atlantic Forest region, the latter implying that, in addition to Brazil, it also occurs in either eastern Paraguay or northeast Argentina, or all three.

Immature: In general terms, any plumage intermediate between juvenile and adult, but note that (at least in those groups considered in this book) this term should not be taken to imply sexual immaturity. Males are usually capable of breeding in immature plumage, although note that many immature male manakins might not actually breed because of the hierarchical system in operation.

Juvenile: A bird in the first complete plumage on leaving the nest, which may be kept only a few months in many manakins.

Monophyletic: A group that contains all of the descendants of a common ancestor (q.v. **polyphyletic**).

Monospecific: A genus containing only a single species, but multiple taxa (i.e. the species is not generally regarded as being monotypic).

Monotypic: The sole member of a grouping, be it species, family, etc.

Neotropical: Refers to the entire Central and South American faunal region, including the West Indies and other related islands, and Mexico north to just south of the Federal District.

Nominate race: The first named race of a given species, characterised by its scientific binomial and trinomial being identical.

Páramo: Humid grassland with some shrubby vegetation that occurs above montane and elfin forests, between southern Central America and northern South America, locally to Bolivia.

Parapatric: Refers to two closely related taxa whose geographical ranges narrowly meet but are nevertheless largely separated, for instance, by altitude. Contact zones between parapatric species pairs are typically narrow if they exist at all. For example, in southeast Brazil the geographical range of Grey-winged Cotinga *Tijuca condita* entirely overlaps that of the congeneric Black-and-gold Cotinga *T. atra*, but the latter is largely (but not exclusively) found at lower elevations, i.e. they occur in elevational parapatry.

Paraphyletic: A term, originating in cladistics, referring to a group whose contents include a common ancestor and some, but not all, of its descendants (q.v. **monophyletic**).

Perch-gleaning: To glean insects from either leaves or bark while a bird is perched.

Polylepis **woodland**: A distinctive high-elevation Andean forest type, found at 3,500–4,500m between northwest Venezuela and northern Argentina and northern Chile. The habitat is by its very nature patchy, blocks of usually relatively low-stature woodland being surrounded by *páramo* (q.v.) or other grassy areas. Epiphytes, mosses and lichens can be prominent features of such forests, which support a distinctive suite of bird species including several high-Andean cotingas. *Polylepis* spp. (Rosaceae) often (but not exclusively) occur in monospecific stands and the trees are probably both fire-resistant and drought-tolerant. Their clearance for firewood and other uses is of considerable conservation concern.

Polytypic: A species comprising two or more subspecies.

Rectrices: Refers to the tail feathers.

Remiges: The wing's main flight feathers, i.e. the secondaries and primaries.

Restinga: Refers to those coastal forests and scrub growing on white-sand soil in eastern Brazil. Such forests are usually low in stature and relatively rich in terrestrial bromeliads.

Sally: Aerial foraging, in which a bird flies out to seize an insect or fruit in flight.

Sandy-belt forest: Humid forest growing on white-sand soil that is not seasonally inundated but is generally less diverse floristically and of lower stature than *terra firme* **forest**. This is the predominant forest type in much of the upper Orinoco and Negro drainages.

Superspecies: Two or more closely related taxa that replace one another geographically, which under some taxonomic treatments might be considered as subspecies, rather than species. It is generally assumed that the different constituents of a superspecies are usually only recently differentiated.

Sympatric: Where two similar species breed in the same region, they are stated to occur in sympatry (contrast **allopatric** and **parapatric**, q.v.). See also **syntopic**.

Synonym: In zoological nomenclature, an alternative name for the same taxon, usually as a result of the same form being named (sometimes multiple times) by different authors, although synonymy may also result from direct taxonomic revision and a decision to recognise fewer subspecies, for example.

Syntopic: Where two similar species breed in the same region and habitat type, they are stated to occur in syntopy.

Taxon: Any named form (plural **taxa**) and frequently used in discussions to refer to forms of debatable status, i.e. there is some doubt as to the best classification, subspecies or species.

Taxonomy: The study of classification and naming of life forms.

Terra firme forest: Renowned for its extraordinary diversity of plant species, *terra firme* forest is the most abundant habitat type in the Amazon Basin and is further characterised in that it is never subject to inundation (q.v. *várzea*).

Type (holotype): Refers to the individual specimen used to describe a species or taxon; where more than one specimen is specifically so used then a **type series** is involved.

Várzea forest: A general term that refers to all types of seasonally flooded tropical evergreen forest, of which four distinct types are sometimes recognised. They are tall in stature but usually less floristically diverse than *terra firme* **forests** (q.v.), although the undergrowth is often rich. We typically differentiate between *várzea* along white-water rivers in Amazonia, and *igapó*, which borders black-water and clear-water rivers in the same region, and which generally grow on sandy soils. The undergrowth is generally more open in *igapós*, and these forests are generally inundated for five months or longer each year.

White-sand forest: Forest and scrub on white-sand soil, which varies strongly from site to site, from relatively low scrub to tall forest, depending on soil type and drainage. Woody plant diversity is relatively low in such forests, but endemism is frequently high. In Brazil, where such forests cover *c*.60,000km², principally in the upper Rio Negro region and more locally elsewhere, they are subdivided into *campinas* (rather open scrub) and *campinaranas* (taller and closed-canopy woodland, also known as Amazonian *caatinga*). In northeast Peru, subdivisions include *varillal* (both dry and humid forest types, with the understorey sometimes poor but in others more developed) and *chamizal* (dense low-stature forests with a partially developed understorey). See also *Restinga* and **sandy-belt forest**.

MOVEMENTS AND MIGRATIONS

Cotingas and manakins are not especially known for their migratory habits, although there is mounting evidence for seasonal altitudinal movements in some species (see below). However, there is evidence that four species of cotingas are latitudinal migrants, as follows. Both Rufous-tailed *Phytotoma rara* and White-tipped Plantcutters *P. rutila* are at least partially migratory, performing latitudinal movements away from more southerly regions of Chile and Argentina in the austral winter. At this season, White-tipped Plantcutter has reached Brazil on several occasions, once as far north as Espírito Santo, and Rufous-tailed Plantcutter has, rather exceptionally, wandered to the Falkland Islands; both species have also been reported to descend from the highest-elevation breeding sites, in Bolivia and Chile, respectively, in winter. Furthermore, it seems that Swallow-tailed Cotinga *Phibalura flavirostris* is also a latitudinal migrant in the Atlantic Forest, being present in the extreme south of its range, for instance in Rio Grande do Sul (Brazil), exclusively between late September and late March (the austral spring/summer), whereas it appears to be principally a winter visitor to northeast Argentina and perhaps exclusively so to southeast Paraguay. However, occasional records of this species deep in the interior of Brazil, in Goiás, come from both May (late autumn) and January (summer), and are therefore difficult to explain in purely migratory terms. *Phibalura* too is perhaps another elevational migrant to a greater or lesser extent, although we speculate here that the scale and frequency of such movements may be dependent on both climatic conditions and food resources. Finally, there are also some data to suggest that Bare-throated Bellbird *Procnias nudicollis* may be at least partially migratory: it is only present in the non-breeding season in northeast Argentina and in summer in southernmost Brazil, while the species seems to be a transient through eastern Paraguay. Like *Phibalura* and the two plantcutters mentioned earlier, this bellbird appears to show also some evidence of elevation migrations in southeast Brazil, but details are still rather fragmentary.

In contrast to such 'extreme cases', the diurnal activities of most cotingas and manakins, especially of course the males, tend to revolve around their lek sites, particularly in the early morning and late afternoon (see the chapter on Breeding biology). For many of these fundamentally sedentary species, dependent on a tropical environment that is comparatively stable throughout the year, there is no logical requirement for anything other than local foraging movements. However, it should be remembered that some manakins have been recorded (via radio-tracking surveys) as moving over a rather wider area in their non-breeding periods (especially in females). For some species, these actually provide the best opportunity for locating them, as they quite frequently perch on exposed snags at the tops of trees, doubtless searching for gatherings of frugivores at fruiting trees.

However, tropical environments are not always as uniform as they initially appear to casual observers, and there is at least some degree of seasonality, e.g. in fruiting seasons, particularly with increasing latitude. As already mentioned, in particular, it is suspected or proven that several species of cotingas are altitudinal migrants, at least partially or occasionally, although the mechanisms determining these movements are not always obvious. However, in some well-documented examples, these movements are known to coincide with and follow highest fruit productivity, which in regions such as southeast Brazil and Central America is more seasonal than in areas closer to the equator. The climate in the montane parts of these regions can be relatively severe in the 'winter' months (particularly compared with adjoining lowlands), with lower temperatures and increased precipitation.

In the northern Costa Rican highlands, such as Monteverde Cloud Forest Reserve, two species, Three-wattled Bellbird *Procnias tricarunculatus* and Bare-throated Umbrellabird *Cephalopterus glabricollis* are now well known to be migrants, with the bellbird initially moving higher following breeding (or to the lowlands of adjacent Nicaragua) and then to the Pacific lowlands of southwest Costa Rica. In the case of the umbrellabird, the birds move downslope following breeding (after July and August) and only return to the highlands in March. Interestingly, it also seems that males and females are to some extent altitudinally segregated during the non-breeding season. In the same general region, there is some (more or less anecdotal) evidence that another globally threatened species, Yellow-billed Cotinga *Carpodectes antoniae*, also performs seasonal altitudinal migrations, at least to some extent. Further south, there is more anecdotal evidence for the appearance of Long-wattled Umbrellabird *Cephalopterus penduliger* in the lowlands of Ecuador and Colombia at certain seasons, but more recently collected data dispute the notion that this rare bird might also perform altitudinal migrations. In southeast Brazil, there is at least some evidence to demonstrate that Elegant Mourner *Laniisoma elegans* must also be considered an altitudinal migrant (see the relevant species account). There are also records of this species from the same region both outside its usual range and from distinctly unusual localities within its overall geographical distribution, which can be assumed to reflect displacement during elevational movements or as being symptomatic of a general predisposition to wander in search of food.

However, one species previously postulated to be an altitudinal migrant seems to be at most only partially so. Snow (2004a) considered that the Brazilian endemic Buff-throated Purpletuft *Iodopleura pipra* probably migrated to the highlands from its sea-level breeding sites following breeding. Although there is some evidence of seasonal elevational movements, at least from Rio de Janeiro and rather more vaguely from Espírito Santo, there are also more robust data from its best-known breeding locality, in the littoral of São Paulo, indicating year-round residency (Whittaker and Kirwan 2008).

Despite being generally considered highly sedentary, there are also fewer than a handful of manakins known to move seasonally over altitudinal gradients, with for instance White-ruffed Manakin *Corapipo leucorrhoa* also descending to the lowlands and foothills in the non-breeding period, at least in Costa Rica. In western South America, there is also some evidence for elevational movements in the Club-winged Manakin *Machaeropterus deliciosus*, but the cumulative evidence is rather less than for the better-studied White-ruffed Manakin.

Turning finally to those species covered here that are generally regarded as 'out-and-out' residents, Thrush-like Schiffornis *Schiffornis turdina* has a much larger home range (at least in French Guiana, where radio-tracking has been used to elucidate the lives of several 'Pipridae') than true manakins that are both more dependent on fruit and possess fixed display areas. As already noted by David Snow (and others), it seems probable, if not certain, that at least some species of cotingas in the Neotropical lowlands wander much more widely than most passerines following fruit-ripening events, and to this extent species such as those Amazonian members of the genus *Cotinga* probably possess 'mobile' display sites. Others too, like the Central American Snowy Cotinga *Carpodectes nitidus* also appear to move erratically, presumably in search of suitable food resources. Nonetheless, it is difficult to envisage that such movements in pursuit of fruit supplies can explain the occasional records of White Bellbird *Procnias albus* from the central Amazon region and those on Trinidad. Snow (2004a: 61–2) speculated that these records may reflect 'pioneers' deliberating seeking new potential areas to breed, and further that the relatively recently discovered, and highly isolated, population of this species in the Serra dos Carajás, south of the Amazon, might signal that such pioneers are occasionally successful. (In this respect, Snow also considered that such pioneers might also have been responsible for the highly disjunct population of Swallow-tailed Cotinga in the Bolivian Andes.) Only with more data, and especially radio-tracking studies such as in the case of the French Guianan manakins or Three-wattled Bellbirds in Costa Rica, will our knowledge advance significantly in the future.

VOICE

The suboscine passerines (woodcreepers, ovenbirds, antbirds, tyrant flycatchers, etc.) of the Neotropics are classified as such because of their less-evolved syringeal anatomy. In purely simplistic terms, they are 'separated' by ornithologists from the true songsters such as thrushes, wrens and other oscines. However, while at least the majority of the suboscine passerines are presumed (or known) to inherit their 'songs', i.e. this information is passed genetically, some cotingas (namely the *Procnias* bellbirds) are known to 'learn' their songs just like oscine passerines. In the case of the Three-wattled Bellbird *P. tricarunculatus*, genetic evidence has been marshalled to demonstrate vocal learning and, furthermore, four regional dialects have been identified for this species (Saranathan *et al.* 2007).

Nonetheless, it is suspected that most Cotingidae and Pipridae are probably 'normal' members of the suboscines and vocal information is inherited, but further studies would be welcome. It is certain that cotingas and manakins exhibit a wide and sometimes spectacular array of vocalisations; indeed, like many other species of tropical forest birds, voice is often the first, vital, indication of a species' presence in a given area. Among the cotingas alone, their vocalisations range from one of, if not, *the* loudest among all birds, to some of the quietest and most difficult to detect. At the time of Snow's (2004a) last review of the family, it was thought that the bellbirds might have the loudest voices of any birds, although the voice of only one (White Bellbird *Procnias albus*) might be deemed 'bell-like', with the others sounding more like metal anvils being struck. However, there are now strong data to indicate that the rather more appropriately named Screaming Piha *Lipaugus vociferans* is the loudest bird on Earth (Nemeth 2004), as well as being one of the best known for its vocalisations. Although not the loudest cotinga, the primary vocalisation of the Capuchinbird *Perissocephalus tricolor* is unquestionably one of the most remarkable, a deep sound somewhat midway between a 'lowing' ox and a chainsaw. At the other end of the spectrum, one must remain highly alert to hear the very thin vocalisations of most of the fruiteaters (*Pipreola*) or the hollow 'booming' notes of the umbrellabirds (*Cephalopterus*). Other genera vocalise comparatively infrequently, among them Swallow-tailed Cotinga *Phibalura flavirostris*, and the related 'white' (*Carpodectes*) and 'purple' or 'white-winged' (*Xipholena*) cotingas, which seem to possess easily overlooked frog-like croaking calls. The blue cotingas (*Cotinga*) were also thought to be exceptionally quiet. However, recent field observations have revealed that Turquoise Cotinga *C. ridgwayi* has a very high-pitched vocalisation (Sánchez *et al.* 2007) and that Spangled Cotinga *C. cayana* regularly utters a low *hooo* call (Chaves 2001), albeit both are probably easily missed. The vocalisations of least two other species of 'cotinga' remain to all intents and purposes completely unknown, namely those of Olivaceous Piha *Snowornis cryptolophus* and Kinglet Calyptura *Calyptura cristata*.

In general, manakins of either sex are (like cotingas) rather silent birds away from their leks, but males at their display grounds are usually extremely vocal, although not all species are audible at longer ranges. Two rather 'quiet' species are Golden-winged *Masius chrysopterus* and Pin-tailed Manakins *Ilicura militaris*, both of whose vocalisations are not usually heard over much distance. The aerial vocalisations of the two *Corapipo* species are also easily missed by the less 'tuned-in' observer. Some of those species no longer considered part of the Pipridae, for instance the *Schiffornis* and *Piprites* species, utter reasonably loud (and very distinctive) vocalisations, but relatively infrequently, unlike the *Neopelma* and *Tyranneutes* tyrant-manakins, whose songs are also highly distinctive, relatively simple, but often given persistently virtually day-long. At the other 'end of the scale', the blue-backed (*Chiroxiphia*) manakins possess some of the most complex and richest repertoires among the Pipridae.

Several cotingas and a larger number of manakins make a diverse range of mechanical sounds. The snapping sounds given by members of the genus *Manacus* are particularly noteworthy for their loudness among the latter group. Those mechanical sounds produced by the three (or more) species of *Machaeropterus*, especially Club-winged Manakin *M. deliciosus*, are also of particular interest, and have apparently developed in response to their unusually weak syrinx. Indeed, Club-winged Manakin has proved an especially interesting subject, with Bostwick *et al.* (2010) finding that the modified wing feathers possess exceptional harmonics and that the quality of their resonance is pre-selected by females. Several of the genus *Pipra*, especially the *P. aureola* group, and White-throated Manakin *Corapipo gutturalis* also produce mechanical sounds during their displays, usually in conjunction with visual signals. Among cotingas, the two red cotingas (*Phoenicircus*) combine mechanical sounds with 'true' vocals, but no visual display, while the even more poorly known mechanical sounds produced by members of the genus *Cotinga* are seemingly 'offered' alone, without any special visual or traditional vocal signals. Perhaps one of the most remarkable examples of mechanical sound production in either family was described only recently, that employed by Dusky Piha *Lipaugus fuscocinereus* during its parachute-like display-flight (López-Lanús 2000).

Although transcriptions of most of the different vocalisations of each species are attempted in the main text, it should be obvious that these can never approach the 'real thing' for authenticity and accurate rendition. In recognition of the fact that access to the now-many commercially available cassettes, CDs and DVDs of vocalisations will enhance an observer's ability to learn the vocalisations of these (and other) birds, we conclude most of the vocal sections with a list of such recordings known to us. We have also attempted to provide some information on the recordings available at the increasingly valuable and well-respected online xeno-canto resource (http://www.xeno-canto.org).

It is unquestionable that the study of vocalisations of Neotropical birds has been one of the key tools of the past three decades; many recently published taxonomic decisions rely heavily on vocal differences as one of the main parameters for 'splitting' similar-looking taxa. Yet, the history of such studies using voice is not long, despite the fact that bird song was first recorded as long ago as 1889 (Alström and Ranft 2003: 124). Indeed, it dates back specifically to Paul Schwartz's seminal study of the systematic relationships of two forest falcons, in which he used vocal differences to establish the status of Barred *Micrastur ruficollis* and Lined Forest Falcons *M. gilvicollis* as separate species (Schwartz 1972). More recently, Alström and Ranft (2003) demonstrated how far our collective appreciation of the use of vocalisations in taxonomic studies has come in the intervening 30 years.

To study vocalisations, field observers are using a variety of recording devices and microphones, as well as playback to lure birds into view. Pre-recorded calls are often used to 'entice' birds, hitherto silent, to reveal their presence. The use of such techniques has gone from being from the privilege of a lucky few at the 'top of the game' to almost mandatory. This has led to a degree of disquiet in some circles, with the main argument revolving around the potential disruption to a bird's regular activities, especially if it is nesting. This is not the forum to discuss the moral issues surrounding use of playback, but although there is no doubt that inventorying the avifaunas of tropical forests would be extremely difficult without such techniques, it should also be used as sparingly as possible, given that the potential for some harm is difficult to deny. At the most positive level, the use of playback has led to the discovery of several new species, arguably the most striking example being the recently discovered Jocotoco Antpitta *Grallaria ridgelyi*, originally found in an area abutting Podocarpus National Park, in southern Ecuador. In the final twist to this story, however, playback of the species is now banned at the same site, now thankfully preserved, and instead visitors are able to enjoy unparalleled views of this stunning bird feeding on worms specially put out for the birds!

Knowledge of the voices of some of the rarer and more secretive cotingas and manakins will undoubtedly prove instrumental in helping to locate species such as the fruiteaters, whose high-pitched calls are often the only clue to their presence. Many species are responsive to playback, or even whistled imitations of their calls; in particular, an imitation of Black-headed Berryeater's *Carpornis melanocephala whaooow* call (nothing like a whistle!) will often elicit a response. Many manakins call incessantly; indeed, the only calls heard at midday in the lowlands of eastern Ecuador are often those of Wire-tailed Manakin *Pipra filicauda* and Dwarf Tyrant-Manakin *Tyranneutes stolzmanni*. Club-winged Manakins near Buenaventura, southwestern Ecuador, vocalise continually during daylight hours, sometimes with only a 15-minute 'break' at midday. Screaming Piha is possibly *the* enduring 'background' sound in Amazonia; interestingly this species quite often appears on soundtracks to films located (allegedly) in Africa or Southeast Asia!

BREEDING BIOLOGY

The emancipation of the majority of male cotingas (two notable but not sole exceptions being the *Pipreola* fruiteaters and Swallow-tailed Cotinga *Phibalura flavirostris*) and apparently all male manakins from most, or more usually all, of the duties involved with nest building and rearing young is a consequence of their principally frugivorous diets (Snow 1982, 2004a, 2004b). This has led to a life strategy centred on sexual dimorphism (often extreme), startling plumage embellishments (in cotingas), extravagant displays or remarkable vocalisations, and relatively complex social interactions (based on a hierarchical system) between individuals in those instances where displays are conducted in an arena. Nonetheless, despite nearly a century of field effort, commencing with early studies in Panama and Costa Rica by Frank Chapman and then Alexander Skutch, subsequently pursued by the likes of David Snow on Trinidad and in Guyana, and now through a dedicated and growing number of modern-day students, of which to name just a few would be unfair to the remainder, there are still many gaps in our knowledge of the specific breeding biology of these birds, especially many of the cotingas.

Typically, a male cotinga or manakin will be brightly or at least strikingly coloured, often with a deep lustrous quality to the plumage, in contrast to the much more cryptically coloured female, although (as noted by Snow 1982, and others) shades of black, brown and grey are also well represented among male cotingas. Nonetheless, it should be remembered that some cotinga genera are sexually monochromatic, for instance *Lipaugus* and *Snowornis* pihas, and the same is true of the *Tyranneutes* and *Neopelma* tyrant-manakins, two genera that have traditionally been placed in the Pipridae but which recent genetic data suggest lie outwith true manakins. The particularly deep vibrant colours found in the males of some species of cotingas are produced by the presence of certain carotenoids concentrated in the feather barbs. However, cotingas are unable to produce these pigments themselves and are presumably dependent on extracting most of them from fruits. These bright colours are determined by the male being 'divorced' from all activities centred on the nest or young, where bright plumage could serve as a signal for predators, whereas in contrast the female needs to blend with the surrounding vegetation to avoid detection. In this respect, the strange colours of the down of some young cotingas appear illogical; for instance, that of the nestling Capuchinbird *Perissocephalus tricolor* is bright orange, in striking contrast to its environs. The periodicity of the female's nest visits is also determined by the nutritious nature of fruit, thereby necessitating fewer nest visits than is the case with many insectivorous birds.

The plumage embellishments exhibited by various cotingas range from the colourful to the bizarre. Bright colours are often centred on the throat area, for example the bright green of the male Bare-throated Bellbird *Procnias nudicollis* and the brilliant red of the male Bare-necked Umbrellabird *Cephalopterus glabricollis* (the latter presumably caused by small blood vessels near the skin's surface). In addition, the three other bellbird species possess extravagant wattles that emanate from the throat and gape area. These are an integral part of the vocalisation process, with the wattles being flicked over the bill in a stereotypical fashion. In the case of White Bellbird *Procnias albus* this is embellished by the inky black gape, which is in startling contrast to the clean white plumage. The bright red coloration of the Bare-necked Umbrellabird actually comprises a sac of bare skin distended during sexual signalling, as is the extravagant wattle of the other umbrellabirds. Although 'physical' embellishments are comparatively rare, one of the most obvious examples being the bizarre tail of the Wire-tailed Manakin *Pipra filicauda*, most male manakins are also 'blessed' with very strikingly patterned plumage.

The extravagant and stereotypical displays so characteristic of many species of cotingas and manakins, especially the Pipridae, which possess the most complex courtship movements among passerines, have been well studied and documented, although those of some species remain decidedly mysterious. The leks of many species are maintained in the same arena for as long as the habitat remains viable, thereby enabling researchers to conduct continual observations over many years, often using banded individuals. Especially over the course of the last *c*.25 years some fine studies of lekking behaviour in the Pipridae have been published, for instance those on Band-tailed Manakin *Pipra fasciicauda* (Robbins 1983), Red-headed Manakin *Pipra rubrocapilla* (Castro-Astor *et al.* 2004), Round-tailed Manakin *P. chloromeros* (Tello 2001), White-crowned Manakin *Dixiphia pipra* (Castro-Astor *et al.* 2007) and Blue-crowned Manakin *Lepidothrix coronata* (Durães 2009), to give just a few examples. Improved knowledge of display behaviour has also proved useful in determining taxonomic relationships (Prum 1990a). Above all, however, an active lek is a magnificent sight, particularly as most of the electrifying activity comes from the brightly coloured males. Arena lekking behaviour is not a phenomenon restricted to these two groups, however, being exhibited in birds as diverse as *Calidris* sandpipers (Scolopacidae), Galliformes (Phasianidae) and the birds-of-paradise (Paradisaeidae). The main focus of any lekking arena is a number of males (occasionally up to 50 individuals in some species, of both cotingas and manakins) performing stereotypical movements in an attempt to attract a female. This frenzy of excited activity is often accompanied by a variety of sounds, both mechanical (produced by modifications to the wing feathers) and 'natural' vocalisations. However, many species of both Cotingidae and Pipridae have evolved what are termed 'exploded leks', wherein each male displays within audible distance of its neighbour, but rarely in sight of each other. Two classic examples involve the *Neopelma* tyrant-manakins and the *Lipaugus* pihas. In their tropical settings, leks are often attended virtually year-round albeit with seasonal surges in activity and an obvious decline in attendance during the moult period, and the imperative for any dominant or 'alpha' male will be to ensure his continued dominance. Male manakins frequently spend up to 90% of daylight hours in close proximity to their lek site. Various manakin species (e.g. the *Pipra aureola* superspecies and the genus *Chiroxiphia*) have evolved what have been termed 'coordinated' displays, in which one male (the 'beta') effectively acts as a foil for the 'alpha' individual, who secures the vast majority of copulations. These displays, which depend for their success on the degree of coordination between the individuals, unquestionably reach their elaborate peak in the blue manakins (*Chiroxiphia*). Perhaps surprisingly to the uninitiated, there appear to be advantages for the subordinate males to such displays, which enable them in turn to succeed to the 'top of the pecking order'. Other manakins (and/or their closest relatives) incorporate ostensibly remarkable above-canopy display flights into their repertoire, namely the genera *Corapipo*, *Heterocercus* and *Tyranneutes*. Knowledge of the vocalisations that accompany such displays can substantially aid the observer in detecting these species. Amongst cotingas, the main focus of activity at any arena is often during the early morning, before the birds disperse to feed, and late afternoon, before roost sites are selected. While the same is to some extent true of the Pipridae, in contrast manakins tend to display more or less throughout the day, albeit with noticeable bursts of activity related to factors such as ambient light and, in particular, the presence of females (just as in cotingas), but 'knocking-off' regularly for short bursts of feeding activity usually close to the lek site.

At the time of David Snow's monograph to the cotingas (1982), descriptions existed for the nests of 15 of the 25 genera then included in the family. However, as he noted the breeding biology of just three species, Bearded Bellbird *Procnias averano*, Rufous Piha *Lipaugus unirufus* and Guianan Cock-of-the-Rock *Rupicola rupicola*, could be regarded as reasonably well known at that time. At the time of writing (late 2010), the 'state of play' is that of the same 26 genera, the nests of 21 genera have been described or are otherwise known to us. (Bear in mind that subsequent to 1982 the two Andean green pihas have been recognised to occupy a separate genus, *Snowornis*, and we recognise the genus *Zaratornis*, which is now usually employed for White-cheeked Cotinga *Z. stresemanni* (the nest of which had been described prior to 1982). On the other hand, at that time Snow recognised Scimitar-winged Piha *Lipaugus uropygialis* in its own genus *Chirocylla*, an assignment since abandoned seemingly universally. Unsurprisingly, given the species' rarity, its nest remains unknown.) Regrettably, it remains the case that the breeding biology of comparatively few species of cotinga is known well, but overall the number of species whose nests have been described has advanced (see below for examples from one genus). However, within the last 30 years studies of the breeding biology of many manakins have increased not quite exponentially. Detailed studies of courtship and breeding of a rather large number of manakin species have been attempted to date, and robust descriptions of the nests of all but three of the genera, *Ilicura*, *Xenopipo* and *Neopelma*, included in the Pipridae by Snow (2004b) are now available. And, in contrast to those genera of Cotingidae whose nests have not been described, some information exists on the nests of all three of these manakin genera.

The nests of cotingas (and manakins) tend to be uncomplicated, relatively small affairs (even among the larger species), presumably to facilitate their concealment (for the Cotingidae, it certainly seems to have worked in respect of human observers!). Most cotinga nests that have been found have been 'flimsy' saucer-shaped structures usually comprising twigs or tendrils from just a few types of plants (this might even prove to be a limiting factor in the distribution of some species), supported by small twigs and branches. Nonetheless, critical examination of such nests, for instance after the birds have departed, has shown them to be surprisingly robust structures, belying their fragile appearance, due either to the degree to which the materials interlock or through the use of a binding substance such as the white fungus used in a nest of Amazonian Umbrellabird *Cephalopterus ornatus* discovered recently (Greeney and Sheldon 2008). Genera such as *Gymnoderus* (Bare-necked Fruitcrow) and *Cotinga* (blue cotingas) construct a seemingly even flimsier pad, which usually rests on a more substantial branch and in the case of the latter genus appears to be usually destroyed after use. This habit is apparently unique within the family to this genus. The major exception to the small-nest 'rule' is Purple-throated Fruitcrow *Querula purpurata*, which possesses a breeding strategy that could be said to celebrate the diversity within the family. Several adults working cooperatively attend a larger and more conspicuous nest, which they protect by mobbing any potential predators that approach. The recent discovery that both male and female Black-faced Cotingas *Conioptilon mcilhennyi* tend their young while calling loudly (Tobias 2003) led Snow (2004a: 58) to suggest that this species, too, might be capable of defending the nest-site against 'all-comers'. Earlier, Snow (1982) had also speculated that Red-ruffed Fruitcrow *Pyroderus scutatus* might employ a similar means of nest defence, but although this species is known to chase other birds as large as raptors from the vicinity of its nest, the tending adult also pursues conspecifics.

Some 'cotingas' such as the tiny purpletufts (genus *Iodopleura*) build a minute cup-like nest bound using cobwebs and externally adorned with lichens, very similar to that constructed by hummingbirds, and placed relatively high on horizontal branches. As an example of the advances noted above, since Snow published his first review of the Cotingidae, when only that of White-browed Purpletuft *I. isabellae* was known, the nests of both of its congenerics have now been discovered and described. The nests of some (but not all) montane genera, e.g. *Ampelioides* (which has yet to be described in the technical literature), *Pipreola*, *Ampelion* and *Zaratornis* (the latter two genera were combined by Snow), comprise more substantial constructions of lichens and mosses, and may sometimes take advantage of the availability of substantial epiphytes to disguise and conceal the nest's outline. However, in some ways, relatively little progress has been made since Snow's monograph: the nests of *Doliornis*, for example, remain unknown. In a relatively predator-free environment (such as the high Andes) these may afford more insulation in regions which can become relatively cold at night, and go several days without radiant heat from the sun. Finally, cocks-of-the-rock are just that, building nests of mud and vegetable matter on vertical rock faces in the case of the Andean species, or in caves or against enormous boulders in the Guianan species.

In those species traditionally placed in the Pipridae, nest architecture is generally even more uniform. The great majority of species (e.g. of the genera *Antilophia*, *Pipra*, *Lepidothrix*, *Dixiphia*, *Chloropipo*, *Xenopipo* and *Tyranneutes*) construct relatively small, compact, cup-shaped nests, placed rather low above the ground, typically in the understorey, suspended in a horizontal fork, often with dead leaves on their outside to 'camouflage' the structure and usually bound together and attached to the substrate using spider webs or fungal fibres. Sometimes a 'tail' of vegetation, such as moss, may be added, dangling below the nest, further disguising its outline. Their apparently flimsy nature often means that the eggs are visible in the nest from below. Differences between the genera in nest placement and construction are generally comparatively minor (for one such comparison between several genera from lowland Ecuador, see Hidalgo *et al.* 2008). The genus *Piprites*, for long placed within the Pipridae, but in recent years consistently confirmed through molecular analysis to lie outside this family, has unsurprisingly been found (at least in one species, Black-capped Piprites *P. pileata*) to construct a spherical moss nest (Cockle *et al.* 2008) quite atypical of the family it was long considered to be part. The nests of the two species of *Schiffornis* described to date are also unusual, compared with the Pipridae within which they were also long placed, for their relative bulk and sometimes position. These examples amply demonstrate the contribution that amateur birdwatchers, who must find many nests during the course of their trips, are capable of making: nest architecture can, in many instances, prove useful for inferring phylogenetic relationships, especially when utilised in conjunction with other data.

The eggs of both cotingas and manakins are almost invariably cryptically coloured and patterned, even those species such as the *Rupicola* that nest in sites with very low ambient light levels, undoubtedly to facilitate their concealment. Some manakins possess eggs with a white base colour, but usually these are still heavily marked with browns and other dark colours. Cotingas are, as noted by Snow (1982: 26), remarkable among passerine birds in laying eggs unusually large compared with the adults' body size, the relationship between the two echoing that found in such non-passerines as kingfishers (Alcedinidae) and rollers (Coraciidae). Snow suggested that this probably reflected the relatively long incubation period, which might enable the young bird to have completed as much of its growth as possible while still in the egg, and we are unaware of any subsequently published research that has disputed this hypothesis. Although less marked, manakins also lay relatively large eggs in comparison with adult body size. Typically, the clutch comprises a single egg in the medium to large tropical forest cotingas, which build small saucer-shaped nests, e.g. in the genera *Cotinga*, *Lipaugus*, *Carpodectes* and *Xipholena*. However, *Pyroderus* and *Rupicola* both lay two eggs, and 2–3 eggs is the norm for such montane genera as *Phibalura*, *Pipreola* and *Ampelion*. We still know nothing concerning the nesting of other higher-elevation genera such as *Tijuca*, even though many birdwatchers visit the range of both species in southeast Brazil each year, especially during the austral spring, the presumed breeding season. Elucidating the breeding strategy of these two small-range Atlantic Forest endemics remains a major 'prize' for any determined resident or visiting birdwatcher. As noted by Snow (1982: 27), the breeding seasons of most cotingas (and manakins) are reasonably closely tied to the overall season among passerines in the relevant region. In relation to climate, breeding by passerines in Central and South America usually commences in the late dry season and continues through the first part of the wet season. As many manakins forage on both fruit and insects, this would be a logical time of year for nesting activity. Snow (1982) also pointed to the extreme paucity of data for cotingas concerning the number of breeding attempts per season by a given individual. Such data remain pitifully few, but intensive studies of Pipridae breeding ecology in some parts of the continent have revealed almost staggeringly high levels of predation (cf. Snow 2004b: 139, for a brief résumé), confirming Snow's (1982: 20) remark 'that a high proportion of nesting attempts end in failure'. The number of nesting attempts is known for very few species, but repeat nesting would be expected in areas of high predation such as lowland tropical forests.

In those manakins studied to date, two-egg clutches are the norm and the incubating female spends relatively long periods at the nest (up to four consecutive hours), with only short breaks (off-bouts) for feeding in the near vicinity. Female manakins often maintain a somewhat vigilant posture on the nest, apparently to aid their ability to 'merge into their surroundings'. The same is true of at least some female cotingas, e.g. *Lipaugus* and *Xipholena*. Although many Neotropical passerines sit 'very tight' during the later stages of incubation (GMK pers. obs.), female manakins do appear to be unusually 'tame' while incubating; Skutch (1949) related how some Red-capped Manakins *Pipra mentalis* would remain steadfast on the nest permitting him to advance within touching distance. Like cotingas, the incubation period (at *c.*17–19 days in some *Pipra*, *Lepidothrix* and *Manacus*) in at least some manakins appears to be relatively protracted (although it might be remarked that data for many species are still rather few). It has been speculated that a long incubation period enhances nestling survivorship, for the same reason as in cotingas, and it certainly seems to be the case that the interval between hatching and fledging is less protracted for manakins (and to a certain extent among the even fewer number of cotingas for which such data are available). However, even for manakins the data in respect of fledging periods are even less robust than those available for incubation periods.

In general, those nestlings of cotingas that have been described are thickly covered in down (see photographs of a nestling Bearded Bellbird *Procnias averano* in Snow 2004a: 66), except for those of cocks-of-the-rock *Rupicola*, although these species do possess unusually long down. However, the diversity in appearance of the nestlings is remarkable, and probably again linked to the requirement for concealment; for example, the hatchling Bare-necked Fruitcrow *Gymnoderus foetidus* resembles lichen, while nestling purpletufts are able to impersonate another piece of tree bark rather impressively (Snow 2004a: 58). In contrast, manakins on hatching are almost naked with just a slight covering of grey down. It is probable that young manakins are more frequently brooded by the adult female than perhaps the majority of cotingas, making heat conservation more important among the latter group. Again, breeding data can prove useful in studies of relationships, as the former 'manakin' Thrush-like Schiffornis *Schiffornis turdina* atypically (for a piprid) is densely covered in down at this stage (Skutch 1969; see also Collins 2010: 98 for a brief review). The nestling of Elegant Mourner *Laniisoma elegans* (another species now placed in the Tityridae) is unquestionably one of the most bizarre-looking nestlings in the avian world, and is depicted on Plate 15. Recent (not-yet published) observations have revealed that the unfledged young of Cinereous Mourner *Laniocera hypopyrra* (which genus has recently been proven to be a close relative of *Laniisoma*) is equally remarkable. Snow (1982: 27) suggested that the *Laniisoma* nestling has evolved to resemble 'a moss covered with fruiting bodies', which would surely prove advantageous in the species' humid foothill habitat where lichens and mosses grow commonly, but the same can hardly be true of the *Laniocera* in its Amazonian range. However, as already noted by Snow (1982), the nestlings of several 'true' cotingas possess down which contrasts in colour with their nest-sites (see also above), so other factors are clearly at work here. Unlike for cotingas, we have a much better knowledge of food provisioning and nestling care among manakins, although it is still true to say that most species of Pipridae require more data in respect of this part of their natural histories. Most manakin chicks are fed both insects and fruit pulp, usually carried in the throat of the female, and feeds are usually infrequent (which is probably also true for nestling cotingas). The nest is generally kept clean by the adults, who remove faecal sacs from the surroundings (and in the instance of a pair of Fiery-throated Fruiteaters *Pipreola chlorolepidota* they even occasionally regurgitated droppings to the nestlings: Gelis *et al.* 2006). However, older Pipridae nestlings often defecate over the side of the nest, which must make the surroundings below the nest clearly visible to potential predators.

All adult female cotingas undergo a complete moult immediately following the end of the breeding season, and the same is true for those manakins studied to date. This is also the case for the males of those cotinga species that partake in nesting activities. Where males are emancipated from nesting activity, they tend to commence their moult prior to the start of the nesting season, sometimes while even still involved in courtship (see Snow 1982: 28–29, for a breakdown of our knowledge by genus).

FOOD AND FORAGING

As is very well known, cotingas and manakins are primarily frugivorous, although insects do feature, to some extent, in the diets of many species and amongst some of the larger cotingas they can be an important dietary component. Indeed, in species such as the Crimson Fruitcrow *Haematoderus militaris* larger insects such as beetles, cicadas and orthopterans are the major items present in analysis of stomach contents, although in recent years evidence of its liking for fruit has become available. Nonetheless, despite such 'discrepancies', large cotingas are amongst the most important seed-dispersers in Neotropical forests, sharing this role with toucans (Ramphastidae). The type of fruit taken largely depends on the overall size of the species in question, and also to some extent on the time of day the foraging activity occurs, but it is still true that many cotingas show some degree of preference for fruits of the families Cecropiaceae and Araliaceae. Other consistently important families in the diets of cotingas include the Lauraceae, Burseraceae, Myristicaceae and Melastomataceae, but it is worth remarking that we are still (like Snow 1982, 2004a) waiting for good qualitative (and quantitative) data for the 'white-winged' (*Xipholena*) and 'blue' (*Cotinga*) cotingas. Overall, however, many species (of both cotingas and manakins) are now known to possess comparatively broad diets in terms of the number of different fruits recorded. As noted by Snow (2004a), classic examples of such catholicity are provided by Guianan Cock-of-the-Rock *Rupicola rupicola*, which has been recorded taking fruits of 65 plant species belonging to 31 families in just one month at a single locality (Érard *et al.* 1989), and Bearded Bellbird *Procnias averano*, which on Trinidad alone has been recorded taking fruits from 20 different plant families (Snow 1982). And, among the Pipridae, Blue-crowned Manakin *Lepidothrix coronata* has been recorded taking the fruits of 49 species of woody plants in the lowlands of eastern Ecuador (Loiselle *et al.* 2007a), but is easily 'topped' by White-bearded Manakin *Manacus manacus* recorded taking the fruits of 105 different plant species on Trinidad (Snow 2004b: 123).

Many of the smaller species (with tinier, but nonetheless still comparatively wide gapes *vis-à-vis* other bird families), including the vast majority of manakins, tend to be highly dependent on smaller melastome (Melastomataceae) fruits; these are high in sugar content and particularly favoured during the early daylight hours for a quick energy 'fix'. The major role of the Melastomataceae followed by the Rubiaceae has been confirmed by dietary studies in French Guiana (Théry 1990c). Larger fruits, which sometimes appear to be almost too large for the bird to deal with comfortably, are often 'juggled' in the bill prior to swallowing, this process presumably enabling the bird to soften the fruit. Many Pipridae are also frequent takers of insects and spiders, even occasionally following army ants in their pursuit of such prey (Willis 1984), and in some cases their young might be largely fed on such items at least during the first few days of life (see, for example, Lill 1975, in respect of White-bearded Manakin). Fewer than a handful of cotingas have also been observed following army ants (see, for example, Willis 1983), but in the cases of both families the lack of suitable perches close to ground level and, especially, the number of other successful, specialised ant-followers presumably act as deterrents to such activity (Snow 2004b: 123). As explained in the overview chapter discussing breeding biology, our knowledge of cotinga nesting is still rudimentary for the vast majority of species, but those data that are available (e.g. for the fruitcrows, Cinnamon-vented Piha *Lipaugus lanioides* and Capuchinbird *Perissocephalus tricolor*) suggest that nestling cotingas are also more dependent on invertebrates, although this is certainly not the case for all species (see Gelis *et al.* 2006). Thrush-like Schiffornis *Schiffornis turdina* is known to be especially insectivorous, and even feeds large caterpillars to its nestlings (Skutch 1969), although it should also be remarked that there is plenty of evidence of the importance of typical fruits in its diet, including both Melastomataceae and Rubiaceae (Poulin *et al.* 1999). Manakins are well known for their efficiency in seed dispersal: the two-species study (one *Manacus* and one *Pipra*) by Andrea Worthington in Panama revealed that larger seeds might be regurgitated in as little as *c.*7 minutes and the minimum time for seeds to pass through the digestive system was similarly short. Pipridae are also significant in seed dispersal because they often defecate at edges or in clearings, or other sites where pioneer plants will find it 'easier' to gain a foothold.

Several species of cotingas and manakins are mistletoe (Loranthaceae) specialists: for example, the high-Andean White-cheeked Cotinga *Zaratornis stresemanni* (which seems particularly dependent on two genera, *Tristerix* and *Ligaria*: Parker 1981), the spectacular Swallow-tailed Cotinga *Phibalura flavirostris* and the tiny purpletufts (*Iodopleura*), which are now known not to be cotingas. The example provided by White-cheeked Cotinga seems to one of the very few (if not the only) instance of a member of the Cotingidae or Pipridae being dependent on such a tiny range of fruit species (see above). The two fruit genera in question are probably almost entirely dependent on this cotinga for seed dispersal. Théry's (1990c) French Guianan research demonstrated that Pipridae in general are certainly extremely important to seed dispersal of their two favoured families of woody plants (see above). The stunningly rare Kinglet Calyptura *Calyptura cristata* is also speculated to belong to this group of mistletoe specialists, but there is no suggestion that it is unusually restricted in its diet. In contrast, larger fruits, among them *Ficus* figs (Moraceae) and laurels (Lauraceae), can only be accommodated by birds with much wider gapes, such as bellbirds (genus *Procnias*). These fruits are protein-rich and constitute an extremely good energy source, thereby emancipating species such as bellbirds from much diurnal foraging activity, and enabling the males, in particular, to spend most of the day vocalising in their territories. This also has implications for breeding strategies, a subject covered in the relevant section. Apart from an old record of snail-eating by Bare-throated Bellbird *P. nudicollis*, the genus appears to be exclusively frugivorous, which might prove to be virtually unique among the Cotingidae. The blue cotingas might also be strongly dependent on *Ficus* fruits.

The three species of plantcutters (*Phytotoma*) are unusual among the species covered here in being herbivores (bud, shoot and leaf specialists), although to some extent the birds also take fruits. Furthermore, Rufous-tailed Plantcutter *P. rara* is known to take at least some insects, and its nestlings are apparently exclusively fed them, which might be speculated to be true of the other two species as well. Unlike most other species covered here, adults of any of the three species can descend to the ground to feed, do not engage in aerial sallies and are also unusual in regularly flocking during foraging behaviour (exceptionally up to 100 individuals of White-tipped Plantcutter *P. rutila* have been recorded together).

Records of more unusual dietary elements are, to date, confined to the Cotingidae, which is relatively unsurprising given their generally larger size. As already mentioned there is a single record of snails being recorded in the diet of a bellbird, and recently one observer reported that *Plekokeilas* land snails were regularly taken using aerial sallies by both sexes of Scaled Fruiteater *Ampelioides tschudii* (this species apparently regularly takes insects) at a site in northwest Ecuador (Williams 2002). Such 'aberrant' behaviour has not been reported for any of the *Pipreola* fruiteaters, which like the genera *Cotinga* and *Xipholena*, was long thought to be exclusively frugivorous. However, all three of these genera probably take advantage of aerial swarms of winged termites (Isoptera) or flying ants (Hymenoptera), as do some manakins. However, note that at the only nest of Fiery-throated Fruiteater *Pipreola chlorolepidota* found to date, the adults apparently brought only fruit to their growing nestlings (Gelis *et al.* 2006). Both of the *Rupicola* species are known to (probably regularly) feed their young small vertebrates, such as lizards and frogs, while Screaming Piha *Lipaugus vociferans* has been recorded taking an *Anolis* lizard and Capuchinbird a roosting bat (Whittaker 1996a).

Among both cotingas and manakins, fruit is usually procured by sallying from a lower perch, plucking the individual fruit and then returning to the same or another lower perch to consume it. Although some fruit is also taken while perched, usually in particularly advantageous situations and using a lunging movement from above, insects are taken almost exclusively in flight. The peculiar Sharpbill *Oxyruncus cristatus* (here placed in it own family) is especially remarkable in its dexterity while foraging, not only hopping sideways along branches and probing clusters of dead leaves and epiphytes, but even hanging upside down from the thin outer branches of trees. In their review of avian frugivory in the Neotropics, Moermond and Denslow (1985) found that birds use four methods for procuring fruit: hovering, stalling, swooping or snatching. The method used depends on the wing loading of the species in question and they discovered that specialised frugivores use any one of the first three methods. Hovering tends to be used by birds weighing less than 20g, e.g. most of the smaller manakins. Stalling is the principal method employed by birds such as trogons (Trogonidae), with short but deeply slotted wing-tips, and swooping is a rather specialised method used by those species with long, broad wings, such as Purple-throated Fruitcrow *Querula purpurata*.

Among cotingas and manakins, foraging is often accompanied by the sound of whirring wings, which often proves a good method of locating larger frugivores, and even small manakins when close to, although the noise could just as easily be caused by an aracari, trogon or larger tanager. Unfortunately, the corollary of this noisy but infrequent foraging is the difficulty involved in locating individual birds during those periods when they are comparatively inactive. This is particularly so for 'sluggish' birds such as fruiteaters and pihas, which do not tend to perch in open situations, unlike the bellbirds or 'blue' cotingas. For those species that are also comparatively less vocal, encountering them can be doubly difficult, and in the case of birds such as Elegant Mourner *Laniisoma elegans*, often incredibly so. It is also axiomatic that the presence of frugivorous birds in a given area also increases the potential for other such species to be located; for example, a foraging group of Pale-mandibled Aracari *Pteroglossus erythropygius* in western Ecuador may well be accompanied by a lone Long-wattled Umbrellabird *Cephalopterus penduliger*. Sitting and watching a fruiting strangler fig anywhere in the Neotropics could yield sightings of a wide variety of frugivores, from thrushes and tanagers to toucans and quetzals, including a variety of cotingas and manakins.

Despite the fact that, away from their leks, most cotingas and manakins are relatively solitary species, they will effectively consort with other species (both conspecifics, congenerics and otherwise) at fruiting trees. Some species will also join mixed-species foraging flocks, although such behaviour, e.g. among some *Pipreola*, might be limited to the confines of their own territory. Aggressive interactions with other frugivores at food sources appear to have been rarely reported in the literature. Such gatherings of frugivorous birds are one of the fascinations of birdwatching anywhere in the tropics. For hornbills (Bucerotidae) and broadbills (Eurylaimidae) in the Oriental region, swap turacos (Musophagidae) in the Afrotropics, and cotingas, manakins, larger tanagers (Thraupidae) and toucans in the Neotropics. The only pantropical frugivorous family is the barbets (Capitonidae), which is relatively poorly represented over most parts of the Neotropics, but a frequent constituent of most sub-Saharan African woodlands.

CONSERVATION AND THE RISE OF NEOTROPICAL BIRDING

Various conservation non-governmental organisations (NGOs) have addressed the issue of ensuring the survival of the world's birds for future generations, and in so doing have proposed various protocols for threat categories, as well as habitat status. Nonetheless, those with most widespread currency are those developed by the International Union for the Conservation of Nature (IUCN) for all biota, and applied to birds by BirdLife International. The first relevant publication in this endeavour was the bird section of the Red Data book's second edition, published in the late 1970s (King 1978–79), which listed just five cotingas as being threatened with extinction; no manakins qualified for the inventory. The International Council for Bird Preservation (now known as BirdLife International) subsequently published the first edition of *Birds to Watch* (Collar and Andrew 1988), which revised the total number of threatened cotingas and manakins (as treated here) to 14. The seminal work, referred to extensively in virtually any publication concerning the conservation of Neotropical birds, is *Threatened Birds of the Americas* (Collar *et al.* 1992). This comprehensive and extraordinarily detailed tome provided in-depth analysis into the status of many species included in the first Red Data book. Relevant specimens in many of the world's major collections were inventoried, with comments regarding the limitations of certain label information (particularly with regard to collection sites). Much anecdotal (and unpublished) information was included from field observers, and the entire publication was a marvellous exercise in synthesis and analysis of the threats facing Neotropical birds.

Particularly since the publication of the latter work, a burgeoning interest in the avifauna of the New World tropics, especially amongst native Latin Americans, has brought a staggering increase in publications concerning the avifauna of the region (the quantity of post-1990 publications listed in our Bibliography offers some testimony to this). Undoubtedly, the publication of high-quality field guides such as those to Panama (Ridgely and Gwynne 1976), Venezuela (Meyer de Schauensee and Phelps 1978 , Hilty 2003), Colombia (Hilty and Brown 1986), Costa Rica (Stiles and Skutch 1989), Mexico (Howell and Webb 1995) and more recently Ecuador (Ridgely and Greenfield 2001), northern South America as a whole (Restall *et al.* 2006) and Peru (Schulenberg *et al.* 2007) have proved major stimuli in this endeavour, enabling amateurs to identify a great many of the region's bird species correctly. These works have been massively abetted by the production of two volumes covering all of the passerines of South America (Ridgely and Tudor 1989, 1994), as well as a superb handbook to the birds of higher elevations in the Andes (Fjeldså and Krabbe 1990). In particular, Tudor's unparalleled 'knack' amongst modern-day bird artists for capturing the essence of a given species from the 'bird continent' (like Louis Agassiz Fuertes before him) has unquestionably played its part in enthusing a new generation of birders and ornithologists to explore the highways and byways once the resort of but a few hardy specialists. It is also imperative to mention in this brief survey how fundamentally the widespread advent of sound-recording of Neotropical birds, pioneered by such 'heroes' as Paul Schwartz (Gorton 2010) and Ted Parker (Parker 1991, Remsen and Schulenberg 1997), has revolutionised our understanding of the distribution, abundance and life histories of many species across the American tropics. Even just 25 years ago, knowledge of the vocal repertoires of the greater percentage of Middle and South American birds was still very much in its infancy. Nowadays the birder afield has ready access to the vocalisations of the majority of species (even taxa) via commercially produced compendiums on CD or DVD, or via the internet (especially the resources offered at http://www.xeno-canto.org). For an excellent overview of this change in knowledge from a single-country perspective, that of Ecuador, see Moore (2008). It is worth emphasising that much of what newcomers to the Neotropical birding 'scene' might already take for granted has its basis in the developments of the last 25–30 years.

The genesis of the Neotropical Bird Club (with its journal *Cotinga* and subsequently the birding magazine, *Neotropical Birding*), coupled with the huge increase in travel to the region by the world's amateur and professional ornithologists, has also produced an enormous increase in the data available to researchers. For some examples of how birders can make a contribution to our cumulative knowledge see Hosner (2010). There is no doubt that the massive increase in data will entail reappraisal of the threat status for many Neotropical bird species (indeed, rediscoveries of hitherto suspected extinct or near-extinct species have been reported fairly regularly during the past two decades). The turn of the last century saw the publication of another landmark treatise by BirdLife International, *Threatened Birds of the World* (listing 16 cotingas and four manakins as at significant risk of extinction, i.e. in the category Vulnerable or higher). Subsequently, the listing was subject to a major overall in 2004 and near-annual revisions have been conducted since, with the result that one additional species of cotinga has now been added to that unfortunate list. For now, two of those species are considered Critically Endangered, the mysterious Kinglet Calyptura *Calyptura cristata* and the recently described Araripe Manakin *Antilophia bokermanni*. Remarkably, the former might yet prove to be less threatened than currently thought, despite the existence of just one reliable record in the past *c.*150

years. On the other hand, it might be working off a very long 'extinction debt', i.e. the time lag between the event precipitating a species' extinction and its loss in nature (see Donald *et al.* 2010: 264–265). As of late 2010, an additional six species of 'cotingas' and one manakin are treated by BirdLife International as Near Threatened, two of which (Cinnamon-vented Piha *Lipaugus lanioides* and Buff-throated Purpletuft *Iodopleura pipra*) were listed as Vulnerable or Endangered, respectively, in *Threatened Birds of the World*. Data provided by the apparently ever-expanding band of travelling amateur birdwatchers have played a significant role in this process of deciding which are the world's rarest birds. Meanwhile, *Key Areas for Birds in the Neotropics* (Wege and Long 1995) and *Endemic Bird Areas of the World: Priority Sites for Biodiversity Conservation* (Stattersfield *et al.* 1998), both also published by BirdLife International, serve to give a perspective on a more holistic approach to conservation, namely preserving critical habitats or sites in their entirety rather than simply focusing on 'flagship species'. This work was furthered via BirdLife's Important Bird Areas (IBA) programme, originally launched in Europe and since extended globally. Most countries in the Neotropics have now published their own IBA inventories, that for Brazil running to two volumes (Bencke *et al.* 2006, De Luca *et al.* 2009), with an overview volume having also been published for the entire Americas (Devenish *et al.* 2009).

The developments summarised above offer hope for the future. But, sad to say, to some (far from insignificant) extent, it is the same processes that have permitted our knowledge to increase by such leaps and bounds that are imperilling the same near-boundless biodiversity we seek to understand and revel in. More infrastructure equals more access to previously inaccessible areas (and formerly near-mythical birds) but these developments are, truth to tell, far too frequently harbingers of doom for wildlife. Until now at least, the arrival of the road meant that the axe, chainsaw and other instruments of habitat change were 'hot on its heels'. Habitat modification and, in the worst-case scenario, complete destruction is the major cause of endangerment of the Neotropical avifauna. But while simultaneously endeavouring to deal with this issue, other conservation problems also require addressing, without even considering the wider issue and challenge posed by climate change (a recent study has attempted to predict the effect of this on the manakins, a group with comparatively few globally threatened species in their midst, with alarming results). The capturing of wild birds for the cagebird trade (both indigenous and for export) has undoubtedly brought some birds close to extinction, even without further stresses caused by other environmental problems. In many cases environmental degradation goes hand in hand with trapping to create a negative synergy which can only hasten a species' extinction. A classic example is the Seven-coloured Tanager *Tangara fastuosa* (Vulnerable), whose northeast Brazilian humid forest habitat has been almost totally converted to sugarcane, at the same time as it has become a popular cagebird for the domestic market (Silveira *et al.* 2003b). Fortunately, the species does seem to be adapting to the new circumstances in which it finds itself: pure serendipity, rather than design. Worse still, Spix's Macaw *Cyanopsitta spixi*, seemingly always rare, had declined to a single known individual by the mid 1990s and had become extinct in the wild by the turn of the century, its population remorselessly eradicated by the capture of both adults and young for the cagebird trade. The gradual, but reversible, deterioration of the species' tenuous gallery forest habitat exacerbated the situation, and such habitat degradation has made the re-establishment of a new population derived from captured individuals even more difficult (Juniper 2004). Fortunately, there are a relatively small number of species of serious interest to the indigenous cagebird trade in Neotropical countries, although there is a well-organised (and often illegal) international trade in particular groups such as the psittacids. The indigenous trade quite often reflects a bird's vocal virtuosity and still relatively common birds such as seedeaters feature strongly in a cagebird inventory. Nonetheless, a species' apparent abundance is no cause for complacency. The once-widespread Great-billed Seed Finch *Sporophila* (*Oryzoborus*) *maximiliani* (Near Threatened) has declined catastrophically across its entire South America range, almost entirely due to an insatiable and unsustainable desire to keep them in cages. The amazing vocalisation of the Bare-throated Bellbird *Procnias nudicollis* (Vulnerable) has made it a popular cagebird in Brazil, to the significant detriment of the wild population. Indeed, within its range, an observer will often be more likely to hear one of these birds calling from a cage in a village home than from the tops of trees in adjacent forest.

The hunting of birds for the pot is a frequently understandable, but nonetheless major problem in some areas. In many remote rural regions, the lack of protein in the diet is militated for by shooting 'bushmeat' in adjacent forests. This has led to the local extinctions of particularly vulnerable groups such as cracids and primates, which can be extremely common and sometimes even relatively tame in protected areas, but which often survive for just a relatively short time following contact with an expanding human population (see, for example, Peres and Palacios 2007, Wright *et al.* 2007, Haugaasen and Peres 2008, Parry *et al.* 2009). Virtually any bird (or mammal) that is relatively slow-moving and large can be 'fair game', which includes some larger cotingas such as umbrellabirds. Indeed, Long-wattled Umbrellabird (Vulnerable) of the Chocó of western Colombia and northwest Ecuador suffers from hunting for food, capture for the cagebird trade *and* the catastrophic loss of its foothill habitat, especially in Ecuador, where extensive forest clearance within the species' range commenced as recently as the 1960s.

The birds themselves, of course, neither know nor care for bureaucratic designations, they simply have to try and survive in a region that seems to regard 'development' as entailing nothing less than wholesale habitat destruction. There is no doubt that particular 'critical habitats' are in major danger (the Atlantic Forest of southeast Brazil, northeast Argentina and eastern Paraguay are good examples). However, the geography of many of these habitats is such that the political realities of conservation entail co-operation by more than one administration. However, some cross-border national parks have been established, for example La Amistad, which straddles the boundary between Costa Rica and Panama.

The realisation that some Neotropical species are altitudinal migrants (including cotingas such as Bare-necked Umbrellabird *Cephalopterus glabricollis* and Three-wattled Bellbird *Procnias tricarunculatus*, both of which are globally threatened) demands the preservation of pristine altitudinal gradients to enable these species to persist. This, in turn, compounds the problems conservationists face in designating proposed protected areas, as it is the lower elevations which are of most importance agriculturally. Very few montane areas in the Neotropics face total devastation, although certain habitat types such as *Polylepis* woodlands, upon which several cotingas are partially dependent, are under severe pressure from over-exploitation. Three globally threatened cotingas, White-cheeked Cotinga *Zaratornis stresemanni*, Chestnut-bellied *Doliornis remseni* and Bay-vented Cotingas *D. sclateri*, are confined to high-altitude Andean woodlands; the first two were discovered within the last *c.*50 years, while all are considered Vulnerable and are at risk due to agricultural encroachment and forest clearance for firewood. However, it is lowland habitats in many areas that are almost inevitably the first to be converted, although vast areas of the Amazon Basin remain in a pristine condition, though for how much longer is increasingly uncertain. In western Peru, the plight of the globally Endangered Peruvian Plantcutter *Phytotoma raimondii* has worsened steadily in recent decades as its riparian thickets and desert scrub habitats are destroyed. Fortunately, *P. raimondii* is now the subject of reasonably intensive work designed to save it. Elsewhere, many lowland biomes to all intents are almost completely 'gone', for example the Atlantic Forest of Alagoas and Pernambuco in northeastern Brazil, and the Chocó forests of northwest Ecuador. Further south in eastern Brazil, the range of the lovely Banded Cotinga *Cotinga maculata* is under extreme threat, with many of its former strongholds reduced in area and others apparently largely abandoned for unknown reasons. Currently listed as Endangered, if its situation does not ameliorate, this species might yet join the select band of Critically Endangered birds. Five other globally threatened cotingas are confined to the Atlantic Forest biome (and four classified as Near Threatened), while three of the four species of globally threatened Pipridae are more or less restricted to the same region. The majority of these birds are now largely confined to protected areas, but it is always those species most dependent on lowland areas, such as Black-headed Berryeater *Carpornis melanocephala* (Vulnerable) whose circumstances are the most threatened. However, one of these, the remarkable Araripe Manakin, might yet serve as a classic test case for how to save a species apparently precariously balanced on the brink of extinction from a seemingly inevitable fate. Another of these Atlantic Forest endemics, Black-capped Piprites *Piprites pileata*, remains to some extent inexplicably rare, especially in Argentina where it has only recently been seen again after going unrecorded for many years. The same is true of another species of this genus, Grey-headed Piprites *Piprites griseiceps* of Central America, which is a very poorly known bird that was formerly listed as Near Threatened, and given the collective state of our knowledge of it is a bird 'crying out' for some decent research into its ecology and requirements.

The soils of many lowland areas are insufficient to promote sustainable agriculture, and are often sacrificed to extensive cattle ranching following just a few productive years. Indeed, this has been one of the major destructive agents in the Amazon Basin in the last few decades, although many parts of eastern and southern Amazonia within the so-called 'Arc of Deforestation' have at least initially been cleared for soya crops. As yet, few birds from the families covered by this book number among the Amazon's most threatened, with the recently rediscovered Golden-crowned Manakin *Lepidothrix vilasboasi* (Vulnerable) being the only high-profile example, principally owing to its relatively small range and the advancing agricultural frontier, the product of an increasing human population and the planned paving of the main road through this region. Provided sufficient forest remains, even probably selectively logged or secondary growth, this species should survive. The geographically and genetically close Opal-crowned Manakin *Lepidothrix iris* was formerly treated as Near Threatened, but improved knowledge of its situation has led to this species being downgraded to of Least Concern, although at least part of its range lies well within the 'Arc of Deforestation'.

The situation in many subtropical areas is even more critical. Elevations between 1,000 and 2,000m are optimum for the growing of cash crops such as coffee and marijuana, and the forests of the entire east slope of the Andes of Colombia, Ecuador and Peru are threatened by these macro-economic factors. Many cotingas and manakins are closely associated with upper tropical and subtropical elevations in the Andes, including several rare fruiteaters (*Pipreola* spp.), most notably Fiery-throated Fruiteater *P. chlorolepidota* (Near Threatened), as well as the rare Scimitar-winged Piha *Lipaugus uropygialis* (Vulnerable) of southeast Peru and adjacent Bolivia, but also others of wider range, including Amazonian Umbrellabird *Cephalopterus ornatus*.

There are protected areas which include a range of elevations within their designations, but these also require adequate protection, rather than being mere 'paper parks'. It was formerly thought that Kinglet Calyptura may have been eradicated by the almost total clearance of forest between sea level and 1,000m in the vicinity of Rio de Janeiro, much of this destruction having occurred in the first half of the 19th century (see Lambert and Kirwan 2010). This highlights another problem facing conservationists: species with restricted ranges. Kinglet Calyptura is an extreme example, although there is another cotingid in the same area which is probably even more geographically restricted, Grey-winged Cotinga *Tijuca condita*, but being a bird of the high mountain tops this is more secure than the calyptura (the danger from dry-season fires and human disturbance notwithstanding).

Virtually all habitat types in the Neotropics are represented within the ranges of cotingas and manakins, from the *Polylepis* woods of the high Andes to the mangrove forests of southern Central America (and their Yellow-billed Cotingas *Carpodectes antoniae*), and anywhere in the region where burgeoning human populations are juxtaposed with exploitable wooded areas will mean the continuing destruction of habitats. One of the great paradigms of the 21st century is the breaking of this umbilical relationship, to the equal benefit of humans and wildlife. Many NGOs throughout the world, including Latin America, are now endeavouring to do just that, sometimes with a degree of success at least in respect of conserving some key flagship species. The work of ProAves in Colombia and Fundación Jocotoco in Ecuador offer two cases in point. However, the issue is not just one of changing the mindset of the general public, but also of producing a mutually beneficial and true partnership between conservationists and scientists. While rarely at loggerheads, it is certainly the case that these two groups could integrate rather better than they frequently do, to the ultimate benefit of wildlife.

SYSTEMATICS

As noted in the Taxonomy and Nomenclature section of How to Use this Book (pp. 14–15), generic and familial relationships among those species traditionally considered part of the Cotingidae or Pipridae have been subject to substantial revision in recent decades, principally with the widespread advent of molecular-based ornithology. This section discusses the state of our knowledge of relationships within these groups, family by family, genus by genus. This approach has both advantages and disadvantages, one of the latter being some degree of repetition across closely related genera in referring to published findings. We make no apology for any duplication, as we suspect many readers will 'dip into' this section somewhat haphazardly.

Despite this book being titled *Cotingas and Manakins*, as will become swiftly apparent, on current knowledge, the species chosen for inclusion are best considered members of five or six different families. Many of the systematic changes described in the text that follows have only become apparent or have garnered deep-rooted support in the course of the past two decades. Within the text for each genus, the accent is firmly on what the results of genetic work tell us, although studies based on anatomy or other factors are mentioned where we consider such work to be especially interesting or insightful. However, we have not attempted to provide an in-depth history of the systematic treatment of every genus, interesting though that might have proven to be, simply because the result would have been too long. In any case, most treatments up to and including the second half of the 20th century were based as much on intuition and informed guesswork as relevant taxonomic characters.

Several notes and disclaimers must be made here. What follows constitutes a brief review of the literature, distilled wherever possible into reasonable layman's terms, although some may find reference to the Glossary (pp. 21–23) helpful in explaining some unavoidable use of taxonomic terminology. We have not included headings for those genera outside the remit of this book, most notably *Pachyramphus*, *Xenopsaris* and *Tityra*, which form the remainder of the Tityridae as constituted here. Our general policy has been to follow the findings of Tello *et al.* (2009) in respect of order, systematics and nomenclature, but occasional deviations became almost 'unavoidable'. (Many of Tello *et al.*'s findings reasonably closely replicate those of other recent phylogenies.) So, for instance we have treated *Oxyruncus* (Sharpbill) as the sole member of a family and have deviated from those authors in our linear arrangement within the Phytotominae, albeit entirely for 'cosmetic' reasons. At the end, we treat three genera as *Incertae Sedis*, but two of them at least appear likely to be members of the Tyrannidae. The third, *Phibalura*, might be expected to 'remain' part of the Cotingidae, once genetic data become available and are tested extensively, but one 'rule of thumb' when considering these groups of taxa has proved to be 'expect the unexpected'. Authors of families, subfamilies and genera are presented, but we have avoided use of complete citations – such information can be found in works such as *Handbook of the Birds of the World* (Snow 2004a, 2004b, and others), and for some genera AOU (1998), as well as online at Alan Peterson's very useful http://www.zoonomen.net. Bock (1994) is a useful source for family-level group names, although see Olson (1996).

FAMILY EURYLAIMIDAE, Lesson, 1831

Genus *Sapayoa*, E. Hartert, 1903 (one species)

Because Fjeldså *et al.* (2003) and Chesser (2004) clearly showed that *Sapayoa* is more closely related to the Old World suboscines than to any of the New World suboscine groups (a concept first postulated by Warter 1965), and Irestedt *et al.* (2006) and Moyle *et al.* (2006) found that it is embedded within the Old World suboscine family Eurylaimidae, we follow Remsen *et al.* (2009) in placing the remarkable Broad-billed Sapayoa *S. aenigma* within that family. Some recent authors, e.g. Sibley and Monroe (1990) and Dickinson (2003), placed *S. aenigma* in its own family, the Sapayoaidae, and this course of action was recently also taken by Chesser *et al.* (2011). Both of the most recent genetic studies found the Old World broadbill (and asity) species to form two sister clades, one consisting of *Calyptomena* (green broadbills) and *Smithornis* (African broadbills), the other comprising a host of generally smaller southern and East Asian and Malagasy genera, namely *Eurylaimus* (Banded *E. javanicus* and Black-and-yellow Broadbills *E. ochromalus*), *Cymbirhynchus* (Black-and-red Broadbill), *Serilophus* (Silver-breasted Broadbill), *Corydon* (Dusky Broadbill), *Psarisomus* (Long-tailed Broadbill), *Pseudocalyptomena* (Grauer's Broadbill), *Neodrepanis* (sunbird-asities) and *Philepitta* (asities). Some doubt remains as to the species' precise position within the family, as Irestedt *et al.* (2006) found *Sapayoa* to be sister to the *Calyptomena*/*Smithornis* clade, whereas Moyle *et al.* (2006) found *Sapayoa* to be sister to the second clade. Incidentally, it is worthy of remark that as long ago as the mid-19th century commentators such as Alfred Russell Wallace were remarking on the probability of a close relationship between the southeast Asian broadbills (Eurylaimidae) and the Neotropical Cotingidae (cf. Olson 1971: 511).

FAMILY PIPRIDAE, Rafinesque, 1815

SUBFAMILY NEOPELMINAE, Tello, Moyle, Marchese & Cracraft, 2009

Genus *Neopelma*, P. L. Sclater, 1860 (five species)

Rêgo *et al.* (2007) in their molecular analysis of the Pipridae found evidence to suggest that both *Tyranneutes* and *Neopelma* might lie outwith the true manakins, but are the most closely related taxa to the latter group, and this position had previously been taken by Lanyon (1985), Prum *et al.* (2000) and Chesser (2004), but rejected by Prum and Lanyon's (1989) study of syringeal morphology, nest characteristics and plumage. McKay *et al.* (2010) also found *Tyranneutes* and *Neopelma* to be sister to all other manakins. To emphasise their somewhat unique position, Gill and Wright (2006) elected to use the genus's scientific name as the English group name too, but also placed *Neopelma* within the Tyrannidae. More recently, however, Tello *et al.* (2009) erected a new subfamily, the Neopelminae (type genus *Neopelma*), for *Neopelma* and *Tyranneutes*, which they found to be sister to all other taxa within the Pipridae (although their taxon sampling was far from complete), thereby to some extent confirming the findings of Rêgo *et al.* (2007).

Genus *Tyranneutes*, P. L. Sclater & Salvin, 1881 (two species)

For a summation of recent genetic findings concerning this small genus, see *Neopelma*. *Tyranneutes* and *Neopelma* are the sole constituents of the recently created Neopelminae (of which the type genus is obviously *Neopelma*).

SUBFAMILY PIPRINAE, Prum 1992

Genus *Pipra*, Linnaeus, 1764 (eight species)

The recent genetic study by Rêgo *et al.* (2007) found that the genus *Pipra* as constituted here is polyphyletic and appears to be split into two groups (although they did not sample all species). They recommended resurrecting *Ceratopipo* (a name originally employed solely for Scarlet-horned Manakin *P. cornuta*) to full generic, rather than subgeneric status (as employed by Prum 1992) for the entire *Pipra erythrocephala* clade (see p. 138). However, the nuclear gene study of Tello *et al.* (2009), who sampled just two species, Golden-headed Manakin *P. erythrocephala* and Wire-tailed Manakin *P. filicauda*, although confirming that Prum's (1992) classification of *Pipra* is indeed polyphyletic, found evidence to suggest that *P. erythrocephala* is closely related to White-crowned Manakin *Dixiphia pipra* and to *Machaeropterus*. (The close relationship to *Machaeropterus* was also recovered by Rêgo *et al.* 2007.) Because *Dixiphia* has priority by some four years as a genus name over *Ceratopipo*, Tello *et al.* (2009) advocated its use. Nonetheless, although *Pipra* remains polyphyletic, we maintain the same order and systematics as Snow (2004b) in the belief that, in this case, stability is the best option until a clear, and we hope unambiguous, multi-loci genetic dataset for all relevant taxa becomes available.

Genus *Lepidothrix*, Bonaparte, 1854 (eight species)

All of the species now included in *Lepidothrix* were previously included in the genus *Pipra* (e.g. by Hellmayr 1929b, Meyer de Schauensee 1970, Snow 1979b, Ridgely and Tudor 1994), but (*L.*) *serena* and (*L.*) *suavissima* (then considered subspecies) were removed to *Lepidothrix* by Prum (1988), and the rest of the species treated here as members of this genus were subsequently transferred herein on the recommendation of Prum (1992). Subsequently, additional genetic support for this position has been uncovered by both Rêgo *et al.* (2007) and Tello *et al.* (2009), thereby confirming that the expanded genus *Pipra* that had been recognised for much of the 20th century is polyphyletic. Tello *et al.* (2009) suggested that *Pipra* and *Lepidothrix* might be closely related, but with weak or no support for this position, and neither of these recent molecular studies was able to resolve satisfactorily the relationship of a monophyletic *Lepidothrix* to other members of the Piprinae (namely the genera *Pipra*, *Manacus*, *Heterocercus*, *Machaeropterus* and *Dixiphia*). Most recently, Paclt (2009) considered the name *Lepidothrix* to be preoccupied by its use for a thysanuran genus that has sometimes been accorded family status, and introduced the name *Neolepidothrix* in its place. However, some doubt seems to exist concerning the validity of this proposal and we have continued to use *Lepidothrix* at least for now.

Genus *Manacus*, Brisson, 1760 (four species)

Snow (1975) commented that *Manacus* and *Machaeropterus* might be each other's closest relatives, based on the thickened shafts to the secondary feathers and their choice of display perches. Prum (1992), in contrast, speculated that *Manacus* was most closely related (sister) to a clade containing *Antilophia* and *Chiroxiphia*. With the advent of genetic techniques to resolve such problems, Brumfield and Braun (2001) noted that *Manacus* is more closely related to the Red-capped Manakin *Pipra mentalis* + Band-tailed Manakin *P. fasciicauda* + White-crowned *Dixiphia pipra* group. Tello *et al.*'s (2009) more wide-ranging nuclear gene study sampled two members of *Manacus*, finding weak support for a relationship to *Heterocercus*. More importantly, they found better resolution for including *Manacus* within their subfamily Piprinae, along with all of the *Pipra* taxa, *Dixiphia*, *Machaeropterus* and *Heterocercus*. McKay *et al.* (2010) also found that *Manacus* groups with *Pipra*, *Dixiphia* and *Machaeropterus* but emphasised the need for additional work to resolve this genus' relationships satisfactorily.

Genus *Heterocercus*, P. L. Sclater, 1862 (three species)

The genus *Heterocercus* comprises a beautiful and strikingly large-sized series of manakins, which on the basis of their syringeal morphology were considered to be perhaps most closely related to *Pipra* (Prum 1992), whilst their displays and nest architecture (which are only incompletely known) suggested the possibility of a sister relationship with *Corapipo* (Prum 1990a, Alvarez Alonso 2001, Snow 2004b). Most recently, genetic (both mitochondrial and nuclear DNA) data from two of the three species have revealed *Heterocercus* to be nestled within the subfamily Piprinae, closest either to some *Pipra* or *Manacus*, although the latter relationship has low bootstrap support (Rêgo *et al.* 2007, Tello *et al.* 2009). The five genera comprising this subfamily – *Lepidothrix*, *Pipra*, *Dixiphia*, *Machaeropterus* and *Heterocercus* – might well form a single clade.

Genus *Machaeropterus*, Bonaparte, 1854 (three species)

At face value, this group appears highly distinctive and unusual amongst the Pipridae, and Prum (1992) recommended tribal status (Machaeropterini) for these three species. The syrinx is unusually weakly developed in all three species, but only in one species has the visual display and mechanical sound production reached new heights, either in response to or as a cause of this. Two recent molecular studies (Rêgo *et al.* 2007, Tello *et al.* 2009) uncovered support for Bostwick's (2000) proposition that Club-winged Manakin *M. deliciosus* forms a monophyletic clade with *Pipra*, by finding that Fiery-capped Manakin *M. pyrocephalus* belongs within the same expanded clade as Red-headed Manakin *Pipra rubrocapilla*, Golden-headed Manakin *P. erythrocephala*, Round-tailed Manakin *P. chloromeros*, Scarlet-horned Manakin *P. cornuta* and Red-capped Manakin *P. mentalis*. Prum's (1992) overall findings had also suggested that *Machaeropterus* might form a clade with *Pipra*. However, the genetic data suggest that *Machaeropterus* forms a single clade not only with *Pipra*, but also with *Lepidothrix*, *Dixiphia* and *Heterocercus* (see also McKay *et al.* 2010).

Genus *Dixiphia*, Reichenbach, 1850 (one species)

Writing in an age prior to the advent of molecular techniques as a solution to the problems of accurately divining avian relationships, Snow (1975) considered the White-crowned Manakin *D. pipra*, which he placed in the genus *Pipra* (and which at that time also included those species herein treated as *Lepidothrix*), to lack obvious close relatives. Subsequently, Prum (1992, 1994a) noted that *pipra* does not seem to belong with other members of the genus *Pipra*, based on syringeal morphology and display, and advocated returning it to the genus *Dixiphia*. In this proposal, he was followed by many authors, but Remsen *et al.* (2009) maintained White-crowned Manakin within *Pipra*, waiting it would seem for more robust genetic (and perhaps other) data to become available. Nonetheless, three very recent genetic analyses (Rêgo *et al.* 2007, Tello *et al.* 2009, McKay *et al.* 2010) have confirmed the distinctiveness of the White-crowned Manakin, and all have suggested that the genus is, perhaps surprisingly, quite closely related to the genus *Machaeropterus*. Where these studies have differed is what to do with the remainder of the species 'left' in *Pipra* following Prum's pioneering revision (i.e. once those species now treated in *Lepidothrix* had been 'removed'). Rêgo *et al.* (2007), who sampled the greater number of relevant taxa, suggested resurrecting the name *Ceratopipo* as a subgenus for the *Pipra erythrocephala* superspecies. In contrast, Tello *et al.* (2009) recommended that, because Golden-headed Manakin *P. erythrocephala* itself was closer to *D. pipra* than to the members of the *P. aureola* superspecies, the entire *erythrocephala* group should be removed to *Dixiphia*, which is the oldest available name. Because the genetic data on this issue are still not definitive, but do strongly support a separate genus for White-crowned Manakin at least, we consider *Dixiphia* meritorious of recognition (unlike Remsen *et al.* 2009) but maintain it as a monospecific genus, at least for now.

SUBFAMILY ILICURINAE, Prum 1992

Genus *Xenopipo*, Cabanis, 1847 (one species)

Genus *Chloropipo*, Cabanis & Heine, 1859 (four species)

Chloropipo is frequently 'sunk' within *Xenopipo* (since the work of Prum 1992), e.g. by Dickinson (2003), Ridgely and Tudor (2009) and the American Ornithologists' Union South American Checklist Committee (SACC; Remsen *et al.* 2009). However, separate genera were maintained by Snow (2004b) and Gill and Wright (2006). Recently, Black Manakin *Xenopipo atronitens* and Olive Manakin *Chloropipo uniformis* have been sampled genetically by Rêgo *et al.* (2007) and Tello *et al.* (2009). The authors of the latter study (which was more expansive) found that both species form part of the subfamily Ilicurinae, along with the genera *Antilophia*, *Chiroxiphia*, *Ilicura*, *Masius* and *Corapipo*, to which taxa the so-called *Xenopipo* group (*Xenopipo* and *Chloropipo*) is sister. Although the two species sampled were closely related, Tello *et al.* (2009) were unable to determine whether Prum (1992) was correct to subsume *Chloropipo* within *Xenopipo* based on syringeal morphology. Because this question has yet to be resolved using molecular techniques, we prefer to maintain the arguably more traditional arrangement of separate genera for now.

Genus *Ilicura*, Reichenbach, 1850   **(one species)**

Traditionally considered to be of uncertain relationships (Ames 1971, Snow 1975, Snow and Snow 1985, Willis 1992), only recently have robust data become available to elucidate the remarkable Pin-tailed Manakin's closest relatives. Using syringeal evidence Prum (1992) recommended that the genera *Corapipo*, *Ilicura* and *Masius* be considered to form a Tribe, the Ilicurini (now given subfamily status by Tello *et al.* 2009). Tello *et al.* (2009) found evidence from their analysis of two nuclear genes to suggest that *Masius* and *Corapipo* constitute a clade that is sister to the genus *Ilicura*, and that these two 'groups' form one of three core constituent groupings within the Ilicurinae (the type genus of which is *Ilicura*).

Genus *Masius*, Bonaparte, 1850   **(one species)**

Described by Snow (1975) in a period prior to the advent of molecular techniques for resolving taxonomic problems as being 'without obvious affinities', in common with the equally difficult to place *Ilicura*, subsequently Prum and Johnson (1987), Prum (1990a) and McKay *et al.* (2010) considered that the monospecific genus *Masius* might be most closely related to *Corapipo* (and the two replace one another elevationally in parts of Colombia: T. M. Donegan *in litt.* 2009), based on similarities in their male displays, as well as on the basis of syringeal evidence (Prum 1992). Most recently Tello *et al.* (2009) found evidence from an analysis of nuclear genes to suggest that *Masius* indeed forms a clade with *Corapipo*, which is sister to the genus *Ilicura*, and that these two 'groups' form one of three core constituent groupings within the Ilicurinae.

Genus *Corapipo*, Bonaparte, 1854   **(two species)**

Relationships are now known with reasonable certainty, since Snow (1975) postulated that, on the basis of plumage and close-to-the-ground display sites, *Corapipo* might be most closely related to *Manacus*. Despite some differences between their displays, as noted by Rosselli *et al.* (2002), the two species of *Corapipo* possess not only substantial heterogeneity in their display behaviours (see Prum 1986, Théry 1990, Rosselli *et al.* 2002) but also some marked similarities to the principal display elements found in the monospecific Andean genus *Masius* (Golden-winged Manakin *M. chrysopterus*, for which see Prum and Johnson 1987, Snow and Snow 1992). Prum (1990a, 1992) proposed that *Corapipo* and the similarly enigmatic *Ilicura* (Pin-tailed Manakin *I. militaris* of the Atlantic Forest) might be close relatives, as well as with *Masius*. J. F. Pacheco (*in litt.* 2010) has also pointed out the similarity in some vocalisations between *Ilicura* and *Corapipo*. Brumfield and Braun (2001), on the other hand, using electrophoretic methods, proposed a close relationship between *Chiroxiphia* ('blue' manakins) and *Corapipo*, but any similarities in displays between these two genera appear coincidental, because such behaviour in *Corapipo* is neither truly cooperative nor synchronised (cf. Rosselli *et al.* 2002). Although the system in *Corapipo* might also be hierarchical, the degree to which this is well established among 'dominant' or 'resident' males and 'visitors' or 'floaters' seems far weaker than in *Chiroxiphia*, or at least remains to be elucidated. The above-canopy element of their displays might be taken as signs of a link with a genus such as *Heterocercus* (Snow 2004b). Recently, the first molecular data have been published for *Corapipo*. Tello *et al.* (2009) found strong support for the relationships suggested by Prum (1992). The latter's tribe, the Ilicurini, formed by the genera *Ilicura*, *Corapipo* and *Masius*, was recognised as one of three groups within the subfamily Ilicurinae, and Tello *et al.* (2009) found *Masius* and *Corapipo* to form a single clade, with *Ilicura* sister to it.

Genus *Chiroxiphia*, Cabanis, 1847   **(five species)**

Prum (1990a, 1992) proposed that *Chiroxiphia* is most closely related to *Antilophia*, as evidenced by the fact that Blue Manakin quite readily hybridises with Helmeted Manakin *A. galeata* in the southern *cerrados* of Brazil, while Blue-backed Manakin has also been recorded interbreeding with *A. galeata* on a couple of occasions. This close relationship has been confirmed by genetic data (Rêgo *et al.* 2007, Tello *et al.* 2009, McKay *et al.* 2010), which have revealed that *Antilophia* and *Chiroxiphia* form a distinct clade apart from most other genera of manakins (see *Antilophia* for further discussion).

Genus *Antilophia*, Reichenbach, 1850   **(two species)**

The position of *Antilophia* within the Pipridae is obviously close to *Chiroxiphia* (as evidenced by their ability to interbreed), and it forms a distinct clade apart from most other genera (Rêgo *et al.* 2007, McKay *et al.* 2010). Tello *et al.* (2009) found very low nuclear gene differentiation between *Chiroxiphia* and *Antilophia*, and these two genera form one of three groups within the subfamily, the others being the *Xenopipo* group (*Chloropipo* and *Xenopipo*) and the *Ilicura* group (formed by the genera *Corapipo*, *Masius* and *Ilicura*).

FAMILY OXYRUNCIDAE, Ridgway, 1906 (1831) (see Bock 1994: 115, 200)

Genus *Oxyruncus*, Temminck, 1820   **(one species)**

The Sharpbill *Oxyruncus cristatus* was first placed in its own family by Sclater (1888), and this arrangement generally persisted for many years (e.g. in Meyer de Schauensee 1970, Wetmore 1972), despite its occasional removal to the Tyrannidae (e.g. Mayr and Amadon 1951). Ames (1971) found its syringeal

41

morphology to resemble those of the becards *Pachyramphus* and the Tyrannidae in general, to which latter grouping the species was again removed by Lanyon (1985), whilst Ericson *et al.* (2006) considered that *Oxyruncus* is the basal member of the Tityridae. In contrast, Sick (1971) suggested that the Sharpbill's affinities might be closer to the Cotingidae, and thereafter Sibley *et al.* (1984), Sibley and Ahlquist (1985, 1990) and Prum *et al.* (2000) uncovered evidence to suggest that it would best placed within the latter family, a course that was adopted by Dickinson (2003) and Snow (2004a). Specifically, Prum *et al.* (2000) suggested a close relationship between *Oxyruncus* and the two genera of principally Andean fruiteaters, *Pipreola* and *Ampelioides*, but subsequent genetic work has refuted this suggestion (e.g. Tello *et al.* 2009). Ohlson *et al.* (2008) found evidence for a relationship between *Oxyruncus* and the Tityridae (including the genera *Schiffornis* and *Laniisoma*) and *Piprites*, as well as all of the Tyrannidae. In the light of additional genetic data (Johansson *et al.* 2002, Chesser 2004), which failed to uncover a close relationship with any likely candidate families, other authorities, notably the SACC (Remsen *et al.* 2009) and Ridgely and Tudor (2009), have preferred to resurrect the single-species family Oxyruncidae, which course has also been adopted here. However, Tello *et al.* (2009) recovered dual nuclear-gene evidence of a close relationship between *Oxyruncus* and the onychorhynchine flycatchers (Onychorhynchini), namely the genera *Onychorhynchus*, *Myiobius* and *Terenotriccus*, which these authors elected to recognise at the level of Tribe. One course of action might be to remove these latter genera to the Oxyruncidae too. Tello *et al.* (2009) placed this group as a subfamily, the Oxyruncinae, of the Tityridae. Fully 70 years since Chapman (1939) first drew attention to the 'riddle of *Oxyruncus*' we seem to be little nearer to solving the conundrum that it poses.

FAMILY TITYRIDAE, G. R. Gray, 1840

SUBFAMILY LANIISOMINAE, Barber & Rice, 2007

Genus *Schiffornis*, Bonaparte, 1854 (three species)
This aberrant genus was placed within the Pipridae by Sclater (1888), a course of action that was followed by such influential commentators as Hellmayr (1929b) and Meyer de Schauensee (1966), based in large part on *Schiffornis* having a typically piprine foot structure. Nonetheless, its unique character has also long been recognised, and Sclater (1888) accorded it a subfamily, in which he presciently also grouped *Laniisoma* amongst others. Indeed, both morphological (Prum and Lanyon 1989) and genetic (Chesser 1994, Barber and Rice 2007, Ohlson *et al.* 2007, Tello *et al.* 2009) data indicate that it does not belong in that family but rather forms a group with the genera *Tityra* through *Pachyramphus*. Within this group Barber and Rice (2007) found genetic evidence for two major clades: (a) *Laniisoma*, *Laniocera* and *Schiffornis*, and (b) *Iodopleura*, *Tityra*, *Xenopsaris* and *Pachyramphus*. These authors recommended that the groups be ranked as subfamilies (Laniisominae and Tityrinae) and, subsequently, in the most recently published genetic study of these families, Tello *et al.* (2009) found additional support for *Schiffornis* to be placed together with *Laniisoma* and *Laniocera*.

Genus *Laniocera*, Lesson, 1840 (two species)

Genus *Laniisoma*, Swainson, 1832 (one species)
As mentioned above, Barber and Rice (2007) found evidence for two major groups within the Tityridae, of which *Laniocera* groups with the genera *Schiffornis* and *Laniisoma* (Elegant Mourner), this relationship having already been predicted by Prum and Lanyon (1989). Ohlson *et al.* (2007, 2008) uncovered evidence for a relationship between *Oxyruncus* and the Tityridae (including *Schiffornis* and *Laniocera*) and *Piprites*, as well as all of the Tyrannidae. Tello *et al.* (2009) too found that the Laniisominae is a strongly monophyletic grouping, and that its closest relatives are the Tityrinae (namely the genera *Iodopleura*, *Pachyramphus* and *Xenopsaris*) and the Oxyruncinae (for which see the Family Oxyruncidae, above).

SUBFAMILY TITYRINAE, Prum, Rice, Mobley & Dimmick, 2000

Genus *Iodopleura*, Lesson, 1839 (three species)
Ames' (1971) study of the syringeal morphology of passerine birds suggested that *Iodopleura* might group with the Tyrannidae, his work revealing a coincidence in syrinx structure and musculature with genera such as *Laniocera*, *Attila* and *Casiornis*. However, recent work by Rick Prum, Terry Chesser and others (Prum *et al.* 2000, Irestedt *et al.* 2002, Chesser 2004, Ericson *et al.* 2006) has revealed that the purpletufts constitute part of the 'Schiffornis' assemblage, which has now been removed from the Cotingidae. As noted above, Barber and Rice (2007) found two major groups within the new family Tityridae, of which *Iodopleura* grouped with the genera *Tityra*, *Xenopsaris* and *Pachyramphus*. The even more recent genetic study, based on an analysis of two nuclear genes, by Tello *et al.* (2009) recovered the same relationship as did Barber and Rice.

FAMILY COTINGIDAE, Bonaparte, 1849

SUBFAMILY PIPREOLINAE, Tello, Moyle, Marchese & Cracraft, 2009

Genus *Pipreola*, Swainson, 1837 (11 species)

Ames (1971) found that the two species of *Pipreola* examined by him seemed most closely allied with the genera *Cotinga*, *Xipholena* and *Ampelion* in terms of their syringeal morphology. However, with the advent of molecular techniques, Prum *et al.* (2000) proposed that *Oxyruncus*, the Sharpbill *O. cristatus*, might also be closely related to *Pipreola* and the other genus of fruiteaters, the single-species *Ampelioides*, but this relationship has been refuted by subsequent genetic work. All of the genetic studies to date have found *Pipreola* to form a single clade with *Ampelioides tschudii* (Scaled Fruiteater), e.g. one of the four recognised within the 'true' cotingas by the study by Ohlson *et al.* (2007). This same close relationship was also strongly supported in the nuclear gene study of Tello *et al.* (2009), who erected a new subfamily, the Pipreolinae (type genus *Pipreola*), for this grouping, which they considered to be sister to all other lineages of Cotingidae.

Genus *Ampelioides*, J. Verreaux, 1867 (one species)

Ampelioides and *Pipreola* were found to represent a single clade, of four recognised in the 'true' cotingas by the molecular study of Ohlson *et al.* (2007). The same close relationship was also strongly supported in the nuclear gene study of Tello *et al.* (2009), whereas Prum *et al.* (2000) proposed that *Oxyruncus*, the Sharpbill, might also be closely related to the two genera of fruiteaters, but this relationship has been denied by subsequent genetic work.

SUBFAMILY COTINGINAE, Bonaparte, 1849

Genus *Lipaugus*, Boie, 1828 (seven species)

Genus *Tijuca*, Férussac, 1829 (two species)

The status of *Lipaugus* as 'true' cotingas has periodically been questioned, e.g. by Wetmore (1972), who removed the genus to the Tyrannidae. However, there are many grounds, including recently accrued genetic data, for retaining them in the Cotingidae (see Warter 1965, Prum 1990, Prum *et al.* 2000, Ohlson *et al.* 2007, Tello *et al.* 2009). On current evidence it is apparent that *Lipaugus* forms part of the present subfamily, i.e. the core cotingas. At least one recent molecular study has recovered evidence of a close relationship between *Lipaugus* (Rufous Piha *L. unirufus* and Dusky Piha *L. fuscocinereus* were sampled) and the southeast Brazilian endemic Black-and-gold Cotinga *Tijuca atra*, but did not establish reciprocal monophyly (Ohlson *et al.* 2007) and thus it is too early to recommend that these two genera be merged, with *Lipaugus* having priority (Tello *et al.* 2009). Screaming Piha *L. vociferans* and Rose-collared Piha *L. streptophorus* were sampled by the second-named study. Tello *et al.* (2009) did not sample either of the two species of *Tijuca*, but both of these studies did confirm the genetic distinctiveness of the genus *Snowornis* (the two species of Andean green pihas formerly also placed in *Lipaugus*).

Genus *Porphyrolaema*, Bonaparte, 1854 (one species)

Recent molecular data have suggested that *Porphyrolaema* is related most closely to *Carpodectes* and *Xipholena*. Ohlson *et al.* (2007) and Tello *et al.* (2009) found that this genus forms part of the monophyletic *Gymnoderus* group, in which *Porphyrolaema* was found to be sister to all of the other constituent genera, namely *Gymnoderus*, *Conioptilon*, *Carpodectes* and *Xipholena*.

Genus *Gymnoderus*, E. Geoffroy Saint-Hilaire, 1809 (one species)

The relationships of the sole species of *Gymnoderus* were for many decades unclear, although various commentators noted that its vocal displays recall those of some of the umbrellabirds and the Red-ruffed Fruitcrow *Pyroderus scutatus*. *Gymnoderus* was considered sufficiently differentiated to warrant its own subfamily, the Gymnoderinae, by Warter (1965), following the earlier recommendation of Salvin and Godman (1891), based principally on its skull structure (which, perhaps surprisingly, recalls that of the genus *Cotinga*). Its plumage, however, especially that of females, is similar to the Amazonian Umbrellabird *Cephalopterus ornatus*, although the blue neck wattles are wholly unique. Thereafter, Snow (1982) speculated that its closest relative might prove to be the more recently described Black-faced Cotinga *Conioptilon mcilhennyi*, which (together with the other fruitcrows) shares a similar syringeal structure (Ames 1971), as well as the powder-down-covered plumage. The latter character is shared with rather few other cotingas, and all possess it to a much less obvious extent. This close relationship between *Gymnoderus* and *Conioptilon* has recently received additional, molecular, support (Ohlson *et al.* 2007, Tello *et al.* 2009).

Genus *Conioptilon*, Lowery & O'Neill, 1966 (one species)

The systematic relationships of *Conioptilon* were until recently rather speculative, but Lowery and O'Neill (1966) and Snow (2004a) both placed it close to *Carpodectes* and *Gymnoderus*, with which two genera it shares the character of possessing powder-down over many parts of the feathers. In his study of syringeal morphology,

Ames (1971) found evidence to suggest that Black-faced Cotinga is most closely allied to *Perissocephalus*, *Gymnoderus*, *Pyroderus* and *Cephalopterus*, but slightly apart from *Querula* and *Carpodectes*, which form a separate group, although in some aspects of its behaviour (e.g. group-living and frequent vocalising) this cotinga is definitely fruitcrow-like. Its especially close relationship to *Gymnoderus* was recently confirmed by the genetic studies of Ohlson *et al.* (2007) and Tello *et al.* (2009).

Genus *Xipholena*, Gloger, 1842   (three species)

Genus *Carpodectes*, Salvin, 1865   (three species)

Ames (1971) found that in terms of syringeal morphology, the genus *Xipholena* seems most closely related to the genera *Cotinga*, *Ampelion* and *Pipreola*. Snow (1982) noted that the feather modification found in *Xipholena* might be considered the extreme in a trend also exhibited by *Haematoderus* (Crimson Fruitcrow), *Querula* (Purple-throated Fruitcrow), *Pyroderus* (Red-ruffed Fruitcrow) and others. In recent years, the superficial relationship to *Carpodectes*, suggested by Haffer (1970), has been confirmed using molecular techniques. Thus Prum *et al.* (2000), Ohlson *et al.* (2007) and Tello *et al.* (2009) all reached a similar conception of the subfamily Cotinginae, at the heart of which lies the well-supported monophyletic *Gymnoderus* group, which comprises five genera, namely *Porphyrolaema* (lying slightly apart from, and sister to, the rest), *Gymnoderus* + *Conioptilon*, and *Xipholena* + *Carpodectes* (following Tello *et al.* 2009).

Genus *Procnias*, Illiger, 1811   (four species)

In his study of syringeal morphology, Ames (1971: 156) considered that the highly muscular syrinx found in bellbirds is 'so specialized that [it] tells us little about the relationships of *Procnias*', and earlier Warter (1965) had placed the bellbirds in their own subfamily based on their skull morphology. Most recently, the results of three genetic studies have confirmed that the bellbirds are members of the so-called core Cotingidae but their closest relatives within this group are unresolved (Tello *et al.* 2009). Prum *et al.* (2000) and Tello *et al.* (2009) found weak and unsupported evidence for a close relationship between *Procnias* and *Cotinga*, but in contrast these two genera were widely separated in the study of Ohlson *et al.* (2007). Tello *et al.* (2009) further opined that *Cotinga* and *Procnias* might form a sister clade to the *Cephalopterus* group, and this finding was better supported. Nonetheless, clearly much further work will be required to fully establish the bellbirds' closest relatives.

Genus *Cotinga*, Brisson, 1760   (seven species)

Ames (1971) found that in their syringeal morphology *Cotinga* grouped with genera such as *Xipholena*, *Pipreola* and *Ampelion*. Subsequent work has refined our knowledge and we now know, largely through the use of molecular techniques, that *Cotinga* is not closely related to any of the above three genera. Both Prum *et al.* (2000) and Tello *et al.* (2009) found some evidence to unite *Procnias* (bellbirds) with *Cotinga*, and that the *Cephalopterus* group might be their sister clade, but without strong support for this hypothesis. In contrast, Ohlson *et al.* (2007) were unable to provide any resolution as to the position of *Cotinga* within the core cotingas, although by sampling *C. cayana* and *C. maynana* they were able to determine monophyly for the genus, thereby supporting the findings of Prum *et al.* (2000). Clearly, further work is required.

Genus *Haematoderus*, Bonaparte, 1854   (one species)

The spectacular Crimson Fruitcrow *H. militaris*, arguably one of the most stunning birds amongst a remarkably beautiful family, has been speculated to be probably most closely related to the *Xipholena* cotingas, with which it shares some features (Snow 2004a). Although our cumulative knowledge of the Crimson Fruitcrow's life history has increased dramatically in recent years, its relationships within the Cotingidae were the subject of considerable guesswork. Only very recently has the molecular work of Ohlson *et al.* (2007) and Tello *et al.* (2009) revealed that it is probably sister to a group comprising *Querula*, *Perissocephalus*, *Pyroderus* and *Cephalopterus*, but this relationship is still not clearly resolved.

Genus *Querula*, Vieillot, 1816   (one species)

Although considered by Ames (1971) to be relatively close to the *Carpodectes* 'white' cotingas in its syrinx structure, this potential relationship was correctly rejected by Snow (1982). Although Snow (1982) considered that the passing morphological resemblance to Red-ruffed Fruitcrow *Pyroderus scutatus* was also misleading, this does offer some clue to the species' relationships, although *Pyroderus* is probably *most* closely related to the *Cephalopterus* umbrellabirds. Thus, *Querula* forms part of the fourth clade of true cotingas defined by Ericson *et al.* (2006) and is most closely related to some of the other species that we label as fruitcrows. Nonetheless, molecular data have proffered support to some of Ames' other findings in respect of this group (see comments on the genus *Cephalopterus*). Most recently, in their nuclear gene study, Tello *et al.* (2009) found that the *Cephalopterus* group represent a well-supported clade comprising four (probably five) genera, namely *Querula*, *Perissocephalus*, *Pyroderus* and *Cephalopterus* (the latter two being particularly closely related), with *Haematoderus* forming an apparent sister group. Ohlson *et al.* (2007) recovered a similar phylogeny, but their data suggested that *Cephalopterus* is most closely related to *Perissocephalus*.

Genus *Perissocephalus*, Oberholser, 1899 (one species)

Capuchinbird *P. tricolor* had long been speculated to be probably most closely related to the *Cephalopterus* umbrellabirds, but perhaps also to the fruitcrow *Pyroderus*, and like many lek-breeding birds, it is monomorphic. In his study of syringeal morphology, Ames (1971) found evidence to suggest that Capuchinbird is most closely allied to *Pyroderus*, *Gymnoderus*, *Conioptilon* and *Cephalopterus*, but slightly apart from *Querula* and *Carpodectes*, which formed a separate group. Genetic data (see previous genera) have revealed it to form part of the so-called *Cephalopterus* group, which comprises several of the above-mentioned genera, but not *Gymnoderus* or *Conioptilon*.

Genus *Pyroderus*, G. R. Gray, 1840 (one species)

Ames (1971) found evidence to suggest that Red-ruffed Fruitcrow is most closely allied to *Perissocephalus*, *Gymnoderus*, *Conioptilon* and *Cephalopterus*, but slightly apart from *Querula* and *Carpodectes*, which form a separate group. The molecular findings of Ohlson *et al.* (2007) and Tello *et al.* (2009) have provided certainty that *Pyroderus* forms a group with the previous three genera and the umbrellabirds. However, a definitive statement regarding intra-group relationships is still awaited.

Genus *Cephalopterus*, E. Geoffroy Saint-Hilaire, 1809 (three species)

In his study of syringeal morphology, Ames (1971) found evidence to suggest that the umbrellabirds are most closely allied to *Perissocephalus*, *Gymnoderus*, *Conioptilon* and *Pyroderus*, but slightly apart from *Querula* and *Carpodectes*. Subsequently acquired molecular data have tended to support some of Ames' findings, albeit not the close relationship between Purple-throated Fruitcrow *Querula querula* and the 'white' cotingas. Most recently, in their nuclear gene study, Tello *et al.* (2009) found the *Cephalopterus* group to represent a well-supported clade (see above). Ohlson *et al.* (2007) recovered a similar phylogeny, but their data suggested that *Cephalopterus* is most closely related to *Perissocephalus*.

Genus *Carpornis*, G. R. Gray, 1846 (two species)

In the past, *Carpornis* was sometimes submerged within the Andean genus *Ampelion* (e.g. by Hellmayr 1929b, Pinto 1944), and many authors have pointed to a superficial similarity between *Carpornis* berryeaters and *Pipreola* fruiteaters. However, recently acquired nuclear gene data do not give succour to either theory. Tello *et al.* (2009) found that *Carpornis* (they sampled only Black-headed Berryeater *C. melanocephala*) represents one of four primary lineages within the Cotinginae subfamily, but that it appears to be sister to all of the other groups (e.g. the two largest, the *Gymnoderus* and the *Cephalopterus* groups) within this crown clade. As noted above, neither *Pipreola* (Pipreolinae) nor *Ampelion* (Phytotominae) are members of the Cotinginae. In contrast, SACC (Remsen *et al.* 2009) places *Carpornis* next to *Pipreola*, at the start of the list, invoking historical tradition until such time as more robust data become available.

SUBFAMILY RUPICOLINAE, Bonaparte, 1853

Genus *Snowornis*, Prum, 2001 (two species)

On the basis of hindlimb morphology (Prum 1990), syringeal data and the phylogeny presented by Prum *et al.* (2000), Prum (2001) erected a new genus, *Snowornis*, to differentiate the mainly olive-green Andean pihas, *subalaris* and *cryptolophus*, from the other species in the old *Lipaugus* genus, which proposal has garnered universal support and is followed here. Snow (1982) had already noted that these two species might prove to be 'only distantly related' to the other pihas. (Prum further recommended that the two *Snowornis* species be called cotingas, rather than pihas, in order to emphasise their distinctiveness from *Lipaugus*, but that proposal has seemingly yet to 'catch on'.) The phylogeny of Prum *et al.* (2000), which recognised four subfamilies within the Cotingidae, although placing *Lipaugus* and *Snowornis* within the same subfamily, the Cotinginae, found the two genera to be far removed from one another within that grouping, and this separation of *Snowornis* from *Lipaugus* was subsequently also strongly supported by the molecular studies of Ohlson *et al.* (2007) and Tello *et al.* (2009).

Genus *Rupicola*, Brisson, 1760 (two species)

The cocks-of-the-rock were formerly placed in their own family, the Rupicolidae, until as recently as Meyer de Schauensee (1970), but their removal to the Cotingidae has gained widespread support since Snow (1979a), although earlier both Pinto (1944) and Phelps and Phelps (1950) had also pursued such a course. Ames (1971) also considered their syringeal morphology to be much like that of the 'typical' cotingas. Nonetheless, the displays of the two species are quite different, as initially noted by Snow (1982), and the skull's ossification in the nasal region also differs in both species (Warter 1965). At least one recent genetic study (Ohlson *et al.* 2007) recovered four clades within the core Cotingidae, placing this genus, together with *Phoenicircus*, in a single clade. This course of action had effectively also been taken by Dickinson (2003) who removed these two genera to their own subfamily, the Rupicolinae, and also recently by Remsen *et al.* (2009). Their moves were only partially confirmed by the study of Tello *et al.* (2009); the last-named authors also included the green pihas *Snowornis* within this subfamily.

Genus *Phoenicircus*, Swainson, 1832 (two species)

Genetic data appear to have resolved the systematics of this group, revealing *Phoenicircus* to be indeed most closely related to *Rupicola*, but also *Snowornis*, the latter appearing to be sister to the *Rupicola* + *Phoenicircus* clade, and these three form a subfamily, the Rupicolinae (Ohlson *et al.* 2007, Tello *et al.* 2009).

SUBFAMILY PHYTOTOMINAE, Swainson, 1837

(first used as a subfamily by Prum, Rice, Mobley & Dimmick, 2000)

Genus *Ampelion*, Tschudi, 1845 (two species)

Ames (1971) considered *Heliochera* (= *Ampelion*) to recall most closely the genera *Cotinga*, *Pipreola* and *Xipholena* in terms of syringeal morphology. Several recent genetic and other studies (e.g. Lanyon and Lanyon 1989) have suggested that these three genera and *Phytotoma* (plantcutters) are closely related, and Ohlson *et al.* (2007) that the four genera form one of the four clades amongst the 'true' cotingas. The nuclear gene study by Tello *et al.* (2009) also found *Ampelion* to be a core member of the Cotingidae and to form a subfamily, the Phytotominae, along with *Phytotoma*, *Zaratornis* and *Doliornis*. Within this grouping, Tello *et al.* (2009) considered that *Phytotoma* is sister to *Ampelion* and *Doliornis*, and *Zaratornis* to be sister to all these three genera.

Genus *Doliornis*, Taczanowski, 1874 (two species)

This genus was subsumed within *Ampelion* in the 1950s, an arrangement that persisted until almost the end of the last century (e.g. followed by Snow 1979a, Fjeldså and Krabbe 1990), despite their apparent morphological distinctiveness. However, Snow (1982) pointed to the narrower, less hooked bill of *Doliornis*, compared with *Ampelion*, and subsequently Lanyon and Lanyon (1989) and Prum (1990) demonstrated the validity of the generic split, based on syringeal and cranial characters, amongst others. Further justification was supplied by Robbins *et al.* (1994), based on the quite different juvenile plumages of the two *Ampelion* species. In this respect, it is worthy of remark that the juvenile plumage of *Zaratornis* is still undescribed. The two *Doliornis* species do, however, share a red erectile crest with *Ampelion* and Red-crested Cotinga *A. rubrocristatus* is frequently found in sympatry with either species of *Doliornis*, these factors pointing towards a common ancestor for high-Andean cotingas, as well as for *Phibalura* (Swallow-tailed Cotinga). As noted above, Tello *et al.* (2009) found *Doliornis* to form part of the subfamily Phytotominae along with the genera *Phytotoma*, *Zaratornis* and *Ampelion*. Within this grouping, Tello *et al.* (2009) considered that *Phytotoma* is sister to *Ampelion* and *Doliornis*, and *Zaratornis* to be sister to all these three genera. We depart from their suggested order within the subfamily.

Genus *Zaratornis*, Koepcke, 1954 (one species)

Like *Doliornis*, this genus was often subsumed within *Ampelion*, but with the array of different analytical methods available to modern-day taxonomists, we now know that *Zaratornis* does indeed represent a distinctive taxon worthy of generic status (see Remsen *et al.* 2009). The nuclear gene study by Tello *et al.* (2009) found *Zaratornis* to form a subfamily with the genera *Phytotoma*, *Ampelion* and *Doliornis*, all of which show some similarities in their vocalisations (Parker 1981) and syringeal morphology (Ames 1971).

Genus *Phytotoma*, Molina, 1782 (three species)

The affinities of this genus have been subject to considerable dispute. The plantcutters were long considered to form their own family (Phytotomidae) of rather uncertain affinities (e.g. Hellmayr 1929b), wherein they were retained as recently as the mid-1990s (Stotz *et al.* 1996). Indeed, Lanyon and Lanyon (1989) uncovered early biochemical evidence to suggest that *Phytotoma* was best placed in its own family. However, only a decade earlier their morphology had led Sibley and Ahlquist (1985) to recommend that the plantcutters were cotingas (treated by them as a subfamily of the Tyrannidae). Ames (1971) had already identified that, in terms of their syringeal morphology, *Phytotoma* are very close to cotingas, especially those of the genus *Ampelion*. Since then, multiple genetic studies have seemingly confirmed their place within the Cotingidae (Johansson *et al.* 2002, Chesser 2004; see Remsen *et al.* 2009). Ohlson *et al.* (2007) found evidence for *Phytotoma* either to (a) be a sister group to a clade comprising the genera *Ampelion*, *Doliornis* and *Zaratornis*, or (b) comprise a direct part of the same clade as the *Ampelion* group. Other lines of evidence are less straightforward and make it unsurprising that the plantcutters have been the cause of so much confusion as to their systematic placement. For instance, with respect to their oval to elliptical-shaped eggs, Walters (2006: 163) commented that they 'are very different in appearance from any eggs I have seen of species in families placed near the Phytotomidae, a few eggs of *Cracticus* (Cracticidae [butcher birds]) are not unlike those of *P. rutila*.'

GENERA *INCERTAE SEDIS*

Genus *Piprites*, Cabanis, 1847 (three species)

Piprites has for some considerable time being recognised as an atypical genus amongst the manakins, where it had previously long rested (cf. Snow 1975). Bill shape, foot structure (the outer toe is almost completely 'free' from the middle one), syrinx development (see below) and musculature are all different from manakins, and in certain characters approach some of the Tyrannidae. In his study of syringeal morphology, Ames (1971) considered the *Piprites* to recall tyrannid genera such as *Myiobius* and *Terenotriccus* (for which see comments on the genus *Oxyruncus* above). Prum (1990a) also noted that *Piprites* has a tyrannid-like syrinx and Ericson *et al.* (2006) uncovered molecular data for placing the genus with the tyrannids. Ohlson *et al.* (2008) found evidence for the existence of an expansive clade that includes *Oxyruncus* and the Tityridae (including *Schiffornis* and *Laniisoma*) and *Piprites*, as well as all of the Tyrannidae. The most recent attempt to reconstruct a detailed phylogeny for tyrant flycatchers, cotingas, manakins and their perceived closest relatives, found *Piprites* to represent an isolated lineage of distinctly uncertain closest affinities (Tello *et al.* 2009). So, for now, the systematic position of *Piprites* remains unclear because none of the different positions claimed for it on the phylogenetic tree possesses strong bootstrap support. In recognition of the fact that *Piprites* has historically been treated as part of the Pipridae we have included it in this book, for now, but we suspect that its true relationships, when fully elucidated, will lie with the Tyrannidae. The IOC has recently removed the genus to the Tyrannidae in their online list (http://www.worldbirdnames.org/updates.html).

Genus *Calyptura*, Swainson, 1832 (one species)

After spending a long period within the Cotingidae, Kinglet Calyptura *C. cristata* has recently been re-evaluated as *Incertae Sedis* and placed with the genus *Piprites* and sometimes also *Phibalura* outwith both the Pipridae and the Cotingidae (Dickinson 2003, Gill and Wright 2006, Remsen *et al.* 2009). Olalla (1943) had erected a new family, Iodopleuridae, for the genera *Iodopleura* and *Calyptura*, but this proposal has long since sunk into obscurity. Tello *et al.* (2009) considered the genus *Iodopleura*, another genus of tiny birds once thought to be true cotingas, to be the sister group of *Tityra* (together with *Pachyramphus* and *Xenopsaris*, similar to the findings of Barber and Rice 2007), and these genera to form a subfamily, the Tityrinae, wherein it has been speculated *Calyptura* might also lie. However, the first genetic samples for *Calyptura* suggest that it belongs within the Tyrannidae, being most closely related to the genera *Platyrinchus*, *Neopipo* and *Tachuris* (Ohlson *et al.* 2010).

Genus *Phibalura*, Vieillot, 1816 (one species)

To date no genetic studies have sampled *Phibalura* and therefore its position within, or potentially outside, the Cotingidae is unknown, but Remsen *et al.* (2009) have chosen to regard the species as *Incertae Sedis* for want of any molecular data to confirm or deny its status as a cotinga. We follow the same course.

PLATE 1: GENERA *NEOPELMA, TYRANNEUTES* AND *SAPAYOA*

Three genera of generally unassuming 'manakins', all of them clad in shades of principally green plumage. Sapayoa is now known to be a sister taxon to Asian and African broadbills, while genetic data demonstrate both genera of tyrant-manakins to be sister to 'true' manakins. Vocalisations are distinctive in all eight recognised species treated here and are the best aid to locating these unobtrusive birds.

Serra do Mar Tyrant-Manakin *Neopelma chrysolophum*   Map and text page 127

Restricted to montane southeast Brazil. Generally, Serra do Mar and Wied's Tyrant-Manakins are elevationally parapatric including within the few areas where they possibly do overlap (for instance in the Novo Friburgo region of Rio de Janeiro state), and the same certainly holds true for this species and Pale-bellied Tyrant-Manakin.

Wied's Tyrant-Manakin *Neopelma aurifrons*   Map and text page 124

Now very rare; Serra do Mar Tyrant-Manakin was formerly regarded as a subspecies of the present species, but is easily distinguished by vocalisations and, to a lesser extent, by the less obvious coronal patch in Wied's, as well as the shorter tail, longer bill and longer wings (thus the tail looks shorter).

Sulphur-bellied Tyrant-Manakin *Neopelma sulphureiventer*   Map and text page 122

The southwest Amazonian member of the superspecies. Only the range of Pale-bellied Tyrant-Manakin approaches this species, although Sulphur-bellied comes quite close to the range of Saffron-crested Tyrant-Manakin in northeast Peru. In plumage, the clear pale yellow belly of Sulphur-bellied separates it from Pale-bellied, but voice is more helpful to species identification.

Saffron-crested Tyrant-Manakin *Neopelma chrysocephalum*   Map and text page 129

The Guianan Shield representative of the genus, although it also occurs in some white-sand forests in northeast Peru. The coronal patch is the largest in the genus and is accentuated by the darker grey sides to the head and nape. These features, as well as the fact that the crown patch is a richer golden-yellow, distinguish the species from the otherwise extremely similar Sulphur-bellied Tyrant-Manakin (no known overlap).

Pale-bellied Tyrant-Manakin *Neopelma pallescens*   Map and text page 119

Of its congeners, this species is only certainly sympatric with Wied's Tyrant-Manakin, from which it can be distinguished by the paler underparts lacking any clear yellow and, more easily, by voice. Pale-bellied Tyrant-Manakin is the most widespread member of the genus *Neopelma*; almost endemic to Brazil, small extensions of its range penetrate Bolivia, Guyana and Surinam.

Tiny Tyrant-Manakin *Tyranneutes virescens*   Map and text page 135

Restricted to the Guianan Shield, both species of *Tyranneutes* tyrant-manakins are most easily located by their voices. They vocalise constantly almost daylong, but they can be difficult to find due to their small size and flycatcher-like greenish plumage, which is easily missed in the forest.

Dwarf Tyrant-Manakin *Tyranneutes stolzmanni*   Map and text page 132

The more widespread member of the *Tyranneutes* superspecies occurs across most of Amazonia. Compared to Tiny Tyrant-Manakin, the present species is marginally larger and longer tailed, but it is most easily distinguished by the pale irides and less stippled effect to the throat and breast.

Broad-billed Sapayoa *Sapayoa aenigma*   Map and text page 117

Found from Panama to northwest Ecuador, this species' plumage resembles some of the other duller Pipridae, but its rather pointed, broad-based and flattened bill is quite unlike any manakin. Any superficial resemblance to a female manakin should further be quickly dispelled by the rather long, full tail. Only Green Manakin *Chloropipo holochlora* approaches it in shape and size but is smaller, with more yellow on the belly and a yellow eye-ring. The sapayoa's size, shape and posture to some extent recall Thrush-like Schiffornis *Schiffornis turdina*, but the latter is much browner above, especially on the wings, and much less yellow below, with a more obvious eye-ring and lacks a coronal-stripe.

Serra do Mar Tyrant-Manakin

Wied's Tyrant-Manakin

Sulphur-bellied Tyrant-Manakin

Pale-bellied Tyrant-Manakin

Saffron-crested Tyrant-Manakin

Tiny Tyrant-Manakin

Dwarf Tyrant-Manakin

Broad-billed Sapayoa

PLATE 2: GENUS *PIPRA* I

The genus *Pipra* as currently constituted comprises eight species and two superspecies, which generally conform to most observers' conceptions of 'classic' manakins, i.e. they are characterised by being small, with brightly coloured males and dull-plumaged females. Their stereotyped displays afford exemplary opportunities for students of avian ecology and colourful spectacles for birdwatchers alike.

Crimson-hooded Manakin *Pipra aureola*   Map and text page 138

Male *aureola* Of the two superspecies in *Pipra*, the first comprises three species, Crimson-hooded, Wire-tailed and Band-tailed Manakins. This species is the northeastern representative; overlap with Band-tailed Manakin has been reported at fewer than a handful of localities, but the nature of any such interactions has yet to be elucidated. Nominate *aureola* is illustrated here, but geographical variation in Crimson-hooded Manakin is notoriously difficult to identify except in long series of specimens.

Female Females of all three recognised subspecies within *P. aureola* are to all intents and purposes identical.

Band-tailed Manakin *Pipra fasciicauda*   Map and text page 144

Male *fasciicauda* The most widespread member of this superspecies, Band-tailed Manakin occurs from east Amazonian Brazil south to northeast Argentina and west to eastern Peru and northern Bolivia. Other races possess considerably more red on the head and underparts. Males are easily recognised by their white tail bands but most readily detected by their somewhat 'whining' vocalisations.

Male *scarlatina* The tail pattern of this subspecies is identical to that of *P. f. fasciicauda*, the ear-coverts and throat feathers are extensively scarlet-tipped, whilst the foreneck and breast are much deeper and redder, and these red feathers extend more sparsely over the flanks and even as far as the undertail-coverts, but are highly variable, apparently individually.

Female Like Crimson-hooded Manakin, geographical variation is scarcely apparent in females of this species. Over much of the eastern part of its range, in the Cerrado this is the only small female manakin with pale irides.

Wire-tailed Manakin *Pipra filicauda*   Map and text page 151

Male *filicauda* Formerly placed in its own genus, both sexes of Wire-tailed Manakin are distinguished by their wire-like tail filaments, which are most exaggerated in males. The species occurs across the western half of Amazonia as well as in northern Venezuela; two subspecies are traditionally recognised.

Female and displaying male Female Wire-tailed Manakin is the most immediately recognisable of female *Pipra* manakins, due to the long curved filaments to the tail. This male is displaying to the female.

Scarlet-horned Manakin *Pipra cornuta*   Map and text page 175

Female and male Both sexes of this species, which is confined to the tepui region of southern Venezuela, westernmost Guyana and northernmost Brazil, are comparatively easily identified by the 'horns' on the hindcrown (albeit reduced in the female). Scarlet-horned Manakin and Round-tailed Manakin *P. chloromeros* do not form part of the *Pipra erythrocephala* superspecies.

male
aureola

Band-tailed Manakin

male
fasciicauda

female

female

Crimson-hooded Manakin

male
scarlatina

female

Wire-tailed Manakin

male
filicauda

displaying

female

male

Scarlet-horned Mankin

The remaining four species that comprise the genus *Pipra* are widely distributed through the Neotropics, with Golden-headed and Red-headed Manakins occupying northern and southern Amazonia, respectively. Males of all four species should be easily identified within their respective ranges, but as always, a lone female will require more care, especially in that part of their ranges where Red-capped and Golden-headed Manakins are found in close geographical proximity to one another.

Round-tailed Manakin *Pipra chloromeros*   Map and text page 171

Male and female Endemic to a relatively small area of western Amazonia, in eastern Peru south of the Amazon, extreme southwest Brazil and northern Bolivia, male Round-tailed Manakin is the only fully red-headed manakin in its range. Females will prove more difficult to identify, but look for the greyish irides (not always present), rounded tail, slightly 'shaggy' crest and pale belly.

Golden-headed Manakin *Pipra erythrocephala*   Map and text page 156

Male and female *erythrocephala* Immediately identified by the golden-yellow head, sometimes with a reddish rear border, this species is found solely north of the Amazon, as well as just into extreme southern Central America, in Panama. In the last-named country, Golden-headed Manakin is apparently at least partially sympatric with Red-capped Manakin. Females of these two species are strikingly similar and will require real care and prolonged or very good views to separate reliably; it might also be noted that hybrids between the two have been reported in the literature.

Red-headed Manakin *Pipra rubrocapilla*   Map and text page 161

Male and female This species forms a superspecies with Golden-headed Manakin and perhaps also with Red-capped Manakin. Red-headed Manakin is found exclusively south of the Amazon making males, at least, immediately recognisable, especially as there is no known overlap with Round-tailed Manakin. It is the only red-headed member of the genus to occur in the Atlantic Forest. Perhaps surprisingly, this isolated population appears not to have differentiated, even subspecifically.

Red-capped Manakin *Pipra mentalis*   Map and text page 165

Male and female *mentalis* The northernmost member of *Pipra*, Red-capped Manakin occurs from southern Mexico south to northwest Ecuador. In areas of apparent sympatry with Golden-headed Manakin, namely around the Panama/Colombia border region, extreme care will be needed to separate females of these two species, but Red-capped has, on average, a slightly longer-looking tail and sometimes has more obviously yellowish thighs. Bare-parts colorations are probably unreliable, although a bird with pale irides is probably Red-capped. The male displays his extensively yellow underwings and yellow thighs in display to the female.

female

Round-tailed Manakin

male

male
erythrocephala

displaying

female

Golden-headed Manakin

Red-headed Manakin

female

displaying

male

male
mentalis

displaying

female

Red-capped Manakin

Following the splitting of the 'old' genus *Pipra* and the resurrection of the present genus for the smaller species with strikingly coloured crown patches, *Lepidothrix* became the largest single genus of manakins. Several species possess relatively tiny ranges.

Blue-crowned Manakin *Lepidothrix coronata*   Map and text page 178

Male and female *coronata* More than one species might be involved in the geographically widespread Blue-crowned Manakin; at least eight subspecies are generally recognised. Males in most races are black with a deep blue crown, whilst females are primarily green with reddish irides.

Male *caelestipileata* This race, endemic to a small corner of southwest Amazonia, is characterised by its bright blue crown but green body. It is one of three races with primarily green bodies, the others being *L. c. exquisita* and *L. c. regalis*. In principle, it might appear that black- and green-bodied birds could be treated as separate species, but genetic data do not support this and there seems to be a relatively broad zone of intergradation between the two colour forms.

Orange-bellied Manakin *Lepidothrix suavissima*   Map and text page 201

Male Until the mid 1990s this and White-fronted Manakin were considered to represent subspecies of a single species. Geographically, the two are apparently entirely allopatric and males are easily identified, given a front-on view, by the lack of a separate yellow breast patch in Orange-bellied.

Female Range is the best feature to separate Orange-bellied and White-fronted Manakins. The present species occurs across southern and southeast Venezuela, north-central Guyana and immediately adjacent, northernmost Brazil, whereas White-fronted Manakin is found from southeast Guyana south to the lower Rio Negro and Amapá, in Brazil.

White-fronted Manakin *Lepidothrix serena*   Map and text page 204

Male Males of this and the previous species are primarily black and yellow, with a striking white forecrown and bright blue rump and uppertail-coverts. Compared to Orange-bellied Manakin, males of the present species have a purer yellow belly and an orange-yellow breast patch, separated from the belly by a narrow black band.

Female Females of this species are similar to the last, although female Orange-bellied has a smaller and yellowish throat patch, and is more extensively washed with olive over the breast. For other potentially discriminatory features see the main text.

Blue-rumped Manakin *Lepidothrix isidorei*   Map and text page 186

Male *leucopygia* This race, which occurs south of the Marañón Gap in northern Peru, is characterised by having a much whiter rump patch than nominate *isidorei*. It apparently only occurs to the north of the range of Cerulean-capped Manakin.

Male *isidorei* Note the obviously bluer rump patch compared to the more southerly ranging *L. i. leucopygia*. The nominate race occurs from eastern Colombia throughout eastern Ecuador.

Female Very difficult to identify with confidence from females of Blue-crowned Manakin *L. coronata* and Cerulean-capped Manakin *L. coeruleocapilla*, although range should assist, especially with respect to the latter. In comparison to the former, note in particular the yellow-tinged forecrown and the contrast between the rump and tail with the rest of the upperparts. However, under certain circumstances it might be necessary to leave some birds unidentified.

Cerulean-capped Manakin *Lepidothrix coeruleocapilla*   Map and text page 189

Male Poorly known but apparently reasonably common within its relatively small range on the east slope of the Andes in central to southeast Peru, Cerulean-capped Manakin is similar in all plumages to either sex of Blue-rumped Manakin. However, the two are not known to overlap in range, and male Cerulean-capped has a blue cap, not a white one, and always has a blue rump patch (white in *L. i. leucopygia*).

Female Females of this species will be extremely difficult to separate from those of Blue-rumped Manakin, although the two are, fortunately, not known to overlap. Compared to the latter species, female Cerulean-capped is slightly larger with a longer tail, but correctly judging such features will require considerable previous experience of both species.

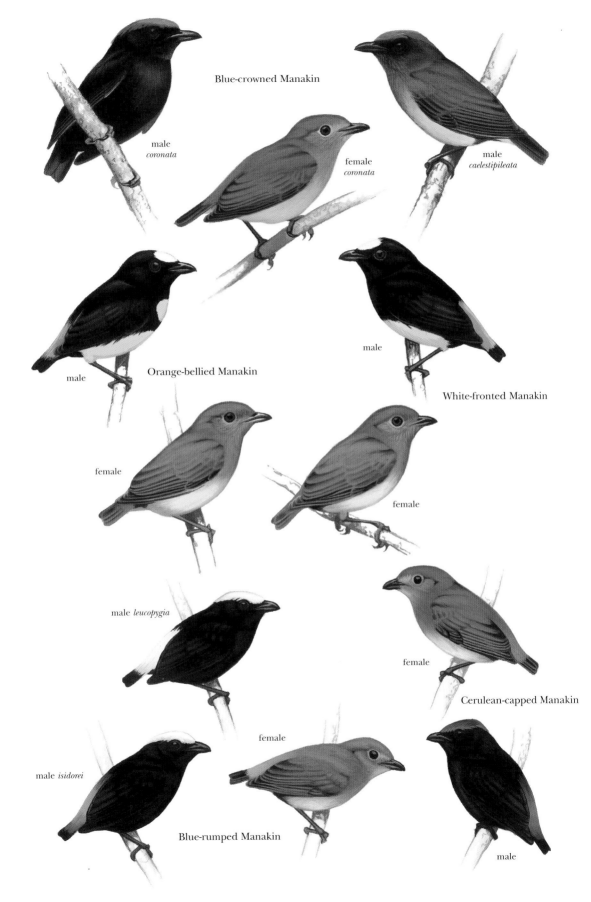

Blue-crowned Manakin

male
coronata

female
coronata

male
caelestipileata

Orange-bellied Manakin

male

male

White-fronted Manakin

female

female

male *leucopygia*

female

Cerulean-capped Manakin

female

male *isidorei*

female

Blue-rumped Manakin

male

White-crowned Manakin was formerly also placed in *Pipra*, but there are strong genetic and other rationale for its placement apart. The three species of *Lepidothrix* included here are all restricted to southern and eastern Amazonia.

White-crowned Manakin *Dixiphia pipra*   Map and text page 252

Male and female *pipra* Males of this species are immediately identifiable, based on their black body, white crown and red irides. Females also have red irides and a noticeably grey head, making them one of the most easily identified female manakins.

Female *anthracina* Some 13 subspecies are frequently recognised within this species, but many are probably better synonymised, dating from a time when according relatively trivial variation was more fashionable than it is now. *D. p. anthracina*, which is the northernmost subspecies, is very similar to most northern South American forms. Compared to the Amazonian nominate race, the female is marginally brighter green above, with paler underparts.

Female *coracina* Females of this race (found in northwest Venezuela to north-central Peru) are characterised by their unusually bright upperparts and in being distinctly yellower below than those of many other subspecies.

Snow-capped Manakin *Lepidothrix nattereri*   Map and text page 192

Male *nattereri* Males of the two races of Snow-capped Manakin are identical, both having an opalescent crown, nape and rump patch, which distinguishes the species from either Golden-crowned and Opal-crowned Manakins (at most, limited overlap with either).

Female *nattereri* The most widespread of the southern Amazonian representatives of the genus. *L. n. nattereri* occurs in the Madeira–Tapajós interfluvium. Females are distinguished from the same sex of the next race by the bluish crown.

Female *gracilis* This subspecies occurs south (reaching to Bolivia) and east of the nominate (as far as the Rio Xingu), and is that most frequently encountered by birders, e.g. at the well-visited Cristalino Jungle Lodge.

Opal-crowned Manakin *Lepidothrix iris*   Map and text page 198

Male *iris* The easternmost representative of the southern Amazonian *Lepidothrix*, this Brazilian endemic is common but apparently has a disjunct range and the two subspecies are not each other's closest relatives, meaning that the poorly known *L. i. eucephala* is probably best treated as a fourth species of south-bank *Lepidothrix*.

Male *eucephala* Compared to the nominate, this subspecies is characterised by having a narrow but distinct green forecrown in the male.

Female *eucephala* Whereas nominate *iris* has the crown and nape green, in this race (or species?) these parts are blue. *L. i. eucephala* is confined to southwest Pará along the right bank of the lower Rio Tapajós.

Golden-crowned Manakin *Lepidothrix vilasboasi*   Map and text page 195

Male and female Discovered as recently as the 1950s and then promptly 'lost' from view for almost half a century, Golden-crowned Manakin has one of the smallest ranges of any manakin. Its range is subject to ongoing human colonisation and consequent deforestation, making it fortunate that this manakin is probably not as susceptible to habitat deterioration as some other forest-based species.

White-crowned Manakin

female
pipra

female
coracina

male
pipra

female
anthracina

Snow-capped Manakin

female
nattereri

female
gracilis

male
nattereri

male
iris

female
eucephala

Opal-crowned Manakin

male
eucephala

male

female

Golden-crowned Manakin

PLATE 6: GENUS *MANACUS*

These four species form a superspecies and indeed all four are sometimes treated as members of a single, very wide-ranging species; they occur from southern Mexico to northeast Argentina, although three species are wholly or almost entirely confined to Middle America. With the exception of the complicated situation in parts of northern and western Colombia, all four species should be readily identified, with even females posing few problems on account of their size, structure and bright legs and feet.

White-collared Manakin *Manacus candei*   Map and text page 208

Male The northernmost representative of the genus occurs from southeast Mexico to northwest Panama, where at the southernmost edge of its range it hybridises with Golden-collared Manakin.

Female Easily identified from other manakins that share the same range through a combination of size and bare-parts coloration; note the brightly coloured legs and feet.

Orange-collared Manakin *Manacus aurantiacus*   Map and text page 212

Male Orange-collared Manakin has the most restricted range of any species of *Manacus*, being confined to a small area of southern Costa Rica and adjacent southwestern Panama.

Female Females of this species would probably prove impossible to separate from White-collared Manakin; fortunately, there is no overlap between them.

Golden-collared Manakin *Manacus vitellinus*   Map and text page 215

Male and female Found from northwest Panama south and east to northern and western Colombia, a well-documented hybrid zone is known between this species and White-collared Manakin. To the south, in western Colombia, the interaction between Golden-collared and White-bearded Manakins are much more poorly known, although hybrids are known from at least two areas and *M. m. flaveolus* shows some approach to the present species in plumage.

White-bearded Manakin *Manacus manacus*   Map and text page 220

Male *flaveolus* This race inhabits the upper Magdalena Valley of central Colombia; note the creamy yellow tone to the throat and collar. It thus approaches, to some extent, Golden-collared Manakin, and the two species are known to hybridise in parts of southwest Cauca and the lower Cauca Valley, both in Colombia.

Male and female *manacus* Some 15 subspecies of White-bearded Manakin are generally recognised, although many are only weakly distinguished from their geographical neighbours. Nominate *manacus* occurs across the Guianan Shield and is characterised by being extensively white below with solidly black upperparts.

Male *gutturosus* The Atlantic Forest representative of the species is quite well differentiated from other subspecies in being the darkest below, with the grey feathering extending from the vent to at least the breast.

Orange-collared Manakin

male

White-collared Manakin

female

female

male

male

Golden-collared Manakin

male
flaveolus

White-bearded Manakin

female

male
gutturosus

male
manacus

female
manacus

White-bearded Manakin

PLATE 7: GENUS *HETEROCERCUS*

This genus represents yet another superspecies and is exclusively Amazonian in distribution. The three species are generally common but quite easily overlooked and not necessarily easily seen (especially females). The ranges of Orange-crested Manakin and Flame-crested Manakin in western Brazil require elucidation.

Flame-crested Manakin *Heterocercus linteatus*   Map and text page 233

Male and female This species has the largest geographical range of the genus, ranging across southern Amazonian Brazil as well south into Bolivia and west into easternmost Peru. Any possible contact with the next species remains to be discovered. The female has a largely grey chin and throat.

Yellow-crested Manakin *Heterocercus flavivertex*   Map and text page 229

Male and female Found north of the Amazon, from northern Brazil to southwest Venezuela and southeast Colombia, males are boldly marked, like those of the previous species. Females will be easily separated from other manakins in range by their large size and the grey throat, among other features.

Orange-crested Manakin *Heterocercus aurantiivertex*   Map and text page 236

Male and female Confined to a relatively small area of western Amazonia, in Ecuador south of the Río Napo and northeast Peru, as well as at one locality in immediately adjacent Brazil, this species is rare in collections and known from comparatively few localities. Note the much less deeply saturated underparts, in both sexes, than either of the previous two species. The orange crown patch is often very difficult to see.

Flame-crested Manakin

male

female

Yellow-crested Manakin

male

female

male

female

Orange-crested Manakin

PLATE 8: GENUS *MACHAEROPTERUS*

This genus comprises three or four species as currently constituted. Many authorities since the publication of *HBW* have preferred to recognise four species, splitting Striped Manakin into two. However, we maintain the more traditional single-species treatment because, while it seems very likely that more than one species is involved, it also seems possible that to recognise just two species might be too simplistic a view. Fuller research into the relationships between this group of taxa than has been possible to date is urgently required.

Striped Manakin *Machaeropterus regulus*   Map and text page 240

Male *regulus* Confined to eastern Brazil, where it ranges from Bahia south to central Rio de Janeiro, this taxon is usually split under the name Eastern Striped Manakin. It is easily separated from other members of the species as constituted here by the only very narrowly streaked underparts.

Female *regulus* Compared to other 'striped manakins', the female is easily separated by the fine small red streaks below, leaving most of the underparts rather white in appearance.

Male *aureopectus* The distinctive yellow breast-band is very striking in males. This race is found in southeast Venezuela and adjacent Guyana, but a very similar or identical population has recently been found in northern Peru, confusing the situation.

Male and female *striolatus* The most widespread of the 'western' races of this species, *M. r. striolatus* occurs from eastern Colombia south to northeast Peru and east into western Brazil. The different 'western' races (*M. r. zulianus*, *M. r. obscurostriatus* and *M. r. antioquiae* are not illustrated here) differ mainly in the depth and intensity of the streaking below. The present taxon is more or less the most strongly streaked below, with the narrowest white areas.

Club-winged Manakin *Machaeropterus deliciosus*   Map and text page 248

Male A very striking manakin of the Chocó of western Colombia and western Ecuador, its remarkable plumage was formerly considered sufficient to afford the species its own genus, *Allocotopterus*.

Female Rather less distinctive than the male of this species, but note the buffy to cinnamon-toned lores and face-sides.

Fiery-capped Manakin *Machaeropterus pyrocephalus*   Map and text page 245

Male and female *pyrocephalus* This manakin has a rather strange distribution, principally across the fringes of southern and eastern Amazonia, but with a small population in Venezuela south of the Orinoco. The latter is recognised subspecifically, as *M. p. pallidiceps*, and is characterised by the male having a paler yellow supercilium and a less prominent median coronal-stripe.

male
regulus

male

female
regulus

Club-winged Mankin

Striped Manakin

female

male
aureopectus

female
striolatus

male
striolatus

Striped Manakin

female
pyrocephalus

male
pyrocephalus

Fiery-capped Manakin

At least some recent authors have preferred to unite these two genera, with *Xenopipo* having seniority, but we maintain the *status quo*, at least for now, because there are no conclusive genetic data that demands their unification and, secondly, the genus *Xenopipo* has a substantially more varied vocal repertoire.

Olive Manakin *Chloropipo uniformis* Map and text page 268

Adult *uniformis* Confined to the pantepui region of southern Venezuela and adjacent parts of northernmost Brazil and westernmost Guyana, this species is generally common within its limited range. It is a rather long-winged and long-tailed manakin, but as befits its scientific name, the species' plumage is rather featureless.

Green Manakin *Chloropipo holochlora* Map and text page 265

Adult *litae* and *holochlora* The most widespread member of the genus *Chloropipo*, Green Manakin might comprise more than one species. It ranges south from eastern Panama to southeast Peru. While subspecies *litae* occurs west of the Andes in Colombia and Ecuador, the nominate race is found on the east slope from southern Colombia to central Peru, and these two might be better treated specifically (see main text).

Jet Manakin *Chloropipo unicolor* Map and text page 270

Male and female Note the distinctive white underwing-coverts in both sexes. This poorly known species is comparatively rarely seen in the field, although it frequently turns-up in mist-nets set at appropriate localities and elevations on the east slope of the Andes in southern Ecuador to Peru.

Yellow-headed Manakin *Chloropipo flavicapilla* Map and text page 263

Male The rarest of the genus is practically endemic to Colombia, but for a handful of records from northeast Ecuador. Note the considerably brighter head of the male, compared to the female; both sexes have reddish irides.

Female Note the much duller head and underparts compared to the male, although at least some females can be brighter yellow on the crown than this bird.

Black Manakin *Xenopipo atronitens* Map and text page 260

Male and female Apparently widespread in white-sand forests across much of Amazonia, this species has recently been found at several localities much further west and south of its previously known range. Males at least are perhaps most likely to be confused with one of the similar all-black tyrant flycatchers that inhabit the same range, rather than another manakin, but none of these Tyrannidae are likely to be found in the same habitat as this species.

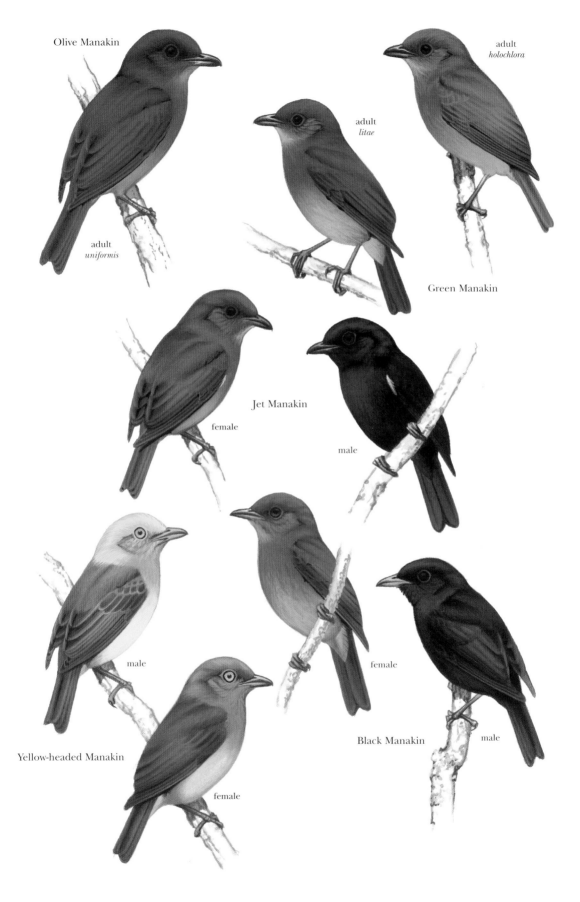

Olive Manakin

adult
uniformis

adult
litae

adult
holochlora

Green Manakin

Jet Manakin

female

male

Yellow-headed Manakin

male

female

female

Black Manakin

male

PLATE 10: GENERA *MASIUS* AND *CORAPIPO*

These two genera form part of the Ilicurini, together with the genus *Ilicura* (see Plate 12). While *Masius* is exclusively Andean in distribution, the two species (as recognised here) that comprise *Corapipo* are decidedly more widespread across northern Southern America and through Costa Rica and Panama.

Golden-winged Manakin *Masius chrysopterus*   Map and text page 277

Male *coronulatus* Another highly distinctive manakin, males appear almost eye-less and bill-less due to the deep black plumage and fancy head adornments. This race occurs in southwest Colombia and adjacent northwest Ecuador, and has a brownish to yellow hindcrown.

Male *chrysopterus* Considered to range from northwest Venezuela to central Colombia (although see the main text for details of the considerable confusion that exists in assigning birds racially in the latter country), the nominate race has an orange hindcrown.

Female The different subspecies recognised within Golden-winged Manakin are separable, to some extent, only in male plumage. Females are relatively easily identified to species, given the pale bill and underparts pattern, but subspecific identification is impossible, except on range.

White-ruffed Manakin *Corapipo leucorrhoa*   Map and text page 281

Male *heteroleuca* Treated as a single species here, although some authorities consider White-ruffed Manakin to comprise two species, *C. leucorrhoa* and *C. altera* (including *C. l. heteroleuca*). We maintain the single-species arrangement given the lack of conclusive evidence published in the peer-reviewed literature of the need to recognise more than one species; see the main text. *C. l. heteroleuca* (Pacific slope in southwest Costa Rica to western Panama) is distinguished, in males, principally by the narrower throat patch but obvious fan-like tips to the feathers.

Male *leucorrhoa* In the field (as opposed to the hand) male *C. l. leucorrhoa* (the South American portion of the species' range) is separated from other taxa in this species-group by the broad white throat patch which continues almost even in width to the rear.

Female Females of the various taxa are not separable, but the broad pale throat patch should distinguish them from those of other manakins that share the same range.

White-throated Manakin *Corapipo gutturalis*   Map and text page 287

Male and female Confined to the Guianan Shield, the diminutive White-throated Manakin should be easily identified in all plumages, males by the triangular white throat patch and females on account of the largely pale bill and mostly greyish-white underparts.

male
coronulatus

male
chrysopterus

Golden-winged Manakin

female

male
heteroleuca

female

White-ruffed Manakin

male
leucorrhoa

female

male

White-throated Manakin

PLATE 11: GENUS *CHIROXIPHIA*

The genus *Chiroxiphia* forms a superspecies of five species, one of which, Yungas Manakin *C. boliviana*, has only recently been recognised (split from Blue-backed Manakin *C. pareola*). It is possible that future taxonomic work might elevate also the subspecies *C. p. regina* (which is yellow-capped) to species rank. Three species possess more or less striking adornments to the tail feathers, and presumably all five (Yungas remains unstudied in this respect) have highly complex cooperative displays.

Long-tailed Manakin *Chiroxiphia linearis*   Map and text page 291

Male The most flamboyantly plumaged of the genus, Long-tailed Manakin ranges from Mexico to northwest Costa Rica. Within this range, males are impossible to mistake, even young birds without their tail streamers.

Female The projecting central tail feathers should serve to immediately identify female Long-tailed Manakins within their Middle American range, especially as few other manakins overlap in distribution, all of which are smaller-bodied.

Lance-tailed Manakin *Chiroxiphia lanceolata*   Map and text page 296

Male This species is found from southern Costa Rica north into South America, where it is distributed as far east as Venezuela. There is no geographical overlap with any other 'blue-backed' manakin, making males immediately recognisable.

Female Although females (and very young males still in largely or entirely green plumage) possess shorter central rectrices than Long-tailed Manakins *C. linearis*, no other manakin in this species' range possesses such tail adornments, and this is also the bulkiest-bodied species of Pipridae in northernmost South America and southernmost Central America.

Blue-backed Manakin *Chiroxiphia pareola*   Map and text page 301

Male *regina* This subspecies is widely distributed across southern Amazonia, and is unique among representatives of this genus in having a yellow crown. Seen reasonably well, this feature alone should eliminate any risk of confusion with other Pipridae.

Male *napensis* The only blue-backed manakin in Amazonia, males should, as ever, be readily identified. This subspecies is generally rather smaller than the rest, albeit with a reportedly larger bill, a marginally brighter red crown patch, and somewhat darker duller blue on the mantle and scapulars.

Immature male Following the first moult, young males acquire some red crown feathers, as well as patchy blue feathering over the mantle.

Female *napensis* Females of this species are probably largely unassignable to subspecies, except on range. *C. p. napensis* is found in the northern half of upper Amazonia.

Yungas Manakin *Chiroxiphia boliviana*   Map and text page 307

Male Recently split from Blue-backed Manakin *C. pareola*, and confined to southeast Peru and northern Bolivia, Yungas Manakin ranges at much higher altitudes than adjacent populations of *pareola*, but in any case Blue-backed in this region is represented by the yellow-crowned form *regina*, further preventing confusion, at least in males.

Female The only *Chiroxiphia* in range: concentrate on body size, overall coloration and bare-parts coloration to separate this species from other manakins.

Blue Manakin *Chiroxiphia caudata*   Map and text page 309

Male and female Endemic to the southern half of the Atlantic Forest, and well named as this is the only 'blue' manakin in which the male is largely blue, rather than black. The slightly forked projecting central tail feathers, which also characterise and help identify females, give rise to the species' alternative vernacular name, Swallow-tailed Manakin. In the north of its range, there is apparently some contact with Blue-backed Manakin *C. pareola*, although the two species are principally allopatric.

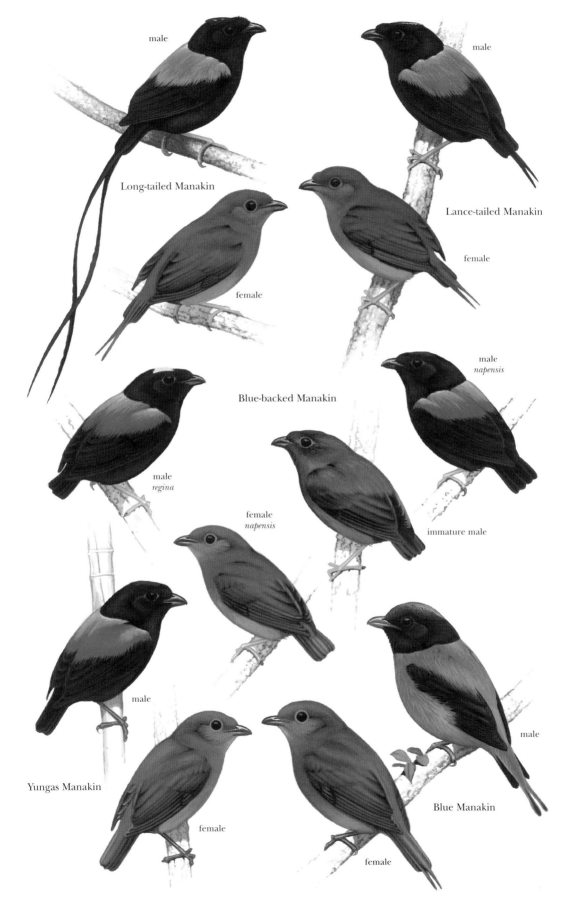

male

Long-tailed Manakin

female

male

Lance-tailed Manakin

female

Blue-backed Manakin

male
napensis

female
napensis

immature male

male
regina

male

Yungas Manakin

female

female

male

Blue Manakin

female

PLATE 12: GENERA *ANTILOPHIA* AND *ILICURA*

Two genera, and three species, almost entirely restricted to Brazil; Helmeted Manakin just penetrates parts of Bolivia and Paraguay. Molecular techniques have recently elucidated the position of the bizarre-looking Pin-tailed Manakin, revealing it to be most closely related to the genera *Masius* (of the Andes) and the more widely distributed *Corapipo*, of southern Central and northern South America.

Helmeted Manakin *Antilophia galeata*   Map and text page 315

Male A widespread Cerrado endemic, the stunning male is immediately identified by its all-black body and red 'shawl' and forehead tuft. This is a large and rather long-tailed manakin, easily detected by its loud vocalisations.

Female Despite their overall green plumage, female *Antilophia* manakins remain easily identified, given their distinctive structure (long tail, bulky body and forehead tuft). Few other manakins are found in the same habitat as this species.

Subadult male Acquisition of adult plumage is protracted in many larger manakins, leaving younger males looking somewhat 'piebald'.

Araripe Manakin *Antilophia bokermanni*   Map and text page 319

Male Critically Endangered and only recently discovered, this is but one of a number of birds endemic to northeast Brazil whose future hangs on a relative knife-edge. The stunning males are similar in virtually all respects to the very closely related Helmeted Manakin, but for their largely white plumage. Their vocalisations too are almost identical.

Female Like the female Helmeted Manakin, the female of this species should pose no identification problems, it being unique within the species' tiny range on the slopes of the Chapada do Araripe in southernmost Ceará.

Pin-tailed Manakin *Ilicura militaris*   Map and text page 272

Male Although predictive modelling suggests that this stunningly distinctive species might occur in northeast Argentina and adjacent Paraguay, there is in fact no real evidence that it is not a Brazilian endemic. The male could hardly be mistaken, even given a brief view.

Female Despite lacking the male's colourful plumage, females remain difficult to confuse with sympatric species of manakins, having a grey face, pale irides and pin-shaped tail feathers.

Helmeted Manakin

male

female

Araripe Manakin

male

female

male

Pin-tailed Manakin

subadult male

female

PLATE 13: GENUS *SCHIFFORNIS*

Long placed in the Pipridae (manakins), molecular (and other) work has recently demonstrated conclusively that the genus *Schiffornis* forms part of the newly recognised family Tityridae, and is one of three genera that collectively form the subfamily Laniisominae, together with *Laniisoma* (Elegant Mourner *L. elegans*) and *Laniocera* (two species of mourners). There is no sexual dimorphism in any of three species that comprise the genus *Schiffornis*.

Greenish Schiffornis *Schiffornis virescens*   Map and text page 333

Adult Endemic to the Atlantic Forest, from eastern Brazil to eastern Paraguay and northeasternmost Argentina, this species forms a superspecies with Thrush-like Schiffornis *S. turdina*. The two species are segregated altitudinally in the area of overlap between them, in southeast Brazil, with Greenish Schiffornis found at higher elevations in this region. With good views confusion should be unlikely, given the distinct eye-ring, greener body plumage and contrastingly rufescent wings and tail.

Várzea Schiffornis *Schiffornis major*   Map and text page 330

Adults *major* There is a great deal of morphological variation in this species, ranging from birds with a wholly rufous-coloured head and neck (concolorous with the rest of the body) and those with an extensively grey head. This variation does not appear to be geographical, with the result that some authorities have doubted the validity of recognising any subspecific variation in this species.

Adult *duidae* This taxon was described from southwest Venezuela. It purportedly differs from the nominate race by virtue of its clearer grey crown extending over the hindneck and the mantle also has a more olive-brown cast than in the nominate race.

Thrush-like Schiffornis *Schiffornis turdina*   Map and text page 335

Adult *panamensis* Virtually all named subspecies are very similar and many probably impossible to separate in the field using morphology, at least in regions where it is unclear which subspecies might occur (although voice may differ). *S. t. panamensis* occurs in eastern Panama and adjacent northern Colombia, and is reported to differ in its brighter rufous crown, wings and tail, and the throat and upper breast are cinnamon-rufous, contrasting with the greyish-olive lower breast and belly.

Adult *turdina* The nominate form is found in eastern Brazil, in the states of Bahia and Espírito Santo. It is uniform dingy brown above with slightly more rufescent fringes to the wing feathers. The underparts are dull olive-brown, becoming slightly more cinnamon on the throat.

Adult *rosenbergi* This subspecies is found in southwest Colombia and western Ecuador as far south as northwest Peru, and is considered to have the wings and tail more olive-grey (with fewer rufous tones), the throat paler and also less rufescent, and to be somewhat smaller in size than the adjacent taxon to the north, *S. t. acrolophites*.

Adult *aenea* Found in eastern Ecuador and northern Peru; compared to *S. t. rosenbergi* it has the upperparts browner and less greenish, with a more rufescent crown, more brownish breast, more greenish belly and the flight feathers warmer brown.

Adult *amazonum* This subspecies is widespread across southern Venezuela, southeast Colombia, eastern Peru and western Brazil east as far as northwestern Mato Grosso. It is similar to the nominate race, but the crown is slightly more cinnamon and it lacks the distinct cinnamon-brown wash to the upper breast of *S. t. turdina*.

Greenish Schiffornis

adult

Várzea Schiffornis

adult *major*
(rufous variant)

adult
duidae

adult *major*
(grey-headed variant)

adult
rosenbergi

adult
turdina

Thrush-like Schiffornis

adult
aenea

adult
panamensis

adult
amazonum

PLATE 14: GENERA *IODOPLEURA* AND *CALYPTURA*

These two genera of diminutive 'cotingas' have recently been reclassified on the basis of genetic evidence, with the result that the purpletufts (genus *Iodopleura*) are now considered part of the recently erected family Tityridae, whilst the remarkable Kinglet Calyptura, a bird practically unknown in life, is now thought to be a tyrant flycatcher.

Dusky Purpletuft *Iodopleura fusca*   Map and text page 359

Adult male and female Endemic to the Guiana Shield, and seemingly nowhere common, this species is the darkest-plumaged of the three purpletufts, with the generally chocolate-brown upperparts relieved solely by the white rump-band. Only the male possesses the striking violet-purple pectoral tufts, which are frequently hidden, unless flared in display or aggression.

White-browed Purpletuft *Iodopleura isabellae*   Map and text page 355

Adult male As in congenerics, only the male White-browed Purpletuft has the deep purple pectoral tufts. White-browed Purpletuft is a widespread Amazonian species, although its range is apparently entirely allopatric with that of Dusky Purpletuft *I. fusca*, making confusion between them unlikely. In any case, the distinctive white face markings of the present species should prevent potential confusion.

Adult female Lacks the purple pectoral tufts of the male, but is still easily separated from other purpletufts by the white facial markings, while the species' tiny size and white rump-band should make it readily identifiable to genus.

Buff-throated Purpletuft *Iodopleura pipra*   Map and text page 362

Adult male and female *pipra* Endemic to southeast Brazil, the nominate subspecies of the Buff-throated Purpletuft is best known from the coastal region of northern São Paulo state and adjacent Rio de Janeiro state. As in other species of *Iodopleura*, only the male has the purple pectoral tufts.

Adult male *leucopygia* Distinguished from the southeastern subspecies mainly by the white rump-band, the northeast Brazilian subspecies is the more poorly known of the two. More work is needed on the taxonomy of this species, as some birds within the range of the nominate sometimes show traces of a rump-band, and if *I. p. leucopygia* can be validated, the boundary between the two subspecies requires more accurate delineation.

Juvenile Comparatively little is known concerning plumage maturation in any of the purpletufts, but the first plumage of all three species closely resembles that of their nest site and thus is heavily camouflaged. Most feathers on the dorsal surface have prominent white tips.

Kinglet Calyptura *Calyptura cristata*   Map and text page 578

Adult male Almost unknown in life, with only one certain, multi-observer sighting within the last 100+ years, Kinglet Calyptura is undoubtedly the most mythical species of the Atlantic Forest, and one of the most enigmatic anywhere in South America. The crest is periodically raised like a frontal shield, thereby reducing the superficial similarity to a North American kinglet (genus *Regulus*).

Adult female Female Kinglet Calyptura differs from the male in having the forehead and forecrown largely dark olive-green, with paler orange-red restricted to the rear crown where it is intermixed with black; although the black is chiefly on the crown-sides, it does not form lateral stripes. Furthermore, the white tips to the wing-coverts and tertials are perhaps generally narrower, but still broad and obvious, and the rump patch is less bright yellow.

male

female

male

Dusky Purpletuft

White-browed Purpletuft

female

female
pipra

male
pipra

male

Buff-throated Purpletuft

Kinglet Calyptura

juvenile

male
leucopygia

female

These three genera belong to three separate families according to the taxonomy adopted here, although they all were frequently placed in the Cotingidae in the recent past. Whilst Scaled Fruiteater *Ampelioides tschudii* is closely related to the *Pipreola* fruiteaters, and remains within the cotingas, we, like many other recent authors, have removed the Sharpbill *Oxyruncus cristatus* to its own family (Oxyruncidae) and *Laniisoma* to the Tityridae. However, unlike at least some other authors, we prefer to view Elegant Mourner *Laniisoma elegans* as a single wide-ranging species, rather than splitting the Andean and Atlantic Forest groups of taxa into separate species.

Sharpbill *Oxyruncus cristatus*   Map and text page 323

Adult *cristatus* The nominate subspecies, which is confined to the Atlantic Forest is also arguably the easiest to see, for the species appears to reach peak abundance in this region, especially in the Brazilian portion of its range in this biome. This subspecies has the most extensively yellow underparts of any subspecies of Sharpbill.

Adult *hypoglaucus* This comparatively widespread but often patchily distributed species is sometimes divided into as many as six subspecies, with some additional, recently discovered populations, e.g. in Colombia, Ecuador and Peru, yet to be identified subspecifically. Race *O. c. hypoglaucus* is known from one locality in extreme southeast Venezuela, as well as elsewhere in the Guianas and in extreme northeast Brazil. It is similar to nominate *cristatus*, but has white underparts (greenish-yellow on the sides and undertail-coverts), white (rather than pale yellow) lores and cheeks, a slightly brighter green mantle and broader yellow fringes to the median coverts.

Scaled Fruiteater *Ampelioides tschudii*   Map and text page 393

Male and female The Andean-distributed Scaled Fruiteater is accorded a monospecific genus, although in some characters it approaches the Barred Fruiteater *Pipreola arcuata*. Both sexes of this cotinga are chunky, with a heavy dark bill, scaled underparts (more boldly marked in the female) and dark crown (in the male), making this species easily identified. All those *Pipreola* fruiteaters that overlap in range with *Ampelioides* have full black hoods (males) or lack the scalloped effect on the underparts (females).

Elegant Mourner *Laniisoma elegans*   Map and text page 349

Male *elegans* Given a reasonable view (which can be difficult), Elegant Mourners are relatively easily identified birds. The differences between the sexes are usually clear, especially the blacker crown and less extensively 'scaled' underparts of the male. Note, however, that there is some individual variation in the amount of scaling below, which can to some extent cloud differences between the sexes, thereby necessitating a clear view of the head.

Female *elegans* The female is easily separated by the much more extensively scaled and vermiculated underparts (virtually the entire ventral surface is so marked, with the exception of the chin and central belly), and the crown appears marginally duskier and less blackish, being more dark olive-green on the sides and the supercilium.

Male and female *buckleyi* The differences that serve to differentiate the sexes of the nominate form also separate males and females in the *buckleyi* group of taxa; here a male with very little scaling below. Nominate *L. e. elegans* in eastern Brazil and *L. e. buckleyi* in the Andes, differ rather marginally, in the smaller size of the *L. e. buckleyi* group, with fewer dark vermiculations on the underparts in either sex and the much paler crown in the female (almost concolorous with the rest of the upperparts).

Chick *buckleyi* One of the most remarkable birds in this book is the chick of this species, which to date has been seen just once. The illustration is based on the unique specimens held in the Natural History Museum (Tring).

Immature *buckleyi* Plumage much as adult of the respective sex or is more female-like, although at least some males partially develop the black crown, and all birds have some ventral scaling; also retains large and irregular rufous-chestnut spots near the tips of the larger, duskier, wing-coverts (making ageing straightforward).

adult
cristatus

Sharpbill

Scaled Fruiteater

male

adult
hypoglaucus

female

male
elegans

male
buckleyi

Elegant Mourner

female
buckleyi

female
elegans

chick
buckleyi

immature
buckleyi

PLATE 16: GENUS *PIPREOLA* I

The five species included on this plate are all part of the *Pipreola aureopectus* superspecies group, with the exception of the distinctly 'oddball' Red-banded Fruiteater *P. whitelyi*, which is confined to the Pantepui region. The other species are all found in the Andes, between Venezuela (Golden-breasted Fruiteater *P. aureopectus*) and southern Peru (Masked Fruiteater *P. pulchra*).

Masked Fruiteater *Pipreola pulchra*   Map and text page 371

Male and female Restricted to Peru, this striking fruiteater is relatively easily identified, as it does not overlap in range with any other member of the *P. aureopectus* superspecies. The male's head is olive but can appear darker in the field, especially around the throat, forehead and ear-coverts. There is no overlap with the similar Orange-breasted Fruiteater *P. jucunda*. Females resemble those of other members of the superspecies, but more frequently demand separation from female Scarlet-breasted Fruiteater *P. frontalis*, which has a similar geographical and partially overlapping elevational range; female Masked has streaked (not scaled) underparts, olive tarsi (red in Scarlet-breasted) and no pale spots on the tips of the tertials.

Orange-breasted Fruiteater *Pipreola jucunda*   Map and text page 368

Male and female The male most resembles the allopatric male Masked Fruiteater *P. pulchra*, but has the entire head glossy black (rather than mainly olive) as well as a fiery orange breast. Females of Orange-breasted and Golden-breasted Fruiteaters *P. aureopectus* are more similar, but the throat is a more uniform olive in Orange-breasted (rather than streaked yellow), and it lacks the faint pale tertial tips of Golden-breasted. Orange-breasted perhaps marginally overlaps with the larger Green-and-black Fruiteater *P. riefferii*, but note the different head and upper-breast pattern of males of the two species, and in females the different underparts patterns, lack of white tertial tips in this species and the grey-green (not orange) legs of Orange-breasted.

Black-chested Fruiteater *Pipreola lubomirskii*   Map and text page 373

Male and female Largely distributed along the humid east Andean slope from southern Colombia to northeast Peru, where it is always rare, this species does not certainly occur alongside any other member of the *P. aureopectus* group, thus making the larger Green-and-black Fruiteater *P. riefferii* the most likely pitfall. Separation of these two species is reasonably straightforward, given a decent view, as both sexes of Green-and-black Fruiteater exhibit pale tertial tips, orange-red legs and dark irides, whilst male Black-chested also lacks the yellow border to the black hood of male Green-and-black and has the central underparts unmarked.

Golden-breasted Fruiteater *Pipreola aureopectus*   Map and text page 365

Male The northernmost member of the superspecies, found in Venezuela and Colombia, the male of this species is unlikely to be confused with any sympatric congener, as in Venezuela male Green-and-black Fruiteater *P. riefferii* has a black hood and both sexes of Handsome Fruiteater *P. formosa* exhibit much larger white tertial spots.

Female Females of all four forms within the *P. aureopectus* superspecies are rather similar, but female Golden-breasted is separated from all of the others by virtue of the yellow throat streaking and white tertial fringes, and there is only any known range overlap with Orange-breasted Fruiteater *P. jucunda* in the Andes of southwest Colombia, where the two are not syntopic and there is no evidence of intergradation, further supporting their specific status.

Red-banded Fruiteater *Pipreola whitelyi*   Map and text page 383

Male and female Restricted to southeast Venezuela and adjacent Guyana, this species is easily identified in its restricted range. Male Red-banded Fruiteater has basically dull moss green upperparts and greyish underparts, with a contrasting orangey-red breast-band and bronze wash to the flight feathers. The female is much duller: greenish on the upperparts, with heavily streaked underparts from the throat to the vent. There are, however, no sympatric congeners in the Pantepui, and the female should not present any identification problems once the two superficially similar, but rather larger female bellbirds (*Procnias* spp.) that occur in the same region, or a Sharpbill *Oxyruncus cristatus*, are eliminated.

Orange-breasted Fruiteater

male

male

Masked Fruiteater

female

female

female

Black-chested Fruiteater

male

female

male

Golden-breasted
Fruiteater

female

male

female

Red-banded Fruiteater

PLATE 17: GENUS *PIPREOLA* II

Three species of brightly coloured and generally very distinctive *Pipreola* fruiteaters are included on this plate, one of which, Scarlet-breasted Fruiteater *P. frontalis*, might be better treated as two species. More research into this species' taxonomy is definitely required. Fiery-throated Fruiteater is the smallest member of the genus and is also the only species to have all-green underparts. Both these species are endemic to the east slope of the Andes. The third species, Handsome Fruiteater *P. formosa* is confined to Venezuela, and is easily identified by its very striking white tertial tips.

Scarlet-breasted Fruiteater *Pipreola frontalis*   Map and text page 375

Male and female *frontalis* This beautiful and distinctive smaller fruiteater appears to be most closely related to the Fiery-throated Fruiteater *P. chlorolepidota*, and some authorities have speculated that their speciation might have been a comparatively recent event. Scarlet-breasted and Fiery-throated Fruiteaters still exhibit rather extensive geographical overlap, although their altitudinal ranges are largely parapatric. Identification of these two species is covered in the next account.

Male *squamipectus* This subspecies (sometimes known as the Bluish-fronted Fruiteater) is found in eastern Ecuador to northeast Peru, and is slightly smaller, with a longer and broader bill. The male has the scarlet on the underparts restricted to the lower throat and chest, and the patch on the face is darker, glossier and distinctly more extensive, thereafter becoming bluish-green over much of the crown. Furthermore, it has some white on the tips to the greater coverts and secondaries.

Female *squamipectus* Compared to female *P. f. frontalis*, the female *P. f. squamipectus* is generally scaled yellow and green from the throat to belly (i.e. it lacks a distinct throat patch), with more solidly green flanks and patchy yellow undertail-coverts (versus more solidly yellow in *P. f. frontalis*). The forehead is only lightly spotted with yellow above the base of the bill, although this is probably difficult to detect in the field.

Fiery-throated Fruiteater *Pipreola chlorolepidota*   Map and text page 378

Male and female Fiery-throated Fruiteater is the smallest of the genus *Pipreola*, and appears to be most closely related to the Scarlet-breasted Fruiteater *P. frontalis*. These two species are largely elevationally parapatric, but they occur syntopically at several localities on the east slope of the Andes between southern Colombia and southern Peru. The male with its orange-red throat could be mistaken for the larger Scarlet-breasted Fruiteater, which also has the remaining underparts yellow rather than green. Female Fiery-throated Fruiteater lacks any yellow on the forehead, is more uniformly and densely scaled below, and has a white (rather than yellow) iris.

Handsome Fruiteater *Pipreola formosa*   Map and text page 381

Male and female *formosa* Although this fruiteater occurs sympatrically with Green-and-black *P. riefferii* and Golden-breasted Fruiteaters *P. aureopectus*, the identification of either sex should usually prove to be a straightforward matter. The black hood of the male immediately excludes Golden-breasted, and the splash of orange across the breast readily separates Handsome from Green-and-black Fruiteater. The female's barred underparts and yellow breast patch (which can be difficult to see) are diagnostic, whilst the particularly bold white tertial spots in both sexes of this fruiteater offers another useful feature.

Male *pariae* Handsome Fruiteater is generally considered to comprise three subspecies, which perhaps form two groups (nominate *P. f. formosa*, and the *P. f. rubidior / P. f. pariae* group). In *P. f. pariae*, which is found in the coastal mountains of extreme northeast Venezuela, the male has the upper breast scarlet in the centre fading to orange on the breast sides, and this patch of colour is more extensive than in *P. f. formosa*. There are broad white fringes to the tertials, the proximal end of the fringe having a black border.

Scarlet-breasted Fruiteater

male
frontalis

female
frontalis

male
squamipectus

Fiery-throated Fruiteater

female
squamipectus

female

male

female
formosa

male
formosa

male
pariae

Handsome Fruiteater

Three species are included on this plate, two of which are widespread and common throughout much of the Andean chain, whereas Band-tailed Fruiteater *Pipreola intermedia* is endemic to eastern Peru.

Green-and-black Fruiteater *Pipreola riefferii*   Map and text page 387

Adult male and female *riefferii* Arguably the most frequently encountered *Pipreola* virtually throughout its very broad range, and for many observers this species will be the first of this genus that they come across.

Adult male and female *tallmanorum* This taxon (which might merit specific status) occurs on the east slope in central Peru, and is most similar to the nominate in plumage, but significantly smaller. The male has the head and upper breast shiny black, the underparts mainly lemon-yellow and less streaked, except on the vent and flanks. In contrast to other populations, the irides are bright red. Females differ from those of all other subspecies in their small size, darker, more bluish-green upperparts and more golden-yellow underparts.

Adult male *melanolaema* This subspecies occurs in northern Venezuela and is smaller than the nominate. The male resembles *P. r. riefferii* but lacks the dull olive wash to the hood and has obviously unmarked yellow central underparts, the pale tips to the tertials are more conspicuous because these feathers are dark-centred, and the greater coverts have yellowish fringes and tips forming a slight wing-bar.

Barred Fruiteater *Pipreola arcuata*   Map and text page 385

Adult male and female *arcuata* A large and easily identified fruiteater of higher elevation cloud forest habitats, Barred Fruiteater is generally common throughout its range from Venezuela to Bolivia. Females lack the black-hooded appearance of the male and the entire underparts from the chin to the undertail-coverts (with the exception of the throat, which is more or less solidly green and concolorous with the rest of the head) are more or less evenly barred pale blackish and pale yellow.

Band-tailed Fruiteater *Pipreola intermedia*   Map and text page 391

Adult male *intermedia* Compared to the sympatric races of Green-and-black Fruiteater (*P. r. chachapoyas* and *P. r. tallmanorum*) both of which are appreciably smaller than Band-tailed, and lack the subterminal tail-band with whitish tips and densely variegated underparts, Band-tailed generally occurs at higher elevations than Green-and-black Fruiteater, although there is some limited elevational parapatry in La Libertad and Huánuco, Peru.

Adult male *signata* Differs from the previous taxon in that males are cleaner yellow on the central underparts (lacking the crescents of nominate *P. i. intermedia*) and have the flanks scalloped dark olive, with a more noticeable chrome yellow half-collar.

Adult female Compared to females of the much more numerous Green-and-black Fruiteater *P. riefferii*, note the relatively broad subterminal tail-band and whitish tail tips, although these are rarely conspicuous.

Green-and-black Fruiteater

male
riefferii

female
riefferii

male
tallmanorum

female
tallmanorum

male
melanolaema

Barred Fruiteater

female
arcuata

male
arcuata

female

male
intermedia

male
signata

Band-tailed Fruiteater

Green-and-black Fruiteater

The genus *Lipaugus* currently constitutes seven species of medium-sized cotingas found virtually throughout the mainland Neotropics, from northern Middle America to southeast South America, although only one species is found in Amazonia. All of the species are most easily located by voice, especially the Screaming Piha *L. vociferans*, which is speculated to be the loudest bird on Earth. Several species are considered globally threatened, including the recently described Chestnut-capped Piha *L. weberi* of Colombia and the range-restricted Scimitar-winged Piha *L. uropygialis* of the Yungas forests of southeast Peru and northern Bolivia.

Scimitar-winged Piha *Lipaugus uropygialis*   Map and text page 415

Adult Formerly placed in a monotypic genus *Chirocylla*, on account of the strangely modified (scimitar-shaped) primaries, this species closely resembles Dusky Piha *L. fuscocinereus* in colour, size and general proportions, but there is no geographical overlap with the latter species. Seen well, Scimitar-winged Piha should prove relatively easy to identify, even if the deep chestnut rear underparts and rump, which are unique within the genus, are not seen.

Cinnamon-vented Piha *Lipaugus lanioides*   Map and text page 410

Adult Endemic to the Brazilian Atlantic Forest, this species might be realistically confused only with the much more widespread Screaming Piha *L. vociferans*, although in their narrow area of overlap the two species usually are altitudinally segregated. The present species is separated from Screaming Piha by the overall more cinnamon-brown, rather than grey, plumage. As the name suggests this colour is at its brightest on the undertail-coverts.

Dusky Piha *Lipaugus fuscocinereus*   Map and text page 396

Adult The largest of the genus *Lipaugus* and confined to the northern Andes, Dusky Piha is a large piha with a short, thick bill that is slightly decurved. It is further characterised by the relatively small, slightly flattened head, narrow 'shoulders', long but relatively narrow body and very substantial, long tail. Its plumage is largely slate grey with slightly browner flight feathers.

Rose-collared Piha *Lipaugus streptophorus*   Map and text page 413

Adult male This 'oddball' piha is the only member of the genus to display sexual dimorphism. The male is far more distinctive than the less brightly plumaged female. Rose-collared Piha remains one of the least known of the genus, in large part because much of the species' range is very difficult to access. It is endemic to a relatively tiny region on the border between southeast Venezuela and adjacent Guyana and Brazil.

Adult female Females lack the rose to magenta collar and similarly coloured undertail-coverts; instead the latter are chestnut to cinnamon-rufous. Fortunately, the sexes often forage together, making the identification of females relatively straightforward.

Screaming Piha *Lipaugus vociferans*   Map and text page 402

Adult The best known of the genus on account of its highly distinctive song and widespread, principally Amazonian range, Screaming Piha is one of the least assuming of a generally unremarkable group in terms of its plumage. It is the only piha in Amazonia and therefore should be easily identified, once the equally uniform Greyish Mourner *Rhytipterna simplex* has been excluded. The mourner is smaller and slimmer, and has a very different song. Furthermore, its plumage shows a strong hint of olive below, especially if viewed in good light, and Greyish Mourner has an obvious reddish iris, which is easy to see.

Chestnut-capped Piha *Lipaugus weberi*   Map and text page 399

Adult Only recently discovered and already threatened, in large part due to it being confined to a small area of the Colombian Andes that has suffered extensive deforestation, Chestnut-capped Piha is closely related and morphologically similar to Dusky Piha *L. fuscocinereus*, but it is considerably smaller and greyer overall, with a distinctive chestnut-brown crown, yellow orbital ring and very different vocalisations. However, in poor light both the crown colour and that of the vent can prove difficult to discern.

Scimitar-winged Piha

Dusky Piha

Cinnamon-vented Piha

male

Rose-collared Piha

female

Screaming Piha

Chestnut-capped Piha

Included here are the predominantly rufous-coloured Rufous Piha *Lipaugus unirufus*, as well as two genera each comprising two species, namely the mourners *Laniocera*, which are part of the Tityridae, and another genus of cotingas, the green pihas, *Snowornis*. The two species that comprise the latter genus are exclusively Andean, while *Laniocera* has representatives in both Middle America and Amazonia; Rufous Piha occurs through Middle America to northwest Ecuador.

Grey-tailed Piha *Snowornis subalaris* Map and text page 524

Adult Both species of green piha are comparatively infrequently observed and are seemingly uncommon to rare; they probably sing only rarely. Grey-tailed Piha is exclusively found on the east slope of the Andes, in southern Colombia, south somewhat discontinuously to southern Peru. It is only likely to be confused with its sibling species, the Olivaceous Piha, whose range extensively overlaps Grey-tailed on the east slope (but is mainly elevationally parapatric). However, Olivaceous Piha is, as its name suggests, a more uniform bird and lacks the contrasting grey belly and tail of Grey-tailed.

Olivaceous Piha *Snowornis cryptolophus* Map and text page 526

Adult The voice of this species is not certainly known, making our knowledge of its distribution and abundance considerably weaker than for its congeneric, which is the only significant confusion risk. Unlike Grey-tailed Piha, which is confined to the east slope of the Andes, Olivaceous Piha is also found on the west slope, where it occurs from western Colombia to northwest Ecuador (subspecies *S. c. mindoensis*). On the east, it is found from southeast Colombia to central Peru (nominate). Although there is considerable overlap in their geographical ranges, Olivaceous generally replaces Grey-tailed at higher elevations. To date the two have been found at very few sites in sympatry (and always at different elevations).

Rufous Piha *Lipaugus unirufus* Map and text page 406

Adult This species' predominantly rufous plumage (and principally Middle American range) means that it can hardly be mistaken for another *Lipaugus*. The most significant risks of confusion are with Rufous Mourner *Rhytipterna holerythra* and Speckled Mourner *Laniocera rufescens*. The former is smaller than Rufous Piha, with a flatter-shaped head and a slimmer bill, whilst the piha also tends to have a paler throat and a darker crown compared with Rufous Mourner. Also smaller, Speckled Mourner *Laniocera rufescens* possesses rufous spotting on the otherwise dusky wings and, although it can be hard to see in the field, also shows fine greyish scaling or barring on the breast. It also lacks the pale eye-ring of the piha and has yellow or orangey pectoral tufts on the wing-bend (although these are usually concealed).

Speckled Mourner *Laniocera rufescens* Map and text page 345

Adult Most likely to be confused with either Rufous Piha *Lipaugus unirufus* or the tyrant flycatcher Rufous Mourner *Rhytipterna holerythra*. This species occurs from Guatemala south to northwest Ecuador, but is always difficult to find, except perhaps in parts of Panama. If visible (they are frequently not), the pectoral tufts of this mourner will readily separate it from either of the other two species, but otherwise note the rufous-spotted dusky wings and the finely grey-barred breast; voice is another good indicator of the species concerned.

Cinereous Mourner *Laniocera hypopyrra* Map and text page 341

Adult The Amazonian representative of the genus *Laniocera* is also found in the Atlantic Forest and is easily separated from its sole congener on both range and plumage (grey vs. rufous-brown); both species possess pectoral tufts (usually difficult to see). Throughout its range the species seems scarce and it is certainly easily overlooked, especially without knowledge of its voice. The most significant confusion risks are almost certainly Screaming Piha *Lipaugus vociferans* and Greyish Mourner *Rhytipterna simplex*, both of which widely overlap in geographical and altitudinal range with the present species, and all three can be found syntopically. Neither the piha nor the *Rhytipterna* possess any rufous spotting on the wing-coverts, on the tail tip, or on the underparts; both of these potential confusion species lack the yellow or orange pectoral tufts of the present species, whilst the piha is also marginally larger and the Greyish Mourner slightly smaller than this species.

Grey-tailed Piha

Olivaceous Piha

Rufous Piha

Cinereous Mourner

Speckled Mourner

PLATE 21: GENERA *TIJUCA* AND *CARPORNIS*

These two genera are endemic to the forested mountains of southeast Brazil. The two *Tijuca* cotingas are highly restricted to the environs of Rio de Janeiro, whereas the two *Carpornis* berryeaters are of more widespread distribution. Hooded Berryeater *C. cucullata* is still reasonably common, but Black-headed Berryeater *C. melanocephala* is much rarer and generally confined to protected areas; it is largely restricted to lower elevations.

Grey-winged Cotinga *Tijuca condita*   Map and text page 420

Adult A long-overlooked cotinga of forested mountains in close proximity to Rio de Janeiro. Described as recently as 1980 and discovered in the field shortly afterwards. Superficially similar to the female Black-and-gold Cotinga *T. atra*, which occurs in elevational parapatry, with the present species usually found at slightly higher altitudes. Compared to Black-and-gold Cotinga, both sexes of Grey-winged Cotinga are marginally smaller and perhaps less plump, with overall brighter green and yellow plumage in the male, which is further distinguished by having a silvery-grey cast to the remiges and rectrices, whilst Grey-winged Cotinga has a smaller and more delicate bill than female Black-and-gold, and is also rather yellower overall with greyer wings. The two species also differ quite markedly in vocalisations.

Black-and-gold Cotinga *Tijuca atra*   Map and text page 417

Adult male and female The adult male is highly distinctive, being largely black with yellow in the wings (visible both at rest and in flight). Females could easily be confused with the congeneric Grey-winged Cotinga *T. condita*; their separation is discussed under the latter species.

Hooded Berryeater *Carpornis cucullata*   Map and text page 518

Adult male and female The larger and more robust of the two berryeaters, this species is relatively common and easily seen, at least locally, in the foothills of its southeast Brazilian haunts. Much of the range of the Hooded Berryeater lies to the south of its only congeneric, the Black-headed Berryeater *C. melanocephala*. Female plumage mirrors that of the male, but the mantle colour is less intense and the hood and wings have an olive cast, whilst the underparts are marked by pale olive chevrons, especially on the breast-sides and flanks.

Black-headed Berryeater *Carpornis melanocephala*   Map and text page 521

Adult male and female This rare cotingid has almost certainly undergone a particularly dramatic decline in numbers and range. Black-headed Berryeater now occurs mainly in conservation areas and continued protection of these is increasingly essential to its long-term survival. Easily distinguished from its more highland counterpart, the Hooded Berryeater *C. cucullata*, by the mainly dull olive-yellow body and wings, and the black hood extending only to the level of the throat (not onto the breast as in Hooded Berryeater). The female has some olive suffusion to the black of the head, but is otherwise inseparable from the male.

Grey-winged Cotinga

adult

Black-and-gold Cotinga

male

Black-and-gold Cotinga

female

male

male

Hooded Berryeater

female

female

Black-headed Berryeater

PLATE 22: GENUS *XIPHOLENA*

Most closely related to the trans-Andean white cotingas (genus *Carpodectes*), the genus *Xipholena* might be almost considered a 'model' group of cotingas, for the males are quite resplendently wonderful birds, with lacquer-like feathering and striking plumage, whilst the females are somewhat dowdy, thrush-like birds, the unassuming plumage an adaptation to their being solely responsible for nesting duties. The three species possess almost entirely allopatric distributions, although Pompadour *X. punicea* and White-tailed Cotingas *X. lamellipennis* apparently meet and perhaps overlap in southern Amazonia between the Tapajós and Madeira rivers.

Pompadour Cotinga *Xipholena punicea*   Map and text page 433

Male and female The most widespread of the genus, the male Pompadour Cotinga is arguably the most beautiful and distinctive of the three species. Compared to female White-tailed Cotinga *X. lamellipennis*, with which there is apparently limited overlap (see main text), female Pompadour is overall darker, especially on the underparts, which appear decidedly less mottled (although note that some have almost clean white bellies and undertail-coverts), with perhaps marginally less white in the wing, and the bill is perhaps marginally paler. Females of this species might also require separating from some female *Cotinga* cotingas, but note the pale irides of this species, in comparison to Spangled Cotinga *C. cayana*, as well as the broader white fringes to the wing feathers.

White-winged Cotinga *Xipholena atropurpurea*   Map and text page 440

Male and female Endemic to the Atlantic Forest, where it ranges from the state of Rio de Janeiro (perhaps only formerly) north as far as Paraíba, this species' numbers have undoubtedly declined as a result of massive deforestation, especially in the northern part of this range. Like those of other *Xipholena*, males should be immediately identifiable, but female White-winged Cotinga might require separation from the same sex of the partially sympatric and now even rarer and more range-restricted Banded Cotinga *Cotinga maculata*. Banded is overall much browner, has dark eyes, heavily brown-scaled (rather than uniform grey) underparts and lacks the striking white fringes to the wing-coverts and tertials that characterise White-winged Cotinga.

White-tailed Cotinga *Xipholena lamellipennis*   Map and text page 437

Male and female White-tailed Cotinga is endemic to east Amazonian Brazil, where it is generally still reasonably common in forested areas. Both sexes should prove unmistakable if seen well, as White-tailed Cotinga is virtually entirely allopatric with other *Xipholena*, although it and Pompadour Cotingas seem to overlap with one another on the west bank of the lower Rio Tapajós (and even as far as the Rio Madeira; see above and main text). Male White-tailed Cotinga is not easily confused with Pompadour, given its overall much darker plumage and longer, white tail, but females of the two are less easily distinguished, and without good views will probably prove inseparable. Female Pompadour is overall darker, especially over the underparts, with perhaps marginally less white in the wings.

Pompadour Cotinga

female

male

White-winged Cotinga

female

male

female

male

White-tailed Cotinga

PLATE 23: GENUS *CARPODECTES*

With the advent of molecular techniques to resolve taxonomic issues, it has been confirmed that the genus *Carpodectes* (the so-called 'white cotingas') is sister to *Xipholena*; these two genera possess similarly plumaged females, but are found on opposite sides of the Andes. Whereas *Xipholena* occurs across Amazonia and the Atlantic Forest, the white cotingas are restricted to southern Central America, with one of the three species, Black-tipped Cotinga *C. hopkei*, ranging south as far as northwest Ecuador.

Yellow-billed Cotinga *Carpodectes antoniae*   Map and text page 448

Male Endemic to the Pacific slope of Costa Rica and western Panama, this species occurs in extensive mangroves and, seasonally, in the nearby forested foothills. It is marginally the smallest and shortest-tailed of the genus, but the male remains unmistakable (given the lack of sympatry between members of the genus) and cannot be confused with any other species in its small range.

Female Identification of the females of the two exclusively Central American *Carpodectes* will largely focus on range, given that Snowy *C. nitidus* and Yellow-billed Cotingas are entirely allopatric. This is fortunate because females of these two species are, to all intents and purposes, probably indistinguishable in the field; although the present species is marginally the smaller of the two and has a yellow base to the bill, these features are extremely unlikely to be of any assistance in most field situations.

Snowy Cotinga *Carpodectes nitidus*   Map and text page 446

Male Certainly the most widespread and probably the commonest of the genus, Snowy Cotinga is distributed from northwestern Honduras through Nicaragua and Costa Rica to westernmost Panama. Males of this medium-sized, stout-bodied cotinga appear completely white in the field, although the upperparts are in fact pale blue-grey. It is restricted to the Caribbean slope, whilst the other entirely Middle American member of this genus, Yellow-billed Cotinga *C. antoniae*, also appears all white but frequents coastal mangroves on the Pacific side.

Female Restricted to the Caribbean slope of Central America, which provides the only certain means of separating females of this species from the very similar female Yellow-billed Cotinga *C. antoniae*, which is found in a relatively small area on the Pacific slope. Females and subadult males of all three species of white cotinga might be confused with a female or immature tityra (*Tityra*), but note the lack of any red on the face in any of the three species and the much smaller bill.

Black-tipped Cotinga *Carpodectes hopkei*   Map and text page 443

Male Black-tipped is the largest of the three white cotingas. The other two species are entirely restricted to Central America, whereas Black-tipped Cotinga is only just represented in the isthmus, in easternmost Panama, in which country Snowy *C. nitidus* and Yellow-billed Cotingas *C. antoniae* are found only in the far west. Male differs from other white cotingas in having red irides, and black tips to tertials and tail.

Female Female Black-tipped Cotinga might be mistaken for a female Blue Cotinga *Cotinga nattereri*, but note the present species' red irides, overall greyer plumage, unmarked underparts and much more striking white fringes to the wing feathers, all of which should be obvious given reasonable views, but might prove difficult to distinguish at long range.

male

male

Yellow-billed Cotinga

Snowy Cotinga

female

female

male

female

Black-tipped Cotinga

PLATE 24: GENUS *PROCNIAS*

Procnias (the bellbirds) is a widespread grouping speculated to have arisen in the Guianas or eastern Brazil. Their nearest relatives remain somewhat obscure, but there is some evidence (from genetics) to suggest that the genera *Cotinga* and *Cephalopterus* are most closely related to the bellbirds. In the modern day they are found from central Middle America in the 'trans-Andean' region (one species), then cross the Darién gap into South America, ranging north of the Andes into northern Venezuela (including Trinidad) and the Pantepui, thence south into the lowlands of Amazonia (where one species is very local), southeast and east to the Atlantic Forest of Brazil.

Bare-throated Bellbird *Procnias nudicollis*　　　　　　　　　Map and text page 463

Male and female Endemic to the Atlantic Forest, where it ranges south as far as northeast Argentina and eastern Paraguay. Like males of the other species, the male Bare-throated Bellbird should be readily identified, but females (and very young males) might be mistaken for a female Bearded Bellbird *P. averano* in northeast Brazil. Unlike the female of the latter species, female Bare-throated Bellbird has a much more solidly dark crown and, especially, throat. These two species generally replace each other altitudinally in northeast Brazil, with Bearded Bellbird probably largely confined to remnant lowland forests, although we have records of both species from the highland forests of this region.

White Bellbird *Procnias albus*　　　　　　　　　　　　　　Map and text page 455

Male and female The White Bellbird has a strange distribution, being largely confined to the Guianan Shield, but the species is also known as a vagrant to Trinidad, and there is a separate, resident population south of the Amazon, in the Serra dos Carajás, Pará, Brazil. There should be little difficulty in identifying the male White Bellbird (there is no range overlap with the Bare-throated Bellbird *P. nudicollis*). The basically green, streaked yellow females are less obviously identifiable. However, in its range, females are only really confusable with the marginally smaller female Bearded Bellbird *P. averano*, from which it is largely separated altitudinally for much of the year. Although the two species are very similar in plumage, Bearded Bellbird has a darker grey-brown crown and more coarsely and extensively streaked throat and underparts; it is also marginally longer-tailed and longer-billed, although whether such characters would be apparent in the field except in comparative views or without extensive previous experience seems unlikely.

Three-wattled Bellbird *Procnias tricarunculatus*　　　　　　　Map and text page 451

Male and female Confined to southern Central America, the globally threatened Three-wattled Bellbird is a highly distinctive species. The bicoloured male especially should present no challenge in identification, particularly if the call is also heard. The female is a rather drab olive cotinga, heavily streaked below; however, the broad gape is always a sure indication of its generic affiliation.

Bearded Bellbird *Procnias averano*　　　　　　　　　　　　Map and text page 459

Male and female Two subspecies of Bearded Bellbird are recognised, the nominate in extreme northeast South America and on Trinidad, while *P. a. carnobarba* (which has greyer body plumage) is endemic to northeast Brazil. Male Bearded Bellbird, with its chocolate-brown hood and black wings contrasting with the white or palest of grey bodies, permits straightforward identification. The female, in contrast, could be mistaken for a female White *P. albus* or Bare-throated Bellbird *P. nudicollis*, depending on where in the species' range the observer is. For separation of these female bellbirds, see above.

male

male

Bare-throated Bellbird

female

female

White Bellbird

Three-wattled Bellbird

female

male

male

Bearded Bellbird

female

PLATE 25: GENERA *PORPHYROLAEMA* AND *COTINGA* I

The genus *Porphyrolaema* consists of a single species that is primarily distributed across upper Amazonia; genetic data suggest it is most closely related to *Xipholena* and *Carpodectes*. In contrast, the genus *Cotinga* (the blue cotingas) is a well-known and comparatively large genus, comprising seven species, whose relations have to date proved difficult to determine with any certainty, although one recent molecular study found some evidence for a close relationship to the bellbirds (*Procnias*).

Purple-throated Cotinga *Porphyrolaema porphyrolaema*   Map and text page 423

Male and female The male should prove unmistakable given good views, as the plumage pattern is unique amongst cotingids. The female is also readily recognised given reasonable views, but care will often be needed to distinguish it from the very marginally larger female Spangled *Cotinga cayana* and Plum-throated Cotingas *C. maynana*. These two species lack the rufous throat of female Purple-throated Cotinga, as well as the barred underparts and spotted crown, and have a subtly different head shape to the present species. Female Plum-throated also has pale, not dark, irides.

Lovely Cotinga *Cotinga amabilis*   Map and text page 467

Male and female Males resemble the two other species of blue cotinga occurring in Middle America, being turquoise-blue with two purple patches on the underparts, which are rather larger when compared with those of its neighbouring congeners, and appear to be separated by a blue breast-band. Females are arguably the most distinctive of the genus, being very pallid, with a whitish ground colour to the underparts, which are overlain with spots rather than scales, and possess whitish (and buffish) spots and scales over the brown upperparts.

Blue Cotinga *Cotinga nattererii*   Map and text page 474

Male and female The blue of the male is rather more turquoise but darker than the other two species in Middle America, and it appears less immaculately plumaged than the Lovely Cotinga *C. amabilis* owing to the presence of randomly exposed black bases to the upperparts feathers. Female Blue Cotingas are rather drab brown above, with very indistinct paler fringes to the wing-coverts. They are only slightly paler below, lacking the scaling or spotting usually associated with females of the genus.

Turquoise Cotinga *Cotinga ridgwayi*   Map and text page 471

Male and female Males most closely resemble the male Blue Cotinga *C. nattererii*. The purple belly patch is slightly larger than that of Blue Cotinga, extending lower onto the belly and towards the flanks, but this feature may be hard to judge in the field. However, the presence of black above the base of the bill, although also difficult to see, is characteristic. Female Turquoise Cotinga has dark brown upperparts with cinnamon tips to each feather (whiter tips on Lovely *C. amabilis*, uniform brown on Blue Cotinga), making the upperparts appear spotted. The throat is cinnamon (whitish on Lovely, dull brown on Blue Cotinga), whilst the feather centres on the breast and belly are dark brown, fringed cinnamon (fringed whitish on Lovely, and again uniform brown on Blue Cotinga).

male

female

Lovely Cotinga

Purple-throated Cotinga

male

male

female

female

male

Blue Cotinga

male

Turquoise Cotinga

PLATE 26: GENUS *COTINGA* II

The remaining four species of *Cotinga* are exclusively South American, three of them being found in Amazonia, with the fourth, very rare, species being restricted to part of the Atlantic Forest.

Plum-throated Cotinga *Cotinga maynana*   Map and text page 481

Male and female The slightly larger male Spangled Cotinga *C. cayana* has much paler turquoise-blue upperparts and scattered black markings above and below, as well as largely black wings. Male Plum-throated possesses a much more immaculate appearance, with yellow irides, smaller purple throat patch and the overall blue plumage. Female Plum-throated Cotinga is more heavily marked than female Spangled, appearing decidedly scaled on the underparts, unlike Spangled which has a rather uniform appearance below.

Spangled Cotinga *Cotinga cayana*   Map and text page 477

Male and female Arguably the commonest and most frequently encountered of the genus, this species overlaps in range with Plum-throated Cotinga *C. maynana* of western Amazonia, which has yellow irides, whilst males lack the black head, wings and upperparts markings of the more widespread and variegated Spangled. Female Spangled Cotinga is rather uniform below, lacking the scaled effect to the underparts prevalent in female Plum-throated. Purple-breasted Cotinga *C. cotinga* is marginally but obviously smaller and less bulky, with much deeper blue upperparts in males and extensively purple underparts. The female is rather dark brown above, with paler tips to the feathers, whilst from below, female Purple-breasted can appear uniform brown at a distance.

Purple-breasted Cotinga *Cotinga cotinga*   Map and text page 483

Male and female The colour of the upperparts in the male Purple-breasted Cotinga is a deep blue, rather than the pale turquoise-blue of the rather larger male Spangled Cotinga *C. cayana* (the only sympatric congener). Females are typical of the genus and most closely resemble the allopatric Banded Cotinga *C. maculata*, being distinguished from Spangled Cotinga by their rather more contrasting appearance to the upperparts: dark brown feathers tipped and fringed whitish, from the crown to the uppertail-coverts, and appearing rather spotted above at close range.

Banded Cotinga *Cotinga maculata*   Map and text page 486

Male and female This threatened species is the only blue cotinga in its limited range. Another rare cotinga – the White-winged Cotinga *Xipholena atropurpurea* – is often found alongside the Banded Cotinga in the Atlantic Forest of Brazil. Although of a different genus, females of the two may be confused, as their general appearance is of a plump, generally brown cotinga. However, female White-winged is a greyer brown bird with much bolder, white, fringes to the wing-coverts and some remiges. If seen feeding or at rest, the pale irides of the White-winged will also confirm the identification.

Plum-throated Cotinga

female

male

male

female

Spangled Cotinga

male

female

Purple-breasted Cotinga

female

male

Banded Cotinga

PLATE 27: GENERA *CONIOPTILON, PYRODERUS, QUERULA* AND *GYMNODERUS*

These four genera, all of which are represented by single species, form part of the so-called 'core' cotingas. Long suspected to be close relatives, due to their sharing powder-down over many parts of the feathers, molecular techniques have proven Black-faced Cotinga *Conioptilon mcilhennyi* and Bare-necked Fruitcrow *Gymnoderus foetidus* to be particularly closely related. One of the most recent genetic investigations found *Querula* and *Pyroderus* to be reasonably closely related as well, and both species to be part of a clade that also contains the umbrellabirds (genus *Cephalopterus*) and Capuchinbird *Perissocephalus tricolor*, and perhaps also Crimson Fruitcrow *Haematoderus militaris*.

Black-faced Cotinga *Conioptilon mcilhennyi*   Map and text page 430

Adult The sexes are basically identical in this species (and genus) endemic to southwest Amazonia, where it occurs in southeast Peru, adjacent northwest Bolivia and extreme southwest Brazil. This is a distinctive species, marked by its jet black face, chin, throat and crown, with a partial whitish border at the rear of the ear-coverts, entirely dark grey upperparts, becoming even darker, almost slate, on the wings and tail, whilst the underparts are also grey, but much paler, and grade to whitish on the lower belly and undertail-coverts.

Red-ruffed Fruitcrow *Pyroderus scutatus*   Map and text page 502

Adult *scutatus* The nominate form is endemic to the Atlantic Forest; it has the ruff orange with bright and broad red feather fringes, a few chestnut spots on the centre of the black belly and glossed upperparts. The species itself is very distinctive among cotingas for the red ruff from which the species takes its vernacular name; once this is seen, Red-ruffed Fruitcrow is immediately identified.

Adult *occidentalis* This subspecies is found in the northwest of the species' range, in western Colombia and northwest Ecuador. It has the feather fringes of the ruff less bright than in all of the other subspecies. The belly is extensively chestnut (much like in *P. s. orenocensis* of eastern Venezuela and adjacent Guyana), and the black upperparts are glossed.

Purple-throated Fruitcrow *Querula purpurata*   Map and text page 493

Adult male and female This is one of the most widespread (and sociable) of the cotinga family and the species is locally common in humid, principally lowland, forests. The male's throat colour can be hard to see at a distance or against the light, but even in such circumstances its calls and behaviour should readily distinguish this species from other large, predominantly all-dark birds. Purple-throated Fruitcrow is easily distinguished even in flight, when its curiously floppy wingbeats and compact shape, with the short block-headed and broad-tailed appearance, render it immediately identifiable with relatively minimal previous experience.

Bare-necked Fruitcrow *Gymnoderus foetidus*   Map and text page 426

Adult male and female Males of this widespread Amazonian species are unmistakable. At rest the cobalt-blue bare skin of the throat and ocular area permit instant identification of this rather 'vulturine' cotingid. The female might recall a female Amazonian Umbrellabird *Cephalopterus ornatus*, and these two species are often found together, but note the fruitcrow's smaller head and longer, slender neck. In flight the male's silvery-grey wing panel is particularly conspicuous at some distance.

Black-faced Cotinga

adult

adult
scutatus

adult

Red-ruffed Fruitcrow

adult
occidentalis

male

Purple-throated Fruitcrow

female

female

Bare-necked Fruitcrow

male

PLATE 28: GENERA *PERISSOCEPHALUS* AND *HAEMATODERUS*

These two species, both the sole components of single-species genera, are among the largest cotingas. Both are entirely, or principally restricted to the Guianan Shield, respectively, with the range of Crimson Fruitcrow *Haematoderus militaris* having, particularly in recent years, proven to be much broader, reaching well into southern Amazonia, albeit sparsely and apparently at low density. The much more readily encountered Capuchinbird *Perissocephalus tricolor* (or Calfbird) emits one of the most distinctive and bizarre avian vocalisations, which is sometimes likened to a cross between a chainsaw and 'lowing' cattle.

Capuchinbird *Perissocephalus tricolor*   Map and text page 497

Adult This monomorphic species is often characterised as being 'ugly'. Whatever its aesthetic qualities, there is no doubting that the Capuchinbird is one of the most remarkable and distinctive cotingas. The only difference between the sexes is that males average slightly larger. Confusion with any other bird seems unlikely. However, female Guianan Cock-of-the-Rock *Rupicola rupicola* also has a somewhat odd shape and generally brown plumage, but lacks the long heavy bill, any contrast between the wings and tail and the body, and the bald head, but does possess a semblance of the male's forehead 'bump'. Seen very poorly, or only partially, a more serious confusion risk than another cotinga might be a Red Howler Monkey *Alouatta seniculus*, whose fur has a similar colour to the Capuchinbird's body feathers and which primate has a very similar geographical range to the bird.

Crimson Fruitcrow *Haematoderus militaris*   Map and text page 489

Male and female With reasonable views the sexes of this remarkable and stunningly plumaged bird will be easily separated, as females possess an all dark, rather than red mantle. In terms of the species' field identification, the largely red plumage is perhaps most likely to promote confusion with the red cotingas, although it only overlaps extensively with one of these, Guianan Red Cotinga *Phoenicircus carnifex*, which is easily distinguished by its midstorey habits (the fruitcrow is principally found in the canopy), much smaller bill and head, and overall much smaller size than the fruitcrow. Recently, Crimson Fruitcrow has been found also to reach as far south and west as the range of the Black-necked Red Cotinga *P. nigricollis* (albeit apparently very locally), but the same features, as well as the striking contrast in the black neck-band of the male *Phoenicircus*, will serve to distinguish them.

adult

Capuchinbird

male

female

Crimson Fruitcrow

displaying Capuchinbirds

PLATE 29: GENUS *CEPHALOPTERUS*

The umbrellabirds (genus *Cephalopterus*) comprise a superspecies of spectacular and unique cotingas that are found in primary forests of southern Central and western and central South America. The three species comprise two restricted-range 'trans-Andean' representatives, Bare-necked *C. glabricollis* and Long-wattled Umbrellabirds *C. penduliger* and a single, much more widespread 'cis-Andean' species, Amazonian Umbrellabird *C. ornatus*. The two first-named species are both threatened by deforestation and hunting.

Long-wattled Umbrellabird *Cephalopterus penduliger* Map and text page 510

Male Despite their all-black plumage, both this species and Amazonian Umbrellabird *C. ornatus* are remarkable birds, first on account of their size, and then their spectacular head and throat adornments. The male Long-wattled Umbrellabird is immediately recognisable as an umbrellabird and is arguably the most bizarre of all the *Cephalopterus*: the crest forms almost a complete 'umbrella' and is full and bushy, virtually entirely covering the bill, whilst the bird's extensible wattle reaches up to 35cm long, and usually hangs well below the perch.

Female The female resembles the female Amazonian Umbrellabird *C. ornatus* (no geographical overlap), but lacks the white irides of the latter species, whilst the vestigial wattle and uniform blackish throat separates it from Red-ruffed Fruitcrow *Pyroderus scutatus*, of the foothills, and from the Purple-throated Fruitcrow *Querula purpurata* at lower altitudes (there is limited geographical overlap with both of the latter species).

Bare-necked Umbrellabird *Cephalopterus glabricollis* Map and text page 514

Male The sole Middle American representative of the genus *Cephalopterus*, male Bare-necked Umbrellabird is unmistakable with a 'Mohican'-style crest that covers the head and bill, and the bare throat and neck are scarlet-coloured, with an unusual 'tassel' at the base.

Female Female Bare-necked Umbrellabird has a smaller crest than the male and lacks the bare skin on the throat, and to a certain degree resembles the all-black female Purple-throated Fruitcrow *Querula purpurata*. This species is larger, however, with a very short tail (especially obvious in flight, but sometimes incorrectly illustrated in field guides) and its plumage is browner in tone.

Amazonian Umbrellabird *Cephalopterus ornatus* Map and text page 507

Male and female The male Amazonian Umbrellabird appears glossy black in the field, with white shafts to the bizarre crest feathers and a long pendulous feathered wattle dangling from the lower throat. The irides are silvery white. Female Amazonian Umbrellabird is less ornate, with only a vestigial crest and wattle. In Amazonia it might therefore be confused with another cotingid, the generally commoner Purple-throated Fruitcrow *Querula purpurata*, the male of which has a deep crimson-purple throat patch, but this can appear much subdued within the dim light of its primary forest haunts; thus, both sexes can appear all black. However, these fruitcrows are considerably more sociable than umbrellabirds, being often found in noisy parties, whereas Amazonian Umbrellabirds usually occur alone. The most widespread and least threatened of the genus *Cephalopterus*, the handsome Amazonian Umbrellabird is nonetheless usually rather uncommon over much of its wide range, only very locally appearing in reasonable numbers.

male

male

Bare-necked Umbrellabird

Long-wattled Umbrellabird

female

female

male

female

Amazonian Umbrellabird

PLATE 30: GENUS *RUPICOLA*

The two species of cocks-of-the-rock are frequently considered to be amongst the most spectacular of the great many extravagant Neotropical birds. Both members of the superspecies possess a highly 'colourful' lekking display, and the wispy processes on the secondary feathers of Guianan Cock-of-the Rock *R. rupicola* match closely the plumage of some birds of paradise, further enhancing the similarities. The cocks-of-the-rock were formerly placed in their own family, the Rupicolidae, until as recently as 40 years ago, but their removal to the Cotingidae has gained widespread support since, and some authors have found a close relationship with the red cotingas (genus *Phoenicircus*).

Andean Cock-of-the-Rock *Rupicola peruvianus*   Map and text page 529

Male *sanguinolentus* One of the best-studied subspecies, this form is found in the West Andes of Colombia and northwest Ecuador. The male has scarlet body plumage and deep red irides. Females (not illustrated) are rather variable but generally slightly more gingery, with pale red irides and a grey to pinkish-grey orbital ring.

Male *aequatorialis* This subspecies occurs in the Andes of northwest Venezuela, the central and eastern cordilleras of Colombia, eastern Ecuador, and south to northern Peru. The body plumage of the male is bright orange and the black bases to the tertials are exposed, whereas in the other three subspecies the grey on these feathers extends over the entire area that can be observed in the field. In parallel, females of this subspecies are the reddest of any of the races.

Male *saturatus* The southernmost subspecies *saturatus* occurs in southeast Peru to northwest Bolivia, and has the body plumage deep orange-red, approaching that of *sanguinolentus*, and males have pale blue to whitish irides with a pale orange-yellow orbital ring.

Female *saturatus* Although plumage variation in male Andean Cocks-of-the-Rock is reasonably marked, it is much less so in females, which are broadly similar between races, but still easily separated from any other species of bird, including the entirely allopatric Guianan Cock-of-the-Rock *R. rupicola*. Females of this subspecies often have brown irides.

Guianan Cock-of-the-Rock *Rupicola rupicola*   Map and text page 534

Male and female Because of the lack of any geographical overlap with the previous species, there is no chance of confusing either sex of this most remarkable bird. The male is adorned with delicate silky plumes on the lower back and scapulars especially, like fine orange peel, and the female, although much less distinctive, still bears the combination of heavy shape, broad-based bill and crest that makes this genus so immediately recognisable.

Andean Cock-of-the-Rock

male
sanguinolentus

male
saturatus

female
saturatus

male
aequatorialis

male

female

Guianan Cock-of-the-Rock

PLATE 31: GENUS *PHOENICIRCUS*

The 'red cotingas' are characterised by their intense carotenoid-rich, saturated red coloration, albeit with much black in the male of one species, Black-necked Red Cotinga *P. nigricollis*. This species-pair inhabits tall lowland forests of the Amazon and its tributaries, mainly in the north of the basin. They are usually treated as being most closely related to the cocks-of-the-rock (genus *Rupicola*), but some researchers have noted that the two *Phoenicircus* possess similar tarsal scutellation to the manakins (and is also similar to *Laniisoma*).

Black-necked Red Cotinga *Phoenicircus nigricollis*   Map and text page 542

Male and female Found exclusively south of the Amazon, and perhaps most easily found in the upper half of the basin, this beautiful cotinga is easily identified over most of the species' range. Females of this species and Guianan Red Cotinga will be difficult to identify in east Amazonian Brazil, where the two species perhaps come into contact in the region of the Rio Tapajós; for their separation see the next species. Males should be reasonably easily identified, if views are good, wherein observers should note that the dark parts of the plumage, including the terminal tail-band, are much darker and blacker in *nigricollis* than in *carnifex*, and the bill of the former is usually deeper-based. Eye colour also differs to some extent, with Black-necked having darker irides.

Displaying males Both species of red cotingas form exploded leks, wherein males usually display within auditory distance of one another. Each male holds the body slightly forward and horizontal on the branch, and the wings drooped, in order to display the red rump and tail to best effect. The birds also perform display-flights between up to five or so different perches, the male uttering a high-pitched whistle and wing noises as they swoop back down onto a branch.

Guianan Red Cotinga *Phoenicircus carnifex*   Map and text page 538

Male and female Largely restricted to the Guianan Shield, this fabulous species also reaches south of the Amazon in eastern Amazonian Brazil, where there is perhaps some overlap with Black-necked Red Cotinga *P. nigricollis*. Males of the two species should be reasonably easily separated, given good views, but females will be more difficult to identify. However, Black-necked tends to have a much darker, redder tail (and rump patch), heavier bill, much more red-saturated underparts extending as high as the lower throat (paler and more washed-out in Guianan, in which this colour generally extends only to the breast), and their eye colours differ as in males (reddish-brown in Guianan, but darker in Black-necked).

Black-necked Red Cotinga

male

female

displaying male
Black-necked Red Cotingas

female

male

Guianan Red Cotinga

PLATE 32: GENERA *AMPELION, DOLIORNIS, ZARATORNIS* AND *PHIBALURA*

The first three genera are apparently most closely related to the plantcutters (genus *Phytotoma*, see Plate 33), which relationship, although yet to be definitively resolved, seems reasonably certain on the available evidence. In contrast, *Phibalura*, a remarkably distinctive bird found in the southeast Atlantic Forest, with an isolated population in the Bolivian Yungas, is yet to be sampled molecularly and its closest relatives consequently are unknown.

Red-crested Cotinga *Ampelion rubocristatus*   Map and text page 545

Adult The sexes are basically identical in this, the commonest and most widespread of the high-Andean cotingas. All of the other species on this page that overlap in range with Red-crested Cotinga lack the distinctive white tail-band of this species (which is only visible from below), and none of the others has such a pale bill, amongst other differences.

Chestnut-crested Cotinga *Ampelion rufaxilla*   Map and text page 549

Adult Arguably the most attractive species amongst the three high-Andean cotinga genera; like the congeneric Red-crested Cotinga *A. rubocristatus* the sexes are fundamentally alike in this species. Chestnut-crested Cotinga is unmistakable and when perched appears 'chestnut-headed' rather than just 'chestnut-crested', as the dark facial markings are often obscure on a distant bird. Two subspecies are recognised, which replace each other along a latitudinal gradient.

Chestnut-bellied Cotinga *Doliornis remseni*   Map and text page 555

Male In all plumages, this species can be distinguished from the entirely allopatric Bay-vented Cotinga *D. sclateri*, which is its southern counterpart, by virtue of its rich rufous-chestnut mid-breast to vent. On Bay-vented Cotinga the rufous is restricted to the vent and this has a more orange hue than in Chestnut-bellied. The face, throat and breast of Chestnut-bellied are darker grey than its congener, and there is less contrast with the crown than in Bay-vented Cotinga.

Female Compared to the male, female Chestnut-bellied Cotinga differs in that the black crown feathers are fringed grey, which in the field renders the crown almost concolorous with the face and throat. The area in front of the eye is pale grey, contrasting with the black lores and imparting an indistinctly spectacled appearance.

Bay-vented Cotinga *Doliornis sclateri*   Map and text page 552

Male and female Throughout its small Peruvian range, this rare cotinga is only likely to be mistaken for Red-crested Cotinga *Ampelion rubrocristatus*, which is much commoner and has a conspicuous white tail-band, whereas Bay-vented Cotingas are much more rarely seen, preferring to perch inconspicuously in the canopy near the tops of the tallest trees. Female Bay-vented Cotinga differs from the male in lacking an all-black crown, which is grey with dusky shaft-streaks and a duller red centre; it also has a short blackish stripe through the lores, a paler belly, back and uppertail-coverts than the male, perhaps a slightly browner throat and slightly paler undertail-coverts.

White-cheeked Cotinga *Zaratornis stresemanni*   Map and text page 557

Adult Endemic to a relatively small area of Peru, and only discovered in the 1950s, this cotinga is a highly distinctive inhabitant of *Polylepis* woodland. It shares the streaked underparts with immature Red-crested Cotinga which, however, always has a white tail-band (particularly conspicuous in flight), and lacks the white cheeks of its rarer relative. There is no overlap with either of the similar-sized, but relatively longer-tailed and smaller-billed *Doliornis* species, both of which are easily distinguished given clear views of the head and underparts.

Swallow-tailed Cotinga *Phibalura flavirostris*   Map and text page 581

Male and female *flavirostris* Endemic to the Atlantic Forest. One of the most distinctive of all cotingas, this species' unique combination of dark head, bright yellow throat, barred underparts, dark green mantle and back, and long, swallow-shaped tail, makes it instantly identifiable.

Male *boliviana* Sometimes considered to be a separate species (Palkachupa Cotinga), this form is well isolated from the nominate. Generally reported to differ in being potentially longer-tailed, with a clean white postocular area, less yellow on the throat, fewer bars below, more orange-toned feet and reportedly weaker sexual dimorphism, but at least some of these differences still require substantiation and detailed clarification.

Red-crested Cotinga

adult

Chestnut-bellied Cotinga

female

male

Chestnut-crested Cotinga

adult

White-cheeked Cotinga

adult

male

female

Bay-vented Cotinga

female
flavirostris

male
flavirostris

male
boliviana

Swallow-tailed Cotinga

PLATE 33: GENUS *PHYTOTOMA*

Long considered to constitute a separate family, the Phytotomidae, but multiple genetic studies have confirmed that the three species of plantcutters that constitute the genus *Phytotoma* are best placed within the Cotingidae. Nevertheless, the *Phytotoma* do seem to lie at the heart of a subfamily whose constituents also comprise the three genera of high-Andean cotingas, namely *Ampelion*, *Doliornis* and *Zaratornis*. Two of the species are confined to the southern third of the continent, and these are both reasonably widespread and common birds of largely open country. The third species, Peruvian Plantcutter *P. raimondii*, is confined to the littoral of Peru, where it has undergone a significant decline in recent decades and is at some risk as a result of ongoing habitat destruction and modification.

White-tipped Plantcutter *Phytotoma rutila*   Map and text page 563

Male Whilst not as striking as the male Rufous-tailed Plantcutter *P. rara*, the White-tipped presents few, if any, identification problems. Although there is no range overlap, male Rufous-tailed Plantcutter can be discounted by the fact that White-tipped has more extensive and deeper red on the underparts and crown, and also more extensive and more noticeable white in the wings.

Female Female plantcutters should be immediately identifiable to genus and, as there is no known geographical overlap between the three different species, should be equally readily identified to species. The potential for this species to occur in the same areas as Rufous-tailed Plantcutter *P. rara* in winter (when both species disperse to some extent) nonetheless exists. Note the rather greyer (less brown) mantle and back of the White-tipped Plantcutter, which also has a paler face, more obvious white tips to the wing-coverts and a much less noticeable pale supercilium than Rufous-tailed.

Peruvian Plantcutter *Phytotoma raimondii*   Map and text page 560

Male The rarest of the plantcutters, given the lack of overlap with either of its two congeners, there is no identification challenge, although the male most closely resembles the White-tipped Plantcutter; however, the Peruvian Plantcutter is a generally grey bird with white wing-bars and rufous patches on the chest and belly.

Female The less distinctively plumage, streaked, female Peruvian Plantcutter might recall a Streaked Saltator *Saltator striatipectus* or another finch species, but various features (including the distinctive bill shape) should easily reveal its true identity.

Rufous-tailed Plantcutter *Phytotoma rara*   Map and text page 566

Male The southernmost species of cotinga, there is no geographical overlap with the ostensibly similar White-tipped Plantcutter *P. rutila*; males of both species have red underparts, but the colour tones are quite different, which should make both species immediately identifiable.

Female Although superficially similar to other female plantcutters, lack of geographical overlap prevents any confusion.

White-tipped Plantcutter

Peruvian Plantcutter

male

male

female

female

male

female

Rufous-tailed Plantcutter

PLATE 34: GENUS *PIPRITES*

The genus *Piprites*, whose systematic placement is still from adequately resolved, comprises three species, two of which form a superspecies. The third species, the strikingly wonderful Black-capped Piprites *P. pileata* is rare, probably declining and confined to the Atlantic Forest region; it is the only member of the genus to exhibit sexual dimorphism, further confirming its distinctiveness. The northernmost representative of the genus, Grey-headed Piprites *P. griseiceps*, which is confined to Central America, is also rare and certainly very poorly known in terms of its biology, but not apparently yet threatened.

Black-capped Piprites *Piprites pileata* Map and text page 575

Male and female Both sexes of this fascinating bird should prove unmistakable. Females are easily separated from the rather brighter males by the green mantle, scapulars and back, and rather duller-coloured underparts. Pairs often maintain reasonably close contact and frequently consort with mixed-species flocks, especially those with many tanagers (Thraupidae). Black-capped Piprites is virtually confined to southern and southeast Brazil, but was recently rediscovered in northeast Argentina, where the species is known from just two sites and has a tiny population.

Grey-headed Piprites *Piprites griseiceps* Map and text page 569

Adult An enigmatic species restricted to lowland Central America, the Grey-headed Piprites is the least studied of the genus and seems to be very infrequently seen throughout much of its range, perhaps most especially in recent years. The rather long-tailed appearance, coupled with the chunky shape, may lead to confusion with a female Barred Becard *Pachyramphus versicolor* or even a *Tolmomyias* flycatcher, especially if the bird remains high in the subcanopy. However, Grey-headed Piprites lacks the scaled underparts of the becard and the wings lack any rufous fringes, whilst if seen well the pale eye-ring should be prominent.

Wing-barred Piprites *Piprites chloris* Map and text page 571

Adult *tschudii* The most widespread of the genus; although the plumage pattern (wing-bars, white tertial fringes, eye-ring, etc.) resembles a tyrannid or a vireo, Wing-barred Piprites is reasonably straightforward to identify if seen well – especially note the large dark eye, emphasised by the yellowish-white eye-ring and loral area. *P. c. tschudii* is found in eastern Ecuador, extreme southeast Colombia and southernmost Venezuela, south through eastern Peru, and western Amazonian Brazil, and is duller olive above than the nominate, with a greyer cast to the head, especially on the nape and hindneck; the underparts are yellow-olive with pale grey flanks. It appears to intergrade with *P. c. chlorion* in western Brazil.

Adult *chloris* The nominate form is virtually endemic to the Atlantic Forest region of eastern Brazil, eastern Paraguay and northeast Argentina, and from southern Mato Grosso do Sul, Brazil, where it is generally uncommon. The recently discovered population in northeast Brazil has yet to be assigned to subspecies. In the nominate, in particular, note the extensively greenish-yellow underparts and the relatively restricted amount of grey feathering on the head; the wing-bars and tertial fringes are generally white.

Adult *chlorion* The range of this subspecies remains to be fully elucidated, but it is generally stated to range over southern Venezuela, parts of eastern Colombia and lower Amazonian Brazil. Within its core range, this bird is rather distinctive, being very grey on the breast and belly (the grey extending as a band over the hindneck), with a contrasting yellow throat, thighs, vent and undertail-coverts, a very narrow wing-bar, rather smaller white tertial tips than other northern South American races, very little yellow on the lores and a greenish forehead.

Black-capped Piprites

female

male

Grey-headed Piprites

adult
tschudii

adult

Wing-barred Piprites

adult
chloris

adult
chlorion

Wing-barred Piprites

FAMILY EURYLAIMIDAE

Genus *Sapayoa*: Broad-billed Sapayoa

The Broad-billed Sapayoa (or 'Manakin') takes its unusual family name from the locality of its type specimen, the Río Sapayo, in northwest Ecuador. Its specific name, *aenigma*, was well chosen, for the species has long baffled ornithologists determined to classify it. From the outset it was recognised to be a fascinating novelty (Hartert 1903). Traditionally placed in the Pipridae (manakins), primarily based on the foot structure of *Sapayoa* appearing to be typically piprine, its similarity to various members of the Tyrannidae (tyrant flycatchers) has long been noted, whilst the recent description of its nest and parental care procedures strengthened calls for its reclassification. Some recent authors (e.g. Chesser *et al.* 2011) have placed this strange bird in its own family, Sapayoidae, on the basis of recently accumulated genetic data (Fjeldså *et al.* 2003, Chesser 2004), but *Sapayoa* is more closely related to the Old World suboscines, broadbills and pittas than to those found in the Western Hemisphere (see Systematics).

BROAD-BILLED SAPAYOA
Sapayoa aenigma   Plate 1

Sapayoa aenigma **E. Hartert, 1903,** *Novit. Zool.* 10: 117, Río Sapayo [= Sapallo Grande], prov. Esmeraldas, Ecuador

One of the visually most unassuming yet intrinsically fascinating of Neotropical birds, the single species of sapayoa is nowhere numerous within its Panamanian and northwest South American range. Unsurprisingly, there is probably still much concerning its natural history that remains to be learned.

IDENTIFICATION 13.5–15.0cm. This 'manakin', of uncertain affinities, is certainly atypical. Its plumage resembles that of some of the other duller members of the Pipridae but its rather pointed, broad-based and flattened bill is quite unlike any member of the latter family. Any superficial resemblance to any number of female manakins with which it shares its range should be quickly dispelled by the powerful bill and rather long, full tail. Only the Green Manakin *Chloropipo holochlora* approaches the sapayoa in shape and size but is still smaller, with more yellow on the belly and a yellow eye-ring. The sapayoa's size, shape and posture to some extent recall Thrush-like Schiffornis *Schiffornis turdina*, but the latter is much browner above, especially on the wings, and much less yellow below, with a more obvious eye-ring and lacks a coronal-stripe. Some of the flatbills *Rhynchocyclus* and *Ramphotrigon* (Tyrannidae) resemble the sapayoa, but can be separated by their conspicuous yellowish wingbars and fringes to the flight feathers, as the sapayoa has essentially unmarked wings. Females of two tanagers, Carmiol's Tanager *Chlorothraupis carmioli* (the sapayoa may occasionally join flocks of this species) and Tawny-crested Tanager *Tachyphonus delattrei*, bear a passing resemblance to Broad-billed Sapayoa, but Tawny-crested is much browner and less olive overall, whilst the former species has an even larger and heavier bill.

DISTRIBUTION Broad-billed Sapayoa occurs from southernmost Central America into northwest South America. The species is found from Panama east from the northern Canal Zone (e.g. along the Pipeline Road) to the Darién, principally on the Caribbean slope, thereafter through Pacific Colombia east as far as the upper Sinú Valley, Córdoba, and the middle Magdalena Valley, in the Serranía San Lucas (Hilty and Brown 1986), thence south as far as extreme northwest Ecuador, in Esmeraldas and northwest

Pichincha; there are two specimens from further south in Pichincha and even Guayas (Ridgely and Greenfield 2001). Elevational range, from near sea level to *c.*1,100m, even at 1,370m on Cerro Pirre (Darién, Panama) and once at 1,800m in southern Colombia (Mazar Barnett *et al.* 1998), but there are no records from above 500m in Ecuador.

MOVEMENTS Apparently sedentary.

HABITAT Principally inhabits humid and wet primary forest, often near streams and ravines.

DESCRIPTION Rather nondescript apart from the bill shape (culmen reasonably well arched and tip hooked), the yellow coronal stripe of the male (which is usually concealed by the olive-green fringes and tips to the crest feathers, and is difficult to see in the field), and the comparatively long tail. *Adult* Sexes are generally alike, with the body and head dull olive above and olive-yellow below, flammulated darker, with a paler, yellower throat and neck-sides, almost orange-coloured central belly, and darker flanks. The wings and tail are dusky-olive, the remiges have slightly brighter olive fringes, but any contrast is effectively minimal. *Juvenile.* – Undescribed, but is presumed to resemble the female (Snow 2004b), though the young male apparently shows emergent yellow on the crown (Restall *et al.* 2006; but see below). Hellmayr (1911) mentioned an 'immature' female that had the upper part of the head more yellowish-green, and the throat slightly paler yellow than in adults, whilst a young male he described as lacking any trace of the yellow coronal patch but having a shorter, smaller bill with a yellow-white lower mandible. The nestling was described by Christian (2001); see below. *Moult.* – No published moult data, but at least some Ecuadorian specimens taken in September–November had the wings and tail heavily worn (MECN). *Bare parts.* – Irides dull reddish- or tawny-brown or dark brown (perhaps slightly paler in the female, and described as tan in immatures); maxilla black with a paler (horn-coloured or blue-grey) lower mandible and even paler (sometimes flesh-coloured or yellow) base, and long rictal bristles; and legs (which appear somewhat short) and feet mid to blue-grey; soles yellow (Wetmore 1972, Robbins *et al.* 1985; UWBM and MECN specimen data).

MEASUREMENTS (from Wetmore 1972; MECN: Panama and northwest Ecuador) Wing of male (*n* = 14) 74.0–83.8mm, wing of female (*n* = 14) 77.4–83.1mm; tail of male (*n* = 14) 56.0–61.0mm, tail of female (*n* = 14) 54.5–60.0mm; bill of male (*n* = 14) 14.8–18.3mm, bill of female (*n* = 14) 15.3–18.7mm; tarsus of male (*n* = 10) 15.0–15.2mm, tarsus of female (*n* = 10) 14.2–15.2mm. Some additional mensural data, including of two young individuals, were presented by Hellmayr (1911). Weight (sexes combined): 18.5–23.0 g (Robbins *et al.* 1985, Snow 2004b; MECN).

GEOGRAPHICAL VARIATION Monotypic. Wetmore (1972) noted a slight propensity for birds from the Serranía de Baudó, in central western Colombia, to be on average more olive, but, like subsequent authors, saw no need to name such variation.

VOICE Poorly known, but Snow (2004b) mentions a somewhat nasal trill, and slightly louder *chip, ch-ch-ch*. The latter call appears to function as an alarm, between members of a pair, and the chip note and short trill may be given together or separately, especially the trill, which can be lengthened. The nasal trill appears to be the territorial song and is delivered on a more or less even pitch lasting *c.*3 seconds (Jahn *et al.* 2002, Krabbe and Nilsson 2003). Recordings of the both the presumed song and call, from Panama, are available online (www.xeno-canto.org).

NATURAL HISTORY Generally found at low to mid levels, often alone and less frequently in pairs. Rather quiet and staid when perched, usually rather upright, peering quizzically around for quite long periods, abruptly making occasional short sallies for insects (both aerial and on leaves, by hover gleaning). Also takes quantities of small fruits, as well as by sallying. Regularly joins mixed-species flocks, especially in the understorey, e.g. containing Western Woodhaunter *Hyloctistes virgatus*, *Myrmotherula* antwrens, Bright-rumped Attila *Attila spadiceus* and Tawny-crowned Greenlet *Hylophilus ochraceiceps*.

BREEDING Breeding-condition birds have been collected in western Colombia in February–April, and in northwestern Ecuador in September–November (MECN), but concrete breeding data are available only from Panama (cf. Christian 2001, for nest dimensions and other details), where the species constructs a pear-shaped nest, from strips of fibrous bark and fibres, with a noticeable 'tail' of the same material, entered from below, and suspended from a branch *c.*2m above a stream. Eggs (two) are laid in late April/early May, and both adults fed the nestlings (insects including moths), often giving a short trill or longer twittering call upon approaching the nest (which they usually did simultaneously). Hartert (1903), in the type description,

also mentioned that the species lays two eggs, but further information is unavailable. Nest shape and construction, and parental care, all clearly demonstrate that this species lies outwith the Pipridae.

STATUS Treated as Least Concern (BirdLife International 2004, 2008), though the species is range-restricted in Ecuador where Ridgely and Greenfield (2001) considered it sufficiently rare (though perhaps almost certainly also overlooked) to merit Near Threatened status. In Ecuador, the species can most profitably be searched for in Fundación Jocotoco's Río Canandé reserve, in Esmeraldas, and at Playa de Oro, in the same province. Reasonably widespread but considered probably local in Colombia, where known from several protected areas (e.g. La Planada and El Pangan reserves, both in dpto. Nariño) and at least formerly Broad-billed Sapayoa was found to be locally abundant in southeast Panama, from which country the majority of museum specimens come (see Wetmore 1972).

REFERENCES Angehr and Dean (2010), AOU (1998), BirdLife International (2004, 2008), Chesser (2004), Chesser *et al.* (2011), Christian (2001), Fjeldså *et al.* (2003), Hartert (1903), Hellmayr (1911, 1929b), Hilty and Brown (1986), Irestedt *et al.* (2006), Jahn *et al.* (2002), Krabbe and Nilsson (2003), Mazar Barnett *et al.* (1998), Olson (1971), Restall *et al.* (2006), Ridgely and Greenfield (2001), Ridgely and Gwynne (1976), Ridgely and Tudor (1994, 2009), Robbins *et al.* (1985), Snow (1975, 2004b), Stotz *et al.* (1996), Tello *et al.* (2009), Warter (1965), Wetmore (1972).

Broad-billed Sapayoa *Sapayoa aenigma.* **Fig. 1.** Male, Playa de Oro, prov. Esmeraldas, northwest Ecuador, June (*Nick Athanas / Tropical Birding*). Note the just-visible yellow central coronal stripe, which identifies the bird as a male, as well as the broad-based, slightly pointed but not long bill, and predominantly green plumage, which features identify it to species.

Genus *Neopelma*: larger tyrant-manakins

This genus comprises a quintet (one species only recently recognised) of unprepossessing, dull 'manakins' of uncertain affinities (they are sometimes speculated to be tyrant flycatchers), whose closest relatives are almost certainly the *Tyranneutes* 'manakins', although the latter morphologically more closely resemble 'true' manakins in the field. There is no sexual dimorphism in any *Neopelma* (or *Tyranneutes*), and the species are all very much alike, but felicitously, for field identification purposes, they are very largely allopatric in distribution.

PALE-BELLIED TYRANT-MANAKIN
Neopelma pallescens   Plate 1

Tyrannula pallescens **Lafresnaye, 1853**, *Rev. Mag. Zool.* 2(5): 57, Bahia [Brazil]

Snow (2004b) considered the genus *Neopelma* to represent a superspecies, of which Pale-bellied Tyrant-Manakin is about the most widespread, although its range is still almost entirely confined to Brazil. Willis (1982) in his review of the biogeography of east Brazilian birds considered *N. pallescens* to be a close relative of *N. aurifrons* (at a time when the latter was universally regarded as constituting a single species) and *N. sulphureiventer*.

IDENTIFICATION 14–17cm. Of its congeners, this species is only certainly sympatric with Wied's Tyrant-Manakin *N. aurifrons* (e.g. in the upper Rio Doce region of Minas Gerais: Faria *et al.* 2006), from which it can be distinguished by the paler underparts lacking any clear yellow and, more easily, by voice. (It is unclear whether *N. pallescens* is truly sympatric with Sulphur-bellied Tyrant-Manakin *N. sulphureiventer* in northeast Bolivia.) Like all *Neopelma* this species will bring to mind a tyrannid of sorts, perhaps most especially one of the *Myiopagis* elaenias. Greenish Elaenia *M. viridicata*, which is often cited as a potential confusion species with any of the *Neopelma*, can be distinguished by its white supraloral stripe and eye-ring, yellower belly, and yellowish fringes to the secondaries. Given brief views, another possible confusion risk might be female Blue-backed Manakin *Chiroxiphia pareola*, which shares some of this species' same forests, e.g. in southern Guyana and parts of northeast Brazil, but aside from being generally darker green the *Chiroxiphia* also has bright orange legs.

DISTRIBUTION Near-endemic to Brazil, where its strange distribution includes a localised population in lower Amazonian Brazil (in the savannas of Amapá westwards along both banks of the Amazon to the lower Rio Tapajós, in central Pará as far east as the Serra dos Carajás, and northern Mato Grosso, at the Serra dos Caiabis), with the bulk of the range focused on central and southeastern Brazil, namely from Maranhão (e.g. at Rosário and Transqueira) south and west through Tocantins, Goiás and northwest Minas Gerais to southern Mato Grosso and Mato Grosso do Sul, thence east and north through western São Paulo, eastern Minas Gerais, eastern and central Bahia (e.g. in the Chapada Diamantina), Alagoas and Pernambuco to Rio Grande do Norte (Pinto 1944, Novaes and Lima 1991, Ridgely and Tudor 1994, Oren and Parker 1997, Sick 1997, Hidasi 1998, 2007, Parrini *et al.* 1999, Pacheco and Olmos 2005, 2006, Pacheco *et al.* 2007, Lees *et al.* 2008, Lopes *et al.* 2008). The species has only very recently been found at one locality in the Brazilian Pantanal, at which it is apparently common (Vasconcelos *et al.* 2008, Lowen 2010). It was also discovered in the 1980s in

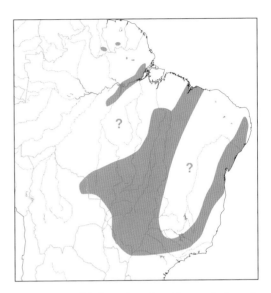

northeastern Bolivia, in northeast Santa Cruz, on the Serranía de Huanchaca (Bates *et al.* 1992), where it is apparently replaced at the base of the plateau by Sulphur-bellied Tyrant-Manakin. Pale-bellied Tyrant-Manakin was discovered recently in southern Guyana at four sites in the Rupununi savannas of Guyana, where it was initially found in 1992, e.g. at the frequently visited Karanambu Ranch (Mees 2000, Robbins *et al.* 2004), and even more recently (June 2007) in southernmost Surinam, in the vicinity of Mamia Pakoro, in the Sipaliwini Savanna (Ottema *et al.* 2009, Mittermeier *et al.* 2010), and at two localities in northernmost Pará, Brazil (Aleixo *et al.* 2011). Finally, Pale-bellied Tyrant-Manakin has been predicted to occur in Roraima, northernmost Brazil (Naka *et al.* 2007) and has also been reported from near Itacoatiara, east of Manaus, Amazonas (Forrester 1993).

MOVEMENTS None known.

HABITAT *N. pallescens* inhabits the lower growth of dense and closed deciduous and gallery woodland (in the main, it inhabits drier areas than Wied's Tyrant-Manakin *N. aurifrons*), to at least 800m, particularly where there is a substantial growth of vines. In eastern Amazonia, it is found at the ecotone between tall *terra firme* and open scrubbier vegetation (GMK pers. obs.) whilst in southern Surinam it occurs solely on forested hillsides (Ottema *et al.* 2009, Mittermeier *et al.* 2010).

DESCRIPTION Flycatcher-like, with proportionately long wings and tail for a 'manakin', and is the largest of its genus. The sexes are similar, but males average larger in most mensural data (see Measurements) and tend to have a larger and brighter yellow coronal patch (though it is rarely visible in the field in either sex). Bill is relatively broad-based with a reasonably arched culmen, and at least some birds have a strikingly hooked tip (completely lacking in others). Rictal bristles well developed. *Adult.* – Dark olive-green above and rather uniform, but is duskier on the outer webs of the tertials and the flight feathers, which have olive-green fringes. There are noticeably darker tips to the greater coverts and the yellow central crown patch has much darker olive borders than the rest of the upperparts. The underparts are pale creamy whitish with the slightest hint of yellow (mainly on the lower belly, sometimes reaching to the lower breast and the flanks), and admixed olivaceous grey on the lower breast and flanks, thus effectively demarcating the paler, more whitish, throat, which in turn is flammulated grey, sometimes strikingly so (there seems to be no obvious seasonal, sexual or geographical bias to this feature). *Juvenile.* – Undescribed to date (Snow 2004b), but based on skull ossification data, there seems to be no noticeable difference between full adults and younger birds (MNRJ). *Moult.* – Few published moult data except from the Chapada do Araripe, in southern Ceará, where approximately 50% of trapped birds were moulting either the head and body feathers or the primaries or secondaries during the period June–September (Nascimento *et al.* 2000). Elsewhere, birds taken in Amapá in September, Pernambuco in March and July, and Ceará in July were either very fresh-plumaged or showed no evidence of moult, whereas one taken in central Bahia in January was renewing the head, body and outermost tail feathers, two primaries and the secondaries, whilst one from Bahia in December was replacing the primaries and wing-coverts (MNRJ). *Bare parts.* – Irides are greyish-white or greyish-mauve (once chestnut) to yellow, with a brownish-red orbital ring; the legs and feet are dark brown to greyish-blue, with ochre soles; and the bill is brown to black with a horn-coloured or greyish-white base (FMNH; MNRJ; Novaes 1978).

MEASUREMENTS (BMNH; MNRJ; RMNH: mainly Brazil, from Amapá, Bahia, Ceará, Goiás, Mato Grosso, Pará, Pernambuco; also Surinam) Wing of male (*n* = 16) 72.5–80.0mm, wing of female (*n* = 9) 67–79mm; tail of male (*n* = 16) 60.5–66.0mm, tail of female (*n* = 8) 55–64mm; bill of male (*n* = 16) 12.87–16.08mm, bill of female (*n* = 9) 12.68–14.28mm; tarsus of male (*n* = 4) 16–19mm, tarsus of female (*n* = 2) 16mm. For other published measurements see Hellmayr (1908) and Novaes (1978). Weight: at least 15–23g (Fry 1970, Snow 2004b, Rodrigues *et al.* 2005, Dunning 2008; DZUFMG; MNRJ; RMNH).

GEOGRAPHICAL VARIATION Monotypic. Work designed to test for any genetic diversity within populations of this species is currently underway (Berv and Zyskowski 2010).

VOICE Published recordings are available on the following compilations: Remold (2002), Boesman (2006a) and Minns *et al.* (2009), and several recordings from various Brazilian states are archived online at www.xeno-canto.org. Gives a rather soft low nasal *wraah, wra-wra* (Ridgely and Tudor 1994, 2009) in display. The warning or alarm-call is a loud *wet, wet, wet* like a tree frog (Sick 1993) or *erk, erk, erk* (Lees *et al.* 2008), given from the understorey, sometimes whilst foraging, sometimes becoming faster and with up to six notes when extremely agitated, or occasionally given as a double-noted call. A variant of the latter (context unknown) is a short and much less harsh *chuk-chuk* (GMK pers. obs.). Occasionally calls in response to a Ferruginous Pygmy Owl *Glaucidium brasilianum* imitation, but this species can be very unresponsive to playback. See also next section.

NATURAL HISTORY Pale-bellied Tyrant-Manakin at least occasionally joins mixed-species foraging flocks (cf. Silva and Oniki 1988, Tubelis 2007), but is easiest to observe when the male is displaying.

FOOD AND FEEDING It can forage in groups of 4–8 birds, usually 3–10m above ground, making short darting flights and upward sallies (Lees *et al.* 2008; GMK pers. obs.). Diet appears to consist predominantly of insects (see Schubart *et al.* 1965, Piratelli and Pereira 2002, Snow 2004b) including larvae (GMK pers. obs.), but also comprises fruits of some melastomes, e.g. *Miconia* spp. (Melastomataceae), and their seeds (cf. Krabbe 2007). Specific insect prey recorded include Coleoptera (beetles), Formicidae (ants) and Hymenoptera (wasps, etc.) (Lima *et al.* 2010). Pale-bellied Tyrant-Manakin has recently been reported to occasionally follow *Labidus predator* and *Eciton burchelli* army ant swarms in search of insect prey disturbed by the ants (Faria and Rodrigues 2009).

DISPLAY The display consists of a vertical jump (revealing the yellow crown) with beating wings, returning to the perch (but often facing in the opposite direction) and vocalising. The display was initially described by Snethlage (1928), then subsequently in more detail by Pinto (1940), whilst Sick (1959d) and Lees *et al.* (2008) also proffered data. Lees *et al.* (2008: 153) regularly encountered leks in June–July in northern Mato Grosso, as follows:

> Males were typically spaced *c.*40 m apart, within vocal (but probably not visual) contact. They perched on thin horizontal limbs, typically 0.5–3.0 m above ground. The display commenced with the exposure of the bright yellow coronal patch and, after a few seconds, the bird made up to three consecutive leaps in the air of 4–8 cm, changing its position on the perch slightly, but typically maintaining the same orientation. Prior to jumping, they often made a mechanical-sounding "knocking" vocalisation, before the main lek vocalisation delivered whilst jumping, a penetrating *scwhe-sizur*. K. J. Zimmer and A. Whittaker (*in litt.* 2006) observed a lekking *N. pallescens* in *campina* forest in Ceará: a displaying male, possibly in the presence of a female, descended from its 2.5-m looping vine perch and flew diagonally 5–6 m to the open forest floor. The bird oriented towards the vine, flaring its coronal patch, and commenced an exaggerated display in transit towards its perch. Each hop took the bird 3–5 cm off the floor, its tail held at 45°. After *c.*3.0–3.5 m the male paused for *c.*15 seconds, its wings and tail slightly open and head lowered to display its crown towards the lek perch. The male then continued hopping for another 3 m, before abruptly turning 180° in one hop and hopping another 1 m, then flying back to its vine and continuing its leap display.

Because the species selects rather unstable perches, the vine or branch often appears to 'bounce' after the bird lands on it, perhaps heightening the visual aspect of the display (Sick 1959d).

BREEDING Largely unknown, except for a bird seen carrying nest material in southern Ceará in early November (Snow 2004b), but as noted above display behaviour seemed strong in northern Mato Grosso in mid-year, and seems most pronounced early in the year (e.g. in January and February) in the Serra dos Carajás and northeast Brazil, e.g. in Alagoas

(GMK pers. obs.). Males in breeding condition have been collected in October–January (Bahia) and October (Amapá) and a female with active ovaries in December (MNRJ; Novaes 1978). Those trapped in southern Guyana in January and March were plainly not breeding (Mees 2000, Robbins *et al.* 2004), but several of those trapped in June and July in the Chapada do Araripe, northeastern Brazil had brood patches (Nascimento *et al.* 2000).

STATUS Uncommon and local but not considered threatened, and BirdLife International (2004, 2008) treats Pale-bellied Tyrant-Manakin as of Least Concern. It appears capable of surviving in relatively fragmented habitats (Marini 2001), although local extinctions have occurred, e.g. in parts of central São Paulo (Willis 2006) and in the upper Paraná Valley, on the Mato Grosso do Sul/Paraná border (Mendonça *et al.* 2009). Furthermore, Anciães and Peterson (2006) predicted that *N. pallescens* might be severely impacted by habitat modification in the face of potential climate change based on modelling techniques. The species is known from a reasonable number of protected areas through its rather large range, these including: Chapada Diamantina National Park, Bahia (Parrini *et al.* 1999), Brasília National Park and Águas Emendadas Ecological Station, both in the Distrito Federal (Braz and Cavalcanti 2001), Carajás National Forest, Pará (Pacheco *et al.* 2007), Chapada do Araripe National Forest, Ceará (Nascimento *et al.* 2000), Cantão State Park, Tocantins (Pinheiro and Dornas 2009a), all in Brazil, as well as in Noel Kempff Mercado National Park, in Santa Cruz, Bolivia (Bates *et al.* 1998).

REFERENCES Albano (2010a, 2010b), Aleixo *et al.* (2011), Anciães and Peterson (2006, 2009), Bates *et al.* (1992, 1998), Berv and Zyskowski (2010), BirdLife International (2004, 2008), Braun *et al.* (2007), Braz and Cavalcanti (2001), Dunning (2008), Faria and Rodrigues (2009), Faria *et al.* (2006), Forrester (1993), Fry (1970), Hellmayr (1908, 1929a, 1929b), Hidasi (1998, 2007), Ingui and Parruco (2009), Krabbe (2007), Lees *et al.* (2008), Lima *et al.* (2010), Lopes and Braz (2007), Lopes *et al.* (2008, 2009), Lowen and Bernardon (2010), Magalhães *et al.* (2004, 2007), Marini (2001), Mees (2000), Melo Júnior *et al.* (2001), Mendonça *et al.* (2009), Minns *et al.* (2009), Mittermeier *et al.* (2010), Naka *et al.* (2007), Nascimento *et al.* (2000), Novaes (1960, 1978), Novaes and Lima (1991), Ohlson *et al.* (2008), Olmos (2003), Oren and Parker (1997), Ottema *et al.* (2009), Pacheco and Olmos (2005, 2006, 2010), Pacheco *et al.* (1997), Parrini *et al.* (1999), Pinheiro and Dornas (2009a), Pinto (1940, 1944), Piratelli and Pereira (2002), Remold (2002), Ridgely and Tudor (1994, 2009), Robbins *et al.* (2004), Rodrigues *et al.* (2005), Santos *et al.* (2010), Schubart *et al.* (1965), Sick (1958, 1959d, 1960, 1993, 1997), Silva and Oniki (1988), Silva *et al.* (1997), Silveira *et al.* (2003a), Snethlage (1928), Snow (2004b), Stotz *et al.* (1996), Tubelis, (2007), Vasconcelos (2007), Vasconcelos and D'Angelo Neto (2007), Vasconcelos *et al.* (2008), Willis (1992, 2006), Willis and Oniki (1990).

Pale-bellied Tyrant-Manakin *Neopelma pallescens*. **Fig. 1**. Chapada do Araripe, Ceará, northeast Brazil, December (*Pete Morris*). **Fig. 2**. Chapada do Araripe, Ceará, northeast Brazil, December (*Ciro Albano*). **Fig. 3**. Chapada do Araripe, Ceará, northeast Brazil, July (*Rafael Bessa*). The underparts typically appear very clean white, only occasionally with yellowish elements, while the yellow coronal stripe is only usually revealed when a bird is singing or in response to playback.

SULPHUR-BELLIED TYRANT-MANAKIN
Neopelma sulphureiventer   Plate 1

Scotothorus sulphureiventer **C. E. Hellmayr, 1903**, *Verh. Zool. Bot. Ges.* 53: 202, 203, [Villa Bella de] Mato Grosso, Mato Grosso, Brazil, and San Mateo, Bolivia

Neopelma sulphureiventer is a very poorly known bird that is seemingly confined to the Inambari Centre of endemism (Cracraft 1985). Given our general lack of knowledge of this typically unassuming member of the genus, and the relative inaccessibility of much of the species' range, it is perhaps surprising that this was the first of the genus for which nesting data became available.

IDENTIFICATION 13.0–13.5cm. Of its congeners, generally only the range of Pale-bellied Tyrant-Manakin *N. pallescens* approaches this species, although *N. sulphureiventer* comes quite close to the range of Saffron-crested Tyrant Manakin *N. chrysocephalum* in northeast Peru. In plumage, the clear pale yellow belly of Sulphur-bellied separates it from Pale-bellied Tyrant-Manakin, but voice is probably more helpful to species identification. As with most species in this poorly known genus, there is a similarity to Greenish Elaenia *Myiopagis viridicata*, but the tyrant-manakin's wing has a more uniform aspect, lacking the yellowish fringes to the remiges, has pale (not dark) irides and has no white on the face.

DISTRIBUTION Restricted to southwestern Amazonia, in western Brazil from Acre, where the species is known from a handful of sites, to southwest Mato Grosso, on the Rio Guaporé at Vila Bela da Santíssima Trindade, west as far as eastern Peru, in dptos. Madre de Dios, Ucayali and Cuzco, and further north in dptos. Loreto and San Martín, and south to northern Bolivia where it reaches south to dptos. Cochabamba and northern Santa Cruz (e.g. at Las Trancas and the Estación Biológica Caparú). It was listed for western Amazonas, Brazil, by Snow (1979b), but on what basis is unclear (Remsen *et al.* 1988). The latter authors presented a near-comprehensive list of specimen localities. Mainly found below 700m in Peru, but occurs locally to 1,000m there (Schulenberg *et al.* 2007). Otherwise the species is generally found below 450m (Snow 2004b).

MOVEMENTS None known.

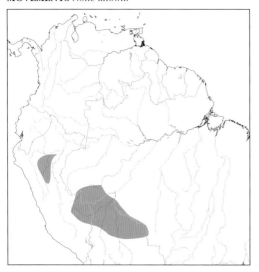

HABITAT Sulphur-bellied Tyrant-Manakin inhabits seasonally flooded forest (*várzea*), with a special preference for thickets of bamboo or vine tangles in some parts of its range, but it also occurs in semi-deciduous scrub on poor soils in northern Peru (Schulenberg *et al.* 2007), in the undergrowth of riverine forest in dpto. Beni, Bolivia (Remsen *et al.* 1988, Brace and Hornbuckle 1998), and in young second growth (S. Mayer recording, XC 1939) and in *Chiquitano* dry forest in the extreme south of its range (Flores *et al.* 2001).

DESCRIPTION The sexes are alike. The bill is relatively broad-based with a reasonably arched culmen, and at least some have a strikingly hooked tip (completely lacking in others). Rictal bristles well developed. *Adult.* – Uniform olive-green above, becoming slightly browner over the wings and tail, with the large yellow coronal patch typical of the genus, and the ear-coverts are slightly paler olive. Throat greyish-white, but this offers very little contrast with the greyish-olive breast. Rest of underparts pale yellow. *Juvenile.* – A bird with dark eyes and a distinctly pale head was considered to be a juvenile, as it was being fed by an obvious adult (Whittaker and Oren 1999). *Moult.* – Data are very few, but Remsen *et al.* (1988) reported that birds collected in Bolivia in June–August were not renewing any feathers. At least one of several seen at a site near Tarapoto, dpto. San Martín, Peru, in late October was in tail moult (D. Beadle and GMK pers. obs.). *Bare parts.* – Bill black or dark over the maxilla and tip, with a paler (and greyer, even pale bluish) mandible, and the legs and feet are horn or dark yellow to greyish or bluish-grey. Irides pale grey to creamy or pinky, or even orange-yellow (Remsen *et al.* 1988, Whittaker and Oren 1999, Snow 2004b; FMNH; see Figs 1–3).

MEASUREMENTS (MNRJ; Gyldenstolpe 1945; J. Hornbuckle unpubl.: Acre, Brazil, and Beni, Bolivia) Sexes combined: wing (*n* = 39) 66–79mm; tail (*n* = 3) 49–62mm; bill (*n* = 2) 13.42–15.0mm; tarsus (*n* = 2) 14.0–16.49mm. Weight (sexes combined): 13.7–19.5g (Remsen *et al.* 1988, Bates *et al.* 1989, Snow 2004b; J. Hornbuckle unpubl. data from Beni, Bolivia).

GEOGRAPHICAL VARIATION Monotypic.

VOICE The first commercially available recordings of this species appeared on the recently issued Boesman (2009) compilation, and there are quite a number of recordings from Bolivia and Peru archived online at www.xeno-canto. org. Schulenberg *et al.* (2007) described a squeaky *dueek* or *duet*, both of these notes being given in short series, and a scratchy series of *djurt* or *djurit* notes. Ridgely and Tudor (2009) mentioned that the song is a nasal *wraanh-wraanh* that is lower pitched than the equivalent vocalisation in *N. pallescens* (based on a J. Hornbuckle recording). Males sing from perches up to 3.5m above ground in the understorey, and will raise the crown feathers to expose the bright central patch in response to playback (Whittaker and Oren 1999).

NATURAL HISTORY Generally presumed to be much as other *Neopelma*, but Sulphur-bellied Tyrant-Manakin appears to be especially inconspicuous and shy, and thus very poorly known. Its general behaviour is completely undescribed, although from our limited field experience with this species it seems much like that of congenerics.

FOOD AND FEEDING The species' diet is known fundamentally only from stomach contents of specimens, and it seems to consist mainly of insects (arthropods) with only a small proportion of fruits taken (Remsen *et al.* 1988).

BREEDING The nest of this species was recently described by Lebbin *et al.* (2007) from observations in dpto. Madre de Dios, southeastern Peru, this representing the first nesting data to be published for any species in the genus. They observed one (presumed to be a female) constructing a nest on 16 October within a patch of *Guadua* bamboo, but were unable to follow it to completion. The partially completed nest was a thin, shallow cup of woven bamboo fibres, slung between two bamboo branches, 10–11m above the ground. It resembled that described here for Serra do Mar Tyrant-Manakin *N. chrysolophum*, though no spiderwebs were visible in the construction, and its placement also resembled that of Dwarf Tyrant-Manakin *Tyranneutes stolzmanni* (which see), except that it was much higher above the ground (see also Serra do Mar Tyrant-Manakin). January, August and October specimens from Bolivia were apparently not in breeding condition, and the same is true of a bird taken in western Brazil in June (MNRJ).

STATUS Treated as Least Concern (BirdLife International 2004, 2008), but the species is certainly uncommon and local in eastern Peru (Schulenberg *et al.* 2007), where it is even only infrequently trapped during mist-netting work in suitable habitat (Robinson and Terborgh 1997). Its status is also poorly known in western Brazil, with few published localities available. Perhaps best known in dpto. Beni, northern Bolivia, but Sulphur-bellied Tyrant-Manakin is also readily found at El Refugio Huanchaca, dpto. Santa Cruz, Bolivia (N. Athanas) and Quebrada Upaquihua, south of Tarapoto, dpto. San Martín, Peru (Valqui 2004). The species seems to be known from comparatively few protected areas within its relatively restricted range, but it has been recorded in the frequently visited Manu National Park and Biosphere Reserve, Peru, the Beni and Caparú Biological Stations, Bolivia, and the Reserva Extravista Chico Mendes, Acre, Brazil.

REFERENCES Aleixo and Guilherme (2010), Anciães and Peterson (2009), Bates and Parker (1998), Bates *et al.* (1989), BirdLife International (2004, 2008), Boesman (2009), Brace and Hornbuckle (1998), Cracraft (1985), Flores *et al.* (2001), Forrester (1993), Guilherme and Dantas (2008), Guilherme and Santos (2009), Haffer (1974), Hellmayr (1929b), Hennessey *et al.* (2003), Lebbin *et al.* (2007), McKay *et al.* (2010), Mestre *et al.* (2010), Pinto (1944), Remsen and Parker (1995), Remsen *et al.* (1988), Ridgely and Tudor (1994, 2009), Robinson and Terborgh (1997), Schulenberg *et al.* (2007), Sick (1997), Silva (1996), Snow (2004b), Stotz *et al.* (1996), Thom and Mestre (2009), Valqui (2004), Vidoz *et al.* (2010), Walker *et al.* (2006), Whittaker and Oren (1999).

Sulphur-bellied Tyrant-Manakin *Neopelma sulphureiventer*. **Fig. 1**. Manu National Park, southeast Peru, July (*Daniel J. Lebbin*). Like others of the superspecies, the southwest Amazonian representative of the genus is more readily censured using mist-nets than by other techniques. Note the striking pinkish-grey iris coloration. **Figs. 2–3**. Rio Branco, Acre, western Brazil, September (*Andrew Whittaker*). The relatively extensive yellowish elements on the posterior underparts should identify this species from Pale-bellied Tyrant-Manakin *N. pallescens*, but voice is always distinctive.

WIED'S TYRANT-MANAKIN
Neopelma aurifrons   **Plate 1**

Muscicapa aurifrons **Wied, 1831**, *Beitr. Naturg. Bras.* 3(2): 829, Camamú, southern Bahia [see comments on types by Hellmayr 1906a]

The sole member of the genus *Neopelma* that is currently considered globally threatened, Wied's Tyrant-Manakin is confined to lowland and foothill forests in a restricted area of eastern Brazil. Much remains to be learned concerning its ecology and life history, like most of its conspecifics. Whitney *et al.* (1995) speculated that *Neopelma aurifrons* might be related more closely to the genus *Tyranneutes* than to other members of *Neopelma*, especially to Dwarf Tyrant-Manakin *T. stolzmanni*. Because *N. aurifrons* is the type species of *Neopelma*, this would have obvious consequences for the remaining species of the genus as currently constituted. To date, however, no further support for this proposition has accrued, and there are no strong reasons for erecting a new name for the other members of the genus.

IDENTIFICATION 13–14cm. This and Serra do Mar Tyrant-Manakin *N. chrysolophum* are most like Sulphur-bellied Tyrant-Manakin *N. sulphureiventer* in appearance, but Sulphur-bellied is entirely allopatric in its distribution. In southeast Brazil, Wied's sometimes occurs alongside Pale-bellied Tyrant-Manakin *N. pallescens* (e.g. at two localities in Minas Gerais) but the latter is larger and paler below with only a hint of yellow to its underparts. Wied's occurs sympatrically very locally with Serra do Mar Tyrant-Manakin, which thus offers the greatest confusion risk. The best means of separating them is by voice and the fact that the two are generally altitudinally segregated. However, Serra do Mar Tyrant-Manakin is also slightly longer tailed, shorter billed and shorter winged, with a larger coronal patch than Wied's Tyrant-Manakin, but all of these plumage and structural characters will be difficult to appreciate, especially without previous experience or the extremely unlikely event of comparative views! Any difficult-to-place nondescript 'flycatcher' in the Atlantic Forests of Brazil should be thoroughly investigated as this species and the next are almost certainly often overlooked by visiting birders. The more vertical stance and long tail are atypical manakin characteristics and the coronal patch illustrated in field guides is sometimes concealed and often impossible to see in the field.

DISTRIBUTION Endemic to the Atlantic Forest of coastal eastern Brazil, *N. aurifrons* is known from Rio de Janeiro north to southern or perhaps central Bahia. It has been reported from ten Important Bird Areas in four states, as follows: Chapada Diamantina National Park (B. C. Forrester *in* BirdLife International 2000) and Boa Nova (both Bahia), Fazenda Santana, Salto da Divisa, and Rio Doce State Park (both Minas Gerais), Sooretama Biological Reserve, Augusto Ruschi (formerly Nova Lombardia) Biological Reserve, Duas Bocas Biological Reserve and Cafundó (all Espírito Santo), and Anil (Rio de Janeiro) (see Whitney *et al.* 1995, Bencke *et al.* 2006). The species has perhaps always been rare: Whitney *et al.* (1995) identified an additional four sites in Bahia, all of them based on old historical records, the furthest north being from 'the vicinity of Salvador' in the early 19th century, as well as an additional five in Espírito Santo and three in Minas Gerais. To these, Vasconcelos *et al.* (2004) added two further sites,

in northeastern Minas Gerais, Acauã Ecological Station and a nearby private fazenda, both in the vicinity of Leme do Prado (see also Vasconcelos and D'Angelo Neto 2007). Garske and Anjos (2005) mentioned an additional locality in Espírito Santo. Forrester's 1990 record in the Chapada Diamantina is unclear, as the more extensive surveys of Parrini *et al.* (1999) only found *N. pallescens* in this area, whilst in his unpublished trip list Forrester makes no mention of the latter species. Further south, it was relocated at Boa Nova in the mid 1990s but not since (GMK unpubl.). Thus, in the present day its definite range extends only from the region of Salto da Divisa, on the border between Minas Gerais and Bahia south perhaps still to central Rio de Janeiro, although Ridgely and Tudor (2009) considered it to be extinct in the latter state. Browne's (2005) listing of *N. aurifrons* from the Serra da Bocaina is based on a misreading of Buzzetti (2000), which clearly listed the species of *Neopelma* in this region as *N. chrysolophum*, and this is confirmed by other observers (Whitney *et al.* 1995; GMK pers. obs.). Goerck (1999: 250) also mentioned a sighting from the environs of Ubatuba, São Paulo, in August 1997, which too presumably refers to *N. chrysolophum*. Elevational range: sea level to *c.*1,000m.

MOVEMENTS None recorded.

HABITAT Wied's Tyrant-Manakin prefers the tall under-storey of undisturbed primary forest or old, well-developed second growth, where it generally seeks the forest interior. It occasionally visits forest borders, both natural and man-made (Whitney *et al.* 1995; GMK pers. obs.).

DESCRIPTION Sexes alike. Essentially a plain olive flycatcher-like 'manakin' with a yellowish belly. The bill is relatively broad-based with a reasonably arched culmen, and at least some have a strikingly hooked tip (but completely lacking in others). Rictal bristles not especially obvious in the field. *Adult.* – Head dull olive with a slightly paler ocular region and ear-coverts. Sulphur-yellow to orange-yellow coronal patch, but compared with other species of *Neopelma* this is rather smaller and even absent in some individuals, and the nape and head-sides are less contrastingly dark than in some congenerics, e.g. Saffron-crested Tyrant-Manakin *N. chrysocephalum* (but there is no difference between Wied's and Serra do Mar Tyrant-Manakins in this respect). The mantle is dull olive-green, becoming slightly paler and brighter over the rump and contrasting with the darker and duskier wings and tail (relieved by olive fringes). In the field the slightly paler rump is the only 'feature' of the otherwise uniform upperparts. The greyish-white throat and upper breast contrast with the pale lemon-yellow belly and ventral region. *Juvenile.* – A specimen in MNRJ appears identical to adults in that collection, but iris colour data are lacking. *Moult.* – The only published moult data involve a male taken in December that was commencing wing moult (Willis and Oniki 2002), but one collected in October was in very fresh plumage (MNRJ). *Bare parts.* – Irides pale grey to yellow-white, the bill is black to horn with a paler base, and the legs are grey to blackish (MNRJ).

MEASUREMENTS (BMNH; CUMZ; MNRJ: Minas Gerais and Espírito Santo; Whitney *et al.* 1995, which see for bill-width, bill-depth and culmen-length to feathers) Sexes combined: wing (n = 24) 65–77mm; tail (n = 24) 47–58mm; bill (n = 13) 12.58–14.39mm; tarsus (n = 13) 14.80–17.20mm. Weight (sexes combined; n = 8): 13.5–17.0g (Willis and Oniki 2002, Dunning 2008; DZUFMG; MNRJ).

GEOGRAPHICAL VARIATION Monotypic, but Serra do Mar Tyrant-Manakin was previously considered conspecific with the present species (Whitney *et al.* 1995).

VOICE Compared with *N. chrysolophum*, the advertising call of Wied's Tyrant-Manakin is shorter and simpler, and comprises a four-syllable phrase rendered *kiú ki-chru-chrrí* (e.g. BirdLife International 2000), which is repeated at regular intervals, but especially in the morning hours, from a thin, horizontal perch up to 7m above the ground. Unobtrusive when singing, like *Tyranneutes* (GMK pers. obs.), the bird remains stolidly in the same position for many minutes, only occasionally flipping round to face the opposite direction. However, the species can respond aggressively to playback approaching the source of the sound more closely, even during the late summer, and the voice in response to playback changes dramatically, becoming obviously agitated (see sonograms in Whitney *et al.* 1995). Published recordings are available on the Remold (2002) and Minns *et al.* (2009) compilations, and two recordings, both from Espírito Santo, are available online at www.xeno-canto.org.

NATURAL HISTORY Much as congenerics. Songposts are usually within 'earshot' of other singing individuals, in an 'exploded lek' (of up to five birds), thus the species tends to cluster loosely, with large areas of apparently suitable habitat unoccupied. Wied's Tyrant-Manakin does not appear to join mixed-species foraging flocks, instead most feeding appears to occur within relatively proscribed territories within close proximity to the song perches.

FOOD AND FEEDING The species employs relatively short (<1.5m) sally-hovers to seize small fruits (which are swallowed whole) and once a small stick-insect (suborder *Phasmodea*) (Whitney *et al.* 1995).

BREEDING Nesting is not definitely known. Euler (1900), reported in Whitney *et al.* (1995), mentioned discovering examples of the long, bag-like nest of '*Elainea brevipes*' near Cantagalo, Rio de Janeiro, always sited below banks or overhanging roots. Notwithstanding the possibility, mooted by Whitney *et al.* (1995), that *N. aurifrons* and *N. chrysolophum* are not each others' closest relatives, but are instead the results of separate colonisation events of southeast Brazil, we note the remarkable uniformity in structure of those few nests of *Tyranneutes* and *Neopelma* discovered to date (see also *N. chrysolophum*). This suggests to us that Euler's description did not pertain to the bird we currently know as *N. aurifrons*.

STATUS Formerly treated as Endangered (BirdLife International 2000, 2004) but since downlisted to Vulnerable (BirdLife International 2008) and Wied's Tyrant-Manakin is given the same categorisation in the state of Espírito Santo (Passamani and Mendes 2007). Anciães and Peterson (2006) predicted that this species could be badly impacted by habitat modification in the face of potential climate change based on modelling techniques. Cracraft (1985) considered *Neopelma aurifrons sensu lato* to be restricted to the Serra do Mar Centre of endemism, but in fact this is only true of *N. chrysolophum*, as *N. aurifrons sensu stricto* ranges further into the interior than was appreciated by Cracraft. The species is known from fewer than ten protected areas and at some of these it is obviously rare, e.g. Sooretama Biological Reserve (Whitney *et al.* 1995; GMK pers. obs.), whilst its current status in southern Bahia is the subject of complete speculation (see Distribution).

REFERENCES Anciães and Peterson (2006, 2009), Bencke *et al.* (2006), BirdLife International (2000, 2004, 2008), Browne (2005), Cracraft (1985), Dunning (2008), Faria *et al.* (2006), Garske and Anjos (2005), Goerck (1999), Hellmayr (1906a, 1929b), Minns *et al.* (2009), Parker and Goerck (1997), Parrini *et al.* (1999), Passamani and Mendes (2007), Pinto (1944), Ridgely and Tudor (2009), Simon (2009), Snow (2004b), Stotz *et al.* (1996), Vasconcelos and D'Angelo Neto (2007), Vasconcelos *et al.* (2004), Whitney *et al.* (1995), Willis and Oniki (2002).

Wied's Tyrant-Manakin *Neopelma aurifrons*. **Figs. 1–2**. Santa Teresa, Espírito Santo, southeast Brazil, June (*Ciro Albano*). Currently treated as globally threatened (Vulnerable), this species is the rarest of its genus and is one of two *Neopelma* endemic to the Atlantic Forest. These photographs were taken at one of its last strongholds.

SERRA DO MAR TYRANT-MANAKIN
Neopelma chrysolophum   Plate 1

Neopelma aurifrons chrysolophum **Pinto, 1944,** *Cat. Aves Bras.* 2: 100, no locality [= Minas Gerais, Brazil]

Despite the suggestion of Meyer de Schauensee (1966), until very recently (1995) this taxon was considered conspecific with *N. aurifrons*, which largely replaces it to the north and at lower elevations in the Atlantic Forest region, but the two differ chiefly in vocal characteristics. Meyer de Schauensee (1966) suggested the name Pinto's Tyrant-Manakin, whereas Snow (2004b) 'reduced' the name to simply Serra Tyrant-Manakin. Given the long obscurity that this taxon has 'endured' – it was not adequately named until the mid-20th century (after one 'false start': Pinto 1933) – and the substantial vocal differences that exist between it and *Neopelma aurifrons* were not recognised for another 50 years, it is perhaps surprising that this is far the easier to find of the two *Neopelma* endemic to the Atlantic Forest.

IDENTIFICATION 12.2–14.5cm. Like other *Neopelma*, this is a rather long-tailed manakin with a superficially tyrannid appearance. It is most likely to be located by voice, which is wholly distinctive and is the best means of separating the present species from the near-identical Wied's Tyrant-Manakin *N. aurifrons* (other differences, which are likely to be of limited use in the field, are covered under the previous species). Generally, Serra do Mar and Wied's Tyrant-Manakins are elevationally parapatric, including within the few areas where they possibly do overlap (for instance in the Novo Friburgo region of Rio de Janeiro state), and the same certainly holds true for this species and Pale-bellied Tyrant-Manakin *N. pallescens*. Nonetheless, it should be remarked that *N. chrysolophum* has recently been discovered at one locality southeast of Belo Horizonte, Minas Gerais, at a much lower altitude than previously recorded for the species (see Distribution), and well within the elevational range of *N. aurifrons*. Fortunately for field observers, *N. aurifrons* has, to date, not been found in central Minas Gerais, thereby reducing the risk of confusion.

DISTRIBUTION Confined to a relatively small area of the Atlantic Forest in southeast Brazil, from east-central Minas Gerais south through Rio de Janeiro state to southernmost São Paulo, and the species perhaps also occurs in adjacent Paraná state, although it has yet to be confirmed there (Pinto 1944, Whitney *et al.* 1995, Snow 2004b). It is known from *c*.30 historical and modern-day localities (Whitney *et al.* 1995). Altitudinal range is chiefly higher than that of the previous species, being almost confined to *c*.1,150–1,800m (Pires *et al.* 1991, Whitney *et al.* 1995, Snow 2004b), although it has recently been confirmed to occur at 700m at a locality in central Minas Gerais (Vasconcelos 2007) and the species also occurs at a similar elevation in the environs of Parati, Rio de Janeiro, and at 860m at Parque Estadual Intervales (GMK pers. obs.). In regions where they may enter into sympatry, e.g. north-central Rio de Janeiro state, Serra do Mar and Wied's Tyrant-Manakins are probably elevationally parapatric (Mallet-Rodrigues *et al.* 2007).

MOVEMENTS None known; Serra do Mar Tyrant-Manakin is apparently resident and highly sedentary given the ease with which singing males are found in the same spot year after year, and in many different months, within certain favoured areas (Whitney *et al.* 1995; GMK pers. obs.).

HABITAT This species generally appears to shun the forest interior, being found in dense and moderately low-stature edge growth, especially with many bamboos and ferns (Whitney *et al.* 1995, Snow 2004b; GMK pers. obs.). It will inhabit secondary forest (Gomes and Silva 2002).

DESCRIPTION Sexes alike. A plain flycatcher-like 'manakin' with a slightly yellower belly. The bill is relatively broad-based with a reasonably arched culmen, and sometimes with a hooked tip. Rictal bristles not especially obvious in the field. Plumage is effectively identical to the previous species, except in the larger coronal patch. *Adult.* – Head dull olive with a slightly paler ocular region and ear-coverts. Bright yellow to deep orange-yellow coronal patch (cf. Vasconcelos 2007), which is much more striking than in Wied's Tyrant-Manakin but is typically difficult to see in most field situations, and the nape and head-sides are less contrastingly darker than in some congenerics, e.g. Saffron-crested Tyrant-Manakin *N. chrysocephalum*, but still obviously darker than the rest of the plumage. Mantle olive-green, becoming slightly paler and brighter over the rump and contrasting with the darker and duskier wings and tail (relieved by olive-green fringes). The greyish-white throat and upper breast contrast with the pale lemon-yellow belly and ventral region. *Juvenile.* – Undescribed (Snow 2004b). *Moult.* – No published moult data. *Bare parts.* – Both sexes have pale greyish-mauve or pale brown irides (once dirty orange in a male and yellow in a bird of unknown sex), the bill is black, greyish or dusky often with a slightly paler, more horn-coloured lower mandible (especially at the base), and greyish to pale flesh-coloured legs and feet (Snow 2004b, Krabbe 2007; GMK pers. obs.; FMNH).

MEASUREMENTS (BMNH; CUMZ; MNRJ; RMNH: all Rio de Janeiro [where known]; Whitney *et al.* 1995, which see for bill-width, bill-depth and culmen-length to feathers) Sexes combined: wing (*n* = 22) 63.0–68.5mm; tail (*n* = 22) 54–61mm; bill (*n* = 13) 10.11–12.03mm; tarsus (*n* = 9) 16.4–17.8mm. Weight: 11.6–23.0g (mainly males; FMNH; MNRJ).

GEOGRAPHICAL VARIATION Monotypic following Whitney *et al.* (1995). This species was previously treated as a subspecies of Wied's Tyrant-Manakin.

VOICE The song is distinctly longer and more complex than that of its presumed sister-species, *N. aurifrons*, comprising three elements, the first being of 1–4 (usually two) very short, sharp notes (this part may be repeated), followed by two further elements, each of 3–4 notes that are given in rapid succession and not repeated. Perfectly rendered as *chip, chip, dree-zee-zee, zéw* by Snow (2004b), and the song does not audibly change in response to playback. Also gives a very sharp *pik* and other quite loud notes, presumably in contact, sometimes intermixed with the song (N. Athanas recording, XC 34596). Song perches are usually 3–6m above the ground, and like those of *N. aurifrons* are usually thin, horizontal or gently upwardly inclined branches (Whitney *et al.* 1995; GMK pers. obs.). Behaviour on song perches is very similar to that of Wied's Tyrant-Manakin. Like Whitney *et al.* (1995), we have never heard more than two birds in 'earshot' of one another, and their territorial system is probably distinctly more linear, less 'clumped, than that of Wied's Tyrant-Manakin. Can be relatively easily attracted using playback, although the species is highly stoical and does not always closely approach the 'intruder' or does so very unobtrusively, though at other times birds can respond swiftly and obviously. Sings at all times of day, like Wied's Tyrant-Manakin, but with perhaps a less obvious tendency for singing to be concentrated in the morning hours. Published recordings are available on the compilations of Gonzaga and Castiglioni (2001), Boesman (2006a) and Minns *et al.* (2009), whilst recordings from Minas Gerais, Rio de Janeiro and São Paulo are available online at www.xeno-canto.org.

NATURAL HISTORY Generally found alone.

FOOD AND FEEDING Diet is poorly known, though like the previous species it probably comprises solely small fruits and arthropods (e.g. insects). Only fruit remains were found in the stomach contents of two birds trapped at Intervales State Park (Gomes and Silva 2002), but others have reportedly held both insects and small fruits (Krabbe 2007), the latter including at least five species of *Rapanea* (Myrsinaceae: Pineschi 1990) and *Psychotria suterella* (Rubiaceae: Manhães and Dias 2009). Serra do Mar Tyrant-Manakin appears to remain independent of mixed-species foraging flocks, even when they pass through its territory. Feeding behaviour as previous species (GMK pers. obs.).

BREEDING Nesting previously undescribed, but nests discovered twice recently, both times in the upper part of Itatiaia National Park, Rio de Janeiro, on the first by K. J. Zimmer and A. Whittaker (pers. comm.) and on the second occasion by GMK *et al.* (pers. obs.). This latter nest, which was found on 19 September 2007, was in the initial stages of construction, sited within 3m of a dirt road and *c.*1m above ground in an understorey shrub (*c.*2m in overall height) shaded by taller trees with a canopy height of *c.*15m. The nest (diameter *c.*5cm) was placed *c.*50cm from the main trunk of the tree, slung between the fork formed by two very narrow, horizontal branches, attached in two places to each branch, mainly using heavily bound spidersweb, with the rest of the construction involving both live and dead black rootlets, some moss and dead leaves for camouflage. Only one bird, presumably the female, attended the nest, occasionally testing it for size, and regularly bringing fresh material to it.

STATUS Treated as Least Concern (BirdLife International 2004, 2008). This recently recognised species (the taxon is not mentioned in Ridgely and Tudor 1994) occurs in two Endemic Bird Areas, the Central Brazilian Hills and Tablelands, and Atlantic Forest Mountains (Stattersfield *et al.* 1998), as well as a number of protected areas (e.g. Intervales and Carlos Botelho State Parks, São Paulo; Serra dos Órgãos National Park and Desengano State Park, Rio de

Janeiro; and RPPN Serra do Caraça and Ibitipoca State Park, Minas Gerais). However, visiting birdwatchers will probably find the species to be most easily and reliably located on the first part of the Agulhas Negras road, in the upper part of Itatiaia National Park, Rio de Janeiro.

REFERENCES Anciães and Peterson (2009), Bauer and Pacheco (2000), BirdLife International (2004, 2008), Boesman (2006a), Buzzetti (2000), Goerck (1999), Gomes and Silva (2002), Gonzaga and Castiglioni (2001), Hellmayr (1929b), Krabbe (2007), Mallet-Rodrigues and Noronha (2009), Mallet-Rodrigues *et al.* (2007), Manhães and Dias (2009), Meyer de Schauensee (1966), Minns *et al.* (2009), Pacheco *et al.* (2008), Pineschi (1990), Pinto (1933, 1944, 1951), Pires *et al.* (1991), Ridgely and Tudor (2009), Snow (2004b), Stattersfield *et al.* (1998), Vasconcelos and Melo Júnior (2001), Vasconcelos (2007), Whitney *et al.* (1995).

Serra do Mar Tyrant-Manakin *Neopelma chrysolophum.* **Fig. 1**. Itatiaia National Park, Rio de Janeiro, southeast Brazil, November (*Hadoram Shirihai / Photographic Handbook to Birds of the World*). **Fig. 2**. Itatiaia National Park, Rio de Janeiro, southeast Brazil, September (*Pete Morris*). Not easily separated from Wied's Tyrant-Manakin *N. aurifrons,* except vocally and by altitude and location, but note the on average longer-tailed and shorter-billed appearance of the present species.

SAFFRON-CRESTED TYRANT-MANAKIN
Neopelma chrysocephalum Plate 1

Heteropelma chrysocephalum **Pelzeln, 1868**, *Orn. Bras.* 2: 125, 186, San Carlos, Río Guainía, Venezuela

This species, the northeastern representative of the genus *Neopelma*, has recently been discovered far from its previously known range in the Guianan Shield in lowland northeast Peru, where it is quite common. Clearly, it should be searched for elsewhere south and west of the Rios Negro and Solimões, in Brazil, wherever there is suitable habitat.

IDENTIFICATION 13.1–14.5cm. This species is largely confined to northeastern South America and has no sympatric congener. Like other *Neopelma*, even given prolonged views (but no or little previous experience of the genus) the species can appear distinctly flycatcher-like, although note the long bill and tail (both longer than most manakins), chunky build and lack of any wingbars (if it is not possible to see the iris colour). Tiny Tyrant-Manakin *Tyranneutes virescens* is much smaller with a stubby tail, and Greenish Elaenia *Myiopagis virescens*, which overlaps with the present species only to a limited extent, can be separated following the same criteria as for other *Neopelma* (see Pale-bellied Tyrant-Manakin). The coronal patch is the largest in the genus and is accentuated by the darker grey sides to the head and nape. These features, as well as the fact that the crown patch is a richer golden-yellow, distinguish the species from the otherwise extremely similar Sulphur-bellied Tyrant-Manakin (no known overlap).

DISTRIBUTION The species' main range lies in northeastern South America, but it has somewhat outlying populations in extreme northeast Peru, in dpto. Loreto, where it was only recently discovered (in May 1994) and is restricted to the vicinity of Lores and the Allpahuayo-Mishana Reserved Zone (Alvarez Alonso 2002, Alvarez Alonso and Whitney 2003, Schulenberg *et al.* 2007), and in eastern Colombia, at Caño Cubiyú, near Mitú, dpto. Vaupés, but is to be expected also in eastern Guainía, given the species' presence in immediately adjacent Venezuela (Hilty and Brown 1986). (This pattern of species dependent on nutrient-poor white-sand soil forests, and mainly restricted to the Guianan Shield region, being found locally as far west as northeast Peru, is mirrored by a number of

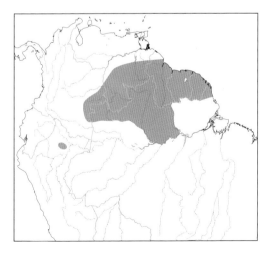

other taxa, including several cotingas and manakins.) Elsewhere, Saffron-crested Tyrant-Manakin occurs in the Rio Negro basin of southern Venezuela, e.g. at Junglaven, Amazonas and from the upper río Caura, northwest Bolívar, through the Guianas (where, for instance, it is rather widespread but generally uncommon in Surinam and is speculated to be quite widespread in French Guiana, although to date its range remains very poorly known) and north of the Amazon in Brazil from Roraima south to the Manaus region, where it occurs in the INPA reserves north of the city, as well as in northernmost Amapá (Tostain *et al.* 1992, Bradshaw and Kirwan 1995, Cohn-Haft *et al.* 1997, Boesman 1998, Hilty 2003, Restall *et al.* 2006, Ottema *et al.* 2009). However, in this region of Brazil, the species may be largely confined to the west bank of the Rio Trombetas (Aleixo *et al.* 2011).

MOVEMENTS None known.

HABITAT Considered to be an obligate white-sand forest specialist by Alvarez Alonso (2002). In all range states it is restricted to the marginally more open parts of stunted, forest and savanna woodland (e.g. *campina* in Brazil) on white-sand soils, for instance scrubby (low-canopy) *varillales* in Peru (Alvarez Alonso and Whitney 2003) and *muri* scrub in Guyana (Ridgely and Tudor 2009), but it has also been reported in *igapó* in Jaú National Park, northern Brazil (Borges *et al.* 2001). The species has been recorded to *c.*850m in Venezuela (Crease 2009), but it is probably mainly found below this elevation (Hilty 2003, Snow 2004b).

DESCRIPTION Sexes alike. Essentially a plain olive flycatcher-like 'manakin' with a more yellow belly. The bill is relatively broad-based with a reasonably arched culmen, and at least some have a hooked tip (completely lacking in others). The rictal bristles are reasonably obvious in the field. *Adult.* – The golden-yellow coronal patch is broader than in all other *Neopelma* and extends back to the nape (where it may incline to orange-rufous), forming a flattish crest. The head is otherwise principally greyish, including the lores and ear-coverts and is darkest abutting the coronal patch. The rest of the upperparts are dull olive with obviously slightly browner wings and tail (no paler fringes). Pale grey chin, throat pale yellowish- or greyish-white, contrasting rather strongly with the olive-washed breast and sides, which grade into the clear, pale lemon yellow flanks, belly and ventral region (the undertail-coverts are marginally the palest part). *Juvenile.* – Apparently undescribed, although this plumage seems unlikely to differ much from the adult, except in having fluffier body feathering, but has apparently been observed by Alvarez Alonso and Whitney (2003) in northern Peru. *Moult.* – Very few published moult data, but in southernmost Venezuela, Willard *et al.* (1991) noted that light body moult was evident in two early March-collected specimens, whereas one taken late the previous month was not moulting. *Bare parts.* – Bill black to blackish-grey over the maxilla, becoming pinkish-white or white, with a greyish-brown tip, on the lower mandible. The irides are white, dull cream, yellowish-white, or coppery yellow to pale reddish (perhaps brighter in males, but there is probably much overlap). Legs and feet pinkish to greyish, once purplish-grey (Willard *et al.* 1991, Alvarez Alonso and Whitney 2003, Snow 2004b; FMNH).

MEASUREMENTS (BMNH; CUMZ; RMNH: Amazonas, Brazil, Guyana and Surinam) Wing of male (*n* = 17) 67–74mm, wing of female (*n* = 7) 64–71mm; tail of male (*n* = 17) 47–56mm, tail of female (*n* = 7) 45–55mm; bill of male (*n* = 17) 12.48–14.31mm, bill of female (*n* = 7) 12.87–15.00mm; tarsus of male (*n* = 7) 14–16mm, tarsus of female (*n* = 7) 13–17mm. Weight (sexes combined): 13.4–17.2g (Haverschmidt 1952, Willard *et al.* 1991, Alvarez Alonso and Whitney 2003, Snow 2004b, Dunning 2008; FMNH; RMNH).

GEOGRAPHICAL VARIATION Monotypic.

VOICE Included in compilations published by Omena Júnior (2007), Naka *et al.* (2008) and Boesman (2009), and recordings from Brazil, Peru (many) and Venezuela are archived online at www.xeno-canto.org. The advertising song is highly nasal and twangy throughout the species' range, recalling the sound made by a Jew's harp: *jewee-jewEE-JEWEE-jewee-jewee* (occasionally shortened to just two or three notes) and described in Hilty and Brown (1986), Hilty (2003) and Schulenberg *et al.* (2007), amongst others. The song is uttered at lower frequency than the call, reaching 3,216kHz (Rodrigues Lima & Anciães 2009b). Saffron-crested Tyrant-Manakin sings persistently at short intervals (usually of just a few seconds), but the sound is somewhat ventriloquial and thus it can be hard to locate the singer. Crouches just slightly on perch in the process of singing and the body almost imperceptibly 'shakes' simultaneously (GMK pers. obs.). Alvarez Alonso and Whitney (2003) described the birds giving a quieter, closely spaced 3–6-note series of buzzing notes, both prior to 'display leaps' and literally at the height of the display (see below), but which was only heard at leks. In alarm, the species gives a loud, sharp *kwip* (up to three times) or *Pew!* (usually uttered in an evenly spaced series at variable speed), also featured on the Naka *et al.* (2008) compilation, or a softer and more nasal *chip* (the latter initially described by Davis 1949). The *pew* note comprises three frequency bands and reaches 4,438kHz, and its frequency and rate of delivery are modified based on the stress of the individual concerned (Rodrigues Lima and Anciães 2009b).

NATURAL HISTORY A detailed study of this species' biology, based at the INPA Campina Biological Reserve north of Manaus, Brazil, is in progress (Rodrigues Lima and Anciães 2009a). Presently poorly known, but the species is mainly solitary and usually keeps within 3–8m of the ground. It occasionally joins other manakins and frugivores at fruiting trees, but does not attend mobile mixed-species flocks. Rather active in bursts (between longer periods of virtually total inactivity) and at least partially insectivorous, performing short aerial sallies or to foliage, but the diet (like that of all *Neopelma*) is poorly known (see below).

FOOD AND FEEDING From their observations in Peru, Alvarez Alonso and Whitney (2003) described the birds making sally-strikes and sally-hovers to leaves or trunks and branches, scanning every few seconds for arthropod prey, but north of Manaus the species has also been observed perch-gleaning small melastome fruits (GMK pers. obs.). Overall it is known to take small fruits (including a species of Rubiaceae), as well as Hymenoptera and Coleoptera prey (Willard *et al.* 1991, Snow 2004b).

DISPLAY As described initially by Davis (1949), then Snow (1961) and Alvarez Alonso and Whitney (2003), males display alone, albeit usually within clear auditory distance of the next. They initially display the crest prominently, fluffing it outwards and even more obviously upwards, while simultaneously performing a 6–15cm upward 'jump' usually from a very slender limb 3–20m above ground (but mainly at the lower end of this spectrum). Sometimes the display branch is a heavier limb at a prominent angle to the ground. During the display the male emits a buzzing vocalisation (described above) whilst flapping the wings a few times, especially at the apex of the jump when the bird appears to hover momentarily. On returning to the perch, landing facing the same direction in which it started, although the display-flight sometimes takes the opposite direction, the male adopts an exaggeratedly horizontal posture, the crest still raised, and performs 10–14 shallow exaggerated wing flicks, neck twitches and tail pumps. Thereafter, another vertical leap usually follows (sometimes as many as seven occurring within a period of just 23 seconds). (Videotape of the display, from coastal Surinam, by W. Vercruysse was also used to compile this section.) Apparent females sometimes perch close by, within a few metres of displaying males.

BREEDING Lekking activity has been noted in Peru in January, when birds (3–10) were spaced 40–60m apart within 1–2ha of forest, but not between February and early June. In Surinam the species is certainly active at leks late and early in the year, and males in breeding condition have been collected in March–April and August–November (RMNH). Seven breeding-condition birds were collected in eastern Colombia in May (Olivares 1964), a male with enlarged gonads in coastal Guyana in late April (FMNH), whilst Alvarez Alonso and Whitney (2003) collected males with greatly enlarged testes in mid November, late January and mid May, and observed an apparent pair (performing an unexplained behaviour) in the company of another individual they considered to be a juvenile, in Peru, on 1 July. The nest and eggs are undescribed.

STATUS Saffron-crested Tyrant-Manakin is treated as Least Concern (BirdLife International 2004, 2008). The species is considered fairly common within its limited range in dpto. Amazonas, Peru (Alvarez Alonso 2002, Schulenberg *et al.* 2007), at several sites in Surinam (Ottema 2009) and in Guyana (Braun *et al.* 2007), but is known from just a single site in eastern Colombia and there is no recent information concerning the species' status within that country. It is regularly found at Awala in French Guiana (Renaudier 2009). Like some other *Neopelma*, it is known from relatively few protected areas, but has been found in Jaú National Park, Amazonas, Brazil (Borges *et al.* 2001) and is common at the INPA reserves north of Manaus in the same state (Cohn-Haft *et al.* 1997; GMK pers. obs.).

REFERENCES Aleixo *et al.* (2011), Alvarez Alonso (2002), Alvarez Alonso and Whitney (2003), Anciães and Peterson (2009), BirdLife International (2004, 2008), Boesman (1998, 2009), Borges (2007), Borges *et al.* (2001), Bradshaw and Kirwan (1995), Braun *et al.* (2007), Cohn-Haft *et al.* (1997), Crease (2009), Davis (1949), Dunning (2008), Haverschmidt (1952), Hellmayr (1929b), Naka *et al.* (2006, 2008), Novaes (1978), Olivares (1964), Omena Júnior (2007), Ottema (2009), Ottema *et al.* (2009), Pinto (1944), Renaudier (2009), Ridgely and Tudor (1994, 2009), Robbins *et al.* (2007), Rodrigues Lima and Anciães (2009a, 2009b), Salaman *et al.* (2008), Schulenberg *et al.* (2007), Sick (1967, 1997), Silva *et al.* (2010), Snow (1961, 2004b), Snyder (1966), Stotz *et al.* (1996), Tostain *et al.* (1992), Willard *et al.* (1991), Zyskowski *et al.* (2011).

Saffron-crested Tyrant-Manakin *Neopelma chrysocephalum*. **Fig. 1**. INPA Campina Biological Reserve, north of Manaus, Amazonas, Brazil, September (*Hadoram Shirihai / Photographic Handbook to Birds of the World*). All species of *Neopelma* can be distinguished from the several species of very superficially similar tyrant flycatchers by their long bills and tails (both longer than most manakins), chunky build and lack of any wingbars, as well as the colour of their irides. The present species is a white-sand soil specialist. **Figs. 2–3**. Allpahuayo-Mishana Reserved Zone, dpto. Loreto, northeast Peru, October (*Hadoram Shirihai / Photographic Handbook to Birds of the World*). This species was only relatively recently discovered in a small region of upper Amazonia, along with a number of other species that are otherwise largely or solely thought to be restricted to the Guianan Shield, which finding has important implications for our understanding of Amazonian biogeography, and the processes shaping it.

Genus *Tyranneutes*: small tyrant-manakins

This genus comprises two tiny, essentially plain 'manakins', which form a superspecies (Sibley and Monroe 1990) and are probably most closely related to the *Neopelma* 'manakins' (Snow 1975, R. O. Prum *in* Ridgely and Tudor 1994). It has been suggested that both genera might be better subsumed within the Tyrannidae, wherein *Tyranneutes* was formerly placed, rather than being placed in the Pipridae, and this course of action was followed by the recently published International Ornithological Congress list. Gill and Wright (2006) further recommended employing the scientific generic name as the English group-name as well, thus *T. stolzmanni* would become Dwarf Tyranneutes. In both species of *Tyranneutes*, the sexes are essentially alike in plumage and both lack any ritualised lekking behaviour. They can be very difficult to observe, but are easily heard, in their lowland rainforest haunts within the Amazon Basin.

DWARF TYRANT-MANAKIN
Tyranneutes stolzmanni   Plate 1

Pipra stolzmanni **C. E. Hellmayr, 1906**, *Ibis* 6: 44, Marabitanas, upper Rio Negro, Brazil

Dwarf Tyrant-Manakin is a dingy, flycatcher-like bird that is far more often heard than seen. Despite its relative abundance and wide range, it is a comparatively poorly known taxon in many aspects of its behaviour.

IDENTIFICATION 7.5–9.0cm. Usually located and identified by virtue of its distinctive voice. This diminutive, drab bird, which somewhat resembles a pygmy tyrant (*Lophotriccus*) or tody-tyrant (*Hemitriccus*), is arguably most likely to be confused with Tiny Tyrant-Manakin *T. virescens* (which see) or females of several true manakins of the genus *Pipra*. Saffron-crested Tyrant-Manakin *Neopelma chrysocephalum* might also represent a confusion risk. It too has pale (usually yellowish to white) eyes, but is significantly larger with a semi-concealed central coronal stripe and quite different vocalisations. Dwarf Tyrant-Manakin has a pale iris, which could also lead to confusion with some of the immature male *Pipra* that acquire a pale iris whilst still in essentially olive attire. Two such species – Golden-headed *P. erythrocephala* (widespread north of the Amazon) and Round-tailed Manakins *P. chloromeros* (southwest Amazonia) – are broadly or locally sympatric, respectively, with *T. stolzmanni*. These are marginally larger birds, however, and are typically far more active, with brown or pinkish mandibles, whilst most tyrannids of a similar size can be distinguished by their wingbars, sleeker appearance and proportionately longer tails.

DISTRIBUTION Dwarf Tyrant-Manakin principally occurs over southern and western Amazonia, including throughout the basin south of the river, but is restricted to the upper Amazon north of it. It occurs from southern Venezuela (in western and southern Bolívar and Amazonas), eastern Colombia (north to Meta and Vaupés, and as far west as the foothills of the Andes), south throughout eastern Ecuador and eastern Peru, to northern Bolivia (south as far as dpto. La Paz), thence east across Amazonian Brazil, where it is known south to Mato Grosso (along the upper Xingu and elsewhere as far south, discontinuously, as the Serra das Araras Ecological Station) and across southeast Pará, central Tocantins (Lopes and Braz 2007) east to northern Maranhão, and north of the Amazon east to the Rio Negro drainage and as far as the west bank of the Rio Branco in Roraima (Pinto 1966, Naka *et al.* 2006). The species was

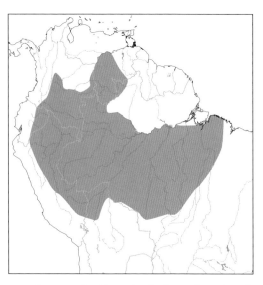

recently reported, without details, in southern Amapá, north of the Amazon (Campos *et al.* 2009), where it must come close to occurring in sympatry with *T. virescens*. Dwarf Tyrant-Manakin is mainly recorded below 400m, but the species occasionally reaches 800m in Peru (Schulenberg *et al.* 2007) and to at least that in Bolivia (Perry *et al.* 1997, Hennessey *et al.* 2003), to 920m in southern Venezuela (Crease 2009) and to 1,000m in Ecuador (Ridgely and Greenfield 2001).

MOVEMENTS None known.

HABITAT *T. stolzmanni* is mainly found in the interior of humid lowland forest, usually at lower and middle levels, and only rarely in clearings and at edges. Recorded in *terra firme* and, more rarely, *várzea* forests (e.g. in Ecuador), especially those on white-sand soils, but the species is rare in Peruvian white-sand *varillales* (Alvarez Alonso 2002).

DESCRIPTION This and the next species constitute some of the most uniform passerine birds. *T. stolzmanni* is small and squat, with a comparatively large bill (considering the bird's minute overall size) and a very short tail. The bill has a slightly arched culmen and a hooked tip. The nostrils are very obvious and the bird has reasonably well-developed rictal bristles (more so than *T. virescens*). The outermost primary is rather shorter than the second outermost primary (the difference is less pronounced in *T. virescens*). The sexes are alike, except that females have on average marginally longer tails than males. *Adult.* – Olive above, perhaps slightly darker on the wings, especially so on the flight feathers, with one or two slightly paler and brighter feathers on the wing bend. Dingy greyish-olive from the chin to breast (the darkest tract on the underparts), where it is obscurely streaked and smudged yellowish-white, with a paler, more yellowish belly. *Juvenile.* – This plumage is apparently undescribed (Snow 2004b); a nestling (of unstated age) was found, but not described, by Greeney *et al.* (2004). *Moult.* – Data are very few, though Willard *et al.* (1991) noted some evidence of feather renewal in one of three early March specimens collected in southern Venezuela, and one collected in eastern Ecuador in February was in full body moult (MECN). Several trapped in eastern Colombia in May were not renewing any feathers, but others in June and September were in body moult (A. Ayala V. and R. Parra/ProAves unpubl. data). One collected in northern Brazil in September was in light body moult (INPA). Singles collected in southeast Peru (late August) and northern Brazil (early October) were moulting their body-feathers and their wing and body feathers, respectively (FMNH). *Bare parts.* – Irides usually whitish-grey, but always pale and range from orange-tinged white, to pale greyish, white or pale brown. The bill is black or dark brown with a paler, greyish lower mandible replete with a black tip and sometimes also with darker cutting edges, and the legs and feet are dark horn to dark greyish or black.

MEASUREMENTS (Hellmayr 1910: Rio Madeira, Brazil; BMNH: Colombia, Ecuador and Peru; INPA: northern Brazil; MECN: Ecuador; Gyldenstolpe 1945: western Brazil; see also Whitney *et al.* 1995 for additional mensural data) Wing of male (n = 10) 46–52mm (<56mm in live birds), wing of female (n = 4) 46.0–49.5mm; tail of male (n = 9) 18–25mm, tail of female (n = 4) 19–25mm; bill of male (n = 6) 9.42–12.0mm, bill of female (n = 4) 10.35–12.0mm; tarsus of male (n = 6) 10–11mm, tarsus of female (n = 2) 12mm (<15mm in live birds). Weight (sexes combined): 6.5–13.0g (Silva *et al.* 1990, Willard *et al.* 1991, Snow 2004b, Dunning 2008; FMNH; INPA; MECN; M. Gutiérrez and R. Parra/ProAves unpubl. data).

GEOGRAPHICAL VARIATION Monotypic, though Friedmann (1948) mentioned that he considered birds from southern Venezuela and northern Brazil to appear slightly brighter yellow on the underparts than those south of the Amazon. However, his sample size was rather small.

VOICE Distinctive; the male advertising vocalisation is an insistent, well-defined, hoarse *jew-jit* (Ridgely and Tudor 1994), *jew-pit* or *ur-jit* (Ridgely and Tudor 2009), which can be repeated constantly for long periods at 4–6-second intervals. Blue-crowned Manakin *Pipra coronata* has a rather similar vocalisation, but which is less emphatic, coarse and with less stress on the second syllable (Hilty and Brown 1986), and which is always given in series, not singly (Hilty 2003). In southern Peru and Ecuador, both sexes may give a melodic *tuee-tuee-tuee-tuee* (the number of notes varies), from the canopy (Ridgely and Greenfield 2001), with the first note slightly higher and of a somewhat nasal quality (Hilty 2003); the notes are usually longer than in the similar call of Slender-footed Tyrannulet *Zimmerius gracilipes* (Schulenberg *et al.* 2007), which, by contrast, is a more or less exclusively canopy-dwelling species. Recordings have been published on the audio compilations of English and Parker (1992), Moore (1994), Boesman (1999, 2006a, 2006b), Mayer (2000), Schulenberg *et al.* (2000), Krabbe and Nilsson

(2003), Marantz and Zimmer (2006) and Boesman (2009), and sound-recordings are also available from Bolivia, Brazil, Ecuador and Peru online at www.xeno-canto.org.

NATURAL HISTORY Generally found solitarily and well dispersed, although 2–3 males usually occur within earshot of one another, and at least occasionally it joins mixed-species foraging flocks (Silva and Oniki 1988, Tubelis 2007). Very retiring and inconspicuous, the Dwarf Tyrant-Manakin will remain on the same, favoured perches, steadfastly, for long periods, often vocalising at regular intervals (principally from late morning and all afternoon), when it will permit close approach by careful observers. Calling birds are, however, unobtrusive and are often only located with some difficulty, perched on side branches at 3–15m above ground, occasionally ascending even higher into the canopy. The same territories are apparently often occupied for many years (GMK pers. obs.).

FOOD AND FEEDING The diet is mainly small fruits, but also includes an unknown percentage of invertebrates (Pinto 1953, Snow 2004b; INPA). There are virtually no specific data on, for example, the species of fruits it favours, but Tello (2003) found *T. stolzmanni* to be one of the more frequent avian visitors to a fruiting *Ficus pertusa* (Moraceae) tree in southeast Peru. As mentioned above, Dwarf Tyrant-Manakin joins mobile mixed-species flocks, both in the canopy and, less regularly, in the understorey (Munn 1985). It also joins other manakins at fruiting trees (Ridgely and Tudor 2009).

DISPLAY The display (context unknown) is rather remarkable for such a small and visually unassuming bird, as the male flies straight up 20–30m into the air above a very tall tree, before diving back down to the same perch in the canopy (Snow 2004a, Walther 2004). Whittaker (2009) provided an even more detailed description of this spectacular behaviour, from observations made at Alta Floresta, northern Mato Grosso, Brazil:

> On the sunny morning of 4 June 2003, at 07h57, I observed a *T. stolzmanni* in the crown of an emergent tree *c.*100m away. The first flight was a steep ascent, at 60–70°, on fast fluttery wingbeats, in a tight spiral and two "steps", to *c.*15m, before folding its wings and "dive-bombing" to the same perch. Thirty seconds later it climbed rapidly in an exaggerated "zigzag" flight up *c.*30m, again "dive-bombing" vertically to the tree crown. Ninety seconds later the bird flew again, climbing rapidly at a steep angle (but less spiralling) to *c.*40m, then "dived" back at *c.*20° to the crown. The final display-flight was performed 50 seconds later, with the bird climbing diagonally in an exaggerated fluttering, in a tight corkscrew to *c.*40–45m, again "dive-bombing" at *c.*30° back into the canopy. The four flights occupied 2.5 minutes, and the final flight was the most spectacular. I could not hear any audible noise associated with the ascent or vertical dives, contrary to flight displays by *Corapipo* or *Heterocercus* manakins (pers. obs.). I have also observed this same display at Ziggylandia, Manacapuru, Amazonas, and the ACEER walkway, Río Napo, Loreto, Peru, in January.

K. J. Zimmer (*in* Walther 2004) mentioned observing similar behaviour from a canopy tower in Pará, Brazil. The only ostensible difference between Walther's observations (made in southern Amazonas, Venezuela, in April) and those of

Whittaker is that Zimmer noted his bird to flick the wings whilst perched. The bird can erect the short frontal crest when particularly excited.

BREEDING This is poorly known, as only one nest has been found to date, at Sacha Lodge Research Station, eastern Ecuador, in mid April. The tiny cup of sparse black rootlets, sited 1.5m up in the horizontal fork of a small sapling, contained a single nestling (Greeney *et al.* 2004, wherein nest dimensions are presented). In addition, breeding-condition birds have been collected in Colombia in March and May (A. Olivares *in* Hilty and Brown 1986), eastern Ecuador in December (MECN), northern Brazil in late October and mid November (INPA), and in southern Venezuela in March–May (Willard *et al.* 1991).

STATUS Considered Least Concern (BirdLife International (2004, 2008). However, Anciães and Peterson (2006) predicted that this species could be severely impacted by habitat modification in the face of potential climate change based on modelling techniques. There are a few robust data on abundance, but Terborgh *et al.* (1990) found up to 20 individuals per 100ha at their study site in extreme southeast Peru. Relatively common (by voice), the Dwarf Tyrant-Manakin is not currently threatened, given the vast areas of undisturbed forest within its range. Despite being very inconspicuous, *T. stolzmanni* is a regular feature of most avifaunas throughout its range and can be encountered at a great many sites, including a widespread network of protected areas in all range states.

REFERENCES Almeida *et al.* (2003), Alvarez Alonso (2002), Anciães and Peterson (2006, 2009), Balchin and Toyne (1998), BirdLife International (2004, 2008), Boesman (1999, 2006a, 2006b, 2009), Borges (2007), Borges *et al.* (2001), Cadena *et al.* (2000), Campos *et al.* (2009), Crease (2009), Dunning (2008), English and Parker (1992), Friedmann (1948), González (1998), Greeney *et al.* (2004), Gyldenstolpe (1945), Haffer (1974, 1992b), Hellmayr (1910, 1929b), Hennessey *et al.* (2003a, 2003b), Henriques *et al.* (2003), Hilty (2003), Hilty and Brown (1986), Hosner *et al.* (2009), Krabbe and Nilsson (2003), Lane *et al.* (2003), Lopes and Braz (2007), Maillard *et al.* (2007), Marantz and Zimmer (2006), Mayer (2000), McKay *et al.* (2010), Mee *et al.* (2002), Mestre *et al.* (2010), Moore (1994), Munn (1985), Naka *et al.* (2006), Novaes (1960), Oren and Parker (1997), Pacheco and Olmos (2005), Pacheco *et al.* (2007), Parker and Wust (1994), Parker *et al.* (1994a, 1994b, 1994c), Peres and Whittaker (1991), Perry *et al.* (1997), Pinheiro and Dornas (2009a), Pinto (1944, 1953, 1966), Restall *et al.* (2006), Ridgely and Greenfield (2001), Ridgely and Tudor (1994, 2009), Salaman *et al.* (2008), Schulenberg *et al.* (2000, 2006, 2007), Sick (1997), Silva (1996), Silva and Oniki (1988), Silva *et al.* (1990), Snethlage (1907), Snow (2004b), Stone (1928), Stotz *et al.* (1996, 1997), Tello (2003), Terborgh *et al.* (1990), Tubelis (2007), Vidoz *et al.* (2010), Walther (2004), Whitney *et al.* (1995), Whittaker (2009), Willard *et al.* (1991), Zimmer (1930).

Dwarf Tyrant-Manakin *Tyranneutes stolzmanni*. **Fig. 1**. Anavilhanas Jungle Lodge, Amazonas, Brazil, December (*Hadoram Shirihai / Photographic Handbook to Birds of the World*). **Fig. 2**. Tupana Lodge, Amazonas, Brazil, December (*Hadoram Shirihai / Photographic Handbook to Birds of the World*). *Tyranneutes* tyrant-manakins are some of the drabbest inhabitants of South American tropical forests, but draw the attention with their persistent, easily recognised vocalisations. Despite this, their small size and habit of remaining still on the same branch for long periods mean they can still be difficult to locate. However, once a favourite perch is known, the observer can sometimes return months (even years) later and find the bird in much the same place.

TINY TYRANT-MANAKIN
Tyranneutes virescens   Plate 1

Pipra virescens **Pelzeln, 1868**, *Orn. Bras.*: 128, 187, Barra do
Rio Negro [= Manaus]

Although principally allopatric with the previous species,
their ranges might well overlap in part of southernmost
Bolívar, in southeast Venezuela, where increased observer
coverage has almost inevitably led to claims of both species
on the same forest trails, a situation which demands clarification. However, complete syntopy, as has been claimed at
the Maracá Ecological Station, in Roraima, northernmost
Brazil, seems unlikely (see Naka *et al.* 2006), and in general
the two species replace one another either side of the
Rio Branco, the lower Rio Negro and the Amazon (Snow
2004b).

IDENTIFICATION 7.0–8.1cm. The principal confusion
species, especially in any possible areas of sympatry, or where
their ranges are known to come close, is the extremely
similar, very marginally larger and slightly longer-tailed
Dwarf Tyrant-Manakin *T. stolzmanni*. They are best separated
by virtue of the dark irides in the present species and the
yellow coronal patch of the male (although this is usually
invisible in the field). Furthermore, at close range in optimal
views, the throat and breast of Tiny Tyrant-Manakin is greyer
than Dwarf's with a distinctly 'stippled' effect produced by
the presence of short yellow streaks, and the belly is even
paler and less yellow. The voice of Tiny Tyrant-Manakin
distinctly differs from that of Dwarf Tyrant-Manakin (see
below). Similar distinguishing criteria to those outlined
under Dwarf Tyrant-Manakin must be used when separating
the present species from any of the number of superficially
similar tyrannids or female-plumaged *Pipra* manakins that
overlap in range.

DISTRIBUTION Tiny Tyrant-Manakin is restricted to
northeast South America. Essentially the species occupies
that part of the Amazon Basin where Dwarf Tyrant-Manakin
is absent, namely throughout the Guianas, although it is
largely restricted to the interior in French Guiana (where

T. virescens was first recorded as recently as the mid 1970s:
Dick *et al.* 1984), but is even found in the savanna forests
of the Rupununi in Guyana, and in extreme southeastern
Venezuela (in eastern and southern Bolívar, in the Sierra de
Imataca and near El Paují), thence south, locally, through
northern Brazil east of the Rio Branco in Roraima, where
the species was only recently discovered (at Vila União: Naka
et al. 2006), to the Amazon, at the confluence with the lower
Rio Negro around Manaus (Cohn-Haft *et al.* 1997), and east
through northern Pará to Amapá, where it seems reasonably
widespread and has been recorded in several conservation
units (Silva *et al.* 2009, Campos *et al.* 2009). The species does
not penetrate south of the Amazon. It has been recorded
to *c.*500m in Venezuela (Gilliard 1941).

HABITAT Regularly visits the canopy and subcanopy, but
is probably mainly found in the lower and middle growth
of humid lowland forest, almost exclusively in *terra firme*,
but including those forests on sandy soils. Also visits forest
borders, at least occasionally, and sometimes clusters around
light gaps, treefalls and other small clearings (GMK pers.
obs.).

DESCRIPTION Similar to Dwarf Tyrant-Manakin except
that it is smaller and even shorter tailed with a darker
iris. Small and squat, with a comparatively large bill
(considering the bird's minute overall size), the sexes
are alike, except that females have marginally longer tails
than males, and the already-mentioned yellow coronal
patch of the male is vestigial or absent in the female. See
comments on the rictal bristles and primaries under the
previous species. *Adult.* – Head and upperparts dull olive,
with darker wings, relieved (in the male) only by the
largely concealed yellow central crown-stripe, becoming
paler and more greyish-olive on the throat to breast, flanks
and thighs (which are slightly flammulated with yellow
'streak-like' markings), and then becoming very pale yellow
over the belly. The axillaries and underwing-coverts are
pale sulphur-yellow becoming pale brown over the flight
feathers. *Juvenile.* – As with its sister-species, this plumage is
apparently undescribed (Snow 2004b). *Moult.* –Unknown.
Bare parts. – Bill dark brown to black with a marginally paler
lower mandible; the legs and feet are dark horn to dark
greyish (once black); and the irides are light brown to pale
sepia (Snow 2004b; INPA).

MEASUREMENTS (BMNH; INPA; RMNH: Amazonas,
Brazil, Guyana and Surinam; see also Whitney *et al.* 1995 for
mensural data) Wing of male ($n = 10$) 45.5–52.0mm, wing
of female ($n = 5$) 45.0–51.5mm; tail of male ($n = 10$) 17.5–
21.0mm, tail of female ($n = 5$) 20.5–22.5mm; bill of male ($n
= 10$) 8.66–9.93mm, bill of female ($n = 5$) 10.82–11.4mm;
tarsus of male ($n = 8$) 10.6–12.37mm, tarsus of female ($n =
5$) 9.01–13.82mm. Weight (sexes combined): 6–11g (Dick
et al. 1984, Snow 2004b, Dunning 2008; RMNH).

GEOGRAPHICAL VARIATION Monotypic.

VOICE Differs noticeably from that of Dwarf Tyrant-
Manakin, the vocalisation being a fast, burry but melancholy-
sounding *whippy-jebree* without any inflection and repeated
at very regular, short intervals (D. W. Finch *in* Ridgely
and Tudor 1994), also rendered as *weedle-de-dee* or *Nicky
the Greek* (Hilty 2003). The first notes are more or less
fine and relatively higher pitched, with the last part more
burry, sometimes pronouncedly so. Haverschmidt and
Mees (1994) described a slightly different, faster-delivered
and more melodious vocalisation, also of three to four

phrases, which is described as a call and features on the Naka *et al.* (2008) and Renaudier and Deroussen (2008) compilations. GMK (pers. obs.) has heard this vocalisation given frequently, albeit at intervals, in the first three hours of the morning by a territorial male in the subcanopy (*c.*30m above ground) in south central Guyana. In Venezuela, Tiny Tyrant-Manakin is described as being more vocal during the first half of the year (Hilty 2003). Like Dwarf Tyrant-Manakin, this species repeats its advertising call over and over, as frequently as every 3–6 seconds throughout the day. Sound-recordings from Brazil and Venezuela are archived online at www.xeno-canto.org.

NATURAL HISTORY Much like that of the previous species. Tiny Tyrant-Manakin forms dispersed leks, with 2–4 males often within hearing distance of one another, each one perched a little above eye level, i.e. the species is usually found at lower levels than *T. stolzmanni*, on an open horizontal perch (usually a narrow twig in a small understorey tree). Exhibits the same tenacity to certain favoured perches, on just 2–3 different trees, and persistent calling habits as the previous species, and has been estimated to call for 86% of the day, thereby emitting *c.*6,000 vocalisations per day (Hilty 2003).

FOOD AND FEEDING The diet is mainly fruits, taken by sally-gleaning, but also hover-gleans small quantities of insects and their larvae. Only occasionally (?) visits the canopy. In French Guiana, Théry (1990c) found that melastome (Melastomaceae) fruits were very important in the species' diet, especially of males, but there seems to be no other specific information concerning food or feeding.

DISPLAY Two displays have been described (Snow 1961). The first is a slow 'floating' butterfly-like flight between branches, which can be given in conjunction with the 'calls' described by Haverschmidt and Mees (1994; GMK pers. obs.), or a short jump with the wings fanned, legs dangling and crest fully erect (with the head and body held upwards). Also has a sideways-peering display on the perch between flights, the eyes always fixed in front and the body held erect, with the head and neck being moved from side to side (Snow 1961). Walther (2004) also reported a similar towering display above the canopy to that of Dwarf Tyrant-Manakin, from observations by K. J. Zimmer at Manaus, and this remarkable facet of both species' natural history was confirmed by Whittaker (2009) for *T. virescens*, based on his August observations, also north of Manaus, Amazonas, Brazil. Such aerial display has also been observed in south central Guyana, from the Iwokrama Canopy Walkway (A. Moses pers. comm.).

BREEDING Very little is known concerning nesting

behaviour, but Beebe and Beebe (1910: 342–343) reported finding a nest in Guyana in late March or early April, in a sapling 2m above the ground in a clearing, suspended in a fork. The nest was a very fragile-looking affiar constructed of rootlets and vegetable matter with two or three dead leaves attached to the base with cobwebs, and the authors were able to lift the female off the nest by hand. It was presumably incubating eggs, although Beebe and Beebe do not mention if this was the case or not. Robbins *et al.* (2004) considered the species to be breeding in March/April at one of their study sites in southern Guyana, and birds of both sexes have been collected in breeding condition in September, November, January and February in Surinam (RMNH), and in Amazonas, Brazil, in October (INPA). In French Guiana the main singing (and presumably nesting) season is December–June (Renaudier 2009).

STATUS Tiny Tyrant-Manakin is generally rare and local in Venezuela, but is locally common throughout the Guianas and in the relevant part of northern Brazil, and at present the species is not considered threatened (Least Concern: BirdLife International 2004, 2008). For instance, at a study site in French Guiana, Thiollay (1994) found this species to be the most abundant Pipridae, with an estimated density of 18 pairs per 100ha. It is relatively easy to see in the vicinity of the trails at km 67 and km 73 south of El Dorado, in southeastern Bolívar, Venezuela; and is regularly found at lower levels of Brownsberg Nature Park and Raleigh Falls-Voltzberg Nature Park, both in Surinam (Ridgely and Tudor 1994), at Saint-Eugène, Sinnamary and Angoulême in French Guiana (Claessens 1997, Renaudier 2009), at the Iwokrama Canopy Walkway, near Atta Rainforest Camp, in Guyana (GMK pers. obs.), as well as being tolerably common north of Manaus (Cohn-Haft *et al.* 1997) and in Parque Nacional Montanhas do Tumucumaque, Amapá (Bernard 2008), both localities in Brazil.

REFERENCES Anciães and Peterson (2009), Beebe and Beebe (1910), Bernard (2008), BirdLife International (2004, 2008), Campos *et al.* (2009), Chubb (1921), Claessens (1997), Cohn-Haft *et al.* (1997), Dick *et al.* (1984), Dunning (2008), Gilliard (1941), Haffer (1974, 1992b), Haverschmidt and Mees (1994), Hellmayr (1929b), Hilty (2003), Naka *et al.* (2006, 2008), Novaes (1978), Ottema *et al.* (2009), Pinto (1944), Renaudier (2009), Renaudier and Deroussen (2008), Restall *et al.* (2006), Ridgely and Tudor (1994, 2009), Robbins *et al.* (2004), Sick (1997), Silva *et al.* (2009), Snethlage (1907), Snow (1961, 2004b), Snyder (1966), Stotz *et al.* (1996), Théry (1990c), Thiollay (1994), Tostain *et al.* (1992), Walther (2004), Whitney *et al.* (1995), Whittaker (2009), Zyskowski *et al.* (2011).

Tiny Tyrant-Manakin *Tyranneutes virescens*. **Fig. 1**. El Palmar, Bolívar, southeast Venezuela, March (*Joe Tobias / Edward Grey Institute, Oxford University*). This singing male is obviously very agitated; the yellow coronal stripe is rarely so obvious! **Fig. 2**. Campamento Río Grande, Serranía de Imataca, Bolívar, southeast Venezuela, March (*Pete Morris*). **Fig. 3**. Fazenda Dimona, Biological Dynamics of Forest Fragments Project, north of Manaus, Amazonas, Brazil, October (*Andrew Whittaker*). **Figs. 4–5**. Iwokrama Canopy Walkway, Guyana, October (*Hadoram Shirihai / Photographic Handbook to Birds of the World*). The species principally occurs in the midstorey and subcanopy, but this singing male has ascended into the canopy and, in Fig. 3, is utilising an unusually large branch to perch. Both *Tyranneutes* also possess a rarely observed above-canopy display-flight in common with several genera of 'true' manakins.

Genus *Pipra*: typical manakins

Following his transfer of those species now treated within *Lepidothrix* from the present genus, Prum (1990a, 1992) considered *Pipra* to comprise two clades: the *P. erythrocephala* clade (comprising Scarlet-horned Manakin *P. cornuta*, Red-capped Manakin *P. mentalis*, Golden-headed Manakin *P. erythrocephala*, Round-tailed Manakin *P. chloromeros* and Red-headed Manakin *P. rubrocapilla*) and the *P. aureola* clade (namely Crimson-hooded Manakin *P. aureola*, Band-tailed Manakin *P. fasciicauda* and Wire-tailed Manakin *P. filicauda*). Advertisement and many other calls differ in their shared characters between these two clades (see Tello 2001), whilst male-coordinated displays appear to be important for the second-named clade in determining male dominance, the *P. aureola* clade having developed a much more highly developed system of display elements than is present in the *P. erythrocephala* clade. Nonetheless, Castro-Astor *et al.*'s (2004) study of Red-headed Manakin has yielded new information as to the diversity of displays in the latter clade.

Wire-tailed Manakin has, in the past, been afforded its own genus, *Teleonema*, Reichenbach, 1850 (e.g. Hellmayr 1929b, Pinto 1944), but was subsumed within *Pipra* by Haffer (1970), a move followed by all subsequent authors. Scarlet-horned Manakin was also frequently placed in a monotypic genus, *Ceratopipo*, C. L. Bonaparte, 1854, during the same period (e.g. Hellmayr 1929b, Pinto 1944).

CRIMSON-HOODED MANAKIN
Pipra aureola   Plate 2

Parus Aureola Linnaeus, **1758**, *Syst. Nat.*, 10th edn., 1: 191, based on Edwards, *Nat. Hist. Birds* 2: 83, pl. 83, fig. 2, 'from some part of South America, near the equinoctial line' [= Surinam; cf. Hellmayr 1906d: 6]

The type species of the genus *Pipra* (Hellmayr 1906d), Crimson-hooded Manakin is the northeasternmost representative of the genus, although it ranges south and west from the eastern Guianan Shield to the southern Middle Amazon. *P. aureola* forms a superspecies with Band-tailed *P. fasciicauda* and Wire-tailed Manakins *P. filicauda*, all of which replace each other geographically (Haffer 1970, Schwartz and Snow 1978). As noted by Robbins (1983), they are united by their similar plumage, vocalisations and displays, and recent genetic data suggest that these three might be the sole representatives of the genus *Pipra* (see Systematics, p. 39).

IDENTIFICATION 10.7–12.0cm. Because this is the sole representative of its superspecies over the vast majority of the species' range, e.g. in Venezuela and the Guianas, males should prove immediately identifiable. Local parapatry has been reported in the Serra dos Carajás, Pará, Brazil (Pacheco *et al.* 2007), where Band-tailed Manakin is unquestionably the more numerous of the two (GMK pers. obs.), and apparently at Utinga, south of Belém (Beebe 1915, Haffer 1997b). It seems likely that the two also come into contact around Humaitá in southernmost Amazonas, given that *P. aureola* has been collected in this region (Hellmayr 1929b) and *P. fasciicauda* has been recently observed there (Santos and Silva 2005), albeit on opposite banks of the Rio Madeira. However, towards its mouth, *P. aureola* has been found on the right bank of the river too. Wire-tailed Manakin comes close to the range of the present species around Manaus, but seems to be separated from it by the Rios Negro and Purus; regardless, the tail adornments present in both sexes should make that species impossible to confuse. Young males yet to acquire substantial tracts of adult feathering might still be readily distinguishable from other manakins by their white irides, except in areas where Band-tailed Manakin might possibly occur. Away from leks, female-plumaged birds are perhaps most likely to be confused with the same sex of

White-bearded Manakin *Manacus manacus* or the smaller Golden-headed Manakin *Pipra erythrocephala* over most of the present species' range. The pale (but not necessarily white) irides, general shape and ochre-coloured throat should serve to separate female Crimson-hooded Manakin from female *M. manacus*, whilst the colour of the irides and the distinctly more yellowish underparts should separate it from female *P. erythrocephala*, even if size cannot be readily judged. At the limits of its distribution, great care would be needed in some areas to separate female *P. aureola* from same-sex Band-tailed Manakin, and in many cases this is probably impossible.

DISTRIBUTION Northeast South America and eastern Amazonia, the species is the sole member of the *P. aureola* superspecies found in the Guianan Shield. It ranges through eastern Venezuela in southeast Sucre (including the Paria Peninsula), eastern Monagas and Delta Amacuro, as well as in Bolívar near the Cerro Roraima (Hilty 2003), thence east throughout much of the Guianas, mainly in coastal areas and the west of Guyana (Snyder 1966), the littoral of Surinam (Ottema *et al.* 2009) and French Guiana, in which latter country the species is practically unknown in

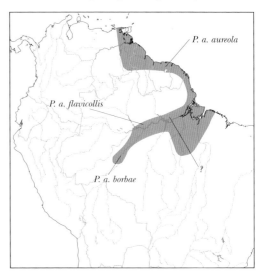

the interior (Tostain *et al.* 1992). The rest of the species' range is in Brazil, where it is found throughout Amapá, much of Pará (including some islands at the mouth of the Amazon), north of the Amazon west to Óbidos, south of the river around Belém and along the lower reaches of the Rios Tocantins, Xingu and Tapajós, as well as in the Serra dos Carajás (Pinto 1944, Pacheco *et al.* 2007), and further west locally in Amazonas, north of the Solimões at Faro and apparently around Manaus (cf. Hellmayr 1906d, 1929b, Zimmer 1936a) and south of it principally along the Rio Madeira as far south as Humaitá in southernmost Amazonas (Hellmayr 1929b, Pinto 1944). Cohn-Haft *et al.* (1997) did not find *P. aureola* north of Manaus, perhaps casting doubt on its occurrence in the region. Crimson-hooded Manakin is principally a lowland species, being rarely found above 300m (even 150m), but it has been recorded to a maximum elevation of 1,200m, near the Cerro Roraima in southern Venezuela, and occurs around the base of tepuis in western Guyana (Hilty 2003).

MOVEMENTS There is no evidence for any movements and the species is generally considered resident and males are noticeably sedentary (Snow 2004b). However, Hilty (2003) mentioned that birds will wander some distance in search of suitable foraging opportunities.

HABITAT Crimson-hooded Manakin is principally a bird of swampy and seasonally flooded forest (*várzea*), including modified areas (Ridgely and Tudor 1994, Sick 1997, Hilty 2003), as well as tangled gallery woodland along watercourses (Silva *et al.* 1997) and dry to moist semi-deciduous woodland in hilly areas, especially where there are many vine tangles, lianas and *Attalea* (Arecaceae) palms (Hilty 2003, Restall *et al.* 2006). Reynaud (1998) provided some further details concerning the structure of riparian forests inhabited by this species in French Guiana, and at two lek sites in Surinam, Snow (1963a) noted many *Heliconia* (Heliconiaceae) and *Psychotria* (Rubiaceae) trees in the understorey, and a predominance of Sandbox *Hura crepitans* (Euphorbiaceae) trees at one. However, it also occurs locally in *terra firme* forest (Aguiar *et al.* 2005) and in mangrove and its edges (Tostain *et al.* 1992, Hayes *et al.* 2003), as well as in second growth (Hilty 2003, Souza *et al.* 2008) and white-sand *campinas* in Amapá (A. Whittaker *in* Hilty 2003). *P. aureola* is also occasionally found on river islands (MNRJ) and Hilty (2003) reported that the species will also visit fruiting trees away from forest.

DESCRIPTION The wing feathers are slightly modified in males, in that the barbs of the secondaries are stiffened with thickened shafts. The bill has a reasonably arched culmen, but the tip is rarely strongly hooked, and then usually in males. The nominate race is described here. *Adult male.* – The crown, nape, neck-sides, ear-coverts, breast and upper belly are entirely crimson-red, with a variable orange-yellow forehead band, which in some is reasonably prominent but in others consists of scarcely a spot of feathers above the bill (see Geographical Variation). The orange-yellow coloration extends across the lores, lower face-sides, chin and throat, merging almost imperceptibly into the red of the breast and ear-coverts. The rest of the upperparts and underparts, including the tail, are velvety black, becoming more charcoal-coloured over the belly and abdomen, with the exception of the creamy to whitish tarsal feathering (some with pale yellow tips) and some reddish or (more usually) orange feathering in the ventral region (usually the centre). The flight feathers have duller outer webs and the

inner webs, especially of the tertials, can have a broad white band (which can be obvious at rest and, more especially, in flight). There can also be some white along the feather shaft at the base of the outer web of the outermost pair of rectrices. The axillaries and underwing-coverts are pale yellowish, and the wing-bend is usually fairly bright yellow. *Adult female.* – Typically rather dull, as are most female *Pipra*. The upperparts are generally dull greenish-olive, becoming dark brown with greenish-olive fringes over the wing-coverts, flight feathers and rectrices. The throat is dull olive-yellow or dull ochre, while the foreneck to belly-sides is also dull greenish-olive, and the lores are yellowish, the middle line of the abdomen is pale olive-yellowish and the rest of the underparts are greyish or dull ochre (palest on the belly). Axillaries and underwing-coverts are yellowish-white with dark tips. There is no white in the remiges or rectrices. Some adult females, perhaps generally older birds, show some red or orange feathers on the crown and underparts (usually the breast), respectively (Haverschmidt 1965, Graves 1981, Haverschmidt and Mees 1994; MNRJ), although this trait of showing some elements of male plumage does not appear to be as commonly displayed as in some congenerics. *Juvenile.* – Younger individuals of both sexes apparently resemble adult females but have dark irides; however, by the time young males are showing some adult plumage their irides are white (sometimes with a hint of reddish) like those of adults (MNRJ). Young males may appear brighter below than adult females (GMK pers. obs.). Beebe *et al.* (1917: 235–237) briefly described chicks in the nest and their development. Plumage maturation is not well described in the literature, but subadult males can retain some green feathering on the wing-coverts, posterior underparts, mantle and rump. Males initially gain red feathering on the crown, chin, throat, breast and/or ear-coverts (MNRJ; ZMA). Younger males (lacking complete adult plumage) are probably capable of breeding, but note that only dominant older males generally mate (see Display). See also comments under Wire-tailed Manakin concerning plumage maturation. *Moult.* – Moult regime is basically unknown, but a young male was moulting the body-feathers in September, at a time when adults in the same region were breeding and thus not undergoing feather replacement (MNRJ). A female collected in northeast Venezuela in November was in body moult (FMNH). *Hybrids.* – Two interesting hybrids have been described in the literature. '*Pipra heterocerca*', Sclater, 1860 (*Proc. Zool. Soc. Lond.* 1860: 313) was described on the basis of a single specimen of uncertain provenance, which was subsequently destroyed (Haffer 2002). Parkes (1961) considered it to represent a hybrid (*Pipra filicauda* × *P. aureola* or *P. fasciicauda*), whilst Haffer (1970, 1974, 2002) regarded it as being a hybrid *Pipra filicauda* × *P. aureola*. For more information see the account of Wire-tailed Manakin. A second hybrid, originally described as '*Pipra anomala*' Todd, 1925 (*Proc. Biol. Soc. Wash.* 38: 97), based on a male specimen (perhaps immature) collected by S. M. Klages at Santarém, Pará, Brazil, is generally considered to be an inter-generic hybrid between *Pipra a. aurantiicollis* and Flame-crested Manakin *Heterocercus linteatus* (Parkes 1961, Mallet-Rodrigues 2008). For more information see the latter species. *Bare parts.* – Males generally have bright white or whitish irides, whilst females have very pale grey, rose-white, white or cream-white irides (Ouellet 1990; FMNH). Legs and feet of both sexes are rosy-pink, reddish or purplish-pink (sometimes greyer in young birds) with browner toes, black claws and ochre or beige-coloured soles. The bill is generally black, blackish-brown or dark brown in many birds, especially over the maxilla, sometimes with a paler (greyer) base to the mandible and even paler cutting edges (FMNH; MNRJ; Novaes 1978, Snow 2004b). Restall *et al.* (2006) described the bill as being vinaceous-red in males, but we have not seen either photographs or well-labelled specimens with such a bill colour.

MEASUREMENTS (CUMZ; MNRJ; ZMA: Amapá, Amazonas and Pará, northern Brazil; Surinam) Subspecies grouped (but most pertain to *P. a. aureola*): wing of male (*n* = 41) 61–69mm, wing of female (*n* = 13) 61–65mm; tail of male (*n* = 43) 27–37mm, tail of female (*n* = 13) 29–38mm; bill of male (*n* = 42) 10.51–13.48mm, bill of female (*n* = 12) 12.15–13.44mm; tarsus of male (*n* = 21) 13.34–16.79mm, tarsus of female (*n* = 9) 14.44–17.68mm. Hellmayr (1906d) presented the following data for the different subspecies (see also Hellmayr 1929d), with female *P. a. flavicollis* from FMNH. *P. a. aureola* (east Venezuela and the Guianas): wing of male (*n* = 14) 62–65mm, wing of female (*n* = unknown) 63–65mm; tail of male (*n* = 14) 28–32mm, tail of female (*n* = unknown) 31–33mm. *P. a. flavicollis* (near Manaus, Amazonas, Brazil): wing of male (*n* = 4) 61.5–64.0mm, wing of female (*n* = 2) 59.0–61.5mm; tail of male (*n* = 4) 27–30mm, tail of female (*n* = 2) 30–32mm. *P. a. aurantiicollis* (Santarém and localities downstream, Pará, Brazil): wing of male (*n* = 3) 62.0–63.5mm; tail of male (*n* = 3) 28–30mm. *P. a. borbae* (Borba, Amazonas, Brazil): wing of male (*n* = 2) 60–63mm; tail of male (*n* = 2) 28–30mm. Additional mensural data for live birds (pertaining to nominate *aureola*) were presented by Aguiar *et al.* (2005). Weight: 14–18g (males) and 15.5–18.5g (females) (Haverschmidt 1948, 1952, Silva *et al.* 1997, Hilty 2003, Snow 2004b, Aguiar *et al.* 2005, Dunning 2008; FMNH; MNRJ). Aguiar *et al.* (2005) gave means of 16.8g and 15.0g for males and females, respectively.

GEOGRAPHICAL VARIATION Polytypic, with four subspecies generally recognised (e.g. by Dickinson 2003, Snow 2004b). Plumage differs between the subspecies only in males, and the following comments therefore refer solely to male plumage. Nonetheless, other perhaps than topotypical material, differences between the different taxa can be rather marginal and difficult to categorise, witness for instance that Hellmayr (1906d) recognised just two subspecies (nominate *aureola* and *P. a. flavicollis*) and pointed to the existence of marked individual variation in the depth of the frontal band, despite having access to material from the ranges of all forms recognised herein. Snethlage (1907) also noted extensive individual differences in discussing the problems presented by lower Amazonian birds (based on a sample from Monte Alegre and the Ilha de Marajó). Some revision of subspecific limits may be necessary, but has not been attempted here. *P. a. aureola* is distributed through eastern Venezuela, all of the Guianas and Amapá, Brazil, as far west (north of the Amazon) as the Rio Maicuru (Pará, but see below), islands at the mouth of the Amazon (e.g. Marajó and Mexiana) and further south in southeast Pará including the lowest reaches of the Amazon. It is described above. Hellmayr (1906d) remarked that amongst specimens collected in Surinam, some had a striking orange-yellow forehead band and others none at all. (Photographs of adult males from French Guiana by M. Dechelle and M. Chrétien also confirm the variability of this feature.) Both he (Hellmayr 1929b) and Zimmer (1936a) unswervingly assigned material from the lower Rio Tocantins and the right bank of the Rio Xingu, in southern

Pará, to nominate *aureola*, thereby leaving that subspecies' range 'curiously interrupted' by that of *P. a. aurantiicollis* (see below). Specimens from the Rio Maicuru were assigned to nominate *aureola* by Hellmayr (1929b) but to *aurantiicollis* by Pinto (1944), revealing again the difficulties of assigning some specimens to a given subspecies, especially in the lower Amazon. All of the following subspecies are confined to Brazil. *P. a. flavicollis* P. L. Sclater, 1852 [for information concerning dating of this taxon see Dickinson *et al.* 2011] ('Yellow-throated Manakin'), is restricted to the middle Amazon on the north bank of the Solimões, from around Óbidos (Pará) to the Manaus region (Amazonas), reaching the south bank locally, e.g. on both sides of the Rio Madeira at its mouth (Zimmer 1936a, Pinto 1944). See below, however, for specimens commensurate with this race from as far east as Monte Alegre (Pará) on the north bank of the Amazon. Compared with the previous race, the forehead band is narrow but clearly demarcated and cleaner and paler yellow (with fewer orange elements) while the yellow throat patch is more extensive, reaching to the upper breast and onto the upper ear-coverts (which are more pure yellow with fewer reddish elements) (see Fig. 3). These features also serve to differentiate *flavicollis* from *aurantiicollis*, on average (Hellmayr 1929b). Hellmayr (1906d) also considered the axillaries and undertail-coverts to be brighter yellow than in *P. a. aureola*. *P. a. aurantiicollis* Todd, 1925 ('Orange-throated Manakin'), ranges west of the previous subspecies, principally south of the Solimões in southwest Pará, from around Santarém, along the lower Rio Tapajós, towards the mouth of the Amazon, and perhaps occurs locally north of the Amazon, e.g. at Monte Alegre, Pará. However, whereas Pinto (1944) treated north-bank specimens as belonging to *aurantiicollis*, Snethlage (1914) and Hellmayr (1929b) treated them within *aureola*, and Zimmer (1936a) as *flavicollis*! We have examined two male specimens in MNRJ (10789–90) from Monte Alegre: both show broad yellow throat patches, which might generally be considered consistent with *flavicollis*, although it should be remarked that we have seen photographs of adult males from coastal French Guiana that also display reasonably prominent and extensive yellow throats (Fig. 4). These questions concerning the range of *flavicollis* and whether the features associated with this taxon are truly geographical rather than individual merit additional attention. Further south along the Tapajós, *P. a. aurantiicollis* is replaced by *P. fasciicauda scarlatina* (Pinto 1944), e.g. in Tapajós (Amazônia) National Park. Pinto (1944) noted that *aurantiicollis* grades into both nominate *aureola* and *P. a. flavicollis*, but because of the perceived impossibility of assigning at least some males from the range of *aurantiicollis* to either of the adjacent subspecies, both Hellmayr (1929b) and Zimmer (1936a), as well as Pinto (1944), were content to uphold *aurantiicollis*. Snow (2004b) considered *aurantiicollis* to be differentiated by its very narrow and poorly defined forehead band, and its rather deep yellow throat, but as noted by Hellmayr (1929b) the heavy orange suffusion to the throat and forehead band are perhaps better distinguishing characters. Amongst the topotypical series from Santarém, Hellmayr (1929b) noted that a small number of specimens show some white in the tail, either as a shaft streak or a sub-basal band. Zimmer (1936a) considered this race to be 'exactly intermediate between *aureola* and *flavicollis*'. We have examined relatively few specimens from within the range of this form, but to our eyes it seems impossible to diagnose confidently. *P. a. borbae* J. T. Zimmer, 1936, is restricted to the Rio Madeira drainage in south central Amazonian Brazil, where it is known to range from Borba (the type locality), on the right bank, south to its upper reaches at Marmelos and Humaitá on the left bank (Pinto 1944), above which it is apparently replaced by *P. fasciicauda calamae* (Zimmer 1936a). Considered by Hellmayr (1929b) to represent an insignificant variation, we have only examined a single young male from the range of this subspecies. Indeed, earlier, Hellmayr (1906d, 1910) had examined material from the type locality of *borbae*, taken by Natterer, without even commenting on any variation within *flavicollis*, to which he assigned these specimens. *P. a. borbae* was described on the basis of the much broader forehead band, which merges with the red of the crown. The ear-coverts are perhaps marginally less suffused with scarlet (Snow 2004b). Snow (2004b) added that the tail is shorter, but this difference, if it is one, seems weak at best.

VOICE The most commonly heard vocalisation (the advertising call) is a rather plaintive, slightly drawn-out and penetrating *eeeeew* or *neeeeeeer* (Hilty 2003, Snow 2004b), given with the bill pointing almost upwards and the throat feathers puffed out, while the tail is held depressed and fanned. If given while displaying to another male, the wings are also quivered and the back feathers raised slightly (Snow 1963a). The advertising call can be uttered as frequently as every ten seconds, but inter-call intervals are usually substantially longer, typically several minutes in duration (Snow 1963a; GMK pers. obs.), although both Snow (1963a) and Hilty (2003) noted that neighbouring males often immediately respond to the first bird, almost like an echo. Snow (1963a) described two other vocalisations: a sharper, doubled *thee-weep*, which can be associated with the display given when a female arrives at the display area; and a much softer *weee-ip*, uttered with the bill held up and given by males in the display area but also when feeding away from it. Hilty's (2003) *eeer-teet* is presumably analogous to the latter. For mechanical sounds, see the section on Display. The vocalisations of Crimson-hooded Manakin have featured on the following commercial audio compilations: Boesman (1999, 2006a, 2006b) and Renaudier and Deroussen (2008). Recordings from Brazil, French Guiana and Venezuela are archived online at www.xeno-canto.org.

NATURAL HISTORY More study is needed as most aspects of the species' biology have not been explored well and most of our knowledge is based on casual observations, or inferred based on information pertaining to other members of the same superspecies. In-depth modern studies are almost entirely lacking.

FOOD AND FEEDING Takes small fruit and insects and spiders, like others of the genus, with some apparent preference for fruits of *Ficus* (Moraceae) (Chubb 1921, Hilty 2003, Restall *et al.* 2006) and Araceae (Tostain *et al.* 1992), although the latter authors mention that *P. aureola* takes a great variety of fruits. Beebe *et al.* (1917) mentioned that nestlings were fed fruit, a small beetle and 'worms'. Crimson-hooded Manakin typically seizes fruit using a short-range sally-hover method.

DISPLAY Males display most of the year (Hilty 2003), but the species' behaviours have not been studied in great detail, other than by Snow (1963a) who provided data from observations in Surinam, with additional data presented by Schwartz and Snow (1978) and Robbins (1983) for other members of the *P. aureola* superspecies. Considered to be generally similar to those of Wire-tailed Manakin, involving coordinated, alternating, display-flights, males display in small loosely associated groups, involving just three and two individuals, respectively, at Snow's two study sites in Surinam. Each male tends to give the advertising call and display from a small number of favoured perches within an 18m radius *c*.36m from the next male, and *c*.9–27m above the ground. Hilty (2003), however, reported that display-perches are much lower, just 2–5m above the ground. Snow observed males plucking leaves or other vegetation from their display-perches in flight, apparently 'gardening' the area to keep it clear. The same observer reported eight different display behaviours as follows. (1) Mechanical-looking *side-to-side slides* consist of rapid steps, first one way then the other, along the display perch. During these moves, the bird appears hunched, but the bill points upward, the tail is depressed and the head feathers are fluffed out. (2) *Backward and forward slides* represent a variant of the previous display, in which the bird performs similar movements but instead of perching at right angles to the branch, the bird faces along the perch. (3) Should another male arrive on the perch, the perch-owner faces away, crouches down, shivers the wings and cocks the tail to display the yellow ventral feathering. This display Snow termed the *facing-away and wing-shivering* posture. (4) When moving between adjacent display-perches, the wings make a clicking noise on landing (*click on landing*). (5) *Slow flight* may be observed should a female arrive in the display-area, during which the white in the wing is distinctly more obvious, as well as during coordinated displays (see 8). (6) Not observed by Snow, *darting back-and-forth* was reported to him by F. Haverschmidt and consists of a male flying rapidly back and forth between two display-perches and seems akin to similar displays in Red-capped *Pipra mentalis* and Golden-headed Manakins *P. erythrocephala*. (7) The *display-flight* consists of the male flying from a display-perch to another, slightly higher branch *c*.18–20m away, then arcing downwards in a return flight that approaches to within 4m of the ground, uttering a soft mechanical *poop* (likened to pulling a piece of cloth taut) as it does so, before arriving at the first perch with a movement designed to show off the white in the wings. On landing, the bird immediately performs an about-face to look back in the direction from which it came, uttering a single or double *eeeeew* call simultaneously. The whole display is so rapid that it is easily missed but for the associated sounds (Snow 1963a, Hilty 2003). (8) The *coordinated display between two males* is perhaps only rarely performed in full, when it lasts 2–3 minutes, but more frequently in part according to Snow's observations. This display commences with two males on the same perch, of which one performs the same display described under (7), whereupon on landing, the second bird ducks and then flies down to a lower perch as the first returns to the initial perch. The doubled *eeeeew, eeeeew* advertising call is given, either with the returning bird giving the first *eeeeew* and the departing bird the second call, or perhaps by both birds in unison. Thereafter, a series of display-flights at short intervals is performed, although Snow was unsure whether one bird was responsible for all of the displays or if, as he thought more likely, they took it in turns. Sometimes, however, the bird on the display-perch will give the *eeeeew* call and then the displaying bird will proceed to land on an alternative branch, or the perched individual does not call and assumes a head-down posture, with the displaying bird again landing on a different branch. Snow assumed that the second male was from an immediately adjacent display-area. In another variation, should a female-plumaged individual arrive at the display-perch, 'she' will drop from the perch when the adult male returns and 'she' does not perform the display-flight. Snow concluded that the coordinated display is presumably more likely to attract a female's attention, but that given the presence of two males would then signal the need for the dominant male to establish his precedence to mate with the female, perhaps using a pre-copulatory display similar to that observed in Blue-backed Manakin *Chiroxiphia pareola*, which also conducts similarly rhythmic coordinated displays between males. Whether this is true has yet to be fully elucidated, because to date (rather remarkably) no one has built substantially on Snow's observations. However, Le Maitre and Reynaud (1994) found that it is true that only older dominant males mate with females.

BREEDING Obviously, the female undertakes all of the nesting duties. The nest is illustrated in Beebe *et al.* (1917: 236), Tostain *et al.* (1992: 139) and Snow (2004b: 136) and is a typical manakin structure: a small, relatively shallow cup slung between a horizontal understorey tree fork and attached with spiderwebs. Nest materials do not appear to have been well described, but one in French Guiana seems to be constructed of black rootlets and pale brown vegetable fibres with some dead leaves on the outer base to disguise the outline (Snow 2004b: 136). Beebe *et al.* (1917) noted that a nest in Guyana had coarse grass and rootlets as its main constituents, and was very fragile looking. A January nest in French Guiana was placed *c.*1m above the ground (Tostain 1988a), as was one (of four) March-discovered nests in northern Guyana, another of which was sited over a small pool of water (Beebe *et al.* 1917). Another nest found recently in French Guiana, in early November, was placed 1.7m above the ground in a mangrove (*Avicennia* sp.) sapling, and held a single newly hatched young (A. Vinot *in litt.* 2010). The outside of the nest was largely constructed of dead leaves fitted neatly together. Dimensions of both nests and eggs were recorded by Beebe *et al.* (1917), and of eggs alone by Hellebrekers (1942). The clutch size is two eggs, which in northeast Brazil Snethlage (1935) described as being proportionately large and pale yellowish-brown with brownish-black markings. In Guyana, Beebe *et al.* (1917: 235) described the eggs as being 'dull yellowish-white with numerous pale brown and lilac markings ... and more numerous at the larger end.' Hellebrekers (1942, 1945), describing eggs collected in Surinam, noted that the ground colour could be variable, being even reddish-white or pale yellowish-brown, with even more variable markings, especially in their extent. Nothing precise is known concerning incubation or fledging periods, but Beebe *et al.* (1917) noted that one ten-day-old young had full-grown flight feathers, but that they were still in their sheaths. Concerning seasonality, many of those trapped or collected in Amapá, Brazil, in September–November were in breeding condition (Novaes 1978, Silva *et al.* 1997; MNRJ). Breeding (egg laying) has been reported in February–March in Guyana (Snow 2004b), October, March–May (Hellebrekers 1942) and December in Surinam (http://webserv.nhl.nl/~ribot/english/index.htm), and October–May in French Guiana (Snow 2004b).

STATUS Crimson-hooded Manakin is treated as Least Concern by BirdLife International (2004, 2008) based on its large range (estimated at 671,000km²) and the lack of evidence for any decline in numbers or distribution area. Nonetheless, the species is generally rather uncommon over much of this large range, with the exception of parts of Amapá, extreme northeast Brazil, and in coastal regions of the Guianas, where *P. aureola* is locally abundant (Snyder 1966, Novaes 1978, Tostain *et al.* 1992, Forrester 1993, Haverschmidt and Mees 1994, Reynaud 1998, Ottema *et al.* 2009). Furthermore, Anciães and Peterson (2006) predicted that Crimson-hooded Manakin could be one of the Pipridae at greatest risk of habitat loss through climate change. Among protected areas known to harbour the species are the following: Área de Proteção Ambiental do Rio Curiaú, and Parque Nacional do Cabo Orange, both in Amapá, as well as the mosaic of protected areas in the Serra dos Carajás, Pará (all Brazil), and the Parque Nacional Paria, Venezuela (Sharpe 1997, Aguiar *et al.* 2005, Pacheco *et al.* 2007, Souza *et al.* 2008).

REFERENCES Aguiar *et al.* (2005, 2010), Anciães and Peterson (2006, 2009), Beebe (1915), Beebe *et al.* (1917), BirdLife International (2004, 2008), Boesman (1995, 1999, 2006a, 2006b), Braun *et al.* (2007), Campos *et al.* (2009), Chubb (1921), Clay (2009), Cohn-Haft *et al.* (1997), Dickinson (2003), Dickinson *et al.* (2011) Dunning (2008), Forrester (1993), Graves (1981), Haffer (1970, 1974, 1992b, 1997b, 2002), Haverschmidt (1948, 1952, 1965), Haverschmidt and Mees (1994), Hayes *et al.* (2003), Hellebrekers (1942), Hellmayr (1906d, 1910, 1929b), Hilty (2003), Kaiser (1999), Le Maitre and Reynaud (1994), Mallet-Rodrigues (2008), Meyer de Schauensee and Phelps (1978), Novaes (1978), Ouellet (1990), Pacheco *et al.* (2007), Parkes (1961), Pinto (1944), Prum (1990a), Renaudier (2009), Renaudier and Deroussen (2008), Restall *et al.* (2006), Reynaud (1998), Ridgely and Tudor (1994, 2009), Robbins (1983), Santos and Silva (2005), Schubart *et al.* (1965), Sharpe (1997), Sick (1993, 1997), Silva *et al.* (1997), Snethlage (1907, 1914, 1935), Snow (1963a, 2004b), Snyder (1966), Souza *et al.* (2008), Stotz *et al.* (1996), Tostain (1988a), Tostain *et al.* (1992), Zimmer (1936a).

1

Crimson-hooded Manakin *Pipra aureola*. **Fig. 1**. Male, *P. a. aureola*, near Maturín, Monagas, northeast Venezuela, March (*Pete Morris*). **Fig. 2**. Male, *P. a. aureola*, Joanes, Ilha de Marajó, Pará, Brazil, November (*Arthur Grosset / www.arthurgrosset.com*). **Fig. 3**. Male, *P. a. flavicollis*, Itacoatiara, east of Manaus, Amazonas, central Amazonian Brazil, July (*William Price / www.pbase/tereksandpiper*). **Fig. 4**. Male, Gulf de Kourou, coastal French Guiana, January (*Maxime Dechelle*). Note the rather striking large yellow throat on this individual compared to the males in Figs. 1 and 2 (see Geographical Variation). **Fig. 5**. Female, *P. a. aureola*, Joanes, Ilha de Marajó, Pará, Brazil, November (*Arthur Grosset / www.arthurgrosset.com*). Note the variation in throat colour and in the width of the orange forehead band in the first two males, despite which all of them can be confidently assigned to the nominate taxon. Four subspecies are generally recognised within *P. aureola*, but they are only differentiated in male plumage (the same is true for the vast majority of Pipridae exhibiting geographic variation).

BAND-TAILED MANAKIN
Pipra fasciicauda   Plate 2

Pipra fasciicauda **Hellmayr, 1906**, *Ibis* (8)6: 9, new name for *Pipra fasciata*, Lafresnaye & d'Orbigny, 1837, 'Yuracarés [= Yungas], eastern Bolivia' [= La Paz / Cochabamba], and Guarayos, Santa Cruz, Bolivia (cf. Paynter 1992: 58–59 & 168). Snow's (2004b) 'restriction' of the type locality to the second of the two localities mentioned is incorrect. *P. fasciicauda* was introduced as a nom. nov. by Hellmayr, to replace *P. fasciata* (preoccupied by *Pipra fasciata* Thunberg, 1822, = *Phyllomyias fasciatus* Planalto Tyrannulet), which was used twice by Lafresnaye and d'Orbigny, initially in 1837 (type locality Yuracarés) and again in 1839, when they referred to Guarayos and Santa Cruz. Hellmayr (1906) himself designated Yuracarés as the type locality, but elsewhere (Hellmayr 1929b) indicated that multiple Bolivian localities might be regarded as 'typical'.

The most widespread member of the *P. aureola* superspecies, it has been suggested that Band-tailed Manakin is the sister species of Wire-tailed Manakin *P. filicauda* based on some specific shared elements of their display repertoire (Tello 2001). Support or contradictory evidence for this theory must await more robust and complete genetic sampling or additional information on the display behaviour of Crimson-hooded Manakin *P. aureola* itself.

IDENTIFICATION 9.5–12.6cm. In common with the other two members of the superspecies, Band-tailed Manakin is readily identified over the greater part of its range. Especially for the highly distinctive males, identification should be rather straightforward, even in areas of potential or proven contact with either Wire-tailed Manakin (both sexes of which possess the 'fancy' tail adornments and so should therefore be easily separated) or Crimson-hooded Manakin. Contact with the latter species is known or suspected in the following areas of Amazonian Brazil: Serra dos Carajás (Pacheco *et al.* 2007) and south of Belém, at Utinga, both in Pará (Beebe 1915, Haffer 1997b) and perhaps around Humaitá, in southernmost Amazonas (see also *P. aureola*) (Hellmayr 1929b, Santos and Silva 2005). In comparison with *P. aureola*, males of the relevant races of Band-tailed Manakin (*P. f. scarlatina* and probably *P. f. calamae*) possess far more yellow (less red, and no black) on the underparts, and a white base to the tail, which given good views should usually be obvious. However, females of the two species will be practically impossible to identify, although *P. fasciicauda* is perhaps more yellowish-green above and slightly more extensively yellowish on the belly. As already noted, separation from Wire-tailed Manakin should be straightforward and contact is potentially more limited, south of the Amazon in the region of Rios Purus and Juruá (Brazil), and perhaps also around the Ucayali in Peru (Haffer 1997b). Female Band-tailed Manakins should be reasonably readily identified from other manakin species, especially in the Cerrado (where the only other Pipridae are often White-bearded Manakin *Manacus manacus* and Helmeted Manakin *Antilophia galeata*), given their obviously pale irides, more green-saturated upperparts and yellowish underparts, e.g. compared with the also slightly smaller Red-headed Manakin *P. rubrocapilla*. In contrast, female *Lepidothrix* that share the same range, e.g. Snow-capped Manakin *L. nattereri*, are paler and heavier-billed, with much brighter yellow posterior underparts and deeper green heads, breasts and upperparts.

DISTRIBUTION Band-tailed Manakin is very widely distributed south of the Amazon. The bulk of the species' range is in Brazil, where it occurs from eastern Pará, in the municipality of Belém (e.g. Beebe 1915, Novaes 1970), and western Maranhão, south (and west) across Amazonia and the Cerrado, to western Minas Gerais, northwest Sao Paulo and northern Paraná, Mato Grosso do Sul, Rondônia and Acre (Pinto 1944, Ridgely and Tudor 1994, Scherer Neto and Straube 1995, Sick 1997, Stotz *et al.* 1997, Scherer Neto *et al.* 2001, Guilherme and Santos 2009). In western Amazonia, Band-tailed Manakin probably comes close to meeting, or does meet with Wire-tailed Manakin in the region of the upper Rio Purus, Rio Juruá and, further west in Peru, the Río Ucayali (Haffer 1974). In the latter region, at least, they do seem to be separated, however (Alverson *et al.* 2001). In the far north of its range, *P. fasciicauda* seems to meet *P. aureola* at two localities in southeast Pará (Haffer 1974, 1997b, Pacheco *et al.* 2007). Thereafter, Band-tailed Manakin occurs west into Peru, where it is found widely across the lowland centre and east of the country, in the north locally crossing the Marañón but not the Huallaga in dpto. San Martín (Ridgely and Tudor 1994, Schulenberg *et al.* 2007). It also penetrates northern Bolivia, where it occurs in the departments of Pando, Beni, La Paz, Cochabamba and northern Santa Cruz (Remsen and Traylor 1989, Hennessey *et al.* 2003b). Even further south, perhaps isolated populations occur in eastern Paraguay, from Matogrosense south to Alto Paraná, and thus largely east of the Río Paraguay (Hayes 1995), and in extreme northeast Argentina, in Misiones (Saibene *et al.* 1996, Mazar Barnett and Pearman 2001). There is another, unquestionably isolated population in northeast Brazil, in the Serra do Baturité, Ceará (Pinto and Camargo 1961, Albano and Girão 2008), where Band-tailed Manakin is common in the Área de Proteção Ambiental do Maciço do Baturité (Rodrigues *et al.* 2003). Ridgely and Tudor (1994), repeated by Haffer (1997b) and Snow (2004b), also listed the species for Alagoas, but this seems erroneous (cf. Albano and Girão 2008). Snow (2004b) listed *P. fasciicauda* as being restricted to elevations below 600m, but the type of *P. f. saturata* was taken at *c*.1,000m (Zimmer 1936a), *P. f. purusiana* has been collected in Pasco (Peru) around 1,000m (FMNH 287940) and Walker *et al.* (2006) recorded

the species in Manu National Park to the same altitude (*P. f. fasciicauda*), whilst Stotz *et al.* (1996) listed occurrences to 800m (more exceptionally 950m), also in Peru, and the species also occurs to at least 700m in the Serra dos Carajás, Pará, Brazil (Pacheco *et al.* 2007).

MOVEMENTS Like most other *Pipra*, the species is not known to move to any extent, other than wandering for fruits (Snow 2004b). Robbins (1985) found that alpha males are extremely sedentary, spending the vast majority of each day on their territories, but elsewhere Piratelli and Mello (2001) registered one bird (of nine captured more than once) that moved 7km across a *Eucalyptus* (Myrtaceae) plantation between patches of suitable habitat. Nonetheless, Pinto (1953) considered that the species' presence in the Belém region might be explained by migrations and presented some circumstantial evidence to support that theory.

HABITAT In eastern Peru and many other areas of western Amazonia, Band-tailed Manakin is heavily dependent on, or even largely restricted to, *várzea* (seasonally flooded forest) (Robbins 1983, Schulenberg *et al.* 2007), but Armacost (2006) found it fairly common in a palm-dominated *terra firme* forest in dpto. Loreto. Understorey palms can also be prominent in the species' habitat in *várzea* (Robbins 1983). However, across Brazil's Cerrado, the Pantanal and parts of northern Bolivia, the species is found solely in the interior of gallery woodland or other dry or seasonally inundated woodlots, including *cerradão*, which are often isolated to some extent (Piratelli and Mello 2001, Antas 2004, Snow 2004b, Piratelli and Blake 2006). It also readily uses secondary growth in these regions (Scherer Neto and Kajiwara 1997, Vasconcelos and Roos 2000) and can even be found in areas that have been partially converted to plantations (GMK pers. obs.). Band-tailed Manakin also occurs in *terra firme* in eastern Amazonia, albeit perhaps especially close to rivers, in areas with a dense understorey, many vine tangles and some palms (GMK pers. obs.).

DESCRIPTION A typical member of the *P. aureola* superspecies. The wing feathers are slightly modified in males, in that the barbs of the secondaries are stiffened with thickened shafts. The bill has a reasonably arched culmen, but the tip is rarely strongly hooked, and then usually in males. The nominate race is described here. *Adult male.* – Superficially similar to *P. aureola*, and is also strikingly attractive. Characterised by the red crown, nape and neck-sides, becoming orangey-yellow over the fore ear-coverts, forehead, lores, chin, throat and breast, where it becomes slightly redder in the form of streaks, and then pale creamy-yellow over the rest of the underparts including the undertail-coverts. The remainder of the bird's plumage is matt to velvety black. The only exceptions are the strip of white on the inner webs of the flight feathers, which is only especially obvious in flight (when it forms a wingbar), but which is sometimes partially visible at rest, and the yellowish-white basal tail-band (see also Geographical Variation). *Adult female.* – Like all female manakins, positively dowdy compared with the male. Principally dull olive-green, especially on the head and upperparts, with slightly browner wing-coverts, flight feathers (including the rectrices) and can be strongly yellow-tinged on the face (lores, chin and throat) and breast (although this probably varies individually, in all races). The posterior underparts are rather paler green, with some yellow and grey admixed. The wing-bend is noticeably bright yellow. As in others of the superspecies, females may occasionally show some red

feathers on the breast (Zimmer 1936a) and, even more frequently, on the crown and nape (Graves 1981). *Juvenile.* – Probably undescribed, but like other *Pipra* (and manakins in general) this plumage almost certainly closely recalls the adult female, although Robbins (1983), repeated by Snow (2004b), reported that younger males possess brown or grey irides (see Bare parts). However, photographs of young males gaining the first vestiges of adult plumage, in eastern Brazil and Argentina, clearly have dull white irides, much like adults. Plumage maturation is not well described in the literature and there is no information concerning the number of moults required to attain adult plumage, but see comments under Wire-tailed Manakin. Young males clearly attain red or orangey-red feathers before any black ones, and these are usually concentrated on the breast, ear-coverts and crown-sides (GMK pers. obs.). Robbins (1983), however, noted that males can acquire variable numbers of red, yellow *and* black feathers following the first post-juvenile moult. One MNRJ specimen has scattered red and orangey feathers over the breast, throat, chin, crown and nape, with black feathers appearing over the back and lower mantle, but the wings and tail are still contrastingly brown. *Moult.* – There are very few published data concerning moult: in Mato Grosso do Sul (southern Brazil), Piratelli *et al.* (2000) and Piratelli and Mello (2001) noted that adults were moulting body and flight feathers in March–April and body feathers in August–September (i.e. immediately prior to breeding), whilst Oniki and Willis (1999) noted body moult in September in the Serra das Araras (Mato Grosso). *Bare parts.* – Irides are white or whitish in males, but reportedly span the range from pale grey to magenta, pink or whitish in females (Robbins 1983, Snow 2004b; FMNH); however, the vast majority of both sexes that we have seen or examined in the field or museum had white or nearly white irides, with the exception of one female that had greyish-yellow irides. The bill is dark grey to blackish in both sexes, sometimes with a paler grey to bluish-grey mandible (sometimes even with a pink base), and occasionally with the cutting edges or mandible tip palest. Both sexes have the legs and feet violaceous-grey, dull reddish or purplish-red, sometimes with sootier or blackish feet, and black claws (Snow 2004b; FMNH; MNRJ).

MEASUREMENTS *P. f. scarlatina* (MNRJ: Goiás, Mato Grosso, Mato Grosso do Sul and Tocantins, Brazil): wing of male (*n* = 16) 62.5–67.5mm, wing of female (*n* = 4) 62.5–66.5mm; tail of male (*n* = 16) 26–37mm, tail of female (*n* = 4) 25–35mm; bill of male (*n* = 15) 11.56–13.20mm, bill of female (*n* = 3) 13.29–13.57mm; tarsus of male (*n* = 4) 14.08–16.63mm, tarsus of female (*n* = 4) 14.15–16.52mm. *P. f. calamae* (MNRJ: Rondônia, Brazil): wing of male (*n* = 3) 61.5–64.5mm, wing of female (*n* = 1) 61mm; tail of male (*n* = 3) 28–33mm, tail of female (*n* = 1) 30.5mm; bill of male (*n* = 3) 11.71–13.17mm, bill of female (*n* = 1) 12.93mm; tarsus of male (*n* = 1) 15.55mm, tarsus of female (*n* = 1) 14.75mm. *P. f. saturata* (Zimmer 1936a: San Martín, Peru): wing of male (*n* = 1) 65mm; tail of male (*n* = 1) 25mm; tarsus of male (*n* = 1) 15mm. Data from live birds (*P. f. scarlatina*: dpto. Beni, Bolivia): wing of male (*n* = 45) 63–71mm, wing of female (*n* = 114) 59–71mm (J. Hornbuckle unpubl.). Additional mensural data were presented by Hellmayr (1908, 1910, 1929b), Oniki and Willis (1999) and Piratelli and Mello (2001), the latter two studies referring to live birds but not segregated by sex. There are no significant mensural differences between the sexes in *P. f. scarlatina* (Piratelli and Mello 2001). Weight (subspecies combined, but vast majority of data pertains to *P. f. scarlatina*): 11.0–22.8g (males) and 11.0–21.2g (females) (Fry 1970, Novaes 1976, Bates *et al.* 1989, Graves and Zusi 1990, Oniki 1990, Silva *et al.* 1990, Oniki and Willis 1999, Piratelli and Mello 2001, Snow 2004b, Dunning 2008, Sorrie ms.; J. Hornbuckle unpubl.; FMNH; MNRJ; MVZ].

GEOGRAPHICAL VARIATION Polytypic with five subspecies generally recognised (Dickinson 2003, Snow 2004b), principally based on the amount and extent of red on the underparts and to a lesser extent the face, as follows. As with Crimson-hooded Manakin, there are no known differences between females of the different races, thus all of the following comments concerning racial separation refer solely to males. However, it might be noted in passing that Zimmer (1936a) considered female *P. f. saturata* to be brighter yellow and olive than same-sex *P. f. purusiana*. *P. f. fasciicauda*, which occurs in dptos. Madre de Dios and Puno, southeast Peru, and north and northeast Bolivia, in dptos. Cochabamba and northern Santa Cruz, is described above. *P. f. purusiana* Snethlage, 1907, is found over the rest of eastern Peru south of the Amazon (from dpto. Loreto to dpto. Cuzco) thence into western Brazil, through Acre and western Amazonas as far east as the upper Rio Purus. It is separated from the previous subspecies by its redder pectoral band, whilst compared with the next taxon the red on the underparts is far more restricted (Schulenberg *et al.* 2007). Hellmayr (1929b) mentioned that, compared with the nominate form, the central rectrices are uniform black and the black tips to the undertail-coverts are more extensive. In this form, the outer rectrices possess a yellowish-white band on both webs, but Peruvian specimens have all six median tail feathers devoid of white, whereas Brazilian ones have white bases to the inner webs of the third pair from the centre (Hellmayr 1910, 1929b). *P. f. saturata* J. T. Zimmer, 1936, occurs in northern Peru in the Huallaga drainage (i.e. between the Huallaga and Marañón rivers, and east of the Andes), in dpto. San Martín, and is diagnosable on the basis of its having the deepest and most extensive red underparts of any of the subspecies. Although closest to *P. f. purusiana*, Zimmer (1936a) noted that the red reaches the lower throat, belly and undertail-coverts, and also postulated that the forehead is paler yellow and more clearly demarcated from the red crown in consequence, whilst the flanks are darker and sootier. *P. f. calamae* Hellmayr, 1910, is confined to a limited area of western Brazil near the upper Rio Madeira, including Rondônia, as far north as Calama and Aliança, and probably into adjacent northwest Mato Grosso (e.g. at Dardanelos: Novaes 1976). This subspecies is said to differ from *P. f. purusiana* by its olive-washed flanks, deeper red breast, and the crimson suffusion to the abdomen and basal undertail-coverts (Hellmayr 1910, 1929b). The tail pattern is identical to that of the adjacent *P. f. purusiana*. We have seen rather too few specimens to comment on the issue of its diagnosability. *P. f. scarlatina* Hellmayr, 1915, occurs over the rest of the species' vast range, over much of central and eastern Brazil, from central Pará, south of Belém, south to Mato Grosso do Sul, western Minas Gerais and northwest São Paulo, with more isolated populations in Ceará and Alagoas in northeast Brazil, as well as in northern Bolivia in dptos. Pando and Beni, southeast Paraguay and northeast Argentina. Whilst the tail pattern of this subspecies is identical to that of *P. f. fasciicauda*, the ear-coverts and throat feathers are extensively scarlet-tipped, whilst the foreneck and breast are much deeper and redder, and these red feathers extend more sparsely over the flanks

and even as far as the undertail-coverts, but are never as extensive on the posterior underparts as in *P. f. saturata*. Furthermore, evidence from photographs (see Figs. 1, 2 and 4) and specimens from most parts of the range of this taxon indicate that the extent of red feathering on the underparts is highly variable, apparently individually.

VOICE The species' vocalisations have been described in some detail by Robbins (1983, 1985), who mentioned four calls and two mechanical sounds produced by the wings, most of which possess clearly analogous elements in Wire-tailed and Crimson-hooded Manakins. Arguably the most frequently heard vocalisation by birdwatchers is the downward-inflected, slightly whining *eeeeew* advertisement call, which serves to announce that a male is on its territory or that a 'visitor' has arrived at a court (see Display). It lasts *c*.0.5 seconds and is audible over *c*.100m. As with the analogous vocalisation given by other members of the superspecies, the bird raises the head, depresses and fans the tail, and slightly puffs-out the throat feathers when giving the advertisement call. Termed by Robbins (1983, 1985) the appeasement whistle, this is an upward-inflected, soft whistled *sweee*, of 0.4–0.6 seconds, uttered with the bill slightly open while perched. These whistles of slightly varying duration may be given in series. It seems to indicate passivity or non-aggression in the male, and may be given early in the morning by an alpha male prior to display or by a visiting male which has no desire to display with an alpha male. This call is also given following a bout of display, signalling the participants wish to cease activity. The display-call has three types, but is always given when perched, with the bill pointing slightly upwards (less so than in advertisement), the throat puffed-out but the tail closed. Robbins (1983) termed the three subtypes 'normal', 'partial' and 'slurred'. The first is a somewhat harsh *we-ee-eeh* and is given by the alpha male should another bird delay in coming to display, while the visitor may give this call between the alpha male leaving the main perch and his return flight. However, when exchanges between alpha and other males are rapid and smoothly coordinated, this vocalisation is given less frequently. Following a break in display, the alpha male may initiate another round of display using this call. The 'partial' display-call comprises a *weee*, and is given by an alpha male if a visitor fails to display. On such occasions, the perch-owner flies close to the uncooperative bird and calls until the visitor either displays or departs. The *weee* call can also be given by either male of a displaying duo when the returning bird flies over the perch instead of landing on it, or when two or more males compete for dominance. The slurred call-type consists of the addition of a fourth note of almost equal length to the rest of the display-call but at lower frequency. This seems to be given most frequently early in the morning and later in the day, apparently to summon other males to display. The final non-mechanical vocalisation described by Robbins (1983) is the so-called culminating call, a drawn-out *eeeooo* given only during the 'swoop-in' flight (see Display) immediately before landing on the main perch. It is rarely omitted during solo performances or between well-acquainted display partners, but immature males rarely give this call. Two mechanical sounds were also identified during Robbins' study, namely a low-intensity *klok* produced using the wings just before a male lands on the perch, and a similar *kloop*, which is given at the lowest point of a 'swoop-in' flight. Both mechanical sounds serve to accentuate the male's conspicuousness and thereby attract females to visit the arena. Robbins (1983) presented sonograms of all these calls, and the species' vocalisations are available on the following commercially available audio compilations: Schulenberg *et al.* (2000), Boesman (2006a, 2009), Marantz and Zimmer (2006) and Minns *et al.* (2009), whilst additional material is archived online at www.xeno-canto.org.

NATURAL HISTORY Generally, Band-tailed Manakins are found alone, except at leks. Piratelli and Mello (2001) found that in their study, the population appears to comprise virtually equal numbers of males and females. The species' social organisation (among males) was very well described by Robbins (1985); his results are summarised under Display. There is a distinct hierarchy among males, from non-territorial males through beta males to alpha males, which seems to be based principally on age. Immature males are only capable of calling imperfectly and are principally observers during lek behaviours (Robbins 1985). Other than at leks, or perhaps at fruiting trees, Band-tailed Manakins are normally encountered solitarily and usually in the understorey. Pearce-Higgins *et al.* (2007) studied survival rates for this species in northern Bolivia. They uncovered significant age-related variation, but that adult survival rates did not differ by sex, and they estimated annual survival at 10% for immatures within an area of contiguous forest, rising to 53% in a 10.9ha forest fragment. Rates for adults were 46% in the year after capture and 68% thereafter. The authors suggested that forest fragmentation may have reduced immature dispersal, leading to inflated apparent survival rates in the forest fragment.

FOOD AND FEEDING Like other *Pipra* species, Band-tailed Manakin takes both small fruits and insects (e.g. beetles, and Diptera: Beebe 1915, Ferreira *et al.* 2008), although it is principally a frugivore, and at least regionally seems to favour fruits of Melastomataceae (*Miconia* sp.), Dilleniaceae (*Curatella americana*) and Rubiaceae (Piratelli and Mello 2001, Snow 2004b). Tello (2003) observed this species visiting a fruiting *Ficus pertusa* (Moraceae) in southeast Peru. *Miconia* sp. (Melastomataceae) fruits have also been observed being taken by the isolated population of Band-tailed Manakin in far northeast Brazil (GMK pers. obs.). Both insects and fruits are taken using a short-range sally-hover movement. Rubio *et al.* (2003) considered the species to be omnivorous, but that the ratio of fruit to insects was 9:6, whilst Piratelli and Pereira (2002) recorded only fruit in this species' diet at a locality in eastern Mato Grosso do Sul. Ferreira *et al.* (2008), who also studied the species in Cerrado localities, confirmed the species' preference for fruit. No differences have been identified between males and females in their diet preferences (Piratelli and Mello 2001, Ferreira *et al.* 2008). Band-tailed Manakin has also been observed following *Eciton burchelli* army ants, taking insect and larval prey disturbed by their passage (Willis 1984, Willis and Oniki 1992).

DISPLAY The study in southeast Peru reported by Robbins (1983) remains unsurpassed to date. At the lek he studied, ten display-arenas or territories were present, of which seven were rather clustered: distances between neighbouring males' main perches varied from 14m to 45m and overall territory sizes from 20 × 20m to 30 × 32m (Robbins 1983). The height of each male's principal perch above the ground was 3–5m. Associated with each court within the lek is an alpha, usually a beta, and occasionally one or more visiting adult males that perform coordinated displays. Visitors are typically short-staying (Robbins 1983, 1985). Whereas alpha males are extremely sedentary and dominate all interactions within their respective territories, betas are less sedentary and may display with more than one alpha per day. They inherit the territory from the alpha male, either by active displacement or death, with the result that subordinate males compete actively for a beta role; there seems to be no advantage in prior territory-ownership for a bird seeking to establish himself at a new arena (Robbins 1985). Territory-owners actively encourage other males to join them in displays, except males that own adjacent territories. Whilst visits to the arena by most other bird species are tolerated, in Robbin's (1985) study he found that other lekking manakins, e.g. Round-tailed Manakin *Pipra chloromeros* and Fiery-capped Manakin *Machaeropterus pyrocephalus*, were actively chased. Perhaps this was due to the fact that Robbins (1985) observed both these other species displaying to female *P. fasciicauda*. On the other hand, Várzea Schiffornis *Schiffornis major* is tolerated. Eleven display elements were identified and described by Robbins (1983) as follows; his terminology is largely adopted here.

Side-to-side display is principally given by the alpha male (perch-owner) and consists of short sideways steps along a branch, the bird perpendicular to the perch, the head and body tilted upwards and held rigid, with the mantle feathers depressed. He moves rapidly up to 10cm in one direction, before either returning or 'about-facing' and displaying in the opposite direction. The display encourages another male to join in a coordinated display and can be given for up to two minutes, usually on the main perch or an immediately joining branch. The *short flight* display is frequently given prior to another display type, and consists of a short flight on a more or less horizontal plane, usually between the main perch and an adjacent branch, with a low *klok* produced prior to each landing (see Voice). In contrast, the *stationary display* is less centred on the main perch, and is most frequently given when three or more birds are present in the territory. The head is tilted forward, the body held nearly horizontal, the wings are lowered slightly and quivered, and the lower back feathers may be slightly erected. This behaviour may precede or follow any other display. The *horizontal freeze* is probably solely given in the presence of a female-plumaged bird and seems to be immediately preceded by a swoop-in flight. The bird's posture recalls that adopted in the stationary display, but the body, wings and tail are all held horizontal, with the feathers sleeked down, and irides slightly contracted. The position is held for 5–10 seconds and the display was postulated by Robbins (1983) to be testing the receptiveness of the female. Designed to show to best advantage the white wing stripe, the *butterfly flight* display is a more or less level flight on stiff deliberate wingbeats between two display-perches, occasionally with a terminating *klok*. It is always performed in the presence of another bird.

Much more rarely seen, at least by Robbins (1983), the *aerial chase* is similar to the butterfly display, but two birds are always involved, one chasing the other in a series of wide loops through and above the display-arena, sometimes for >1 minute, exceptionally for *c.*3.5 minutes. Always three or more adult males were present and, because Robbins never saw an alpha male involved in such chases, he postulated that this display serves as a means for non-alpha males to establish dominance over the others. In the *flutter display* the male appears to be falling backwards off a perch, his wings spread and rapidly beating. This behaviour simulates copulation and is frequently performed following a swoop-in flight. Robbins (1983) also observed immature males performing flutter displays, perhaps in response to rising hormone levels. The *tail-up freeze* (cf. Robbins 1983: 334) is performed should either another male or female visit the display-perch. The male orients himself directly away from the visitor, facing downwards but erecting the lower back and tail, drooping and quivering the wings slightly (to reveal some white), and exposing the cloacal region for 3–4 seconds. Although usually performed while wholly stationary, the bird's body sometimes moves from side to side. A swoop-in flight usually follows. The *swoop-in flight* itself usually commences on the main perch, and is almost invariably given in the presence of a second male. The perch-owner flies up to a perch some 15–30m distant, usually producing a *klok* on landing, before immediately returning in a looping flight, accompanied by a *kloop* at its lowest point, and turning around in mid-air immediately before landing at the main perch, so that the bird faces the same direction from which it has just come. The whole performance lasts up to eight seconds. *Coordinated (joint) displays* between two males are typically initiated following a series of short flights, rarely a butterfly display, or a tail-up freeze; however, 'well-acquainted' partners rarely require such 'preambles'. The birds then perform a series of swoop-in flights, taking turns, with the visitor giving the advertisement call while the perch-owner is displaying, and the alpha male giving the culminating call (see Voice) on his return to the main perch. These displays are usually most impressive and particularly sustained (lasting several minutes) between an alpha and beta male, but are poorly coordinated if one male is immature or if the visitor is especially aggressive (Robbins 1983). As with most other manakins, copulations are only rarely seen, and Robbins' experience was similar. Thus most *male–female interactions* that he observed did not culminate in mating. Females do not join displays and rarely if ever call on the lek. The alpha male (which is apparently the only bird at a given arena who will mate with visiting females: Robbins 1985) will try to attract the female to the main perch using short flights, a butterfly flight and eventually a side-to-side display on the perch itself. In the only successful copulation he observed, the female flew to the main perch following the alpha male's side-to-side display, whereupon the male immediately performed a swoop-in flight, which terminated in him landing directly on the female and mating with her bent slightly forwards. However, on all other occasions, the female would leave the main perch again, following which the male would use a variety of other behaviours such as side-to-side displays, advertisement calls, swoop-in flights, butterfly flights and horizontal freezes, to tempt her back. Should the female leave the arena, the male never gave chase.

At least in southern Brazil, display-arenas are occupied year-round (Antas 2004) and the same seems true in other areas too, although Robbins (1985) noted some variation in male attendance at territories.

BREEDING The nest is unsurprisingly similar to those of other, closely related piprids, and the female is entirely responsible for the parental duties. It is a tiny open-cup structure sited in a two-way horizontal fork well above the ground and constructed of dark fungal rhizomorphs, small twigs, rootlets, vegetable fibres and rachises of leaves. Some or many dead leaves may be integrated within the base, principally to disguise the outline of the nest (see Fig. 6, and photograph in Raine 2007: 57). Dimensions of a typical nest were presented by Oniki and Willis (1983). Nests are typically placed 1.2–3.0m above the ground (Oniki and Willis 1983, Piratelli and Mello 2001, Snow 2004b, Raine 2007; GMK pers. obs.) and are heavily attached to the support branches using spiderwebs (GMK pers. obs.). Band-tailed Manakin generally selects understorey trees or shrubs in which to build its nest, once a *Theobroma cacao* (Malvaceae) tree (Oniki and Willis 1983). However, GMK has observed a nest of this species placed *c*.6m above the ground in northeast Peru (race *P. f. saturata*). Most nests examined by GMK (pers. obs.) have been situated where nearby live foliage provides a degree of shade for the incubating female and the young, and may also assist in preventing predation; however, other nests have been in more open situations (Raine 2007). Clutch size is the two eggs typical of all manakins; these are cream or whitish with streaks and blotches of brown or reddish-brown (Willis and Oniki 1983, de la Peña 1989, Raine 2007). Egg dimensions/mass were presented by de la Peña (1989) and Willis and Oniki (1983) but there are no data concerning incubation or fledging periods. Seasonality, however, is much better known. Raine (2007) found a February nest in southeast Peru and GMK (pers. obs.) a November nest in northeast Peru (San Martín), both with eggs. MVZ and FMNH have examples of both sexes in breeding condition (including females with eggs in the oviduct) from southeast Peru taken in December, and FMNH a male from the same general region taken in August. From northwest Bolivia (dpto. La Paz), FMNH has a female with an egg in the oviduct taken in late October. At the northernmost edge of the species' range, around Belém (Brazil), the species commences breeding in December (Pinto 1953, Willis and Oniki 1983). In southern Brazil, Oniki and Willis (1999) noted birds with brood patches in January–February and June–July in the Serra das Araras, in southwest Mato Grosso. Antas (2004) stated that the species breeds in July–November in the Pantanal, whilst Piratelli *et al.* (2000) and Piratelli and Mello (2001) reported breeding in August–November (with a smaller peak in April–May) at a locality in eastern Mato Grosso do Sul.

STATUS Like other members of the superspecies, Band-tailed Manakin is not considered threatened, being categorised as Least Concern (BirdLife International 2004, 2008) with an estimated range of 4,780,000km². Although the species' overall population is speculated to be declining, the nature of this is not suspected to be sufficient to trigger any threat levels. However, possible habitat loss as a result of projected levels of climate change was postulated to have the potential to very severely affect this species' population (Anciães and Peterson 2006). In southeast Peru, Terborgh *et al.* (1990) found densities of up to 45 individuals per 100ha at their study site, making Band-tailed Manakin the commonest piprid at Cocha Cashu. However, the species seems to be generally rare to uncommon in Paraguay (Hayes 1995) and Argentina (Saibene *et al.* 1996). It can also be very common at certain sites in Brazil, e.g. at a locality in Mato Grosso do Sul (Pina *et al.* 2005), but declines have, unsurprisingly, been noted in response to deforestation (Scherer Neto and Kajiwara 1997). In Brazil, which constitutes the bulk of the species' range, it is known from several conservation units, among them the mosaic of protected areas in the Serra das Carajás, Pará (Pacheco *et al.* 2007), Tapajós (Amazônia) National Park, Pará (Oren and Parker 1997), Parque Estadual Cantão, Tocantins (Pinheiro and Dornas 2009a), Chapada dos Guiramães National Park (Lopes *et al.* 2009) and Estação Ecológica Serra das Araras,

Mato Grosso (Silva and Oniki 1988), Parque Estadual do Morro do Diabo, São Paulo (Vasconcelos and Roos 2000) and Parque Estadual de Vila Rica do Espírito Santo, Paraná (Scherer Neto and Kajiwara 1997). Elsewhere, Band-tailed Manakin is known from conservation units in Argentina, namely Parque Nacional Iguazú (Saibene *et al.* 1996), Bolivia, e.g. Pilón Lajas Biosphere Reserve, La Paz (Hennessey *et al.* 2003a), Beni Biological Station, Beni (Brace *et al.* 1997), Estación Biológica Caparú (Vidoz *et al.* 2010) and Parque Nacional Noel Kempff Mercado, Santa Cruz (Bates *et al.* 1998), in Paraguay, e.g. San Rafael, Cerro Corá, Ybycuí, Serranía San Luis, and Caaguazú National Parks (Hayes and Scharf 1995a, 1995b, Madroño *et al.* 1997a, 1997b, Robbins *et al.* 1999), and in Peru, e.g. Tambopata Reserved Zone, and Manu National Park and Biosphere Reserve (Ridgely and Tudor 1994, Walker *et al.* 2006). A couple of the few localities where the species can be found in Argentina are the Posada Puerto Bemberg (Lowen 2010) and Parque Provincial Cruce Caballero (Bodrati *et al.* 2010).

REFERENCES Albano and Girão (2008), Aleixo and Guilherme (2010), Almeida *et al.* (2003), Alverson *et al.* (2001), Anciães and Peterson (2006, 2009), Antas (2004), Armacost (2006), Bates *et al.* (1989, 1998), Beebe (1915), BirdLife International (2004, 2008), Blake and Loiselle (2009), Bodrati *et al.* (2010), Boesman (2006a, 2009), Botêlho *et al.* (2003), Brace *et al.* (1997), Bueno *et al.* (2008), Chebez *et al.* (1999), Clay (2009), Dickinson (2003), Dunning (2008), Ferreira *et al.* (2008), Fry (1970), Graves (1981), Graves and Zusi (1990), Guilherme (2004), Guilherme and Santos (2009), Gyldenstolpe (1951), Haffer (1970, 1971, 1974, 1992b, 1997b, 2002), Hayes (1995), Hellmayr (1906d, 1908, 1910, 1929b), Hennessey *et al.* (2003a, 2003b), Hidasi (1998, 2007), Lane *et al.* (2003), Lopes *et al.* (2009), Lowen (2010), Lowen *et al.* (1996), Madroño *et al.* (1997a, 1997b), Maillard *et al.* (2007), Marantz and Zimmer (2006), Mazar Barnett and Pearman (2001), Mestre *et al.* (2010), Minns *et al.* (2009), Naumburg (1930), Novaes (1970), Oniki (1990), Oniki and Willis (1983, 1999), Oren and Parker (1997), Pacheco and Olmos (2010), Pacheco *et al.* (2007), Parker *et al.* (1982, 1994a, 1994b, 1994c), Parkes (1961), Paynter (1992), Pearce-Higgins *et al.* (2007), de la Peña (1989), Pina *et al.* (2005), Pinheiro and Dornas (2009a), Pinto (1944, 1953), Pinto and Camargo (1961), Piratelli and Blake (2006), Piratelli and Mello (2001), Piratelli and Pereira (2002), Piratelli *et al.* (2000), Prum (1990a), Raine (2007), Remsen and Traylor (1989), Ridgely and Tudor (1994, 2009), Robbins (1983, 1985), Robbins *et al.* (1999), Robinson and Terborgh (1997), Rodrigues *et al.* (2003), Rubio *et al.* (2003), Saibene *et al.* (1996), Santos and Silva (2005), Scherer Neto and Straube (1995), Scherer Neto and Kajiwara (1997), Scherer *et al.* (2001), Schulenberg *et al.* (2000, 2007), Sick (1967, 1993, 1997), Silva and Oniki (1988), Silva *et al.* (1990), Snethlage (1908a), Snow (2004b), Stotz *et al.* (1996, 1997), Tello (2001, 2003), Terborgh et al. (1990), Tubelis and Tomas (2003), Vasconcelos and Roos (2000), Vidoz *et al.* (2010), Walker *et al.* (2006), Whittaker (2009), Wiley (2010), Willis (1984), Willis and Oniki (1990, 1992), Zimmer (1936a), Zimmer *et al.* (1997).

1

2

Band-tailed Manakin *Pipra fasciicauda*. **Fig. 1**. Male, *P. f. scarlatina*, Vila Bela da Santíssima Trindade, Mato Grosso, Brazil, July (*William Price / www.pbase.com/tereksandpiper*). **Fig. 2**. Adult and immature male, *P. f. scarlatina*, Puerto Bemberg, prov. Misiones, northeast Argentina, September (*Emilio White*). These birds are at a lek; young males of most manakins attend leks but rarely get the chance to mate with females. **Fig. 3**. Male, *P. f. fasciicauda*, Explorer's Inn, Río Tambopata, dpto. Madre de Dios, southeast Peru, July (*Harvey van Diek*). This race is separable from *P. f. scarlatina* on the basis of its overall much yellower underparts and face, with many fewer reddish elements. **Fig. 4**. Male, *P. f. scarlatina*, Guaramiranga, Ceará, northeast Brazil, January (*Ciro Albano*). Despite being isolated in a few upland forest fragments of Alagoas and Ceará, the northeast Brazilian population of this species can be confidently ascribed to the subspecies *P. f. scarlatina* on plumage. Males of this form are highly variable in the amount of red feathering below (see text). **Fig. 5**. Male, *P. f. scarlatina*, Puerto Bemberg, prov. Misiones, northeast Argentina, April (*Emilio White*). Note the tail pattern. **Fig. 6**. Female, *P. f. scarlatina*, Guaramiranga, Ceará, northeast Brazil, February (*Ciro Albano*). The outer wall in the nest of this species is typically constructed predominantly of dead leaves. **Fig. 7**. Female, *P. f. scarlatina*, Baturité, Ceará, northeast Brazil, January (*Nick Athanas / Tropical Birding*).

WIRE-TAILED MANAKIN
Pipra filicauda   Plate 2

Pipra filicauda **Spix, 1825**, *Av. Bras.*, 2: 6, pl. 8, figs. 1, 2, São Paulo de Olivença, Rio Solimões, Brazil

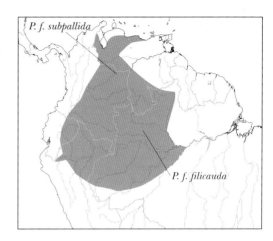

P. f. subpallida

P. f. filicauda

The strikingly beautiful Wire-tailed Manakin was for long placed in the monospecific genus *Teleonema*, e.g. by such influential authors as Hellmayr (1929b), Pinto (1944) and Gyldenstolpe (1951), primarily on the basis of its highly modified rectrices. Even earlier it had often been placed in the genus *Cirrhipipra* (e.g. by Chapman 1917), but Hellmayr (1929b) showed that Bonaparte's name lacked priority. However, Haffer (1970), who has been followed by all subsequent authors (e.g. Snow 1975, 1979b, Prum 1992, Dickinson 2003, Remsen *et al.* 2009), demonstrated that *Teleonema* should not be upheld because Wire-tailed Manakin obviously forms part of the *P. aureola* superspecies. Haffer based his proposal on the three species' largely similar plumage and virtually wholly allopatric ranges. Subsequent publications dealing with the ecology and natural history of Wire-tailed and Band-tailed Manakins have revealed that, even more tellingly, all three have generally analogous vocalisations and displays.

IDENTIFICATION 10.7–11.5cm (exclusive of the tail filaments, which measure up to 3.8–5.1cm in males and 2.5cm in females). Identification of either sex should prove very straightforward. See Band-tailed *P. fasciicauda* and Crimson-hooded Manakins *P. aureola* (both of which are marginally smaller) for known or potential overlap with those two species, which are the Wire-tailed Manakin's closest relatives. However, even those two species should be easily distinguished from either sex of Wire-tailed given reasonable views, as the present species' remarkable hair-like tail extensions, once seen, are unmistakable. Males are further characterised by having the cleanest yellow underparts, no white on the tail (unlike Band-tailed) and the palest red coloration, which is more or less confined to the crown and nape. Should the female's tail not be noticed or be obscured, her whitish eyes, yellowish belly and relatively large size, especially in combination, should offer safe identification features. Over much of this species' range relatively few other manakins share the same habitats with it, further decreasing the likelihood of confusion.

DISTRIBUTION Wire-tailed Manakin is the northwestern representative of the *P. aureola* superspecies. It ranges through humid parts of northern Venezuela, as far east as Miranda, somewhat discontinuously through the Coastal Cordillera and on both sides of the Andes to the Sierra de Perijá and Táchira, with a few scattered records from the *llanos*, including western Apure and Portuguesa to southern Cojedes (Hilty 2003), then across eastern Colombia, from Norte de Santander to Putumayo and Amazonas (Hilty and Brown 1986). Thereafter, Wire-tailed Manakin ranges across lowland eastern Ecuador (Ridgely and Greenfield 2001) and northeast Peru east of the Andes and south of the Amazon as far as the Ríos Yavarí and middle Ucayali (Alverson *et al.* 2001, Schulenberg *et al.* 2007, Wiley 2010). In adjacent western Brazil it reaches south of the Amazon to northwest Acre, at Cruzeiro do Sul (Novaes 1957), the headwaters of the Rio Juruá and the middle reaches of the Rio Purus, in Amazonas (Snethlage 1908a, Pinto 1944, Gyldenstolpe 1945, 1951), and north of the river east to the mouth of the Rio Negro. It also ranges north along the Rio

Branco into the state of Roraima (Hellmayr 1929b, Pinto 1966, Naka *et al.* 2006), and over southern and western Amazonas, Venezuela, as far north as Puerto Ayacucho (Hilty 2003). In terms of the species' elevational range, Wire-tailed Manakin is largely found below 300m, but ascends to 500m in Colombia (Hilty and Brown 1986), to 750m in Ecuador (Ridgely and Greenfield 2001), to 1,000m north of the Orinoco in Venezuela (Hilty 2003) and 1,148m in northern Peru (Brooks *et al.* 2009).

MOVEMENTS None known.

HABITAT Over much of lowland Amazonia the species is principally associated with *várzea* (seasonally flooded forests), including on river islands (e.g. the Anavilhanas archipelago in the upper Rio Negro). Nonetheless, it is at least occasionally found in *terra firme* forest, e.g. in Jaú National Park (Borges *et al.* 2001). However, elsewhere, e.g. in parts of eastern Colombia and northern Venezuela, its habitat preferences are less specialised. Nonetheless, even in these regions it prefers the vicinity of watercourses, in gallery woodland, tall second growth and even plantation-like areas, including old cocoa and coffee plantations, often with a relatively open understorey (Schwartz and Snow 1978, Hilty and Brown 1986, Hilty 2003, Snow 2004b, Verea and Solórzano 2005). In Amazonian Ecuador and Venezuela lek sites are closely correlated with open forest on low-lying ground that is seasonally inundated, and thus are usually close to rivers (Heindl 2002, Loiselle *et al.* 2007a).

DESCRIPTION The 'oddball' of the *P. aureola* superspecies on the basis of its uniquely adapted tail feathers: the bare shafts of the three outer pairs of rectrices project by about the same length as the main tail (or even slightly more than this) in the form of wire-like filaments, which curve outwards and downwards. This modification has a tactile function apparently unique in birds (see Display, and illustration in Schwartz and Snow 1978: 53). The wing feathers are slightly modified in males, in that the barbs of the secondaries are stiffened with thickened shafts. The bill has a reasonably arched culmen, but the tip is rarely strongly hooked, usually in males. The nominate race (but see Geographical Variation) is described here. *Adult male.* – The crown, nape and upper edge of the mantle are bright scarlet-red, contrasting beautifully with the pale bright yellow forehead, lores, head-sides, face and entire underparts as far as the undertail-coverts. Parts of the ear-coverts and flanks may appear slightly olive-yellow in the field. The rest of the upperparts are virtually entirely velvety black, with the exception of a white band across the inner flight feathers, which is rarely visible at rest but is obvious in flight (see photograph in Schwartz and Snow 1978: 52) and matches the same feature in other members of the superspecies. The underwing-coverts and tibial feathers are black. *Adult female.* – Largely uniform olive-green upperparts, with marginally browner wing feathers, contrasting slightly with the marginally paler and more yellow underparts, being palest on the throat and pale yellow over the belly, with olive-green undertail-coverts. Some grey elements also appear on the posterior underparts, as in other members of the superspecies. The tail filaments are similarly developed as in the male, but are distinctly shorter (see Identification). Like many other *Pipra* (and some other Pipridae genera), Schwartz and Snow (1978), Graves (1981), Heindl (2002) and Ryder and Durães (2005) noted the presence of scarlet feathers in the crown and nape of some adult females, and occasionally even a partial white wing patch. *Juvenile.* – Probably more or less identical to adult female plumage, except for the brownish irides and much less developed tail (Restall *et al.* 2006), but young birds are poorly described in the literature, as was plumage maturation until recently. *Moult.* – It is now known that the species requires three moults to reach fully adult plumage, and the same is likely to be true of other members of the superspecies and most other small manakins, given that this is the case for *Dixiphia* and one *Lepidothrix* species. Ryder and Durães (2005) found that the body feathers are replaced but not the rectrices or remiges, and moult limits are discernible in the coverts. Young males may acquire some signs of adult plumage, e.g. brighter yellow underparts, a yellowish band across the forehead, some scarlet feathers on the crown and white irides, by which time the tail filaments are almost as long as in the adult (Schwarz and Snow 1978). Restall *et al.* (2006) stated that red on the nape is developed later, and the second pre-basic moult occurs at the end of the first breeding season (*c.* 1 year later). At this point young males typically acquire a significant percentage of adult plumage and no longer show any moult limits in the wing-coverts. Adult moult has only been described in the 'grey literature' and we have seen no published data on patterns of feather replacement, although it is presumably similar to that in other *Pipra*. Reckardt (2000 *in* Heindl 2002) reported that in southern Venezuela the annual moult was completed during the wet season (April–November) prior to the onset of breeding (see below). In eastern Colombia, birds (of both sexes) have been recorded in body and/or wing moult in March, May, September and November (M. Gutiérrez and R. Parra/ProAves unpubl. data). *Hybrids.* – Several intriguing hybrids have been reported in the literature, two of them apparently inter-generic specimens. The first, *Pipra heterocerca*, P. L. Sclater, 1860 (*Proc. Zool. Soc. Lond.* 1860: 313), was described on the basis of a single specimen speculated to be from Pará, Brazil, which differed from *P. filicauda* in having the 'outer rectrices acuminate and produced; the second, third, and subsequent pairs in a less degree than the first; the outer pair exceeding the medial rectrices, which have nearly the ordinary normal form, by nearly half a inch; the crimson color extending lower down the back above, and pervading the breast and upper part of the belly.'

The type specimen, formerly in Paris, was subsequently destroyed (Haffer 2002). Parkes (1961) considered it to represent a hybrid (*Pipra filicauda* × *P. aureola* or *P. fasciicauda*), and Haffer (1970, 1974, 2002) regarded it as being a hybrid

Pipra filicauda × *P. aureola*. Secondly, Gyldenstolpe (1951: 241–242) described and depicted a most remarkable specimen taken at Redempção on the Rio Purus, apparently a male hybrid Wire-tailed Manakin × White-bearded Manakin *Manacus manacus*, as follows. *M. manacus* is apparently absent from this region. Gyldenstolpe reported:

> The shape of the tail and primaries is exactly what might be expected from a cross between these two genera. The beard and crest are typical *Manacus*, while the slender legs and short reddish toes are as in *Teleonema*. The yellow frontal band of the latter is suggested by its indistinct yellowish forehead. The entirely black wings, upper- and under tail-coverts are apparently inherited from *Teleonema*. Besides the characteristics already mentioned, the specimen in question differs from any of the members of the genus *Manacus* by reason of its long, forked tail, and by its differently-shaped primaries. […] Altogether it gives an abnormal impression. The absence of any trace of red in the plumage need not disturb us. Both yellow and red are lipochromes, the latter being merely a more specialized type.

A full description and measurements were also presented. Parkes (1961) endorsed Gyldenstolpe's conclusions. Most recently, Graves (1993) identified a hybrid male held at MECN (2748) as being a *Dixiphia pipra* (White-crowned Manakin) × *P. filicauda* cross. The bird was collected at a locality in prov. Pastaza, eastern Ecuador. Photographs of the specimen were published therein (Graves 1993: 437) illustrating its most striking (and diagnostic) characters, namely the golden-yellow crown and nape, the yellow-and-black mottled underparts, dark face patch, glossy black mantle, wings and tail, and shallowly forked tail (11mm). The bird has broadly rounded central rectrices with tapered outer ones, but no rachi extensions. We too have examined this specimen and concur with Graves' analysis. *Bare parts.* – The irides are white or nearly white in adult males (but see Geographical Variation) and at least in some females, but some adult females have darker (beige-coloured) irides (INPA). The bill is usually blackish with slightly paler cutting edges, or dark brown over the maxilla with a marginally paler mandible, and the legs and feet are sooty-reddish or rose-grey, generally rather dark, with paler, pinker soles (Snow 2004b; INPA).

MEASUREMENTS *P. f. filicauda* (CUMZ; INPA; MNRJ: Amazonian Brazil, southern Venezuela): wing of male (*n* = 7) 62.0–66.5mm, wing of female (*n* = 3) 62.5–69.5mm; tail of male (*n* = 7) 73–98mm, tail of female (*n* = 3) 38–48mm; bill of male (*n* = 7) 11.45–12.76mm, bill of female (*n* = 3) 11.91–13.08mm; tarsus of male (*n* = 2) 16.91–18.80mm, tarsus of female (*n* = 1) 17.25mm. Tail measurements include the filaments. Live birds: *P. f. subpallida* (M. Gutiérrez and R. Parra/ProAves unpubl. data): wing of male (*n*=6) 61–69mm, wing of female (*n* = 11) 56–65mm; tail of male (*n* = 5) 68.5–71.5mm, tail of female (*n*=11) 42–75mm; bill of male (*n* = 6) 8.5–11.6mm, bill of female (*n* = 11) 7.8–11.9mm; tarsus of male (*n* = 6) 16.0–18.9mm, tarsus of female (*n* = 9) 15.0–18.5mm. Gyldenstolpe (1945, 1951) and Graves (1993) presented additional mensural data for specimens, whilst Ryder and Durães (2005) did the same for live birds. Weight: 11.0–14.5g (males), 13.6–20.0g (females) (Hilty 2003, Snow 2004b, Ryder and Durães 2005, Dunning 2008; FMNH; INPA; MVZ; M. Gutiérrez and R. Parra/ProAves unpubl. data). Loiselle *et al.* (2007a) listed the mean weight as 15.2g.

GEOGRAPHICAL VARIATION Probably best treated as monotypic. Birds from coastal Venezuela, in Carabobo, Lara and Zulia, were described as *P. f. subpallida*, Todd, 1928 (*Proc. Biol. Soc. Wash.* 41: 112), and this race is now considered to occupy that part of the range between Miranda, Venezuela, and eastern Colombia (Snow 2004b). Although many authors have upheld this race, it is known to intergrade with the nominate race around the Colombia/Ecuador border, and it is considered 'very like nominate but slightly paler' (Snow 2004b). But, this on average slightly larger race was subsumed within *P. f. filicauda* already by Hellmayr (1929b), a decision supported cautiously by Gyldenstolpe (1951), who also noted the extensive individual variation in western Brazil specimens. Other features used in its description (the depth of the yellow coloration of the rear underparts, and the colour of the tibial feathering) appear to reflect individual variation. It is also worth mentioning that Phelps (1944) considered that males taken in the Serranía de Perijá, on the Venezuela/Colombia border, are much darker on the throat and breast, less lemon-yellow, than birds from Carabobo and Miranda, Venezuela. However, note that Restall *et al.* (2006) upheld *P. f. subpallida* based on a presumably extensive sample of specimens of both forms, albeit solely from Venezuela. They considered *subpallida* to have the three outermost rectrices gently (rather than steeply) graduated (a feature first noted by Schwartz and Snow 1978), more intense yellow on the underparts, black (rather than olive-green) thighs, pale brown (rather than white) irides, and black legs and feet. The issue of geographical variation in this species clearly demands further consideration.

VOICE The species' vocalisations and mechanical sounds are strongly analogous to those of the other two members of the superspecies (see, in particular, Band-tailed Manakin). Wire-tailed Manakin is generally quiet away from leks, and the advertising call is a downward-inflected, nasal and drawn-out *eeeeeeeeeaaa* or *eeeeeeu* (lasting *c.*0.25 seconds), with a somewhat hard quality but is not loud (Schwartz and Snow 1978, Hilty and Brown 1986, Ridgely and Greenfield 2001, Hilty 2003, Snow 2004b). Although this vocalisation can be given very infrequently, it is frequently answered immediately by another territorial male, the two calls sometimes overlapping (Schwartz and Snow 1978). It serves to signal that a territory is occupied and is given with the head held up and the throat feathers puffed-out, but the bill closed. Other calls include a short *eeeo* given when a male in swoop-in flight passes the main perch (termed the pass-by call), a more prolonged *eeeooo* when the bird does land on the main perch (the culminating call) and a short, upward-inflected *swee* whistle, with the bill slightly open but not held up, during competition for a display area. Schwartz and Snow (1978) consider this latter to be perhaps the most frequently heard call at leks, especially during displays. The appeasement whistle is a more prolonged *sweeee*, which indicates a lack of aggression, but neither of these last two calls lasts more than 0.5 seconds. Appeasement whistles may be more prolonged in the presence of females, but both longer and shorter such whistles may be given to encourage other males to display with a calling male. Females also give these soft whistles, including sometimes at the lek but also around the nest. Fledglings in the nest gave what Schwartz and Snow described as a 'scratchy whistle' when handled. Schwartz and Snow (1978) were also seemingly the first to describe the species' mechanical sounds, a very low-pitched *kloop*, given at the lowest point during the display-flight, and a sharp but low-intensity *klok*, which is made in terminating

the same flight. The latter was likened to a tongue-clicking sound by its describers. Both are apparently made using the wings. Schwartz and Snow (1978) published sonograms of some of the Wire-tailed Manakin's vocalisations. The species' vocalisations have been presented on the following commercially available audio compilations: Moore (1993), Boesman (1999, 2006a, 2006b, 2009) and Krabbe and Nilsson (2003), and examples from Ecuador and Peru have been archived online at www.xeno-canto.org.

NATURAL HISTORY Generally quiet and easily overlooked away from the species' leks. Blake and Loiselle (2008) published data on annual survival rates for this species in eastern Ecuador, and the same authors (and co-workers) found that males participating at a given lek are not more closely related than would be expected based on chance (Loiselle *et al.* 2007c).

FOOD AND FEEDING Like others of the genus *Pipra*, this species feeds solely on small fruits and insects but specific details of its diet seem to be very few (Snow 2004b). Loiselle *et al.* (2007b) mentioned that their analysis of faecal samples in eastern Ecuador had produced records of 33 plant species in the diet of Wire-tailed Manakin, but did not list them. However, all of the manakins sampled by the latter study showed some preference for fruits of the following genera: *Anthurium* and *Philodendron* (Araceae), *Coussapoa* and *Cecropia* (Cecropiaceae), *Miconia* and *Henriettea* (Melastomataceae), *Besleria* (Gesneriaceae) and *Ficus* (Moraceae). Hilty (2003) also mentioned a preference for *Ficus* spp., based on non-systematic observations, and Blendinger *et al.* (2009) noted that Wire-tailed Manakin is one of the few avian frugivores in eastern Ecuador to take the fruits of *Miconia fosteri* and *M. serrulata* (Melastomataceae). It performs short-range sally-hovers at least when taking fruit (Hilty 2003).

DISPLAY Described by Schwartz and Snow (1978) and since studied in much greater detail by Heindl (2002), Heindl and Winkler (2003a, 2003b) and Ryder *et al.* (2008a, 2008b, 2009, 2010), based on work in southern Venezuela and Amazonian Ecuador. Leks are 'exploded' like others of the superspecies, with each male's territory being widely spaced, defending an area of *c.*40m in diameter and 10–15m between the borders of each territory (Ryder *et al.* 2010). At their study sites in eastern Ecuador, Loiselle *et al.* (2007a) found 2–12 males at each lek site and that each one measured *c.*3,000 to 16,500m², with 300m between different leks. However, in a second publication, the same authors also mentioned a lek attended by as many as 19 males (Loiselle *et al.* 2007c). Heindl (2002) found that in southern Venezuela leks average 1.1ha in size (range 0.3–1.8ha), but are more widely separated, usually by several kilometres. Individual territories are separated by 10–42m and thus only in auditory contact, and can each measure 10–60m in diameter. Display perches are 1.4–3.5m above the ground, and usually close to horizontal. In this region at least, activity at leks is most pronounced between 06.30 and 10.30 hours and 13.00 and 16.30 hours. Male display seems to be more prevalent during sunny conditions (Heindl and Winkler 2003a). The latter authors also determined that Wire-tailed Manakins usually display within shady sites, thereby reducing their conspicuousness at longer distances (an anti-predator device), whilst maximising the visual contrast of their plumage colours at close range.

As in Band-tailed Manakin, there is an obvious hierarchy amongst males, from immature males (which visit leks), through adult males without territories and territorial males, to the highest category, territory-owners, which spend the greater part of the time within their territory (Heindl 2002).

Ryder *et al.* (2008b, 2011) further refined this social network in an effort to understand how the coordinated male–male displays that have evolved in the *P. aureola* superspecies fit within the continuum of courtship-related behaviour in Pipridae. One of the results of their study was the finding that territory ownership was, indeed, the most reliable predictor of mating success and that the likelihood of siring offspring increased dramatically with time spent as a territory-owner. Ryder and his colleagues also noted that, while all males acquire social affiliations to both territorial and non-territorial males, those that acquire and maintain more of these connections are more likely to ascend the hierarchy; these birds effectively act as 'social hubs'. It is possible that successful dominance interactions with non-territorial birds could be contributory to this process, especially if it enables relationships with territory-holders. Their data show that coalitions were most often formed between males of different status and that the presence of coalition partners increased a male's display rate via social facilitation. Display coalitions were non-random and varied in stability with male age. And, while birds can establish new territories, relationships with territorial individuals are an essential prerequisite for inheritance because most males acquire territories via a social partnership. However, in terms of copulations it is possible that the hierarchy is only fully functional within a territory, and Heindl (2002) postulated that coordinated displays in this species may lack an obvious beneficiary among the two males, but could ultimately signal the right to inherit the territory. The skew in copulations noted in some other manakins, especially *Chiroxiphia*, is far less pronounced in *P. filicauda*. This indicates that males other than territory-owners are far from being at a complete disadvantage (Ryder *et al.* 2009) and further emphasises the very complex social network at play in this species (Ryder *et al.* 2008b). Unlike in *P. fasciicauda*, Heindl (2002) found that strong associations with so-called beta males were distinctly less common and of shorter duration in Wire-tailed Manakin. Thus, the majority of coordinated displays observed in his study were between the territory-owner and a visiting non-territorial male.

Schwartz and Snow (1978) provided the first description of the male's display behaviours, which can be categorised as follows. As with the species' vocalisations, many of these are strongly analogous to those of the other members of the *P. aureola* complex, especially the better known *P. fasciicauda* (which see). The mechanical-looking *side-to-side jump* consists of a series of jumps sideways over 8–10cm then back again, which serves as an invitation to other males to display with a territory-owner, and calls frequently punctuate the display. The *stationary* display consists of the territory-owner vibrating and drooping the wings while holding the head downwards, the tail horizontal, and raising the back and rump feathers slightly. It is adopted during other displays or prior to them, and seems to signal 'frustration' at the reticence of another male to display. The *butterfly flight* is a relatively slow, deliberate, near-level flight designed to show the white wingbar to best advantage, with or without a terminating *klok* and usually over 2–6m. The *twist* display nearly always involves two birds, one of which is active and the other passive. It commences with the stationary display, with the displaying male facing away from the passive individual, following which the first-named bird tilts its body further downwards and commences to twist the tail from side to side, increasing the tempo with time, during which the observing bird shuffles towards the

other male until the tail filaments are brushing its face and throat. Usually one of the main perches is selected for this display and in well-coordinated displays the birds take turns to assume the passive and active roles. However, should the partners include a less experienced (or immature) bird the display will often 'break down'. Immature males may 'nip' the displaying bird's tail with the bill, but adults rarely exhibit such behaviour. The twist display also forms an extremely important part of courtship, with the male sometimes performing this ritual for several minutes in the presence of adult females on the main display-perch. As with Band-tailed Manakin (which see), male *P. filicauda* uses a combination of displays to 'coax' a visiting female to arrive at the main perch, but once there he will concentrate on using the twist and a variant thereof, the *tail-up-freeze*, with an occasional butterfly flight to 'woo' her. What Schwartz and Snow (1978) termed the *breakaway* consists of a sudden departure from the display-perch in which the bird rapidly turns around during its descent and which is sometimes accompanied by a loud wing-snap. The *swoop-in flight* is performed as in Band-tailed Manakin, and is accompanied by very similar mechanical sounds (see also Voice). This display is usually directed at a partner, either male or female. The initiator performs a level or slightly upwards flight of 10–15m to another branch, which it barely touches before returning, swooping low uttering a *kloop* (during which the white wing patch is more visible) and giving the pass-by call if it lands on a perch near to the start branch or the culminating call if landing on the same perch. The partner may also fly to the nearby perch as the first bird is landing on it, but regardless of this they both return to the main perch to recommence the display, with the passive partner in the previous display now performing the swoop-in flight. If the partner is 'reticent', the territory-owner or display's initiator may perform the stationary display or side-to-side jumps. Bouts of this display may last as long as 15–20 minutes, especially in a well-coordinated partnership. Finally, the *flutter* display, which is also observed in Band-tailed Manakin, consists of the bird appearing as if to lose its balance on the perch and is accompanied by rapid wing flapping; it presumably serves an identical purpose to the analogous movement in *P. fasciicauda*. This display is sometimes given following a swoop-in flight. Although Schwartz and Snow (1978) did not describe such flights as separate display behaviour, Wire-tailed Manakin also performs *short flights* between display-perches 0.6–6.0m apart, each terminating with a *klok* sound.

In terms of choice of mates, Ryder *et al.* (2010) revealed that females select more heterozygous males as their partners. However, females do not appear to select their mates based on genetic dissimilarity, because Ryder and his team found that 'pairs' were more related than would have been expected if mating was totally random. Heterozygosity of territorial males was correlated with two morphological traits (wing and tarsus length), suggesting that females assess male genetic quality using phenotypic characters. The study also revealed that heterozygosity was related to male social rise (territory acquisition) and suggests that heterozygosity may act as a filter of male reproductive potential.

BREEDING This aspect of the species' life history is not particularly well known, with for instance as yet no information on fledging or incubation periods. However, recent work in eastern Ecuador has substantially increased our knowledge. As with all other *Pipra*, the females are entirely responsible for building the nest, incubating the eggs and tending the young. Nests are very often (but far from exclusively) sited close to or overhanging streams, seasonal or permanent (Schwartz and Snow 1978, Hidalgo *et al.* 2008) and they are usually placed in a horizontal fork of an understorey tree or shrub, 2–4m above the ground (range 0.9–8.4m in eastern Ecuador: Hidalgo *et al.* 2008). The nest is a shallow open-cup affair typical among Pipridae, constructed externally largely of dead leaves with some live moss, and lined with dark rhizomorphs, bound together and to the support plant with spiderwebs. At least in eastern Ecuador, the nest usually lacks any 'tail' of dead leaves or other detritus below it. In their detailed east Ecuadorian study, during which they located >70 nests of Wire-tailed Manakin, Hidalgo *et al.* (2008) noted that the species often selects a rather open understorey dominated by *Rinorea* (Violaceae) treelets in which to nest. In their study support plants for nests included *Rinorea viridifolia, R. lindeniana* and *R. apiculata,* as well as *Psychotria, Rudgea* and *Ixora* (Rubiaceae), *Sorocea* (Moraceae) and *Neea* spp. (Nyctaginaceae). The same authors presented a detailed series of dimensions for their nests. Compared with the smaller *Pipra, Dixiphia* and *Lepidothrix* species, the nest of Wire-tailed Manakin is slightly larger, although not necessarily deeper overall. As in other manakins, the clutch is of two eggs (illustrated in Hidalgo *et al.* 2008: 59). Colour photographs provided by T. B. Ryder show the eggs to be pale whitish with brown and slightly reddish-brown markings, which are obviously heaviest at the larger end. As in Blue-crowned Manakin *Lepidothrix coronata,* Ryder *et al.* (2008a) discovered that this manakin is subject to nearly astonishing rates of predation; thus of 61 nests monitored, 84% failed. Females may give a type of fluttering distraction display when their nest is discovered, at least in the presence of human observers (Schwartz and Snow 1978). In northern Venezuela, the breeding season is considered to be mid April–mid July (Schwartz and Snow 1978), although display persists into other months, but in the south of the country breeding activity increases between November and mid March (Heindl 2002). In southern Colombia a female with a begging young was observed in November (J. V. Remsen *in* Hilty and Brown 1986) and a male in breeding condition was collected in July in the north (M. A. Carriker *in* Hilty and Brown 1986). A male in breeding condition was collected in eastern Ecuador (Napo province) in February (FMNH). There are very few nesting data available from Brazil or Peru, but a male collected in October on the Rio Negro, Amazonas, was in breeding condition (MNRJ) while four (both sexes) from northeast Peru in July–September were not (MVZ).

STATUS Wire-tailed Manakin is considered Least Concern by BirdLife International (2004, 2008) given that its population is apparently stable and its known range is very large (*c.*2,610,000km²). Indeed, the species can be locally abundant, e.g. along the Rios Juruá and Purus, in western Brazil (Gyldenstolpe 1945, 1951), and on the Anavilhanas archipelago at the mouth of the Rio Negro, also in Brazil (Cintra *et al.* 2007). However, at the relatively nearby Jaú National Park, Wire-tailed Manakin is considered rare (Borges *et al.* 2001). Blake and Loiselle (2009) also found Wire-tailed Manakin to be locally abundant in parts of eastern Ecuador, as did Cherrie (1916) in western Amazonas, Venezuela. *P. filicauda* is known from the following protected areas: Jaú National Park, Brazil (Borges *et al.* 2001), Tinigua National Park and Amacayacu National Park, both Colombia (Cadena *et al.* 2000, Snow 2004b) and Yasuní Biosphere Reserve (Ridgely and Greenfield 2001) and Cuyabeno Faunal Reserve (Ecuador) (Williams *et al.* 1997).

REFERENCES Alverson *et al.* (2001), Anciães and Peterson (2006, 2009), Anon. (1982), Blake (1962), BirdLife International (2004, 2008), Blake and Loiselle (2008, 2009), Blendinger *et al.* (2009), Boesman (1999, 2006a, 2006b, 2009), Borges *et al.* (2001, 2007), Brooks *et al.* (2009), Cadena *et al.* (2000), Chapman (1917), Cherrie (1916), Cintra *et al.* (2007), Clay (2009), Dickinson (2003), Dugand and Phelps (1946), Friedmann (1948), Graves (1981, 1993), Gyldenstolpe (1945, 1951), Haffer (1970, 1974, 1992b, 1997b, 2002), Heindl (2002), Heindl and Winkler (2003a, 2003b), Hellmayr (1906d, 1929b), Hidalgo *et al.* (2008), Hilty (2003), Hilty and Brown (1986), Krabbe and Nilsson (2003), Lane *et al.* (2003), Loiselle (2007a, 2007b, 2007c), Meyer de Schauensee and Phelps (1978), Moore (1993), Naka *et al.* (2006), Novaes (1957), Parker *et al.* (1982), Parkes (1961), Phelps (1944), Pinto (1944, 1966), Prum (1990a), Remsen *et al.* (2009), Restall *et al.* (2006), Ridgely and Greenfield (2001), Ridgely and Tudor (1994, 2009), Robbins (1985), Ryder and Durães (2005), Ryder *et al.* (2008a, 2008b, 2009, 2010, 2011), Salaman *et al.* (2008, 2009), Schubart *et al.* (1965), Schulenberg *et al.* (2007), Schwartz and Snow (1978), Sick (1967, 1993, 1997), Snethlage (1908a), Snow (1975, 2004b), Stotz *et al.* (1996), Tello (2001), Verea and Solórzano (2005), Wiley (2010), Williams *et al.* (1997).

Wire-tailed Manakin *Pipra filicauda.* **Figs. 1–2**. Male, *P. f. filicauda,* Shiripuno Lodge, prov. Pastaza, eastern Ecuador, November (*Hadoram Shirihai / Photographic Handbook to Birds of the World*). One of the most immediately recognisable of all manakins!

GOLDEN-HEADED MANAKIN
Pipra erythrocephala   Plate 3

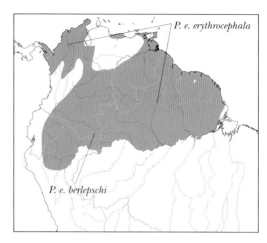

[*Parus*] *erythrocephala* **Linnaeus, 1758**, *Syst. Nat.*, 10th edn., 1: 191, based on Edwards, *Nat. Hist. Birds* 1: 21, America australi [= Surinam]

Arguably one of the easiest manakins to see, Golden-headed Manakin is very widespread in northern South America. It is the only member of its superspecies to have a yellow rather than red head, making males usually identifiable with ease.

IDENTIFICATION 7.5–10.0cm. Male should be immediately recognised, given a good view, by virtue of its bright yellow head and otherwise all-black plumage, and tiny size. No other small manakin in range has a golden-yellow head. Females, not seen in the company of the distinctive male, will be harder to identify, but close attention to bare-parts colorations in particular should permit identification in most instances under which reasonable views are obtained. In western Panama, on the country's Pacific slope, and at one locality (Mutatá) in northwest Colombia (Haffer 1967b), this species overlaps with Red-capped Manakin *P. mentalis*, e.g. on the Río Chepo (Griscom 1933) and at Majé on the Río Bayano, in eastern Panama province (Ridgely and Gwynne 1976). However, the latter species always has a dark bill and legs, as well as a marginally longer tail, and at least some possess obviously yellow thighs. In addition, female *P. erythrocephala* is generally duller and dingier plumaged than female Blue-crowned Manakin *Lepidothrix coronata* (which see), with which there is rather substantial overlap in range, but is easier to separate from female Blue-rumped Manakin *L. isidorei*, which displays reasonably marked contrast between the crown, mantle, rump and tail, unlike the uniformly patterned upperparts of the present species. In many parts of the Golden-headed Manakin's range, *L. isidorei* is absent making this species even less of a problem. More or less equally widespread, however, female White-crowned Manakin *Dixiphia pipra* should be distinguished more easily than *L. coronata* or *P. mentalis* at least, due to its generally grey head (a field mark that is usually obvious) and red irides. In a tiny area of northern Peru, south of the Marañón, this species comes into contact with another congeneric, Round-tailed Manakin *P. chloromeros*. Males of the latter, being red-headed, are again straightforward to distinguish, but female *P. chloromeros* will require more careful separation, based on the slightly crested appearance and, especially, on the slightly graduated tail shape of the latter. Finally, in parts of the Guianan Shield, from southern Venezuela to northern Brazil east of the Rio Negro and the Guianas, confusion with White-throated Manakin *Corapipo gutturalis* is perhaps possible for the inexperienced, but the latter appears if anything even smaller and slighter, lacks any real yellowish tones on the underparts and has a slightly greyish-toned throat.

DISTRIBUTION Golden-headed Manakin is widespread north of the Amazon in South America, with a small extension of its range into southernmost Central America, and is also present on Trinidad. In Central America, *P. erythrocephala* is solely found in Panama, where it occurs south of the Canal Zone, from eastern Panama (from Chepo) and eastern San Blas provinces (from the Bahía Caledonia) through the Darién. Thereafter, Golden-headed Manakin reappears in Colombia on the Pacific coast south to the middle Atrato Valley (although it is generally replaced in the wettest forests on this slope by *P. mentalis*) and thence east through the humid lowlands north of the Andes to the lower and middle Magdalena Valley as far as Tolima, as well as at the northern base of the Sierra Nevada de Santa Marta, and in the Perijá Mountains, and throughout the eastern lowlands of Colombia (Hilty and Brown 1986) and all of Amazonian Ecuador (Ridgely and Greenfield 2001) to northern Peru, where the species occurs throughout the eastern lowlands north of the Río Marañón, and also creeps south of it as far as the northern slopes of the Cordillera Azul, in San Martín (Schulenberg *et al.* 2007). From here, Golden-headed Manakin is found throughout northern Brazil, i.e. north of the Amazon, as far as Amapá, thence through the Guianas, where *P. erythrocephala* is generally very common and widespread in French Guiana (Tostain *et al.* 1992), Surinam (Ottema *et al.* 2009) and Guyana (Snyder 1966, Braun *et al.* 2007), and in Venezuela, where it is found virtually throughout Bolívar and Amazonas states, south of the Orinoco River, but is decidedly more uncommon north of the latter river, being locally found in Delta Amacuro and on the Paria Peninsula to western Sucre, as well as in the northern cordilleras from Miranda to western Carabobo (e.g. at Palmichal), and then reappearing in the Andes, from northwest Barinas to northern Táchira on the east slope, and from Trujillo to Mérida in the west, and on the Venezuelan side of the Sierra de Perijá (Phelps 1944, Meyer de Schauensee and Phelps 1978, Hilty 2003). It is very common and widespread on Trinidad, but there are no records from Tobago (Kenefick *et al.* 2007). Overall, the species is recorded from sea level to *c.*2,000m, the latter elevation being reached in southern Venezuela (Hilty 2003), but in Panama it does not seem to reach above 1,200m (Angehr and Dean 2010) and elsewhere in South America it is generally restricted to elevations below this (Stotz *et al.* 1996, Ridgely and Greenfield 2001, Salaman *et al.* 2002a) though it reaches 1,500m in the Sierra Nevada de Santa Marta, Colombia (Todd and Carriker 1922), 1,450m on the east slope of the Andes in Colombia (Salaman *et al.* 2002) and 1,350m in northern Peru (Schulenberg *et al.* 2007) and on the Serranía de los Yariguíes, Santander, Colombia (Donegan *et al.* 2010).

MOVEMENTS No altitudinal or seasonal migrations have been recorded to date, and adults are highly sedentary during the breeding season. Strong site fidelity was noted for this species on Trinidad by Snow and Lill (1974).

However, post-breeding when adults are moulting, radio-tracking studies (in French Guiana) have revealed that they are capable of moving over several hundred hectares (Théry 1990c) with a young male recorded wandering over 22.7ha.

HABITAT Principally inhabits humid forest including tall *terra firme*, as well as more open second-growth woodland, gallery forest in the Gran Sabana and Roraima, Brazil, and sandy-belt forest elsewhere in southern Venezuela (Hilty 2003, Santos and Silva 2007), *campinaranas* in northern Brazil (Borges *et al.* 2001), but also hill forest on the tepuis and locally in the northern Andes and the Venezuelan Coastal Cordillera. It regularly visits forest borders and clearings, especially where there are fruiting trees, and the species is capable of using shade-coffee plantations (Jones *et al.* 2002) and cacao plantations, the latter at least seasonally (Verea and Solórzano 2005).

DESCRIPTION A relatively typical tiny, short-tailed *Pipra* manakin. Both sexes have the outer primaries emarginated and very pointed. The nominate race is described here. *Adult male.* – The entire crown, head-sides and hindneck are bright golden or orange-yellow, becoming darkest on the head-sides and hindneck, and often with a line of orange-red at the base of the hindneck of varying width, but this is generally reasonably broad in birds of the Guianan Shield. Most of the rest of the bird's plumage is glossy black, sometimes with a slight hint of bluish, e.g. on the wings and breast, with more dusky-coloured undersides to the wing feathers and greyish-black axillaries and underwing-coverts. The tibia feathers are white, becoming scarlet-red on the lower outer part (see Display). *Adult female.* – Can be very variable. The upperparts are entirely dull olive-green, becoming dusky-grey over the wings and tail, the feathers of which still possess olive-green fringes. The foreneck and lower breast are pale olive, becoming yellowish-olive over the lower belly and undertail-coverts, whilst the axillaries, underwing-coverts and inner webs of the primaries and secondaries are all yellowish-white. Some (presumably older) adult females possess a few scattered bright yellow feathers on the hindneck (Snow 1962b, Wetmore 1972), but this condition appears to be quite rare (we have not examined any such specimens) and is usually difficult to detect (Graves 1981). *Juvenile.* – Considered inseparable from adult females (Snow 2004b) but immature males gradually acquire male-like plumage, as well as having yellowish irides (Wetmore 1972). *Hybrids.* – There is apparently a record of a hybrid Golden-headed × Red-capped Manakin from the Pacific slope in Panama (J. Strauch *in* Ridgely and Gwynne 1976) but no additional details appear to have been published (see also Haffer 1975). '*Manacus coronatus*' (originally '*Chiromachaeris coronata*'), a name based on a specimen from 'Bogotá', was already noted by Hellmayr (1929b: 75) to be very probably a hybrid between Golden-headed Manakin and White-bearded Manakin *M. manacus*. Sibley (1957) and Parkes (1961) seconded this view. *Moult.* – Few detailed data, but in southern Venezuela (Amazonas state), Willard *et al.* (1991) found that most specimens collected between February and March were not moulting, except one in wing moult and two in body moult in early March. *Bare parts.* – The irides are white in males but dark to mouse brown or grey in females and young, whilst the bill is sometimes all-yellow in males, but in others the maxilla is dark to pale brown, with a pale brown to yellowish or whitish mandible, and the legs, feet and claws are pinkish- or reddish-brown to pale brown or even whitish (Junge and Mees 1958, Wetmore 1972, Ridgely and Gwynne 1976, Novaes 1978, Robbins *et al.* 1985, Ouellet 1990, Willard *et al.* 1991).

MEASUREMENTS (CUMZ; MNRJ; RMNH: Amapá and Amazonas, Brazil; Guyana; Surinam) *P. e. erythrocephala*: wing of male (*n* = 29) 53.5–60.0mm, wing of female (*n* = 23) 54.0–60.5mm; tail of male (*n* = 27) 18.5–26.0mm, tail of female (*n* = 23) 20.5–30.0mm; bill of male (*n* = 29) 9.91–11.61mm, bill of female (*n* = 23) 11.16–12.55mm; tarsus of male (*n* – 7) 13.51–15.72mm, tarsus of female (*n* = 8) 12.64–14.43mm. Wetmore (1972: eastern Panama) found: wing of male (*n* = 10) 56.0–58.5mm, wing of female (*n* = 10) 57.5–59.5mm; tail of male (*n* = 10) 17.0–19.5mm, tail of female (*n* = 10) 19.5–21.0mm; bill of male (*n* = 10) 9.9–11.3mm, bill of female (*n* = 10) 10–12mm; tarsus of male (*n* = 10) 13.5–14.9mm, tarsus of female (*n* = 10) 14–15mm. *P. e. berlepschi* (Colombia and Ecuador: RMNH; ZMA): wing of male (*n* = 2) 57.0–61.5mm; tail of male (*n* = 2) 23–26mm; bill of male (*n* = 2) 10.46–10.49mm; tarsus of male (*n* = 1) 14.23mm. Live birds, but note probable variation in culmen measurement protocols (*P. e. berlepschi*): wing of male (*n* = 108) 51–62mm, wing of female (*n* = 158) 53–61mm; tail of male (*n* = 91) 17.0–34.5mm, tail of female (*n* = 142) 17.5–33.5mm; bill of male (*n* = 83) 7.7–13.5mm, bill of female (*n* = 144) 6.7–14.1mm; tarsus of male (*n* = 97) 12.6–18.8mm, tarsus of female (*n* = 144) 12.5–18.9mm (Colombia: A. Ayala V., P. Castañeda, M. Gutiérrez, C. F. Londoño, J. C. Luna, E. Machado, J. Medina, C. Olaciregui, R. Parra, A. Quevedo, B. Ramirez, D. Y. Ramírez, R. Reinosa, J. M. Ruiz, C. E. Ureña and D. M. Velasco/ProAves unpubl. data). For other measurements see Friedmann (1948), Junge and Mees (1958), Pinto (1966) and Graves (1993). Weight (most values pertain to *P. e. erythrocephala*): 10.0–13.5g (*n* = 13 males from eastern Panama), 10.2–15.0g (*n* = 47 males from Venezuela), 11.0–13.5g (*n* = 7 males from Trinidad), 9.0–13.8g (*n* = 13 males from Surinam), 9.5–12.5g (*n* = 4 males from French Guiana), 12–13g (*n* = 2 males from Brazil); 10–14g (*n* = 36 females from eastern Panama), 11.8–17.2g (*n* = 18 females from Venezuela), 11.5–14.5g (*n* = 4 females from Trinidad), 10.8g (*n* = 1 female from Surinam), 11.8–14.5g (*n* = 6 females from French Guiana), 13–14g (*n* = 4 females from Brazil); 9.0–16.5g (males) and 8.0–19.3g (females) (*P. e. berlepschi*: Colombia and Peru) (Haverschmidt 1952, Junge and Mees 1958, Burton 1975, Dick *et al.* 1984, Robbins *et al.* 1985, Willard *et al.* 1991, Verea *et al.* 1999, Pérez-Emán *et al.* 2003, Snow 2004b, Dunning 2008; FMNH; MNRJ; MVZ; RMNH; A. Ayala V., P. Castañeda, M. Gutiérrez, C. F. Londoño, J. C. Luna, E. Machado, J. Medina, C. Olaciregui, R. Parra, A. Quevedo, B. Ramirez, D. Y. Ramírez, R. Reinosa, J. M. Ruiz, C. E. Ureña and D. M. Velasco/ProAves unpubl. data).

GEOGRAPHICAL VARIATION Polytypic; three subspecies are frequently recognised (Dickinson 2003), but we concur with Wetmore (1972) and Snow (2004b) that recognition of *P. e. flammiceps* for eastern Colombian populations seems unnecessary. Nominate *P. e. erythrocephala* (described above, including *P. e. actinosa*, Bangs and Barbour, 1922, and *P. e. flavissima*, Junge and Mees, 1958) ranges from eastern Panama across northern Colombia, Venezuela, the Guianas and Brazil north of the Amazon and east of the Rio Negro, but appears to intergrade with *P. e. berlepschi* in the upper regions of the latter river (Hellmayr 1929b), although Pinto (1944) considered Tonantins (02°47'S, 67°47'W), on the north bank of the Rio Solimões, to be the only certain locality for the latter subspecies in Brazil. Not accepted as valid herein, the range of *P. e. flammiceps* Todd, 1919, is defined as eastern Colombia. It was tentatively upheld, e.g. by Hellmayr (1929b), on the basis of it being slightly smaller, with a strongly orange-coloured hindneck and head-sides, but no distinct red posterior border to the cap. However, as already admitted by Hellmayr (1929b), the plumage features he used to delimit *flammiceps* appear individually variable, even at the type locality (El Tambor, dpto. Santander), whilst his sample size (two) is inadequate to validate any size differences. *P. e. berlepschi* Ridgway, 1906, occurs over the rest of the species' range in western Amazonia, from southeast Colombia and eastern Ecuador to northeast Peru and across Brazil west of the Rio Negro. It differs from nominate *P. e. erythrocephala* in having a paler and yellower crown with a narrower but more sharply defined red border (sometimes entirely absent). Nonetheless, despite its continued acceptance, including here, even this race is scarcely very well marked (cf. Friedmann 1948) and probably demands more careful re-examination than we have had time to conduct. Golden-headed Manakin has, in the past, been considered conspecific with Red-headed Manakin, e.g. by Hellmayr (1929b), with the expanded species being referred to as Flame-headed Manakin, but the two are sympatric in northeast Peru along the Río Ucayali and lower Río Huallaga.

VOICE Like other *Pipra*, Golden-headed Manakin is noisy when displaying but its vocalisations have not been subject to very detailed study. Males give varied sharp, dry, chipping and trilling notes (Hilty 2003). Snow (1962b) described the advertisement call as a clear *pu*, which may be prolonged into a trill *pu-prrrrrr-pt* or even an expanded *pir-pir-prrrrrrrr-pt-pt!* It generally sounds very similar to the analogous vocalisation of Red-headed Manakin. A very short, sharp *zit, zit* or *kew* sound is given between or during flight displays, and Golden-headed Manakin produces a buzzing sound with the wings on landing following a display-flight (Snow 1962b, Wetmore 1972), but lacks any true mechanical sounds associated with wing-flicks, unlike in Red-headed Manakin (Castro-Astor *et al.* 2004). This species' vocalisations appear on the following audio compilations: English and Parker (1992), Moore (1997), Boesman (1999, 2006a, 2006b, 2009), Krabbe and Nilsson (2003), Hammick (2004), Naka *et al.* (2008) and Renaudier and Deroussen (2008), with many additional recordings archived online at www.xeno-canto.org.

NATURAL HISTORY Golden-headed Manakin principally inhabits the upper understorey to subcanopy of humid forest. On Trinidad, Snow and Lill (1974) documented males living to 11.5 years old and females to 12.0 years old, and calculated that both sexes may remain reproductively active for at least eight years.

FOOD AND FEEDING Golden-headed Manakin is a melastome specialist, especially preferring the small berries of the genus *Miconia* (Melastomataceae), although small insects (Beebe 1909) and spiders are also taken, and even fruits of up to 11×15mm (Snow 2004b). It visits fruiting trees from the understorey to the canopy, but is mainly observed at between 5 and 15m off the ground (Wetmore 1972, Hilty and Brown 1986). The most detailed study to date was conducted on Trinidad (Snow 1962b), which identified the fruits of 43 species in this manakin's diet, although 79% belonged to just three families (Araliaceae, Euphorbiaceae

and Melastomataceae). Loiselle *et al.* (2007b) recorded 27 species of fruit in the species' diet during their work in eastern Ecuador, but did not report more details. However, the related study by Blendinger *et al.* (2009) revealed that *P. erythrocephala* is, like several other manakins in east Ecuador, important for the dispersal of *Miconia fosteri* and *M. serrulata* seeds. In another study, in French Guiana, Melastomataceae, followed by Rubiaceae, were again found to be the most important dietary constituents (Théry 1990c). In southern Venezuela, Willard *et al.* (1991) found *Pagamea plicata* (Rubiaceae) and a *Ficus* sp. (Moraceae) seeds in stomach contents, and in northern Brazil *Heliconia acuminata* (Heliconiaceae) fruits are dispersed by this species (Silva *et al.* 2010).

DISPLAY Considering the species' abundance (it is the commonest *Pipra* north of the Amazon), its lekking behaviour has been rather inadequately described in the literature, and the only dedicated studies are those by Snow (1962b) and Lill (1976), both of which were conducted on Trinidad. At least on that island, but also in Venezuela, leks comprise 6–20 (including young) males (sometimes even more) in a concentrated area, not dispersed as in *P. rubrocapilla* (see Castro-Astor *et al.* 2004). Thus, it seems that *P. erythrocephala* is unique within the genus *Pipra* in not having evolved a dispersed lek. The birds' display-perches, which are free of foliage (like those used by other *Pipra*), are horizontal or near-horizontal branches or vines sited 5–20m above the ground (Snow 1962b, Wetmore 1972, Hilty 2003). Both adults and young males display (Wetmore 1972). Snow (1962b) and Lill (1976) described the species' displays (see also Prum 1990a), among which the following are most frequently seen. *Backward-slide* displays recall those of the other members of the superspecies; the males stretch the legs upward, hold the body low but cock the tail, and appear to slide sideways along the perch. *Short flights*, like those of other *Pipra*, consist of the male engaging in rapid back-and-forth horizontal flights between the display-perch and a nearby bough, with the wings producing a humming sound in mid-air and the buzzing sound on alighting (see also Voice). *S-shaped flights* cover up to 20–40m in a semi-circular route, swooping back up onto the display-perch uttering an accelerating series of buzzy *kew* notes (see Voice) and the wings humming in flight. Because the displays of the Golden-headed Manakin are generally very similar to those of Red-headed Manakin and Round-tailed Manakin *P. chloromeros*, which are described in detail under those species, we refer those interested in this aspect of the species' life history to that account. However, it should be noted that the vertical-wing and forward-jump with backward-slide displays are not linked in Golden-headed Manakin, and the latter is completely unknown in *P. erythrocephala* (or indeed any other of the *P. erythrocephala* superspecies: Castro-Astor *et al.* 2004). Furthermore, Lill (1976) only once observed a male land directly on a female to copulate following a display-flight, in contrast to *P. rubrocapilla*, in which males customarily do so. Unlike *P. rubrocapilla*, which has strikingly white underwing-coverts, in Golden-headed Manakin wing and body movements designed to reveal certain colour patches are limited to accentuating the thigh coloration, because *P. erythrocephala* lacks any contrast on the underwing. Displays in this species are probably performed almost year-round as in other members of the *P. erythrocephala* superspecies, albeit with noticeably increased activity during the main reproductive season, which can vary with locality (see below).

BREEDING Nests and nest building have been described by Snow (1962b), Hilty and Brown (1986), Tostain (1988b) and Valsko and Anciães (2008). On Trinidad, Snow (1962b) considered the breeding season to be prolonged, extending from January to August and he described the nest as a small, shallow and very thin-based cup sited in a horizontal fork in the lower branches of a tree or in a sapling or understorey shrub, at between 1 and 10m above the ground. It is constructed of brownish fibres and rootlets, with (as is typical of many manakin nests) a few dead leaves in the bottom of the cup or hanging from below the nest, presumably to disguise its shape. In northern Colombia, M. A. Carriker (*in* Hilty and Brown 1986) found a nest with eggs in southern Bolívar in the fourth week of May, and he collected a female about to lay eggs at the end of the third week of June in Guajira. In French Guiana, a nest was discovered in the fourth week of November, 3m above the ground, and another nest was found under construction, 6m above the ground in a *Pouteria torta* (Sapotaceae) tree, 1.5m from the trunk, with the female bringing new material (including *Marasmius* fibres and small dead leaves) every 2–4 minutes (Tostain 1988b). North of Manaus (Amazonas, Brazil), Valsko and Anciães (2008) observed a female constructing a nest, commencing with vegetable fibres taken from an understorey tree 30m from the nest tree and the web of an arthropod. After five days, the nest was completed also using fine flakes of tree bark, dead leaves and lined with dark strips of palm fibres. Dimensions of two nests were presented by Tostain (1988b) and Valsko and Anciães (2008). Concerning the eggs, the typical clutch size is two and, again from Trinidad, Belcher and Smooker (1937) described them as being pale greenish-yellow with dense spots and longitudinal streaks of umber brown that form a wreath at the larger end. Dimensions were presented by Belcher and Smooker (1937) and repeated by Wetmore (1972). The fledging period is unknown but incubation takes 16–17 days (Snow 1962b). Other breeding data, principally concerning seasonality, are as follows. In northwest Colombia, M. A. Carriker (*in* Haffer 1975 and Hilty and Brown 1986) collected 19 breeding-condition birds in December–March, whilst there is a female that was about to lay and three males with enlarged testes in late April/May from the northeast of the country (MVZ 152314–16) and two others with partially formed eggs from August and early October in the same region (MVZ 154551–52). In northeast Peru, between July and September, very few of either sex of those collected seemed to be in breeding condition (MVZ). In northeast Venezuela, Beebe (1909) found birds to be in full breeding condition in the March. In southern Venezuela (Amazonas state), at the frontier with Brazil, Willard *et al.* (1991) found both males and females in breeding condition (the latter with eggs in the oviduct) in January and especially February and March, but others of both sexes collected during the same period were not. Further north in the same state, Bradshaw and Kirwan (1995) noted a female feeding two fledged young in mid March. Dick *et al.* (1984) collected a female in breeding condition in French Guiana in early February, and Tostain *et al.* (1992) mentioned the discovery of a nest under construction in late October. In Amapá, Brazil, Novaes (1978) mentioned birds collected in breeding condition in October and February.

STATUS Categorised as Least Concern by BirdLife International (2004, 2008), although Anciães and Peterson (2006), using modelling techniques, predicted that Golden-headed Manakin would be significantly impacted by forecast levels of climate change. In French Guiana, Thiollay (1994) estimated the density of *P. erythrocephala* to be seven pairs per 100ha at one study site. The species is known from a great many protected areas across its wide range (see, for example, Borges *et al.* 2001, Trolle and Walther 2004, Salaman *et al.* 2008, 2009, Bernard 2008, Souza *et al.* 2008).

REFERENCES Anciães and Peterson (2006, 2009), Angehr and Dean (2010), AOU (1998), Beebe (1909), Belcher and Smooker (1937), Bernard (2008), BirdLife International (2004, 2008), Blake (1962), Blake and Loiselle (2009), Blendinger *et al.* (2009), Boesman (1999, 2006a, 2006b, 2009), Borges (2007), Borges *et al.* (2001, 2006), Bradshaw and Kirwan (1995), Braun *et al.* (2007), Burton (1975), Campos *et al.* (2009), Castro-Astor *et al.* (2004), Cherrie (1916), Chubb (1921), Cohn-Haft *et al.* (1997), Dickinson (2003), Donegan *et al.* (2010), Doucet *et al.* (2007), Dugand and Phelps (1946), Dunning (2008), English and Parker (1992), Friedmann (1948), Graves (1981, 1993), Griscom (1933), Haffer (1967b, 1975, 1992b), Hammick (2004), Haverschmidt (1952), Haverschmidt and Mees (1994), Hellmayr (1906d, 1929b), Hilty (2003), Hilty and Brown (1986), Hudon *et al.* (1989), Jones *et al.* (2002), Junge and Mees (1958), Kenefick *et al.* (2007), Krabbe and Nilsson (2003), Lill (1976), Loiselle *et al.* (2007b), Meyer de Schauensee and Phelps (1978), Mittermeier *et al.* (2010), Moermond and Denslow (1985), Moore (1997), Naka *et al.* (2008), Novaes (1978, 1980a), Ottema *et al.* (2009), Ouellet (1990), Parker *et al.* (1982), Parkes (1961), Pérez-Emán *et al.* (2003), Phelps (1944), Pinto (1944, 1966), Prestel (1984), Prum (1990a), Quevedo *et al.* (2006), Rego *et al.* (2007), Renaudier and Deroussen (2008), Restall *et al.* (2006), Reynaud (1998), Ridgely and Greenfield (2001), Ridgely and Gwynne (1976, 1989), Ridgely and Tudor (1994, 2009), Robbins *et al.* (1985, 2004), Salaman *et al.* (1999, 2002a, 2002b, 2008, 2009), Santos and Silva (2007), Schubart *et al.* (1965), Schulenberg *et al.* (2007), Sibley (1957), Sick (1993, 1997), Silva *et al.* (2010), Snethlage (1914), Snow (1962b, 2004b), Snow and Lill (1974), Snyder (1966), Souza *et al.* (2008), Stotz *et al.* (1996), Tello (2001), Théry (1990b, 1990c, 1992, 1997), Thiollay (1994), Todd and Carriker (1922), Tostain (1988a, 1988b), Tostain *et al.* (1992), Trolle and Walther (2004), Valsko and Anciães (2008), Verea and Solórzano (1998, 2001, 2005), Verea *et al.* (1999), Wetmore (1972), Willard *et al.* (1991), Wiley (2010), Zimmer and Hilty (1997), Zyskowski *et al.* (2011).

Golden-headed Manakin *Pipra erythrocephala*. **Fig. 1**. Male, *P. e. erythrocephala*, Trinidad, May (*Steve Garvie / www.pbase.com/rainbirder*). Song perches are not always high in the subcanopy. **Fig. 2**. Male and female, *P. e. berlepschi*, Shiripuno Lodge, prov. Pastaza, eastern Ecuador, November (*Hadoram Shirihai / Photographic Handbook to Birds of the World*). Here a female visits a displaying male in the perch zone; note the latter's red and white tibial feathering. **Fig. 3**. Female, *P. e. erythrocephala*, El Paujil Bird Reserve, dpto. Boyacá, Colombia, January (*Hadoram Shirihai / Photographic Handbook to Birds of the World*). **Fig. 4**. Male, *P. e. erythrocephala*, Junglaven, Amazonas, southern Venezuela, March (*Pete Morris*). Note the deeper yellow head (in both examples here) compared to subspecies *P. e. berlepschi*, although characters are perhaps not entirely constant and the two intergrade in western Amazonia.

RED-HEADED MANAKIN
Pipra rubrocapilla   **Plate 3**

Pipra rubro-capilla **C. J. Temminck, 1821**, *Nouv. Rec. Pl. Col.* livr. 9, pl. 54, fig. 3, Bahia [see Hellmayr 1929b: 31], Brazil

Pipra rubrocapilla is the geographically most widespread of the red-headed members of the *P. erythrocephala* super-species, whose other constituents are confined to southwest Amazonia (Round-tailed Manakin *P. chloromeros*), the Pantepui region (Scarlet-horned Manakin *P. cornuta*) and Middle America to the Pacific seaboard of extreme northwest South America (Red-capped Manakin *P. mentalis*).

IDENTIFICATION 9.7–11.2cm. As intimated above, over much of its southern Amazonian and Atlantic Forest range, *P. rubrocapilla* is the only species of 'red-headed' manakin, which should make males automatically distinctive. Red-capped Manakin does not occur east of the Andes and Scarlet-horned Manakin is confined to a limited area of the Guianan Shield. There is some limited geographical overlap with Round-tailed Manakin *P. chloromeros* in southwest Amazonia, but they seem to be rarely if ever syntopic (see that species). In any case, males of the two species can be separated by the rounded (i.e. slightly graduated) rather than square-cut tail tip of Round-tailed Manakin, which frequently also appears rather crested, due to the feathers of the hindcrown being slightly 'shaggy'. Further minor but noticeable differences, given optimal views, are the whitish irides and yellow tibial feathering of male Round-tailed. Female Round-tailed Manakin shares the male's graduated tail, which should serve as the main distinguishing feature, although the crest can also be 'shaggy' like that of the male. Compared to Golden-headed Manakin (which see), with which there is perhaps very limited geographical overlap in part of northeast Peru (but see Schulenberg *et al.* 2007), should it prove impossible to assess head colour, then identification might need to rest on the slightly longer tail and darker irides of Red-headed Manakin. Separating females of these two species will be a much tougher challenge, and while female Golden-headed should show greyish or whitish irides this will not necessarily serve for young birds. Female Red-headed is said to be very slightly more yellowish on the throat and belly, but assessing this difference in the forest shade might prove difficult. Other female manakins in range over southern Amazonia are either larger with brighter-coloured legs, e.g. *Chiroxiphia* and *Manacus*, or have distinctly greener upperparts and much deeper yellow posterior underparts, e.g. the marginally smaller Snow-capped Manakin *Lepidothrix nattereri*, as well as quite different bill and iris colours. Female White-crowned Manakin *Dixiphia pipra* (relatively limited overlap, including in eastern Brazil) has an obvious grey cast to the crown and deep red irides, although reasonably close views might be needed to establish these features.

DISTRIBUTION This member of the *P. erythrocephala* complex is restricted to southern Amazonia and the northern part of the Atlantic Forest, where it is generally rather scarce. In Amazonia, the Red-headed Manakin occurs south of the Amazon and the Marañón from eastern Peru, in southern dpto. Loreto and extreme eastern dpto. Madre de Dios (Schulenberg *et al.* 2007), across virtually all of southern Amazonian Brazil east as far as northern

Maranhão, southern Pará and northern and western Tocantins, and south to eastern Acre, Rondônia and northern Mato Grosso (Fry 1970, Sick 1997, Zimmer *et al.* 1997, Hidasi 1998, Guilherme and Santos 2009, Lees *et al.* 2009, Pinheiro and Dornas 2009a), locally to south-central Mato Grosso, e.g. around Vila Bela da Santíssima Trindade (Silveira and D'Horta 2002), and northern Bolivia, in dptos. Pando, Beni and Santa Cruz (Bates *et al.* 1989, Remsen and Traylor 1989). There is a separate population in the Atlantic Forest of Brazil, from Pernambuco and Alagoas, in the north, where it is known from many forest fragments, locally south to northern Espírito Santo, as far at least as Aracruz and Serra, and at least formerly at Cantagalo (21°58'S, 42°22'W), northeast Rio de Janeiro (Berla 1946, Sick 1997, Silveira *et al.* 2003a, Antas *et al.* 2009). In terms of elevational range, Red-headed Manakin is largely found below 500m in Amazonia, but locally it reaches higher, e.g. to *c.*700m in the Serra dos Carajás, Pará, Brazil (Pacheco *et al.* 2007). In the Atlantic Forest region *P. rubrocapilla* is also largely confined to lowland regions, but even here it locally reaches as high as 590m in Alagoas (Silveira *et al.* 2003a) and even higher in southern Bahia, in the Serra das Lontras (Silveira *et al.* 2005).

MOVEMENTS Snow (2004b) considered that the species is almost certainly sedentary and we too have seen no definitive evidence to suspect that Red-headed Manakin performs any kind of movements. However, Henriques and Wunderle (2001) found that they trapped the species more frequently during the wet rather than the dry season in the Floresta Nacional do Tapajós (Brazil).

HABITAT Principally found in humid lowland *terra firme* forest and dense secondary woodland, including edges, especially where there are fruiting trees. However, Novaes (1970) noted *P. erythrocephala* (= *P. rubrocapilla*) regularly in *várzea* forest at the lower Rio Guamá, Pará, in northern Brazil.

DESCRIPTION A typical small *Pipra* manakin. Males have the inner secondaries unusually stiffened (as in congeners) with the shafts somewhat enlarged over two-thirds of their length, slightly curved and laterally compressed. The bill has a reasonably arched culmen, sometimes with a hook tip and often quite prominent nostrils. *Adult male.* – The

161

entire head and hindneck are bright scarlet (although the feathers are either white or pale yellow at their bases). The lower two-thirds of the slightly 'puffy' tarsal feathering are also red, but the rest of the bird's plumage is entirely matt black. The axillaries and underwing-coverts are whitish-cinnamon. *Adult female.* – The plumage is very similar, if not practically identical to that of female Golden-headed Manakin. The upperparts are predominantly bright greenish-olive, with dusky primary-coverts fringed bright green, uniformly bright green remiges, and dusky-green outer primaries. Below, paler over the foreneck and breast, with a duller greenish-yellow throat, abdomen, tibia and undertail-coverts. The axillaries and underwing-coverts are pale. Females can very rarely exhibit some tiny red feathers in the ocular region or on the crown (Graves 1981, Castro-Astor *et al.* 2004). *Juvenile.* – Probably more or less identical to adult females (though not actually described), except for the loosely textured feathering typical of all juvenile passerines, while immature males start to show some adult feathers on the head and body. Young birds, in contrast to adults, will doubtless show moult limits in the greater coverts, with the retained wing-coverts, and remiges, duller, while the outer primaries and rectrices are narrow, pointed and brownish (as in Red-capped Manakin: see Wolfe *et al.* 2009). Plumage maturation has not been well described in the literature, but small orange-red feathers initially appear on the crown and nape, and by the time that the head is extensively red some charcoal black coloration will have appeared over the flanks, across the breast, throat, mantle, scapulars, larger wing-coverts and tertials, and the entire tail is black (MNRJ). Castro-Astor *et al.* (2004) considered that adult plumage must be attained during or before the second year of life. *Moult.* – There are no published moult data, but this species' regime is presumably similar to those *Pipra* for which reasonably robust data exist (see, e.g., Red-capped Manakin and Band-tailed Manakin *P. fasciicauda*). Birds in east Amazonian Brazil were not replacing any feathers in June (MNRJ). *Bare parts.* – The irides are generally grey-brown, coffee- or hazel-brown (occasionally yellow-brown) to amber in both sexes, although one male from the Atlantic Forest had the irides milky white and one from Rondônia had them off-white, while the bill is usually dark to black over the maxilla with a paler grey- or brownish mandible (occasionally reddish at the base), and the legs and feet are orange-brown to dull pinkish (flesh) or dull red, sometimes with a hint of purple (Snow 2004b; FMNH; MNRJ).

MEASUREMENTS (CUMZ; MNRJ: Atlantic Forest of Bahia, Espírito Santo and Pernambuco, Brazil) Wing of male (*n* = 14) 60.5–65.5mm, wing of female (*n* = 8) 62–66mm; tail of male (*n* = 14) 27.0–35.5mm, tail of female (*n* = 8) 30–35mm; bill of male (*n* = 14) 10.41–12.12mm, bill of female (*n* = 7) 12.03–12.56mm; tarsus of male (*n* = 7) 12.72–15.66mm, tarsus of female (*n* = 7) 12.74–14.58mm. (MNRJ: Amazonia, in Mato Grosso, Pará and Rondônia, Brazil) Wing of male (*n* = 10) 59–64mm, wing of female (*n* = 8) 59.0–62.5mm; tail of male (*n* = 10) 27.0–35.5mm, tail of female (*n* = 8) 30–33mm; bill of male (*n* = 9) 9.72–11.86mm, bill of female (*n* = 8) 10.99–11.93mm; tarsus of male (*n* = 5) 13.79–15.81mm, tarsus of female (*n* = 4) 13.24–14.50mm. Weight: 10.9–16.5g (males) and 10.0–17.5g (females) (Fry 1970, Novaes 1976, Bates *et al.* 1989, Graves and Zusi 1990, Snow 2004b, Dunning 2008; FMNH; MNRJ).

GEOGRAPHICAL VARIATION Monotypic.

VOICE The species' vocalisations are generally somewhat

similar to those of *P. erythrocephala*, especially the flight-calls (Snow 2004b). Its vocal repertoire was detailed recently by Castro-Astor *et al.* (2004), who also presented sonograms, and this is by far the most comprehensive study of the Red-headed Manakin's voice. These authors identified nine vocal types (including mechanical sounds) as follows. The *advertisement call* is the most frequently heard of these and is audible >100m away. Its function is territory defence and advertisement to females. The call comprises two notes (*tsi-gheh* or *tslit*) with a total length of <1 second, of which the second is the longer of the two, and which is sometimes varied to give just the first note or to add a very short, high-pitched note between the first and second notes, or following both of them. The *short-whistle* call is a short, sharp note (*TSIK*) given when returning to the display-perch during the back-and-forth display (see below) and appears to denote the non-aggressive state of the caller, whereas the *long-whistle* call is uttered on leaving the perch during the same display. It lasts c.0.25 seconds (i.e. about three times the length of the short whistle). The *display-flight call* lasts c.2.5 seconds, the first part (0.8 seconds) thin and descending, then an ascending whistle that ends with two sharp shrill notes (*tsi-ewww, tsi-ewww, tsi-ewww, seeeeeeee, gheh-gheh*: Sick 1993). Sometimes the first part is varied to comprise 1–3 thin, sharp, descending calls followed by the descending–ascending calls, and ending with 1–5 harsh notes. What Castro-Astor *et al.* (2004) termed the *modulated trill* is an ascending–descending call given when a female-plumaged bird leaves the display-perch immediately after landing. The about-face with wing-spreading call (see Display) is given between males from different display sites and includes two different notes lasting c.0.4 seconds (*seeeee-gheh*). Usually the second note is repeated 2–3 times, but sometimes only the second note, which recalls the second note of the advertisement call, is given. The *trill* call, like the last vocalisation, is given only during male–male interactions, and is followed in quick succession by two pure-tone quavering whistles. Castro-Astor *et al.* (2004) found that the trill comprises a very short, broad-frequency series of pulses ranging from 2.5 to 8.0kHz. The trembling whistle forms part of the vertical-wing display (see below) and typically comprises eight notes, both ascending and descending elements, and lasting c.2.6 seconds. The *whistle-snap* (see Display) typically consists of 1–2 whistles, followed by a short note at a much lower frequency and a sharp slapping sound that is produced by 2–8 uninterrupted wing-flicks, e.g. *tsew, tsew-tschew SEEEEEEEE'BZZANG* (Schulenberg *et al.* 2007). However, the snapping sound can be made without uttering the whistle. Red-headed Manakin features on the following published audio compilations: Schulenberg *et al.* (2000), Remold (2002), Boesman (2006a, 2009), Marantz and Zimmer (2006) and Minns *et al.* (2009), and additional recordings are archived online at www.xeno-canto.org.

NATURAL HISTORY Red-headed Manakin is generally an inhabitant of the midstorey and subcanopy of tall forest. Its display-perches are typically sited in the upper part of the understorey or the lower midstorey. Given its relative abundance, our cumulative knowledge of its life history was comparatively weak until very recently, but further data, especially on its breeding biology and diet, would still be very welcome.

FOOD AND FEEDING Relatively little known, at least in terms of specifics. However, in the northeast Brazilian

Atlantic Forest, Red-headed Manakin is known to be an important disperser of seeds (Pereira *et al.* 2008). The species takes both small fruits, e.g. *Miconia ciliata* (Melastomataceae), *Symphonia globulifera* (Clusiaceae), *Psidium guajava* (Myrtaceae) and *Croton matourensis* (Euphorbiaceae) (Gomes *et al.* 2008, Marceliano *et al.* 2009), and insects, which are plucked during short-range sally-hover manoeuvres typical of the genus.

DISPLAY Best studied just recently by Castro-Astor *et al.* (2004) at Poço das Antas Biological Reserve in the Atlantic Forest of southeast Brazil. This study found that some males displayed more or less alone, but that one lek numbered 13 different display-courts, and that mean distance between each court was 72.5m (range 34–157m), i.e. that each site was only within auditory distance of the next. In northeast Brazil, Xavier and Silva (2008) found that the distance between display-courts varied from 50 to 200m, with the highest densities being found in dense lowland forest and the lowest at forest borders, but no more than four males attending each lek site. Castro-Astor *et al.* (2004) noted that most display-perches were on slender trees (including a Myrtaceae, Flacourtiaceae, Moraceae and several legumes) and were generally bereft of foliage; some had been used for up to seven years. Display-perches themselves were sited 4.4–7.1m above the ground.

Castro-Astor *et al.* (2004) described the following 11 different display behaviours. In the *upright posture* the male holds his head almost vertical, with the bill pointing upwards, which position is also assumed by the female on arrival at the display-perch. Like others in the *P. erythrocephala* complex, *about-faces* involve a rapid 180° turn, landing on the same place, between *back-and-forth* flights, which occur mainly when a female-plumaged bird is present. The male makes rapid flights between the display-perch and an adjacent limb, giving the long whistle call (see Voice) on leaving and usually gives the short whistle call on his return, as well as sometimes a snapping sound, which is assumed to be of mechanical origin. The *side-to-side slide* is most frequently performed with the arrival of a female-plumaged bird, but is also given alone or with another adult male. The male perches at right angles to the display-perch with the tail depressed and quivering, then jumps sideways while simultaneously raising his wings horizontally or vertically. Should a female-plumaged bird land on the display-perch, the male raises his wings slowly umbrella-like and lands beside her, quivering his tail, before turning parallel to the perch to reveal his red-and-white thighs, and then commencing a *backward slide*. The throat-feathers may also be expanded slightly (GMK pers. obs.). The latter display is performed with the body held almost parallel to the perch, the tail elevated and quivering, legs stretched to reveal the thighs, and head lowered. The male takes short rapid steps back along the perch increasing his speed, his tail pointing towards the 'female', which stays silent facing him. If the 'female' leaves the display-perch, the male raises his wings vertically and vocalises. At the end of the slide, the male crouches and performs a *display-flight*. This involves an initially downward then upward flight to a slightly higher limb 25–30m from the display-perch, from where the male immediately returns in an S-shaped flight in front of the female, which ends with the male landing on her back to copulate with her, or if the female 'rejects' him, he lands beside her wings raised, then repeats the side-to-side slide, backward-slide and the display-flight. (However, display-flights are also sometimes performed alone or in the sole presence of another male, usually quietly in such cases; Sick 1993.) Should copulation ensue, which is very brief, the male will sometimes face away from the female raising the rear half of his body and expanding the tibial feathering, while the female may vibrate her tail and occasionally raises her wings slightly (GMK pers. obs.). What Castro-Astor *et al.* (2004) termed the *frenzied-flutter* has analogous displays in both Golden-headed and Round-tailed Manakins, and seems to be only performed in the absence of a female-plumaged bird, usually following a display-flight. It is a pseudo-copulatory movement, which is also observed in the *P. aureola* superspecies. Males from adjacent arenas are known to regularly perch together on one display-perch or in the area between different courts. In male–male displays, near neighbours may be capable of performing slower, better coordinated displays. While non-adult males regularly take part in displays and vocalise like adults, they are not capable of engaging in well-coordinated displays and seemingly do not display directly with adults (Castro-Astor *et al.* 2004). The *about-face with wing-spreading* display is only given in the presence of other males, sometimes two others and occasionally as many as five in the general vicinity. The perch-owner bends forward, exposing the thigh feathers, spreads his wings horizontally, raises his tail, lowers his head below the perch, and performs a 180° turn without any lateral movement. Seconds later, the male turns again and repeats the display, during which time the other male/s also spread/s his/their wings horizontally or vertically. The perch-owner usually gives the display-call (see Voice) as he lowers the head. Also given solely to other males is the *vertical-wing* display, in which the perch-owner raises his wings vertically, fans the tail and gives a trill and (on some occasions) trembling whistles (see Voice). This display may be accompanied by a slow side-to-side slide. The *forward jump with backward slide* is also a male–male display. Legs stretched, tail cocked, head lowered and body leaning slightly forward, one male quivers his tail and jumps forward then back. Thereafter, with his body held almost in line with the perch, he jumps forward again then slides back with his tail toward the other male, exhibiting his thigh-feathers, and sometimes almost touching the other male with his tail, although the second male usually retreats. Following several repetitions, the displaying male backs toward the other male until his tail almost touches the other bird, freezes for a few seconds, then turns around and flies rapidly towards the other male, which flies away. Usually, the two then switch positions and roles. The *wing-flick with whistle-snap* commences with a male performing a display-flight, returning with a thin whistle and then landing silently. He then slides towards the other male, exposing his red thighs and flicking his wings vertically to expose the whitish underwing-coverts. A sharp slapping sound accompanies the wing-flicks, which may be given up to eight times, each accompanied by a sharp slapping sound.

BREEDING This aspect of the species' natural history is still surprisingly poorly known (given the species' general abundance and widespread occurrence). At Belém, Pará (east Amazonian Brazil), Red-headed Manakin breeds in September–December (Pinto 1953), and nests are sited between 2 and 5m above the ground. The nest has not been well described to date, but it is similar to those of all other *Pipra*. A completed nest with eggs found in relatively open forest in northeast Brazil was placed *c.*2m above the ground in the two-way fork of an understorey tree (GMK pers. obs.). The nest's outer layer was constructed largely of dead leaves, while the main structure comprising small pieces of bark, fungal rhizomorphs and rootlets, and the nest was attached to the narrow support branches with many spiderwebs. A few dead leaves also hung below the nest, disguising the overall outline of the structure, while from above it was partially shaded by life leaves. The clutch size is two eggs, as in all manakins, and these are pale brownish or yellowish-white with vinous-brown or brownish markings, which are very variable in size and strength, but are often heaviest towards the broad end (Velho 1932, Pinto 1953; GMK pers. obs.). Egg dimensions were presented by Velho (1932) and Pinto (1953). The incubation period is unknown. However, the young fledge in 13–14 days. Novaes (1976) found males in breeding condition in northwest Mato Grosso, Brazil, in October, and birds in breeding condition in Bahia and Espírito Santo (Atlantic Forest) have been collected in late September/October and December (MNRJ). Further north, in Alagoas, a female was flushed from a nest with lightly incubated eggs in the fourth week of January (GMK pers. obs.). In southwest Amazonia (northern Bolivia and Rondônia, Brazil), birds were in breeding condition in October–November (FMNH).

STATUS Categorised as Least Concern by BirdLife International (2004, 2008), based on its large range (estimated at 3,390,000km²) and relative abundance throughout, although Anciães and Peterson (2006), using modelling techniques, predicted that Red-headed Manakin could be very severely impacted by forecast levels of climate change. The Red-headed Manakin is known from many protected areas throughout its range, in Brazil, for example, the Serra dos Carajás mosaic of protected areas, Pará (Pacheco *et al.* 2007), Parque Nacional da Amazônia, Pará (Oren and Parker 1997), Floresta Nacional do Pau-Rosa, Amazonas (Dantas *et al.* 2010), Parque Estadual do Cantão, Tocantins (Pinheiro and Dornas 2009a), Parque Estadual Ricardo Franco, Mato Grosso (A. Grosset *et al.* unpubl.), Pedra

Talhada Biological Reserve, Alagoas (Forrester 1993), Sooretama Biological Reserve, Espírito Santo (Parker and Goerck 1997), and União Biological Reserve (Castro-Astor *et al.* 2004). Elsewhere, *P. rubrocapilla* is found, for example, in Parque Nacional Noel Kempff Mercado and Estación Biológica Caparú, both in Bolivia (Acheson and Davis 2001, Vidoz *et al.* 2010), and the Tambopata Reserve in southeast Peru (Parker *et al.* 1994c).

REFERENCES Acheson and Davis (2001), Aleixo and Poletto (2007), Almeida *et al.* (2003), Anciães and Peterson (2006, 2009), Antas *et al.* (2009), Bates *et al.* (1989), Beebe (1915), Berla (1946), BirdLife International (2004, 2008), Boesman (2006a, 2009), Castro-Astor *et al.* (2004), Dantas *et al.* (2010), Dunning (2008), Forrester (1993), Fry (1970), Gomes *et al.* (2008), Graves and Zusi (1990), Guilherme and Santos (2009), Gyldenstolpe (1945, 1951), Haffer (1992b), Hellmayr (1906d, 1929b), Henriques and Wunderle (2001), Henriques *et al.* (2003), Hidasi (1998), Hohnwald (2009), Hudon *et al.* (1989), Lamm (1948), Lees *et al.* (2008), Lima *et al.* (2001), Magalhães *et al.* (2004), Maillard *et al.* (2007), Marantz and Zimmer (2006), Marceliano *et al.* (2009), Mestre *et al.* (2010), Minns *et al.* (2009), Naumburg (1930), Novaes (1970, 1976), Oren and Parker (1997), Pacheco and Olmos (2005), Pacheco *et al.* (2007), Parker and Goerck (1997), Parker *et al.* (1982, 1994c), Peres and Whittaker (1991), Pereira *et al.* (2008), Pinheiro and Dornas (2009a), Pinto (1944, 1953), Pinto and Camargo (1957), Prum (1990a), Remold (2002), Remsen and Traylor (1989), Restall *et al.* (2006), Ridgely and Tudor (1994, 2009), Schubart *et al.* (1965), Schulenberg *et al.* (2000, 2006, 2007), Sick (1959d, 1967, 1993, 1997), Silva (1996), Silveira and D'Horta (2002), Silveira *et al.* (2003a, 2005), Simon (2009), Snethlage (1907, 1908a, 1908b, 1935), Snow (2004b), Stotz *et al.* (1996, 1997), Velho (1932), Vidoz *et al.* (2010), Whittaker (2009), Wiley (2010), Willis and Oniki (2002), Wolfe *et al.* (2009), Xavier and Silva (2008), Zimmer *et al.* (1997).

Red-headed Manakin *Pipra rubrocapilla.* **Fig. 1**. Male, RPPN Frei Caneca (Jaqueira), Pernambuco, northeast Brazil, September (*Ciro Albano*). **Fig. 2**. Male, RPPN Frei Caneca (Jaqueira), Pernambuco, northeast Brazil, December (*Pete Morris*). Despite being isolated in the Atlantic Forest of eastern coastal Brazil, no subspecies are recognised within Red-headed Manakin, which is otherwise found widely south of the Amazon.

RED-CAPPED (YELLOW-THIGHED) MANAKIN
Pipra mentalis   Plate 3

Pipra mentalis **P. L. Sclater, 1857**, *Proc. Zool. Soc. Lond.* 1856: 299, pl. 121, Cordova [= Córdoba], Veracruz, Mexico

Formerly widely known as the Yellow-thighed Manakin, we would advocate returning to that name to avoid potential 'confusion' with Red-headed Manakin *P. rubrocapilla*. Both species have red heads of equal extent, but only *P. mentalis* has yellow thighs, which are used prominently in the species' displays. Of course, the southwest Amazonian Round-tailed Manakin *P. chloromeros* also has yellow thighs but this species' name is sufficiently distinctive to prevent confusion. If providing sufficiently distinctive and appropriate English names for all of the world's birds is a worthwhile goal, then we would reason that use of Yellow-thighed Manakin should be preferred over Red-capped for this species.

IDENTIFICATION 9.0–11.2cm. There is no geographical overlap with any other 'red-headed' *Pipra*, making the adult male Red-capped Manakin automatically identifiable. Indeed, over virtually all of the species' Middle American range this is the sole member of its genus and the only other genuinely small-sized manakin is Blue-crowned Manakin *Lepidothrix coronata* (in Costa Rica and Panama), which should make females of the present species fairly readily identifiable too. Female *L. coronata* are distinctly brighter and deeper green over the entire upperparts than the same sex of *P. mentalis*, and further differ in having slightly shorter tails and reddish irides, as well as favouring lower storeys within the same forests (Stiles and Skutch 1989). In extreme northwest Colombia, there is some overlap in the vicinity of the middle Atrato Valley with the marginally smaller Golden-headed Manakin *P. erythrocephala* (see Fig. 5 in Haffer 1967b: 350). To date, the two have only been found sympatrically at one locality, Mutatá, where Haffer (1967b) collected both species within 100m of each other, and in general Red-capped appears to favour wetter forests in this region (Hilty and Brown 1986). Further south in Colombia, Chapman (1917) reported the collection of Golden-headed Manakin at Buenaventura, near Cali, well within the range of *P. mentalis*, but there have been no subsequent reports of the former species from this region (Haffer 1967b). Griscom (1933), Wetmore (1972: 316) and Ridgely and Gwynne (1976) stated that in southwest Panama there is definite overlap between the two species (for further details see *P. erythrocephala*). Lone females of these two species will probably be virtually inseparable in the field, although Hilty and Brown (1986) postulated that Red-capped might appear marginally longer-tailed and a bird with pale irides must be Red-capped Manakin. Some female Red-capped Manakins have noticeably yellow thighs, but this is not a feature common to all. None of the species of *Manacus* manakins that occur in sympatry with *P. mentalis* should offer real confusion; all of their females are larger with bright red legs, and are principally found in the lower understorey. There is also limited geographical overlap with White-crowned Manakin *Dixiphia pipra* and White-ruffed Manakin *Corapipo leucorrhoa*, but females of both these species have reddish irides, and the former has a grey cast to the crown and the latter an obviously pale (whitish) throat.

DISTRIBUTION The northernmost representative of the genus *Pipra*, Red-capped Manakin is found from southeast

Mexico, in south-central Veracruz, northern Oaxaca (to a point just west of the Valle Nacional), Tabasco, Campeche, northern Chiapas and the eastern Yucatán (Binford 1989, Howell and Webb 1995) south throughout Belize (Jones 2004), northern Guatemala, northern Honduras, eastern Nicaragua and Costa Rica (where it also occurs on the Pacific slope north to the environs of Manuel Antonio National Park) to Panama, where it occurs locally on the Pacific slope from Chiriquí east to the Serranía de Majé in eastern Panamá province, but is absent from much of the Azuero Peninsula (except the west) and the savannas of southern Coclé, and on the Caribbean slope from Bocas del Toro (including some near-shore islands) to eastern Colón and western San Blas (e.g. at Mandinga) (Wetmore 1972, Ridgely and Gwynne 1976, Cooper 1999). *P. mentalis* is, however, absent from the highlands of the Darién. In South America, it ranges along the Pacific coast of Colombia south from the middle Atrato Valley, at the Río Uva and Mutatá, in northern dpto. Chocó (Hilty and Brown 1986) to northwest Ecuador, where *P. mentalis* is regularly found south only to Esmeraldas and northwest Pichincha, although there are two older records from northern Manabí and northern Los Ríos, and two more recent records in northwest Azuay (Ridgely and Greenfield 2001). Generally, Red-capped Manakin is found from sea level to *c.*500m. However, it does range higher, reaching 1,050m in Costa Rica (Stiles and Skutch 1989), 950m in western Colombia, to 850m in Mexico (Andrle 1967) and locally to 600m in Panama (Wetmore 1972). Furthermore, Monroe (1968) reported, perhaps erroneously, that the species ascends, locally, to 1,500m in Honduras.

MOVEMENTS Although the species is generally considered to be sedentary and resident, in parts of eastern Costa Rica some Red-capped Manakins (but not all) are suspected to make regular movements to lower altitudes in the non-breeding season (Levey 1988, Blake and Loiselle 2001, 2002). These movements are more or less identical to those performed by White-ruffed Manakin (which see). Local movements of up to *c.*6km were also recorded during the latter study, and it might also be true that young males, seeking to establish themselves, might wander further than females.

HABITAT Red-capped Manakin inhabits humid evergreen and semi-deciduous forest, as well as tall second growth and even thickets (Levey 1988), occasionally visiting forest borders (perhaps especially where there are fruiting trees). When foraging, the species regularly visits clearings, including around buildings, and more scrubby areas. However, at least in eastern Costa Rica, Red-capped Manakin seems to breed more or less exclusively in old-growth forest (Blake and Loiselle 2002) and Loiselle *et al.* (2007b) noted a preference for ridge top localities.

DESCRIPTION A typical small *Pipra* manakin. Males have the inner secondaries unusually stiffened (as in congeners) with the shafts somewhat enlarged over two-thirds of their length, slightly curved and laterally compressed. The rectrices are also to a lesser extent stiffened. The bill has a reasonably arched culmen, sometimes with a hook tip, and often quite prominent nostrils. Nominate *mentalis* is described here. *Adult male.* – The entire head and hindneck are bright orange-red (although the feathers are either white or pale yellow at their bases), but the chin is yellow or yellowish-white, and the feathers of the malar can also be yellow. The lower two-thirds of the slightly 'puffy' tarsal feathering are pale yellow, but the rest of the bird's plumage is entirely matt black, with the exception of the greyish-brown inner webs to the primaries and the pale yellow fringes to the secondaries (which are rarely, if ever, visible in the field). The axillaries and underwing-coverts are yellow. *Adult female.* – The upperparts are predominantly bright greenish-olive, with dusky primary-coverts fringed bright green, uniformly bright green remiges, and dusky-green outer primaries. Below, the plumage is paler over the foreneck and breast, with a duller greenish-yellow throat, abdomen, tibia and undertail-coverts. In some, at least, the thigh feathers can be noticeably yellow, but this is certainly not always the case. The axillaries and underwing-coverts are as in the adult male. Females can exhibit some red feathers in the ocular region or on the crown (Graves 1981; MNCR) and females (and young males) can often show whitish inner webs to the larger tertials. However, the tertials never show any dusky wash to the inner webs, permitting sexing (and/or ageing) opposed to young males that have not yet developed any red or black feathering (see below). *Juvenile.* – Probably more or less identical to adult females, except for the loosely textured feathering typical of all juvenile passerines (Wolfe *et al.* 2009), while immature males possess white irides (or the eyes are flecked brown and white) and start to show some adult feathers on the head and body. These sometimes commence with a few red feathers immediately around the eyes (S. Easley photograph). Skutch (1949) provided brief notes on the appearance of nestlings and their development. Young birds, in contrast to adults, will show moult limits in the greater coverts, with the retained wing-coverts, and remiges, duller, while the outer primaries and rectrices are narrow, pointed and brownish (Wolfe *et al.* 2009). Plumage maturation has not been well described in the literature, but small orange-red feathers initially appear in the ocular region, on the lores, cheeks, neck-sides and nape, and these individuals usually have a dusky to blackish wash to the outer web of at least one of the tertials and one or more blackish body feathers (Wolfe *et al.* 2009). However, the plumage probably does not become extensively dusky over the underparts, from the throat to undertail-coverts, or any blackish feathers appear on the mantle, back and scapulars, until many red feathers are present on the head. Howell and Webb (1995) stated that adult plumage

is attained when *c.*1 year old. *Moult.* – Moult was studied in detail by Wolfe *et al.* (2009), who found that the species' first post-juvenile moult is partial (in March–October) and is followed the next year by a complete moult during the same period, to attain adult plumage. Post-juvenile moult includes a variable number of greater coverts, but no remiges or rectrices. *Hybrids.* – Haffer (1975) reported the existence of specimens from eastern Panama, which he considered to be hybrids between this species and Golden-headed Manakin (the two species overlap in range over *c.*100km). Furthermore, J. Strauch (*in* Ridgely and Gwynne 1976) mentioned the record of a hybrid Golden-headed × Red-capped Manakin from the Pacific slope in Panama, but no additional details appear to have been published. However, in northwest Colombia, there is no evidence to date of any introgression (Haffer 1967b). *Bare parts.* – The irides are generally white, whitish or pale yellow in adult males, but varying shades of brown (or occasionally yellow, rarely white) in adult females (typically brown in younger birds), while the bill (in both sexes) is usually dark grey to fuscous over the maxilla with a paler horn- or even flesh-coloured mandible, which becomes paler towards the base from the tip, and the legs and feet are dull reddish to lead grey or dull brown, with horn-coloured soles and greyish-brown claws (Wetmore 1972, Hilty and Brown 1986, Stiles and Skutch 1989, Snow 2004b; MNCR).

MEASUREMENTS *P. m. mentalis* (CUMZ; MNCR: Guatemala and Costa Rica): wing of male (*n* = 15) 54.5–62.0mm, wing of female (*n* = 9) 56–62mm; tail of male (*n* = 15) 26–33mm, tail of female (*n* = 9) 25–33mm; bill of male (*n* = 14) 9.85–12.30mm, bill of female (*n* = 9) 11.09–12.39mm; tarsus of male (*n* = 13) 13.50–15.55mm, tarsus of female (*n* = 6) 13.25–14.91mm. *P. m. ignifera* (Wetmore 1972: western Panama): wing of male (*n* = 16) 54.5–59.5mm, wing of female (*n* = 18) 55.5–61.0mm; tail of male (*n* = 16) 23–27mm, tail of female (*n* = 18) 24.0–28.5mm; bill of male (*n* = 16) 9.9–12.0mm, bill of female (*n* = 18) 10.0–12.6mm; tarsus of male (*n* = 16) 13.4–15.9mm, tarsus of female (*n* = 18) 13.3–15.8mm. *P. m. minor* (Hellmayr 1911, 1929b, Haffer 1967b: western Colombia) wing of male (*n* = 10) 57–60mm, wing of female (*n* = 6) 59.0–62.5mm; tail of male (*n* = 10) 28–29mm, tail of female (*n* = 6) 26.0–30.5mm. Live birds: *P. m. minor* (J. Hornbuckle unpubl. data: northwest Ecuador) wing of male (*n* = 3) 59–60mm, wing of female (*n* = 3) 60–62mm. Additional mensural data were published by Hellmayr (1906d, 1929b) and Wolfe *et al.* (2009), the latter referable to live birds. Weight (*P. m. mentalis*): 13–18g (males) and 11–18g (females); *P. m. ignifera*: 12.8–15.5g (males) and 13.4–14.7g (females); *P. m. minor*: 10.9–15.7g (males) and 15.9–16.4g (females) (Tashian 1952, Wetmore 1972, Burton 1975, Strauch 1977, Hilty and Brown 1986, Stiles and Skutch 1989, Snow 2004b, Dunning 2008; J. Hornbuckle unpubl. data; FMNH; MNCR; MVZ).

GEOGRAPHICAL VARIATION Polytypic with three subspecies generally recognised (Hellmayr 1929b, Snow 1979b, Dickinson 2003, Snow 2004b), although differences are generally very marginal (chiefly involving the depth of the red head coloration and relative size) and are probably not detectable in the field. Hellmayr (1906d) and Wetmore (1972) considered that female *P. m. ignifera* might be separated from same-sex *P. m. mentalis* in being somewhat brighter green above with more extensive yellow on the lower breast and abdomen, but in general we consider that even differences in males are not readily detectable, especially within shorter series. This is exemplified by many disagreements in the literature over the ranges of the three subspecies (see below). The reputedly smaller size of *P. m. minor* is not readily appreciated in the data presented above (see Measurements), although beware that these data are from varied sources and therefore not necessarily directly comparable. Nonetheless, further work has the potential to rationalise the number of taxa currently recognised based on a modern approach to subspecific designation, and it is worth mentioning that Hartert (1898) described *P. m. minor* based on just a single type (with reference to two other 'Bogotá' specimens) and it is unclear how critically subsequent commentators have re-analysed Hartert's claim of its small size. *P. m. mentalis*, which occurs from southeast Mexico south over the Caribbean slope perhaps as far as eastern Costa Rica, is described above. However, Wetmore (1972) argued that only those from northwest Costa Rica strongly approached nominate *mentalis* in having the head colour more orange, and he therefore considered that the range of the next race should also embrace Costa Rica. *P. m. ignifera* Bangs, 1901, is nowadays at least sometimes considered to be restricted to Panama (e.g. by Snow 2004b), where it occurs principally on the Caribbean slope. However, much earlier Hellmayr (1929b) had delimited this race's range as being in western Costa Rica and western Panama as far east as the Canal Zone. This treatment was reversed subsequently, but see above the comments of Wetmore (1972). It is considered to have a deeper red head and a more intense black body and wings (Snow 2004b), as well as averaging slightly smaller with a shorter tail, a smaller yellow chin and darker yellow tibial feathering (Wetmore 1972), but we have seen photographs of birds from east of the Panama Canal with more obvious yellow chin patches than in birds from as far afield as Mexico (see Fig. 2). *P. m. minor* E. Hartert, 1898, is restricted to northwest South America, in western Colombia and western Ecuador. Subspecies *minor* is considered to be smaller than the other subspecies (Hellmayr 1929b, Snow 2004b), and was also postulated to have the red forehead and crown deeper red still, paler yellow thighs and narrower and fewer yellowish fringes to the secondaries by Hellmayr (1929b), who thought that this race ranged as far north as Panama east and south of the Canal, including Barro Colorado Island. The latter author also suggested that females might be distinguished by their more yellowish underwing-coverts, in addition to their smaller size. Again, modern treatment of its range was revised by Wetmore (1972).

VOICE Vocalisations of the Red-capped Manakin were first described in detail by Skutch (1949), whose classic work represents one of the first in-depth single-species studies undertaken of a Neotropical bird. He listed the following elements. An exceedingly short, high-pitched, sputtering *psit*, or the same note delivered very rapidly in series but more softly: *psit psit psit psit psit*. This same note may also be given 2–3 times followed by a buzzing sound (*zzzzrk*). The song can be rendered *psit psit psit p'tsweee-e – psip*, with the final *psip* sometimes omitted, but when given it is sharp and emphatic. It is uttered intermittently by males on their display perches, and this or the long *p'tsweee-e* is the call most frequently noticed. The whistled *p'tsweee* is long-drawn-out, high-pitched and thin sounding. Finally, males give a high, shrill, rather harsh-sounding *tseeee* or *eeee* on returning to the display-perch after a short circling flight, or when alighting on the back of a female to copulate. Skutch reported that if one male at a lek utters this call, it immediately stimulates

the rest to vocalise. Chapman (1935) was the first to comment on the species' mechanical wing-snaps, which were subsequently described by Skutch (1949). His remarks bear extensive quotation:

> The snapping sounds may be made singly or in rapid sequence, producing a whirr or a sort of snapping roll. [...] While remaining on his perch, he often produces a short snapping whirr by beating his wings with the utmost rapidity. Indeed, the whole series of wingbeats … is over so soon, that unless I happened to be looking directly … through my binoculars … I could not be sure that he moved his wings at all. More rarely, while resting quietly on his perch, a manakin will raise his wings and beat out a series of loud snaps in a more deliberate fashion, the crackling sounds coming more slowly … and … with greater force. Correspondingly the wingbeats are more distinct to the eye … and it is easy to see that the movements of the wings are somehow associated with the production of the sound. Both the single snaps and the snapping roll … are less loud than the corresponding noises of … *Manacus*. In addition … the male manakins produce various whirring and rustling noises … either while they fly or by beating their wings while perching. As they approach the display perch in the short circling flight … they make a surprisingly loud noise such as may be imitated by holding a piece of stout cloth between both hands and suddenly jerking it taut. At the instant this noise is made there is a momentary break in the bird's flight. After delivering this flourish the manakin alights upon his display perch or upon the back of the waiting female.

Tello (2001) noted that the double wing-snap is common to *P. chloromeros*, *P. cornuta* and the present species. Females are generally silent, even at the lek, as in other small *Pipra* species (Wetmore 1972, Stiles and Skutch 1989), except apparently in defence of the nest or small young just fledged (Skutch 1949). Nestlings give quiet *peep* calls when the female arrives to feed them (Skutch 1949). Various examples of the species' voice have been published on the following commercial audio compilations: Moore (1992), Ross and Whitney (1995), Jahn *et al.* (2002), Krabbe and Nilsson (2003), Boesman (2006c) and Knapp and Will (2008). There are also many recordings archived online (at www.xeno-canto.org) from Belize, Costa Rica, Ecuador, Nicaragua and Panama, thereby encompassing all subspecies.

NATURAL HISTORY Red-capped Manakin is principally found in the midstorey of humid forest, but ranges from the upper understorey to the subcanopy. It occasionally visits the canopy (Loiselle 1988). In Costa Rica, Blake and Loiselle (2002) found that female survival was markedly higher than for males while, in Panama, Brawn *et al.* (1995) noted that juvenile survival rates were much lower than for adults of either sex in the Costa Rican study. Bucher and Worthington (1982) found that this species and Golden-collared Manakin *Manacus vitellinus* reduce their metabolic rates when resting, e.g. overnight, during which period body temperature may be lowered significantly (see also Vleck and Vleck 1979). Roosting behaviour is generally poorly known in Pipridae, but E. Bonaccorso and J. M. Guayasamin (*in litt.* 2004) found four separate individuals of *P. mentalis* (none adult males) roosting along a 400m stretch beside a stream, each one perched 2–3m above the ground. One individual returned to the same perch on two consecutive evenings.

FOOD AND FEEDING Reasonably well known due mainly to studies based in eastern Costa Rica. Like other *Pipra*, it is generally omnivorous in that it takes both fruit and insects (and spiders), but Red-capped Manakin is primarily a frugivore. Both fruit and insects are taken using a short-range sally-hover movement, and larger insects are beaten against the branch prior to being swallowed (Skutch 1949, Wetmore 1972). In respect of insect prey, Red-capped Manakin has been reported to not infrequently join mixed-species bird parties following army ants (Skutch 1949). The same author also witnessed in a female-plumaged bird an unsuccessful attempt to take a small lizard, which it beat against a branch but which subsequently escaped. In terms of its fruit diet, at least 74 species have been recorded. Favoured are species of Melastomataceae (including *Miconia simplex*, *Clidemia densiflora*, *Henriettea tuberculosa* and *Ossaea macrophylla*), Rubiaceae, Sapindaceae, Ulmaceae and *Guatteria* (Annonaceae), at least in Costa Rica (Worthington 1982, Moermond and Denslow 1985, Stiles and Skutch 1989, Loiselle and Blake 1999, Loiselle *et al.* 2007b). Arils, such as *Alchornea costaricensis* (Euphorbiaceae), are taken by Red-capped Manakin (Skutch 1980). Forty-five species including four *Miconia* (Melastomataceae) and 12 *Psychotria* spp. (Rubiaceae) were recorded being taken by *P. mentalis* during a study in central Panama (Poulin *et al.* 1999). Skutch (1949) reported that the diet of nestlings is principally fruit. The species' diet was also studied by Graham (1996) but we have not seen the results of this study. In a study of captive birds, Levey (1987) found that this and White-collared Manakin *Manacus candei* apparently cannot taste sugar (unlike at least some tanagers).

DISPLAY Brief descriptions of the Red-capped Manakin's display behaviour have been published by, among others, Wetmore (1972), Ridgely and Gwynne (1976), Hilty and Brown (1986) and Stiles and Skutch (1989), and some additional data were added by Tello (2001), who mentioned that males of this species at least occasionally perform coordinated flight-displays (as also reported in certain circumstances for *P. chloromeros* and Band-tailed Manakin *P. fasciicauda*). Tello (2001) also noted that *P. mentalis* has a type II flight-display, as described for *P. chloromeros* (and also seen in *P. erythrocephala*) but did not provide specific details. Display-perches are narrow horizontal or near-horizontal boughs, occasionally vines, 5–15m, more exceptionally >20m, above the ground (Skutch 1949, Wetmore 1972) and 3–30m apart (Stiles and Skutch), such that rival males must be rarely if ever in visual contact. On Barro Colorado Island, in Panama, Skutch (1949) found two leks comprising four and five adult males, respectively. Displaying males remain near or on these perches most of the day, with only short breaks to feed, but high-intensity displays seem to be limited to the first 2.5–3.0 hours of daylight, unless a female visits. Whenever a female arrives at a male's display-perch this stimulates much-increased activity, not only from the male whose perch she visits but also in the surrounding males. Neighbouring adult (and perhaps also young) males will frequently perch together but apparently never on their display-perches, rather in some 'neutral ground' between their courts. In such circumstances they will alternately display 'half-heartedly' to one another, giving wing-snaps and other sounds, partially raise the thighs and perform weak backward-slides (see below). Adult males appear to

never visit the display-perch of another male and young males seem to perform more perfunctory displays than adults (Skutch 1949). The first observations on the species' displays were published by Chapman (1929a, 1935), which were followed by the detailed account of its life history by Skutch (1949), upon which the following is strongly based. Remarkably, this seems to be the only detailed study of this manakin's behaviour to be published. Although he produced in many ways a very full account, there is no doubt that an enterprising modern worker could still capitalise on Skutch's groundwork. Skutch described four principal display behaviours exhibited by males, as follows. This species' *about-face* display involves the male standing on the display-perch legs stretched up to prominently reveal the yellow thighs, and his body horizontal or tilted slightly forward, in which position the bird flips round to face the other direction in a swift movement with one foot grasping the perch and the other moving sideways as the bird pivots. The changes in the position of the foot are so rapid to be easily overlooked, although with each about-face the bird gives a resonant wing-snap. Subsequently termed the *wing-snapping twist display*, this specific modification of 'about-face' behaviour is unique within the *P. erythrocephala* superspecies. The *backward-slide* commences in the same position adopted at the onset of the about-face display, i.e. 'standing tall' to display the yellow thighs, but thereafter the bird leans forward, sometimes almost touching the branch with his head, and cocks the tail. Using short, very rapid steps, the male moves backward along the perch in a sliding motion over several centimetres, following which the bird sometimes turns and slides back to his original position. This display is often accompanied by wing-whirring or the tail being moved rapidly from side to side, and Skutch (1949) observed one male to hold his wings up above his back as he slid towards a female that had arrived on the display-perch (a behaviour that is also seen in Red-headed Manakin). Both these displays are frequently employed whenever a female arrives at or in the vicinity of the display-perch, during which he endeavours to advance closer to her, as she remains quiet and relatively still more or less throughout. As in other *Pipra*, males conduct *short flights* by flying rapidly back and forth between the display-perch and another nearby, producing a loud wing-snap (see Voice) on commencing each flight. However, this display is probably less commonly given in the actual presence of a female. The *circling flight* comprises a rapid departure from the display-perch, following which the male circles round before returning. In the final stage of the descent, the male appears to 'stall', making the surprisingly loud tearing-cloth sound (see Voice) and then the shrill *eeee* on landing. This display also marks the culmination of a successful courtship, with the male landing on the back of the female to copulate, rather than on the display-perch itself, in such instances. Skutch (1949) several times observed females resist copulation, by either 'side-stepping' the incoming male or 'threatening' him using the bill.

BREEDING The nest, which was initially described and illustrated by Skutch (1949: Plate 1), is (as in all manakins) constructed by the female alone in the fork of a horizontal branch. It is placed in a shrub or small tree *c.*1.5–10.5m above the ground, although usually at the lower end of this range and perhaps only high up in second growth or in light-gaps (Skutch 1949). At least one nest was well shaded by surrounding vegetation, in this case by a *Euterpe* palm (Skutch 1949). The nest itself is a very shallow and tiny cup, typical of *Pipra*, constructed of pale brown vegetable fibres with fragments of dead leaves attached to the outside, especially on the base, and attached to the support branches using spiderwebs or similar material. Dead leaves can completely cover the outside and sometimes the inner part of the nest may contain some dark fungal hyphae or fern parts. Nest building can be a protracted affair. One nest that Skutch discovered in the early construction phase was only ready for eggs after c.8 days. Skutch (1949) and Wetmore (1972) presented dimensions of the nest. Skutch (1949, 1969) mentioned that the two-egg clutch is greyish-buff in their ground colour but heavily mottled brown, forming a wreath at the larger end (see Plate 1 in Skutch 1949). Robinson et al. (2000b) mentioned a single one-egg clutch; whether another egg had been predated is unknown. Wetmore (1972) mentioned another clutch that was more pinkish-white in ground colour, and both he and Skutch (1949, 1969) presented dimensions of eggs. Less is known concerning the incubation and fledging periods, but the eggs are laid c.24–72 hours apart and the female incubates for at least 80% of each day during the first few days, with mean on-bouts of c.65 minutes and off-bouts of 14 minutes based on a relatively small data sample (Skutch 1949). Skutch (op. cit.) thought that the incubation period was about 15–19 days, and Robinson et al. (2000b) found it to be c.21 days based on two nests in central Panama. These latter authors considered the nestling period to be just 13 days (based on four nests). Skutch (1949) also found that the females could incubate remarkably tightly, remaining on the nest even when he touched them, but occasionally using an apparent injury-feigning display, or elements of the male's about-face display, or even hovering and calling at him while Skutch inspected the contents. Ricklefs (1977) also noted how females did not flee the nest on human approach. The breeding season is reasonably well known in southern Central America, with egg laying in March–June/July in Costa Rica (Skutch 1949, Wetmore 1972) and perhaps occasionally, earlier, from January (MNCR), and later (to September: Wolfe et al. 2009), and in (December) February–August in Panama (Wetmore 1972, Willis and Eisenmann 1979; MVZ). Elsewhere, data are sparser and less detailed: from Mexico, Tashian (1952) and Binford (1989) reported single males in breeding condition in August in northern Chiapas and in June in Oaxaca, and in western Colombia M. A. Carriker (in Hilty and Brown 1986) took ten birds in breeding condition between December and March. As in several other manakins for which good data are available, it seems that predation rates in this species are high: of seven nests that Skutch (1949) followed in Panama or Costa Rica, all failed.

STATUS Although the overall population of Red-capped Manakin is considered to be declining, its overall range (estimated at 559,000km²) and the extent of remaining habitat offer some protection. BirdLife International (2004, 2008) currently categorises the species as Least Concern. Furthermore, Anciães and Peterson (2006) predicted that Red-capped Manakin might be substantially less at risk due to habitat loss in the face of predicted rates of climate change than many other species of manakins. The species is generally fairly common over much of its range. Monroe (1968) considered Red-capped Manakin to be 'exceedingly abundant' in forested areas of Honduras, and Blake and Loiselle (2002) found it to be the most frequently mist-netted piprid at their study site in eastern Costa Rica. Elsewhere, however, Wetmore (1972) already found that its range and numbers had probably declined in western Panama. Ridgely and Greenfield (2001) considered that the species must have declined massively in both numbers and probably range in Ecuador in recent decades, and local extinctions, e.g. at Río Palenque in southwest Pichincha have been reported. Red-capped Manakin is known from a reasonable number of protected areas through its wide range, among them: Yaxchilán Natural Monument, Mexico (Puebla-Olivares et al. 2002), Cockscomb Basin Wildlife Sanctuary, Belize (Wheatley and Brewer 2001), Laguna del Tigre National Park, Guatemala (Selvin and Castillo 2000), Río Indio-Maiz National Park, Nicaragua (Wheatley and Brewer 2001), Tortuguero National Park, La Selva Biological Station, Hitoy Cerere Biological Reserve and Corcovado National Park, Costa Rica (Lawson 2010), Soberanía National Park, Panama (Poulin et al. 1999), and Río Canandé reserve and Bilsa Biological Station, Ecuador (Williams et al. 1997).

REFERENCES Anciães and Peterson (2006, 2009), Andrle (1967), Angehr and Dean (2010), AOU (1998), Bartholomew et al. (1983), Binford (1989), BirdLife International (2004, 2008), Blake and Loiselle (2001, 2002, 2009), Boesman (2006c), Bostwick and Prum (2003), Brawn et al. (1995), Bucher and Worthington (1982), Burton (1975), Chapman (1917, 1929a, 1935), Cooper (1997, 1999), Dickinson (2003), Dunning (2008), Eisenmann and Avendaño (2007), England (2000), Garrigues and Dean (2007), González-García et al. (1993), Graham (1996), Graves (1981), Griscom (1932, 1933), Haffer (1967a, 1967b, 1975), Hartert (1898), Hellmayr (1906d, 1929b), Hilty and Brown (1986), T. R. Howell (1957), Howell (1999), Howell and Webb (1995), Hudon et al. (1989), Jahn et al. (2002), Jenkins (1982), Jones (2004), Kennard and Peters (1928), Knapp and Will (2008), Krabbe and Nilsson (2003), Land (1963), Lawson (2010), Levey (1987, 1988), Loiselle (1988), Loiselle and Blake (1999), Loiselle et al. (2007b), McDonald et al. (2001), McKay et al. (2010), Moermond and Denslow (1985), Monroe (1968), Moore (1992), Peters (1929), Piaskowski et al. (2006), Poulin et al. (1999), Prum (1990a), Puebla-Olivares et al. (2002), Restall et al. (2006), Ricklefs (1977), Ridgely and Greenfield (2001), Ridgely and Gwynne (1976, 1989), Ridgely and Tudor (1994, 2009), Robinson et al. (2000a, 2000b), Ross and Whitney (1995), Salaman et al. (2008, 2009), Selvin and Castillo (2000), Skutch (1949, 1969, 1980), Slud (1964), Snow (2004b), Stiles and Skutch (1989), Stotz et al. (1996), Strauch (1977), Tashian (1952), Tello (2001), Vallely and Whitman (1997), Vleck and Vleck (1979), Wetmore (1972), Wheatley and Brewer (2001), Williams et al. (1997), Willis and Eisenmann (1979), Wolfe et al. (2009), Worthington (1982, 1989).

Red-capped Manakin *Pipra mentalis*. **Fig. 1**. Male, *P. m. mentalis*, Las Guacamayas, Chiapas, southern Mexico, March (*Nick Athanas / Tropical Birding*). **Fig. 2**. Male, *P. m. mentalis*, Bosque del Río Tigre Lodge, Osa Peninsula, southwest Costa Rica, February (*Kevin Easley / Costa Rica Gateway*). **Fig. 3**. Male, *P. m. ignifera*, Soberanía National Park, Colón, central Panama, December (*Nick Athanas / Tropical Birding*). The range of this subspecies has been the subject of some discussion in the literature and in the past some authors have suggested that it reaches as far as western Costa Rica. As can be seen here, separating these taxa based on the depth of the red head or other features (see text) can be difficult. *P. m. ignifera* is generally stated to possess a smaller yellow chin than the nominate, but this individual belies that (see text). **Fig. 4**. Female, *P. m. mentalis*, southwest Costa Rica, April (*Steven Easley / Costa Rica Gateway*). Some individuals have very pale irides, even whitish-looking, but there is much variation (see text). The depth of the yellow thighs also varies considerably, but they are reasonably bright in this bird. **Fig. 5**. Displaying male, *P. m. mentalis*, Bosque del Río Tigre Lodge, Osa Peninsula, southwest Costa Rica, February (*Kevin Easley / Costa Rica Gateway*).

ROUND-TAILED MANAKIN
Pipra chloromeros   Plate 3

Pipra chloromeros **Tschudi, 1844**, *Arch. Naturg.* 10(1): 271, Montañas of northwestern Peru [= Valley of Vitoc, dept. Junín, *fide* Hellmayr 1929b]

Despite at least part of this species' range lying within a comparatively well-studied part of the New World tropics, Round-tailed Manakin is one of the poorest known members of the *Pipra erythrocephala* clade. However, in recent years, the first detailed observations of its lekking behaviour have been published, and its nest was also recently described for the first time.

IDENTIFICATION 10.5–11.0cm. There is only limited geographical overlap with the ostensibly very similarly plumaged Red-headed Manakin *P. rubrocapilla*, which has an extensive range in southern Amazonia, but is largely allopatric with the Round-tailed Manakin. In at least some areas of sympatry (e.g. easternmost dpto. Madre de Dios, Peru) the two are apparently rarely if ever syntopic; for instance, Schulenberg *et al.* (2007) considered that in such cases, *P. rubrocapilla* is largely restricted to *terra firme* forests, whilst *P. chloromeros* inhabits seasonally flooded areas. The same might be true in Bolivia but there seem to be no data on the mechanisms at work separating the two species there. Males of these species can be separated by the rounded (i.e. slightly graduated) rather than square-cut tail tip, and Round-tailed Manakin frequently appears rather crested, due to the feathers of the hindcrown being somewhat 'shaggy'. Further minor but noticeable differences, given optimal views, are the whitish irides and yellow tibial feathering of males of the present species. Female Round-tailed Manakin shares the male's graduated tail, and this will serve as the main distinguishing feature from other female *Pipra* that inhabit the same range, whilst the crest can be 'shaggy' like that of the male. The irides of females can be either greyish or whitish; if the latter, this will serve as a further identification feature versus Golden-headed *P. erythrocephala* or Red-headed Manakins. Female Round-tailed Manakin might also be separated from either of the two latter species by the rather yellower underparts, but this is only likely to be useful in extremely good-quality comparative views.

DISTRIBUTION Round-tailed Manakin is restricted to southwestern Amazonia. Cracraft (1985) considered the species to be restricted to the Inambari Centre of endemism. It occurs from northern Peru, in northern San Martín and southernmost Amazonas (i.e. entirely south of the Río Marañón), southwards in the Amazon lowlands and the foothills of the Andes through the eastern half of the country to Madre de Dios and northern Puno (Schulenberg *et al.* 2007), thence across the northern half of Bolivia, where it occurs in the departments of Pando, Beni, La Paz, Cochabamba and western Santa Cruz (Remsen and Traylor 1989), and into westernmost Brazil, in the state of Acre, where *P. chloromeros* was discovered as recently as 1995 at two localities, Tapuara (09°16'S, 72°42'W) and Largo Ceará, both sites on the left bank of the Rio Juruá (Whittaker and Oren 1999), and then at Estação Ecológica do Rio Acre, in 2005 (Aleixo and Guilherme 2008, 2010). Further west, the Round-tailed Manakin seems to be replaced again by Red-headed Manakin, e.g. at Ramal Jarinal, in eastern Acre (Guilherme and Santos 2009), and in the RESEX Chico

Mendes, in the extreme southeast of the state (Mestre *et al.* 2010). The species is recorded to 1,500m in the Andean foothills of Peru, e.g. in Manu National Park and Biosphere Reserve (Walker *et al.* 2006, Schulenberg *et al.* 2007).

MOVEMENTS None is known and the species is presumed to be resident like other red-headed manakins. Graves *et al.* (1983) reported that females are considerably more dispersive than adult males, whilst immature males show dispersal abilities somewhat intermediate between adults of the two sexes.

HABITAT Inhabits humid forest, with a preference in areas of overlap with Red-headed Manakin for seasonally flooded (*várzea*) forests. Nonetheless, Round-tailed Manakin does inhabit dry-land forests, sometimes being found in areas of tall bamboo (FMNH) wherever *P. rubrocapilla* is absent, e.g. in Acre, Brazil (Whittaker and Oren 1999), and Tello (2001) even found that density of leks is marginally higher in *terra firme* as opposed to floodplain forest. Merkord *et al.* (2009) noticed a marked preference for the forest interior in the Cordillera Azul, in northern Peru.

DESCRIPTION A relatively typical *Pipra* manakin, with the exception of the slightly graduated tail shape and somewhat pronounced crest. Males have modified secondary feathers, which are enlarged, curved and stiffened, with thickened shafts (Snow 2004b), and the shafts of the outer rectrices are also stiffened with thickened bases (Hellmayr 1929b). The bill is reasonably well arched, with relatively large nostrils and often a slightly hooked tip. Hudon *et al.* (1989) investigated the carotenoids in the head-feathers of this species and other members of the *P. erythrocephala* superspecies. *Adult male.* – Entirely black body, wings and tail with a slight velvet blue cast, relieved only by the red head, over the entire crown and nape, reaching below the eye to the malar region and the hindneck. The nape-feathers protrude from the line of the head, giving males the appearance of a 'shaggy' crest. The long tibial feathers are quite bright yellow, intermixed with black and sometimes with some orange. *Adult female.* – The upperparts are entirely dull olive with a slight grey cast and slightly darker tips to the feathers of the crown and nape, with a very slightly tufted appearance to the rear crown and paler olive-grey underparts, which become vaguely yellowish over the belly, with yellowish tibial feathering and sometimes a very slightly yellow-mottled throat patch. However, some can have the yellow parts of the ventral surface much less contrasting. The flight feathers are generally browner than the rest of the upper surface, with pale green fringes, and white outer webs to the tertials and innermost secondaries. Graves (1981) reported a tiny number of females with some red feathers on the crown and head. *Juvenile.* – Snow (2004b) considered that young birds are identical to females but have darker grey irides. *Moult.* – There are no published data concerning moult, but Tello (2001) reported that immature males probably achieve adult plumage only in their third year. Individuals of both sexes collected in southeast Peru (dpto. Madre de Dios) in August–September were not moulting, but one male taken in November was said to be replacing its feathers (FMNH). *Bare parts.* – Males are stated to possess white or whitish irides, with a blackish or dark brown bill that becomes greyer, but sometimes flesh-coloured over the culmen, and smoky flesh-coloured legs and feet, whilst in females, the irides are either greyish or whitish (Snow 2004b, Schulenberg *et al.* 2007; FMNH).

MEASUREMENTS (BMNH; FMNH: Bolivia and Peru) Wing of male (*n* = 15) 58.0–65.5mm, wing of female (*n* = 15) 59.0–66.5mm; tail of male (*n* = 15) 26–37mm, tail of female (*n* = 15) 26–33mm; bill of male (*n* = 15) 10.82–12.66mm, bill of female (*n* = 15) 11.54–13.38mm; tarsus of male (*n* = 15) 14.92–16.99mm, tarsus of female (*n* = 15) 14.52–17.60mm. Additional mensural data were published by Haffer (1967b). Traylor (1950) found no evidence for an increase in wing-length with altitude in this species. Weight: 12–21g (males) and 14–23g (females) (FMNH; Snow 2004b, Dunning 2008).

GEOGRAPHICAL VARIATION Monotypic. Zimmer (1930) noted apparent differences between single young males collected in eastern Peru and northern Bolivia, but there is no suggestion of identifiable geographical variation.

VOICE Round-tailed Manakin's vocalisations are broadly homologous to those of other members of the *P. erythrocephala* superspecies group. Sonograms and full descriptions of the various components were presented by Tello (2001) based on his work in southeast Peru (see also Natural History). Perhaps most characteristic is the multisyllabic advertisement call, rendered *fui-ii-ii-i—chi-awaaak*, which lasts *c.*1.7 seconds and is audible to 100m away. The introductory phrase is rarely given alone, but the *chi-awaaak*, which lasts just 0.3 seconds, is commonly given on its own. Both the introductory and main phrases decline in frequency and were considered by Tello to be used to attract females to the male's court but were never heard by him once a female had arrived at the arena. The display-call was the second-most frequently uttered vocalisation and is used during encounters between territorial males; it is a three-note *fi-cuac-cuac* lasting 0.6 seconds, comprising a whistle followed by two (sometimes three) buzzing notes, or alternatively may consist of three buzzes followed by several whistles. Appeasement whistles and double wing-snaps were heard much less frequently than other vocalisations. The former is a sharp double-noted *fi-u* lasting 0.1 seconds on a declining frequency, and appears to signify a male's desire to desist in displaying against a dominant rival. Double wing-snaps comprise two pulses of sound emitted by the wings on landing during to-and-fro flights (see Natural History) and appear designed to accentuate the male's arrival on the perch. Both type I and II flight-displays (see Natural History)

are accompanied by specific vocalisations used only during such contexts: type I displays are marked by a high-pitched *fu-fi-fu* on a downward scale lasting 0.5 seconds, whilst the type II display-call is a series of 6–7 whistles of increasing intensity culminating in a single buzzing note (which recalls that uttered by *P. mentalis*), the whole lasting just 0.3 seconds. Finally, the frenzied-flutter display (see Natural History) also possesses its own special call, in this case a quite prolonged *eeeee-eeeee* lasting just less than 2.0 seconds. The species' vocalisations feature on the following audio compilations: Schulenberg *et al.* (2000) and Boesman (2009). A handful of recordings from Bolivia and Peru are archived online at www.xeno-canto-org.

NATURAL HISTORY Round-tailed Manakins are found in the understorey to midstorey. Tello (2001) noted that females and young males can join mobile mixed-species foraging flocks.

FOOD AND FEEDING There are very few details concerning the species' diet and foraging behaviour, although Tello (2003) reported that fruits are taken using a sally-hover typical of the genus (Snow 2004b) and in his earlier work (Tello 2001) reported that Round-tailed Manakins consume berries of the following species: *Psychotria* (Rubiaceae), *Miconia* (Melastomataceae), *Neea* (Nyctaginaceae) and *Ardisia* (Myrsinaceae). Furthermore, Tello (2003) noted that *P. chloromeros* was one of the most frequent feeding visitors to a fruiting *Ficus pertusa* (Moraceae).

DISPLAY The species' displays have been well studied recently by Tello (2001). In southeast Peru, he found that Round-tailed Manakins appear to breed mainly in the period from early August to late November and to operate a dispersed lek system with 220–1,000m between each lek, each of which is attended by 2–5 males (Whittaker and Oren 1999, Tello 2001). The larger leks seem to be the focus of the most intensive activity and may support more than one alpha male (Tello 2001). At a study site in La Paz, Bolivia, in June, Graves *et al.* (1983) found no evidence of breeding, either from field observations or examination of trapped birds. Lek sites, which are maintained for many years, appear to be characterised by an unusually dense understorey, with a higher preponderance of vines, shrubs and understorey trees than non-lek sites. The males space themselves at anything from 8 to 87m between individuals, i.e. always within auditory but more rarely in visual contact, and each male defends a territory of 20–50m in diameter, with apparent neutral zones at the edge courts over which no one male is dominant (Tello 2001). Within his court, the male usually has one or two horizontal display perches, one to three accessory perches adjacent to these and up to 19 advertising perches, from which they sing. Perches are kept clear of vegetation and are between 4 and 16m above the ground.

Tello (2001) identified the following displays during his study (his terminology is adopted throughout): to-and-fro flight, type I and II flight-displays, backward slide, wing-flick and pivot, about-face, squat, frenzied flutter, side-to-side slide and upright posture, in a more less decreasing order of importance (i.e. usage). *To-and-fro flights* are most frequently given when a female-plumaged bird enters the male's court and consist of short flights of 0.5–1.0m between a main perch and accessory perches, the male performing an about-face on landing and sometimes part of the advertisement call. A double wing-snap may also be given in some cases. In *type I flight-displays* the male flies down and then up to a perch 12–15m above the ground and up to 20m from the display perch, before returning within seconds to the latter perch tracing a S pattern through the air, and uttering the flight-display call on landing, whereupon the male may also perform several backward slides or squatting displays, before going to repeat the flight-display. In contrast, *type II flight-displays* were observed much less frequently by Tello (2001) and seemed to fulfil a mainly agonistic function towards juvenile *P. chloromeros* or other bird species, unlike type I displays, which were mainly given in the presence of a female. Type II flight-displays commenced in the same way, but the male describes a U shape in returning to the display perch, on which he then vocalises and produces a buzzing sound, which Tello considered to be probably of mechanical origin. Thereafter, the male may perform about-faces, wing-flicks and pivots, and further flight-displays. *Backward slides* were the third-commonest display observed by Tello. The male faces lengthwise along the branch, raises the tail and the body onto its haunches and takes short, rapid steps backwards for up to 30cm, thereby appearing to slide down the perch. In climax, the male will either (1) raise his tail and head into a briefly held U posture, accompanied by a soft *hick* sound, (2) perform wing-flicks and pivots, before entering into a flight-display, (3) face out from the perch, spread his wings and fan the tail in tandem with a display-call, (4) vibrate his wings rapidly or (5) about-face and then backward slide in reverse to his starting point. *Wing-flicks* are given both in courtship and territorial interactions, and consist of a series of flicks of the wings, alternating with pivoting movements, whereby the male turns 45° on the perch. Marginally less frequently given, *about-face* movements consist of a rapid 180° turn on the perch between to-and-fro flights (see above) and may be accompanied by wing-flicks. The *squat display* is mirrored by Golden-headed Manakin: the male crouches on the perch whilst fanning his tail, quivering the wings and making rapid side-to-side jumps, which sometimes culminate in a mechanical noise similar to but quieter than the double wing-snap of Red-capped Manakin *P. mentalis*. Tello noted that this display seemed most frequent if another male entered the displaying male's court or a female was visiting the display perch of a rival. The *frenzied-flutter display* simulates copulation and comprises a brief hovering flight above the display perch accompanied by frantic calling (see Voice); in Tello's experience it was usually provoked by the departure of an unreceptive female from the court. An exclusively territorial display, *side-to-side slides* involve the male facing outward from the perch taking very short sideways steps for 5–10cm. The *upright posture* is also assumed by males engaged in territorial rivalry, but is also adopted when a female arrives at the display perch; the male holds the head nearly vertically with the bill pointing skywards.

Social status amongst males increases with age, passing from immature to non-territorial to territorial, with the last category being dominant over all other males, although immature males can display against adult territorial males (Tello 2001). Females appear to visit the lek sites most frequently in the early afternoon (usually singly, but Tello once witnessed two females arrive at a male court simultaneously). All of the copulations observed by Tello were on the main display perch, and these were immediately preceded by either type I flight-displays, backward slides or squatting displays. This time of the day also coincides with the peaks in male displays and their territory attendance, although inter-male territorial disputes, which rarely end in fights, are commonest during the morning hours (Tello 2001). Other manakins, Blue-crowned *Lepidothrix coronata* and Band-tailed Manakins *Pipra fasciicauda*, are chased from lek sites, as are some other bird species, including the comparatively large White-winged Shrike-Tanager *Lanio versicolor*.

BREEDING The nest of *P. chloromeros* has only recently been described, based on brief observations in Madre de Dios, southeast Peru, on 1 December (Doucet and Mennill 2005). The observers were only able to observe the initial construction, during which time the female worked constantly for several hours, so no data are available concerning the eggs, or the incubation and fledging periods. The shallow open-cup nest was sited 4–5m above the ground, in the horizontal fork of a dead branch supported within a vine tangle (an unusual nest-site for a manakin). It was attached to the branch using numerous spiderwebs, which the female collected first, followed by the additional material to provide the structure and bulk of the nest, namely dead leaves (which formed the majority of the outer layer of the nest) and fungal rhizomorphs. The only other data involve individuals of both sexes taken in the same area of Peru which were in breeding condition between early August and November, including one female taken in late October with an unshelled egg in the oviduct (FMNH).

STATUS Round-tailed Manakin is currently treated as a species of Least Concern (BirdLife International 2004, 2009), although Anciães and Peterson (2006) considered that the species might be moderately impacted by potential and predicted levels of climate change. It was considered to be locally fairly common in Peru by Schulenberg *et al.* (2007) but in the southeast of the country, Terborgh *et al.* (1990) found mean densities of just one bird per 100ha in suitable habitat. Round-tailed Manakin is known from several protected areas in Bolivia and Peru, including Amboró National Park, Madidi National Park (Perry *et al.* 1997), Carrasco National Park (XC 3702) and Pilón Lajas Biosphere Reserve, all in Bolivia (Hennessey *et al.* 2003a), and Manu National Park and Biosphere Reserve (Terborgh *et al.* 1984, Walker *et al.* 2006) and Tambopata-Candamo Reserved Zone, in Peru (Parker and Wust 1994, Parker *et al.* 1994a, 1994b).

REFERENCES Aleixo and Guilherme (2008, 2010), Anciães and Peterson (2006, 2009), BirdLife International (2004, 2008), Boesman (2009), Chapman (1921), Cracraft (1985), Doucet and Mennill (2005), Dunning (2008), Graves (1981), Graves *et al.* (1983), Haffer (1967b, 1992b), Hellmayr (1906d, 1929b), Hennessey *et al.* (2003a, 2003b), Hudon *et al.* (1989), Mee *et al.* (2002), Merkord *et al.* (2009), Mestre *et al.* (2010), Niethammer (1956), Parker and Wust (1994), Parker *et al.* (1982, 1994a, 1994b), Perry *et al.* (1997), Prum (1990a), Remsen and Traylor (1989), Ridgely and Tudor (1994, 2009), Robbins *et al.* (2011), Robinson and Terborgh (1997), Schulenberg *et al.* (2000, 2007), Sick (1997), Snow (2004b), Tello (2001, 2003), Terborgh *et al.* (1984, 1990), Traylor (1950), Walker *et al.* (2006), Whittaker and Oren (1999), Zimmer (1930).

Round-tailed Manakin *Pipra chloromeros*. **Fig. 1**. Male, Santa Cruz, dpto. Beni, Bolivia, September (*Joe Tobias / Edward Grey Institute, Oxford University*). **Figs. 2–3**. Male, Mazuco–Puerto Maldonado road, dpto. Madre de Dios, Peru, October (*Hadoram Shirihai / Photographic Handbook to Birds of the World*). Fig. 2 represents a useful study of the species' tail shape, and also note the white irides well displayed in both images. **Fig. 4**. Female, upper Río Madre de Dios, dpto. Madre de Dios, southeast Peru, May (*Claudia Torres*).

SCARLET-HORNED MANAKIN
Pipra cornuta   Plate 2

Pipra cornuta Spix, 1825, *Av. Bras.* 2: 5, pl. 7, fig. 2, in sylvis flum. Amazonum [error = Mount Roraima, Venezuela]

Scarlet-horned Manakin occurs syntopically with another member of the *P. erythrocephala* superspecies group, namely Golden-headed Manakin *P. erythrocephala* itself, but is the only red-headed, black-bodied manakin north of the Amazon and east of the Andes. It was formerly placed in its own genus, *Ceratopipo*, and *P. cornuta* also occupies the smallest range of any of its superspecies, being practically confined to the Pantepui region (Mayr and Phelps 1967) and the BirdLife-delimited Tepuis Endemic Bird Area (Stattersfield *et al.* 1998).

IDENTIFICATION 12.5–12.7cm. The beautiful male should be immediately recognisable given that this species is the only red-headed manakin with a black body in its range, even if the remarkable double horns are not immediately seen. Females will certainly prove more difficult to distinguish, but note the relatively long tail (common to both sexes) in comparison with that of female Golden-headed Manakin, which frequently shares the same forests (Snow 1977a, Willard *et al.* 1991). Female *P. cornuta* is also more greyish-toned above than the latter species, but this might prove difficult to evaluate correctly in the shade of the forest. Other potential confusion risks for female Scarlet-horned Manakin are Olive Manakin *Chloropipo uniformis*, which also shares the same forests, but this species has longer wings, darker legs on average, lacks any suggestion of horns on the rear crown and is larger overall with white underwing-coverts, although this last feature is not necessarily easily appreciated. Female White-bearded Manakin *Manacus manacus* is another potential stumbling block, but has brighter legs than the present species, also lacks any tuft effect on the nape and is overall marginally smaller.

DISTRIBUTION Scarlet-horned Manakin occupies a relatively small range within the Guianan Shield, principally in Venezuela throughout the tepui region south of the Orinoco, where it is found on the Cerros Yavi and Sipapo south to the Cerro de la Neblina in Amazonas, and in Bolívar

from the northwest (e.g. on the upper Río Cuchivero) and on the Sierra de Lema south to Uei-tepui (Hilty 2003). In adjacent Guyana, the species occurs along the Adaroo River, in the headwaters of the Mazaruni (Snyder 1966) and on Mt Kowa on the Potaro Plateau (Barnett *et al.* 2002), and in northern Brazil, in northernmost Roraima, where *P. cornuta* was initially found in June 1948 on the Brazilian side of the Cerro Uei-tepui (Cerro de Sol) at 1,300–1,720m (Phelps and Phelps 1962) and on the Cerro Urutaní in 1977 (Dickerman and Phelps 1982). However, it is worth remembering that specimens were collected by Natterer at the Rio Marou, which locality was supposed by Pinto (1944) to lie near Manaus, but has subsequently been judged to lie within the upper Rio Branco drainage (Snow 1977a). Furthermore, the species is also present on the Brazilian side of the Pico da Neblina, in northernmost Amazonas (R. Czaban; www.wikiaves.com.br/71868&t=s&s=11426). The species' elevational range in Venezuela is 500–1,800m (Hilty 2003).

MOVEMENTS None recorded to date and Snow (2004b) considered the species to be almost certainly sedentary.

HABITAT Scarlet-horned Manakin is an inhabitant of humid and wet primary forest, and mature second growth with a tall canopy, always in montane regions. It visits borders, but leks appear to be widely scattered, being usually concentrated in areas with abundant slender-stemmed saplings or dense old second growth (Hilty 2003).

DESCRIPTION Relatively the longest-tailed of the *P. erythrocephala* superspecies and males are further distinguished from the other red-headed members of this group by the tufted (horned) rear crown-feathers. *Adult male.* – Entirely deep black body, wings and tail with a velvet blue sheen especially on the upperparts, relieved only by the all-red head reaching to the throat and neck-sides, and the red thighs, which are revealed to advantage during the species' displays (as in all of this superspecies). The rear crown-feathers are elongated and protrude from the line of the head, forming two tufts that project either side of the head and curve slightly upward. *Adult female.* – The upperparts are entirely dull olive with a slight grey cast and slightly darker tips to the feathers of the crown and nape, with a very slightly tufted appearance to the rear crown ('shadowing' the male's plumage) and paler olive-grey underparts, which become vaguely yellowish over the throat and belly, with yellowish tibial feathering. However, some can have the yellow parts of the ventral surface much paler and less striking. The flight feathers are generally browner than the rest of the upper surface, with pale green fringes, and white outer webs to the tertials and innermost secondaries. *Juvenile.* – Hilty (2003) and Snow (2004b) considered that young birds are identical to females but have paler bills and darker irides. We have seen a very young male in BMNH, in which there are a few black feathers on the breast-sides. *Moult.* – Nothing has been published, although feather replacement presumably follows a similar pattern as in *Pipra* for which such data are available. *Bare parts.* – Males are stated to have white irides, with a pale flesh-coloured bill and flesh-coloured or brownish legs and feet, whilst in females (and immatures) the irides are either creamy white or dark brown, the bill is dusky brown (paler in young birds), and the legs and feet are yellowish-flesh to pale brownish-orange (Willard *et al.* 1991, Hilty 2003, Snow 2004b).

MEASUREMENTS (BMNH; FMNH: Guyana, southern Venezuela) Wing of male (*n* = 5) 65–68mm, wing of female (*n* = 5) 64–69mm; tail of male (*n* = 5) 40.5–44.0mm, tail of female (*n* = 5) 41–44mm; bill of male (*n* = 5) 12.30–14.23mm, bill of female (*n* = 5) 13.24–14.54mm; tarsus of male (*n* = 5) 14.97–18.66mm, tarsus of female (*n* = 5) 12.78–17.69mm. Weight: 22–25g (five males) and 18.0–28.5g (six females) (Snow 1997a, 2004b, Willard *et al.* 1991, Dunning 2008; COP; FMNH).

GEOGRAPHICAL VARIATION Monotypic.

VOICE The commonest vocalisation is a trisyllabic, rather squeaky or metallic-sounding *wrrt-pit-arrk*, or *squee-ke-slick*, which is sometimes preceded by another *pit* note and lasts *c.*1 second (Snow 2004b). Snow (1977a) also mentioned a sharp disyllabic *ker-zeek* (also rendered *ee-slick*) and a monosyllabic *zeek*. All of these are rather abruptly given. The mechanical sound made by the wings was described by Hilty (2003) as an 'abrupt crackling or rough-sounding *P'R'ROP* (like electric bug-zapper)'. Tello (2001) noted that the wing-snapping sound in *P. cornuta* is very similar to that in *P. mentalis* and *P. chloromeros*, and that wing-snaps are given both in flight and immediately on landing, but are not associated with the squat display (cf. *P. chloromeros*). Sonograms of both mechanical wing noises and the advertisement song were presented by Snow (1977a). Vocalisations of Scarlet-horned Manakin have been presented on the Boesman (2006a, 2006b) audio compilations, and there are also a few recordings from Venezuela archived online at www.xeno-canto.org.

NATURAL HISTORY Scarlet-horned Manakin principally is found in the upper understorey and midstorey of forest.

FOOD AND FEEDING The species' diet is very poorly known, although it has been recorded feeding on the berries of Melastomataceae using a sally-hover technique typical of small manakins (Barnett *et al.* 2002, Hilty 2003).

DISPLAY Displays in this species were most extensively reported on by Snow (1977a) based on his observations on the Gran Sabana in southeastern Venezuela during April, at which season he did not witness any female visits to leks, although Barnett *et al.* (2002) observed female visits to leks in neighbouring Guyana in July. Hilty (2003) thought that display might occur year-round, at least from November to June or July, albeit with peak activity in January–March. Unfortunately, our cumulative information is much less than for the previous species. Snow found leks of Golden-headed Manakin in relatively close proximity to the dispersed display grounds of the present species. Males seem to spend much of the daytime hours on the lek ground, where they generally keep to the upper understorey to midstorey (5–15m above the ground, although Hilty 2003 noted perches as low as 2m), where they tend to use the same few perches. Displays tend to be synchronised between the different males present at the lek (2–20, although smaller numbers seem to be more usual), with bouts of display lasting 1–5 minutes and one bird stimulating the others into displaying, and the males occasionally spend periods of time perched in relatively close proximity without displaying. Snow identified three ritualised displays, all of which are known amongst other *Pipra* species; these are the backward slide (considered the commonest by Hilty 2003), side-to-side slide and the display-flight. *Backward slides* are performed with the body aligned along the perch, the head lowered, the tail slightly depressed and the body raised

up on its haunches to prominently exhibit the red thighs, with the bird taking rapid short steps backwards along the display branch for *c.*15cm. At the close of the backwards slide, the bird either suddenly vibrates the wings at high speed, producing an explosive *prrt* sound, whereupon the bird jumps back, like a cork from a bottle, to its original position then repeats the display, or alternatively the display session is terminated with the bird spreading the wings and fanning the tail. The *side-to-side slide* consists of a series of very rapid short steps sideways along the perch for *c.*10cm, while the bird faces outwards (rather than along the perch), terminating with the wing noise described above and the bird jumping back to its original position. A lower-intensity version of this display also seems to exist (Barnett *et al.* 2002). Both of these displays can be given on various perches within a male's court. The *display-flight* commences at the main display perch (a horizontal branch within a small understorey tree, and *c.*5m above the ground) from where the male flies downwards and then upwards to a similar-level perch up to 20m distant. After 5–12 seconds, the bird returns to the display perch in a fast flight with a U-shaped trajectory. On landing again, the male either gives a series of (up to five) buzzing calls while fluttering the wings, or it performs several backward or side-to-side slides. Males usually perform 3–5 displays and then depart the court for up to 15 minutes (Hilty 2003). Should a female arrive at the court, the male will slide backwards towards her, twitching his tail up and down, tickling the female's body (Hilty 2003).

BREEDING To date, nothing has been published concerning this species' nest and eggs, but Willard *et al.* (1991) collected females in breeding condition (one with a fertilised egg in the ovaries, and another with a brood patch) in February in southernmost Venezuela, and a juvenile has been collected in Amazonas, Venezuela, also in February (COP 70745).

STATUS Scarlet-horned Manakin is currently considered Least Concern by BirdLife International (2004, 2008) and is generally fairly common to common in Venezuela (Hilty 2003), as well as within its limited range in Guyana (Braun *et al.* 2007). However, it seems extremely local in the far north of Brazil, where it is restricted to fewer than a handful of tepuis on the border with Venezuela (Sick 1997). This species' range is relatively well protected, with comparatively low levels of human impact; all of the tepuis are designated Natural Monuments by the Venezuelan government, and furthermore the following protected areas have been established that cover the Scarlet-horned Manakin's range: Parque Nacional Canaima, Parque Nacional Jaua-Sarisariñama, Parque Nacional Parima-Tapirapecó and Parque Nacional Serranía de la Neblina.

REFERENCES Anciães and Peterson (2009), Barnett *et al.* (2002), BirdLife International (2004, 2008), Boesman (2006a, 2006b), Braun *et al.* (2007), Chubb (1921), Dickerman and Phelps (1982), Dunning (2008), Gilliard (1941), Haffer (1970), Hellmayr (1906d, 1929b), Hilty (2003), Mayr and Phelps (1967), Meyer de Schauensee and Phelps (1978), Naka *et al.* (2006), Pérez-Emán *et al.* (2003), Phelps and Phelps Jr (1962), Prum (1990a), Restall *et al.* (2006), Ridgely and Tudor (1994, 2009), Snow (1977a, 2004b), Snyder (1966), Stattersfield *et al.* (1998), Stotz *et al.* (1996), Tello (2001), Willard *et al.* (1991).

Scarlet-horned Manakin *Pipra cornuta*. **Fig. 1**. Male, Sierra de Lema, Bolívar, southeast Venezuela, March (*David J. Southall*). **Fig. 2**. Male, Sierra de Lema, Bolívar, southeast Venezuela, October (*Nick Athanas / Tropical Birding*). The red-headed members of the *P. erythrocephala* group are all allopatric, making identification of the present species straightforward, even if the distinctive 'horns' are not seen.

177

Genus *Lepidothrix*: 'crowned' manakins

The eight current members of this genus were predicted to form a superspecies by Snow (1975). A year earlier, Haffer (1974) had suggested that only the lowland white- and blue-crowned species should be included in the superspecies, and this position was supported by AOU (1983) and Sibley and Monroe (1990), whereas Snow (1979b) decided to also include Blue-rumped Manakin *L. isidorei* and Cerulean-capped Manakin *L. coeruleocapilla* in this grouping. In contrast, Sibley and Monroe (1990) considered the last two-named taxa to represent their own superspecies, and this position was later accepted by Snow (2004b).

BLUE-CROWNED MANAKIN
Lepidothrix coronata   Plate 4

Pipra coronata **Spix, 1825**, *Av. Bras.* 2: 5, pl. 7. São Paulo de Olivença, Rio Solimões, Brazil

Blue-crowned Manakin perhaps consists of three species-level groups. The so-called Velvety Manakin *L. (c.) velutina* (including *minuscula*) is found in Middle America and northwest South America west of the Andes. East of the Andes black-bodied populations occur from eastern Colombia to south of the Amazon in eastern Peru and western Brazil; and green-bodied male populations further south again, to northern Bolivia. However, the situation with respect to the latter two populations is decidedly complicated by the presence of intergrades.

IDENTIFICATION 8.0–11.2cm. In Middle America, in the western foothills of the Andes and across northwestern Amazonia, males of this species are easily identified, as this species is the only black-bodied, blue-crowned manakin in range (although note that the colour of the crown is not always obvious in the forest shade). There is no blue or white patch on the rump. Females might be confused with either sex of Green Manakin *Chloropipo holochlora* in southeasternmost Panama and northwestern South America, but the latter species is distinctly larger, has duller upperparts in the case of race *C. h. litae* (on the Pacific slope in Colombia) and east of the Andes has a much duller breast (Hilty and Brown 1986). Female Blue-crowned Manakin often shows reddish or red irides (especially in Central America and northernmost South America), which can help to distinguish this species from many similar female manakins, except female White-crowned Manakin *Dixiphia pipra*, which has more extensively yellowish underparts. There is some overlap in southern Venezuela with Orange-bellied Manakin *L. suavissima*, females of which possess an obviously pale throat (males are impossible to mistake). The situation on the east slope of the Andes, where two other species replace each other north to south, Blue-rumped Manakin *L. isidorei* and Cerulean-capped Manakin *L. coeruleocapilla*, is discussed under those species, but note that both these species are typically less commonly encountered than *L. coronata* and generally occur at higher altitudes, e.g. in foothill and cloud forests. Further south, in extreme southeast Amazonia, males of the pale blue-crowned and green-bodied races should not be confused, as there is no overlap with any other species of *Lepidothrix*, most particularly the white-crowned Snow-capped Manakin *L. nattereri*.

DISTRIBUTION This, the most wide-ranging of the genus *Lepidothrix*, occurs across southern Central America and western South America south as far as northern Bolivia.

In the north of the species' range, Blue-crowned Manakin is distributed along the Pacific slope from Quepos (more rarely Carara), in southern Costa Rica (Stiles and Skutch 1989), to western Chiriquí, the lowlands of central Bocas del Toro and at one locality in Veraguas, in western Panama (Wetmore 1972, Ridgely and Gwynne 1989), and on the Caribbean slope in the Sixaola region of southeasternmost Costa Rica, where it is uncommon (Stiles and Skutch 1989). Thereafter, the species reappears in Panama's Canal Zone, whereupon it occurs eastwards on both slopes (Ridgely and Gwynne 1989), and into Colombia, where it is found mainly in the foothills and lowlands north of the Andes, and in the western and central Andes, to the lower Cauca and middle Magdalena valleys (south to dpto. Caldas), whilst east of the Andes it is found locally in the Sierra Macarena (dpto. Meta) south to dpto. Caquetá, and then reappears in southeast Nariño and dpto. Putumayo, thence east to Guainía and Vaupés (Hilty and Brown 1986, Stiles *et al.* 1999). In the west the species extends in the lowlands and foothills to northwest Ecuador, principally in Esmeraldas but also locally to northern Pichincha and northern Manabí, with one older record in Los Ríos (Ridgely and Greenfield 2001). It also extends east across southern Venezuela south of the Río Orinoco, except northeast Bolívar state (Hilty 2003), and south through Brazil west of the Rio Negro (north of the Amazon) and of the Rio Madeira (south of the Amazon) to northern Rondônia (Sick 1997), as well as throughout eastern Ecuador (Ridgely and Greenfield 2001) and eastern Peru to the east base of the Andes (Schulenberg *et al.* 2007),

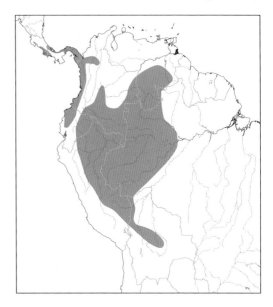

and south into Bolivia, in dptos. Pando, La Paz, Beni and Cochabamba (Schmitt and Schmitt 1987, Remsen and Traylor 1989). The species has recently been reported (but the occurrence is undocumented) in Guyana, in the Burro Burro watershed north of Surama (c.04°15'N, 59°01'W), in May 2001 (W. Burke *in litt.* 2003).

MOVEMENTS Blue-crowned Manakin is considered to be resident or probably sedentary, but see comments under White-fronted Manakin *L. serena.*

HABITAT Blue-crowned Manakin principally inhabits humid primary forest and taller second growth, including, in Amazonia, *terra firme* forest, flooded areas (*igapós*), *campinaranas* and disturbed areas at edges, but also, locally, stunted ridge-top cloud forest (Hilty and Brown 1986, Ridgely and Tudor 1994, Stotz *et al.* 1996, Stiles *et al.* 1999, Alverson *et al.* 2001, Borges *et al.* 2001, Ridgely and Greenfield 2001, Hilty 2003, Restall *et al.* 2006). In southeast Peru, *L. c. caelestipileata* prefers forest on sandy clay soils (H. Lloyd *in litt.* 2010). The species is generally found below 900–1,100m (e.g. in Panama, eastern Ecuador and southeast Colombia), and below 500m in southeast Peru (H. Lloyd *in litt.* 2010), but locally it reaches 1,350/1,400m (e.g. on the Pacific slope of Costa Rica, and in eastern e. Peru, respectively) and, in Venezuela, Blue-crowned Manakin locally ascends the slopes of some of the tepuis to 1,200m (Stiles and Skutch 1989, Stotz *et al.* 1996, Salaman *et al.* 1999, Ridgely and Greenfield 2001, Hilty 2003, Snow 2004b, Schulenberg *et al.* 2007; FMNH).

DESCRIPTION The sexes differ. The narrow bill has an arched culmen and usually a slightly hooked tip (sometimes obvious, in both sexes, but occasionally absent). However, it has less of a propensity to possess a hook tip than in White-crowned Manakin *Dixiphia pipra*, and the culmen is on average marginally less well arched. It has reasonably pronounced rictal bristles. Nominate race/*L. c. carbonata* is described here (although note that females of all races are to all intents and purposes identical). *Adult male.* – Crown and nape bright blue, with the entire rest of the plumage sooty black (including the frontal band), becoming sootier and slightly browner when heavily worn, and has a purplish-bluish gloss to the rump patch (including the uppertail-coverts). The crown patch becomes slightly more violet-coloured just above the bill and at the sides and rear. *Adult female.* – The upperparts are grass green, brightest on the rump and uppertail-coverts, with a duskier tail and wing-feathers (dull green fringes to all of the feathers). The face from the forehead to the rear of the ear-coverts and chin and throat are pale greyish-green, with a dull green breast and flanks, and a olive-greyish ventral region (mid-belly to the undertail-coverts) tinged slightly yellowish. The underwing-coverts are pale greenish-white (like other *Lepidothrix*). On close inspection, females occasionally show bright (male-like) feathers in the crown, although these are even less obvious at a distance (Graves 1981). Ryder and Durães (2005) also noted that older females can assume some attributes of male plumage. *Juvenile.* – Resembles adult female plumage, but the upperparts are more greyish and the underparts are greyish-buff, whilst in Amazonian Brazil at least, young males initially resemble females, but are marginally paler and less bright green above in the majority of individuals. Thereafter, young males acquire the blue crown, more or less in a single moult, although usually a few black feathers are admixed on the central crown (which becomes violet laterally just like in adults)

but not the blue rump patch, whilst possessing a marginally darker breast and throat than females. Birds in their first year generally retain some juvenile greater coverts and or primary-coverts (Ryder and Durães 2005). First-year (juvenile) males are bright green, whilst subadults (two years old) retain variable amounts of green over the body. It is only in their third year that males fully acquire the definitive plumage characterised by a sooty black body and bright blue crown (Ryder and Durães 2005), although these individuals may retain some green feathering on the rump, upper- and undertail-coverts at least (MNRJ), or on the abdomen and wing-coverts (ProAves unpubl. data). The nestling was briefly described by Skutch (1969) and Wetmore (1972). *Moult.* – Very few moult data have been published, but Willard *et al.* (1991) presented information from southernmost Venezuela, where heavy moult of the wing- and body-feathers was noted in early February to early April, especially in subadult males, and light body moult in one late January specimen. Data from mist-netting studies in northern and eastern Colombia suggest that the season is similar, but occurs probably one month later in these regions than in southern Venezuela. Based on the same dataset, it seems likely that young commence their first moult to adult plumage *c.*2–4 months after fledging (C. F. Londoño, R. Parra, B. Ramirez, D. Y. Ramírez and J. M. Ruiz/ProAves unpubl. data). Specimens collected in northwest Brazil were not in moult in July–October (MNRJ) and others from western Brazil, taken both north and south of the Amazon, were also not replacing any feathers in May or November (INPA). A female collected in Costa Rica in September was replacing the body- and wing-feathers (MNCR). *Hybridisation.* – Stotz (1993) collected a hybrid Orange-bellied Manakin *L. suavissima* × *L. coronata* in northernmost Roraima, Brazil. He described the bird, which is held in the Field Museum of Natural History, Chicago (FMNH 344171), as being primarily non-glossy black, although the feathers of the flanks and lower breast have a blue tone, lacking over the rest of the body (a similar blue tone to the abdominal feathers occurs in subspecies *L. c. carbonata*, which is found in the region the bird was collected). Crown sky blue, becoming darker on the nape. Rump and uppertail-coverts cobalt blue. Feathers of abdomen basally black, broadly tipped dull yellow with a greenish tone, forming an irregular patch from the lower edge of the breast to the vent; undertail-coverts green. *Bare parts.* – Irides dark (coffee or caramel) brown to reddish-brown or simply deep red (occasionally yellowish-chestnut in both sexes of *L. c. carbonata*), bill blackish or dark grey over the maxilla with a paler grey or slightly browner mandible, the gape pink, and the legs and feet are dark brown or greyish to black, sometimes with even darker feet (occasionally yellowish-horn or dark horn-grey in young birds, once plumbeous in an adult female) and brownish soles (Burton 1975, Robbins *et al.* 1985, Willard *et al.* 1991, Snow 2004b; INPA; MNRJ).

MEASUREMENTS *L. c. velutina* (from Wetmore 1972: Costa Rica and Panama): wing of male (*n* = 10) 59.5–64.0mm, wing of female (*n* = 10) 58.5–63.0mm; tail of male (*n* = 10) 24.5–27.5mm, tail of female (*n* = 10) 25.0–27.5mm; bill of male (*n* = 10) 9.6–11.3mm, bill of female (*n* = 10) 9.9–11.5mm; tarsus of male (*n* = 10) 13.5–14.4mm, tarsus of female (*n* = 10) 12.6–14.6mm. *L. c. minuscula* (from Wetmore 1972: Panama): wing of male (*n* = 10) 56.5–59.0mm, wing of female (*n* = 10) 54–58mm; tail of male (*n* = 10) 24–26mm, tail of female (*n* = 10) 24.0–26.5mm;

bill of male ($n = 10$) 8.8–10.0mm, bill of female ($n = 10$) 9.4–10.6mm; tarsus of male ($n = 10$) 13.0–14.6mm, tarsus of female ($n = 10$) 13.0–14.1mm. **L. c. caquetae** (FMNH: dptos. Caquetá and Meta, Colombia): wing of male ($n = 3$) 61mm, wing of female ($n = 4$) 57–61mm; tail of male ($n = 3$) 27–31mm, tail of female ($n = 4$) 28–30mm; bill of male ($n = 3$) 8.72–9.62mm, bill of female ($n = 2$) 9.71–9.85mm; tarsus of male ($n = 3$) 13.13–15.83mm, tarsus of female ($n = 3$) 13.63–14.83mm. **L. c. carbonata** (INPA; MNRJ: Amazonas, Brazil): wing of male ($n = 10$) 58.5–61.0mm, wing of female ($n = 8$) 55.5–60.5mm; tail of male ($n = 10$) 26–35mm, tail of female ($n = 8$) 25–33mm; bill of male ($n = 10$) 10.49–10.95mm, bill of female ($n = 2$) 9.63–11.75mm; tarsus of male ($n = 4$) 13.24–14.77mm, tarsus of female ($n = 10$) 14.18–14.59mm. **L. c. coronata** (from Gyldenstolpe 1945, except bill and tarsus, INPA; MNRJ: Amazonas and Rondônia, Brazil): wing of male ($n = 8$) 59.5–61.0mm, wing of female ($n = 5$) 57–59mm; tail of male ($n = 8$) 26–29mm, tail of female ($n = 5$) 27.5–29.0mm; bill of male ($n = 5$) 9.92–11.04mm, bill of female ($n = 2$) 9.11–9.25mm; tarsus of male ($n = 4$) 13.21–13.73mm, tarsus of female ($n = 1$) 13.84mm. **L. c. exquisita** (FMNH: central Peru): wing of male ($n = 4$) 57–61mm, wing of female ($n = 1$) 55.5mm; tail of male ($n = 4$) 26–30mm, tail of female ($n = 1$) 28mm; bill of male ($n = 4$) 9.89–10.72mm, bill of female ($n = 1$) 10.99mm; tarsus of male ($n = 4$) 13.42–15.11mm, tarsus of female ($n = 1$) 14.29mm. **L. c. caelestipileata** (FMNH: dpto. Madre de Dios, southeast Peru): wing of male ($n = 13$) 57.0–60.5mm, wing of female ($n = 7$) 55.5–60.5mm; tail of male ($n = 13$) 30–36mm, tail of female ($n = 7$) 27.0–33.5mm; bill of male ($n = 13$) 9.32–10.99mm, bill of female ($n = 7$) 10.15–12.05mm; tarsus of male ($n = 11$) 12.61–15.56mm, tarsus of female ($n = 5$) 13.76–14.53mm. Additional data from Hellmayr 1929b (western Brazil and southeast Peru): wing of male ($n = $ unknown) 58–62mm; tail of male ($n = $ unknown) 29–31mm. Data from live birds as follows. **L. c. minuscula** from Darién, Colombia: wing of male ($n = 27$) 55–63mm, wing of female ($n = 52$) 54–61mm; tail of male ($n = 22$) 23.0–33.5mm, tail of female ($n = 44$) 21–30mm; bill of male ($n = 21$) 7.9–12.9mm, bill of female ($n = 47$) 7.8–13.2mm; tarsus of male ($n = 27$) 13.7–20.9mm, tarsus of female ($n = 51$) 10.9–19.5mm (C. F. Londoño, D. Y. Ramírez and J. M. Ruiz/ProAves unpubl. data). **L. c. carbonata** from southern Colombia: wing of male ($n = 43$) 51–66mm, wing of female ($n = 31$) 56–61mm (T. M. Donegan *et al.* unpubl. data). Additional mensural data were presented by Hellmayr (1911) and Snethlage (1914). Weight (races combined): 5.7–10.5g (males) and 5.7–16.9g (19.0g) (females) (Burton 1975, Robbins *et al.* 1985, Willard *et al.* 1991, Snow 2004b, Dunning 2008; FMNH; INPA; MNCR; MNRJ; MVZ; T. M. Donegan *et al.* unpubl. data; C. F. Londoño, R. Parra, B. Ramirez and D. Y. Ramírez/ProAves unpubl. data).

GEOGRAPHICAL VARIATION Eight subspecies are currently recognised as follows below (e.g. Dickinson 2003, Snow 2004b). Differences between them are marked only in male plumage and, to a certain extent, in male advertisement song (see also Voice), but two, perhaps three species might be involved, although the situation is in part complicated by intergradation. Several other subspecies have been described but have long been considered synonyms: Pinto (1944) drew early attention to the problem of recognising so many forms in western Amazonia, several of them occupying relatively tiny ranges. Cheviron *et al.* (2005), who sampled all but one of the traditionally recognised subspecies, uncovered strong evidence that this

named variation does not reflect phylogeny of the *L. coronata* group. For instance, in central Peru, typical *L. c. coronata* males (with black bodies), primarily green males (typical of *L. c. exquisita*) and various intergrades between these two plumage types all formed a well-supported monophyletic clade to the exclusion of other pure black or green clades (Cheviron *et al.* 2005). In complete contrast, populations of identically plumaged (black-bodied males) north and south of the Amazon River are separated by large genetic breaks, whilst populations from southern Venezuela (*L. c. carbonata*) and northern Peru (*L. c. coronata*), which are to all intents and purposes identical in male plumage, appear to be highly divergent genetically. Nonetheless, see Remsen (2010) for a commentary on the dangers of over-interpreting genetic data *vis à vis* more traditional taxonomic classifications. In a second publication, Cheviron *et al.* (2006) revealed that the gene usually associated with melanistic phenotypes in birds does not play any role in plumage polymorphism in Blue-crowned Manakins. Cheviron *et al.* (2005) further identified six major haplotype clades within this species, a trans-Andean clade, a southern Venezuela clade, a Napo/Marañón clade, a north Amazon clade, a central Peru clade and south Peru/Bolivia clade. This phylogeographical structure exhibited some obvious congruence with eco-geographical barriers, especially major rivers and, to some extent, mountains, e.g. the Mérida Andes, the Sierra de Perijá and the northern end of the East Andes.

L. c. velutina (Berlepsch, 1883) occurs on the Pacific slope of Costa Rica and western Panama (Chiriquí, Bocas del Toro and Veraguas), as well as in the extreme east of Costa Rica. Characterised by being less solidly and more lustrous black than males of the next subspecies, with the deepest blue crown, but it is perhaps most easily differentiated mensurally (see Measurements). **L. c. minuscula** (Todd, 1919) is found in eastern Panama from the Canal Zone into South America through Colombia south to northwest Ecuador. It differs from *L. c. velutina* in being smaller (see Measurements) with a deeper blue (more ultramarine) crown. Hellmayr (1911) had already drawn attention to the smaller size of the northwest South American populations. Wetmore (1972) considered females to be slightly deeper green than those of *L. c. velutina*. **L. c. caquetae** (Meyer de Schauensee, 1953) occurs in southern Colombia east of the Andes in southern dpto. Meta (in the Sierra Macarena: Blake 1962) and dpto. Caquetá, and closely resembles the nominate race. Males possess a 'cool' blue crown and lack any blue gloss on the uppertail-coverts (Restall *et al.* 2006). **L. c. carbonata** (Todd, 1925) is distributed across south-central Colombia east to southern Venezuela and south to northeast Peru (north of the Marañón) and in northwest Brazil north of the Amazon River. It differs from other subspecies in that males have the lower belly and undertail-coverts patchily tinged greenish-blue (Hilty and Brown 1986, Restall *et al.* 2006; MNRJ), whilst the crown is more azure-blue than in *L. c. minuscula* (Ridgely and Greenfield 2001). However, some males have the greenish tinge restricted to the undertail-coverts and in others this coloration appears to be virtually or entirely absent (MNRJ). Nominate **L. c. coronata** (described above) includes *L. c. hoffmannsi* (Hellmayr, 1907), *L. c. arimensis* (Todd, 1925) and *L. c. chloromelaena* (Todd, 1925); the latter two forms were described from opposite banks of the Rio Purus, and this form is found over eastern Ecuador, northeast Peru south to northern Ucayali and adjacent western Brazil south of the Amazon River, perhaps even as far as northern Rondônia, e.g. around Porto Velho, although it is far more likely that *L. c. caelestipileata* occurs in this region (we have been hampered in our analysis due to a lack of adult males from this region in collections examined by us). There remains the possibility, as intimated by Ridgely and Tudor (1994), that many populations throughout the Madeira–Purus interfluvium, as well as elsewhere across western Brazil, and in northern Peru around the Marañón/Amazon 'divide' are 'compromised' by intermediates, making their subspecific designation very difficult, especially given often short series' of specimens. Hellmayr (1929b) considered *L. c. coronata* to be duller, more brownish-black above than in race *L. c. carbonata*, which replaces it north of the Amazon. The taxa *L. c. hoffmannsi* (type locality Tefé on the upper Rio Solimões), *L. c. arimensis* (from Arima, on the right bank of the lower Rio Purus) and *L. c. chloromelaena* (Nova Olinda, on the left bank of the lower Rio Purus) represent intermediates between black-bodied *L. c. coronata* and the green-bodied forms, further south and west. *L. c. hoffmannsi* shows just some green on the wing fringes, but the other two races have distinctly more green over the body (including below) and the wings and tail. For example, there is a male in the INPA collection, Manaus, from the RESEX Baixo Juruá, Amazonas, that is yellowish-green from the central belly to the undertail-coverts, with some very dark green fringes to the tertials and flight feathers (including the tail). These intermediate populations cast some doubt on the theory that the black-bodied and green-bodied populations represent separate species, as was already noted by Hellmayr (1929b). **L. c. exquisita** (Hellmayr, 1905), which includes *L. c. circumpicta* (Zimmer, 1929), is found east of the Andes in central Peru, from Amazonas south, and is very different from previously mentioned taxa in having a paler blue crown, mainly green upperparts and breast, black lores, face and flight feathers, pale yellow lower belly, and a white vent. Females of this and the following two forms are probably on average brighter, more viridian green, especially on the upperparts than those forms that possess black-bodied males. Gyldenstolpe (1951) suggested that green-bodied taxa like *L. c. exquisita* might be better treated at species level, but intergradation with black-bodied forms was already noted by Haffer (1970). **L. c. caelestipileata** (Goeldi, 1905) replaces all but subspecies in southeast Peru (in dpto. Madre de Dios) and adjacent western Brazil (in Acre and southwest Amazonas, as far as the upper Rios Juruá and Purus, and has even been claimed as far north as the Rio Urucu: Peres and Whittaker 1991, and east to the Rio Madeira, at Humaitá: Hellmayr 1910: 307). This subspecies is also widespread in dpto. Pando, northwest Bolivia (J. A. Tobias *in litt.* 2010). It differs from *L. c. exquisita* in its deeper blue crown (with no purplish posterior border), yellower green upperparts with duller and less extensive yellow on the underparts. **L. c. regalis** (Bond and Meyer de Schauensee, 1940) occurs in north-central Bolivia, in dptos. Cochabamba and Beni (see Fig. 6), and differs from *L. c. caelestipileata* only in having a slightly paler and less deep-coloured crown.

VOICE There is noticeable geographical variation in the species' primary vocalisations, offering support to the idea that more than one species is involved (see Geographical variation). In northwest Brazil, Cerqueira *et al.* (2008) found that singing males call up to 45% of the time whilst on their territories, and utter up to six different vocalisations. In eastern Ecuador, Durães (2009) reported only four distinct vocalisation types. In Central America and west of the Andes,

males in advertisement give a *pi pipipipipi chu-WAK*, the final notes being described as 'harsh, nasal and frog-like' (Stiles and Skutch 1989). East of the Andes, in Colombia, Ecuador, Venezuela, etc., males principally advertise with a *Tyranneutes stolzmanni*-like *thó-wiik*, or *chi-weer*, which is generally given slowly and steadily, often repeated five to six times, and is sometimes preceded by a sharp *hist* or faint *sweeeee?* (Hilty and Brown 1986, Ridgely and Tudor 1994, Ridgely and Greenfield 2001, Hilty 2003, Durães 2009). Each *chi-weer* call lasts c.0.5 seconds but comprises three distinct parts when examined spectrographically, and spans frequencies ranging from 1 to 5kHz.

Further, Durães (2009) reported in detail on other vocalisations given in eastern Ecuador. Most common there is the *swee* call, which is used in contact by males and females of all ages, and by territorial males when vocalising from song perches, while foraging, during interactions with either sex or in some display behaviours (Durães 2009). Softer versions are given by females and fledglings during foraging and by females when visiting males' territories. The *swee* call is given as a single note or in bouts with a variable number of repetitions. The *preew* call (which lasts slightly >0.1 seconds) was given only by males, during interactions with birds of either sex that entered their territories. Throughout at least the Central American range, both sexes and all ages are reported to give a semi-musical and somewhat rattling trill, *prrrreew* or *chk-rrreew* (Hilty and Brown 1986, Stiles and Skutch 1989, Ridgely and Tudor 1994, Sick 1997, Ridgely and Greenfield 2001, Hilty 2003). This seems to be the same call Snow (2004) described as *prrrreew* for *L. coronata* and Skutch (1969) as *p'rrr* for *L. c. velutina* of Central America, and is probably also rather similar to the song of *L. c. caelestipileata* in southeast Peru (see below). Durães (2009) noted that the *preew* call was usually associated with display behaviour, especially wing-flicks, perch-to-perch chases, to-and-fro flights, and whirring to-and-fro flights, but she noted it only very infrequently. The *pee* call is apparently given only by males during display, but is not always audible since males usually emit it when close to the ground but not necessarily at the display court. Durães (2009) also heard the *pee* call during an actual copulation and simulated copulations, as well as in unison with some display behaviours. It can be repeated up to ten times. Further south, Schulenberg *et al.* (2007) described green-bodied males as singing a 'thin, rising whistle followed by a froglike croak: "*SWEE? tuk'URT*" ', as well as giving a rising *wee* (which resembles that of Cerulean-capped Manakin: H. Lloyd *in litt.* 2010) and a 'thin, sputtered, tinkling "*ti'i'ir*" '. A female gave a sharp *zreeep*! note while defending an egg and nest from a *Labidus* army ant swarm (Greeney 2006).

Blue-crowned Manakin vocalisations have featured on the following audio compilations: English and Parker (1992), Moore (1993, 1994), Boesman (1999), Mayer (2000), Ross (2000), Schulenberg *et al.* (2000), Jahn *et al.* (2002), Krabbe and Nilsson (2003) and Boesman (2006a, 2006b, 2009). In addition, recordings from Bolivia, Ecuador, Panama and Peru are archived online at www.xeno-canto. org. Sonograms were presented by Durães (2009).

NATURAL HISTORY Very well studied. Like its congenerics, the Blue-crowned Manakin is chiefly found in the undergrowth of primary forest or taller second growth, and is most easily found by listening for their highly distinctive song at leks, or when visiting a fruiting tree.

FOOD AND FEEDING Small fruits or insects are plucked from the underside of leaves using short sally-strikes, after which the bird returns to a slightly lower perch (Stiles and Skutch 1989). Females and young probably regularly join mixed-species foraging flocks (Snow 2004b). Detailed information concerning diet is generally lacking, but fruits taken include those of *Miconia* (Melastomataceae) and *Ficus* (Moraceae) (Skutch 1980, Tello 2003), berries of 49 species of woody plants (many of them recorded just once) especially of the families Moraceae, Bromeliaceae and Araceae (Loiselle *et al.* 2007a, 2007c), and Blendinger *et al.* (2008) studied fruit removal by manakins at the same study site in Amazonian Ecuador, where Blue-crowned Manakin was one of the few bird species to disperse fruits of *Miconia fosteri* and *M. serrulata* (Melastomataceae). In central Panama, Poulin *et al.* (1999) found that *L. coronata* takes at least 26 species of the genera *Miconia* and *Psychotria* (Rubiaceae) alone. Skutch (1980) also recorded *L. coronata* feeding on *Souroubea guianensis* (Marcgraviaceae) and *Casearia arborea* (Flacourtiaceae) in Costa Rica.

DISPLAY Lek behaviour, dynamics and influence on population structure have been well studied, principally in eastern Ecuador. It is presently unclear whether geographical variation in display behaviour might exist or not (Durães 2009). Males display either alone or in 'exploded leks' of up to seven individuals (often the latter in Central America, and either alone or in very small groups in northwest Brazil), with each bird *c.*25m apart, and its own display area of 3–10m in diameter (see Skutch 1969, Wetmore 1972, Durães 2007, 2009, Cerqueira *et al.* 2008). In eastern Ecuador, Durães (2009) noted that a small number of males might also visit a second display area within their overall territory. The birds periodically depart their arenas to visit fruiting trees (Hilty 2003). Males of all ages attend leks (juveniles usually associating with a specific adult male), but only two-year-old individuals (or older) are territorial, and leks are quite dynamic in their structure with relatively high annual recruitment rates (Durães 2007, 2009). Territories are usually contiguous, at least in eastern Ecuador, and can range in size from 200 to 5,000m² but on average cover 1,000m²: territories seem to be more clearly defined in Ecuador and in southeast Peru than in Costa Rica (Durães 2009; H. Lloyd *in litt.* 2010). Males sing (see Voice) from slender horizontal or slightly angled branches or lianas, typically 3–4m above the ground but range from 0.5 to 9(12)m (Stiles and Skutch 1989, Durães 2009). They occasionally flick or hit their wings and make short, rapid (looping or level zigzag) flights, either high or low above ground, to adjacent perches (sometimes to displace neighbouring males), or irregularly drop down into the undergrowth before assuming a special low perch, where the male lowers the head, flattens and spreads the crown-feathers, and beats the wings while calling (Skutch 1969, Hilty and Brown 1986, Ridgely and Greenfield 2001, Durães 2009). Females that arrive at a male's court can also perform the low flights.

Various facets of the different flight and perched displays of *L. coronata* resemble those of the *Pipra erythrocephala* clade, as well as of White-fronted Manakin *L. serena*, White-crowned Manakin *Dixiphia pipra* and the clade including Crimson-hooded Manakin *Pipra aureola*, with the side-to-side bowing display resembling a display of Golden-winged Manakin *Masius chrysopterus* (Durães 2009). Display behaviour was intensively studied by Durães (2009) at her study site in eastern Ecuador, and in Brazil Cerqueira *et al.* (2008)

identified six different types of flights used in display. In addition to those mentioned above, these are the 'butterfly' flight (the display used most frequently in northwest Brazil, during which two to three males may chase each other), a U-shaped seesaw flight (given between perches at the same level, following which *swee* or *preew* calls are given on landing) and two different types of S-shaped flight displays (one of them during group chases amongst males). There is also what Durães (2009) termed a frenzied flutter flight, which appears to simulate copulation.

Typically, five different stereotyped movements are given by males while perched, some of them coordinated displays between rivals, which apparently determine hierarchies and perhaps serve as sources of information exchange (Durães 2009). *Wing-flicks*, where the bird opens and closes its wings once and utters the *preew* call, are commonly given following flight displays during interactions with birds of either sex. *Side-to-side bowing displays* involve the territorial male stretching its neck out, bending the body slightly forward, and, without moving its feet, turning *c.*45° first to one side and then to the other. This behaviour is used when displaying to females at the court and also during group displays among perched males. *Side-to-side jump displays* are used during group displays by perched males. The male's body remains erect while the bird makes a short hop to the side, without opening its wings, sometimes landing to face in the opposite direction. *About-face* movements are performed usually in conjunction with one of the flight displays or wing-flicks; the male makes a rapid 180° turn on a horizontal branch. Durães (2009) only observed *vertical-wing displays* twice, during which the bird raises both wings (without them touching) above its head, sometimes making a short jump upwards simultaneously and uttering a *pee* call. Both occasions involved male–male interactions. All of these perched displays are given much less frequently than calling (Cerqueira *et al.* 2008).

Females are generally much more inconspicuous at leks or display courts, and their presence is often signalled by a rapid change in adult male display behaviour. It is only at certain points that a female will visit the male to permit copulation, but Cerqueira *et al.* (2008) found differences in the rates of visitation by females to lone males or those belonging to 'exploded leks'. Durães (2009) only observed adult females visiting leks in either the early morning or mid afternoon.

In the recent study led by Durães (2007), in eastern Ecuador, it was found that males at larger leks sang more frequently and were more successful in mating than lone singing males or individuals at smaller leks, but male eviction rates were also noted as being higher at larger leks. She also found that Blue-crowned Manakins do not appear to locate leks at female 'hotspots' nor in particularly optimal habitat, although females nesting close to small leks travel further to reach larger leks (Durães 2007, Durães *et al.* 2007). In addition, she also found that males participating at a given lek are not more closely related than would be expected based on chance (Durães *et al.* 2007, Loiselle *et al.* 2007c). 'New' males are equally likely to take over an existing territory as establish a new territory. Interestingly, lek size does not affect the probabilities of a male recruiting or persisting at a territory, and vocalisation rate, which was a correlate of mating success in the Ecuadorian population studied, did not affect male persistence. Research has also shown that leks in eastern Ecuador rapidly stabilise in size despite changes in territory ownership, whilst rates of male recruitment and disappearance compensate for each other, so leks can persist for several decades after the original males have been lost (Durães *et al.* 2008b). In a further publication, Durães *et al.* (2009) suggested that males at larger leks are not more likely to sire young than those at smaller leks; that within a lek, high-display males are more likely to produce young; and that both male heterozygosity and display rate increased with lek size, thus display does not reflect male genetic quality across leks.

In one of the most comprehensive studies of its kind, Loiselle *et al.* (2007a), working at the same study site in Yasuní National Park, in eastern Ecuador, found relatively strong segregation (principally being separated along axes of elevation and slope heterogeneity) between leks of different manakin species. Blue-crowned Manakin leks were generally sited at mid elevations within the Ecuadorian study area. When spatial overlap occurred, it was almost always between Blue-backed Manakin *Chiroxiphia pareola* and *L. coronata*; one *P. erythrocephala* lek with just one displaying male was nestled within a *L. coronata* lek.

BREEDING Compared with other species of *Lepidothrix*, this species' breeding biology is comparatively well known, principally based on studies in Costa Rica (Skutch 1969) and eastern Ecuador (Hidalgo *et al.* 2008). For nesting, the species prefers relatively open forest with a variable understorey and often nests beside seasonal creeks, at least in Amazonian Ecuador (Hidalgo *et al.* 2008). However, it will sometimes even use relatively recently regenerating wooded patches (Skutch 1969). The nest is a typical manakin structure, a small, but quite deep, cup-shaped affair typically placed in the fork of a slender horizontal branch, attached and bound to the supporting branches using spiderwebs. The nest is constructed of fine pale-coloured (brown to whitish) vegetable fibres, with some dry fragments of leaves/bark (including of palms) with green moss often covering the outer rim and frequently hanging below it. Nests are generally placed 0.3–2.0m above ground, often in Rubiaceae or Violaceae shrubs (Skutch 1969, Stiles and Skutch 1989, Snow 2004b, Greeney 2006, Hidalgo *et al.* 2008), and constructed by the female alone (Skutch 1969). Clutch size is two dull white to pale grey eggs (with many pale to dark brown, or sometimes rufous markings, heaviest at the large end), which are incubated for 17.5–19.0 days (based on just two records), whilst fledging occupies 13–15 days (Skutch 1969). Greeney (2006) observed a female incubating a single egg; whether the clutch had been reduced by predation or if females sometimes lay just one egg is unclear.

Dimensions of the eggs were presented by Skutch (1969) and repeated in Wetmore (1972). Detailed nest dimensions (based on 41 nests) were given by Hidalgo *et al.* (2008). A nest with eggs was depicted in Hidalgo *et al.* (2008: 59). All incubation and other parental duties are undertaken by the female, which feeds the young on insects and fruit pulp (Hidalgo *et al.* 2008). Greeney (2006) observed a female in eastern Ecuador defending a single egg from an attack by *Labidus* army ants. Predation rates were found to be extremely high (84%), especially during the incubation period, at the Amazonian Ecuador study site worked by Ryder *et al.* (2008a).

In Costa Rica, Blue-crowned Manakin lays eggs in February–June, perhaps peaking in March–May (Stiles and Skutch 1989). Further south, in northwest and central Colombia, birds in breeding condition have been collected or mist-netted in October–May (Haffer 1975, Hilty and

Brown 1986, Stiles *et al.* 1999; MVZ; C. F. Londoño, R. Parra, B. Ramírez and D. Y. Ramírez/ProAves unpubl. data). Both sexes of the taxon *L. c. caquetae*, from dpto. Meta, eastern Colombia, were mist-netted in breeding condition in September/October (i.e. unsurprisingly similar to birds from northwest Amazonian Brazil) (ROM). In eastern Ecuador, Greeney (2006) observed an incubating female in late January, and T. M. Donegan *et al.* (*in litt.* 2009) mist-netted juveniles in late July and early August in southern Colombia. In northwest Brazil, in the Rio Negro drainage, the species appears to commence breeding around September/October (INPA; MNRJ), whilst a female was collected along the lower Rio Juruá, Amazonas, with two yellowish eggs in the ovaries in June (INPA). Based on their fieldwork in lowland eastern Ecuador, Blake and Loiselle (2008) presented data on annual survival rates for this and several other species of manakins.

STATUS Treated as Least Concern by BirdLife International (2004, 2008) and the species is generally fairly common to abundant, at least locally, across much of its Amazonian range (Ridgely and Tudor 1994, Ridgely and Greenfield 2001, Hilty 2003, Snow 2004b, Blake 2007), although it is more local in southeast Peru (e.g. Robinson and Terborgh 1997, Schulenberg *et al.* 2007), and western Panama (Wetmore 1972, Ridgely and Gwynne 1989). Blake and Loiselle (2009) noted that it is one of the commonest members of the understorey bird community, based on mist-net capture rates, at their study site in eastern Ecuador, and reported that this manakin was also reasonably abundant at study sites in Panama and Peru. In southeast Peru, Terborgh *et al.* (1990) recorded densities of up to seven individuals per 100ha, whilst in Panama's Canal Zone, in Soberania National Park, Robinson *et al.* (2000a) noted densities of 36 individuals per 100ha. Nonetheless, Anciães and Peterson (2006) foresee that this species could be moderately impacted by habitat modification in the face of potential climate change predicted using modelling techniques. In western Ecuador there have been some local extinctions due to habitat loss, e.g. at Río Palenque (Ridgely and Greenfield 2001). Blue-crowned Manakin is known from a great many protected areas, including the following: Carara National Park, Oro Verde Biological Reserve, Corcovado National Park and Las Cruces Biological Station, all in Costa Rica (Lawson 2010); Tinigua National Park, dpto. Meta (Cadena *et al.* 2000), Reserva Natural Tambito, dpto. Cauca (Donegan and Dávalos 1999), Reserva Natural de las Aves El Paujil, dpto. Boyacá, Reserva Natural de las Aves Arrierito Antioqueño, dpto. Antioquia, and Reserva Natural de los Anfibios Ranita Dorada, dpto. Tolima (Salaman *et al.* 2009), in Colombia; Yasuní National Park, Ecuador; Jaú National Park, Amazonas (Borges *et al.* 2001), and Reserva Extrativista Chico Mendes, Acre (Thom and Mestre 2009), both in Brazil; Manu National Park and Biosphere Reserve, Peru (Walker *et al.* 2006); and Pilón Lajas Biosphere Reserve, dpto. Beni, Bolivia (Hennessey *et al.* 2003a).

REFERENCES Aleixo and Guilherme (2010), Alverson *et al.* (2001), Anciães and Peterson (2006, 2009), Angehr and Dean (2010), BirdLife International (2004, 2008), Blake, E. R. (1962), Blake, J. G. (2007), Blake and Loiselle (2008, 2009), Blendinger *et al.* (2008), Boesman (1999, 2006a, 2006b, 2009), Borges (2007), Borges *et al.* (2001), Burton (1975), Cadena *et al.* (2000), Cerqueira *et al.* (2008), Cheviron *et al.* (2005, 2006), Dickinson (2003),

Donegan and Dávalos (1999), Durães (2007, 2009), Durães *et al.* (2007, 2008b, 2009), English and Parker (1992), Garrigues and Dean (2007), Graves (1981), Greeney (2006), Gyldenstolpe (1945, 1951), Haffer (1959, 1970, 1975, 1992b), Hellmayr (1906d, 1911, 1929b), Hennessey *et al.* (2003a), Hidalgo *et al.* (2008), Hilty (2003), Hilty and Brown (1986), Hosner *et al.* (2009), Jahn *et al.* (2002), Krabbe and Nilsson (2003), Loiselle *et al.* (2007a, 2007b, 2007c), Mayer (2000), McKay *et al.* (2010), Merkord *et al.* (2009), Mestre *et al.* (2010), Moore (1993, 1994), Novaes (1957), Peres and Whittaker (1991), Pinto (1944), Poulin *et al.* (1999), Prum (1990a), Remsen (2010), Remsen and Traylor (1989), Restall *et al.* (2006), Ridgely and Greenfield (2001), Ridgely and Gwynne (1989), Ridgely and Tudor (1994, 2009), Robbins *et al.* (1985), Robinson and Terborgh (1997), Robinson *et al.* (2000a), Ross (2000), Ryder and Durães (2005), Ryder *et al.* (2008a), Salaman *et al.* (1999, 2009), Schmitt and Schmitt (1987), Schulenberg *et al.* (2000, 2007), Sick (1997), Skutch (1969), Snethlage (1908a, 1914), Snow (2004b), Stiles and Skutch (1989), Stiles *et al.* (1999), Stotz (1993), Stotz *et al.* (1996), Tello (2003), Terborgh *et al.* (1990), Thom and Mestre (2009), Tori *et al.* (2008), Walker *et al.* (2006), Wetmore (1972), Wiley (2010), Zimmer (1930).

Blue-crowned Manakin *Lepidothrix coronata*. **Fig. 1**. Male, *L. c. velutina*, Carara National Park, prov. Puntarenas, Costa Rica, November (*Nick Athanas / Tropical Birding*). Populations from Costa Rica south to northwest Ecuador are sometimes suggested to represent a separate species, under the name Velvety Manakin *L. velutina*, but taxonomy is extremely complex and further complicated by the fact that major haplotype groups within *L. coronata* do not necessarily conform to named subspecies. **Fig. 2**. Male, *L. c. coronata*, Shiripuno Lodge, prov. Pastaza, eastern Ecuador, November (*Hadoram Shirihai / Photographic Handbook to Birds of the World*)). **Fig. 3**. Female, *L. c. velutina*, Carara National Park, prov. Puntarenas, Costa Rica, February (*Jason Horn / Costa Rica Gateway*). **Fig. 4**. Female, *L. c. coronata*, Shiripuno Lodge, prov. Pastaza, eastern Ecuador, November (*Hadoram Shirihai / Photographic Handbook to Birds of the World*). **Fig. 5**. Male, *L. c. caelestipileata*, Durand Lodge, dpto. Madre de Dios, southeast Peru, October (*Hadoram Shirihai / Photographic Handbook to Birds of the World*). See also Fig. 51. **Fig. 6**. Male, *L. c. regalis*, Padilla, dpto. Beni, Bolivia, March (*Joe Tobias / Edward Grey Institute, Oxford University*). Note the paler and less deep-blue crown coloration compared to the next subspecies. **Fig. 7**. Male, *L. c. caelestipileata*, Los Amigos, dpto. Madre de Dios, southeast Peru, August (*Joe Tobias / Edward Grey Institute, Oxford University*). Green-bodied populations have been suggested to represent another species, but they intergrade with black-bodied birds in western Amazonian Brazil.

BLUE-RUMPED MANAKIN
Lepidothrix isidorei   Plate 4

Pipra isidorei **P. L. Sclater, 1852**, *Rev. Mag. Zool.* (2) 4: 9, 'Nouvelle-Grenade' [= Bogotá = Buenavista, above Villavicencio, dpto. Meta, Colombia]

This beautiful manakin of the east slope of the Andes can be surprisingly difficult to see and there are relatively few localities where it can be considered common. Symptomatic of how unobtrusive this bird can be is the fact that until less than 20 years ago Blue-rumped Manakin was scarcely known in Colombia, yet it has since proved to be widespread from north of the country's capital Bogotá to the Ecuadorian border.

IDENTIFICATION 7.5–9.0cm. Most likely to be confused with either Blue-crowned *L. coronata* or White-crowned Manakins *Dixiphia pipra*. Ridgely and Greenfield (2001) stated that *L. coronata* and *L. isidorei* have not been found together, and that is probably still true of the situation in Ecuador, but in Colombia there seems to be significant elevational parapatry, at least locally (Salaman *et al.* 1999). *D. pipra*, which occurs to at least 1,500m on the east slope of the Andes, is also known to overlap quite extensively with the present species at several sites in Colombia and at least locally in Ecuador (Ridgely and Greenfield 2001, Salaman *et al.* 2002b). The extremely similar Cerulean-capped Manakin *L. coeruleocapilla* replaces *L. isidorei* somewhere on the east slope of the Andes in Huánuco, Peru; its separation from Blue-rumped Manakin is covered under Cerulean-capped. Given reasonable views, male Blue-rumped Manakin should be easily separated from male White-crowned by the latter's noticeably larger and bulkier-looking body, dark red irides and lack of a blue rump patch (although this can be hidden), and from male Blue-crowned Manakin by that species' blue crown patch and lack of any different-coloured rump patch. Females are more difficult to identify with certainty, but female *D. pipra* is again notably chunkier than Blue-crowned Manakin, has a strong bluish cast to the crown in the relevant subspecies (*D. p. coracina*), paler legs than *L. isidorei* and much greener, less yellow, underparts. Female *L. coronata* and *L. isidorei* are extremely similar and very difficult to distinguish in the field, although the forecrown of the latter is tinged yellow, and the rump and tail offer some contrast with the rest of the darker upperparts.

DISTRIBUTION Endemic to the east slope of the East Andes. The true extent of the species' range in Colombia has only recently (post-1980s) been elucidated. In Colombia, it is now known to occur from eastern dpto. Boyacá, where only recently discovered, and western dpto. Meta, southwards, probably continuously, to western dpto. Putumayo (Hilty and Brown 1986, Salaman *et al.* 2002b), thence through eastern Ecuador in western Napo south to Zamora-Chinchipe (Ridgely and Greenfield 2001), and into northern Peru, from dpto. Amazonas south to northern dpto. Huánuco (Schulenberg *et al.* 2007). However, it seems to be inexplicably absent from certain apparently suitable localities/regions, e.g. the northern Cordillera Azul, San Martín, where Blue-crowned Manakin has been recorded to *c*.1,500m (Alverson *et al.* 2001, Merkord *et al.* 2009).

MOVEMENTS Blue-rumped Manakin is generally considered to be resident, but see comments under White-fronted Manakin *L. serena*.

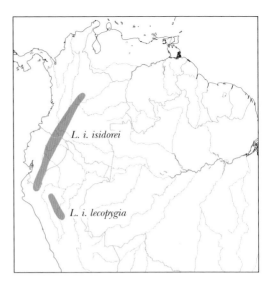

HABITAT Blue-rumped Manakin inhabits the understorey and lower midstorey of humid montane forest in the upper tropical and lower subtropical zones. It is generally recorded at 700–1,800m, but is occasionally observed down to 300m in Colombia, at the foot of the Serranía de los Churumbelos, dpto. Cauca (Salaman *et al.* 1999). Highest altitude record (1,800m) is from the Cordillera del Condor, dpto. Cajamarca, Peru (T. Mark recording; XC 7059). The species' elevational range is distinctly narrower in northern Peru, where it is found mainly at 1,100–1,400m (Schulenberg *et al.* 2007), than elsewhere, e.g. 800–1,700m in Ecuador (Ridgely and Greenfield 2001).

DESCRIPTION Sexes differ. The narrow bill has an arched culmen and usually a slightly hooked tip (sometimes obvious, but occasionally absent). The nominate race is described here. *Adult male.* – The crown and nape are shiny white, with a pale azure-blue lower back, rump and uppertail-coverts patch, whilst the entire rest of the plumage is matt black. *Adult female.* – The upperparts are bright grass green, becoming more yellowish over the forecrown (sometimes virtually the entire crown), and brightest on the rump and uppertail-coverts, with a duskier tail. Females have not been reported to show bright (male-like) feathers in the crown to date, unlike some other female *Lepidothrix* (Graves 1981). The face from the forehead to the rear of the ear-coverts and chin and throat are pale greyish-yellow, with a slightly duller green breast and a yellowish-grey mid-belly to the undertail-coverts. *Juvenile.* – Unknown (Snow 2004b), but probably the immature male initially gains a few blue spots on the crown as in Cerulean-capped Manakin (cf. Mee *et al.* 2002). At least in some individuals, the green feathers on the lower back and larger wing-coverts are the last immature feathers to be shed by young males (BMNH). *Moult.* – There are no published data on moult. *Bare parts.* – Irides dark brownish-red, and appear tiny within the white crown patch. The bill has a blackish maxilla with a paler grey mandible and cutting edges, and the legs and feet are greyish (Snow 2004b).

MEASUREMENTS (RMNH; ROM; ZMA: Colombia, Ecuador and Peru) Races combined, but most data pertain to the nominate. Wing of male (*n* = 10) 47–54mm, wing of female (*n* = 6) 50.5–56.0mm; tail of male (*n* = 9) 25.5–

30.0mm, tail of female ($n = 6$) 24–30mm; bill of male ($n = 9$) 8.66–9.64mm, bill of female ($n = 6$) 8.95–10.36mm; tarsus of male ($n = 1$) 13.49–15.82mm, tarsus of female ($n = 4$) 13.28–14.74mm. Data from live birds (in southern Colombia): wing of male ($n = 13$) 48–52mm, wing of female ($n = 5$) 51–55mm (T. M. Donegan *et al.* unpubl. data). See also Salaman and Donegan (2007) for wing length and overall body length data from live birds, albeit solely expressed as means and not segregated by sex. Hellmayr (1929b) stated that *L. i. leucopygia* has the wing 48–50mm and tail 20–21mm (sexes and sample size unknown). Weight: 7.0g (one male) and 8.5–9.0g (two females) (Rahbek *et al.* 1993, Dunning 2008), but Salaman and Donegan (2007) gave mean weight as 7.8g ($n = 25$, sexes combined).

GEOGRAPHICAL VARIATION Two subspecies are recognised. *L. i. isidorei* (described above) occurs on the east slope of the East Andes from central Colombia south through eastern Ecuador to northernmost Peru in dpto. Amazonas, whilst *L. i. leucopygia* (Hellmayr, 1903) is endemic to northern Peru south of the Río Marañón, occurring on the east slope of the Andes through dptos. Amazonas, San Martín and northern dpto. Huánuco (Schulenberg *et al.* 2007). The latter probably differs only in male plumage, which compared with *L. i. isidorei* has the rump and uppertail-coverts milky white, with a blue tinge and narrow blue borders to the upper and lower edges of the rump patch. Hellmayr (1929b) stated that females of *L. i. leucopygia* differ in having the rump 'slightly more yellowish green' than the nominate race, but even if true it seems unlikely that this difference could be appreciated in the field or except with a long series of birds in a museum. Ridgely and Tudor (1994) and Ridgely and Greenfield (2001) speculated that *L. i. leucopygia* ('Milky-rumped Manakin') might represent a separate species. We see no strong reason to recognise more than one species for now, at least without more and stronger evidence to the contrary.

VOICE The male's advertisement song is a frequently repeated, rising *wing?*, *wreee* or *koooit*, given at 2–5-second intervals, and with the slightly squeaky quality common to most *Lepidothrix* (Ridgely and Greenfield 2001, Snow 2004b, Schulenberg *et al.* 2007). Males also give *prew* or *shew* calls on their courts, but the significance and function of these vocalisations are currently unknown (M. Anciães and D. Calderón). Female 'alarm call' is a high-pitched, short, sharp *weeep* note, also given at regular intervals of >2 seconds (T. Mark recording XC7059). The Blue-rumped Manakin's vocalisations have featured on the following audio compilations: Álvarez-Rebolledo (2000), Krabbe and Nilsson (2003), Lysinger *et al.* (2005), Alvarez *et al.* (2007) and Boesman (2009), and recordings from Colombia, Ecuador and Peru are archived online at www. xeno-canto.org.

NATURAL HISTORY Surprisingly little is known given the species' relatively wide range, although many aspects of its ecology are considered similar to those of Blue-crowned Manakin (Ridgely and Greenfield 2001). It is most readily found in edge habitats, e.g. around clearings or along trails, particularly when visiting fruiting trees and shrubs, sometimes with other species of manakins.

FOOD AND FEEDING Known to feed on *Miconia* (Melastomataceae) fruits (R. S. Ridgely *in* Hilty and Brown 1986), and seeds (ROM), though published data on diet and feeding behaviour are otherwise chronically lacking (but doubtless recall other *Lepidothrix*). We have observed this species feeding in company with other Pipridae (namely Golden-winged Manakin *Masius chrysopterus*, Striped Manakin *Machaeropterus regulus striolatus*, White-crowned Manakin *Dixiphia pipra* and Green Manakin *Chloropipo holochlora*) on fruiting melastomes, principally using short (<50cm) upward or horizontal sally-hovers, before returning to a lower perch, but also by taking fruits while perched, with a short lunging movement (GMK pers. obs.).

DISPLAY Lekking behaviour and display repertoire require adequate description in the literature (but songs at a lek, with multiple birds audible in the recording, have been archived online at www.xeno-canto.org; N. Athanas recording XC6617). A solitary male in Ecuador was reported to have perched 4–8m above ground, singing from thin horizontal branches, and to have occasionally crouched forwards and conspicuously raised the crown and fluffed the rump-feathers (Ridgely and Tudor 1994, Snow 2004b). Song perches can be very hard to pinpoint. Courtship behaviour was briefly described by M. Anciães and D. Calderón (a poster presented at the VII Neotropical Ornithological Congress in Chile, in 2003) based on observations in May in southeast Ecuador. They identified 13 potential courts, *c.*20–50m apart, where males displayed on horizontal, diagonal and vertical perches *c.*1–3m apart and <1m to 7m above ground. The following display behaviours were observed. The *S-shaped flight* is butterfly-like with the bird upright, performing an undulating trajectory over up to 3m within the court. *Round flight* is also butterfly-like, but performed in a circular trajectory. The *chin-down* posture is assumed on a display perch, the bird crouching while lowering the head and simultaneously erecting the crown and rump feathers. During *side-to-side turning* while in chin-down posture, the bird turns its body 180° parallel to the perch, facing opposite directions. Finally, *wing-shivering* while in chin-down posture serves to expose the blue rump, and is similar to the wing-flick behaviour of *L. coronata* (Durães 2009). In *L. isidorei*, however, the male assumes a chin-down posture and 'shivers' the wings, rather than giving a single flick. Blue-rumped Manakins also perform *about-faces* when perched either horizontally or when more upright, as well as *whirring to-and-fro* flights, both of which behaviours have been observed in lekking *L. coronata* (Durães 2009). In southeast Ecuador group displays were semi-coordinated, performed by up to three males, and more frequent than solitary displays, peaking in the mid morning. However, males attend courts from dusk to late afternoon, calling for more than 66% of the time and performing just 7.9% of the time. *Wreee* calls intensified when neighbouring males were calling. Salaman *et al.* (2002b) reported 'leks' at two study localities in Colombia, but nothing has been published on their nature, structure or the number of birds attending them.

BREEDING The nest of this species is unknown and no other indications of breeding appear to have been published.

STATUS The species is categorised as being Least Concern by BirdLife International (2004, 2008). Anciães and Peterson (2006) foresee that this species could be moderately impacted by habitat modification in the face of potential climate change predicted using modelling techniques. Blue-rumped Manakin is generally fairly common to uncommon in Colombia and Ecuador (Hilty and Brown 1986, Ridgely and Greenfield 2001, Salaman *et al.* 2002b), and race *L. i. leucopygia* is also considered to be fairly common in northern Peru (Schulenberg *et al.* 2007). Blue-rumped Manakin is known from the ProAves-owned Halcón Colorado Bird Reserve, near Villavicencio, dpto. Meta, Colombia (Salaman *et al.* 2009), and is common at the recently opened Wild Sumaco lodge, above Loreto, eastern Ecuador (GMK pers. obs.). The species is also regularly found along certain nearby stretches of the Loreto road, in Napo province. It also occurs in Podocarpus National Park, in southern Ecuador (Bloch *et al.* 1991), where the Río Bombuscaro trail represents one of the best localities for finding the species (Williams *et al.* 1997, Ridgely and Greenfield 2001).

REFERENCES Álvarez-Rebolledo (2000), Alvarez *et al.* (2007), Alverson *et al.* (2001), Anciães and Peterson (2006, 2009), BirdLife International (2004, 2008), Bloch *et al.* (1991), Boesman (2009), Chapman (1917), Dunning (2008), Durães (2009), Graves (1981), Haffer (1997a), Hellmayr (1906d, 1929b), Hilty and Brown (1986), Krabbe and Nilsson (2003), Lysinger *et al.* (2005), Merkord *et al.* (2009), Parker *et al.* (1982), Rahbek *et al.* (1993), Restall *et al.* (2006), Ridgely and Greenfield (2001), Ridgely and Tudor (1994, 2009), Salaman and Donegan (2007), Salaman *et al.* (1999, 2002b, 2009), Schulenberg *et al.* (2007), Snow (2004b), Stotz *et al.* (1996), Williams *et al.* (1997).

Blue-rumped Manakin *Lepidothrix isidorei.* **Fig. 1**. Male, *L. i. isidorei*, Río Bombuscaro, Podocarpus National Park, prov. Zamora-Chinchipe, southeast Ecuador, November (*Hadoram Shirihai / Photographic Handbook to Birds of the World*).

CERULEAN-CAPPED MANAKIN
Lepidothrix coeruleocapilla　　　　　　**Plate 4**

Pipra coeruleo-capilla **Tschudi, 1844**, *Arch. Naturg.* 10(1): 271, Peru [type locality designated as Montañas de Vitoc, dpto. Junín, Peru, by Hellmayr 1929b]

With the exception of the Blue-crowned Manakin *L. coronata* and White-fronted Manakin *L. serena*, the life histories of most species of the genus *Lepidothrix* are rather poorly known, and the Cerulean-capped Manakin is certainly no exception to this rule. Indeed, this Peruvian endemic, which is one of the most striking and contrastingly coloured of all the *Lepidothrix* manakins, is long overdue serious study. To date, it seems that virtually nothing has been published on any aspect of its behaviour.

IDENTIFICATION 8.5–9.0cm. Unique and unmistakable within its elevational and geographical range in the foothills of south and central Peru, as there is no known geographical overlap with the extremely similar, albeit slightly smaller and shorter tailed Blue-rumped Manakin *L. isidorei*, which replaces the present species to the north (reaching as far south as northern dpto. Huánuco). Note that it is the whiter crowned and rumped race *L. i. leucopygia* of Blue-rumped that comes closest in range to Cerulean-capped. Range, but not usually elevation, also overlap with the rather less similar Blue-crowned Manakin, males of which lack the azure-blue rump/lower back patch shown by male Cerulean-capped. Females would be extremely difficult to distinguish from other similar species in the field, although the present species might be inclined to appear slightly duller on the underparts, especially compared with *L. c. exquisita* of central Peru (Ridgely and Tudor 1994, Schulenberg *et al.* 2007). Most identifications will surely be based on elevation and habitat. However, note that Stotz (1993) reported that '*P. coeruleocapilla* and *P. coronata* … occur syntopically (captured on the same mistnet line in southeastern Peru, specimens in FMNH), apparently without hybridizing.' Compared with female Blue-rumped Manakin, female *L. coeruleocapilla* lacks any trace of yellow on the face. Clearly extreme care will be needed to identify the present species at the lower edge of its altitudinal range, or in the extreme north of its geographical range. Males of the *L. c. exquisita* race of Blue-crowned have the blue of the crown extremely similar to the coloration of the crown patch in Cerulean-capped, but are green-bodied so the risk of confusion is only possible with young males of the present species.

DISTRIBUTION Endemic to central and southern Peru, where it is found only on the east slope of the Andes, from southern dpto. Huánuco discontinuously south to northern dpto. Puno (Schulenberg *et al.* 2007). The species' range seems to be more or less confined to the South Peruvian Andean subcentre of endemism as defined by Cracraft (1985).

MOVEMENTS None known, and like congenerics the species is presumed to be resident. However, see comments under White-fronted Manakin.

HABITAT The species is principally known from humid, mossy foothill and subtropical forest habitats of the upper tropical zone, at 600–1,900m (Stotz *et al.* 1996, Schulenberg *et al.* 2007). Reports of its occurrence down to 500m and as high as 2,100m (Ridgely and Tudor 1994, Stattersfield *et al.* 1998, Snow 2004b) require verification. At the Cerros

del Sira, dpto. Huánuco, the species has been mist-netted in stunted ridge-top forest (Mee *et al.* 2002).

DESCRIPTION Sexes differ. The narrow bill has an arched culmen and usually a hooked tip (sometimes pronounced, but occasionally absent), with quite prominent nostrils. *Adult male.* – Crown and nape bright cerulean blue, becoming deeper posteriorly, with an even deeper, electric cerulean blue lower back, rump and uppertail-coverts patch (faintly shaded bluish), contrasting strongly with the remainder of the plumage, which is matt black. *Adult female.* – The upperparts are bright grass green, becoming brightest on the rump and duskier over the tail, with browner wing-coverts (especially the larger feathers) and the flight feathers have pale green fringes. Females very occasionally, on close inspection, show bright (male-like) feathers in the crown (Graves 1981) and sometimes show bluish-tipped scapulars and larger wing-coverts (Zimmer 1930). The face from the forehead to the rear of the ear-coverts and chin and throat are pale greyish, with a slightly duller green breast and a yellowish-grey belly to the undertail-coverts. *Juvenile.* – Very similar to the adult female; especially the face and throat show quite fluffy feathering (H. Lloyd). The immature male initially gains a few cerulean blue feathers on the centre of the nape and then the crown (Mee *et al.* 2002; H. Lloyd *in litt.* 2010). *Moult.* – There are no published data on moult. Two males taken in southeast Peru in late November were moulting their body feathers and wing and body feathers, respectively. However, single females collected in eastern Peru in August and November were not replacing any feathers, and the same was true for males taken in April, July, August and November (FMNH). *Bare parts.* – Irides brown, dark brown or dark brownish-red (seemingly at all ages and in both sexes), but two males had the irides blue and black, respectively. The bill has a blackish (occasionally grey) maxilla usually with a paler grey (occasionally silvery) mandible and cutting edges, and the legs and feet are greyish to black, but sometimes pinkish-grey or dark pink in females (FMNH; Snow 2004b).

MEASUREMENTS (BMNH; FMNH; ROM: dptos. Huánuco, Madre de Dios, Puno and Cuzco, Peru) Wing of male (*n* =

15) 51.0–55.5mm, wing of female (*n* = 15) 53–58mm; tail of male (*n* = 15) 23–27mm, tail of female (*n* = 15) 26–31mm; bill of male (*n* = 15) 9.95–10.40mm, bill of female (*n* = 15) 9.54–11.19mm; tarsus of male (*n* = 15) 13.51–15.80mm, tarsus of female (*n* = 15) 13.46–17.22mm. Zimmer (1930) stated that it is possible to differentiate females from the same sex of *L. coronata* in eastern Peru by virtue of their shorter wings and tail, and smaller bill. Weight: 7.8–12.1g (males, once 17.0 g), 8.6–13.3g (females) (FMNH; Snow 2004b, Dunning 2008).

GEOGRAPHICAL VARIATION Monotypic, but forms a superspecies with Blue-crowned Manakin (Sibley and Monroe 1990), which it replaces at higher elevations, there currently being no known overlap in altitudinal range between the two species in Peru (Schulenberg *et al.* 2007). Subspecies *L. c. grandior* (Carriker, 1931, *Proc. Acad. Nat. Sci. Philadelphia* 83: 456, type locality La Aroya, Puno, Peru) has long been regarded as a synonym (Snow 1979b). It was described on the basis of its larger size and smaller and darker blue rump patch, while Carriker reported the female to have a longer tail, yellower abdomen, darker green upperparts and brighter green breast. However, we can see no reason to uphold *grandior* on the basis of the limited material that we have seen.

VOICE Only in the last decade have ornithologists become familiar with the song of this species. The regularly given and highly distinctive advertising song of males is typical of the genus, being burry and frog-like, *prr-uut*, with the accent on the second note; also rendered as a sharp *tee-zeek* (Snow 2004b) or *djee-HAI!* (Schulenberg *et al.* 2007). The song features on two recent audio compilations (Schulenberg 2000a, Boesman 2009). Recordings archived online (www. xeno-canto.org) by H. Lloyd and D. Geale also reveal that the species emits a low, steadily rising whistle lasting just <1 second, which is easily imitated, just like many of its congenerics. This call is sometimes given at a rate of once per two or three seconds, but also at longer intervals (e.g. nine times in *c*.50 seconds), and its 'insistence' can also vary, the call sometimes sounding rather flatter, other times marginally more 'piercing' (e.g. in response to playback). It can be used in response to playback or in the hand, but there is no information to date as to whether it is given by both sexes, as in corresponding vocalisations by other *Lepidothrix*.

NATURAL HISTORY Cerulean-capped Manakin is apparently primarily an inhabitant of the forest midstorey and subcanopy, where males of all ages regularly follow large mixed-species flocks, especially if there are many trees and shrubs in fruit; usually just one (rarely two) follows such flocks (H. Lloyd *in litt.* 2010). However, in response to playback and when visiting fruiting trees, males may come lower to the ground (H. Lloyd *in litt.* 2010). One and sometimes two males will roost in dense vine tangles in the midstorey, but they apparently do not use the same site on consecutive nights (H. Lloyd *in litt.* 2010). *L. coeruleocapilla* is arguably the most poorly known of the genus, which is especially remarkable given that the Brazilian endemic, Golden-crowned Manakin *L. vilasboasi*, was described only just over 50 years ago and until recently had only been seen in the field by two scientists. Yet even the latter species' nest and eggs have been described.

FOOD AND FEEDING No detailed dietary information is available, and the only published information on feeding appears to be that Cerulean-capped Manakin sometimes visits fruiting trees at the forest edge (Snow 2004b). Snow assumed that the species' diet and feeding behaviour, when known, would prove to be closely similar to those of *L. coronata*. H. Lloyd (*in litt.* 2010) reports that Cerulean-capped Manakins regularly feed at *Miconia* (Melastomataceae) and other shrubs in southeast Peru when these are in peak production, typically in August/early September in the Manu region. Stomach contents from the fine series of this species held at FMNH usually involved small fruits, but one female held beetle fragments.

BREEDING Lekking behaviour is unknown (Walker and Fjeldså 2001) and nothing has been published concerning any other aspects of the species' breeding behaviour and biology (Snow 2004b). Based on the long series of specimens held at FMNH, it seems that in dptos. Cuzco and Madre de Dios (southeast Peru) at least, the breeding season commences in around October, from where females have been collected with a yolking ovum in the second week of November and a brood patch at the end of the same month. Recently, however, A. Durand, D. Beadle and H. Shirihai discovered an active nest of Cerulean-capped Manakin, along the Manu road, in dpto. Cusco, at the end of the first week of November 2010. The female was incubating eggs. It was a typical small cup-like nest constructed of rootlets and sited in small tree fork, *c*.2m above the ground. Live vegetation and some dead leaves hanging from the support branches provided a natural 'cloak' largely or partially obscuring the nest from view from several angles (Kirwan *et al.* submitted).

STATUS Cerulean-capped Manakin is currently treated as a species of Least Concern by BirdLife International (2004, 2008). Its range is confined to the East Andean Foothills Endemic Bird Area (Stattersfield *et al.* 1998), within which the most important conservation unit is Manu National Park and Biosphere Reserve, where the species occurs from 750 to 1,600m (Walker *et al.* 2006). It is known from five Important Bird Areas (Boyla and Estrada 2005). Anciães and Peterson (2006) predicted that this species could be moderately affected by habitat modification in the face of potential climate change based on modelling techniques. This manakin is generally considered uncommon to locally fairly common, but it is an extremely inconspicuous and easily overlooked species, unless observers are familiar with its vocalisations. Cerulean-capped Manakin is perhaps most easily seen along the Manu Road, which runs from Shintuya in the lowlands to Paucartambo in the dry intermontane valleys above the eastern slope, in dpto. Cuzco (Ridgely and Tudor 1994). Along this road the species has been found at various localities including around Cock-of-the-Rock Lodge and the immediate San Pedro area (1,200–1,500m) and Quita Calzones (*c*.1,000m). The species has recently been reported to be common in the Cerros del Sira, dptos. Huánuco/Pasco.

REFERENCES Anciães and Peterson (2006, 2009), BirdLife International (2004, 2008), Boesman (2009), Boyla and Estrada (2005), Cracraft (1985), Dunning (2008), Graves (1981), Hellmayr (1906d, 1929b), Kirwan *et al.* (submitted), Mee *et al.* (2002), Parker *et al.* (1982), Ridgely and Tudor (1994, 2009), Robbins *et al.* (2011), Schulenberg (2000a), Schulenberg *et al.* (2007), Sibley and Monroe (1990), Snow (2004b), Stattersfield *et al.* (1998), Stotz (1993), Stotz *et al.* (1996), Walker (2009), Walker and Fjeldså (2002), Walker *et al.* (2006), Zimmer (1930).

Cerulean-capped Manakin *Lepidothrix coeruleocapilla.* **Fig. 1**. Male, Manu Road, dpto. Cuzco, southeast Peru, July (*Harvey van Diek*). **Fig. 2**. Female, near San Pedro, Manu Road, dpto. Cuzco, southeast Peru, June (*Huw Lloyd*). This species replaces Blue-rumped Manakin *L. isidorei* in southern Peru. **Fig. 3.** Female, Manu Road, dpto. Cuzco, southeast Peru, November (*Hadoram Shirihai / Photographic Handbook to Birds of the World*).

SNOW-CAPPED MANAKIN
Lepidothrix nattereri   Plate 5

Pipra nattereri **P. L. Sclater, 1865**, *Proc. Zool. Soc. Lond.* 1864: 611, pl. 39, Borba, Rio Madeira, Brazil

This beautiful manakin with its amazing matt white crown and lower back patches, which have the quality of recently dried paint, is one of *the* loveliest birds of the rainforests of southeast Amazonia. The Snow-capped Manakin's specific name commemorates one of the most prolific of natural history collectors who worked in South America, the Austrian-born Johann Natterer, who spent the years 1817–1835 in Brazil, in the process collecting a prodigious number of birds still scarcely known to modern-day ornithologists. Remarkably, the full magnitude of his discoveries was to some extent overlooked, as Natterer's bird collections were not written up for almost another 30 years, by Pelzeln, during which time some of 'his' new species were discovered and published by other workers.

IDENTIFICATION 8.5–10.6cm. Allopatric with the two (geographically and morphologically) closest species, Opal-crowned Manakin *L. iris* and Golden-crowned Manakin *L. vilasboasi* (both of which occur to the north and east of the range of the present species). There is no known overlap between the three species, although Oren and Albuquerque (1991) speculated that two or more members of the superspecies might yet be found in sympatry. Females are quite possibly indistinguishable from females of either of the other two species (although the present species has a smaller bill than *L. iris*). Males (including young males) are easily separable from Golden-crowned Manakin by the brilliant and shiny white crown/nape and rump patches, and the rump/lower back patch and slightly different colour of the crown (purer white, less opalescent) separate it from the geographically more distant Opal-crowned Manakin.

DISTRIBUTION Endemic to south-central Amazonia, basically occupying the Madeira–Tapajós interfluvium, although it reaches just west of the former river's major tributary, the Guaporé, in the far south of its range, and it crosses the latter into the Serra do Cachimbo, in southwest Pará, as well as occurring along the Rio Von Den Steinen, a

left-bank tributary of the upper Rio Xingu, in Mato Grosso (A. Whittaker pers. obs.). Cracraft (1985) listed Snow-capped Manakin as a Rondônia centre endemic. In Brazil, *L. nattereri* is found from the Serra do Cachimbo, in southwest Pará, in the Tapajós–Xingu interfluvium, south to northern Mato Grosso (e.g. around Alta Floresta: Zimmer *et al.* 1997, Lees *et al.* 2008; and Igarapes-Juruena State Park, between the Rios Juruena and Aripuanã: Oliveira *et al.* 2008) and west to the Rio Madeira in Amazonas and Rondônia. Only relatively recently discovered in northeast Bolivia, initially by Bates *et al.* (1989) at three localities in the Serranía de Huanchaca, in dpto. Santa Cruz. It might be expected to occur in extreme northern dpto. Beni, given the species' presence on the right bank of the Rio Mamoré, near Guajará-Mirim, Rondônia (GMK pers. obs.). Snow-capped Manakin has been recorded as high as *c.*550m in Bolivia (Bates *et al.* 1989).

MOVEMENTS None recorded, and there is no reason to suppose that the species is not resident. However, see comments under White-fronted Manakin.

HABITAT Snow-capped Manakin is typically found in humid *terra firme* forest, usually on level ground, but canopy height varies from 15 to 30m at least, and the undergrowth can range from relatively open to heavily disturbed, with many vine tangles and some bamboo (Bates *et al.* 1989, Zimmer *et al.* 1997; GMK pers. obs.). It is at least occasionally found at the ecotone between *campinarana* and tall humid forest. At least in some areas, the species appears able to persist in relatively small forest patches, despite certain levels of habitat degradation and disturbance (GMK pers. obs.), but in others, e.g. around Alta Floresta, Snow-capped Manakin seems unable to adapt to forest patches smaller than 700ha (A. C. Lees *in litt.* 2010). The species also seems to be patchily distributed and is seemingly absent from large tracts of apparently suitable *terra firme* (A. C. Lees *in litt.* 2010).

DESCRIPTION A tiny manakin. Sexes differ. The narrow bill (slightly broader in females) has an arched culmen and usually a hooked tip (sometimes pronounced, but occasionally absent). *Adult male.* – Crown and nape brilliant white, like the icing on a cake, in some bordered laterally and posteriorly very narrowly bluish, with a relatively bright green mantle, back and wing-coverts (in some slightly duller more olive-green), and an almost equally brilliant white lower back, rump and uppertail-coverts patch (faintly shaded bluish, especially at the upper and lower edges), whilst the tail is generally dark with broad dull green webs. The remiges are generally brownish-black with relatively broad greenish inner webs and paler tips, although these are not so obvious in the field. Ear-coverts, chin, throat, breast and body-sides green, becoming brighter ventrally (but duller overall than the upperparts), the face appearing slightly mottled, and becoming variably bright yellow over the belly to undertail-coverts (perhaps brightest over the central belly), with a dark underside to the tail. *Adult female.* – Differs from the male in lacking the striking white crown and nape, instead having a slightly bluish cast to these parts, and has otherwise entirely bluish-green upperparts, with blackish-brown wing-feathers (including the coverts) and tail (with duller greenish webs). Face and chin to breast much as adult male, but the green is generally slightly duller and less bright, and the rest of the underparts are also, on average, distinctly less bright yellow than in the male, although some still possess some very bright elements over

L. n. nattereri

L. n. gracilis

the central belly and ventral region. *Juvenile.* – Reported to resemble the female (Snow 2004b, presumably based on vague statement in Naumburg 1930), whilst the immature male has a distinctly brighter yellow belly to undertail-coverts than the female (but duller than the adult male) contrasting with the breast, with a few emerging white feathers in the crown (equally appearing to be 'plastered on'). *Moult.* – There are no published data on moult, but birds collected in the Rio Madeira drainage between April and June were not moulting any part of their plumage (INPA). *Bare parts.* – Data principally based on adult male specimens. The irides are very dull white to grey or even pale yellow (no sexual variation apparent). The bill has a dark grey to black maxilla with a bluish-grey mandible and cutting edges (latter rarely buffish), and the legs and feet are pinkish-flesh, orangey or rose-coloured to fuscous yellow (Snethlage 1908b, Hellmayr 1910, Sick 1997, Snow 2004b; INPA; MNRJ).

MEASUREMENTS (Hellmayr 1910: Amazonas and Rondônia, Brazil; INPA, MNRJ: Amazonas, Mato Grosso, Pará and Rondônia, Brazil) Wing of male ($n = 24$) 50.5–54.5mm, wing of female ($n = 14$) 50.5–59.0mm; tail of male ($n = 24$) 24–29mm; tail of female ($n = 12$) 25–34mm; bill of male ($n = 7$) 9.98–11.16mm, bill of female ($n = 10$) 9.92–11.73mm; tarsus of male ($n = 4$) 12.73–13.76mm, tarsus of female ($n = 5$) 13.11–14.68mm. Some additional mensural data were presented by Hellmayr (1910), Snethlage (1914) and Sick (1959c). Weight: 6–9g (males) and 7.0–9.6g (females) (Bates *et al.* 1989, Sick 1959c, 1997, Snow 2004b; INPA; MNRJ).

GEOGRAPHICAL VARIATION Two subspecies are recognised, although Snow (1979b) treated the species as monotypic, presumably because Hellmayr (1910) had subsequently stated that he believed his own description of *L. n. gracilis* (Hellmayr 1903) to be in error and that variation in this species is purely individual. Recent observations in southwest Amazonian Brazil have confirmed the validity of two subspecies (Stotz *et al.* 1997). **L. n. nattereri** (described above) is endemic to Brazil and occurs across central Amazonia, from the Rio Madeira east to the Rio Tapajós drainage, and south to Calama (on the Amazonas/ Rondônia border) and Nova Prainha (on the Rio Aripuanã, Amazonas). **L. n. gracilis** (Hellmayr, 1903) occurs to the south of the previous taxon, from the upper Rio Madeira (south of Aliança) in southwest Amazonian Brazil east to the upper Rio Xingu in Mato Grosso, and south to extreme northeast Bolivia in northeast dpto. Santa Cruz. Males of the two subspecies are identical, but female *L. n. gracilis* differs from the blue-crowned nominate race female in having the crown concolorous with the green back. Hellmayr (1929b) speculated that *L. nattereri* might prove to be simply a western race of *L. iris.*

VOICE Two main vocal types are known. A whistled, rising *seeeep* or *pweeee* call, with a slightly squeaky quality, is given quite persistently, at irregular intervals, by both sexes and young birds. The male advertisement song is a slightly rasping, frog-like vocalisation typical of the superspecies (Zimmer *et al.* 1997, Snow 2004b). The latter has been rendered *chi-wrrr* (Snow 2004b) or *tak-eet* (Sick 1997) and is also given persistently in series' of up to six or more calls, sometimes as few as three, each series sometimes consisting of up to, for example, three 'couplets', with slightly longer pauses between each 'couplet' than the two calls that comprise it. However, the species' calls can also appear much less patternless on many occasions. Playback can frequently result in the bird moving away from the source

of the sound. The species' vocalisations feature on the audio compilations of Boesman (2006a) and Marantz and Zimmer (2006), and several recordings are also available online at www.xeno-canto.org.

NATURAL HISTORY Surprisingly poorly known, given its wide range across south-central Amazonia. Males sometimes perch as little as 10m apart, generally assuming positions 1–6m above ground (especially at 3–4m) and calling continuously for several minutes before moving to a new song perch up to 5–25m away (Zimmer *et al.* 1997). Females and immatures generally perch very quietly.

FEEDING Oren and Parker (1997) reported an observation of a female apparently attending an ant swarm, presumably searching for insects disturbed by the ants. Stomach contents generally recorded as being small fruits (MNRJ), but seeds, insects and a spider have also been recorded (Schubart *et al.* 1965, Snow 2004b; INPA).

BREEDING Behaviour and biology were completely unknown until very recently, although male specimens from two localities in Rondônia had been collected in breeding condition in July–September (MNRJ), with a female also in breeding condition taken in southern Amazonas in late June (INPA). Novaes (1976) found some males in breeding condition in northwest Mato Grosso in September/October. A nest was recently found in Amazônia National Park, on the Rio Tapajós, in southwest Pará (Whittaker *et al.* 2010a). It was found in *terra firme* forest 1m from a narrow trail within very open understorey, and sited in a small sapling *c.*65cm tall. The nest was a neatly woven standard cup, slung between two horizontal branches off the trunk and woven tightly to these branches by spiderwebs along the nest's rim. The walls of the cup were constructed of one larger dead palm leaves lined with thin pale strips of bark, and the entire nest was neatly bound together with spiderwebs. The outer walls and base of the nest had several large dead leaves also attached using spiderwebs and below the cup there was a 'tail' formed by a dead leaf 6.5–7.0cm long, which disguised the nest's shape. The nest was 4.5–5.0cm from the sapling's trunk, and was 50cm above the ground. The incubating female sat very tight, perhaps suggesting that the eggs were close to hatching. The two eggs were pinkish with irregular brown blotching more concentrated at the larger end, forming a ring, with only tiny brown flecks over the remainder.

STATUS Treated as Least Concern by BirdLife International (2004, 2008), Snow-capped Manakin is generally locally common (e.g. at sites in Bolivia and Rondônia) to uncommon across its reasonably wide range. It has been recorded in two Important Bird Areas in Bolivia (BirdLife International 2008). Anciães and Peterson (2006) predicted that this species could be badly affected by habitat modification in the face of potential climate change based on modelling techniques. It is known from a number of protected areas, such as: Amazônia (Tapajós) National Park, Pará (Oren and Parker 1997), Terra Indígena Nove de Janeiro, Amazonas (Santos and Silva 2005), Sucunduri State Park, Amazonas (INPA), and Igarapes-Juruena State Park, Mato Grosso (Oliveira *et al.* 1997), all in Brazil, as well as Parque Nacional Noel Kempff Mercado (Bates *et al.* 1998) and Estación Biológica Caparú (Vidoz *et al.* 2010), both in Santa Cruz, Bolivia. In Brazil, the species is well known at the famous Cristalino Jungle Lodge, near Alta Floresta, Mato Grosso, as well as at the relatively nearby Pousada Rio Azul, in southern Pará, and at Borba, on the east bank of the Rio Madeira, Amazonas.

REFERENCES Acheson and Davis (2001), Anciães and Peterson (2006, 2009), Bandeira *et al.* (2008), Bates *et al.* (1989, 1998), BirdLife International (2004, 2008), Boesman (2006a), Boyla and Estrada (2005), Haffer (1992b, 1997a), Hellmayr (1903, 1906d, 1910, 1929b), Hennessey *et al.* (2003b), Lees *et al.* (2008), Marantz and Zimmer (2006), Naumburg (1930), Novaes (1976), Oliveira *et al.* (2009), Oren and Albuquerque (1991), Oren and Parker (1997), Pacheco and Olmos (2005), Pinto (1944), Rêgo *et al.* (2007), Remsen and Traylor (1989), Ridgely and Tudor (1994, 2009), Santos and Silva (2005), Schubart *et al.* (1965), Sick (1959c, 1997), Snethlage (1908b, 1914), Snow (1979b, 2004b), Stotz *et al.* (1996, 1997), Vidoz *et al.* (2010), Whittaker (2009), Whittaker *et al.* (2010a), Zimmer *et al.* (1997).

Snow-capped Manakin *Lepidothrix nattereri*. **Fig. 1**. Male, *L. n. gracilis*, Cristalino Jungle Lodge, Alta Floresta, Mato Grosso, east Amazonian Brazil, December (*Arthur Grosset / www.arthurgrosset.com*). **Fig. 2**. Female, *L. n. nattereri*, Floresta de Maués, Amazonas, central Amazonian Brazil, June (*Andrew Whittaker*). Note the blue crown (green in *L. n. gracilis*). Differences between the two subspecies are only observable in females. There is no overlap with the only similar species, Opal-crowned Manakin *L. iris*, which ranges further east in Amazonian Brazil.

GOLDEN-CROWNED MANAKIN
Lepidothrix vilasboasi
Plate 5

Pipra vilasboasi **Sick, 1959**, *J. Orn.* 100: 111, headwaters of the Rio Cururu-ri, southwest Pará, Brazil

The Golden-crowned Manakin is one of the most recently described species of Pipridae, being initially discovered by Helmut Sick and Raimundo Costa in July 1957 near a small left-bank tributary of the upper Rio Cururu-ri in the Brazilian Amazon (Sick 1959a). Named for the renowned Villas-Bôas brothers (note the *lapsus* in the spelling of the species name), explorers and champions of the rights of indigenous peoples, whom Sick had joined in 1946 on a famous overland expedition to the Rio Xingu (recounted in his travelogue *Tukani*), Golden-crowned Manakin slipped into relative obscurity during most of the 50 years following its discovery. Firstly, doubts seemed to creep in as to the precise type locality due to the existence of two tributaries of the Rio Teles Pires with similar names, the Cururu-ri and the Cururu-açu, which flow, however, in quite different directions (see Olmos and Pacheco 2003). Secondly, Haffer (1997a) had postulated that *L. vilasboasi* in all probability represented a hybrid swarm between Snow-capped Manakin *L. nattereri gracilis* and Opal-crowned Manakin *L. iris eucephala*, thereby to some extent dampening interest, temporarily, in the taxon. Molecular markers have recently demonstrated that Haffer's hypothesis can be satisfactorily discounted, and that *L. vilasboasi* appears to be most closely related to *L. iris eucephala* (Bandeira *et al.* 2008), not *L. nattereri* as often predicted (Snow 2004b). Finally, Sick (1959c), advised by Alexander Wetmore, had himself 'muddied the waters' by also describing a second, obviously very similar taxon, '*Pipra obscura*', the so-called Sick's Manakin, based on a female and immature male specimen (held in the Museu Nacional Rio de Janeiro), which he had collected at the same locality as the three males of Golden-crowned Manakin. It was treated specifically by Meyer de Schauensee (1970), but subsequently, following Mayr (1971), Sick (1997) reversed his position, stating that he considered '*P. obscura*' to be a synonym of *L. vilasboasi* and the five specimens that he had collected to belong to a single species. These problematic specimens were also re-examined and formally reassigned to the *L. vilasboasi* type series by Gonzaga (1989), and are treated as such here too. They were also discussed by Mallet-Rodrigues (2008).

IDENTIFICATION 8.5cm. Allopatric with two (geographically and morphologically) closest species, Opal-crowned Manakin *L. iris* (which replaces it to the north and east) and Snow-capped Manakin *L. nattereri* (found to the south and west). Females will be quite possibly indistinguishable from females of either of the other two species (although the present species has a smaller bill, especially compared to *L. iris*). In contrast, males (including young males) are easily separable due to the striking yellow crown and nape patches (opalescent or snow-white, respectively, in the other two species), whilst Snow-capped Manakin also has a white rump and lower back.

DISTRIBUTION Golden-crowned Manakin is endemic to eastern Amazonian Brazil, more specifically to a tiny area of the Pará centre of endemism (Cracraft 1985). The species is known from just three published localities, all in southwest Pará, in the headwaters of the Rio Cururu-ri (07°12'S 58°03'W), a right bank tributary of the Tapajós

(not the Teles Pires, as frequently stated), and 200km to the northeast at Consórcio Jamanxim (07°09'S 55°29'W; incorrectly spelt Jamunxim by Olmos and Pacheco 2002, and Snow 2004b), 12km southwest of Novo Progresso (Sick 1959a, 1959b, Olmos and Pacheco 2002, 2003). In 2006, the rediscovery site was found to have been completely logged, but two 'exploded leks' were found in selectively logged forest 20km away, and the species has now also been found at two further localities on the east bank of the Rio Jamanxim, at *c.*07°13'S, 55°32'W (A. C. Lees *in* BirdLife International 2008). Pacheco and Olmos (2005) suggested that the species' range might be constrained by the Rios Tapajós, Cururu-ri, in the west, the lower to mid Jamanxim, in the east, and the north face of the Serra do Cachimbo, in the south, where the latter authors found only Snow-capped Manakin.

MOVEMENTS None recorded, although there is no reason to suppose that the species does perform strict movements of any type. However, see comments under White-fronted Manakin *L. serena*.

HABITAT Golden-crowned Manakin inhabits humid riverine *terra firme* forest, which at Consórcio Jamanxim is characterised by tree species belonging for instance to the families Euphorbiaceae, Lecythidaceae, Burseraceae and Sapotaceae (Olmos and Pacheco 2002, Pacheco and Olmos 2005), and the species is recorded to *c.*200m (Snow 2004b). Olmos and Pacheco (2001, 2002) reported that it can be found in edge habitats and A. C. Lees (*in litt.* 2010) found the species in relatively poor-quality forest that had been selectively logged within the last 15 years.

DESCRIPTION A tiny manakin. Sexes differ. The narrow bill has an arched culmen and usually a hooked tip (sometimes pronounced, but occasionally absent). *Adult male.* – Bright glistening greenish-gold crown and nape, with much less bright yellow-green mantle and back, then becoming yellower over the rump and uppertail-coverts, and the tail is dull green with prominent dark webs. The remiges are brownish-black with greenish inner webs to the flight feathers and creamy whitish outer margins to the tertials, although these are not obvious in the field. Ear-coverts, chin, throat and breast dull green, the face appearing slightly mottled, becoming yellow over the belly to undertail-coverts, with a dark underside to the tail. *Adult female.* – (based on the holotype of '*Pipra obscura*') Differs from the male in lacking the striking golden-yellow crown and has entirely dull grass green upperparts (perhaps marginally darker on the crown), with blackish-brown wing-feathers and tail (and dull green fringes). Face and chin to breast much as adult male, but remainder of underparts distinctly less bright yellow than in male (and immature male). *Juvenile.* – Unknown, but the immature male (based on a specimen labelled as '*Pipra obscura*') has a distinctly brighter yellow belly to undertail-coverts than female (but duller than adult male) contrasting with the breast, unlike in the female wherein the breast and belly colorations show little contrast. The immature male also has distinctly more yellow elements in the upperparts than the adult female, especially in the rump and uppertail-coverts, and the crown and nape are extensively greenish-gold, but it becomes obviously darker on the forecrown than adult males and is overall paler on the crown than the latter. Compared with the adult female, the fringes of the wing-feathers, especially the primaries and secondaries, are brighter green and narrower, and the wing-coverts are overall more yellow-green. *Moult.* – There is no evidence of any moult in the three MNRJ specimens. *Bare parts.* – Adult males have pale greyish or whitish irides, a black bill with a whitish tip and blue-grey mandible, and yellow-brown legs and feet (Sick 1959a), whilst females have brown-yellow irides, a black maxilla and blue-grey mandible, and yellow-brown legs and feet (Sick 1959c).

MEASUREMENTS (MNRJ: southwest Pará, Amazonian Brazil, with data from an additional (live) bird in parentheses: Olmos and Pacheco 2003) Wing of male (n = 2) 52–55mm (51.6mm), wing of female (n = 1) 52mm; tail of male (n = 2) 27–32mm (31.4mm), tail of female (n = 1) 30mm; bill of male (n = 2) 10.06–10.40mm (exposed culmen 7.8mm), bill of female (n = 1) 11.27mm; tarsus of male (n = 2) 13.66–14.72mm (13.4mm), tarsus of female (n = 1) 13.68mm. Weight (sexes and ages combined): 6–8g (n = 5) (Sick 1959c; MNRJ).

GEOGRAPHICAL VARIATION Monotypic.

VOICE Sick (1997) described the male's advertising call as a double-noted *tak-ewt*, similar to the corresponding vocalisations of Opal-crowned and Snow-capped Manakins. A recording by S. M. Dantas (XC 24091) of the male advertising song sounds practically identical to *L. nattereri*, a series of up to ten slightly rasping, frog-like notes, usually given in couplets, with a longer space between each 'couple' of calls, and sometimes with the last call in a series fading abruptly off. This is presumably the same as the 'burry *preee*, sometimes in series' mentioned by Snow (2004b). There are no published recordings to date, but the species' voice can be heard online at www.xeno-canto.org.

NATURAL HISTORY This species is certainly one of the most poorly known covered by this book: almost nothing has been published concerning its life history. Another piprid, Fiery-capped Manakin *Machaeropterus pyrocephalus*, was found to frequent the banks of the same stream as Golden-crowned Manakin at the type locality, and five other Pipridae occurred in the general vicinity (Sick 1959c).

FOOD AND FEEDING Golden-crowned Manakin is known to take both small fruits and insects, the former apparently predominating (Schubart *et al.* 1965, Sick 1959a). Olmos and Pacheco (2002) trapped a male, which was apparently part of a mixed-species foraging flock, also containing

Pectoral Sparrow *Arremon taciturnus*, Pará Foliage-gleaner *Automolus paraensis* and Black-faced Antbird *Myrmoborus myotherinus*. The same authors noted the possibility that the species might consort with other manakins, e.g. White-crowned Manakin *Dixiphia pipra*, at fruiting trees in the understorey, whilst A. C. Lees (*in litt.* 2010) observed Golden-crowned Manakin at a fruiting *Cecropia* (Moraceae) also visited by toucans and tanagers.

DISPLAY A. C. Lees (*in* BirdLife International 2008) reported that the species has an 'exploded lek' system, whereby males display solitarily, but often within earshot of their neighbours, like other members of the genus *Lepidothrix*.

BREEDING Concerning breeding biology, the three adult males collected were all in breeding condition, and Sick (1959c) also reported collecting a typical manakin nest, with two eggs, from the crown of a 1.6m-high understorey tree (on 21 July) that belonged to the female manakin he had described as '*Pipra obscura*' (treated here as *L. vilasboasi*). This nest itself was placed 1m above the ground in a two-branched tree fork, bound to the supporting branches with spiderwebs, and the eggs were white with small red-brown flecks over the central part that became paler and mixed with grey-violet spots towards the ends. Dimensions of the nest and the eggs were presented by Sick (1959c). Unfortunately, the whereabouts of this material are presently unknown; certainly they are not in MNRJ, where most of Sick's collection is housed (J. Nacinovic pers. comm.).

STATUS BirdLife International (2000, 2004, 2008) treats this species as Vulnerable, but at the time of writing (December 2010) was considering a proposal to upgrade Golden-crowned Manakin to Endangered. Data concerning the species' current status, distribution and the threats it faces are urgently required. Although known from just two published sites, the type locality (from where there have been no subsequent records) lies within the Reserva Florestal do Mundurucu (= Munduruku), a 400,000ha protected area owned by the Brazilian air force, to which access is severely restricted and logging banned on paper. Consórcio Jamanxim, Novo Progresso, where the species was rediscovered in May 2002, in forest 'very disturbed by logging' (Pacheco and Olmos 2005), lies just to the south of another proposed conservation unit, the FLONA de Jamanxim (Capobianco *et al.* 2001: 436), but even this is being logged at unsustainable rates (F. Olmos *in* BirdLife International 2008). Given that the rediscovery site has been selectively logged and large areas have already been clear-cut for pastures (Pacheco and Olmos 2005), the species is perhaps able to withstand substantial habitat disturbance. Nonetheless, this region, which lies on the Santarém–Cuiabá highway, a road apparently scheduled to be paved, is subject to considerable and increasing human pressure, due to its expanding population, which locally doubled between 1996 and 2000 (Olmos and Pacheco 2002, BirdLife International 2004).

REFERENCES Anciães and Peterson (2009), BirdLife International (2000, 2004, 2008), Bandeira *et al.* (2008), Capobianco *et al.* (2001), Collar *et al.* (1992), Cracraft (1985), Gonzaga (1989), Haffer (1970, 1992b, 1997a), Mallet-Rodrigues (2008), Mayr (1971), Meyer de Schauensee (1970), Olmos and Pacheco (2002, 2003), Pacheco and Olmos (2005), Ridgely and Tudor (1994, 2009), Schubart *et al.* (1965), Sick (1959a, 1959b, 1959c, 1997), Snow (1979b, 2004b), Stotz *et al.* (1996).

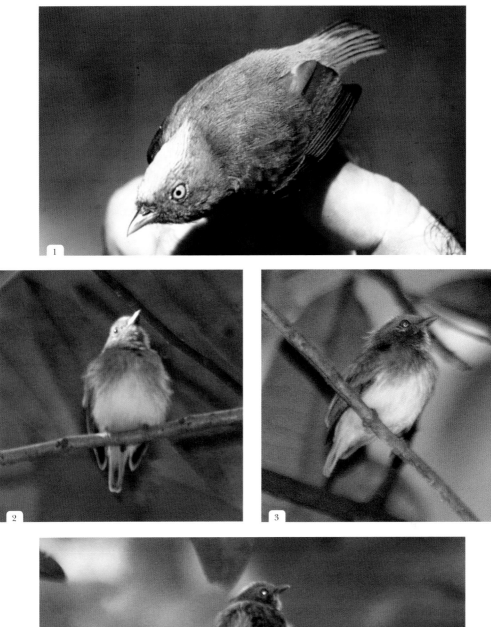

Golden-crowned Manakin *Lepidothrix vilasboasi.* **Fig. 1**. Male, Consórcio Jamanxim, Novo Progresso, Pará, east Amazonian Brazil, May (*Fábio Olmos*). One of just two manakin species to be considered globally threatened, a Golden-crowned Manakin was discovered as recently as 1957, by Helmut Sick, but then went unseen until this male was trapped in May 2002, *c.*200 km northeast of the type locality. **Figs. 2–4**. Male, Novo Progresso, Pará, east Amazonian Brazil, November (*Gabriel Leite*). The first-ever published field photographs of this, one of the rarest and most poorly known manakins in South America.

OPAL-CROWNED MANAKIN
Lepidothrix iris   Plate 5

Pipra iris Schinz, **1851**, *Naturg. Vogel.*, second edn., livr. 7: 91, pl. 39, Guyana [error = Pará, Brazil, *cf.* Hellmayr 1929b]

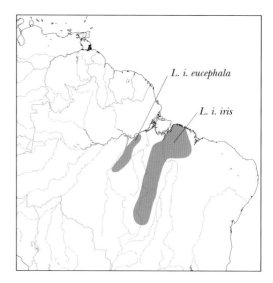

L. i. eucephala

L. i. iris

Opal-crowned Manakin is confined to the northeasternmost portion of that part of Amazonian Brazil south of the Amazon. It has a relatively small range, which is apparently separated into two blocks by a largely unsurveyed area of the lower Amazon between the lowermost reaches of the Tapajós and Tocantins rivers, and the two subspecies that occupy the different regions have recently been revealed to be genetically distinct. Considerable additional fieldwork is needed to establish the range of the present species, especially in northernmost Mato Grosso, and vis-à-vis Golden-crowned *L. vilasboasi* and Snow-capped Manakins *L. nattereri* along the Tapajós and Jamanxim rivers, and at the borders of the Serra do Cachimbo, respectively. A particularly interesting subject for future research, in the field, museum and laboratory, is the relationship between *L. i. eucephala* and *L. vilasboasi*. The nominate race of Opal-crowned Manakin is arguably most profitably searched for in the Serra dos Carajás, in the state of Pará.

IDENTIFICATION 9.0–9.1cm. Like the other members of the superspecies, the Opal-crowned Manakin is theoretically unique within its comparatively restricted range, which on current knowledge is allopatric with Golden-crowned and Snow-capped Manakins. The latter plainly comes very close in range to *L. iris* around Itaituba, where they occupy opposite banks of the Tapajós, at the northern flank of the Serra do Cachimbo, in Pará, and possibly in the region of the Rio Teles Pires in northernmost Mato Grosso, and Golden-crowned Manakin is equally if not more geographically proximate in a restricted region on the east bank of the Rio Tapajós and between there and the Rio Jamanxim. Males of all three species should be easily separable, given reasonable views, as male Snow-capped has a brighter and purer white crown than the present species' opalescent coronal patch, and furthermore in rear views shows a magnificent white lower back and rump, which is not shared by *L. iris*. Golden-crowned has a striking yellow crown patch, which is likely to appear more concolorous with the rest of the upperparts in dim forest light. Females of all three species are plainly very similar (see Golden-crowned, the plumage type of which is still more or less unknown, and Snow-capped Manakins), although Opal-crowned has much the largest bill, and this character, with experience and appropriately close and lengthy views, might be accurately assessed for field identification. Female Snow-capped is perhaps more bluish-tinged above than either of the other two species, and along the Tapajós should show a blue cast to the crown in close views, whilst further south, in the region of the Rio Teles Pires, the females of *L. nattereri* and *L. iris* are likely to appear more similar, other than in bill size.

DISTRIBUTION Endemic to east Brazilian Amazonia, and Cracraft (1985) treated the nominate form as being endemic to the Belém centre of endemism, whose western boundary is formed by the Rio Tocantins, but *L. i. iris* actually penetrates almost as far west as the Rio Xingu (Haffer 1971). Two disjunct ranges occupied by different subspecies. The nominate race is principally known from around Belém, Pará, on the south bank of the Amazon at its mouth, as far east as Ourem on the Rio Guamá, thence

south to northwest Maranhão (Oren 1991), as well as south through Pará across the Rio Tocantins as far as the drainage of the upper Rio Xingu, in northern Mato Grosso (Snethlage 1914, Pinto 1944, Haffer 1997a, Sick 1997a). It probably occurs even further south in eastern Mato Grosso, at the Serra do Roncador, based on records mentioned by Fry (1970), whilst Zimmer *et al.* (1997) speculated that it might yet be found in the region of Rio Teles Pires, further west in the same state, in very close proximity to *L. nattereri*. The other part of the species' distribution is centred on the east bank of the lower Rio Tapajós, along which it ranges as far south as Tucunaré and Trairão (04°40'S, 55°37'W), on the Rio Jamanxim, as well as east along the south bank of the Amazon at least as far as Cussary (<100km east of Santarém), opposite Monte Alegre (Snethlage 1914, Pinto 1944, Pacheco and Olmos 2005). Although Snow (2004b) listed its altitudinal range as lying entirely below 200m, the species ranges as high as *c.*800m in the Serra dos Carajás, Pará (Pacheco *et al.* 2007).

MOVEMENTS Presumed resident like this entire group of species. However, see comments under White-fronted Manakin *L. serena*.

HABITAT Humid, dense *terra firme* forest, at Trairão characterised by tree species belonging for instance to the families Euphorbiaceae, Lecythidaceae, Rubiaceae, Apocynaceae and Arecaceae (Pacheco and Olmos 2005), sometimes in edge habitats, e.g. along roads and vehicle trails, and often in areas with a rather dense understorey and a canopy height of *c.*20–30m (GMK pers. obs.). Vasconcelos *et al.* (2007) reported the species as persisting in an urban forest fragment, at Marabá, Pará, in which no other Pipridae was present.

DESCRIPTION The sexes differ. A tiny manakin, with a disproportionately heavy-based 'chunky' bill (slightly broader in females; *c.*4mm in depth) characterised by its (sometimes markedly) arched culmen and usually by a slightly hooked tip (can be pronounced, but occasionally absent altogether). The nominate race is described here. *Adult male.* – Crown and nape opalescent blue (silvery in some lights), appearing less 'plastered on' than the crown patch in *L. nattereri*, posteriorly becoming much whiter and tapering to a point on the nape, at least in some individuals, and with a green frontal band over the bill. Relatively bright green mantle, back and wing-coverts (in some slightly duller more olive-green), becoming slightly more yellowish-green over the lower back, rump and uppertail-coverts, whilst the tail is generally dark with broad reasonably bright green webs. Remiges are generally brownish-black with relatively broad greenish inner webs and paler (greyer) tips over the terminus of inner web, although these are not always so obvious in the field. Ear-coverts, chin, throat, breast and body-sides green, appearing very slightly mottled around the eyes and lower cheeks, and becoming brighter ventrally (but duller overall than the upperparts), and variably bright yellow over the belly to undertail-coverts (brightest over the central belly), with a generally dark underside to the tail. *Adult female.* – Differs from the male in lacking the bluish-white coronal patch, and has entirely green upperparts, with blackish-brown wing-feathers (including the coverts) and tail (with greenish webs). Face and chin to breast much as the adult male, but the green is generally slightly duller and less bright, and the remainder of the underparts are also, on average, distinctly less bright yellow than in male, although some still possess some bright elements over the central belly and ventral region. *Juvenile.* – Reported to resemble the female but to have dark irides (Snow 2004b). No information concerning plumage maturation, but doubtless similar to its closest relatives. *Moult.* – Well described by Beebe (1915), who found that tail moult commenced in the two pairs of rectrices either side of the central pair, and then in succession outwards. Primary moult proceeds from the innermost, which are replaced first, outwards, whereas in the secondaries moult proceeds inwards, with the outermost shed first. Two specimens collected by him around Belém, Pará, were moulting the crown-, tail- and wing-feathers in early May. *Bare parts.* – Irides vary from almost white to dull grey (in both sexes), or even clear buff-brown in at least one female. The bill is mainly greyish with a slight bluish cast and very marginally darker cutting edges, and the legs and feet are pinkish-flesh to yellowish buff-brown (Hellmayr 1910, Sick 1997, Snow 2004b; MNRJ).

MEASUREMENTS (Hellmayr 1906b; BMNH; MNRJ: eastern Pará, Amazonian Brazil) Wing of male (*n* = 15) 48.5–54.5mm, wing of female (*n* = 7) 53–55mm; tail of male (*n* = 15) 26–31mm, tail of female (*n* = 7) 27–32mm; bill of male (*n* = 14) 10.71–12.32mm, bill of female (*n* = 5) 11.77–12.61mm; tarsus of male (*n* = 5) 12.94–14.34mm, tarsus of female (*n* = 4) 13.88–15.24mm. Weight: 6.0–10.6g (males) and 7.5–11.5g (females) (Fry 1970, Snow 2004b; MNRJ; MPEG).

GEOGRAPHICAL VARIATION Two subspecies are described, which recently acquired mitochondrial DNA data suggest are not each others' closest relatives and therefore that two species-level taxa might well be involved (Bandeira *et al.* 2008). *L. i. eucephala* (Todd, 1928) occurs in southwest Pará along the right bank of the lower Rio Tapajós, immediately to the north of the range of *L. vilasboasi*, which appears to be its closest relative (not the nominate race). This taxon differs inasmuch as the white crown extends to the forehead in the male, whilst females have a bluish cast to the crown and nape (Fig. 3). Nominate *L. i. iris* (described above) occurs over the rest of the species' range, from eastern Pará to northwest Maranhão and south to northern Mato Grosso.

VOICE The male's advertisement song is typical of the superspecies, it being a slightly rasping frog-like call (seemingly identical in both subspecies: GMK pers. obs.; see also recordings mentioned below). The advertising call is a double-noted *chi-wir*, very similar to, but sharper and more staccato than the corresponding vocalisations of Golden-crowned and Snow-capped Manakins, sometimes with three or four calls given in rapid succession, or with several seconds between each call. Both sexes (and probably younger birds) also give a slightly squeaky sounding whistled *sweeep*, at *c.*2–3-second intervals, the quality of which is very similar to, but slightly more 'burry' than the corresponding vocalisation of Snow-capped Manakin (and probably Golden-crowned Manakin?). The species' vocalisations feature on the compilations of Boesman (2006a; nominate *L. i. iris*) and Marantz and Zimmer (2006; both subspecies), and also appear online (nominate *L. i. iris*) at www.xeno-canto.org.

NATURAL HISTORY Very poorly known to date, with an extreme paucity of published information. Opal-crowned Manakin is usually seen alone, occasionally in pairs and typically perches relatively low, on a slender horizontal branch, in the understorey and lower midstorey, most usually at 1–8m above the ground (GMK pers. obs.).

FOOD AND FEEDING Snow (2004b) knew of no data on diet for this species; GMK (pers. obs.) watched a male taking unidentified small fruits at an understorey tree just 2m above ground beside a dirt road, using short (<30cm) sally-strikes, and several females taking melastome fruits in the canopy of *c.*8m-tall trees utilised by a lek of Fiery-capped Manakin *Machaeropterus pyrocephalus*. Gomes *et al.* (2008) reported *Miconia ciliatta* (Melastomataceae) berries in the Opal-crowned Manakin's diet at Belém, and Marceliano *et al.* (2009) noted *Psidium guajava* (Myrtaceae) and *Geonoma macrostachys* (Arecaceae) as well. A specimen held in MNRJ had solely insects for stomach contents, but Beebe (1915) mentioned collecting one with fruit alone in the stomach.

BREEDING The only previously published information on breeding is that a female with an egg in the oviduct was collected in the Belém area, in early August (Pinto 1953). This egg was described as being dirty white with pale vinous-brown markings. The species sings frequently between late August and December (especially in the latter half of this period) in the Serra dos Carajás, suggesting that the species is breeding at this period in this region.

STATUS Formerly treated as Near Threatened (Collar *et al.* 1994), but despite ongoing deforestation within much of the species' range, BirdLife International (2004, 2008) has since downlisted the Opal-crowned Manakin to Least Concern. There have been very high rates of deforestation in Mato Grosso (23.6% of forest cleared by 1988) and Maranhão (19.2%), with large areas also being cleared in Pará (9.6%), due to road building, ranching and land speculation (Cleary 1991). Furthermore, Anciães and Peterson (2006) predicted using modelling techniques that this species could be severely affected by habitat modification in the face of potential climate change. Opal-crowned Manakin has been considered reasonably numerous in the environs of Belém, at least formerly (e.g. Snethlage 1914, Stone 1928, Pinto 1944). It certainly survives in selectively logged areas (Pacheco and Olmos 2005) and relatively small patches of forest (Vasconcelos *et al.* 2007), and the species is also known from several protected areas, including the Serra dos Carajás mosaic of conservation units (Pacheco *et al.* 2007) and the FLONA do Tapajós (Henriques *et al.* 2003), where it is one of the commonest members of the understorey bird community based on mist-net captures (Wunderle *et al.* 2006).

REFERENCES Anciães and Peterson (2006, 2009), Bandeira *et al.* (2008), Beebe (1915), BirdLife International (2004, 2008), Boesman (2006a), Cleary (1991), Collar *et al.* (1994), Cracraft (1985), Fry (1970), Gomes *et al.* (2008), Haffer (1971, 1992b, 1997a), Hellmayr (1906b, 1906d, 1929b), Henriques *et al.* (2003), Marantz and Zimmer (2006), Marceliano *et al.* (2009), Oren (1991), Pacheco and Olmos (2005), Pacheco *et al.* (2007), Pinto (1944, 1953), Rêgo *et al.* (2007), Ridgely and Tudor (1994, 2009), Snethlage (1907, 1914), Snow (2004b), Stone (1928), Stotz *et al.* (1996), Vasconcelos *et al.* (2007), Wunderle *et al.* (2006), Zimmer *et al.* (1997).

Opal-crowned Manakin *Lepidothrix iris*. **Fig. 1**. Male, *L. i. iris*, Serra dos Carajás, Pará, east Amazonian Brazil, October (*Arthur Grosset / www. arthurgrosset.com*). **Fig. 2**. Female, *L. i. iris*, Belém, Pará, east Amazonian Brazil, November (*Ciro Albano*). Two subspecies are known and a recent genetic study has revealed that they are not each other's closest relatives. *L. i. eucephala* is further differentiated in having a blue crown in females and no green forehead patch in males. Its voice seems to have been undescribed, but all members of this superspecies possess similar male advertisement songs. **Fig. 3**. Female, *L. i. eucephala*, FLONA Tapajós, Pará, east Amazonian Brazil, November (*Alexander C. Lees*). The blue crown, which distinguishes females of this taxon from nominate *L. i. iris*, is just visible.

ORANGE-BELLIED MANAKIN
Lepidothrix suavissima   **Plate 4**

Pipra suavissima **Salvin and Godman, 1882**, *Ibis* (4) 6: 79, pl. 1, Merumé Mountains and Bartica Grove, Guyana

Also called the Tepui Manakin (cf. Sibley and Monroe 1993, Prum 1994b), *Lepidothrix suavissima* has 'enjoyed' a somewhat checkered taxonomic history. Described as a species, this ranking was subsequently upheld then rejected by Hellmayr, who eventually decided in favour of subspecific status, although some authorities persisted in treating it specifically until the 1920s. Thereafter the taxon was virtually ignored until the early 1990s when Prum uncovered evidence of its vastly different syrinx and vocal repertoire, as well as pointing out the plumage differences between males of *L. serena* and *L. suavissima*, in addition to elucidating their ranges.

IDENTIFICATION 9.1cm. In range, males should be immediately identifiable, but the female could be confused with the same-sex Blue-crowned Manakin, which overlaps in range widely with this species in Venezuela and Brazil (but not Guyana). The latter species' females lacks the bluish tone to the green upperparts and is less contrastingly yellow on the underparts. It also generally occurs at lower elevations than Orange-bellied Manakin, but beware there is some overlap. See White-fronted Manakin *L. serena*, with which the present species is apparently entirely allopatric, for discussion of plumage differences between them, and for remarks on where their distributions come closest. Voice is also extremely useful in separating these two species. Hilty (2003) also pointed out how the female could recall a female *Euphonia*, especially Plumbeous *E. plumbea* and White-lored Euphonias *E. chrysopasta*, particularly for the inexperienced observer. The bill is considerably less chunky in the manakin, which also can be distinguished by its considerably more contrasting underparts.

DISTRIBUTION Orange-bellied Manakin is known from throughout the tepui highlands of southern Venezuela, across Bolívar and Amazonas, just reaching into Brazil, where the species is principally known from the Cerro Uei-tepui and Pico da Neblina, Roraima, and into western, central, and eastern Guyana, as far as Tiger Creek, a small west bank tributary of the Courantyne River (Phelps and Phelps 1962, 1965, Snyder 1966, Hilty 2003, Prum 1994b). It occurs north almost to the Río Orinoco in Amazonas, Venezuela, and there is a sight record from the Río Grande, near the Sierra de Imataca, in northeast Bolívar, which represents the northernmost record (Hilty 2003). There are no records from the southern third of Guyana or anywhere in the Rio Branco drainage in Brazil (Sick 1997, Robbins *et al.* 2004, Naka *et al.* 2006). Moskovits *et al.* (1985) recorded Orange-bellied Manakin at the Maracá Ecological Station on the Rio Uraricoera, Roraima (03°25'N, 61°40'W), which seems to mark the species' southernmost limit in Brazil. Cracraft (1985) treated *L. suavissima* as being restricted to the Gran Sabana subcentre of the Pantepui centre of endemism. Hellmayr (1929b) mentioned that Beebe (1916) had reported a specimen of this taxon from 'Utinga, near Pará' (= Belém), Brazil, i.e. south of the Amazon, which Hellmayr had been unable to examine; however, this record must be in error.

MOVEMENTS The species is presumed resident, but see *L. serena*.

HABITAT Principally found in humid *terra firme* forest in the foothills and on the lower slopes of tepuis, as well as at shrubby borders and even in upland scrub atop Mt Kowa (Guyana) (Ridgely and Tudor 1994, Barnett *et al.* 2002, Hilty 2003). Recorded to 1,800m (Phelps and Phelps 1965, Hilty 2003, Snow 2004b) and generally down to 500m, but locally the species has been recorded to 250m (Hilty 2003).

DESCRIPTION Like others of the genus, the sexes differ. Males are smaller than females, just as in White-fronted Manakin. Slightly sturdy bill shape/structure are typical of the genus. *Adult male.* – A particularly gorgeous manakin. Its plumage is mainly velvety black with an obvious snow white forecrown patch (with a very pale blue rear border and some scattered blue feathers over the rest), which appears to cover the base of the maxilla. Stunning deep azure-blue rump and uppertail-coverts patch (often not immediately visible in the field, but which virtually covers the entire tail). The underparts below the black breast and body-sides are relieved by a striking deep orange-yellow belly to undertail-coverts patch. *Adult female.* – The upperparts are largely bright grass green, although the forecrown (sometimes to the mid crown) and rump are tinged bluish, becoming duller and greyer over the lores and face, with a very pale yellow throat, extensively olive breast then becoming fairly bright yellow over the central belly and undertail-coverts (this colour varying in its extent over the underparts, very occasionally reaching the lower breast). The wing- and tail-feathers are very dark with green inner webs. The axillaries and underwing-coverts are greyish-white. *Juvenile.* – Reported to resemble adult females (Snow 2004b), whilst immature males gradually acquire black in the plumage (Hilty 2003) but there is no detailed information concerning plumage maturation. *Moult.* – Very few published moult data are available, but the breeding-condition bird collected in February (see Habits) was not in moult, whilst general body moult was noted on three late March specimens in Venezuela (Willard *et al.* 1991, Pérez-Emán *et al.* 2003). Stotz (1993) trapped and collected a hybrid between Orange-bellied Manakin and Blue-crowned Manakin *L. coronata* in northernmost Roraima, Brazil. He described the hybrid, which is retained in the Field Museum of Natural History, Chicago (FMNH

344171), thus. Plumage primarily non-glossy black, although the feathers of the flanks and lower breast have a blue tone, lacking over the rest of the body (a similar blue tone to the abdominal feathers occurs in *L. coronata carbonata*, which subspecies occurs in the region the bird was collected). Crown sky blue, becoming darker on the nape. Rump and uppertail-coverts cobalt blue. Feathers of abdomen basally black, broadly tipped dull yellow with a greenish tone, forming an irregular patch from the lower edge of the breast to the vent; undertail-coverts green. *Bare parts.* – Irides dark brown or reddish brown, bill black, and the legs and feet are greyish or blackish-brown to black (Willard *et al.* 1991, Prum 1994b, Snow 2004b).

MEASUREMENTS (BMNH; ZMA: Guyana) Wing of male (*n* = 10) 54.5–59.5mm, wing of female (*n* = 10) 57–62mm; tail of male (*n* = 10) 26.5–31.0mm, tail of female (*n* = 10) 27–32mm; bill of male (*n* = 10) 10.94–12.07mm, bill of female (*n* = 10) 11.27–12.97mm; tarsus of male (*n* = 9) 14.01–16.67mm, tarsus of female (*n* =10) 14.23–15.81mm. See Stotz (1993) and Prum (1994b) for additional mensural data (expressed solely as means). The latter author found that males are significantly smaller than females in wing- and tail-lengths, but similar in tarsus-length. Weight: 8.5–10.8g (males) and 10.2–11.5g (females) (Willard *et al.* 1991, Stotz 1993, Pérez-Emán *et al.* 2003, Snow 2004b, Dunning 2008; FMNH).

GEOGRAPHICAL VARIATION Formerly treated as a subspecies of White-fronted Manakin, but it was separated by Prum (1994b) on the basis of syringeal morphology (which differs as much as between some families of passerines), vocalisations and male plumage. Chapman (1931) and Gilliard (1941) both found that males from three tepuis in southern Venezuela appeared to have richer orange underparts than those from Guyana, but Friedmann (1948) was of the opinion that any such variation could be accounted for by the relative age of the specimens concerned.

VOICE The Orange-bellied Manakin's repertoire has been subject to much less study than its presumed sister species. Nonetheless, Prum (1994b) provided a reasonably comprehensive analysis, on which the following is based (with additional data from Hilty 2003). The main vocalisation (advertisement call) given by territorial males is a sharp, nasal, slightly upward-inflected *aank*, which is frog-like and easily 'overlooked' by would-be observers. Males also give a more noticeable, rapid, emphatic, piping series of 7–8 notes that rise and fall in pitch and emphasis: *whee-pee-pee-…-pee*, or a quavering *wu WE WE wa we we wit* (heard on the Sierra de Lema, Venezuela). Prum found that this call was given following playback of the *aank* call and during countersinging among males. Each note rises rapidly in frequency and then drops back. The first and last notes have initial and maximum frequency ranges of 2.3–3.5kHz, and each note increases in frequency until the middle notes, which vary from 2.6 to 4.3kHz, and then tapers off to resemble the initial notes. Hilty (2003) also mentioned a short trill, rendered *pr'r'r'r*, which recalls a call of Short-crested Flycatcher *Myiarchus ferox*. The species was included on the Boesman (2006a, 2006b) audio compilations, and also appears online (www.xeno-canto.org).

NATURAL HISTORY Compared with *L. serena*, the natural history of this species is very poorly known, despite Venezuela being a popular destination with birdwatchers and considerable ornithological work there. Hilty (2003), who has provided much of our basic knowledge of the species' habits, recounted that the species is usually encountered singly.

FOOD AND FEEDING Often individuals visit fruiting understorey trees or shrubs, quickly hovering to feed before disappearing again. The appearance of a mixed-species foraging flock can encourage a bird in its territory to feed more actively.

DISPLAY Males generally display alone, perching on slender branches 2–8m above the ground, but sometimes in an 'exploded lek' wherein males are in audible distance of their neighbours (Hilty 2003). Males often sit quietly for long periods, but always seem poised for high-intensity display.

BREEDING Biology, although presumably similar in many respects to White-fronted Manakin, is to all intents and purposes unknown. Several of both sexes collected in southernmost Venezuela in March were in breeding condition (Willard *et al.* 1991), as was another male collected at a different locality in southern Venezuela in February (Pérez-Emán *et al.* 2003). Three juvenile males were collected in January / early February (Phelps and Phelps 1965).

STATUS Treated as Least Concern by BirdLife International (2004, 2008) as the species occupies a comparatively large range that has not been impacted by deforestation to the same extent as many other tropical regions. However, using niche modelling Anciães and Peterson (2006) predicted that this species could be severely impacted by habitat modification as a result of potential climate change. The species is known from five Important Bird Areas in Venezuela (BirdLife International 2008) and it is considered endemic to the Tepuis Endemic Bird Area (Stattersfield *et al.* 1998). Orange-bellied Manakin is considered fairly common in Guyana (Braun *et al.* 2007) and locally fairly common in Venezuela (Hilty 2003), where the most accessible site to find the species in the world is surely the Escalera Road, which ascends the Sierra de Lema. Orange-bellied Manakin is known from Canaima, the Serranía de la Neblina and Duida-Marahuaca National Parks in Venezuela.

REFERENCES Anciães and Peterson (2006, 2009), Barnett *et al.* (2002), BirdLife International (2004, 2008), Boesman (2006a, 2006b), Braun *et al.* (2007), Chapman (1931), Chubb (1921), Cracraft (1985), Friedmann (1948), Gilliard (1941), Hellmayr (1906d, 1929b), Hilty (2003), Mayr and Phelps (1967), Moskovits *et al.* (1985), Naka *et al.* (2006), Pérez-Emán *et al.* (2003), Phelps and Phelps (1962, 1965), Prum (1985, 1988, 1994b), Restall *et al.* (2006), Ridgely and Tudor (1994, 2009), Robbins *et al.* (2004), Sibley and Monroe (1993), Sick (1997), Snow (1975, 1979b, 2004b), Snyder (1966), Stattersfield *et al.* (1998), Stotz (1993), Stotz *et al.* (1996), Willard *et al.* (1991).

Orange-bellied Manakin *Lepidothrix suavissima*. **Fig. 1.** Male, Sierra de Lema, Bolívar, southeast Venezuela, November (*David J. Southall*). **Fig. 2.** Adult male, River Amaila, Guyana, March (*Andrew Whittaker*) **Fig. 3**. Female, River Amaila, Guyana, March (*Jaqueline Rizzi Fortuna*). Compare this female with the female White-fronted Manakin *L. serena* in Fig. 2, p. 207. **Fig. 4.** Same female as in Fig. 3, River Amaila, Guyana, March (*Jaqueline Rizzi Fortuna*). **Fig. 5.** Young male, River Amaila, Guyana, March (*Andrew Whittaker*).

WHITE-FRONTED MANAKIN
Lepidothrix serena   Plate 4

Pipra serena **Linnaeus, 1766**, *Syst. Nat.*, 12th edn., 1: 340, Cayenne and Surinam [based on Brisson, 1760, *Orn.* 4: 457, pl. 36], sometimes delimited as Crique Ipoucin, River Approuague, French Guiana

The more southerly ranging of the *L. serena* species-group, White-fronted Manakin is a generally common but stunningly attractive resident of *terra firme* forests in the Guianan Shield.

IDENTIFICATION 9.0–10.5cm. Apparently, the present species is entirely allopatric (to some extent also elevationally) with the similar, and until recently conspecific, Orange-bellied Manakin *L. suavissima*, making their identification theoretically straightforward. However, in southern Guyana their ranges are known to be separated by just 150km (Robbins *et al.* 2004) and Prum (1994b) considered it possible that the two might come into parapatric contact somewhere on the lower Courantyne or New Rivers in Guyana, unless they are wholly separated there by a lack of appropriate habitat for either species. Males should be easily separated, with reasonable views, given the present species' larger and yellower belly patch divided by a narrow black band. Females are usually considered to be practically indistinguishable, although female Orange-bellied has a smaller and yellowish throat patch and is more extensively washed with olive over the breast, while the posterior underparts are clearly brighter and yellower. Furthermore, female Orange-bellied Manakins appear to show some blue elements in the upperparts (cf. Fig. 4, p. 203 Their voices also differ.

DISTRIBUTION Restricted to extreme northeast South America, in the Guianan centre of endemism (Cracraft 1985). White-fronted Manakin occurs from southernmost Guyana, in the Acary Mountains, where it was first reported by Blake (1950), and at Parabara in the southern Rupununi Savanna (Robbins *et al.* 2004), through much of Surinam (but especially the east of the country and it has not been recorded west of the Nickerie River) and French Guiana. This manakin also occurs in far northeastern Brazil in the state of Amapá, as well as around Manaus, Amazonas, (Cohn-Haft *et al.* 1997), at least as far north as Balbina (Willis and Oniki 1988c) and the Rio Uatumã (INPA), and on the Rios Trombetas (INPA) and Paru du Leste (Novaes 1980a), in adjacent Pará. It can also be expected to occur in extreme northeastern Pará, at the border with Surinam and Guyana, within the huge Reserva Florestal Nacional do Tumucumaque protected area, as well as probably more widely north of the Amazon in the same state (Prum 1994b).

MOVEMENTS Considered to be basically resident like others of the genus, although a radio-tracking study in French Guiana revealed that in the non-breeding season, whilst moulting, adults wander over an area of probably several hundred hectares and an immature male had a range of 24.1ha. However, during the breeding season, two adult males had home ranges of 2.8 and 3.2ha, respectively, which were centred on a single display site and bathing area, whilst the home ranges of two adult females were much larger, at 11.2 and 13.0ha, thus encompassing the display areas and bathing sites of several males (Théry 1990c). Such sexual differences in home range, although

unstudied in others of the genus, are probably common to all *Lepidothrix* species.

HABITAT White-fronted Manakin inhabits the understorey of humid lowland tropical forest, apparently with a preference for edge habitats, to *c.*700m (Restall *et al.* 2006). In Surinam, at least, White-fronted Manakin is absent from coastal and lowlands forests below 200m (Prum 1985), but it does occur more rarely in islands of forest within the savanna zone in both Guyana and Surinam (Robbins *et al.* 2004; J. H. Ribot website).

DESCRIPTION Generally similar in morphology to the previous species and, like others of the genus, the sexes differ in White-fronted Manakin. Males are smaller than females, just as in Orange-bellied Manakin. Slightly sturdy bill shape/structure are typical of the genus, and can have rather large nostrils, at least in the male. *Adult male.* – Startlingly beautiful. Principally velvety black with an obvious white forecrown patch (tinged very pale blue), which appears to cover the base of the maxilla, and a stunning azure-blue rump and uppertail-coverts patch, which virtually covers the entire tail. The underparts, below the black breast and body-sides, are marked by an orange-yellow lower breast patch separated from the yellow belly and undertail-coverts by a black bar of slightly uneven width. There are usually a few scattered pale yellow feathers on the chin and throat, and the yellow belly patch is normally brightest on the upper belly, whilst the flanks and tibial feathering are black. *Adult female.* – The upperparts are largely bright grass green, although the crown is tinged bluish, becoming duller and greyer over the lores, face and throat, then yellower over the rest of the underparts, especially on the lower breast, central belly and undertail-coverts (the upper breast and flanks are greener). The wing- and tail-feathers are very dark with green inner webs. *Juvenile.* – A specimen labelled as being a juvenile (MNRJ) is identical to adult females in the same collection, whilst immature males gradually acquire black in the plumage but there is no detailed information concerning plumage maturation. Immature males also perform displays (Prum 1985, Théry 1990a). *Moult.* – There are no published data on moult, other than that feather replacement occurs post-breeding. *Bare parts.* – Irides vary from almost yellowish (once red) to dark brown, with perhaps a tendency for the colour to be darker in females but our sample size is still relatively small (although indicative of more variation than was admitted by Prum 1994b). The bill is black sometimes with a paler, greyer or even whitish, mandible, and the legs and feet are very dark brown, greyish to black (Novaes 1978, Prum 1994b, Snow 2004b; INPA; MNRJ).

MEASUREMENTS (BMNH; CUMZ; INPA; MNRJ; RMNH: Amapá, Amazonas and Pará, Brazil, French Guiana and Surinam) Wing of male ($n = 22$) 51–56mm, wing of female ($n = 12$) 51.5–57.0mm; tail of male ($n = 22$) 24.5–30.5mm, tail of female ($n = 12$) 24–31mm; bill of male ($n = 22$) 9.11–12.29mm, bill of female ($n = 12$) 11.38–12.57mm; tarsus of male ($n = 6$) 14.86–16.12mm, tarsus of female ($n = 4$) 15.13–16.54mm. See also Prum (1994b) for additional mensural data (expressed solely as means). The same author found that males are significantly smaller than females in wing-length but larger in tarsus-length, and that the sexes do not differ in mean tail-length. Weight: 9.5–11.4g (males) and 9.9–12.9g (females) (Dick *et al.* 1984, Snow 2004b, Dunning 2008; INPA; RMNH; ROM).

GEOGRAPHICAL VARIATION Monotypic. Previously considered conspecific with *L. suavissima*, but the rationale (voice, syringeal morphology and male plumage differences) for treating them as separate species was well documented by Prum (1994b) and has been followed by virtually all subsequent commentators. Intermediates between the two are unknown (Prum 1994b). On the basis of their plumage traits, Prum (1988) considered these two, *L. suavissima* and *L. serena*, to form a monophyletic species group, and subsequently, with syringeal morphology data to hand, Prum (1992) removed these two taxa from *Pipra*, in which genus they were then usually placed (Snow 1975, 1979b), to *Lepidothrix*. Subsequent work revealed that *Pipra* was still polyphyletic leading to the other species treated herein also being transferred to *Lepidothrix* and this move has since received further support (Rêgo *et al.* 2007, Remsen *et al.* 2009, Tello *et al.* 2009)

VOICE Well described by Prum (1985, 1994b) based on work in, and recordings from, Surinam and Brazil, respectively, and on which the following is heavily based. The male advertisement call is 'a soft, throaty, rolling *whree* with the quality of a toy police-whistle' (Prum 1994b), given in rapid series (e.g. six calls in *c.*5 seconds) and occasionally interspersed with low, throaty, bell-like, whistled *boop* notes (Prum 1985). During their coordinated displays (see Habits), males also give a soft, descending and emphatic *puurr* note. The *whree* call is primarily at 1.5 and 2.2kHz, with no identifiable harmonics. It either rises slightly in pitch, from 1.5/1.8kHz to 2.0/2.2kHz or remains centred on a single frequency band, but always shows rapid oscillations between the maximum and minimum frequencies over very short time intervals, giving the call its rolling quality. The *boop* is a very short note that rises slightly from 0.8 to 1.0kHz, whilst the *puurr* is a series of 10–12 very short notes that begin near 1.5kHz and descend to *c.*1kHz. The advertisement song was published on the audio compilations of Naka *et al.* (2008) and Renaudier and Deroussen (2008), and sonograms were published by Prum (1985, 1994b). Recordings are also available online at www.xeno-canto.org.

NATURAL HISTORY In Brazil, at least, this species is frequently found side by side with White-crowned Manakin *Dixiphia pipra* and Golden-headed Manakin *Pipra*

erythrocephala (Sick 1997). White-fronted Manakin is typically recorded alone or sometimes in pairs foraging in low growth inside forest (Prum 1985).

FOOD AND FEEDING This species performs aerial sallies for fruits and insects, with a special fondness reported for berries of Melastomataceae (up to 70% of the diets of males in French Guiana: Théry 1990c), followed in importance by Rubiaceae (Snow 2004b, Restall *et al.* 2006). Silva *et al.* (2010) noted that this manakin disperses the seeds of *Heliconia acuminata* (Heliconiaceae), at least in northern Brazil. White-fronted Manakin forages at 1–6m above the ground (Prum 1985).

DISPLAY Breeding behaviour and biology have been rather well documented in comparison with most congenerics, with most data on lek behaviour and courtship based on observations by Prum (1985) and Théry (1990a) in Surinam and French Guiana, respectively, and on nesting by Tostain and others in French Guiana. Several display behaviours closely recall those recently described in detail for Blue-crowned Manakin *L. coronata* (Durães 2009). Like others of the genus, males usually display alone within territories of 30–40m diameter, grouped with two to seven others (Prum 1985, Théry 1990a), calling for long periods (see Voice) from 1–5m-high perches throughout the territory, and performing whirring flights between them. Théry (1990a) found that not all leks are stationary, indicating that there might be geographical variation in lek behaviour. He described what he termed the 'double-spot lek' phenomenon thus:

> Five groups of males systematically moved from an initial site, only used early in the day … to a second site … 80–100 m lower down on the slope, only occupied later in the day. […] During the breeding season, all banded males … and all radio-tracked males … showed a similar daily movement and used the same display territories. Each male defended both territories against the intrusions of unestablished males or neighbors and called throughout the day, with two periods of increasing activity when females visited the arenas.

The movement seemed to be based on changes in lighting conditions and a desire to use the best-illuminated arena, a factor presumably determined by the topography of the study site (cf. Endler and Théry 1996). Prum (1985) noted male incidence on the territory, monitoring one individual for almost 10 consecutive hours.

> He called 7,400 times during this period and was present for 72% of the time. Observation on other dates indicated that territorial attendance may have varied to over 90%. Calling activity continued throughout the day, with occasional periods of increased excitement. … In general, the most intense calling activity developed in response to calling by neighboring males and often resulted in vigorous countersinging along territorial boundaries.

While calling, males erect the small puff of orange-yellow feathers on the lower breast and occasionally fly rapidly to another perch, tracing a horizontal S-pattern *c.*1m wide in the air, or by swooping down from the first perch then rising and approaching the second perch from above. Prum (1985) sometimes witnessed males perform a series of erratic to-and-fro flights, lasting *c.*20 seconds, between ten or more perches and barely stopping to land before proceeding to the next perch. Furthermore, males also perform intermittent stereotypical displays, considered to be most similar to those of *L. coronata* (although in the latter species the coordinated display is most frequently performed after the nesting season and females visit only single males). Male White-fronted Manakins display at 'courts' 1m in diameter near the forest floor, either alone or in 'pairs', which coordinate their display during a bout of countersinging, after one male enters another's territory. In the coordinated display, which can last up to ten minutes (in the presence of a female), both males give multiple *puurr* calls before falling silent and dropping to within 1.0m of the ground. They then commence to fly back and forth between five and ten small vertical saplings that form the court (the birds landing and taking off simultaneously from alternate perches, appearing to chase one another). Flights are either whirring or more hummingbird-like, in which the males hold their bodies nearly vertical and beat their wings rapidly. When perched the males adopt a rigid, horizontal posture, occasionally flicking their wings open to expose the bright blue rump, and facing the centre of the court. The solo form of the display, which is given much less frequently, is identical in its format, but is not preceded by any *puurr* calls. Théry (1990a: 124) presented a schematic representation of the birds' behaviour at the court. Perhaps surprisingly, 'courts' do not appear to be kept clear of vegetation (unlike, for instance some *Pipra* and *Ilicura*, in which males 'garden' their display sites) and to the human observer do not appear different from other parts of a male's territory. Théry (1990a) added information about display and courtship leading to copulation; the latter seems only to occur when males are displaying alone, indicating that the coordinated displays are competitive, rather than cooperative (Prum 1985). When a female approaches, a male flies between two horizontal perches producing a low rustling sound with the wings, before landing facing the centre of the 'court'. The female joins in, following his flights between perches, whereupon they concentrate on two vertical perches between which they cross each other in flight. Théry (1990a) witnessed some 87 such courtship displays, but copulation occurred only three times, when the male flew above the female as they crossed between perches. The female landed on a thin branch 1–2m above ground while the male perched above her, then performed a ritualised S-shaped display flight, approaching the female from below and landing directly on her. The observer considered it possible that the female's lower position might have served as a signal for copulation, like in White-bearded Manakin *Manacus manacus*, and noted that the display-flight is virtually identical to that of Golden-headed Manakin *Pipra erythrocephala*.

BREEDING The nest is a small cup of whitish woody or herbaceous fibres, the exterior being partially camouflaged using long filaments of moss, some of which trail below the nest to disguise its shape. It is usually placed 1–2m above the ground in the horizontal fork of a shrub or small understorey tree, and the clutch is two eggs, but data on incubation and fledging periods as well as parental care and the appearance of the young are wholly lacking. Egg laying is reported to commence in the wet season in French Guiana, in October/November, and probably continues until April there. Occupied nests have been reported in October (Dujardin 1987) and May (two) and November (two) (Tostain 1988a), whilst Tostain *et al.* (1992) reported other nests with single eggs (incomplete or partially predated clutches) found in the second week of June and early March. The first May nest was found in an area rich in *Euterpe oleracea* (Arecaceae) palms and was placed 1.05m above ground at the border of a light gap, in a two-way fork. The nest cup itself was constructed of pale dead vegetable fibres but the entire structure was disguised by many live and dead mosses, which dangled pendant-like below the nest by up to 33cm. The second May nest was similar but was found in an understorey rich in epiphytes and close to a small creek; live mosses fell up to 27cm below this nest, which like the first May nest was subsequently found abandoned. Finally, Tostain (1988a) found two nests in early November, of similar structure, one placed 1.4m above ground almost ready but still under construction and another just 30cm from a stream and 1.8m above ground in a *Duguessia surinamensis* (Annonaceae) tree. The second November nest (a photograph of which appears in Snow 2004b: 136) had two pale rose-coloured eggs with brown markings. Unfortunately, the finder was unable to follow the nest to report observations on the incubation period, etc. All of the nests were found in areas with a dense understorey. Dimensions of all four of these nests, and of the eggs, were presented by Tostain (1988a) who also presented the same colour photograph of a female on a nest as mentioned above (p. 164). Tostain (1988a) also reported the observation of a female with a dependent but fledged juvenile in early April. Juvenile and immature males were collected in the same country in February and May (Dick *et al.* 1984), and adults have been collected in breeding condition in May in French Guiana (ROM) and September/October, with a juvenile in May in Amapá, Brazil (Novaes 1978; MNRJ). A female collected in Pará, Brazil, in November was also in breeding condition (INPA). There is one other record of breeding, a nest with eggs in Surinam in February, but in southern Guyana, Robbins *et al.* (2007) considered that the species' breeding season might last from February to at least September.

STATUS White-fronted Manakin is currently treated as Least Concern by BirdLife International (2004, 2008) owing to its occupying a comparatively large range that has not been impacted by deforestation to the same extent as in many other tropical regions. However, using niche modelling Anciães and Peterson (2006) predicted that this species could be severely affected by habitat modification in the face of potential climate change. White-fronted Manakin is considered common and frequent in the interior of both French Guiana and eastern Surinam (Tostain *et al.* 1992, Haverschmidt and Mees 1994, Restall *et al.* 2006, Ottema *et al.* 2009) where the species is known from 11 proposed Important Bird Areas (BirdLife International 2008). At a study site in French Guiana, Thiollay (1994) found this species to be the second-most numerous manakin with an estimated density of eight pairs per 100ha. Restall *et al.* (2006) also considered the species to be 'widespread' and common in Guyana, but the former adjective seems inappropriate for its quite restricted range within the latter country. Given the number of specimens taken at localities such as the Serra do Navio, the White-fronted Manakin appears common in Amapá, Brazil (Novaes 1978), and is also reasonably numerous at localities north of Manaus, Amazonas (Cohn-Haft *et al.* 1997). Known from protected areas such as Brownsberg Nature Park, Surinam (Ottema 2009), Réserve Naturelle de Trésor, French Guiana (Renaudier 2009), and Reserva Ducke, Amazonas (Willis 1977), Parque Nacional do Cabo Orange (Souza *et al.* 2008) and Parque Nacional Montanhas do Tumucumaque (Bernard 2008), Amapá, all in Brazil.

REFERENCES Anciães and Peterson (2006, 2009), BirdLife International (2004, 2008), Berlepsch (1908), Bernard (2008), Blake (1950), Boss and Aguiar (2008), Campos *et al.* (2009), Cohn-Haft *et al.* (1997), Cracraft (1985), Dick *et al.* (1984), Dujardin (1987), Dunning (2008), Durães (2009), Endler and Théry (1996), Haverschmidt and Mees (1994), Hellmayr (1906d, 1929b), Naka *et al.* (2008), Novaes (1978, 1980a), Ottema (2009), Ottema *et al.* (2009), Prum (1985, 1988, 1990a, 1992, 1994b), Prum *et al.* (2000), Rêgo *et al.* (2007), Renaudier (2009), Renaudier and Deroussen (2008), Restall *et al.* (2006), Reynaud (1998), Ridgely and Tudor (1994, 2009), Robbins *et al.* (2004, 2007), Silva *et al.* (2010), Snow (1975, 1979b, 2004b), Snyder (1966), Souza *et al.* (2008), Stotz *et al.* (1996), Tello *et al.* (2009), Théry (1990a, 1990b, 1990c, 1992, 1997), Thiollay (1994), Tostain (1988a), Tostain *et al.* (1992), Willis (1977), Willis and Oniki (1988c), Zyskowski *et al.* (2011).

1

2

White-fronted Manakin *Lepidothrix serena*. **Fig. 1**. Male, Montagne de Kaw, French Guiana, July (*Marc Chrétien*). **Fig. 2**. Female, Petit-Saut, French Guiana, May (*Marc Chrétien*). Compare the differences in underparts and face pattern between this female and the female Orange-bellied Manakin *L. suavissima*, on p. 204. Formerly considered conspecific with Orange-bellied Manakin *L. suavissima*, there are obvious differences in male plumage and vocalisations. Fortunately, the two are also allopatric, reducing any potential confusion risk (only really applicable to females of the two species).

Genus *Manacus*: 'bearded' manakins

The four currently recognised species of *Manacus* represent a superspecies (AOU 1998) and have occasionally been regarded as the members of a single species, *M. manacus*, although this 'conservative' option has rarely found favour in recent decades, except by the SACC (Remsen *et al.* 2009). Otherwise, Snow (1975, 1979b) was probably the last author to entertain this notion. In terms of their biogeographical history, the four allospecies unquestionably represent a peculiar headache for systematists and species limits are especially problematic, with hybrid zones between taxa that differ strongly in colour, and paraphyly of *M. manacus sensu stricto* (Brumfield and Braun 2001, Brumfield *et al.* 2001, 2008).

WHITE-COLLARED MANAKIN
Manacus candei   Plate 6

Pipra candei **Parzudaki, 1841**, *Rev. Zool.* 4: 306, Truxillo [= Trujillo], Honduras

White-collared Manakin is the second most widespread of the genus *Manacus* and is also one of the most northerly ranging species covered in this work. The males are, like those of its congenerics, beautiful and easily identified birds, which in common with other *Manacus* readily draw the observer's attention via their loud wing-snapping displays. The much less obtrusive females are most likely to be observed at a fruiting tree.

IDENTIFICATION 11–12cm. Over most of this species' range it should be automatically identifiable, being the only manakin on the Atlantic (Caribbean) slope over much of Middle America, other than the rather smaller and less bulky-bodied Red-capped Manakin *Pipra mentalis*, which also has dark legs. White-collared Manakin also overlaps in range, principally in Costa Rica, with White-crowned Manakin *Dixiphia pipra*, White-ruffed Manakin *Corapipo leucorrhoa* and Blue-crowned Manakin *Lepidothrix coronata*, all of which are very marginally smaller in size than the present species. Of these, *M. candei* is the only species to display orange legs, making even the otherwise less-readily identifiable females separable from these other species given reasonable views. Furthermore, female Red-capped Manakin has a flesh-coloured bill (not dark) and is more uniformly olive (far less yellow) below. Jones (2004) pointed to the possibility of confusing female White-collared Manakin with female euphonias, for instance Olive-backed *Euphonia goudi*, but noted that the latter has a much heavier bill, grey legs and feet, and reddish undertail-coverts.

DISTRIBUTION White-collared Manakin is the northernmost representative of the genus *Manacus*, with a range that extends from southeast Mexico, in northern Oaxaca (from the vicinity of the Valle Nacional: Binford 1989), to northwest Panama in western Bocas del Toro, to around Almirante and including Isla Bastimentos (Wetmore 1972). It does not occur east of the Río Teribe (Parsons *et al.* 1993); see below. *M. candei* has only recently been discovered in Panama, although it was predicted to occur by Slud (1964). From northern Oaxaca, it ranges through southern Veracruz, Tabasco, northern Chiapas, southern Campeche and southern Quintana Roo, all in Mexico (Howell and Webb 1995), thence south on the Atlantic slope of Central America through northern Guatemala, all of Belize except the northernmost tip, Honduras, Nicaragua and Costa Rica (Monroe 1968, Stiles and Skutch 1989, AOU 1998, Jones 2004). In northern Costa Rica, it almost

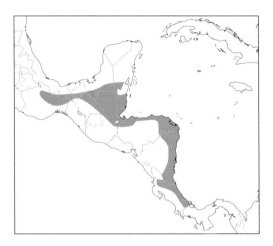

penetrates the Pacific slope in the Cordillera de Guanacaste via the lowest passes (Stiles and Skutch 1989). In terms of the species' elevational range, White-collared Manakin is apparently restricted to the lowlands and foothills, reaching just 500m in Mexico (Howell and Webb 1995), at least 600m in Guatemala (Land 1963), 750m in Honduras (Monroe 1968) and 700m in Costa Rica (Stiles and Skutch 1989). However, occurrence has been reported to 950m (Stotz *et al.* 1996, AOU 1998), and the species at least locally reaches 1,000m, e.g. at El Copal Biological Reserve, Costa Rica (Lawson 2010; GMK pers. obs.).

MOVEMENTS None definitely known and the species is generally assumed to be sedentary.

HABITAT White-collared Manakin is generally a bird of humid evergreen forest, especially its margins, as well as along the banks of wooded streams. In Mexico and northern Central America, Howell and Webb (1995) noted a preference for patches of *Heliconia* (Heliconiaceae). It also inhabits dense, tall second growth, scrub, and old cacao and other plantations.

DESCRIPTION A typical member of the genus *Manacus*, with wing structure and elongated throat-feathers like *M. vitellinus*. The sexes differ. Adult males have the wing feathers somewhat modified, with the outermost five primaries very narrow and stiff over the distal half and the other remiges possess noticeably thickened and bowed shafts and stiff outer webs. The throat-feathers are elongated, projecting slightly forwards toward the tip of the bill, and reaching beyond this especially when flared in display. The culmen is reasonably well arched, often with a hooked tip in both sexes, and the nostrils are comparatively large for the bird's overall size. *Adult male.* – The head from the forehead to the rear crown is deep black, contrasting markedly with the clean white face, ear-coverts, broad neck-collar, neck-sides, throat and upper breast. In turn, the white (which terminates in a ragged pectoral band) contrasts with the rest of the underparts, which are chrome-yellow, becoming slightly orangey on the lower belly, duller on the undertail-coverts and greenish-yellow on the tarsal feathering. The mantle, wings and tail are black, albeit slightly duller than the pileum (and dullest on the flight feathers), becoming deep olive-green on the back, rump and uppertail-coverts, with paler fringes to the rectrices. The largest tertials can have pale grey-white outer webs, whilst most of the scapulars and smaller wing-coverts are also white. The underwing is principally dark grey with whitish axillaries and underwing-coverts. *Adult female.* – Principally deep olive-green above, including the wing-coverts, perhaps marginally darkest on the crown and more obviously so on the tail, whilst the flight feathers are overall dark with greenish fringes to the secondaries. Below, the chin and throat are also olive-green, although marginally paler and brighter than the upperparts, and offering some contrast with the rest of the underparts, which are largely bright greenish-yellow with some hints of orange on the belly and undertail-coverts. *Juvenile.* – Considered to be more or less identical to the adult female except that the belly is pale olive with a little yellow, and the legs are pinkish-orange. Howell and Webb (1995) and Snow (2004b) reported that adult male plumage is assumed after *c.*1 year, whilst Stiles and Skutch (1989) stated that non-adult males recall the adult female but sometimes have a paler more greyish throat and upper breast. Wolfe *et al.* (2009) provided considerably greater detail concerning plumage maturation based on work at La Selva Biological Station, in Costa Rica. They found that birds of either sex in their first or second year between August and July had green body plumage, showed moult limits among the wing-coverts, and that some males (in September–August) possess a grey or pale grey throat; however, only older females can display a greyish throat. Leg colour is sometimes brighter orange in older (second-year or above) rather than young females. Second-to third-year males assume the black cap, lower back, wings and tail, as well as the white throat and upper back, green rump and yellow belly. In September, a moulting male can be identified as being in at least its third year if the outer primary is blackish and narrow, being <2.5mm wide over the distal 8–10mm. Furthermore, second- or third-year males can show less white in the greater coverts than younger males, and any white on the outermost two greater coverts can be washed yellowish at this age. *Moult.* – There are very few published data concerning moult, and the only specimen data are negative; unsurprisingly, given the species' breeding season in Costa Rica (see below), available specimens from that country taken between March and October were not replacing their feathers (MNCR). However, Wolfe *et al.* (2009) recently presented moult data from the same country. These authors found that the first moult from juvenile plumage is partial and occurs in August–January, whilst the moult to adult plumage is complete and is undertaken in July–January. The partial post-juvenile moult includes a variable number of greater coverts but no flight feathers. *Hybrids.* – Peters (1927) was effectively the first person to notice that *M. candei* hybridises with *M. vitellinus* in northwest Panama, but he mistakenly considered the hybrid to represent a previously undescribed

species, *M. cerritus*, which taxon was subsequently considered a subspecies of *M. vitellinus* (AOU 1983). The true identity of '*M. cerritus*' was initially divined by E. Eisenmann *in* Haffer (1967a). This hybrid swarm has been the subject of recent detailed studies by Parsons *et al.* (1993), McDonald *et al.* (2001) and Yuri *et al.* (2009). Parsons *et al.* (1993) found that in Panama pure *M. candei* occurs west of the Río Teribe in Bocas del Toro, but east of this, between at least the Río Changuinola and Tierra Oscura, males intermediate between *M. candei* and *M. vitellinus* are found. Apparently similar populations also occur on the islands of the region, but their identity has yet to be definitely determined (although Cooper 1999 reported *M. vitellinus* on the large island of Isla Popa). The intermediate populations of the mainland are remarkably variable, to a large extent clinally, in having an intermediate-width lemon-yellow collar, yellow-green underparts and an intermediate-sized wing patch (Parsons *et al.* 1993). Brumfield (1999) presented a detailed analysis of colour variation across the hybrid zone. However, typical *M. candei* has also been observed in this region (Parsons *et al.* 1994). Still further east, e.g. at Chiriquí Grande and on the Valiente Peninsula, *Manacus* populations display the pure *M. vitellinus* phenotype, although even here Parsons *et al.* (1993) found limited evidence of the *M. candei* haplotype when these birds were tested genetically, and Yuri *et al.* (2009) found that the cline in characters could be up to 250km broad. The nature, degree and forces driving the introgression are, however, to some extent unclear (Parsons *et al.* 1994), because of the clear shift from white- to golden-collared birds around the Río Changuinola, but the dramatic shift in mitochondrial DNA haplotype and morphometric parameters at the eastern end of the 60km hybrid zone (Parsons *et al.* 1993). The latter authors postulated that the border between white- and golden-collared birds might be moving westwards. It is worth mentioning that there is a more than 50km gap between pure *M. vitellinus* and hybrid populations, from where data on *Manacus* populations are lacking (cf. Parsons *et al.* 1993: Fig. 1, Olson 1993: Fig. 1, McDonald *et al.* 2001: Fig. 1). Subsequently, McDonald *et al.* (2001) provided additional genetic information on this hybrid population. Hybrid males are practically indistinguishable from *candei* genetically and morphometrically, but strongly resemble *vitellinus* due to the introgression of secondary sexual plumage traits, especially the lemon collar. As the observed introgression can be explained either by sexual selection for golden-collared traits or by non-sexual mechanisms, McDonald *et al.* (2001) decided to test this. If sexual selection was at work, they postulated that behavioural differences among the plumage forms should be observable, in this case that golden-collared individuals would be more aggressive than white-collared males. McDonald *et al.* (2001) presented males with taxidermy mounts of the three forms, and then monitored the vocalisations and attacks on the mounts by subject males. They found that yellow-collared (i.e. both lemon- and golden-collared) males were more likely to attack than white-collared males, and that lemon-collared males were more vocally reactive than either parental form, thereby leading them to reject any non-sexual hypothesis as a driver for the observed introgression. Subsequently, Uy and Stein (2007) presented an abstract summarising further work in this hybrid zone, which they report has demonstrated that sexual selection is favouring yellow-collared males. For a review of this hybrid zone see Tori *et al.* (2008). *Bare parts.* – Both sexes usually have the irides brown to sepia, occasionally fiery orange in males and sometimes olive-grey in females. The bill has the maxilla black or blackish, occasionally with the basal part grey, and the mandible is typically grey (occasionally dark brown). The legs and feet are generally orange to reddish-orange, usually with grey to blackish soles and claws (FMNH; MNCR).

MEASUREMENTS (BMNH; MNCR: Costa Rica) Wing of male (*n* = 14) 54–56mm, wing of female (*n* = 10) 50.0–58.5mm; tail of male (*n* = 14) 34–37mm, tail of female (*n* = 10) 35–40mm; bill of male (*n* = 14) 11.65–12.80mm, bill of female (*n* = 11) 11.50–13.56mm; tarsus of male (*n* = 14) 19.8–22.5mm, tarsus of female (*n* = 11) 18.45–22.45mm. Wolfe *et al.* (2009), based on a greater sample of live birds from Costa Rica, gave wing length as 49–59mm in both sexes, and Jenkins (1982) reported wing length as 54–59mm in Belize. Additional mensural data, from northwest Panama, were presented by Wetmore (1972) referring to '*M. v. cerritus*' (see Geographical Variation) and by Parsons *et al.* (1993) from the same region. Weight: 18.5–20.2g (males), 15.0–20.9g (females) (MNCR; Jenkins 1982, Stiles and Skutch 1989, Snow 2004b, Dunning 2008; MVZ). Jenkins (1982) reported a maximum weight of 23g, but did not specify the sex involved.

GEOGRAPHICAL VARIATION Most recent authorities treat *M. candei* as a monotypic species (e.g. Sibley and Monroe 1990, Stotz *et al.* 1996, AOU 1998, Dickinson 2003, Snow 2004b, Gill and Wright 2006). Genetic data reveal *M. candei* to be a basically monophyletic grouping (Brumfield and Braun 2001). However, Snow (1975, 1979b) had treated it, along with *M. aurantiacus* and *M. vitellinus*, as a subspecies of *M. manacus*. The name *Manacus cerritus* (Almirante Manakin), J. L. Peters, 1927, from Almirante Bay, northwest Panama, although treated specifically by Hellmayr (1929b) and considered closest to (probably a subspecies of) *M. vitellinus* therein (and by AOU 1983), is nowadays known to refer to hybrids between *M. candei* and *M. vitellinus* (see above, under Description). Hellmayr (1929b) presented a description and measurements of one such bird (see above) and Parsons *et al.* (1993) provided morphometrics for several characters, including tail length. Wetmore (1972) also presented mensural data from Panama. At that time, *M. candei* was not known to range further south than northeast Costa Rica and this particular problem was only recently resolved (see Ridgely and Gwynne 1989). The name *M. c. electilis* O. Bangs, 1903, from Buena Vista, Vera Cruz, has also been treated as a synonym, virtually since its introduction (Peters 1929).

VOICE The species' vocalisations can be simply subdivided into clapping, scolding, churring and buzzing sounds. White-collared Manakin, in common with other *Manacus* species, is usually first detected by its loud 'firecracker' wing-snaps, *crrrack*, likened to cracking nuts, given during displays. Five different vocalisations were identified and described by Jones (2004). These were as follows. Among the most commonly heard is the loud, slightly machine-gun-like burst of 5–6 hard, rattling notes, rendered *pee-eww*, lasting *c*.0.3 seconds, which in display are slightly more buzzy and are preceded by a sharp snapping (*pitt*) or popping produced by the wings. Thirdly, like those of congenerics, the male's wings make a strong, slightly musical, buzzing sound in flight: a series of *brrr* sounds usually audible over several metres. Finally, the birds (both sexes) give a squeaky *cheerie*, and a rough- or slightly squeaky-sounding *cheuur*

or *cheuur wit*, both of which can be given by males at their leks and again are preceded by wing-snaps. The species' voice features on the following audio compilations: Moore (1992), Ross (2000), Boesman (2006c) and Knapp and Will (2010), and recordings from Belize, Costa Rica and Nicaragua are archived online at www.xeno-canto.org.

NATURAL HISTORY Like other *Manacus*, White-collared Manakin inhabits low to mid levels, although it may ascend into the canopy when foraging at a fruiting tree.

FOOD AND FEEDING The species' diet seems to be very much like that of other *Manacus* species, comprising small fruits and insects, taken during a brief sally-hover to the vegetation. There are few specifics concerning diet constituents, but Skutch (1980) listed fruits of *Alchornea latifolia* (Euphorbiaceae), and White-collared Manakins have been observed visiting a fruiting *Miconia penduliflora* (Melastomataceae) along with a host of other small frugivores, including *Pipra mentalis*, and another unidentified *Miconia* sp. together with many *Tangara* tanagers (GMK pers. obs.). In a study of captive birds, Levey (1987) found that this and other species of manakins apparently cannot taste sugar (unlike at least some tanagers).

DISPLAY The species' displays are generally very similar to those of Orange-collared Manakin *Manacus aurantiacus*, but White-collared Manakin clears a rather larger court than those of the next species, up to 1.2m wide (Stiles and Skutch 1989). Howell (1957) described an ovaloid display court measuring *c*.1.2 × 1.0m. The male removes all litter from this patch of ground and each such court is in clear auditory distance of the adjacent male's arena, but the two are not in visual contact (GMK pers. obs.). Up to four males may be present within an area of 250m^2 (Jenkins 1982). In northwest Panama, McDonald *et al.* (2001) found inter-court spacing to be <5m and *c*.25m, and overall numbers of males at leks ranged from 15 to 30 individuals. Above the arena, the male makes short (*c*.0.5m) mechanical-looking 'leaps' back and forth between slim upright stems, either side of the arena, making loud snapping sounds and single flits of the wings to accompany each jumping movement, performing an 'about-face' on landing. The bird or birds often make a circuit during these displays. Bouts of display are punctuated by longer periods of relative inactivity with the male remaining in the relatively close vicinity of the 'mating stem' (see below), but not displaying, generally staying quiet on a favoured perch up to 2.5m above the ground, preening and occasionally calling in response to displays by neighbouring males (GMK pers. obs.). Time away from the lek, if not spent feeding, is probably generally devoted to visiting a rival male's arena to display. Occasionally, the male crouches with the head appearing retracted, the body swaying, the wings beating and the throat-feathers projected forwards beyond the bill tip. Should a female arrive in the vicinity of the lek, initially usually above the display area, the male and female will make coordinated leaping movements, crossing each other in mid-air above the bare area of the court, landing either on the 'mating stem' or adjacent perches, until finally the female lands on the 'mating stem'. At this point the male jumps down to the ground, then up onto the 'mating stem', before sliding down the perch prior to copulation.

BREEDING The nest is typical of many manakins, being a shallow cup placed in a horizontal fork 1–3m above the ground, constructed of black fungal rhizomorphs and fine brown fibres, and bound to the supporting branches using spiderwebs. However, the nest is somewhat unusual amongst the Pipridae in being comparatively large. It is often lined with filamentous brown *Myriocarpa* (Urticaceae) inflorescences that can dangle up to 1.2m below the nest, and the outside of the nest is usually decorated with green moss (see photographs in Snow 2004b: 134–135). A typical clutch comprises two eggs, with a whitish background but speckled brown, and a broad wreath of brown streaks at the larger end (Stiles and Skutch 1989, Howell and Webb 1995). The incubation and fledging periods are presently unknown (Snow 2004b). In Costa Rica, the breeding season is reported to occupy the period April–August (Stiles and Skutch 1989; MNCR; MVZ) or March–November (Wolfe *et al.* 2009). In northwest Panama, in the hybrid zone between *M. candei* and *M. vitellinus*, display apparently reaches its peak in May (McDonald *et al.* 2001). Howell (1957) collected males in breeding condition in July and August in Nicaragua, and Land (1963) noted breeding evidence in February in Guatemala.

STATUS Like the other members of the genus, BirdLife International (2004, 2008) treats this species as being Least Concern, especially given its comparatively wide range (estimated at 284,000km²). It is known from more than 20 Important Bird Areas and White-collared Manakin is generally fairly common to common throughout its wide range, although it is rather uncommon in northern Belize (Jones 2004), and is relatively tolerant of partially degraded habitats. Given this wide range and some degree of plasticity, Anciães and Peterson (2006) predicted that the species is likely to be much less affected by predicted levels of climate change than are many other manakins. Nonetheless, some local extinctions might have occurred, e.g. in westernmost Panama (Wetmore 1972). White-collared Manakin is known

from many protected areas, among them Montes Azules Biosphere Reserve and Yaxchilán Natural Monument, Chiapas, Mexico (González-García 1993, Puebla-Olivares *et al.* 2002), Rio Bravo Conservation and Management Area, and Lamanai Archaeological Reserve, Belize (Vallely and Whitman 1997, England 2000), Laguna del Tigre National Park, Guatemala (Selvin and Castillo 2000), and Arenal Volcano National Park, Tortuguero National Park, La Selva Biological Station, Hitoy Cerere Biological Reserve and Río Negro Jaguar Preserve, Costa Rica (Cooper 1997, Lawson 2010).

REFERENCES Anciães and Peterson (2006, 2009), AOU (1983, 1998), Binford (1989), BirdLife International (2004, 2008), Boesman (2006c), Bostwick and Prum (2003), Brumfield (1999), Brumfield and Braun (2001), Brumfield *et al.* (2001, 2008), Cooper (1997, 1999), Dickinson (2003), Dunning (2008), Eisermann and Avendaño (2007), England (2000), Garrigues and Dean (2007), Gill and Wright (2006), González-García (1993), Haffer (1967a), Hallinan (1924), Hellmayr (1929b), Höglund and Shorey (2004), Howell and Webb (1995), Howell (1957), Jenkins (1982), Jones (2004), Knapp and Will (2010), Land (1963), Lawson (2010), Levey (1987), McDonald *et al.* (2001), Moermond and Denslow (1985), Monroe (1968), Moore (1992), Olson (1993), Parsons *et al.* (1993, 1994), Peters (1927, 1929), Piaskowski *et al.* (2006), Ridgely and Gwynne (1976, 1989), Ross (2000), Selvin and Castillo (2000), Sibley and Monroe (1990), Skutch (1980), Slud (1964), Snow (1973c, 1975, 1979b, 2004b), Stein and Uy (2006), Stiles and Skutch (1989), Stotz *et al.* (1996), Tori *et al.* (2008), Uy and Stein (2007), Vallely and Whitman (1997), Wetmore (1972), Wolfe *et al.* (2009), Yuri *et al.* (2009).

White-collared Manakin *Manacus candei*. **Fig. 1**. Male, Rancho Naturalista, prov. Cartago, Costa Rica, August (*Jason Horn / Costa Rica Gateway*). Note the white throat feathers can reach beyond the bill tip. **Fig. 2**. Male, La Selva Biological Station, prov. Heredia, northeast Costa Rica, May (*Steven Easley / Costa Rica Gateway*). This is the northernmost representative of the *Manacus* superspecies.

ORANGE-COLLARED MANAKIN
Manacus aurantiacus   **Plate 6**

Chiromachaeris aurantiaca Salvin, 1870, *Proc. Zool. Soc. Lond.* 1870: 200, Mina de Chorcha and Bugaba, Chiriquí, Panama

Arguably the most beautiful of its genus, the Orange-collared Manakin is endemic to western Costa Rica and western Panama, but in comparison with most other members of *Manacus* it is a surprisingly poorly studied species.

IDENTIFICATION 9.3–10.0cm. The exceptionally striking and beautiful male should be impossible to mistake, especially as no other *Manacus* manakin occurs within its relatively limited range. Given the lack of sympatry with congenerics, females too should prove reasonably easy to identify once the bird has been accurately assigned to genus. Female White-collared Manakin *M. candei* occurs only on the Caribbean slope of Central America, and the marginally larger Golden-collared Manakin *M. vitellinus* replaces the present species further west in Panama (the two are not known to meet). Consequently, the only real risk of confusion is with females belonging to other genera of manakins. However, female Lance-tailed Manakin *Chiroxiphia lanceolata* (mainly overlaps with the present species in Panama) is larger, bulkier and has obviously elongated central rectrices. There is only limited overlap with either Blue-crowned *Lepidothrix coronata* or Red-capped Manakins *Pipra mentalis*, both of which are slightly smaller (particularly the first-named) than Orange-collared Manakin, and *P. mentalis* is more of a canopy-dweller than the present species. Especially note the leg colour, dark in *P. mentalis* and *L. coronata* but usually reddish-orange, or similar, in *M. aurantiacus*, and female Blue-crowned Manakin is also decidedly greener in plumage, especially on the upperparts.

DISTRIBUTION Endemic to southern Central America, where it ranges on the Pacific slope through southwest Costa Rica, from the environs of Carara, on the east side of the Gulf of Nicoya, south to western Panama, through southern Chiriquí and southeastern Veraguas, to both sides of the Azuero Peninsula in Los Santos (Wetmore 1972, Ridgely and Gwynne 1976, Stiles and Skutch 1989). Orange-collared Manakin has been recorded to 1,100m in Costa Rica (Stiles and Skutch 1989) but apparently only to 700m in Panama (Wetmore 1972).

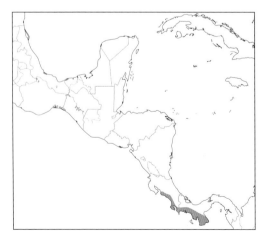

MOVEMENTS None known.

HABITAT Orange-collared Manakin prefers mature wet forest, as well as older second growth, gallery woodland and tall thickets with a canopy height of up to 20m, and it also regularly visits forest borders, especially where there are fruiting trees. It is also found in shade plantations and gardens (Stiles and Skutch 1989). Leks can be found in relatively open-canopy forest with many treefalls and other light gaps, and many vines in the understorey.

DESCRIPTION A typical member of the genus *Manacus*, with wing structure and elongated throat-feathers like *M. vitellinus*. The sexes differ. Adult males have the wing feathers somewhat modified, with the outermost five primaries very narrow and stiff over the distal half and the other remiges possess noticeably thickened and bowed shafts and stiff outer webs. The throat-feathers are elongated, projecting slightly forwards toward the tip of the bill, and reaching beyond this especially when flared in display. The culmen is reasonably well arched, often with a hooked tip in both sexes, and the nostrils are comparatively large for the bird's overall size. *Adult male.* – Crown, from bill base, and lores to upper nape deep black, concolorous with the mantle, whilst the throat, upper breast, face and neck are all brilliant orange, albeit usually the upper ear-coverts are somewhat paler and yellower, as is sometimes that part of the neck abutting the mantle. The bases of all these feathers are white. The remainder of the underparts are bright yellow, sometimes tinged slightly with olive, especially at the sides, or streaked with very pale orange, whilst the lower back is olive-green, becoming yellower over the rump, with an olive tail becoming darker basally and along the feather shafts. The wings appear solidly black in the field, but the secondaries can have olive-green fringes and the fringes to the greater wing-coverts are usually slightly paler (i.e. somewhat greyer or slightly olive) than the feather centres, whilst the median and lesser wing-coverts have pale yellow and orange tips. The underwing is largely greyish-brown except the axillaries and inner coverts which are pale yellow. *Adult female.* – Principally olive-green above, albeit slightly darker on the crown, but becoming paler and slightly more yellowish over the rump and uppertail-coverts, whilst the throat is yellowish-olive, the breast, sides and flanks are olive-green (darkest on the chest), and the belly and undertail-coverts are bright olive-yellow. The tarsal feathering is marginally paler and less bright. The dark (dusky-coloured) wing-feathers are extensively fringed olive-green, especially on the flight feathers. The rectrices are also dusky with olive-green fringes. The underwing-coverts and axillaries are paler than in the male. *Juvenile.* – This plumage is apparently identical to the adult female, except that the legs and feet are yellowish to flesh orange (i.e. paler than that of the adult) (Stiles and Skutch 1989) although Wetmore (1972) considered juveniles to be more greyish-green below. The nestling has grey down and a yellow gape (Skutch 1969, Wetmore 1972). Young males initially gain a golden tinge to the breast- and throat-feathers (Stiles and Skutch 1989), but there is no detailed information concerning plumage maturation and we have examined no immature specimens to comment further on this issue (see also Chapman 1935). *Moult.* – Very few published data, but a male in January was replacing its rectrices (MNCR) and another male taken in July was moulting its wing and body feathers, and the rectrices (FMNH). *Bare parts.* – The maxilla is sepia-coloured to blackish in males, and sepia to dark grey in females, whilst the mandible is rosy-pink to vinaceous-pink to plumbeous or blackish, sometimes with a sepia or pale brown tip or yellow-white base. The legs and feet are sepia to orangish or dark orange, with blackish soles and pale brown claws. Irides are usually warm brown or dark brown to sepia-coloured (Wetmore 1972; FMNH; MNCR).

MEASUREMENTS (BMNH; FMNH; MNCR: Costa Rica) Wing of male (*n* = 11) 47.0–51.5mm, wing of female (*n* = 6) 48.5–51.5mm; tail of male (*n* = 10) 29–35mm, tail of female (*n* = 7) 28–33mm; bill of male (*n* = 11) 11.30–12.06mm, bill of female (*n* = 7) 11.25–12.40mm; tarsus of male (*n* = 11) 17.80–20.45mm, tarsus of female (*n* = 7) 17.1–20.6mm. Additional mensural data were published by Wetmore (1972). Weight: 11–17g (males), 14–18g (females) (FMNH; MNCR; Stiles and Skutch 1989, Snow 2004b, Dunning 2008).

GEOGRAPHICAL VARIATION Monotypic, but this species was formerly sometimes classed as a subspecies of *M. vitellinus*, although the vast majority of current authorities recognise it as a separate species (e.g. Stiles and Skutch 1989, Sibley and Monroe 1990, Stotz *et al.* 1996, AOU 1998, Dickinson 2003, Snow 2004b, Gill and Wright 2006). Prum (1990a), however, included it within *M. vitellinus*, and Snow (1975, 1979b) had regarded *aurantiacus* as a subspecies of *M. manacus*. Genetic data reveal *M. aurantiacus* to be a monophyletic grouping (Brumfield and Braun 2001) and a subsequent study demonstrated this species to be sister to White-collared Manakin *M. candei* (Brumfield *et al.* 2008), which might seem surprising given the zone of hybridisation between *M. candei* and *M. vitellinus*. The name *Manacus aurantiacus flaviventris*, Aldrich, 1937, described from the Bahía Montijo, Veraguas, Panama, is a synonym of nominate *aurantiacus*, with *M. a. flaviventris* having been incorrectly named on the basis of a lack of appreciation of colour fading in specimens (Wetmore 1972).

VOICE The male's primary vocalisation is a rising *chewwe* or *teeeou*, also rendered *cheeu*, usually given singly, sometimes doubled and occasionally more accented at the end, *teeeoU*. Stiles and Skutch (1989) mentioned a 'thin, tense *chee*' given when disturbed, or alternatively a *chee-yu*. Ridgely and Gwynne (1976) also mention a clicking *tick* note. Mechanical sounds are an important feature of the male's displays, and these most commonly include loud single snaps, recalling the crack of a dry twig, but also volleys of snapping and whirring sounds, given during more intense bouts of display, all of which are made using the wings. Also a surprisingly loud wing rustling sound is given in flight, this sound being produced by the modified wing feathers (see Description). The species' vocalisations are also archived online at www.xeno-canto.org.

NATURAL HISTORY Except at the display grounds, the species is generally found alone (Stiles and Skutch 1989) and can be shy and difficult to see within the dense undergrowth (Wetmore 1972). Largely an inhabitant of the understorey but regularly ascends to the midstorey (*c.*10m above the ground). Males spend long periods within the confines of the lek, perching between 30cm and 1.5m above the ground, but most time is probably spent either resting (sitting quietly but watchfully) or preening, often with the flank and throat feathers slightly inflated, rather than actively displaying.

FOOD AND FEEDING Lekking males will regularly break off from displaying to feed, sometimes ascending up to

10m above the ground to so do. Feeding areas may be very close to or even within the lekking arenas, but temporary (*c.*15-minute) departures might suggest that the birds also visit areas slightly further afield to forage. Skutch (1980) listed fruits of the following species as being taken by *M. aurantiacus*: *Protium* spp. (Burseraceae), *Davilla kunthii* (Dilleniaceae), *Clusia* spp. (Clusiaceae), *Casearia sylvestris* (Salicaceae), *Lacistema aggregatum* (Lacistemataceae) and *Miconia trinervia* (Melastomataceae). Small fruits are taken using short aerial sally-hovers, typically upwards, for up to 30cm, but also from a perch, whilst at least occasionally small insects are taken (MNCR), including once while on the ground in the centre of the lekking arena (GMK pers. obs.). Skutch (1969) regularly noted Orange-collared Manakins taking insects flushed by ant swarms in company with some species of antbirds. Seeds are regularly regurgitated from perches within the lek.

DISPLAY This species' ritualised display behaviours are typical of the genus *Manacus*. Bouts of display do not appear to be especially stimulated by ambient light conditions or adjacent males calling (GMK pers. obs.). Remarkably, given interest in manakins as subjects for study, the only detailed remarks on the displays and breeding biology of this species date back to Skutch (1969). The male removes all litter from a small, usually circular, but sometimes more elliptical-shaped patch of ground (30–70cm wide), which is usually smaller than that cleared by Golden-collared Manakin (Skutch 1969, Wetmore 1972). Each such court will be in auditory distance of the adjacent male's arena, but the two will not be in clear visual contact (GMK pers. obs.). Above this, the male makes short (<1m) mechanical-looking 'leaps' back and forth between slim upright stems, making loud snapping sounds and single flits of the wings to accompany each jumping movement, performing an 'about-face' on landing, and with the bird sometimes following a triangular course. Bouts of display are punctuated by longer periods of relative inactivity with the male remaining in the relatively close vicinity of the 'mating stem' (see below), but not displaying, generally remaining quiet on a favoured perch, preening and occasionally calling in response to displays by neighbouring males (GMK pers. obs.). Time away from the lek, if not spent feeding, is probably generally devoted to visiting a rival male's arena to display. It is unclear how such visits are determined, as for instance one adult male observed for a total of four hours on two consecutive mornings in southwest Costa Rica regularly left its own lek site, apparently to visit that of its closest rival, but never appeared to be visited 'in return', given that it was the only male ever seen in the vicinity of its arena (GMK pers. obs.). Occasionally, the male crouches with the head appearing retracted, the body swaying, the wings beating and the throat-feathers projected forwards beyond the bill tip. Should a female arrive in the vicinity of the lek, two or three males will make coordinated leaping movements, crossing each other in mid-air above the bare area of the court, landing either on the 'mating stem' or on adjacent perches. The female will join in this display, until finally she lands on the 'mating stem', whereupon the male jumps down to the ground, then up onto the 'mating stem', before sliding down the perch prior to copulation.

BREEDING The nest has been described from observations in Costa Rica, where Skutch (1969) found it to be a shallow cup constructed principally of pale bast fibres, but also including fine strips of bark, rootlets and grasses, slung loosely between the fork of a horizontal branch 0.6–2.5m above the ground, occasionally higher, to 5.5m, and sited in forest, a coffee plantation, a shady garden or above a stream. The nest is attached to the supporting branches with spiderwebs or caterpillar silk. The materials used in the nest's construction are rarely dark in colour. Unusually for a manakin nest, no dead leaves or moss seems to be used in the nest's construction, and there is usually no material hanging below to disguise its outline. Concerning seasonality, in Costa Rica, the species typically nests between March and June, but occasionally also in September (Stiles and Skutch 1989; MNCR; MVZ) and perhaps also as early as late January (MNCR). Wetmore (1972) mentioned the discovery of a nest with small nestlings in western Panama in the second week of June. Orange-collared Manakin lays two eggs, which range from dull white or pale grey to blue-grey in their ground colour, mottled heavily with brown, either uniformly throughout, in a wreath at the larger end, or with reduced markings at both ends (Skutch 1969, Schönwetter 1969). Measurements of the eggs were repeated in Wetmore (1972). The incubation period lasts 18–20 days and the young fledge in 13–15 days (Skutch 1949, 1969).

STATUS Orange-collared Manakin is currently categorised as Least Concern by BirdLife International (2004, 2008), despite the species' relatively small range (estimated at *c.*29,600km² by BirdLife International) and that the species is probably in decline, especially perhaps in western Panama as a result of increasing deforestation (cf. Wetmore 1972, Sekercioglu *et al.* 2002) although *M. aurantiacus* is possibly still reasonably numerous in parts of western Chiriquí (Snow 2004b). Overall, it is considered locally common in Costa Rica (Stiles and Skutch 1989) and fairly common in western Panama (Wetmore 1972, Ridgely and Gwynne 1976). However, Anciães and Peterson (2006) considered that habitat change in the face of predicted levels of climate change could very severely affect the range and population of this manakin. Protected areas known to harbour the species include Carara National Park, Oro Verde Biological Reserve and Corcovado National Park, all

in Costa Rica (Lawson 2010), and El Montuoso de Chepo reserve, on the Azuero Peninsula, in Panama (Wheatley and Brewer 2001).

REFERENCES Anciães and Peterson (2006, 2009), AOU (1998), BirdLife International (2004, 2008), Bostwick and Prum (2003), Brumfield and Braun (2001), Brumfield *et al.* (2008), Chapman (1935), Dickinson (2003), Dunning (2008), Garrigues and Dean (2007), Gill and Wright (2006), Hellmayr (1929b), Höglund and Shorey (2004), Lawson (2010), Prum (1990a), Ridgely and Gwynne (1976, 1989), Schönwetter (1969), Sekercioglu *et al.* (2002), Skutch (1949, 1969, 1980), Slud (1964), Snow (1975, 1979b, 2004b), Stiles and Skutch (1989), Stotz *et al.* (1996), Tello *et al.* (2009), Wetmore (1972), Wheatley and Brewer (2001).

Orange-collared Manakin *Manacus aurantiacus*. **Fig. 1**. Male, southwestern Costa Rica, December (*Hadoram Shirihai / Photographic Handbook to Birds of the World*). **Fig. 2**. Male, Carara National Park, western Costa Rica, February (*Steven Easley / Costa Rica Gateway*). **Fig. 3**. Female, southwestern Costa Rica, December (*Hadoram Shirihai / Photographic Handbook to Birds of the World*). Confined to southern Costa Rica and western Panama, more or less 'sandwiched' between the ranges of White-collared *M. candei* and Golden-collared Manakins *M. vitellinus*.

GOLDEN-COLLARED MANAKIN
Manacus vitellinus   Plate 6

Pipra vitellina, **Gould, 1843**, *Proc. Zool. Soc. Lond.* 1843: 103,
Panama (= Panama City, Panama)

Golden-collared Manakin is exclusively found in Panama
and western Colombia, and is known to hybridise with
two congenerics, White-collared Manakin *M. candei* in
northwest Panama and White-bearded Manakin *M. manacus*
in Colombia, this evidence having sometimes been used
to maintain all four *Manacus* species as recognised here
within a single species. Alternatively, some authors have
preferred to unite Orange-collared *M. aurantiacus* and
Golden-collared Manakins in a single species, thereby
treating *Manacus* as comprising three species.

IDENTIFICATION 10–12cm. The male Golden-collared
Manakin should be readily identified, given that over the
vast majority of its distribution there is no known overlap
with any other *Manacus.* Only on the Pacific slope in western
Panama does the present species come close to the range
of Orange-collared Manakin (which see), but there is no
known overlap, with the latter species reaching no further
east than the Azuero Peninsula. In northwest Panama, the
ranges of Golden-collared Manakin and White-collared
Manakin are basically separated by the Laguna de Chiriquí,
with *M. candei* to the west and *M. vitellinus* to the east. The
situation is confused by the presence of a hybrid zone
(see below and under White-collared Manakin) between
the ranges of the two species and west and south of the
Laguna, as well as on some of the near-shore islands, within
which males largely or exclusively display the *M. vitellinus*
phenotype. Any bird in this region with a white collar is
almost certainly pure *M. candei*. In northwest Colombia,
especially in the vicinity of the middle Cauca Valley, where
forest cover has been dramatically reduced, there is also
some hybridisation with the neighbouring race of White-
bearded Manakin *M. manacus abditivus* (see below for
a description and discussion of such birds). A potential
additional complication in this part of Golden-collared
Manakin's range is the presence of another subspecies
of White-bearded Manakin, *M. m. flaveolus* of the upper
Magdalena Valley, which has the white underparts and
collar washed with pale yellow, but this coloration never
approaches the intensity displayed by pure *M. vitellinus* and
it never has greenish-coloured posterior underparts as in
the present species. Over most of the species' range female
Golden-collared Manakin might be confused with other
female manakins, but should be generally separable on the
basis of its bright orange legs, this character being shared
only by the larger female Lance-tailed Manakin. The latter
species is further distinguished by the projecting central
tail feathers. However, as noted above, in parts of western
Colombia (and see also below under Hybrids), Golden-
collared Manakin overlaps in range with White-bearded
Manakin and females of these two species are probably
more or less inseparable in the field, although female *M.
manacus* is, on average, slightly paler below and has a pale
greyish throat (rather than yellowish-olive).

DISTRIBUTION Golden-collared Manakin ranges from
northwest Panama south and east to western Colombia. In
Panama, the species ranges on the Pacific slope from eastern
Veraguas (around Santa Fé) through the Canal Zone to
Darién, and on the Caribbean slope from central Bocas

del Toro, on the east side of the Laguna de Chiriquí, east
through the Canal Zone to the province of Panamá and the
Comarca de San Blas (Wetmore 1972). In South America,
Golden-collared Manakin ranges south along the Pacific
coast of Colombia as far as southwest Cauca (at Guapí) and
perhaps also western Nariño, and from the Gulf of Urabá
in northernmost Antioquia to the lower Río Cauca and
the upper Río Nechi, as well as formerly the upper Cauca
Valley (Hilty and Brown 1986). The species was erroneously
listed for northwest Ecuador (in northern Esmeraldas) by
Snow (1979b) and Restall *et al.* (2006), the latter despite the
clarification proffered by Ridgely and Greenfield (2001).
However, there is a specimen from Esmeraldas, collected
at Paramba, in January 1900, which Hellmayr (1929b)
considered to be unusual variant of *M. manacus leucochlamys*
but Haffer (1967a) regarded as almost certainly a hybrid *M.
manacus × M. vitellinus*. Nonetheless, given the situation in
northwest Panama, with *M. candei* and *M. vitellinus*, it does
not necessarily follow that *M. vitellinus* must have occurred
in Ecuador. On the other hand, Ridgely and Gwynne
(1976) speculated that Golden-collared Manakin might
be eventually discovered in adjacent Caribbean Costa Rica,
but this theory was espoused prior to the knowledge that
White-collared Manakin reaches into extreme northwest
Panama. Concerning the species' elevational range, Golden-
collared Manakin ranges through the lowlands and foothills
to 1,200m in Colombia (Hilty and Brown 1986) but to just
450m in Panama (Ridgely and Gwynne 1989).

MOVEMENTS None known to date (Snow 2004b) and
the species is considered resident (Wetmore 1972, Hilty
1997).

HABITAT Golden-collared Manakin is principally found in
mature secondary woodland and at forest borders, as well as
in clearings that are regenerating. Leks are often sited close
to an opening such as a stream (Uy and Endler 2004).

DESCRIPTION Typical *Manacus*, with wing structure and
elongated throat-feathers like *M. candei* and *M. aurantiacus*.
The sexes differ. Adult males have the wing-feathers
somewhat modified, with the outermost five primaries
very narrow and stiff over the distal half and the other
remiges possess noticeably thickened and bowed shafts and
stiff outer webs, this adaptation being used to control the
snapping and other mechanical sounds produced by the
wings. This was first noted by Lowe (1942) and the unusual
musculature, common to all *Manacus*, needed, especially in

males, has been the subject of several recent publications (Schlinger *et al.* 2001, Schultz *et al.* 2001). Three different wing muscles differ in one or more characteristics across sex, suggesting they are specialised for faster contraction and greater force production in male manakins. The throat-feathers are elongated, projecting slightly forwards toward the tip of the bill, and reaching well beyond this (by up to *c.*8cm) especially when flared in display (cf. Uy and Endler 2004). The culmen is reasonably well arched, often with a hooked tip in both sexes, and the nostrils are comparatively large for the bird's overall size. The nominate race is described here. *Male.* – The entire crown down to the lores and superciliary region and nape are black, being separated from the scapulars, wings and tail, which are also deep black, by a reasonably broad orange-yellow collar. This further extends from the hindneck onto the head- and neck-sides, the face, throat and upper breast. The rest of the underparts from the lower breast and including the flanks and undertail-coverts are pale greenish, whilst the rump and uppertail-coverts are rather darker greyish-green, and the lesser wing-coverts are yellow and black. The axillaries and underwing-coverts are pale yellow, whilst the rest of the underwing is dusky grey. *Female.* – The entire upperparts are rather bright olive-green, perhaps dullest and darkest on the head, becoming paler and more yellowish over the breast and abdomen, while the wings and tail are duller than the rest of the plumage. *Juvenile.* – This plumage is reported to resemble that of the adult female (Snow 2004b). Wetmore (1972) reported that immature males are identical to adult females, but there are some data to suggest that young birds might differ from adults in having paler, more yellowish tarsi. *Moult.* – There are very few if any published moult data, but in northernmost Colombia males and females have been trapped replacing their body-feathers (and sometimes their wing-feathers) in June–November, and November–January and late May–June, respectively (C. F. Londoño, D. Y. Ramírez and J. M. Ruiz/ProAves unpubl. data). *Hybrids.* – The existence of a zone of hybridisation, presently known to be *c.*60km wide, in Bocas del Toro, northwest Panama, between *M. candei* and *M. vitellinus* was initially revealed when Peters (1927) described '*M. cerritos*'. At that time *M. candei* was not known to be present in Panama. Recent research, by Parsons *et al.* (1993, 1994), Brumfield (1999), Brumfield and Braun (2001), McDonald *et al.* (2001), Uy and Stein (2007), Tori *et al.* (2008) and Yuri *et al.* (2009), has largely elucidated the extent and nature of this hybrid population, which is detailed under the text for White-collared Manakin. Hybridisation, perhaps as a result of ongoing deforestation at relevant altitudes, is also known between *M. vitellinus* and *M. manacus* in the middle Cauca Valley in Colombia (cf. E. O. Willis *in* Wetmore 1972). Willis's observation merits quoting.

> At Caucasia, in an isolated woodlot in the pastures […] west of town […], I found males of both types displaying in the same dancing ground, no more than ten meters apart. In between males of seemingly pure types in this same dancing ground, there were several intermediate or hybrid males displaying. Out of some ten males displaying […], two at the north end were white, one or two at the south end were yellow and six or so in between were pale yellow in the parts of the plumage which differ in the two taxa. I collected one of the pale yellow birds [now MVZ 148593] … and one of the white birds […] Examination of the hybrid male

from Caucasia and comparison with specimens of *Manacus vitellinus milleri* here at The American Museum of Natural History show that it is like *milleri* but much paler on the underparts and collar. The collar and cheeks are especially pale, being straw yellow like the throat and breast rather than bright yellow. The collar is wider than in *milleri*, and the belly is tinged with much less yellow so that it looks grayish-green. The edges of the throat are especially pale, almost white. In all these respects it is almost exactly intermediate between *milleri* and the specimen of *Manacus manacus abditivus* which I took at Caucasia. The latter is white wherever *milleri* is tinged with yellow, and shows none of the yellowish tint seen in *M. m. flaveolus*.

Furthermore, Haffer (1967a) was able to point to a second zone of contact, for Olivares (1958) had collected both *M. manacus* and *M. vitellinus* at Guapí in southwest Cauca, and from even further south, at Paramba, in Esmeraldas, northwest Ecuador, Hellmayr (1929b: 70) had already revealed the existence of an apparently intermediate specimen. Males with straw colours have been observed around Guapí even more recently (Brumfield *et al.* 2008: 728) revealing ongoing introgression. *Bare parts.* – The irides are generally dark brown, sometimes more mouse brown, while the tarsi and feet are typically orange to dark orange (sometimes slightly paler in females), with grey to black claws. The bill is principally black, especially over the maxilla and mandible tip, but can have a dark neutral grey base to the mandible (Wetmore 1972, Robbins *et al.* 1985, Snow 2004b).

MEASUREMENTS *M. v. vitellinus* (Wetmore 1972: eastern Panama): wing of male (n = 47) 50.5–55.5mm, wing of female (n = 46) 50.5–55.0mm; tail of male (n = 47) 26.0–31.5mm, tail of female (n = 46) 27.5–31.5mm; bill of male (n = 47) 11.0–13.0mm, bill of female (n = 46) 11.1–12.7mm; tarsus of male (n = 47) 20.4–22.4mm, tarsus of female (n = 46) 18.3–20.7mm. *M. v. amitinus* (Wetmore 1972: Isla Escudo de Veraguas, Panama): wing of male (n = 3) 59.5–61.5mm, wing of female (n = 2) 59.5–60.0mm; tail of male (n = 3) 39.0–42.0mm, tail of female (n = 2) 38.0–38.5mm; bill of male (n = 3) 14.0–14.8mm, bill of female (n = 2) 14.7mm; tarsus of male (n = 3) 23.8–24.5mm, tarsus of female (n = 2) 21.0–21.5mm. *M. v. milleri* (Hellmayr 1911: southern Chocó, Colombia): wing of male (n = 4) 53–54mm, wing of female (n = 2) 54–55mm; tail of male (n = 4) 28–30mm, tail of female (n = 2) 29mm. Data from live birds (*M. v. vitellinus*: Darién, Colombia): wing of male (n = 27) 46–57mm, wing of female (n = 59) 49–55mm; tail of male (n = 22) 28–37mm, tail of female (n = 48) 26.0–37.5mm; bill of male (n = 23) 10.1–14.5mm, bill of female (n = 51) 10.2–14.4mm; tarsus of male (n = 23) 20.5–26.3mm, tarsus of female (n = 50) 17.9–23.7mm (C. F. Londoño, D. Y. Ramírez and J. M. Ruiz/ProAves unpubl. data). Stein and Uy (2006) provided additional mensural data for males of *M. v. vitellinus* also pertaining to live birds. Weight: 13.8–24.1g (males) and 14.9–20.6g (females) (Wetmore 1972, Burton 1975, Strauch 1977, Vleck and Vleck 1979, Bucher and Worthington 1982, Robbins *et al.* 1985, Snow 2004b, Stein and Uy 2006, Dunning 2008; C. F. Londoño, D. Y. Ramírez and J. M. Ruiz/ ProAves unpubl. data).

GEOGRAPHICAL VARIATION Polytypic, formerly also including *M. aurantiacus*, although the vast majority of current authorities now recognise it as a separate species (e.g. Wetmore 1972, Stiles and Skutch 1989, Sibley and Monroe 1990, Stotz *et al.* 1996, AOU 1998, Dickinson 2003, Snow 2004b, Gill and Wright 2006, Ridgely and Tudor 2009). In contrast, Prum (1990a) included *M. aurantiacus* within *M. vitellinus*, separate from *M. manacus*, whilst Remsen *et al.* (2009) continued to unite all *Manacus* populations within a single species. Salaman *et al.* (2008, 2009) too continued to regard *M. vitellinus* as a subspecies of *M. manacus*. Genetic data reveal *M. vitellinus* to be a monophyletic grouping sister to *M. manacus*, but that it might be better to consider west Andean populations of the latter species as conspecific with *M. vitellinus* (Brumfield and Braun 2001, Brumfield *et al.* 2008). To date, efforts to date the divergence between *M. vitellinus* and *M. manacus* have proven unsuccessful, but it seems probable that western and eastern populations of *M. manacus* diverged later than *M. vitellinus* (Brumfield *et al.* 2008). However, Brumfield and his colleagues have identified that there is ongoing gene flow between the two allospecies (as evidenced by the hybrid zones discussed above), whereas there is none between eastern and western *M. manacus*. Further adding to the complicated taxonomic history of many *Manacus* populations, the hybrid swarm in northwest Panama was originally described as a species, '*M. cerritus*' (Peters 1927), but thereafter was treated as a subspecies of the present species (AOU 1983). See also Description and under White-collared Manakin. The following subspecies are currently recognised. **M. v. vitellinus** (Gould's Manakin) occurs through much of Panama, from central Bocas del Toro, then into extreme northwest Colombia, in northern Chocó on the lower Río Atrato and along the Golfo de Urabá as far east as Necolí, in northern dpto. Antioquia (Haffer 1959). Small differences have been noted between Colombian *M. v. vitellinus* and Panamanian birds (Haffer 1959). **M. v. amitinus** Wetmore, 1959, is confined to the Isla Escudo de Veraguas, Bocas del Toro, Panama, and is generally very similar to the nominate race, other than in being obviously larger (see Measurements). Furthermore, the green parts of the plumage in males are reportedly darker (Wetmore 1972), as apparently are females and immatures. **M. v. milleri** Chapman, 1915 (Miller's Bearded Manakin), occurs in northwest Colombia, through Antioquia, Córdoba and Bolívar, from the Río Sinú valley to the lower Río Cauca and the middle Río Magdalena. Although Snow (2004b) considered that this race does not differ noticeably from nominate *vitellinus*, Restall *et al.* (2006) described males as having the yellow of the face, breast and collar brighter and more lemon-coloured than in *vitellinus*, whilst the belly, upper and undertail-coverts are paler olive-green washed yellow. Chapman (1915) further considered the female to be also paler below, having the central abdomen, in particular, yellower. (Anciães and Peterson 2006 referred to this form as Milleri Bearded Manakin, but given that the taxon was named for Leo E. Miller it should properly be called Miller's. This and the next form are sometimes collectively known as Greenish-bellied Manakin.) **M. v. viridiventris** Griscom, 1929 (Lemon-throated Manakin), is distributed in western Colombia from central Chocó and northwest Antioquia on the east side of the upper Río Cauca valley and south to the Río Dagua in western Valle and southwest Cauca (Hilty and Brown 1986). Snow (2004b) considered that this form can be distinguished from *M. v. milleri* and *M. v. vitellinus* by its brighter lemon-yellow throat, but Restall *et al.* (2006) disagreed, considering the yellow to be more orange-toned and the belly to be more solid green.

VOICE The species' voice and mechanical sounds are generally very similar to those of White-bearded Manakin. The commonest vocalisations involve a clear *chée-pooh* and a slightly trilled *peerr*. As in other *Manacus* species, the males vocalise most intensely should a female approach their court. The species' vocalisations (from Colombia) are featured on the following commercial audio compilations: Álvarez-Rebolledo and Córdoba-Córdoba (2002) and Alvarez *et al.* (2007); in addition, a range of recordings of the subspecies *vitellinus* from Panama are available online at www.xeno-canto.org.

NATURAL HISTORY Very similar in all respects to that of congenerics: except at the display grounds, the species is generally found alone and can be shy and difficult to see within the dense undergrowth (Wetmore 1972). Rather remarkably, the most detailed general study of the species' ecology remains that by Chapman (1935) based on observations in Panama's Canal Zone. Vleck and Vleck (1979) and Bucher and Worthington (1982) found that this species, and Red-capped Manakin *Pipra mentalis*, reduce their metabolic rates when resting, e.g. overnight, during which period body temperature may be lowered significantly. Currently, Golden-collared Manakin is being used as a focal species in studies of brain adaptations and evolution in relation to complex displays by Lainy Day and Barney Schlinger, among others (see, e.g., Schultz and Schlinger 1999, Saldanha *et al.* 2000, Schlinger *et al.* 2001, Schultz *et al.* 2001, Day *et al.* 2007, 2008).

FOOD AND FEEDING Like other *Manacus* species, Golden-collared Manakin feeds predominantly in the understorey taking small fruits and insects using a short-range sally-hover movement. Fruits of at least 38 species of plants are known in the species' diet, with species of Araceae, Dillineaceae, Melastomataceae and Rubiaceae particularly favoured (Worthington 1982, Moermond and Denslow 1985). In central Panama, Poulin *et al.* (1999) found that *M. vitellinus* takes at least 18 species of the genera *Miconia* (Melastomataceae) and *Psychotria* (Rubiaceae) alone, while Leck (1972) noted the mistletoe *Oryctanthus occidentalis* (Loranthaceae) in the species' diet.

DISPLAY The species' high-speed acrobatic displays are generally very similar to those of other *Manacus*, especially White-bearded Manakin, although it lacks the 'fanning' display of the latter species (Snow 1962a). Detailed analyses using high-speed videography have shown that male displays require an amazing accuracy in neuromuscular coordination. Females mate preferentially with males able to perform their displays at a faster pace and yet maintain perfect control of their posture (Fusani 2010). Leks of Golden-collared Manakin generally number fewer than 20 males, with Chapman (1935) counting six to 15 males, but sometimes as few as three, at display grounds in central Panama (see also Stein and Uy 2006). Willis and Eisenmann (1979) noted that at least one lek studied by Chapman was still in the same place >30 years later. Three to eight courts within each lek were found in central Panama (Chapman 1935, Uy and Endler 2004, Stein and Uy 2006). The arena is defended permanently by the court-owner. Each court-owning male removes the sticks and leaves from a small (*c.*1m) circular court surrounded by at least two and usually several small upright terms, amongst which the birds 'leap', performing an 'about-face' on landing, and accompanied by the 'snap-grunt' display (Chapman 1935). Uy and Endler (2004) recently demonstrated that by clearing the court, males of *M. vitellinus* (and doubtless other *Manacus*) increase the visual impact of their displays, because of the enhanced contrast against the cleared background devoid of leaf litter. Furthermore, the same authors also postulate that females might be less conspicuous as a result of the clearance work, making them less susceptible to predation when visiting the court (Uy and Endler 2004). As with other *Manacus*, male Golden-collared Manakins also occasionally crouch with the head retracted, the body swaying and wings beating, and the throat-feathers splayed forwards reaching in front of the bill-tip (see photograph in Snow 2004b: 131). As in others of the genus, after a female arrives at the court (usually up to 2m above it), both sexes perform coordinated criss-crossing flights between perches, until the female lands on the 'mating' perch waiting for the male to approach. The male lands below her, with the 'beard' extended and the wings beating, before dropping to the ground and bouncing upwards to perch above the female in a single 'lightning' movement, before then sliding down the perch to copulate with her, at which point the male has one foot on the perch and one on the female's back. However, females may visit several courts within an arena before deciding to engage with a male and copulate. Stein and Uy (2006) analysed male mating success and found that it could be related to lek centrality, male body size and plumage brightness, but plumage is apparently the overall best predictor of mating success. At least in Colombia, the species displays all year (Hilty and Brown 1986), but displays (and copulations) show notable peaks in the early morning (06.00–08.00hrs) and early to mid afternoon (13.00–15.00hrs) (Stein and Uy 2006).

BREEDING Like all species of manakins, the female alone constructs the nest and tends the young. Clutch size is typically two eggs and the nest is placed 0.6–1.5m above the ground. Stone (1918) briefly described the nest and eggs of this species (*M. v. vitellinus*), based on observations made in mid April and early May in Panama's Canal Zone. Like other manakin nests, Stone described that of this species as being a frail, shallow cup constructed of plant bark, hair-like rootlets and grass stalks, and placed *c*.1.5m above the ground. Additional data, published subsequently, have revealed that rootlets and fungal hyphae are the principal nest constituents, although finer material can be used as lining, and spiderwebs are used to attach the nest to the horizontal fork in which it is slung. The eggs described by Stone were greyish, streaked longitudinally in varying shades of brown. Golden-collared Manakin has elliptical to long elliptical-shaped eggs, which are generally similar to those of *M. manacus* (Chapman 1935). Wetmore (1972) mentioned additional eggs found in the Canal Zone at the end of March as being pale buff in ground colour, streaked and blotched longitudinally with dull reddish-brown or greyish-brown, forming a slight wreath at the larger end. Those belonging to *M. v. milleri* are similar, being buffy-white with cinnamon to chocolate-brown and greyish-brown markings of varying intensity. Egg measurements were presented by Stone (1918), Schönwetter (1969) and Wetmore (1972). The incubation period was 19 days at one nest (J. Van Tyne *in* Chapman 1935) and fledging reportedly takes 13–15 days (Worthington 1982). Concerning seasonality, Wetmore

(1972) considered that the breeding season in Panama extends from late February to August based on nests with eggs (cf. Willis and Eisenmann 1979), which is supported by the fact that rather few of those examined on Cerro Pirre, Darién, Panama, in July and August appeared to be in breeding condition (Robbins *et al.* 1985). In northwest Colombia, the species has been found in breeding condition in February–May (M. A. Carriker *in* Haffer 1975) and, further south, in dpto. Valle, a female with a dependent juvenile has been observed in early September (Hilty and Brown 1986).

STATUS Golden-collared Manakin is currently treated as Least Concern by BirdLife International (2004, 2008), which estimated the species' range at 119,000km^2 and considered its population to be currently stable. Nevertheless, Anciães and Peterson (2006) predicted that the species was likely to be rather badly affected by predicted levels of climate change and their effects on the species' habitat. These authors separately evaluated the effects on *M. v. viridiventris* (much less severe) and *M. v. milleri* (extremely severe). Wetmore (1972) considered *M. v. amitinus* to be amongst the most abundant bird species present on Isla Escudo de Veraguas, and *M. v. vitellinus* seems to be generally common across mainland Panama, perhaps most especially in the vicinity of the Canal (Ridgely and Gwynne 1976). Golden-collared Manakin is known from a number of protected areas throughout its range, including the following: Soberanía National Park, Panama (Poulin *et al.* 1999, McDonald *et al.* 2001), and Reserva Natural Tambito and Los Katios National Park, Colombia (Wheatley 1994, Donegan and Dávalos 1999).

REFERENCES Álvarez-Rebolledo and Córdoba-Córdoba (2002), Alvarez *et al.* (2007), Anciães and Peterson (2006, 2009), AOU (1983, 1998), Bartholomew *et al.* (1983), BirdLife International (2004, 2008), Brumfield (1999), Brumfield and Braun (2001), Brumfield *et al.* (2008), Bucher and Worthington (1982), Burton (1975), Chapman (1915, 1917, 1935), Cracraft (1985), Cooper (1999), Day *et al.* (2006, 2007), Dickinson (2003), Donegan and Dávalos (1999), Dunning (2008), Fusani (2010), Fusani *et al.* (2007), Gill and Wright (2006), Greenway (1987), Haffer (1959, 1967a, 1975), Hellmayr (1911, 1929b), Hilty (1997), Hilty and Brown (1986), Holland and Shorey (2004), Leck (1972), Lowe (1942), McDonald *et al.* (2001), Moermond and Denslow (1985), Parsons *et al.* (1993, 1994), Peters (1927), Piertney *et al.* (2002), Poulin *et al.* (1999), Prum (1990a), Remsen *et al.* (2009), Restall *et al.* (2006), Ridgely and Greenfield (2001), Ridgely and Gwynne (1976, 1989), Ridgely and Tudor (1994, 2009), Robbins *et al.* (1985), Robinson *et al.* (2000a), Salaman *et al.* (2008, 2009), Saldanha *et al.* (2000), Schlinger (2010), Schlinger *et al.* (2001, 2010), Schönwetter (1969), Schultz and Schlinger (1999), Schultz *et al.* (2001), Sibley and Monroe (1990), Snow (1962a, 1975, 1979b, 2004b), Stein and Uy (2006), Stiles and Skutch (1989), Stone (1918), Stotz *et al.* (1996), Strauch (1977), Tori *et al.* (2008), Uy and Endler (2004), Uy and Stein (2007), Vleck and Vleck (1979), Wetmore (1972), Wheatley (1994), Wheatley and Brewer (2001), Willis and Eisenmann (1979), Worthington (1982, 1989), Yuri *et al.* (2009).

Golden-collared Manakin *Manacus vitellinus*. **Fig. 1**. Male, Canal Zone, Panama, November 2005 (*Mike Danzenbaker*). **Fig. 2**. Male, Soberanía National Park, Colón, central Panama, December (*Nick Athanas / Tropical Birding*). This taxon ranges south to western Colombia, where hybrids with White-bearded Manakin *M. manacus* have been reported on several occasions (see text). **Fig. 3**. Female, central Panama, February (*Peter Burke*). Note the bright orange legs just visible in this photo, which should identify this species versus most other Pipridae in range. However, bear in mind that females of this species and White-bearded Manakin *M. manacus* are likely to be inseparable where they overlap.

WHITE-BEARDED MANAKIN
Manacus manacus   Plate 6

Pipra manacus **Linnaeus, 1766**, *Syst. Nat.* 12th edn. 1: 340, based on Edwards, 1764, *Glean. Nat. Hist.* 1: 107, pl. 260, and Brisson, 1760, *Orn.* 4: 442, Surinam

One of the commonest manakins, White-bearded Manakin positively favours areas of second growth, where its 'firecracker' display sounds are one of the most distinctive 'voices' of the forest. Our knowledge of this stunning manakin still owes much to the efforts of David Snow and Alan Lill, whose research into this species on Trinidad enabled Lack (1966, 1968) to develop some of his theories as to how tropical avian frugivores are able to 'free' males from the vast majority of reproductive duties.

IDENTIFICATION 10.6–14.4cm. Over the greater part of South America, including on Trinidad, White-bearded is the only *Manacus* manakin, making recognition in all plumages generally straightforward. The males are wholly unique and readily identifiable, as no other manakin is the same size and shape, with the same pattern of almost equal amounts of black and white in the plumage. Females are perhaps less immediately identifiable, but most other species of Pipridae with which there is geographical overlap are smaller, less confined to the understorey and many do not have orange legs (e.g. female *Pipra* and *Lepidothrix*). There is also overlap with several species of *Chiroxiphia*, for example Blue-backed Manakin *C. pareola* in parts of Amazonia, Lance-tailed Manakin *C. lanceolata* in parts of Colombia and northwest Venezuela, and Blue Manakin *C. caudata* in the Atlantic Forest. All of these are slightly larger and both of the two last-named have tail shapes that mirror those of their males. Female Blue-backed Manakin has generally greener upperparts, with a shorter tail and on average marginally paler legs. There is also some geographical overlap with Helmeted Manakin *Antilophia galeata*, but females of the latter are obviously larger, obviously duller-plumaged and have a unique head shape. Only in parts of western Colombia is White-bearded Manakin replaced by Golden-collared Manakin *M. vitellinus* and at fewer than a handful of known localities these two species hybridise (see below). The morphological characters of such hybrids are discussed under the latter species. Compared with female Golden-collared Manakin, same-sex White-bearded Manakin is less yellow below, while male *M. vitellinus* is always much yellower over the underparts than any race of *M. manacus*.

DISTRIBUTION Widespread over the northern two-thirds of South America, White-bearded Manakin is one of the most frequently observed Pipridae over the majority of its range. In mainland South America, the species occurs from northern Colombia, where it ranges from the mouth of the Rio Sinú in Cordoba east to Guajira and the Sierra de Perijá, and south to the lower Cauca Valley, at Puerto Valdivia in dpto. Antioquia and the upper Magdalena Valley in dpto. Tolima (Chapman 1917, Todd and Carriker 1922, Hilty and Brown 1986), as well as throughout the lowlands and foothills of the east of the country. It also reappears in south-west Colombia, in southwest dpto. Cauca, from where it ranges south throughout much of western Ecuador as far as dpto. Tumbes in extreme northeast Peru (Wiedenfeld *et al.* 1985, Hilty and Brown 1986, Ridgely and Greenfield 2001, Schulenberg *et al.* 2007). White-bearded Manakin is also found in northwest Venezuela, in Zulia, on the west

slope of the Andes from Trujillo to Táchira and on the east slope from Barinas to Táchira (Hilty 2003). It is also found throughout much of southern Venezuela, except eastern and northeast Bolívar (Hilty 2003), as well as over much of the Guianas (Snyder 1966, Tostain *et al.* 1992, Ottema *et al.* 2009), throughout northern Brazil north of the Amazon (Pinto 1944, Sick 1997), over eastern Ecuador (Ridgely and Greenfield 2001) and eastern Peru south to southern dpto. Loreto and reappearing in dpto. Madre de Dios (Schulenberg *et al.* 2007). In northern Bolivia, White-bearded Manakin has been recorded from dptos. Pando, La Paz, Beni and Santa Cruz (Bates *et al.* 1989, Remsen and Traylor 1989, Maillard *et al.* 2007, Vidoz *et al.* 2010). In Amazonian Brazil, south of the river, it reaches east to northern Maranhão and south to northern Tocantins (Hidasi 1998), northern and western Mato Grosso and Rondônia (Sick 1997). White-bearded Manakin also reappears in eastern Brazil. Here it occurs in the Atlantic Forest from the littoral of Rio Grande do Norte, Paraíba and Pernambuco south to northernmost Rio Grande do Sul, and inland as far as Minas Gerais, the Distrito Federal and southeastern Mato Grosso (Pinto 1944, Berla 1946, Lamm 1948, Scherer-Neto and Straube 1995, Rosário 1996, Sick 1997, Bencke *et al.* 2000, Mähler Junior *et al.* 2007, Oliveira Junior *et al.* 2008). *M. manacus* is also present on at least some near-shore islands off southeast Brazil (Marsden *et al.* 2003, Clausi 2005). At the southern edge of its range, the species reaches southeast Paraguay, where it is exclusively found east of the Río Paraguay, in Alto Paraná and Central Paraguay (Hayes 1995, Lowen *et al.* 1996) and extreme northeast Argentina in Misiones (Mazar Barnett and Pearman 2001). There is a population on the island of Trinidad, off northeast South America, where it is a common resident (ffrench 1991, Kenefick *et al.* 2007), and the species also occurs on the Bocas Islands, which lie between Trinidad and Venezuela's Paria Peninsula (Hayes and Samad 2002). White-bearded Manakin principally occurs below 1,000m, but there are old records in south-west Ecuador as high as 1,300m (Ridgely and Greenfield 2001) and *M. manacus* occurs locally to 1,700m in the Serranía de Yariguíes, eastern Colombia (Donegan *et al.* 2010) and to 1,900m elsewhere in the same country (Hilty and Brown 1986).

MOVEMENTS Resident and largely sedentary, especially adult males and during the breeding season. Snow and Lill (1974) recorded remarkable site faithfulness amongst males in the Arima Valley on Trinidad, although Höglund and Shorey (2003) found evidence for limited male dispersal in northern Trinidad. The latter authors revealed that levels of kinship declined with distance from a given lek. The only other detailed data are from French Guiana, where Théry (1990c) found that during the moulting period adults have a home range of up to several hundred hectares and two immature males wandered 20.1 and 20.3ha. However, during the breeding period two adult males ranged no further than over 2.1 and 2.5ha (i.e. their display area and a single bathing site). Two females, in contrast, had breeding-season home ranges of 13.0 and 14.1ha, thereby encompassing the territories of several males and multiple bathing sites.

HABITAT White-bearded Manakin is reliant on second-growth areas, especially where there is dense undergrowth and often beside streams, including gallery forests and islands of forest in savanna regions (Tostain *et al.* 1992, Robbins *et al.* 2004, Santos and Silva 2007, Santos *et al.* 2010) and *restinga* forest in the littoral of south-east Brazil (Cestari *et al.* 2010). In Surinam and French Guiana, it is often found on the scrubby forested slopes of granitic inselbergs, where *Clusia* spp. (Clusiaceae) are often a dominant part of the vegetation (Olson and McDowell 1983, Krijger *et al.* 1994). In southeast Peru and northwest Bolivia, *M. m. expectatus* lives mainly in flooded or riverine forest and palm swamp (J. A. Tobias *in litt.* 2010). In general, the species prefers shrubby forest and edge habitats, including overgrown plantations, e.g. of bananas or coffee, but in Amazonia also inhabits modified *várzea* and *caatingas* (Novaes 1970; MNRJ).

DESCRIPTION The general structure is very similar to that of congeners. The sexes differ. Adult males have the wing-feathers somewhat modified, with the outermost four primaries very narrow and stiff over the distal half and the other remiges possess noticeably thickened and bowed shafts and stiff outer webs, this adaptation being used to control the snapping and other mechanical sounds produced by the wings. As in other *Manacus*, the throat-feathers are somewhat elongated and can be projected forwards in display. The culmen is reasonably well arched, often with a hooked tip in both sexes, and the nostrils are comparatively large for the bird's overall size. The nominate race is described here. *Adult male.* – Crown and nape level to the eye are deep black, contrasting beautifully with the clean white face, throat, ear-coverts and neck-collar, while the rest of the underparts are also largely white, as far as the undertail-coverts. However, in close views, a grey cast might be visible over the flanks and belly, and very fine grey-black tips might be evident to the ear-coverts and neck-collar. With the exception of some feathers on the upper mantle, the lesser and some median wing-coverts, which are white, the mantle, back, wings and tail are also deep black, offering slight contrast to the mid to dark grey rump and uppertail-coverts. *Adult female.* – The upperparts are principally olive-green, becoming paler and greyer over the underparts, especially over the throat and belly. *Juvenile.* – As is typical of the genus and the family, this plumage is

generally considered to be more or less identical to that of the adult female, although in the hand, and perhaps the field, it might be separated on the basis of the fluffier body-feathers. Young males frequently have dark shaft-streaks to the crown-feathers (MNRJ). Immature males acquire some adult feathers following the first moult when a few months old, and they are reported to gain full adult plumage when one year old (Snow 2004b). Oniki and Willis (1983) provided brief details concerning the development of the young in the nest. *Moult.* – Very few published data. Hilty (2003) considered feather renewal to be mainly late year in Venezuela. None of those examined from the Atlantic Forest region collected between July and October was in moult, but a female taken in March was in post-juvenile moult and another female from April was replacing the axillaries (MNRJ). *Hybrids.* – The existence of a zone of hybridisation, perhaps as a result of ongoing deforestation at relevant altitudes, is known between *M. vitellinus* and *M. manacus* in the middle Cauca Valley in Colombia (cf. E. O. Willis *in* Wetmore 1972). Haffer (1967a) also pointed to a second zone of contact: Olivares (1958) collected both *M. manacus* and *M. vitellinus* at Guapí in southwest Cauca, and from even further south, at Paramba, in Esmeraldas, northwest Ecuador, Hellmayr (1929b: 70) had already revealed the existence of an apparently intermediate specimen. For more details see the account for *M. vitellinus*. More remarkably, Gyldenstolpe (1951: 241–2) described and depicted an exceptional specimen taken at Redempção on the Rio Purus, in western Brazil, apparently a male hybrid Wire-tailed Manakin *Pipra filicauda* × White-bearded Manakin: full details are presented in the account for Wire-tailed Manakin. A third form, '*Manacus coronatus*' (originally '*Chiromachaeris coronata*'), a name based on a specimen from 'Bogotá', was already noted by Hellmayr (1929b: 75) to be very probably a hybrid between Golden-headed Manakin and White-bearded Manakin *M. manacus*. Sibley (1957) and Parkes (1961) seconded this view. *Bare parts.* – The irides are various shades of brown to black (the latter seemingly more prevalent in males) and occasionally more yellowish (in young), while the legs and feet are reddish-orange or orange, with yellow to orange soles. Some, perhaps especially females and young, can have the legs and feet lemon-yellow, ochraceous or mustard-coloured. The bill is usually blackish over the maxilla with the mandible and cutting edges typically greyer (even bluish-grey), or even rose- to horn-coloured at the base of the mandible (Junge and Mees 1958, Novaes 1978, 1980, Wiedenfeld *et al.* 1985, Snow 2004b, Krabbe 2007; FMNH; MNRJ).

MEASUREMENTS *M. m. abditivus* (ProAves unpubl. data: northern Colombia): wing of male (*n* = 25) 47–51mm, wing of female (*n* = 22) 47–53mm (live birds). Hellmayr (1929b) presented additional mensural data for this race (sample sizes unstated). *M. m. flaveolus* (Hellmayr 1929b: upper Magdalena Valley, Colombia): wing of male (*n* = unknown) 49–53mm; tail of male (*n* = unknown) 27–31mm. *M. m. bangsi* (Hellmayr 1929b: southwest Colombia): wing of male (*n* = unknown) 52–53mm; tail of male (*n* = unknown) 25.5–27.0mm. *M. m. leucochlamys* (FMNH: Los Ríos, Ecuador): wing of male (*n* = 3) 56–58mm, wing of female (*n* = 3) 55.0–56.5mm; tail of male (*n* = 3) 34.0–35.5mm, tail of female (*n* = 3) 33.0–37.5mm; bill of male (*n* = 3) 12.47–12.97mm, bill of female (*n* = 3) 12.33–12.80mm; tarsus of male (*n* = 3) 19.58–21.25mm, tarsus of female (*n* = 3) 19.94–20.25mm. Additionally, J. Hornbuckle (unpubl. data: Esmeraldas, Ecuador): wing of female (*n* = 1) 58mm (live bird). Hellmayr

(1929b) published additional mensural data pertaining to this race. *M. m. interior* (Hellmayr 1929b: Venezuela, eastern Ecuador and northwest Brazil): wing of male (*n* = unknown) 52–55mm; tail of male (*n* = unknown) 31–34mm. *M. m. trinitatis* (CUMZ; Junge and Mees 1958: Trinidad): wing of male (*n* = 7) 55–56mm, wing of female (*n* = 7) 54–59mm; tail of male (*n* = 7) 28.5–33.0mm, tail of female (*n* = 7) 32–35mm; bill of male (*n* = 2) 11.95–12.41mm; tarsus of male (*n* = 7) 16.82–22.32mm, tarsus of female (*n* = 7) 18–21mm. Additional mensural data were presented by Hellmayr (1929b). *M. m. umbrosus* (Friedmann 1944: Cerro Yapacana, southern Venezuela): wing of male (*n* = 6) 52–54mm; tail of male (*n* = 6) 30–32mm; bill of male (*n* = 6) 11.9–12.5mm. *M. m. manacus* (CUMZ; MNRJ: Brazil north of the Amazon, and Guyana): wing of male (*n* = 13) 51.0–57.5mm, wing of female (*n* = 4) 53.5–55.0mm; tail of male (*n* = 13) 30–37mm, tail of female (*n* = 4) 31–35mm; bill of male (*n* = 13) 10.94–12.67mm, bill of female (*n* = 4) 12.44–13.38mm; tarsus of male (*n* = 4) 19.14–20.97mm, tarsus of female (*n* = 3) 16.85–18.76mm. *M. m. expectatus* (Gyldenstolpe 1945: upper Rio Juruá, Amazonas, Brazil): wing of male (*n* = 2) 52mm, wing of female (*n* = 1) 54mm; tail of male (*n* = 2) 29mm, tail of female (*n* = 1) 28mm; bill of male (*n* = 2) 9.5–9.8mm, bill of female (*n* = 1) 9.5mm; tarsus of male (*n* = 2) 18mm, tarsus of female (*n* = 1) 17mm. *M. m. subpurus* (MNRJ: Rondônia, Brazil): wing of female (*n* = 1) 51.5mm; tail of female (*n* = 1) 30mm; bill of female (*n* = 1) 11.42mm. Hellmayr (1929b) and Oniki and Willis (1999) listed additional mensural data for this race (males and sexes combined, respectively). *M. m. purus* (MNRJ: southern Amazonas and Pará, Brazil): wing of male (*n* = 13) 50.5–55.0mm, wing of female (*n* = 3) 52–55mm; tail of male (*n* = 13) 28–35mm, tail of female (*n* = 3) 30–35mm; bill of male (*n* = 13) 10.81–14.06mm, bill of female (*n* = 3) 11.75–11.96mm. *M. m. purissimus* (CUMZ; FMNH; MNRJ: eastern Pará, Maranhão and Tocantins, Brazil): wing of male (*n* = 10) 52.0–58.5mm, wing of female (*n* = 6) 49–55mm; tail of male (*n* = 10) 32–39mm, tail of female (*n* = 6) 31–40mm; bill of male (*n* = 10) 10.66–12.58mm, bill of female (*n* = 6) 11.33–12.41mm; tarsus of male (*n* = 7) 19.54–20.42mm, tarsus of female (*n* = 5) 17.31–20.35mm. *M. m. gutturosus* (MNRJ: Bahia, Distrito Federal, Espírito Santo, Minas Gerais, Paraíba, Pernambuco, Rio de Janeiro and São Paulo, Brazil): wing of male (*n* = 34) 49.5–55.0mm, wing of female (*n* = 31) 51–57mm; tail of male (*n* = 35) 31–40mm, tail of female (*n* = 31) 31–41mm; bill of male (*n* = 35) 11.68–14.13mm, bill of female (*n* = 31) 11.64–13.37mm. Weight: *M. m. abditivus*: 13.5–17.0g (males), 10–16g (females) (ProAves unpubl. data). *M. m. flaveolus*: 12–17g (three males), 12–18g (three females) (MVZ). *M. m. leucochlamys*: 13.3–18.9g (two males), 12.6–18.7g (five females) (FMNH; J. Hornbuckle unpubl. data). *M. m. interior*: 15.80–19.75g (males), 12.9–17.6g (FMNH; MVZ). *M. m. trinitatis*: 12.5–21.0g (males), 16.0–17.5g (females) (Junge and Mees 1958, Snow 1962a, 2004b; MVZ). Lill (1975) also provided nestling weights for this subspecies. *M. m. manacus*: 14–20g (males), 11–20g (females) (Haverschmidt 1948, 1952, Olson and McDowell 1983, Dick *et al.* 1984, Snow 2004b; FMNH; MNRJ; MVZ). *M. m. subpurus*: 15.7g (one male), 13.2–15.0g (four females) (Bates *et al.* 1989, Snow 2004b; MNRJ). Oniki and Willis (1999) listed weights for this race (sexes combined) as 14.5–17.0g. *M. m. purus*: 13.5g (one female) (MNRJ). *M. m. longibarbatus*: 14.8–17.2g (males), 12.8–16.2g (females) (Fry 1970). *M. m. purissimus*: 10–13g (three females) (Silva *et al.* 1990). *M. m. gutturosus*: 13–19g (males), 12.0–18.5g

(females) (Castro Astor *et al.* 1997, Faria and Paula 2008; FMNH; DZUFMG; MNRJ). Magalhães *et al.* (2007) listed an upper weight limit of 24g for the last-named subspecies, but did not break down their mass data by sex.

GEOGRAPHICAL VARIATION Polytypic with 15 subspecies generally recognised under modern treatments (see, e.g., Dickinson 2003, Snow 2004b), although the trans-Andean populations are sister to the *M. vitellinus* allospecies rather than to *M. manacus* east of the Andes (Brumfield and Braun 2001). Although Remsen *et al.* (2009) suggest the possibility of recognising trans- and cis-Andean populations of *M. manacus* specifically, lumping the trans-Andean taxa within *M. vitellinus* might be the most appropriate option when considering all of the available data. Racial differences revolve around mainly relative sizes, the width of the white neck-collar and the extent of any grey or other tones to the underparts. Many subspecies are only weakly distinguished and very few, if any, can be reliably separated in female plumage. Thus the remarks that follow refer solely to males unless otherwise stated. We concur with Ridgely and Greenfield (2001) that probably all of those populations west of the Andes could be treated under a single name, for which *M. m. bangsi* would have priority, on the basis of page (all three names were described by Chapman, in two different publications). Zimmer (1936) already noted examples of intergrades between these populations. To date, genetic data (Brumfield and Braun 2001, Höglund and Shorey 2004) have not revealed any significant differentiation amongst cis-Andean populations, other than the unsurprising findings that *M. m. trinitatis* (of Trinidad) differs from *M. m. manacus*, and that these two plus *M. m. interior* differ from southern Amazonian populations. Höglund and Shorey (2001) speculated that both *M. m. trinitatis* and *M. m. gutturosus* (of the Atlantic Forest) might have been isolated for *c.*10,000 years, but Brumfield *et al.* (2008) suggested that populations either side of the Amazon, and in the Atlantic Forest, diverged from one another earlier than this. *M. m. abditivus* Bangs, 1899, of northern Colombia, south to the lower Cauca Valley and the lower to middle Magdalena Valley, is reported to have the throat-feathers very long and stiff. Restall *et al.* (2006) reported it to be very small, but this claim seems dubious to us. Some authors (e.g. Phelps 1944) considered that this race reaches extreme northwest Venezuela. *M. m. flaveolus* Cassin, 1851, is restricted to the upper Magdalena Valley of central Colombia, and has the throat and collar creamy yellow, rather than pure white. Chapman (1917) noted that some specimens from the southernmost range of *M. m. abditivus* show evidence of intergradation into *M. m. flaveolus*, between Malena and Honda (cf. also Todd and Carriker 1922). A 'Bogotá' specimen held in the Cambridge University Museum of Zoology (27/Pip/10/e/9) also seems representative of this trend. *M. m. bangsi* Chapman, 1914, is found in southwest Colombia, from southwest Cauca, to extreme northwest Ecuador, in northern Esmeraldas and Imbabura. This subspecies is considered to be small and grey-bellied with a narrow white neck-collar (Snow 2004b, Restall *et al.* 2006). *M. m. leucochlamys* Chapman, 1914, is endemic to Ecuador, where it occurs from western Esmeraldas and Pichincha south to northern Guayas, and is distinguished from the last-named subspecies by its broader white neck-collar extending onto the mantle and white belly. This taxon is easily found at the Río Silanche reserve in Pichincha province (GMK pers. obs.). *M. m. maximus* Chapman, 1924, replaces the previous subspecies in southwest Ecuador, in eastern Guayas and westernmost Chimborazo south to western Loja, and thereafter into extreme northwest Peru, in Tumbes. As befits its name, this subspecies is reportedly larger than *M. m. leucochlamys* with longer throat- and neck-feathers. *M. m. interior* Chapman, 1914, is a very wide-ranging subspecies, being found across much of Venezuela, the eastern lowlands of Colombia, eastern Ecuador, northeast Peru and northwest Brazil on the upper Rio Negro. In this subspecies, the rump and uppertail-coverts are paler grey than in the nominate. Restall *et al.* (2006) considered it to be diagnosable from *M. m. umbrosus* by its smaller cap. Phelps (1944) treated the birds in the Sierra de Perijá as *M. m. abditivus*, but Hilty (2003) considered that all those populations in northern Venezuela as *M. m. interior*. *M. m. trinitatis* (E. Hartert, 1912) is endemic to the island of Trinidad, and is defined by its large size and very broad white neck-collar, while the female is stated to be either yellower or paler below (Snow 2004b, Restall *et al.* 2006). Olson and McDowell (1983) noted that wing length of adults on Trinidad is on average almost 2mm longer than in mainland *M. m. manacus* in Surinam. *M. m. umbrosus* Friedmann, 1944, is confined to a limited area of southern Venezuela, on the Cerro Yapacana in the upper Orinoco in central Amazonas. It is considered generally similar to *M. m. interior* but has the posterior underparts, over the lower breast to the undertail-coverts, much darker grey, becoming slate grey on the thighs and the undertail-coverts. The neckband is also heavily suffused with grey (Friedmann 1944). Restall *et al.* (2006) stated it to be very similar to *M. m. bangsi* of the Chocó region, but that the white and grey parts of the underparts are less cleanly separated. *M. m. manacus* is found over the Guianas, southern Venezuela in the drainage of the Río Casiquiare (southern Amazonas), as well as in northeast Brazil north of the lower Amazon. Salaman *et al.* (2009) speculated that this race might also be present in the extreme northeast of the Colombian Amazon. It is described above. Compared with other races in northern South America, Restall *et al.* (2006) considered it to be especially marked by its fairly narrow neck-collar and more extensive black cap. *M. m. expectatus* Gyldenstolpe, 1941, occurs in western Brazil on the Rio Juruá and also in adjacent northeast Peru south of the Amazon, in eastern dpto. Loreto and dpto. Madre de Dios (Schulenberg *et al.* 2007). We assume that it is also this race that occurs in northwest Bolivia in dptos. Pando and La Paz west of the Río Beni: it is worth remarking that Snow (1979b, 2004b) and Dickinson (2003) all erroneously omitted Bolivia from the species' range. *M. m. expectatus* is distinguished from geographically proximate subspecies in that the white neck-collar extends prominently over the upper mantle and smaller wing-coverts, sometimes discontinuously, but also rather solidly. In this region, it is probably the case that this subspecies and the next are separated by the Río Beni. *M. m. subpurus* Cherrie & Reichenberger, 1923, occurs over south-central Brazil, east of the Rio Madeira in southern Amazonas, Rondônia and east into western Mato Grosso, as well as in dpto. Santo Cruz, Bolivia. An adult male photographed at Guayaramerin, dpto. Beni (J. A. Tobias), also seems to belong to this form (Fig. 5). The rump is rather dark grey with a faint greyish wash over the breast and abdomen, more extensive and darker grey over the flanks and breast-sides, and white undertail-coverts. The range of *M. m. purus* Bangs, 1899, is slightly unclear, but it is found south of the lower Amazon in Brazil, from the lower Rio Madeira probably as far east as the Rio Xingu.

Compared with *M. m. subpurus*, it has less black on the upperparts, a paler grey rump area, no grey wash to the breast, and a paler and less extensive grey wash to the flanks. *M. m. longibarbatus* J. T. Zimmer, 1936, occurs from the right bank of the Rio Xingu east to the right bank of the Rio Tocantins, Pará (see also below), Brazil, south as far as northern Mato Grosso, and has longer throat-feathers than adjacent races (including the nominate and *M. m. purissimus*) with broader and purer white feathering on the upper mantle, a broader grey rump patch, white subterminal marks to the median and some greater wing-coverts, and paler grey thighs and belly. However, Pinto (1994), at least, declined to recognise this race, despite the fact that Zimmer (1936) also claimed that it had a shorter wingtip and slenderer outer primaries than those of the next race. The difficulties associated with ascribing birds in this region of the lower Amazon to subspecies was further illustrated by Zimmer (1936) himself, who noted birds from the right bank of the Xingu that approached nominate *manacus* in their features! *M. m. purissimus* Todd, 1928, is also endemic to Brazil, where it is found from the right bank of the Rio Tocantins, Pará, east to northern Maranhão (Hellmayr 1929a), and is whiter over the lower belly and thighs, while the wings are longer (with a broader outermost primary) and the throat-feathers are shorter. Zimmer (1936) noted the presence of both *longibarbatus* and *purissimus* from the vicinity of Baião (Pará), on the right bank of the Rio Tocantins near its mouth, which demands further explanation, unless *longibarbatus* is indeed best synonymized within the present subspecies. *M. m. gutturosus* (Desmarest, 1806) is endemic to the Atlantic Forest, where it is found from northeast Brazil south to southeast Mato Grosso and northernmost Rio Grande do Sul, as well as southeast Paraguay and northeastern Argentina. It is characterised by being darkest grey below (with the exception of *M. m. umbrosus*), with the grey tones extending from the breast to the ventral region.

VOICE Vocalisation and mechanical sounds closely recall those of other *Manacus*. During displays the commonest vocalisations are a loud high-pitched *chwee* and an even more excited *pee-you* or *chee-poo* at the onset of a bout of display (Snow 1962a), but a softer trilled *peerr* (which sounds plaintive) is also frequently given, including away from the display grounds. The male's wings produce a dry rustling sound in normal flight and the modified outer primaries (see Description) are also responsible for the loud wing-snaps and 'Bronx cheer' rolls that accompany the species' displays. The species' voice features on the following commercial audio compilations: Murphy (1991), Moore (1994, 1997), Boesman (1999, 2006a, 2006b, 2009), Mayer (2000), Jahn *et al.* (2002), Krabbe and Nilsson (2003), Remold (2003), Hammick (2004), Naka *et al.* (2008), Renaudier and Deroussen (2008) and Minns *et al.* (2009). No geographical variation in vocalisations has been reported to date, but calls from a wide variety of localities are archived online at www.xeno-canto.org.

NATURAL HISTORY Generally seen in loose groups, as males may even feed in loose association away from the leks (Hilty 2003). Like those of other *Manacus*, the display grounds of this species are amongst the most obvious to even relatively casual watchers because of the noise associated with them. That they are typically sited in accessible areas of scrubby forest, often close to roadsides and in other disturbed areas, merely heightens their attractiveness. In many ways, this is one of the easiest manakins to observe within its range. White-bearded Manakin is, unsurprisingly, a well-studied species in consequence. Whereas data for some *Pipra* and *Lepidothrix* species reveal a lack of relatedness amongst males at leks, Höglund and Shorey (2003) in their Trinidad study found high levels of kinship in White-bearded Manakins displaying together. Shorey *et al.* (2000) had already found that at two of the same leks, the males clustered into two separate groups of more closely related individuals. Some of the few available records of longevity in Pipridae are for this species, with reports of birds at least nine years old in the Brazilian Atlantic Forest (Scopel *et al.* 2005) and at least 14 years old on Trinidad (Lill 1974b, Snow and Lill 1974). Snow (1962a) also noted rather remarkable inter-annual survival in adult males of this species, in excess of 85% (but see Breeding for losses at nests).

FOOD AND FEEDING Like most manakins both insects and fruit are taken, the latter typically snatched in flight using a short-range (<75cm) sally-hover movement, although they are occasionally seized while perched. Insects are principally taken in flight. Most feeding is at very low levels in the undergrowth, sometimes in <50cm-tall herbaceous growth outside forest (GMK pers. obs.). The birds return either to the same perch or to a nearby perch. Feeding flights may be horizontal or venture upwards. The most detailed study was made on Trinidad, where Snow (1962a) recorded 66 species of fruit in the White-bearded Manakin's diet. Snow (1962a) recorded that the most important families were Melastomataceae (47%), Euphorbiaceae, Moraceae and Rubiaceae. Subsequent studies on the island have revealed the presence of 105 species belonging to 27 families in the diet (Snow 2004b: 123). In French Guiana, Théry (1990c) recorded even higher levels of dependence on Melastomataceae (65% in males and 57% in females). There are few other detailed studies, but Galetti and Pizo (1996) noted species of Ulmaceae, Rubiaceae, Meliaceae, Burseraceae, Araliaceae and Amaranthaceae being taken in southeast Brazil. In the same general region, Pineschi (1990) recorded fruit of a single species of *Rapanea* (Myrsinaceae) being consumed by *M. manacus*, and Carrano and Marins (2008) added *Symplocos uniflora* (Symplocaceae) to the species' diet. Concerning the species' insect and arthropod consumption, spiders (Araneae), ants (Formicidae), bugs (Hemiptera), beetles (Coleoptera), flies (Diptera), wasps (Hymenoptera) and termites (Isoptera), as well as larvae, have been all recorded being taken (Snow 1962a, Lopes *et al.* 2005, Lima *et al.* 2010). White-bearded Manakin is regularly recorded following army ants, taking insects disturbed by them (Willis 1984). In northern Brazil, Oniki and Willis (1983) mentioned that the young were fed fruits of *Guarea* sp. (Meliaceae) and *Byrsonima* sp. (Malpighiaceae), but Lill (1975) considered that insects are probably more important in the diet of nestlings (constituting on average 50%) than in that of adults.

DISPLAY In comparison with the leks of *Pipra* and *Lepidothrix* manakins, that of White-bearded Manakin is highly compact. Leks can number up to 60 males (Lill 1974a, Hilty 2003), but smaller numbers are more usual, e.g. 4–13 males in French Guiana (Théry 1992) or just 2–5 males in Surinam (Olson and McDowell 1983). On Trinidad, Snow (1962a) noted a mean 29 males at seven leks. However, smaller leks with up to 10–15 males also seem to be the rule in southeast Brazil (GMK pers. obs.). Each male displays within close range of the next, the individual display

courts being separated by just 0.9–4.6m on Trinidad (Snow 1962a) but 6.2–21.5m in Surinam (Olson and McDowell 1983). The overall dimensions of leks is also variable: a maximum of 18.3m × 9.2m on Trinidad (Snow 1962a), up to 548m² in Surinam (Olson and McDowell 1983) and 15–20m in diameter in French Guiana (Théry 1992, Krijger *et al.* 1994). Individual leks on Trinidad were also closer spaced than in Surinam, with an inter-lek distance of 371m versus 706m (Snow 1962a, Olson and McDowell 1983). Cestari *et al.* (2010) have recently reported males clearing and displaying at up to four so-called auxiliary arenas, up to 2.4m distant from each male's main arena, albeit only for very short periods of each day. Each male's court comprises a roughly circular patch of ground containing 2–4 narrow vertical stems among which the males display, following routines strongly akin to those described for the other members of the *Manacus* superspecies. The ground below the stems is cleared of leaves and other debris. The commonest display comprises low 'jumps' between the bases of the stems, combined with a loud wing-snap and an 'about-face' following each landing during which the elongated throat-feathers are projected even further forwards (as they are during all of the described displays). Occasionally, the males also 'jump' to the ground and then back to one of the stems, where it appears to 'crouch' with the head retracted into the neck, the body swaying and the wings rapidly beating and fanned. Whenever a female arrives at the court, at which point all of the adjacent males produce a cacophony of sound, the visited male will commence a series of jumps, which becomes coordinated with the female, as they cross to and fro in mid-air between the 'mating stem' and an adjacent perch. Eventually, when the female lands on the 'mating stem', the male 'jumps' down to the ground, then leaps back up onto the 'mating stem' above the female, before sliding down and landing on her back (this ritual is more or less identical to that in other *Manacus*). Displays can continue periodically for much of the day, with males spending very long periods of time continually at the lek (with just brief foraging sorties), but in Surinam, most copulation events were in the afternoon, between midday and 16.00hrs (Olson and McDowell 1983). On Trinidad and in Surinam, and doubtless elsewhere, a number of (alpha) males at each lek secure the majority of copulations (Lill 1974b, Olson and McDowell 1983). Skewed ratios in copulation success appear to be related to successful territory defence. Males seek to displace rival 'resident' territory-holding males and 'floating' males from nearby perches. Old males may remain in the vicinity of the lek for at least another year after ceasing to be reproductively active (Snow and Lill 1974).

BREEDING Like the nests of other manakins, that of *M. manacus* is a small, shallow open-cup structure of thinly woven rootlets, black fungal hyphae (*Marasmius* sp.) and in some nests dead leaves. There is a softer inner lining, which on Trinidad and northern Brazil is usually constituted of grass stems and fruit panicles of *Nepsera aquatica* (Melastomataceae) and the nest is usually, if not always, attached to the horizontal fork using spiderwebs (Todd and Carriker 1922, Oniki and Willis 1983, Castelino and Saibene 1989). Nests are often sited close to streams and are usually sited between 0.4 and 2.0m above the ground (Pinto 1953, Oniki and Willis 1983, Castelino and Saibene 1989, Castro Astor *et al.* 1997); these authors also provided nest dimensions. Oniki and Willis (1993) mentioned nests on *Theobroma cocoa* (Malvaceae) and *Licania kunthiana*

(Chrysobalanaceae) trees. The clutch size is two eggs as in all manakins, and the eggs are dull white to yellowish-white, sometimes with a slight hint of green, with very variable brown to grey or lavender markings either covering the entire egg or concentrated at the larger end (Ihering 1900, Todd and Carriker 1922, Snethlage 1928, Velho 1932, Hellebrekers 1942, Pinto 1953, Snow 1962a, Oniki and Willis 1983, Castelino and Saibene 1989, de la Peña 1989). Egg dimensions were presented by Todd and Carriker (1922), Velho (1932), Hellebrekers (1942), Pinto (1953), Oniki and Willis (1983), Castelino and Saibene (1989) and de la Peña (1989). The eggs are relatively large considering the size of the adult bird, and this is presumably yet one more adaptation to the single-parent form of parental care known in all manakins, whereby the chicks require less time in the nest between hatching and fledging (Lill 1975). Nestlings hatch either asynchronously or synchronously (with one or two days between hatching events), and the same is true of fledging at the same nest (Lill 1975), although Snow (1962a) considered that incubation would only commence once the second egg has been laid. Lill (1975) found no evidence for significant weight differences between the two chicks on hatching, even though he felt it probable that females must, at least occasionally, commence incubating once the first egg is laid. The same author also considered that because asynchronous and synchronous hatching is known in the same species in the same area, it could be that females are able to gauge the availability of food in advance, and regulate their incubation accordingly. By 'staggering' the nestlings hatching dates, the female reduces her workload to some extent, but might only do so if she considers that food availability might be reduced. The incubation period is 18–19 days and the young fledge in 12–15 days (Snow 1962a, Oniki and Willis 1983, Sick 1997). Females only depart the nest briefly to feed, and Lill (1975) presented information concerning growth rates in nestlings. On Trinidad, however, nest success is very low. Of 227 nests with eggs that were monitored, just 19% produced fledged young, with a mean 0.33 fledglings per nesting attempt (Snow 1962a). Many predation events are nocturnal (Lill 1975). However, females may attempt to breed up to five times per annum (Snow 1962a) and sometimes reuse material from an earlier nest; apparently, on Trinidad at least, there is considerable intra- and inter-specific competition (especially with Ochre-bellied Flycatcher *Mionectes oleagineus*) for nest material (Snow 1962a, Lill 1975). Castro Astor *et al.* (1997) noted that it is not only the eggs and nestlings that may be predated, as they reported a female *M. manacus* being taken on the nest by a boa constrictor *Corallus hortulanus*. Snow (1962a) predicted that snakes were major causes of egg and nestling losses on Trinidad, but did not observe any such cases. These remarkable rates of loss (which are common to at least some *Lepidothrix* and *Pipra* species) are compensated for by comparatively high inter-annual survival in adults (see Natural history). Females are capable of breeding at one year old and are known to be reproductively active until at least ten years old, whereas males probably do not breed until at least three years old but remain active until at least 12 years old (Snow and Lill 1974). Seasonality of breeding is reasonably well known. In northern Colombia, Allen (1905) reported on a mid-May nest found in the Sierra Nevada de Santa Marta, there are two May specimens in breeding condition from Antioquia (FMNH), and M. A. Carriker *in* Hilty and Brown (1986) collected six in breeding condition during July/August elsewhere in northern Colombia (all *M.*

m. abditivus). S. L. Hilty watched a female (*M. m. interior*) nest building in Amazonian Colombia in January (Hilty and Brown 1986). Others from this region of the country have been collected in breeding condition in January, April and May (FMNH). In the upper Magdalena Valley, multiple females of *M. m. flaveolus* have been collected in late January with brood patches and in October with eggs in the oviducts, respectively (MVZ). From southwest Ecuador, H. F. Greeney photographed an active nest in February (Fig. 10). In southern Venezuela (*M. m. umbrosus*) a male was collected in breeding condition at the end of March (Friedmann 1944). In eastern Peru, birds have been collected in breeding condition in August (MVZ). On Trinidad eggs are laid in January–September (exceptionally December), although the peak months are May and June in the early wet season (Snow 1962a, Lill 1974a, 1975). In Surinam, nests have been recorded in January, March and September (Hellebrekers 1942, Haverschmidt and Mees 1994), and Olson and McDowell (1983) considered that the main breeding season in the north was between mid December and March, coinciding with the start of the dry season. Around Belém, Pará (Brazil), nests have been found in June–April (Snethlage 1928, Pinto 1953, Oniki and Willis 1983), in Amapá birds are in breeding condition in February (Novaes 1978), while in southeast Brazil the season is late August to February (Euler 1900; MNRJ). The only Argentine nest described to date was initiated in mid December (Castelino and Saibene 1989).

STATUS Like all *Manacus*, White-bearded Manakin is treated as Least Concern by BirdLife International (2004, 2008), given its large range (estimated at 7,490,000km^2) and preference for secondary and edge habitats. Piratelli *et al.* (2001) documented its persistence in a small woodlot surrounded by sugar cane. The species is generally numerous over the greater part of its range, in many areas being among the commonest species present (Amaral *et al.* 2003, Piratelli *et al.* 2003, Carrano *et al.* 2004, Magalhães *et al.* 2004), but nonetheless Anciães and Peterson (2006) noted that *M. manacus* could be severely impacted by projected levels of climate change. It seems to have been particularly numerous on Trinidad at the time of Snow's (1962a) study, but had already declined a decade later (Lill 1975) apparently due to a reduction in available secondary forest. Olson and McDowell (1983) reported that mean density at their study site in Surinam was considerably less than on Trinidad even during Lill's time. In comparison with its status in most areas, White-bearded Manakin is considered generally rare or uncommon in Paraguay (Hayes 1995) and in northeast Argentina (Mazar Barnett and Pearman 2001). It is also often less common over much of Brazilian Amazonia than elsewhere, e.g. Cohn-Haft *et al.* (1997), Oren and Parker (1997), Stotz *et al.* (1997), Zimmer *et al.* (1997), Henriques *et al.* (2003) and Whittaker (2009), presumably due to the lack of suitable secondary habitats. Some local extinctions have also been reported or predicted, e.g. in the upper Paraná Valley in southern Brazil (Mendonça *et al.* 2009). The species is known from many protected areas across the range; see, for example: Olson and McDowell (1983), Hilty and Brown (1986), Lowen *et al.* (1996), Saibene *et al.* (1996), Oren and Parker (1997), Parker and Goerck (1997), Williams *et al.* (1997), Chebez *et al.* (1999), Henriques *et al.* (2003), Trolle and Walther (2004), Pacheco *et al.* (2007), Bernard (2008), Souza *et al.* (2008), Mallet-Rodrigues and Noronha (2009), Pinheiro and Dornas (2009a), Salaman *et al.* (2009), Donegan *et al.* (2010) and Vidoz *et al.* (2010).

REFERENCES Allen (1905), Almeida *et al.* (2003), Amaral *et al.* (2003), Anciães and Peterson (2006, 2009), Balchin and Toyne (1998), Bates *et al.* (1989), Bencke (2001), Bencke *et al.* (2000), Berla (1946), Bernard (2008), Berres (2002), BirdLife International (2004, 2008), Blake (1962), Bloch *et al.* (1991), Boesman (1999, 2006a, 2006b, 2009), Bostwick and Prum (2003), Braun *et al.* (2007), Breitwisch and Pliske (1974), Brooks *et al.* (2009), Brumfield (1999), Brumfield and Braun (2001), Browne (2005), Brumfield *et al.* (2008), Buzzetti (2000), Campos *et al.* (2009), Carrano and Marins (2008), Carrano *et al.* (2004), Castelino and Saibene (1989), Castro Astor *et al.* (1997), Cestari *et al.* (2010), Chapman (1917), Chebez *et al.* (1999), Chubb (1921), Clausi (2005), Clay (2009), Cohn-Haft *et al.* (1997), Dick *et al.* (1984), Dickinson (2003), Donegan *et al.* (2010), Dunning (2008), Euler (1900), Faria and Paula (2008), ffrench (1991), Friedmann (1944, 1948), Fry (1970), Galetti and Pizo (1996), Gill and Wright (2006), Goerck (1999), Greenway (1987), Guix (1995), Gyldenstolpe (1945, 1951), Haffer (1967a, 1975), Hammick (2004), Haverschmidt (1948, 1952), Haverschmidt and Mees (1994), Hayes (1995), Hayes and Samad (2002), Hellebrekers (1942), Hellmayr (1906b, 1910, 1929a, 1929b), Hennessey *et al.* (2003b), Henriques *et al.* (2003), Hidasi (1998), Hilty (2003), Hilty and Brown (1986), Höglund and Shorey (2003, 2004), Hohnwald (2009), Ihering (1900), Jahn *et al.* (2002), Junge and Mees (1958), Kenefick *et al.* (2007), Kirwan and Marlow (1996), Krabbe (2007), Krabbe and Nilsson (2003), Krijger *et al.* (1997), Lack (1966, 1968), Lamm (1948), Lees *et al.* (2008), Lill (1974a, 1974b, 1975), Lima *et al.* (2010), Lopes *et al.* (2005), Lowen *et al.* (1996), Magalhães *et al.* (2004, 2007), Mähler Junior *et al.* (2007), Maillard *et al.* (2007), Mallet-Rodrigues and Noronha (2003, 2009), Mallorquin and Quevedo (2002), Marsden *et al.* (2003), Mayer (2000), Mazar Barnett and Pearman (2001), McKay *et al.* (2010), Mendonça *et al.* (2009), Meyer de Schauensee (1982), Meyer de Schauensee and Phelps (1978), Minns *et al.* (2009), Mitchell (1957), Moermond and Denslow (1985), Moore (1994, 1997), Murphy (1991), Naka *et al.* (2006, 2008), Naumburg (1930), Novaes (1970, 1978, 1980), Olivares (1958), Oliveira Junior *et al.* (2008), Olson and McDowell (1983), Oniki and Willis (1983, 1999), Oren and Parker (1997), Ottema *et al.* (2009), Pacheco *et al.* (2007), Parker and Goerck (1997), Parker *et al.* (1982, 1994b), Parkes (1961), de la Peña (1989), Pereira *et al.* (2008), Phelps (1944), Pineschi (1990), Pinheiro and Dornas (2009), Pinto (1944, 1953, 1966), Piratelli *et al.* (2001, 2003), Prum (1992), Remold (2003), Remsen and Parker (1995), Remsen and Traylor (1989), Renaudier and Deroussen (2008), Restall *et al.* (2006), Reynaud (1998), Ridgely and Greenfield (2001), Ridgely and Tudor (1994, 2009), Robbins *et al.* (2004, 2007), Rosário (1996), Saibene *et al.* (1996), Santos and Silva (2007), Santos *et al.* (2010), Scherer-Neto and Straube (1995), Schubart *et al.* (1965), Schulenberg *et al.* (2006, 2007), Scopel *et al.* (2005), Shorey *et al.* (2000), Sibley (1957), Sibley and Monroe (1990), Sick (1993, 1997), Silva *et al.* (1990, 1997), Silveira *et al.* (2003a, 2005), Snethlage (1907, 1914, 1928), Snow (1962a, 1979b, 2004b), Snow and Lill (1974), Snyder (1966), Souza *et al.* (2008), Stotz *et al.* (1996, 1997), Strewe and Navarro (2004), Théry (1990c, 1992, 1997), Thiollay (1994), Todd and Carriker (1922), Tostain *et al.* (1992), Trolle and Walther (2004), Velho (1932), Vidoz *et al.* (2010), Walker *et al.* (2006), Whittaker (2009), Wiedenfeld *et al.* (1985), Williams *et al.* (1997), Willis (1984), Willis and Oniki (1990), J. T. Zimmer (1936), Zimmer and Hilty (1997), Zimmer *et al.* (1997), Zyskowski *et al.* (2011).

White-bearded Manakin *Manacus manacus*. **Fig. 1**. Male, *M. m. abditivus*, El Paujil Bird Reserve, dpto. Santander, north-central Colombia, October (*Fundación ProAves / www.proaves.org*). Throat and collar colour already approaching that of palest *M. m. flaveolus*, showing degree of apparently clinal variation between these two forms in this region of Colombia (see also text and next caption). **Fig. 2**. Male, *M. m. flaveolus*, Ibagué, dpto. Tolima, upper Magdalena Valley, central Colombia, May (*Fundación ProAves / www.proaves.org*). Racial identification based on range, but this race might be expected to be creamier yellow on the collar than this individual.

White-bearded Manakin *Manacus manacus*. **Fig. 3**. Male, *M. m. interior*, Mapiripan, dpto. Meta, eastern Colombia, August (*Fundación ProAves / www.proaves.org*). The rump and uppertail-coverts are reportedly paler grey than in *M. m. manacus* (not illustrated here) and the dark cap smaller in extent than in *M. m. umbrosus* (also not illustrated here). **Fig. 4**. Male, *M. m. trinitatis*, Trinidad, May (*Steve Garvie / www.pbase. com/rainbirder*). Note the very broad white neck collar, which is considered to distinguish this race, as well as the rather pale underparts with few grey elements. **Fig. 5**. Male, *M. m. subpurus*, Guayaramerin, dpto. Beni, northern Bolivia, April (*Joe Tobias / Edward Grey Institute, Oxford University*). Racial identification based on the rather dark grey rump with a faint greyish wash over the breast and abdomen, more extensive and darker grey flanks and breast-sides, and white undertail-coverts (not visible here). **Fig. 6**. Male, *M. m. purissimus*, near Senhor do Bonfim, Tocantins, Brazil, January (*William Price, www.pbase.com/tereksandpiper*). Tentatively ascribed to *M. m. purissimus*, but the apparent amount of grey on the thighs suggests the possibility of *M. m. longibarbatus*. Racial limits in eastern and southern Amazonia require revision and several names might be better synonymized.

White-bearded Manakin *Manacus manacus.* **Fig. 7** Male, *M. m. gutturosus,* Mambucaba, Rio de Janeiro, southeast Brazil, October (*Hadoram Shirihai / Photographic Handbook to Birds of the World*). This race, endemic to the Atlantic Forest, is the most extensively grey below. **Fig. 8.** Male, *M. m. gutturosus,* Iguazú National Park, prov. Misiones, northeast Argentina, October (*Emilio White*). Male at a lek site, showing the elongated throat feathers typical of males of all *Manacus,* perched on a vertical sapling. **Fig. 9.** Female, *M. m. manacus* (?), Anavilhanas Jungle Lodge, Amazonas, central Amazonian Brazil (*Hadoram Shirihai / Photographic Handbook to Birds of the World*). Presumed to pertain to this race, but no males were seen at this site during our fieldwork and the possibility exists that *M. m. interior* occurs to the lower Rio Negro. This female seems to be collecting spiderwebs for a nest. **Fig. 10.** Female, *M. m. maximus,* Buenaventura Reserve, prov. El Oro, near Piñas, southwest Ecuador, February (*Harold F. Greeney*). Note how the nest is bound to the supporting branches using spiderwebs.

Genus *Heterocercus*: 'crested' manakins

This genus of three allopatric species, which form a superspecies (Snow 1975) and which have sometimes been considered conspecific (e.g. Parkes 1961 questioned whether *aurantiivertex* might not prove to be a subspecies of *flavivertex*), is exclusively Amazonian in distribution. A fourth 'species', the so-called 'Golden-crested Manakin' *Heterocercus luteocephalus*, described by René Primevère Lesson in 1832, is known solely from the holotype, collected at an unknown locality in South America, and is now generally regarded as probably pertaining to a hybrid (Parkes 1961, Snow 2004b), although the type, once in the Paris Museum, is currently considered to be lost. Oustalet (*in* Hellmayr 1906a) suggested that the bird might have come from 'the interior of Cayenne' (French Guiana); this hypothesis appears incorrect given the lack of any *Heterocercus* species in the latter country. Hellmayr (1929b) described the type, which he had examined and indeed reassigned to *Heterocercus* (Hellmayr 1906a: 326), as having a bright yellow coronal stripe and being otherwise similar to a Pale-bellied Tyrant-Manakin *Neopelma pallescens*, but for the crown-sides, post-ocular region, neck-sides and hindneck being ash-grey, and the posterior underparts being much brighter (sulphur) yellow. Bill structure, tail shape and tarsus length supported the bird's inclusion in *Heterocercus*, but parts of the plumage were in moult; the specimen's measurements were presented by Hellmayr (1906a).

YELLOW-CRESTED MANAKIN
Heterocercus flavivertex   Plate 7

Heterocercus flavivertex **Pelzeln, 1868**, *Orn. Bras.*, pt. 2: 125, 186, Marabitanas, Rio Negro, Brazil [type locality restricted by Pinto (1944)]

Yellow-crested Manakin is arguably the best known of this trio of bulky manakins, although most of our cumulative knowledge derives from a single study made in southern Venezuela more than a decade ago, illustrating again the incredible paucity of information for many Neotropical forest birds. It is confined to forests north of the River Amazon, but is generally uncommon and local across much of its range.

IDENTIFICATION 14.0–16.3cm. Once identified to genus, this species is easily identified, it being the sole *Heterocercus* in range. The striking-plumaged male is easily recognised, but the duller females may be confused with other female manakins or some flycatchers; in all cases the large size, chestnut- or cinnamon-coloured breast and whitish-grey throat/cheeks (forming a very slight ruff, but far less obvious than in males) are keynote features. Bill shape offers an extra clue, *vis-à-vis* some potential confusion tyrannids, such as the White-crested Spadebill *Platyrinchus platyrhynchos*, which, however, is restricted to *terra firme* forest.

DISTRIBUTION The Yellow-crested Manakin is endemic to the Imeri centre of endemism (Cracraft 1985). Confined to northern Amazonia, where it is found from northern Brazil, in the Rio Negro/Rio Branco drainage east to northwest Pará on the Rio Trombetas (Sick 1997), and north to Roraima (Pinto 1966, Naka *et al.* 2006). Sometimes mentioned for Amapá (Ridgely and Tudor 1994) but records for there are seemingly best discounted; indeed, the species is not mapped as occurring there by Ridgely and Tudor (2009). Elsewhere, the Yellow-crested Manakin occurs over southeast Colombia, in eastern Vichada to southernmost Vaupés and west to northeast Meta, at Carimagua, as well as in southwest Venezuela, principally across western and central Amazonas but north as far as extreme southeast Apure at Puerto Páez and Cinaruco-Capanaparo National Park (Prum *et al.* 1996, Hilty 2003).

MOVEMENTS None known and Yellow-crested Manakin is presumed to be resident like the entire genus.

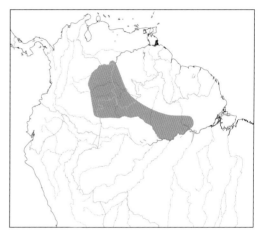

HABITAT Yellow-crested Manakin generally prefers scrubby, sandy-belt woodland, including *campinas*, sometimes also gallery forests, at the borders of streams and oxbow lakes, especially black water, as well as seasonally flooded, stunted *várzea* forests (including *igapós*). It seems commonest in low-canopy woodland on white sand, and will at least occasionally venture into shrubs in open savanna to forage (Prum *et al.* 1996). Although Hilty (2003) and Prum *et al.* (1996) noted a preference for dense areas with many vines, palms and small trees in southern Venezuela, in northern Brazil that has not always been our experience (GMK pers. obs.). Yellow-crested Manakin has been recorded only to *c.*300m (Hilty and Brown 1986, Hilty 2003, Snow 2004b, Ridgely and Tudor 2009).

DESCRIPTION The sexes differ. Large and long-tailed, both sexes possess the graduated tail with the outermost rectrices shortest and narrowest (being about half the length and width of the central tail feathers: see diagram in Prum *et al.* 1996: 723). Furthermore, the feather rachises of the rectrices are curiously unstiffened. The seventh primary is longest, with the eighth and sixth equal. Bill is relatively long and narrow, like others of the genus, with a reasonably well-arched culmen and poorly developed rictal bristles, but large nostrils. *Adult male.* – The upperparts are deep olive-green with a concealed, but when visible extremely striking, orange- or golden-yellow coronal stripe/patch (with greyish bases to the feathers and some white posterior to the base), with contrasting dark grey to blackish head-sides, forming a mask from the lores to the ear-coverts, and grey cheeks. The bright silky white chin and throat consist of elongate feathers that form a small (spur-like) ruff or plume laterally (not in the middle), bordered below by a darkish, sooty-olive band (of variable width but usually rather narrow). In contrast, the breast is deep chestnut grading to warm cinnamon on the belly/ventral region, and olive admixed dark grey on the body-sides and flanks. The wing-feathers have olive-green fringes, i.e. they are concolorous with the mantle, but with dark brownish to dull black centres, and the tail feathers are more solidly dark over both surfaces. *Adult female* – Differs from the male in lacking the yellow coronal stripe and very dark head-sides, with an off-white to greyish (not bright white) and smaller throat patch, a weaker breast-band, and variably but always paler cinnamon-buff underparts (see Geographical Variation). Wing-length is generally shorter than in males (see below; Prum *et al.* 1996, Snow 2004b). *Juvenile.* – Restall *et al.* (2006) described and illustrated this plumage as having a much darker grey throat, with faintly olive-washed underparts, and brown irides, but our own examination of specimens reveals that immature (i.e. somewhat older) males similarly recall females (MNRJ; Snow 2004b), suggesting to us that Restall *et al.* (2006) did not necessarily describe true juveniles. Given that some birds in such non-adult plumage have fully ossified skulls, they might well be capable of breeding at such ages (Prum *et al.* 1996, Hilty 2003; MNRJ). Furthermore, at least some adult males have brown irides, meaning that this is not a characteristic of juvenile plumage (MNRJ). *Moult.* – Very few moult data have been published; Willard *et al.* (1991) mentioned that one of several collected in late February in Venezuela was moulting the tail- and body-feathers. None of the birds examined by us at MNRJ collected on the Rio Negro, northern Brazil, in July, was moulting (GMK pers. obs.). *Bare parts* – Irides fuscous or brown to chestnut or even reddish, bill black, sometimes with a greyish or horn-coloured base to the mandible, with a bright yellow gape, and the tarsus and feet are dusky-brown or greyish to blackish (Willard *et al.* 1991, Snow 2004b, Restall *et al.* 2006; FMNH; MNRJ; GMK pers. obs.).

MEASUREMENTS (BMNH; FMNH; MNRJ; RMNH: Amazonas, Brazil, southern Venezuela; Prum *et al.* 1996; southern Venezuela) Tail measurements refer to the length of the central rectrices. Wing of male (*n* = 12) 81–88mm, wing of female (*n* = 16) 75–83mm; tail of male (*n* = 12) 50–61mm, tail of female (*n* = 3) 48–53mm; bill of male (*n* = 12) 13.76–16.56mm, bill of female (*n* = 3) 14.04–15.14mm; tarsus of male (*n* = 2) 14.57–15.77mm, tarsus of female (*n* = 2) 13.50–14.47mm. Also, tarsus of male (*n* = 16) 15.15mm (mean: Prum *et al.* 1996), tarsus of female (*n* = 14) 14.97mm (mean: Prum *et al.* 1996). For additional mensural data see Prum *et al.* (1996). Weight: 18.3–24.0g (males) and 19.8–23.2g (females) (Willard *et al.* 1991, Prum *et al.* 1996, Hilty 2003, Snow 2004b, Dunning 2008; FMNH; MNRJ).

GEOGRAPHICAL VARIATION Monotypic, although Friedmann (1948) considered that the name *H. f. angosturae*, Berlepsch and Leverkühn, 1890, the type of which is a female, might after all be applicable to Venezuelan birds, males of which he considered to be slightly darker, especially on the forehead, crown-sides and nape. Friedmann (1948) had already remarked that females differ only individually across the species' range, but we agree with other subsequent (and prior) commentators, despite not having seen many specimens of this bird, that *angosturae* is clearly a mere synonym of *flavivertex*.

VOICE As with this species' natural history (see below), much of our information concerning the vocalisations of *H. flavivertex* comes from the work of Prum *et al.* (1996) in southern Venezuela, which remains the only detailed study of the Yellow-crested Manakin to date. Male Yellow-crested Manakins possess at least five distinct vocalisations, with minor variations. The advertisement call, given as the bird perches notably erect, is a loud, three-note, whistled *weeee-pitch-ooo*, which lasts *c.*3 seconds, the first note of which rises slowly from 4.5 to 5.25kHz over 1.6 seconds. There is then a slight pause, before the second note, which rises rapidly from 4.5 to 6.0kHz over 0.2 seconds. Then, after an even briefer pause, the third note descends slowly from 6.0 to 3.8kHz over 0.8 seconds; because of the pauses, the whole sounds somewhat hiccuped. Sometimes the introductory note is doubled, whilst other variations include a partial 'song' wherein only the *weeee* note is given, doubled or not. Although most 'frequently' given in the morning, the advertising call can be heard at any time of day, even in the hottest hours, but is never sung very repetitively, unlike *Tyranneutes* for instance, with usually three to four, or at most *c.*7, songs per hour. However, in mid December, near Novo Airão, on the south bank of the Rio Negro, Brazil, one male was singing at almost 2–5-minute irregular intervals, gradually opening the bill to the widest extent during the first part of the song, then appearing to 'gulp' and snap the bill shut during the final note (GMK pers. obs.). This advertisement call features on the following sound-recording compilations: Boesman (1999, 2000a, 2000b), and a sonogram was presented by Prum *et al.* (1996). The second call is an emphatic *weer-weer . . . weer* (3–6-note) chatter call during aggressive interactions with other individuals of the same species, or different species. These sharp, squeaky notes become successively lower in volume, length and frequency, and each note is composed of two strong harmonics that rise rapidly in frequency and then drop slowly (a sonogram was presented by Prum *et al.* 1996). Other vocalisations involve a querulous *kweip* (which sounds like a very short and rather quiet rattle: GMK pers. obs.) and a loud *keek*, both heard on a few occasions by Prum *et al.* (1996), and given immediately following the tail-shiver display (see Natural History). Heard more frequently is a dry, emphatic *chip*, given as the bird flies from a perch immediately after giving the tail-shiver display. In addition, there is a 0.75-second mechanical *whoosh* sound that is audible when the bird returns to the perch following the tail-shiver display, and a *chip* note.

NATURAL HISTORY A huge amount of our knowledge of the general life history of this manakin is drawn from the studies of Rick Prum and colleagues (Prum *et al.* 1996) at Junglaven, southern Venezuela. Yellow-crested Manakin is generally quiet, undemonstrative and unobtrusive except when singing, being found in the understorey of reasonably open forest.

FOOD AND FEEDING Yellow-crested Manakin occasionally and briefly forages within mixed-species flocks (Hilty and Brown 1986, Hilty 2003) and feeds between 1 and 10m above the ground (Prum *et al.* 1996). The diet is relatively typical of many piprids, consisting of small fruits and insects, although based on the available data (Prum *et al.* 1996) the species appears to be more insectivorous than many other manakins. Arthropods, spiders and caterpillars are seized from branches and leaves, usually via aerial sally-gleans, and only rarely when perched. Birds occasionally leave their display territories to feed at a nearby fruiting tree. Details of the species' frugivorous diet are very poorly known, although Prum *et al.* (1996) mentioned that trees of Melastomataceae, Lauraceae and Rubiaceae were visited, and Willard *et al.* (1991) mentioned that one bird had apparently been feeding at a *Pagamea plicata* (Rubiaceae) tree. Fruiting trees visited by this manakin in southern Venezuela were attended by a variety of other frugivores, including Spangled Cotinga *Cotinga cayana*, Pompadour Cotinga *Xipholena punicea*, Black Manakin *Xenopipo atronitens* and Golden-headed Manakin *Pipra erythrocephala* (Prum *et al.* 1996).

DISPLAY Males defend small, non-resource-based territories of *c.*10–20m diameter within which they spend approximately 75% of daylight hours at the height of the early breeding season, and spend much time preening and, to a lesser extent, sunbathing. Territories generally appear to be very well spaced, perhaps up to 250m distant, even in highly suitable habitat. Birds sit quietly on their perches, typically 2–6m above the ground, but these are sometimes just 1.5m above the ground (GMK pers. obs.). Females apparently rarely visit these territories for more than a few seconds, but might perch in sight of the territories as Prum *et al.* (1996) found that males sometimes appear to peer intently into the distance immediately prior to displaying. The most frequently given ritualised behaviour, observed most often during the hottest hours of the day, was described as the *tail-shiver display* by Prum *et al.* (1996) as follows:

> In the conspicuous tail-shiver display … a male perches on a branch with the body horizontal and the tail cocked at a nearly right angle above its back. The white throat is erected into a puff, and the wings are folded against the body. The male moves the tail forward and back over approximately 15°, and simultaneously rocks its body slightly in the opposite direction, producing a rapid, syncopated "shivering" movement. The male then flies conspicuously from the perch, holding its entire body horizontal, flapping its wings very deeply, and giving an emphatic *chip* call … four rapid tail and body twitching movements [were recorded] in less than one second.

Rivals are sometimes pursued rapidly through the forest understorey, but this species also has a rarely seen above-the-canopy flight display, described by Prum *et al.* (1996) thus:

> J. Pierson saw an elaborate flight display from a trail through open savanna bordering on white-sand woodland approximately 2km from the focal male territories. Following a series of aggressive chatter calls by one or two unseen individuals, a male *flavivertex* flew rapidly and rather vertically from one side of a trail up about 15–20m above the woodland canopy. It then flew horizontally in a semicircle about 10–12m in diameter, and dropped abruptly down into the woodland on the other side of the trail. The entire flight took between 6 and 8 seconds.

BREEDING Prum *et al.* (1996) considered the breeding season to be February to mid May (or the late dry season) in Amazonas, Venezuela, but only one nest has been found to date, in April, which was subsequently abandoned. It was being constructed, of rootlets, small twigs and a large number of wiry, round grass-like fibres, by a female-plumaged bird, and was a cup-shaped structure attached using spiderwebs to the fork of a descending tree branch *c.*2m above the surface of an 8m-wide stream (Prum *et al.* 1996). The incomplete nest's dimensions were presented by Prum *et al.* (1996). There are no data on eggs, incubation, fledging periods, etc. Breeding data from elsewhere are very few, but Olivares (1955) collected a female in breeding condition in mid December in Vaupés, Colombia, while FMNH has a series (both sexes) from the same general area (Carimagua, dpto. Meta) that were in breeding condition between late January and mid May. Finally, Willard *et al.* (1991) took several breeding-condition specimens, of both sexes, in February to April in southern Amazonas, Venezuela at the frontier with Brazil. Populations along the upper Rio Negro, Brazil, are not breeding in July (MNRJ), but on the lower reaches of the same river males were displaying intensively near Novo Airão in mid December, suggesting that the breeding season was starting in this region at that time (GMK pers. obs.).

STATUS Anciães and Peterson (2006) predicted that this species could be severely affected by habitat modification in the face of potential climate change based on modelling techniques. For now, however, it is treated as Least Concern by BirdLife International (2004, 2008), although the species generally appears to occur at rather low densities (Prum *et al.* 1996) and is generally scarce in Colombia (Restall *et al.* 2006), where it was initially recorded as recently in the 1940s (Dugand and Phelps 1946, 1948). Yellow-crested Manakin is known from several protected areas throughout the species' range, including the Parque Nacional Cinaruco-Capanaparo, Apure, Venezuela (cf. Prum *et al.* 1996), and Reserva Natural Xixaua, Roraima (Trolle and Walther 2004), and Jaú National Park, Amazonas (Borges *et al.* 2001), both in Brazil. However, two of the most accessible localities to find this species are Junglaven camp, Amazonas, Venezuela (Zimmer and Hilty 1997), and Anavilhanas Jungle Lodge, Amazonas, Brazil, at both of which the species can be found directly around the accommodation (GMK pers. obs.).

REFERENCES Anciães and Peterson (2006, 2009), BirdLife International (2004, 2008), Boesman (1999, 2006a, 2006b), Borges (2007), Borges *et al.* (2001), Cherrie (1916), Cohn-Haft *et al.* (1997), Cracraft (1985), Dugand and Phelps (1946, 1948), Dunning (2008), Friedmann (1948), Hellmayr (1929b), Hilty (2003), Hilty and Brown (1986), Naka *et al.* (2006), Olivares (1955), Pinto (1944, 1966), Prum *et al.* (1996), Restall *et al.* (2006), Ridgely and Tudor (1994, 2009), Sick (1997), Snethlage (1914), Snow (2004b), Stotz *et al.* (1996), Trolle and Walther (2004), Willard *et al.* (1991), J. T. Zimmer (1936), Zimmer and Hilty (1997).

Yellow-crested Manakin *Heterocercus flavivertex.* **Figs. 1–2.** Male, Anavilhanas Jungle Lodge, Amazonas, central Amazonian Brazil, December (*Hadoram Shirihai / Photographic Handbook to Birds of the World*). Some manakins are among the few species that sing almost interrupted daylong; this bird sang throughout the hottest period of the day. Notice how wide the bill is opened.

FLAME-CRESTED MANAKIN
Heterocercus linteatus   **Plate 7**

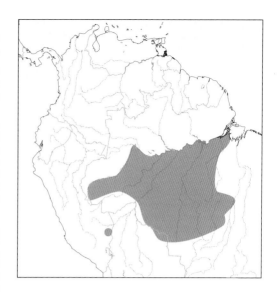

Elaenia linteata **Strickland** *in* **Jardine, 1850**, *Contrib. Orn.*: 121-15, Pl. LXIII, upper branches of the Amazon River [restricted to Borba, Rio Madeira, Brazil, by Gyldenstolpe (1951)]

Despite it having the widest range of any of the genus, the Flame-crested Manakin is a surprisingly poorly known and studied bird, and much of our knowledge is based on purely incidental observations, whilst even its range remains to be fully elucidated. The species is frequently stated to occur in southeast Mato Grosso (e.g. Ridgely and Tudor 1994, Snow 2004b), but this seems to be based on a misapprehension as to the whereabouts of the Serra do Roncador.

IDENTIFICATION 13.8–15.7cm. Once identified to genus, this species is easily identified, it being the sole member of the genus *Heterocercus* to occur across southern Amazonia. The striking-plumaged male is easily recognised, and indeed the most brightly plumaged of the genus. There is no known overlap with either Yellow-crested *Heterocercus flavivertex* or Orange-crested Manakin *H. aurantiivertex*, although the situation in far-western Amazonian Brazil is not yet clear *vis-à-vis* the latter species, but the largely black head-sides of male Flame-crested Manakin should always be obvious, even if the deeper red coronal patch is not visible. Furthermore, male Orange-crested (and Yellow-crested) Manakins are less deep reddish-chestnut below. However, the duller females might be confused with other female manakins or some flycatchers; observers should note the large size, chestnut- or cinnamon-coloured breast and whitish-grey throat/cheeks, which are the critical features. Female Yellow-crested Manakin is brighter olive above with more contrasting grey cheeks than female Flame-crested (Ridgely and Tudor 1994). Compared with female Orange-crested Manakin, females of the present species are probably on average brighter cinnamon below, with slightly darker cheeks and darker upperparts, but the distinction would be very difficult without the presence of males (Ridgely and Tudor 1994, Schulenberg *et al.* 2007). Bill shape offers an extra clue, *vis-à-vis* some potential confusion tyrannids, such as the White-crested Spadebill *Platyrinchus platyrhynchos*, which is restricted to *terra firme* forest.

DISTRIBUTION The southern Amazonian representative of the genus, Flame-crested Manakin is largely restricted to Brazil, where it occurs east to southern Pará in the Rio Xingu drainage (e.g. at the Serra do Cachimbo: Pinto and Camargo 1957, and further east at Santana do Araguaia: A. Aleixo *in* Pinheiro and Dornas 2009b) and as far north as Caxiuanã, at Melgaço, just west of Belém, and south to northeast Mato Grosso, at the Rio Von Den Steinen (A. Whittaker pers. obs.) and the Serra do Roncador (Fry 1970). It has also very recently been recorded on the right bank of the Rio Tocantins, in the state of Tocantins (Pinheiro and Dornas 2009a, 2009b). From Brazil, it occurs south and west to extreme northeast Bolivia, in dptos. Santa Cruz, where it was only recently discovered at a handful of sites (Bates *et al.* 1989, 1998, Williams 1995, Vidoz *et al.* 2010), Beni and La Paz (Maillard *et al.* 2007), where it was predicted to occur by Remsen and Parker (1995), and to southeasternmost Peru, at the Pampas del Heath, near Puerto Maldonado, in southeast Madre de Dios, where it is known from just two recent sight records close to the Bolivian border (Parker

et al. 1994b, Schulenberg *et al.* 2007). The latter authors speculated that it might be also looked for in northeast Peru on the south bank of the Amazon close to the border with Brazil. However, records earlier ascribed to this species by Zimmer (1936) at 'Puerto Indiana' north of the Amazon and from vague localities in upper Amazonia presumably refer to Orange-crested Manakin *H. aurantiivertex*, a species with which Zimmer was unfamiliar. And, in August 2004, B. M. Whitney and D. J. Stejskal (Field Guides tour report) found the latter species on the Brazilian side of the Rio Javari, at Palmari Lodge (see Orange-crested Manakin). The range limits of *linteatus* in the northwest of its range, in Brazil, are unclear, but it has been found at Tefé, as well as on the upper Rio Juruá (Pinto 1944), where it seems to be rare (Gyldenstolpe 1945, 1951), and in a *campinarana* at Guajará (07°22'S, 73°00'W) (Poletto and Aleixo 2005). A specimen labelled Monte Alegre, Pará, from north of the Amazon (Snethlage 1907), was speculated, no doubt correctly, to be from a nearby south-bank locality by Snethlage (1914), and was further discussed by Hellmayr (1929b) and Pinto (1944).

MOVEMENTS None known and presumed resident like the entire genus.

HABITAT This manakin generally prefers riparian and gallery woodland as well as seasonally flooded *várzea* and *igapós*, and well-wooded river islands, but is occasionally found in *terra firme* forest (L. E. Lopes *in* Pinheiro and Dornas 2009b). Sometimes found in stunted sandy-belt woodland (*campinas*) with or without bamboo (Bates *et al.* 1989, Whittaker 2009; A. Whittaker pers. comm.). It has been recorded to *c*.500m (Snow 2004b, Ridgely and Tudor 2009).

DESCRIPTION The sexes differ. Large and long-tailed, both sexes possess the graduated tail with the outermost rectrices shortest and narrowest (being about half the length and width of the central tail feathers). Furthermore, the feather rachises of the rectrices are curiously unstiffened. The seventh primary is longest, with the eighth and sixth equal. The bill is relatively long and narrow, like others of the genus, with a reasonably well-arched culmen, prominent nostrils and weakly developed rictal bristles, but rather large nostrils. *Adult male.* – The upperparts are dark olive-green with a concealed, but when visible extremely striking, fiery red to orange-chrome coronal stripe/patch (with off-whitish bases to these feathers), with a contrastingly black head (grading into the green lower nape) and darker, blackish-brown flight feathers (including the tail). The bright silky white chin and throat consist of elongate feathers that, when flattened, form a small (spur-like) ruff or plume laterally (not in the middle), bordered below by a very dark and relatively broad, sooty-olive band. In contrast, the breast is deep chestnut grading to warm cinnamon-rufous over the belly and entire undertail-coverts, and dark olive (slightly admixed grey) on the body-sides and flanks. The wing-coverts are generally olive-green, i.e. concolorous with the mantle, but with slightly darker centres, becoming duskier (with olive-green fringes) on the primaries and secondaries. *Adult female* – Differs from the male in lacking the red coronal stripe and the rest of the head is concolorous with the dark olive mantle (the crown-feathers have very narrow dusky tips), with a duskier face (ear-coverts and lores down) and an off-white to greyish (not bright white) and smaller throat patch (no elongate feathers although some show some evidence of a slight 'spur'). Furthermore, the female also has a weaker breast-band (sometimes hardly evident at all), greyish-olive flanks, and variably but always much paler cinnamon-buff underparts (see Geographical Variation). Wing-length is generally shorter than in males (see below; Prum *et al.* 1996, Snow 2004b). *Juvenile.* – This plumage is apparently undescribed (Snow 2004b). Plumage maturation is presumably similar to that in congeners, although these too are incompletely known in this respect. Young males have paler underparts, with a slightly duller white throat, and a more orange-red coronal patch. *Moult.* – Nothing seems to have been published concerning this species' moult strategy, but none of those examined by us at MNRJ collected in Mato Grosso, Pará and Rondônia, in June to August, was moulting, and most were in heavily worn plumage at this season (GMK pers. obs.). Two collected in northeast Bolivia in late October and early November were also not moulting (FMNH). *Hybrids.* – The name '*Pipra anomala*' Todd, 1925 (*Proc. Biol. Soc. Wash.* 38: 97), based on a male specimen (perhaps immature) collected at Santarém, Pará, Brazil, is generally considered to represent an inter-generic hybrid, between Crimson-hooded Manakin *Pipra aureola aurantiicollis* and the present species (Parkes 1961, Mallet-Rodrigues 2008), despite the fact that the generally acute Hellmayr (1929b) had maintained it as a good species. In structure, e.g. tail shape and relative lengths of the primaries, and plumage, e.g. throat, head and mantle colorations, as well as the very slightly elongate lateral throat-feathers, '*Pipra anomala*' seems indeed to be entirely intermediate. Three colour images of the specimen were presented in Mallet-Rodrigues (2008). *Bare parts* – Irides brown to very dark brown, bill black to dark brown or grey, sometimes with a horn-coloured base to the mandible, with a bright yellow gape, and the tarsus and feet are dark brown or slate grey (sometimes with a reddish cast) to blackish (Snethlage 1908b, Naumburg 1930, Snow 2004b; FMNH; MNRJ; GMK pers. obs.).

MEASUREMENTS (MNRJ: Mato Grosso, Pará and Rondônia, Brazil; Gyldenstolpe 1945, 1951: Amazonas, Brazil; Prum *et al.* 1996: geography of sample unknown) Wing of male (*n* = 18) 85–91mm, wing of female (*n* = 10) 78–84mm; tail of male (*n* = 8) 47–56mm, tail of female (*n* = 3) 50–51mm; bill of male (*n* = 6) 14.27–15.32mm,

bill of female (3) 14.16–15.80mm; tarsus of male (*n* = 10) 12.94–15.34mm, tarsus of female (*n* = 3) 13.86–15.54mm. For additional mensural data see Hellmayr (1910), Snethlage (1914), Prum *et al.* (1996) and Pinheiro and Dornas (2009b). Weight (sexes combined): 19.8–26.0g (one female 16.0g) (Fry 1970, Bates *et al.* 1989, Graves and Zusi 1990, Snow 2004b, Poletto and Aleixo 2005, Maillard *et al.* 2007, Dunning 2008, Pinheiro and Dornas 2009b; FMNH; MNRJ).

GEOGRAPHICAL VARIATION Monotypic, although Gyldenstolpe (1951) drew attention to a specimen from the Rio Juruá, Amazonas, Brazil, that is more bronzy above than specimens even from as far west as the Rio Purus, which are identical to those from eastern Amazonia.

VOICE Snow (2004b) noted the fact that this species' vocalisations have not been well described in the literature, referring only to its loud calls, which were considered to have a curassow-like quality by Ridgely and Tudor (2009). In fact, Sick (1997) had described the male's advertising 'song', which is given at irregular, sometimes long, intervals, as a loud *pit-iu*, with a very similar quality to that of Yellow-crested Manakin, the first part sounding shrill and as if spat out, the second part more prolonged and following a short pause. It was rendered *skeeeeééeuw, skeeeu* by Ridgely and Tudor (2009), and this call is often given twice in rapid succession, the first call being sometimes preceded by a clicking note (*ts-ik*). Also reported to utter a *psia* during male–male chases through the forest. Marantz and Zimmer (2006) presented another vocalisation, a *c.*1-second, rather flat, throaty, loud *whioou*, given more frequently, sometimes at *c.*4-second intervals, and which is uttered prior to the males ascending into the canopy prior to making its above-canopy display flight (A. Whittaker pers. comm.). The species' advertising call is presented on Boesman (2006a, 2009) and this vocalisation was also included on the Marantz and Zimmer (2006) compilation. Several different vocalisations, all recorded in Mato Grosso, Brazil, are also represented on the online database at www.xeno-canto.org.

NATURAL HISTORY In comparison with the Yellow-crested Manakin, this species is (surprisingly) poorly known and to date no detailed studies of its life history have been attempted. Like the latter species, Flame-crested Manakin is usually encountered alone or, much less frequently, in pairs, and undoubtedly is most easily found when males are singing. Unlike *H. flavivertex*, the present species is much less a species of the undergrowth, it being most frequently found in the subcanopy, albeit of relatively low-stature woodland, although singing males can still also be found at eye level, just like Yellow-crested Manakin. Perches quietly and almost motionless for long periods (Ridgely and Tudor 2009).

FOOD AND FEEDING The species' diet is very poorly known, with the only published data being that it consumes small fruits, insects and spiders (Schubart *et al.* 1965). There is no information on the relative proportion of non-fruit items, and nothing has been published on feeding behaviour; like Yellow-crested Manakin, the species probably takes most food in flight using short sally-strikes.

DISPLAY These are also in need of clarification, but males are described as displaying with 'a few' others (apparently quite unlike *H. flavivertex*), flaring the white throat feathers into a prominent 'Elizabethan' ruff, and chasing their rivals (Sick 1959e, 1997, Snow 2004b, Ridgely and Tudor

2009). Whittaker (2009: 34) recently noted that *H. linteatus* performs aerial displays similar to those recorded in the other two species of *Heterocercus*, without providing further details, although A. Whittaker (pers. comm.) has clarified their essentially identical nature to those of Yellow-crested and Orange-crested Manakins.

BREEDING Data are virtually non-existent. Kirwan (2009) recently drew attention to a specimen (MNRJ 1375) of a nestling, collected by H. Sick, which was considerably less than half adult size, with extensive down over the breast, head and upperparts (but the wing feathers were no longer in pin), taken on 2 August 1949, at Diauarum, on the upper Rio Xingu, Mato Grosso (11°12'S 53°14'W). The entire underparts were very pale, almost buffish-white and the upper surface was mainly brownish-olive with largely darker flight feathers. Another MNRJ specimen, a male collected in Rondônia, Brazil, also in August, had enlarged gonads. Maillard *et al.* (2007) took several of both sexes in breeding condition in September–November in northern Bolivia, whilst Poletto and Aleixo (2005) collected several in breeding condition in late August in southwest Amazonian Brazil. Males are generally singing at Cristalino Jungle Lodge, in northern Mato Grosso, at the same season (GMK pers. obs.).

STATUS Like its congeners, Anciães and Peterson (2006) predicted that this species could be severely affected by habitat modification in the face of potential climate change based on modelling techniques. Treated as Least Concern by BirdLife International (2004, 2008), but other than at a few localities in eastern Amazonian Brazil, e.g. along the Rio Tapajós, Para, and into northern Mato Grosso, e.g. at Alta Floresta, on the Rio Cristalino, Flame-crested Manakin generally appears to be rather uncommon. In Tocantins, where it has only very recently been discovered, the species is considered very rare (Pinheiro and Dornas 2009). Elsewhere in Brazil, Gyldenstolpe (1946, 1951) considered the species to be rare along the Rio Juruá, Amazonas, whilst Peres and Whittaker (1991) found it to be uncommon on the Rio Urucu, Amazonas, and this manakin is also far from numerous along the Rio Roosevelt, Amazonas (Naumburg 1930, Whittaker 2009), or along the Rio Ji-paraná, Rondônia (Stotz *et al.* 1997). Further afield, the relative lack of records and its only recent discovery in Bolivia and Peru also hints at the species' overall rarity in western Amazonia. Flame-crested Manakin is known from rather few protected areas, but these include Amazônia National Park, Pará (Oren and Parker 1997), Cantão State Park, Tocantins (Pinheiro and Dornas 2009), both in Brazil, and Noel Kempff Mercado National Park and the nearby Estación Biológica Caparú, in Bolivia (Williams 1995, Bates *et al.* 1998, Vidoz *et al.* 2010). Undoubtedly, the most frequently visited locality by birdwatchers within the species' range is Cristalino Jungle Lodge, Alta Floresta, Mato Grosso, Brazil (Zimmer *et al.* 1997), but it can also be found at the Ferreira Penna Ecological Station, Caxuianã, Pará, Brazil.

REFERENCES Aleixo and Poletto (2007), Anciães and Peterson (2006, 2009), Bates *et al.* (1989, 1998), BirdLife International (2004, 2008), Boesman (2006a, 2009), Cracraft (1985), Dunning (2008), Fry (1970), Graves and Zusi (1990), Gyldenstolpe (1945, 1951), Hellmayr (1906, 1910, 1929b), Hennessey *et al.* (2003), Kirwan (2009), Lees *et al.* (2006), Maillard *et al.* (2007), Mallet-Rodrigues (2008), Marantz and Zimmer (2006), McKay *et al.* (2010), Naumburg (1930), Novaes (1960, 1976), Oren and Parker (1997), Parker *et al.* (1982, 1994b), Parkes (1961), Peres and Whittaker (1991), Pinheiro and Dornas (2009a, 2009b), Pinto (1944), Pinto and Camargo (1957), Poletto and Aleixo (2005), Prum *et al.* (1996), Remsen and Parker (1995), Ridgely and Tudor (1994, 2009), Schubart *et al.* (1965), Schulenberg *et al.* (2007), Sick (1959e, 1967, 1997), Snethlage (1907, 1908b, 1914), Snow (2004b), Stotz *et al.* (1996, 1997), Todd (1925), Vidoz *et al.* (2010), Whittaker (2009), Williams (1995), J. T. Zimmer (1936), Zimmer *et al.* (1997).

Flame-crested Manakin *Heterocercus linteatus*. **Fig. 1**. Male, Cristalino Jungle Lodge, Alta Floresta, Mato Grosso, east Amazonian Brazil, November (*Hadoram Shirihai / Photographic Handbook to Birds of the World*). **Fig. 2**. Male, Rio Cristalino Jungle Lodge, Alta Floresta, Mato Grosso, east Amazonian Brazil, December (*Arthur Grosset / www.arthurgrosset.com*). The southern and eastern representative of this super-species. Note the variation in the depth of the underparts coloration between these two birds. Females are even paler below and have a grey, not white, throat, as well as lacking any black on the head-sides.

ORANGE-CRESTED MANAKIN
Heterocercus aurantiivertex   Plate 7

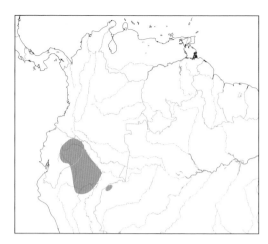

Heterocercus aurantiivertex **P. L. Sclater and Salvin, 1880**, *Proc. Zool. Soc. Lond.* 1880: 157, Sarayacu, Ecuador

This taxon, which remains very poorly represented in ornithological collections, was long speculated to be 'just' a western race of the Yellow-crested Manakin *H. flavivertex*, e.g. by Hellmayr (1929b), and, in particular, its rightful place as part of the Peruvian avifauna was only unambiguously accepted by Zimmer (1936). Indeed, until the 1990s, in Peru Orange-crested Manakin was definitely known solely from a single locality, Chamicuros on the Río Huallaga. Even more recently, it has been found on the Brazilian bank of the Rio Javari, which forms the boundary with Peru, bringing into focus the possibility that somewhere *aurantiivertex* might be in contact with Flame-crested Manakin *H. linteatus*.

IDENTIFICATION 14cm. Once identified to genus, this species should be easily identified, it being the sole member of the genus *Heterocercus* in westernmost Amazonia. The striking-plumaged male is easily recognised, and there is no known overlap with either Yellow-crested or Flame-crested Manakins, although the situation in far western Amazonian Brazil is not yet clear *vis-à-vis* the latter species. However, the largely black head of male Flame-crested Manakin should always be obvious, even if the deeper red coronal patch is not visible. Furthermore, male Flame-crested Manakin is much deeper red below. However, the duller females might be confused with other female manakins or some flycatchers; observers should note the large size, cinnamon-coloured breast and whitish-grey throat/cheeks, which (like all *Heterocercus*) are the critical features. Compared with female Flame-crested Manakin, females of the present species are probably on average slightly paler cinnamon below, with marginally paler cheeks and paler upperparts, but this distinction would be very difficult in the absence of males (Ridgely and Tudor 1994, Schulenberg *et al.* 2007). Bill shape offers an extra clue, *vis-à-vis* some potential confusion tyrannids, such as the Cinnamon-crested Spadebill *Platyrinchus saturatus*, which also occurs in *varillales* in the Allpahuayo-Mishana Reserved Zone.

DISTRIBUTION The western Amazonian representative of the genus, Orange-crested Manakin is more or less restricted to the North Amazon (Napo) centre of endemism (Cracraft 1985). It is found in eastern Ecuador, principally along the Río Napo but also the Ríos Aguarico and Lagarto (and at least formerly the Río Pastaza), and in northeasternmost Peru, in dpto. Loreto, where principally but not exclusively found north of the Amazon, e.g. at Allpahuayo-Mishana Reserved Zone, near Iquitos, and at Jenaro Herrera, on the south bank (Alvarez Alonso 2000, Schulenberg *et al.* 2007). In August 2004, B. M. Whitney and D. J. Stejskal (Field Guides tour report) found Orange-crested Manakin on the Brazil side of the Rio Javari, at Palmari Lodge, although subsequently it became apparent that the species had also been observed there two years earlier by A. Whittaker (pers. comm.), who was at the time inexperienced with the species. The species was long speculated to occur in south-easternmost Colombia, in dpto. Putumayo (Hilty and Brown 1986), but to date Orange-crested Manakin has still not been recorded in that country (Salaman *et al.* 2009). Records earlier ascribed to Flame-crested Manakin by Zimmer (1936) at 'Puerto Indiana' north of the Amazon

and from vague localities in upper Amazonia presumably refer to Orange-crested Manakin, a species with which Zimmer was unfamiliar.

MOVEMENTS None known and the species is presumed to be resident and sedentary, like the entire genus.

HABITAT In Ecuador, Orange-crested Manakin favours the understorey and midstorey of seasonally flooded *várzea* and *igapó* forests (principally along black-water streams and rivers), and perhaps especially beside oxbows, but in northern Peru it is also frequently found in tall humid *varillal* woodland (on white sand soils), often with a canopy height of 15–35m (Ridgely and Greenfield 2001, Alvarez Alonso 2000, 2002, Snow 2004b, Schulenberg *et al.* 2007; GMK pers. obs.). In terms of elevational range, the species has been recorded to *c.*300m (Ridgely and Greenfield 2001, Snow 2004b).

DESCRIPTION The sexes differ as in all *Heterocercus*. The species' general structure also closely recalls others of the genus. Large and long-tailed, both sexes possess the graduated tail with the outermost rectrices shortest and narrowest (being about half the length and width of the central tail feathers: see diagram in Prum *et al.* 1996: 723). Further, the feather rachises of the rectrices are curiously unstiffened. Like the entire genus, the seventh primary is longest, with the eighth and sixth equal. Bill is relatively long and narrow, like others of the genus, with only a slightly arched culmen (perhaps more prominently so in males), at least a slightly hooked tip in some males, and in a few (of either sex) reasonably well-developed rictal bristles (but usually these are typical of the genus in being weakly expressed). *Adult male.* – The upperparts are dull olive with a concealed, but when visible very striking, vivid orange coronal stripe/patch (however, usually it appears, at most, as a very narrow line most prominent at the rear), with contrasting greyish head-sides, forming a very weak mask from the lores to the ear-coverts, and grey cheeks. The off-white chin and throat often possess a few dark striations, and consist of elongate feathers that form a very small (spur-like) ruff or plume laterally, bordered below by a very narrow and hardly distinct, darkish olive band. In contrast, the breast to belly/ventral region is entirely dull cinnamon-buff (i.e. it does not grade paler rearwards, unlike this species' congenerics), becoming somewhat olive-grey on the body-sides and flanks. The wing-feathers are generally very dull, nondescript olive-green, i.e. they are virtually concolorous with the mantle, as is the tail, which might average fractionally darker, especially on the underside. *Adult female* – Differs from the male in lacking the orange coronal stripe but unlike congeners has equally dark (grey) head-sides as the male, and the throat is also off-white to greyish and scarcely any smaller than in the male, whilst the underparts pattern is also basically identical to that of the male. Indeed, we have seen females with brighter underparts overall than males on display courts (GMK pers. obs.). Wing-length is generally shorter than in males (see Measurements; Prum *et al.* 1996, Snow 2004b). *Juvenile.* – Restall *et al.* (2006), perhaps simply following Snow (2004b), stated that young birds recall females, whilst Ridgely and Greenfield (2001) mentioned that some males, which they assumed must be non-adults, lack the crown patch. To all intents and purposes, we know nothing concerning plumage maturation in this species. *Moult.* – Very few moult data have been published; Alvarez Alonso (2000) mentioned that birds moult outside the period June–February, and one collected in northern Ecuador in late March was in body moult (MECN). *Bare parts* – Irides dark brown to dark reddish, bill black, occasionally with a paler base to the mandible and perhaps slightly paler cutting edges, and the tarsus and feet are dark grey to blackish grey, with all-dark claws (Snow 2004b, Restall *et al.* 2006; MECN; GMK pers. obs.).

MEASUREMENTS (BMNH; MECN: Sucumbíos, Ecuador, and northeast Peru; Prum *et al.* 1996: geography of sample unknown) Wing of male (*n* = 7) 81.5–87.0mm, wing of female (*n* = 4) 75.5–81.0mm; tail of male (*n* = 4) 43–48mm, tail of female (*n* = 2) 46–52mm; bill of male (*n* = 4) 13.87–14.65mm, bill of female (2) 12.50–13.95mm; tarsus of male (*n* = 4) 13.82–15.62mm, tarsus of female (*n* = 1) 15.95mm. For additional mensural data see Hellmayr (1929b) and Prum *et al.* (1996). Weight (sexes combined): 21–23g (Snow 2004b, Dunning 2008; MECN).

GEOGRAPHICAL VARIATION Monotypic, although several authorities (e.g. Hellmayr 1929b) speculated that this species might prove to be a subspecies of *H. flavivertex*, a theory that has lacked currency for about half a century since then.

VOICE The species' vocal repertoire was most comprehensively detailed by Alvarez Alonso (2000), wherein sonograms are presented, and some of the vocalisations described below are also featured on three audio compilations (Moore 1996, Krabbe and Nilsson 2003, Boesman 2009) as well as being available online at www.xeno-canto.org. The following is very heavily based on the paper by Alvarez Alonso (2000). *H. aurantiivertex* makes at least nine distinct types of vocalisations, primarily by males at their courts. The advertisement call is given only by displaying males on perches within the court, presumably both to attract females and to repel any rival males, and in northern Peru this is most frequently heard between June and February. It consists of 'a thin meandering trill [lasting 1–3 seconds] … sometimes introduced by weak, rapidly delivered whistles of slightly lower frequency.' Unlike the Yellow-crested Manakin, males do not open the bill especially wide. This call is given throughout the day, usually at 1–6-minute intervals, but more sporadically during the hottest periods. So-called 'interaction' vocalisations, which might serve to establish a display site, are also given by males, usually when another male approaches his court, but also in response to another calling male, or even when a different bird

species passes close to the display ground. It consists of a series of syllables much like the advertisement call but with a metallic quality. In the early breeding season, this vocalisation is given more frequently than the advertisement call, but Alvarez Alonso heard it only irregularly through the main breeding season. A female was heard to utter a similar call several times from or near a nest (Alvarez Alonso 2000, 2001). Agonistic vocalisations are given during aggressive chases and other encounters between males, and comprise a loud, rapid, chattering series that rises and falls. During especially aggressive encounters, this vocalisation is sometimes terminated using:

> strange, vibrating, metallic calls … given repeatedly by a male as it furiously pecked at the head of a stuffed specimen placed in its court. When a female specimen was placed in another male's court, the male emitted the *chi-chi* series … but not the hyper-aggressive metallic calls, and he repeatedly attempted copulation ... These hyper-aggressive [calls] appeared to be reserved for male–male interactions.

Chattering calls are less metallic than the agonistic call, and are given by females when another bird species passes near a nest with young, and Alvarez Alonso (2000) also heard them during chases at leks, but was unable to determine which sex gave these calls in this context. A short, 'stuttering' two- (or rarely one-) note call is virtually always given immediately before a bout of jumps in the log display (see Display), whilst similar notes also sometimes preceded the advertisement call. A thin, sibilant whistle (*tsiiii*) at *c*.6kHz is given occasionally, and was speculated by Alvarez Alonso (2000) to be an alarm-call.

NATURAL HISTORY Better known than Flame-crested Manakin, but like the Yellow-crested Manakin our knowledge of the present species' life history has to date been dependent almost entirely on the efforts of a single researcher, in this case the Peruvian José Alvarez Alonso. Just as in the previous two species, Orange-crested Manakin is usually encountered alone or, much less frequently, in pairs, and undoubtedly is most easily found when males are singing. Unlike *H. flavivertex*, but like Flame-crested Manakin, singing males of *H. aurantiivertex* usually favour specific perches in the upper midstorey or subcanopy (varying with the overall forest canopy height), although sometimes they occupy perches just 0.5m above the ground.

FOOD AND FEEDING Foraging birds regularly venture into the upper understorey (*c*.4m or lower above the ground). The species' diet is very poorly known, with the only published data being that it consumes small fruits and insects, and that small *Ficus* (Moraceae) fruits are an important constituent (Snow 2004b). There is no information on the relative proportion of non-fruit items, and nothing has been published on feeding behaviour. However, like Yellow-crested Manakin, the species probably takes most food in flight using short (<20cm) sally-strikes, e.g. to the underside of leaves (GMK pers. obs.), and it sometimes visits fruiting trees along streams.

DISPLAY The species' courtship and displays were well studied and described by Alvarez Alonso (2000), who found that males maintain 'courts' (of 8–25m diameter) inside 'exploded leks' or 'quasi leks', which can extend for up to 1.2km, and are often characterised by treefalls, with a relatively open understorey, many *Ficus* or palm species, and once was situated in a *Mauritia* (Arecaceae) palm swamp. Most courts are 100–300m (rarely 400m) from the closest neighbouring male, but once they were just 65m apart. Males are never in visual contact, but adjacent males can hear each other's advertisement calls (which are audible up to *c.*200m; see Voice) and flight displays were audible more than twice this distance. Within their courts, which are active from one year to the next and defended virtually year-round, males can vocalise day-round (and spend 70–90% of the day in the court). Birds can utilise a mere handful of particularly favoured perches for a significant percentage of each day, sometimes remaining virtually immobile for long periods between bouts of singing. Males occasionally perform two distinctly different solitary displays. We have not witnessed either of these and the following is entirely based on the paper by Alvarez Alonso (2000). The aerial flight display lasts 20–40 seconds and commences as the male moves from its 'court' perch into the canopy, whereupon it flies upwards, with either a zigzagging trajectory or in 30–50m-diameter spirals that become successively tighter as the bird rises, until it reaches 60–100m above the canopy, at which point it plummets toward its court, gaining momentum through the first 15–20m using rapid wingbeats, before partially closing its wings, which produce a peculiar hissing sound that steadily becomes louder as the bird's velocity increases. When just 2–3m above the canopy, the bird abruptly changes its trajectory nearly 90°, producing a dry, explosive pop, perhaps due to it suddenly opening the wings and spreading its tail to break its descent. Finally, the bird describes an arc, sometimes very wide, before entering the trees still at high speed. Some flight displays, especially the first of the morning, which tend to be shorter, lack the explosive pop, and some plummets take less acute angles, of *c.*75°. Sometimes males perform 'failed' flight displays in which no sound is produced by the point of mid-descent, whereupon the display is aborted. One male performed 23 flight displays in 11 days during July but just three displays over six days in November–December of the same year, whilst another performed three flight displays with <1-minute intervals between them, but usually inter-display intervals were of 1–2 hours. The second courtship behaviour is the 'log display', wherein the male descends to a horizontal branch, approximately 6–30cm in diameter and 0.1–2.0m above the ground. Alvarez Alonso (2000) speculated that less effort is expended on this display type, which is usually performed *c.*3 times per day, occasionally up to five times. Typically a male uses various display logs within his court. Soon after landing on such a log, the male performs a series of vertical dancing jumps of 15–20cm, with the head held upright and the brilliant orange crest fully erect. Each jump is accompanied by a sharp pop like the sound made by cracking a thin, dry branch, and much like the display sounds described for White-throated Manakin *Corapipo gutturalis* and White-ruffed Manakin *C. leucorrhoa*, and probably involving the same method, by slapping the wings. The male's posture is perpendicular to the substrate but jumps are interspersed with occasional 90° aerial pirouettes after which it lands briefly in various positions, sometimes about-facing. If the male lands other than perpendicularly to the substrate, he regains orientation using a short jump. Pirouettes are performed with the tail erect and head down, the bird resembling a bundle of feathers as it spins in the air. A variation sees males hovering to display height in a horizontal position on shallow wingbeats.

BREEDING Alvarez Alonso (2001) reported the discovery of a nest in northern Peru, in late February, wherein photographs and approximate dimensions of the nest were presented. It was not sited in a male's territory, and was placed in the fork of a thin branch of a large *Parkia* sp. (Leguminoseae) tree, *c.*4m above the surface of a black-water stream. The finder described the nest as a shallow, loosely woven structure of vegetable fibres and apparently attached to the branch using spiderwebs. It contained two greenish-white eggs with a broad ring of reddish-brown speckling at the larger end, from one of which a chick was observed in the process of hatching in the mid afternoon. When Alvarez Alonso (2000) returned in the mid-morning of the following day, the second chick had also hatched. Throughout her attendance at the nest, the female adopted a very upright position, as if merely perching on the adjacent branch, and indeed the nest was so small and slight that it was practically invisible when the female was present. The chicks were fed regularly, principally small arthropods but once a red *Ficus* fruit, by the female, at a rate of 6–8 feeds per hour, with each foraging sortie lasting 1–10 minutes. The same author found another abandoned nest nearby, 5.5m above the ground in a *Ficus* tree on the opposite side of the same creek, which he speculated might have been from a previous breeding attempt by the same female. There are no other published breeding data, but given that Alvarez Alonso (2000) found that males gave the advertising call most frequently between June and February, this might be assumed to be the height of the breeding season.

STATUS Treated as Least Concern by BirdLife International (2004, 2008), but Orange-crested Manakin generally appears to be a rather uncommon or locally scarce species, especially in Ecuador, where it is known from a relatively small number of localities, most of them along the Napo River (Ridgely and Greenfield 2001). The species is endemic to the Upper Amazon–Napo lowlands Endemic Bird Area (Stattersfield *et al.* 1998). In northeast Peru, recent fieldwork has revealed it to be reasonably common at less than a handful of localities (Alvarez Alonso 2002) and it is plainly a very local species even there (Schulenberg *et al.* 2007). Only recently discovered in Brazil, we have no information to date concerning its status there: it is currently only known from the environs of Palmari Lodge, Amazonas. Orange-crested Manakin is known from very few protected areas, including Parque Nacional Yasuní and Reserva de Producción Faunística Cuyabeno in northern Ecuador (Williams *et al.* 1997), and especially the Allpahuayo-Mishana Reserved Zone, in dpto. Loreto, Peru (Shany *et al.* 2007), which is one of the most frequently visited localities by birdwatchers within the species' range. Other regular sites for the species include Sacha Lodge, Napo Wildlife Centre, Yuturi Lodge, Sani Lodge and La Selva, all in Ecuador (Ridgely and Greenfield 2001; GMK pers. obs.).

REFERENCES Alvarez Alonso (2000, 2001, 2002), Anciães and Peterson (2009), BirdLife International (2004, 2008), Boesman (2009), Cracraft (1985), Dunning (2008), Hellmayr (1929b), Hilty and Brown (1986), Krabbe and Nilsson (2003), Moore (1996) Parker *et al.* (1982), Prum *et al.* (1996), Restall *et al.* (2006), Ridgely and Greenfield (2001), Ridgely and Tudor (1994, 2009), Salaman *et al.* (2009), Schulenberg *et al.* (2007), Shany *et al.* (2007), Snow (2004b), Stattersfield *et al.* (1998), Stotz *et al.* (1996), Williams *et al.* (1997), J. T. Zimmer (1936).

Orange-crested Manakin *Heterocercus aurantiivertex*. **Fig. 1**. Male, Sani Lodge, prov. Orellana, eastern Ecuador, November (*Leif Gabrielsen*). **Fig. 2**. Female, Reserva Nacional Allpahuayo-Mishana, dpto. Loreto, northeast Peru, October (*Hadoram Shirihai / Photographic Handbook to Birds of the World*). **Fig. 3**. Male, Sani Lodge, prov. Orellana, eastern Ecuador, November (*Leif Gabrielsen*). The dullest member of the superspecies is also the most restricted in range, being confined to a relatively small area of upper Amazonia. Differences between the sexes are arguably the least obvious in the entire genus. This male rarely displayed his diagnostic orange crown patch, and other differences are confined to the marginally whiter throat and deeper saturated underparts.

Genus *Machaeropterus*

This genus comprises three small manakins confined to lowland to premontane forests; two of the species are relatively widespread, mainly in the forests of the Orinoco and Amazon drainages (one of them also west of the Andes), whereas the third is found only in a limited area of Colombia and Ecuador.

STRIPED MANAKIN
Machaeropterus regulus   Plate 8

M. (r.) *striolatus*

M. (r.) *regulus*

Pipra regulus **Hahn, 1819**, *Vogel aus Asien, Africa, Amerika Neuholland* 4, pl. 4, figs. 1 & 2, [Bahia,] Brazil

The taxonomy of this beautiful bird clearly requires renewed attention in the light of the recent realisation that the voice of nominate *M. r. regulus* differs markedly from other, Amazonian populations (Whittaker and Oren 1999). There are also less striking differences in plumage, and reportedly size, between *M. r. regulus* and the other members of the species (the *striolatus* group), and cumulatively these differences led Snow (2004b) to treat them as separate species, Eastern Striped Manakin *M. regulus* and Western Striped Manakin *M. striolatus*. This proposed treatment, which had been earlier suggested by Sibley (1996), was followed by Gill and Wright (2006) and Ridgely and Tudor (2009) but has not yet been implemented by the SACC (Remsen *et al.* 2009). Given that Alverson *et al.* (2001), followed by Schulenberg *et al.* (2007), speculated that the subspecies *M. r. aureopectus* ('Golden-chested Manakin') might prove to be specifically distinct from *M. r. regulus*, and stated that this (or a similar undescribed) race also occurs in Peru, thousands of kilometres from the type locality in the Pantepui (see Geographical Variation), we prefer to await the obviously long overdue, but rigorous, overhaul of this species' taxonomy that is needed. J. P. O'Neill and D. F. Lane *in* Alverson *et al.* (2001) speculated that the Peruvian population, initially located on the Cordillera Azul, might represent a separate taxon and that further populations of '*aureopectus*' might be discovered in similar regions with nutrient-poor soil and stunted forest in intervening regions, such as southeast Colombia and eastern Ecuador. Populations of Western Striped Manakin west and east of the Andes also differ vocally (see below).

IDENTIFICATION 9.0–10.3cm. Males are easily identified by their bright red caps that contrast with the olive upperparts. From below, the reddish (or olive and dull chestnut in the nominate race) streaks are always evident, even as an aggressive male moves swiftly through the lower branches to oust another piprid. Females lack the red cap of the male and the uniform olive upperparts may bring other female manakins to mind. The underparts are, however, streaked on the lower flanks with reddish-brown and she retains the rather diminutive aspect of the male. In northeast Peru (e.g. in San Martín) and southwest Brazil (Acre) this species' range overlaps with that of the Fiery-capped Manakin *M. pyrocephalus*, the male of which is lightly streaked below. Male Fiery-capped shows a distinct yellow crown with a scarlet centre, whilst the female has only subtle underparts streaking and that is restricted to the mid-belly.

DISTRIBUTION Striped Manakin occurs in western and southern Venezuela on the lower slopes of the Sierra de Perijá, in the Maracaibo basin, in the foothills of the Andes

north to Barinas, and in dptos. Amazonas and southern Bolívar; then through northern and eastern Colombia in the Caribbean lowlands, south on both slopes of the Cauca Valley to dpto. Valle and in the Magdalena Valley south to Boyacá, locally on the western slope of the Andes in Chocó, also locally in the eastern lowlands; in the lowland forests of eastern Ecuador and northeastern Peru (south to northern Ucayali in the Pucallpa region and the Serra del Divisor); south of the Amazon in western and northern Brazil as far east as Roraima and south of the Amazon to the region of the Rio Urucu, and south to Acre (along the Rio Juruá). The species was also recently listed for Guyana on the basis of a specimen from Ourumee (= the Merumé Mountains) collected in October 1890 (Agro and Ridgely 1998). There is a disjunct population in the Atlantic Forest region of coastal Brazil in eastern Bahia (north to at least Ilheus and Valença, and at least locally to the environs of Salvador) south to central Rio de Janeiro, e.g. to the region of Nova Friburgo, and, at least formerly, to the municipality of Rio de Janeiro itself (Pelzeln 1871, Mitchell 1957, Maciel 2009).

MOVEMENTS The species is usually considered to be resident and sedentary (e.g. Hilty 2003), but Willis and Oniki (2002) reported trapping a 'vagrant' male at the Santa Lúcia reserve, Santa Teresa, Espírito Santo, eastern Brazil, during a period of drought. At over 600m altitude, this was above the species' normal elevational range in the Atlantic Forest.

HABITAT Striped Manakin is confined to the lower and mid levels of humid primary forests (especially *terra firme*), including disturbed edges, shade-coffee plantations (Jones *et al.* 2002) and mature second growth to *c.*1,350m in Peru and to 1,500m in Colombia, with most records from above 300m (e.g. in Venezuela). In Ecuador the species is usually found below 700m, although it occurs locally to 1,000m

(Ridgely and Greenfield 2001, Freile 2004). In eastern Brazil the species is usually confined to extreme lowlands, below 300m (but see Movements). Striped Manakin is sometimes found at forest borders, usually where trees are fruiting, and in stunted forest on ridgetops with nutrient-poor soil in eastern Peru, where it reaches peak abundance in this region (Alverson *et al.* 2001).

DESCRIPTION A tiny manakin in which the sexes differ, and there is also considerable racial variation, perhaps reflecting the presence of multiple species (see the introduction and Geographical Variation). Bill has an arched culmen and usually a hooked tip (sometimes pronounced, but occasionally entirely absent). Males possess modified secondaries, the tips of these feathers being thickened and enlarged, albeit not to the same extent as in Club-winged Manakin *Machaeropterus deliciosus*, whilst the tail feathers also have thickened rachi. *Adult male.* – Crown is bright glistening red, forming a flattened crest; the ear-coverts, rest of the upperparts and tail are bright olive-green. Remiges greyer with white tips to the tertials and inner webs of the flight feathers, although these are extremely difficult to see in the field under most circumstances. Chin and throat buff or whitish. Males of most races are whitish below and heavily but cleanly streaked. The streaks are broad, red and extensive, or thinner and duller, chestnut-brown and restricted to the belly and flanks (see Geographical Variation for details). Some races are stained with either red or yellow across the upper breast (see below). Underwing-coverts generally white, but are sometimes stained cinnamon (racially dependent?). *Adult female.* – Plain olive-green above with white inner fringes to the tertials. Throat buffish-white. The rest of the underparts are yellowish-white coarsely streaked with reddish-brown on the belly and, especially, the flanks. *Juvenile.* – Resembles the female (Snow 2004b), but young males swiftly gain a few red feathers (basally white) solely on the rear crown. *Moult.* – Almost nothing is known concerning moult strategy in this species, but in central and eastern Colombia moulting females have been trapped in April, September and December, and males in April–July and September–November (P. Castañeda, F. Guerrero, J. C. Luna, E. Machado, A. Quevedo, R. Reinoso, G. A. Suárez, Y. Vargas and D. M. Velasco/ProAves unpubl. data). *Bare parts.* – Both sexes have dark red irides (brown in some females, at least in the Atlantic Forest of Brazil) and flesh-coloured legs with rose-coloured soles to the feet. The bill is rather dark horn to black on the upper mandible and tip to the lower, becoming paler (and greyer) towards the base, especially in females, which have this part straw-coloured or rosy flesh-coloured.

MEASUREMENTS *M. r. striolatus* (BMNH; MNRJ; RMNH; ZMA; Gyldenstolpe 1945: Amazonas, Brazil, southeast Colombia, eastern Ecuador and eastern Peru): wing of male (*n* = 9) 52.0–56.5mm, wing of female (*n* = 5) 51–54mm; tail of male (*n* = 18) 19–26mm, tail of female (*n* = 7) 15–25mm; bill of male (*n* = 18) 8.75–9.90mm, bill of female (*n* = 9) 8.01–11.05mm; tarsus of male (*n* = 7) 14.28–16.18mm. Tail length seems to increase north to south. *M. r. antioquiae* (Hellmayr 1929b: Colombia; sexes combined): wing (*n* = 25) 51–53mm; tail (*n* = 25) 21–23mm. *M. r. obscurostriatus* (Phelps and Gilliard 1941: western Venezuela): wing of male (*n* = 1) 50.5mm; tail of male (*n* = 1) 20.5mm; bill of male (*n* = 1) 10mm; tarsus of male (*n* = 1) 14mm. *M. r. zulianus* (Phelps and Gilliard 1941: northwest Venezuela): wing of male (*n* = 1) 49.5mm; tail of male (*n* = 1) 19.5mm; bill of

male (*n* = 1) 10mm; tarsus of male (*n* = 1) 14.5mm. *M. r. aureopectus* (Phelps and Phelps 1946: southeast Venezuela): wing of female (*n* = 1) 53mm; tail of female (*n* = 1) 18mm; bill of female (*n* = 1) 11mm; tarsus of female (*n* = 1) 14mm. *M. r. regulus* (BMNH; MNRJ; ZMA: Bahia, Espírito Santo and Rio de Janeiro, Brazil): wing of male (*n* = 12) 51.0–55.5mm, wing of female (*n* = 7) 50.5–54.5mm; tail of male (*n* = 17) 20–27mm, tail of female (*n* = 11) 19.5–27.0mm; bill of male (*n* = 15) 8.99–9.98mm, bill of female (*n* = 11) 9.05–10.84mm; tarsus of male (*n* = 9) 13.34–15.95mm, tarsus of female (*n* = 5) 13.21–14.43mm. Data from live birds (*M. r. antioquiae* and *M. r. striolatus*) (variation in culmen-length suggests mix of measuring protocols): wing of male (*n* = 68) 49–54mm (61mm), wing of female (*n* = 126) 48–54mm (61mm); tail of male (*n* = 66) 14.5–23.5mm, tail of female (*n* = 122) 18.5–30.0mm; bill of male (*n* = 49) 6.9–11.1mm, bill of female (*n* = 112) 5.8–11.6mm; tarsus of male (*n* = 67) 13.4–17.7mm (22.5mm), tarsus of female (*n* = 122) 13.7–18.7mm (Colombia: P. Castañeda, F. Guerrero, J. C. Luna, E. Machado, A. Quevedo, R. Reinoso, G. A. Suárez, Y. Vargas and D. M. Velasco/ProAves unpubl. data). Weight (sexes combined): 6.4–12.5g (*M. r. regulus, M. r. striolatus* and *M. r. antioquiae*; FMNH; MVZ; MNRJ; ROM; T. M. Donegan *et al.* unpubl. data; P. Castañeda, F. Guerrero, J. C. Luna, E. Machado, A. Quevedo, R. Reinoso, G. A. Suarez, Y. Vargas and D. M. Velasco/ProAves unpubl. data) and 10.5–11.5g (*n* = 3; *M. r. aureopectus*; FMNH). Dunning (2008) listed means of 9.6g (males) and 9.1g (females).

GEOGRAPHICAL VARIATION Six races are currently recognised principally based on the depth and width of the streaking on the underparts in males, and the colour staining on the upper breast. In the following races males have red staining over the breast, and the remainder of the underparts (except the throat) is streaked reddish-chestnut and white. Generally it is only the males that are identifiable to taxon. The following leans heavily on Restall *et al.* (2006). *M. r. antioquiae* Chapman, 1924 (in the Magdalena and Cauca valleys, and Caribbean region of western and central Colombia), is very much like the next race, but is slightly more yellowish above with a darker red crown and broader white breast streaking. According to Hellmayr (1929b) females are inseparable from those of *M. r. striolatus*. *M. r. striolatus* (C. L. Bonaparte, 1838) (in eastern Colombia, south to eastern Ecuador, northeast Peru and western Amazonian Brazil as far as the Rio Urucu) like the last race has reddish-brown irides and vinaceous-flesh tarsi, whilst the bill is blackish above and paler on the lower mandible. The chest-band, although dominated by red feathering, also contains some greenish-yellow elements. *M. r. obscurostriatus* W. L. Phelps, Sr. & Gilliard, 1941 (on the west slope of the Andes in western Venezuela, from western Trujillo south to western Mérida), has the rump tinged orange-yellowish, reddish streaking on the upper breast that becomes rufous over the rest of the underparts and orange-yellow irides. Females have a dull olive throat and upper breast, and the tarsi in both sexes are greyish olive-green, whilst the bill is described as being brown. *M. r. zulianus* W. L. Phelps, Sr. & W. L. Phelps, Jr., 1952 (in northwestern Venezuela, at the base of the Sierra de Perijá, in the Maracaibo basin, at the west base of the Andes in Táchira and along the east slope of the Andes from southeast Táchira to northwest Barinas), has a red breast with white centres to the dark chestnut streaks. Females are whitish on the underparts, overlain with weak chestnut streaking, whilst immature males have slightly darker streaks than adult females. Both sexes have orange irides (yellow in the young). Difficulties in racial identification meant that both *M. r. striolatus* and *M. r. antioquiae* were originally considered part of the Venezuelan avifauna (Phelps 1944), in place of the present subspecies and *M. r. obscurostriatus*. **M. r. aureopectus** W. L. Phelps, Sr. & Gilliard, 1941 (of southeast Venezuela, in central Amazonas and northwestern and southeastern Bolívar, as well as adjacent northern Brazil, and presumably western Guyana) has black centres to the chestnut underparts streaking, and the chest is stained yellow in males, whilst the uppertail-coverts are washed with orange. Females are more whitish below, but still show some evidence of the yellow upper breast. Both sexes have red irides, whilst immature males have brown eyes and an olive flush to the breast (see also Phelps and Phelps 1946). Another population (set to be described as a new taxon by Dane Lane *et al.*) with a yellow breast-band (Fig. 5), has been found in northern Peru, in the foothills of the Mayo Valley, e.g. at Quebrada Mishquiyacu, near Moyobamba, dpto. San Martín, and in the Cordillera Azul (Alverson *et al.* 2001, Schulenberg *et al.* 2007, Merkord *et al.* 2009). At least in Peru this form appears to have rather smaller white tips to the tertials than in *M. r. striolatus*. **M. r. regulus** (Hahn, 1819) (of eastern Brazil) is slightly larger than the other races; males are yellow-buff on the chest and the dark streaks are narrow and olive, becoming browner on the belly. This imparts an overall paler effect to the underparts than in other populations.

VOICE Geographical variation rather pronounced, with quite distinct vocalisations documented for three different populations, thereby fuelling speculation that multiple species are involved (see introduction and above). Published recordings are available on the following compilations: English and Parker (1992), Moore (1993), Remold (2002), Álvarez-Rebolledo *et al.* (2003), Krabbe and Nilsson (2003), Minns *et al.* (2009) and Boesman (2009), and recordings from Brazil (*M. r. regulus*), Colombia (*M. r. antioquiae*), Ecuador (*M. r. striolatus*) and Peru (San Martín) are archived online at www.xeno-canto.org. In Amazonia (*M. r. striolatus*) the male's advertisement is a soft, insect-like, whistled *whoo-eet* or *pit-sink*, with a quiet overtone to the second part, which is difficult to track down, usually given at 10–30-second intervals in an 'exploded lek' of 2–4 males (see below). This is sometimes followed by short sneezing or quavering buzz or, less frequently, a sneezing *tease-zip* (Hilty and Brown 1986). The song is described by Schulenberg *et al.* (2007) as a loud, hollow *BOOP*, also followed by a quavering buzz, which is perhaps produced by the modified secondaries. However, birds with a yellow breast-band (*aureopectus?*) in Peru give 'a very different, rising, whistled "*chiwee?*" reminiscent of Eastern Wood-Pewee [*Contopus virens*]' (Schulenberg *et al.* 2007). A mechanical wing rattling is also given in display (see below). As noted by Whittaker and Oren (1999) males of *M. r. regulus* in eastern Brazil have a quite different advertisement, described by those authors as 'a shorter, very fast metallic buzzing which is repeated more quickly than *M. r. striolatus* of Amazonia.' This call was rendered *eeeuw* by Ridgely and Tudor (2009). Populations of Western Striped Manakin west and east of the Andes also differ vocally but less strikingly, with a two-note call in each case west of the Andes, the second note being closer in frequency to the first (T. M. Donegan *in litt.* 2009).

NATURAL HISTORY Except when foraging this species can be remarkably unobtrusive, and the best chance of observing it lies in tracking down a calling male to its perch in the lower to mid levels of the forest. Birds often remain silent and inconspicuous on their perches, usually a slender branch 2–15m above the ground, for several minutes at a time.

FOOD AND FEEDING The species' diet appears to comprise small fruits and insects taken via typical short rapid sallies, but very little specific information is available. However, Sick (1997) records that when attending the same fruiting trees as White-bearded Manakin *Manacus manacus* and Red-headed Manakin *Pipra rubrocapilla*, both of the latter two species are dominant over *M. regulus*. Blendinger *et al.* (2008) studied fruit removal by manakins at a study site in Amazonian Ecuador, where Striped Manakin was one of the few bird species to disperse fruits of *Miconia fosteri* and *M. serrulata* (Melastomataceae).

DISPLAY The 'exploded lek' system is well established for this species, with males displaying for several minutes at a time, then departing to feed, before returning to the lek, at which birds are usually within 'earshot' but not sight of each other (each territory usually being up to 30m in diameter). Leks may be attended by up to 11 males in some parts of the range, but in eastern Ecuador leks are rarely attended by more than three males and these are usually located atop low hills (Loiselle *et al.* 2007a, Durães *et al.* 2008a). Loiselle *et al.* (2007a), working at a new study site at the Tiputini Biodiversity Station in Yasuní National Park, in eastern Ecuador, found relatively strong segregation (principally along axes of elevation and slope heterogeneity) between leks of different manakin species. Ridgetop sites were favoured by both the present species and Golden-headed Manakin *Pipra erythrocephala*, but there was no geographical overlap between individual leks of these two species. Each male has several favoured perches that are used regularly. In Colombia, if a male succeeds in attracting a female, he switches to making a series of short vertical 'jumps', which are accompanied by vibrating wing movements and insect-like buzzing notes (Haffer 1967b), whilst in northeast Ecuador a male was described to revolve repeatedly around its display branch in the presence of a female (Skutch 1969). The only other information concerning this facet of the species' natural history comes from the observations of Sick (1967), who described two males displaying together in the same manner as mentioned for Fiery-capped Manakin *Machaeropterus pyrocephalus* below, during which a whirr apparently produced by the modified secondaries may be given.

BREEDING Only recently were the first breeding data for any of the Striped Manakin taxa published, based on observations of 12 nests of *M. r. striolatus* (seven of them active) at two sites in eastern Ecuador. All of the nests were similar to those of other manakin nests, being small, open cups suspended in the 'Y'-shaped gaps formed by horizontal branch forks, except one nest, which was between a living stem and a dead branch that had fallen over it. All of the nests were lined internally with whitish fibres and externally decorated with whitish, yellowish or pale brown fibres and dry palm leaves and strips thereof, which usually hung well below the nest in a 'skirt-like' fashion, considered by H. F. Greeney (*in litt.* 2010) to be most similar to nests of *Lepidothrix* spp. Nest material was bound together and to the supporting fork using spiderwebs. Most nests were situated on slopes or on flat areas atop hills, in areas with a relatively open understorey. All were between 0.4 and 0.8m above the ground, in low shrubs or saplings. All six active nests had two eggs, which were whitish with chestnut speckling. Nest and egg dimensions were presented in Durães *et al.* (2008a), as was some information concerning adult behaviour at the nest. Remarkably, one female was apparently attending two different active nests. In addition, M. A. Carriker collected 12 breeding-condition birds in northern dpto. Antioquia (*M. r. antioquiae*) during May–August (Hilty and Brown 1983), whilst MVZ has another, a male, from this region, taken in late April with large testes, and a female with partially formed eggs in the oviduct (July). H. Shirihai (pers. comm.) observed a female carrying nesting material, in dpto. Huila, in January (Fig. 3). In eastern Colombia, females of the race *M. r. striolatus* have been trapped with brood patches in April and May (ProAves unpubl. data), ROM has two females in breeding condition collected in October, and T. M. Donegan *et al.* (unpubl.) trapped four juveniles between 18 July and 6 August. There are no published breeding data from the Atlantic Forest biome, but G. M. Kirwan and H. Shirihai (pers. obs.) watched a female carrying nesting material to an unseen nest in mid January in Bahia.

STATUS The species is treated as Least Concern (BirdLife International 2004, 2008). Nominate *M. r. regulus* is confined to the Serra do Mar Centre of endemism (Cracraft 1985) and is considered Vulnerable in the state of Espírito Santo (Passamani and Mendes 2007). Striped Manakin is generally uncommon to locally fairly common (e.g. in Venezuela) throughout the species' ample range, but must be rare in Guyana (given the complete lack of recent records) and is considered to be very local south of the Orinoco River in Venezuela (Hilty 2003). Anciães and Peterson (2006) predicted that both Western and Eastern Striped Manakins, which they assessed separately, might be moderately to badly impacted by habitat modification in the face of potential climate change based on modelling techniques. Known from many protected areas throughout its range, especially in Amazonia, but localities elsewhere include, e.g., Tayrona National Park, in Colombia,

Podocarpus National Park, in Ecuador and Una Biological Reserve, Reserva Michelin, Estação Veracel, and Monte Pascoal National Park, in Brazil. Westernmost populations might be threatened to some extent, but in Colombia are protected within two ProAves reserves (Salaman *et al.* 2009, Donegan *et al.* 2010). Nominate *M. r. regulus* is also rather easily found at the privately owned RPPN Regua, near Cachoeiras de Macacu, in Rio de Janeiro state (Pimentel and Olmos 2011). This taxon seems to have formerly occurred within the city limits of Rio de Janeiro itself (Pelzeln 1871, Mitchell 1957), but there are no recent records therein (Maciel 2009).

REFERENCES Agro and Ridgely (1998), Albano (2010b), Álvarez-Rebolledo *et al.* (2003), Alverson *et al.* (2001), Anciães and Peterson (2006, 2009), Balchin and Toyne (1998), BirdLife International (2004, 2008), Blake (1962), Blendinger *et al.* (2008), Boesman (2009), Braun *et al.* (2007), Brooks *et al.* (2009), Cadena *et al.* (2000), Cracraft (1985), Cuervo *et al.* (2008b), Dekker (2003), Donegan *et al.* (2010), Dunning (2008), Durães *et al.* (2008a), English and Parker (1992), Forrester (1993), Freile (2004), Freitas (2008), Gill and Wright (2006), Gyldenstolpe (1945), Haffer (1967b, 1974), Hellmayr (1929b), Hilty (2003), Hilty and Brown (1983, 1986), Jones *et al.* (2002), Krabbe and Nilsson (2003), Loiselle *et al.* (2007a), Maciel (2009), Mallet-Rodrigues *et al.* (2007), Merkord *et al.* (2009), Minns *et al.* (2009), Mitchell (1957), Moore (1993), Naka *et al.* (2006), Passamani and Mendes (2007), Pearman (1994b), Pelzeln (1871), Peres and Whittaker (1991), Phelps (1944), Phelps and Phelps (1946), Pimentel and Olmos (2011), Pinto (1944), Quevedo *et al.* (2006), Remold (2002), Remsen *et al.* (2009), Restall *et al.* (2006), Ridgely and Greenfield (2001), Ridgely and Tudor (1994, 2009), Salaman *et al.* (1999, 2008, 2009), Schulenberg *et al.* (2006, 2007), Sibley (1996), Sick (1959d, 1967, 1997), Silva *et al.* (2000), Silveira *et al.* (2005), Simon (2009), Skutch (1969), Snow (2004b), Stotz *et al.* (1996), Whittaker and Oren (1999), Wiley (2010), Willis and Oniki (2002).

1

Striped Manakin *Machaeropterus regulus*. **Fig. 1**. Male, *M. r. antioquiae*, El Paujil Bird Reserve, dpto. Santander, central Colombia, February (*Nick Athanas / Tropical Birding*). Note the depth of colour of the streaking below (and its breadth) compared to the nominate form in eastern Brazil. Northwest South American populations are often separated as Western Striped Manakin *M. striolatus*, but we maintain a single species because variation in this group is sufficiently complex that more than two species might be involved, and more data are required (see text). **Fig. 2**. Male, *M. r. striolatus*, Shiripuno Lodge, prov. Pastaza, eastern Ecuador, November (*Hadoram Shirihai / Photographic Handbook to Birds of the World*). The underparts streaking is much narrower and less bright in this race. **Fig. 3**. Female, *M. r. antioquiae*, Campo Alegre, dpto. Huila, central Colombia, January (*Hadoram Shirihai / Photographic Handbook to Birds of the World*). Note the nest material in the bill. **Fig. 4**. Male, *M. r. regulus*, Porto Seguro, Bahia, eastern Brazil, November (*Ciro Albano*). Strikingly pale below, with streaking concentrated at the sides, browner (less red) and confined to the feather fringes. This Brazilian endemic taxon is frequently separated specifically, under the English name Eastern Striped Manakin. **Fig. 5**. Male, *M. r. aureopectus*-type, 77km west-northwest of Contamana, dpto. Loreto, Peru, July (*Andrew Kratter*). Closest to *aureopectus* in plumage, this individual represents a new taxon, to be described by Dan Lane *et al.*

FIERY-CAPPED MANAKIN
Machaeropterus pyrocephalus   Plate 8

Pipra pyrocephala **P. L. Sclater, 185**2, *Rev. Mag. Zool.* (2)4: 9, locality unknown; upper Amazonas, Ucayali, by substitution, Berlepsch and Hartert, 1902

Another *Machaeropterus* with a curiously disjunct range, this species and the last were considered by Snow (1975) to form a superspecies, although even with his powers of acuity he was at a loss to explain the apparent geographical replacement mechanisms at work.

IDENTIFICATION 8.0–10.4cm. Small and short-tailed, and like the Striped Manakin *M. regulus* the male has streaked underparts. However, the streaking on male Fiery-capped is far less distinct than in its sister taxon, whilst the yellow crown and rufous upperparts should also separate this species from Striped in its narrow zone of sympatry (across northern and eastern Peru and western Amazonian Brazil). The female is slightly less straightforward: being bright olive above with only vestigial streaking on the underparts, there is some resemblance to a female *Pipra* manakin. However, no female manakin in the latter genus possesses the combination of purplish-flesh legs and a reddish iris, whilst, if seen, the rather indistinct streaking on the underparts should confirm the identification. Female Fiery-capped differs from female Striped Manakin in having marginally darker underparts with less obvious streaking that is olive (not pinkish).

DISTRIBUTION Fiery-capped Manakin is principally found in upper Amazonia. There are isolated populations in southern Venezuela, on the lower Río Caura (Berlepsch and Hartert 1902), and middle Río Paragua, in Bolívar, with a single sight record from northwest Amazonas, near Puerto Ayacucho (Hilty 1999, 2003), and another, apparently, isolated population occurs in extreme northern Brazil (at the Maracá Ecological Station in Roraima: Moskovits *et al.* 1985, Naka *et al.* 2006). It is also known from localities in

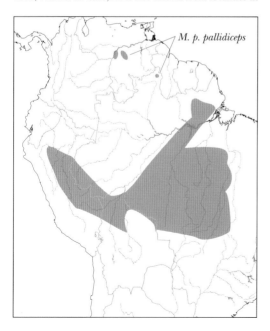

M. p. pallidiceps

southern Amapá (Novaes 1978, Campos *et al.* 2009) and on the upper Rio Paru do Leste and elsewhere in northernmost Pará (Novaes 1980a, Aleixo *et al.* 2011). Elsewhere in Brazil the species is found south of the Amazon, in Acre near Porangaba, Assis Brasil, and in Rio Branco, as well as southeast through Rondônia to Mato Grosso, south as far as the Serra das Araras and Chapada dos Guiramães, and east to Goiás (Zimmer 1936a, Pinto 1944, Hidasi 2007), thence north along the lower Rio Tapajós, as well as east to Palmas, Tocantins (Diniz *et al.* 2009), and the Serra dos Carajás, Pará (Pacheco *et al.* 2007). Further south and west, Fiery-capped Manakin is present in eastern Peru, where it occurs locally in dpto. San Martín, e.g. at Quebrada Mishquiyacu, near Moyobamba, and on the Cordillera Azul, south to dptos. Puno and Madre de Dios (Schulenberg *et al.* 2007), as well as in northern Bolivia south to dpto. La Paz and northeastern dpto. Santa Cruz (Hennessey *et al.* 2003b).

MOVEMENTS None definitely known, although Willis and Oniki (1990) speculated that the species might move from more humid forests (in winter) to drier woodlots in summer.

HABITAT Somewhat catholic in its habitat requirements, Fiery-capped Manakin inhabits the lower to middle levels, and borders, of humid woodland, mature second growth and even transitional forest. In areas where this and the previous species are found in sympatry, e.g. in parts of Acre, western Brazil, and the Serra del Divisor, on the border with Peru, it is possible that *M. pyrocephalus* shows a greater preference for areas with substantial bamboo in the understorey (Whittaker and Oren 1999). Locally, Fiery-capped Manakin occurs to 1,500m in Peru (more usually to 1,100m: Schulenberg *et al.* 2007), but to just 200m in Venezuela (Hilty 2003).

DESCRIPTION Sexes differ. Very short-tailed like the previous species. The bill has an arched culmen and usually a hooked tip (sometimes pronounced, but occasionally entirely absent). Males possess modified inner secondaries, their tips being thickened and enlarged, albeit not to the same extent as in *M. deliciosus*, whilst the tail feathers also have thickened rachi. Nominate race is described here. *Adult male.* – Superbly plumaged male has a golden-yellow crown and nape with a contrasting but inconspicuous scarlet median stripe. The ear-coverts and head-sides are olive. Mantle and rump deep cinnamon-rufous, appearing plum-coloured in the darkness of the forest interior. Tail dull olive. Scapulars, wing-coverts and most remiges are brighter olive; the modified inner remiges being whitish on the outer fringes and the tertials being further adorned with black spots (conspicuous in display). Underwing-coverts white (inconspicuous in the field). Underparts pale plumbrown to pinkish-white, lightly streaked with white and rosy brown. *Adult female.* – Uniform bright olive above. Throat is greyish with whiter bases to the feathers; the rest of the underparts are washed yellow-olive, sometimes with some brownish elements over the breast (becoming yellower on belly), with faint olive streaking. Undertail- and underwing-coverts (the latter sometimes obvious in flight) and rear flanks whiter. *Immature male.* – Female-like, but has usually acquired some golden-yellow on the forecrown at this stage (Hilty 2003) and perhaps also some reddish coloration on the throat-sides (MNRJ). *Juvenile.* – Essentially female-like, but male specimens without any trace of the head and upperparts coloration, and thus presumably true juveniles, have distinctly brighter underparts than adult females, being greenish-yellow throughout, including the rear flanks and undertail-coverts (MNRJ). Young males in entirely female-like plumage do sing just as adult males. *Moult.* – There are no published data on moult, but birds taken in Pará, Brazil, in July–August were in very fresh plumage, and two from Rondônia, Brazil, taken in August and October were not in moult (MNRJ). *Bare parts.* – Legs purplish-flesh, dark yellow or yellowish-pink (males) to bright flesh (females); the irides are red to orange, slightly duller (chestnut or brown) in females. Bill dark horn to black over the maxilla with a paler (flesh- or horn-coloured) base to the lower mandible (FMNH; MNRJ; Ridgely and Tudor 1994, Hilty 2003, Snow 2004b, Restall *et al.* 2006).

MEASUREMENTS (BMNH; MNRJ; RMNH: Mato Grosso, Pará and Rondônia, Brazil, and eastern Peru; see also mensural data in Oniki and Willis 1999) *M. p. pyrocephalus*: wing of male ($n = 15$) 51.5–55.0mm, wing of female ($n = 8$) 48–53mm; tail of male ($n = 15$) 18–25mm, tail of female ($n = 7$) 22–27mm; bill of male ($n = 15$) 9.06–10.31mm, bill of female ($n = 8$) 9.74–10.34mm; tarsus of male ($n = 5$) 12.68–14.12mm, tarsus of female ($n = 5$) 13.36–14.72mm. Live birds from southeast Peru (dpto. Madre de Dios): wing of male (chord) ($n = 5$) 51–53mm, wing of female (chord) ($n = 8$) 51–54mm (B. Sorrie MS.). Weight (sexes combined, although females perhaps average very marginally heavier): 7.8–12.5g (Fry 1970, Novaes 1976, Bates *et al.* 1989, Oniki and Willis 1999, Hilty 2003, Dunning 2008; FMNH; MNRJ).

GEOGRAPHICAL VARIATION Two races generally recognised. *M. p. pallidiceps* J. T. Zimmer, 1936, in southern Venezuela and extreme northern Brazil resembles the nominate race, but is considered to have the yellow of the head paler and the central crown-stripe much less prominent, being golden-brown at the front and less bright red at the rear. It is unknown whether females of the two forms differ, but it seems unlikely. *M. p. pyrocephalus* (described above) occurs in Amazonian Peru, Bolivia and Brazil.

VOICE Male's advertising song given in an 'exploded lek' is a high-pitched bell- or frog-like *pling* or *tink*, usually given at intervals of up to one minute and easily overlooked until learnt (Ridgely and Tudor 1994, Hilty 2003; GMK pers. obs.). Even observers familiar with the species' voice will frequently find the birds difficult to pinpoint, as the sound is rather quiet and it is sometimes hard to judge their distance from the observer. Songs are given irregularly throughout the day, even during the hottest hours, and with perhaps no special frequency during the early morning. No other vocalisations have apparently been reported or recorded. Commercial recordings are available on the following compilations: Mayer (2000), Schulenberg *et al.* (2000), Boesman (2006a, 2006b, 2009) and Marantz and Zimmer (2006), and recordings from Brazil and Peru are archived online at www.xeno-canto.org.

NATURAL HISTORY Inconspicuous and often difficult to observe, even at leks, and away from them Fiery-capped Manakin is only regularly seen at fruiting trees and shrubs.

FOOD AND FEEDING Seems particularly fond of melastomes, e.g. *Miconia* spp., sometimes visiting these with other manakins, including Opal-crowned Manakin *Lepidothrix iris* in the Serra dos Carajás, Pará, Brazil (GMK pers. obs.), apparently without any interaction between them. Fruits are taken both whilst perched and following a short fluttering flight and brief sally-hover. Insect remains

have also been recorded in the stomach contents of this species (FMNH).

DISPLAY Males can sing alone (low ranking or young?) or, more usually, at loose 'exploded' leks (see above) containing up to 5–6 birds that seem rarely to be in more than 'earshot' of one another (i.e. with no visual contact), each bird perching on typically very slender branches 4–15m above the ground, sometimes slightly lower (Hilty 2003, Snow 2004a; GMK pers. obs.). Each male has several favoured perches, just like the previous species, generally flying at high speed between them, but occasionally adult males perform a much slower flight, in which the bird appears to fluff-out the back and rump feathers, and flies on slightly bowed wings in the manner almost of a dipper *Cinclus* sp., the purpose of which is unknown (GMK pers. obs.). In Brazil, Helmut Sick observed males displaying in 'pairs' that perched together, with one hanging downwards and twisting so rapidly from side to side as to blurr, whilst producing a *zsssss* sound apparently using its enlarged secondaries (Sick 1967).

BREEDING The one nest found, south of Maripa, Bolívar, Venezuela, in mid March 1995, was a leafy cup nest, lined with coarse grass-like fibres suspended within the fork of a sapling 1m above the ground and well shaded by the surrounding vegetation. It held two dull white eggs streaked and mottled with brown; the nest was tended by the female although a male was seen nearby, suggesting that nests might be sited within territories or close to them (Bradshaw and Kirwan 1995). In southeast Peru both sexes appear to be in breeding condition between late August and November at least (FMNH). The only other breeding data come from Brazil and involve birds with brood patches trapped in February, September and October in Mato Grosso (Oniki and Willis 1999), a juvenile collected in northwest Mato Grosso in November (R. Gaban-Lima; MNRJ) with males in breeding condition collected in the same region in mid October (Novaes 1976), and a male with active gonads taken in Rondônia in October (MNRJ).

STATUS Treated as Least Concern (BirdLife International 2004, 2008). Anciães and Peterson (2006) predicted that Fiery-capped Manakin could be severely impacted by habitat modification in the face of potential climate change based on modelling techniques. Uncommon and generally rather local (considered inexplicably so in Venezuela; Hilty 2003), although no sub-population can be considered threatened at present. Relatively easy to observe at Tambopata Reserve, dpto. Madre de Dios, and around Amazonia Lodge, in Manu National Park and Biosphere Reserve, Peru (Walker 2009); at certain sites within the Serra dos Carajás, Pará, and at Portão da Fe, in the Chapada dos Guiramães, near Cuiabá, Mato Grosso, Brazil (Forrester 1993); and along the Maripa–Trincheras road, Bolívar, Venezuela. Fiery-capped Manakin seems to be known from rather few protected areas within its range, but is present in Cantão State Park and Fazenda Ecológica, both in Tocantins, Brazil (Pinheiro and Dornas 2009a, Diniz *et al.* 2009), Tapajós National Park, Pará, Brazil (Oren and Parker 1997), Igaparé-Gelado APA, Pará, Brazil (Pacheco *et al.* 2007); Manu National Park and Biosphere Reserve, Peru (Walker *et al.* 2006); and, in Bolivia, in Madidi National Park, dpto. La Paz (Hosner *et al.* 2009), Pilón Lajas Biosphere Reserve (Hennessey *et al.* 2003a), Noel Kempff Mercado, dpto. Beni (Bates *et al.* 1998, Acheson and Davis 2001), and Estación Biológica Caparú, dpto. Santa Cruz (Vidoz *et al.* 2010).

REFERENCES Acheson and Davis (2001), Aleixo *et al.* (2011), Alteff *et al.* (2009), Anciães and Peterson (2006, 2009), Bates *et al.* (1989, 1998), Berlepsch and Hartert (1902), BirdLife International (2004, 2008), Boesman (2006a, 2006b, 2009), Bradshaw and Kirwan (1995), Campos *et al.* (2009), Diniz *et al.* (2009), Dunning (2008), Forrester (1993), Fry (1970), Guilherme (2004), Hellmayr (1929b), Hennessey *et al.* (2003a), Hidasi (1998, 2007), Hilty (1999, 2003), Hosner *et al.* (2009), Lees *et al.* (2008), Lopes *et al.* (2009), Maillard *et al.* (2007), Mayer (2000), Merkord *et al.* (2009), Mestre *et al.* (2010), Moskovits *et al.* (1985), Naka *et al.* (2006), Novaes (1976, 1978, 1980a), Oniki and Willis (1999), Oren and Parker (1997), Pacheco *et al.* (2007), Parker *et al.* (1994a, 1994b, 1994c), Pinheiro and Dornas (2009a), Pinto (1944), Rêgo *et al.* (2007), Remsen *et al.* (1987), Restall *et al.* (2006), Ridgely and Tudor (1994, 2009), Robbins *et al.* (2011), Robinson and Terborgh (1997), Schulenberg *et al.* (2000, 2006, 2007), Sick (1959d, 1967, 1997), Silva (1996), Snow (1975, 2004b), Stotz *et al.* (1996), Tavares and Guilherme (2000), Vidoz *et al.* (2010), Walker (2009), Walker *et al.* (2006), Whitney (1997), Whittaker and Oren (1999), Wiley (2010), Willis and Oniki (1990), J. T. Zimmer (1936a), K. J. Zimmer *et al.* (1997).

Fiery-capped Manakin *Machaeropterus pyrocephalus*. **Figs. 1–2**. Male, *M. p. pyrocephalus*, Cock-of-the-Rock Lodge, Manu Road, dpto. Cuzco, southeast Peru, July (*Harvey van Diek*). **Fig. 3**. Male, *M. p. pyrocephalus*, near Quincemil, dpto. Cuzco, southeast Peru (*Hadoram Shirihai / Photographic Handbook to Birds of the World*). **Fig. 4**. Female, *M. p. pyrocephalus*, Serra dos Carajás, Pará, east Amazonian Brazil, September (*Hadoram Shirihai / Photographic Handbook to Birds of the World*). In comparison to the amazingly dazzling males, females are 'dowdy' and easily overlooked.

CLUB-WINGED MANAKIN
Machaeropterus deliciosus   Plate 8

Pipra deliciosa P. L. Sclater, 1860, *Proc. Zool. Soc. Lond.* 28: 60, Nanegal, [Pichincha,] Ecuador

This is the most range-restricted *Machaeropterus*, and was formerly placed in its own monophyletic genus, *Allocopterus* (e.g. by Hellmayr 1929b). However, even Hellmayr questioned the necessity of recognising *Allocotopterus*, given that the more striking modification of the secondaries is the only truly differentiating feature and in that character is not so different (see Snow 1975, who was first to recommend that the two genera be merged, this proposal being supported by Prum and Wilson 1987, Prum 1992, 1994a).

IDENTIFICATION 9.0–10.5cm. Male unmistakable due to its rufous-chestnut body and contrasting black (and white) wings, whilst the forecrown is bright scarlet. Females also exhibit the white on the inner webs of the tertials possessed by the male, although this feature may prove difficult to see. However, the pale cinnamon or buffy face-sides (sometimes more confined to the lores) provides an additional feature, whilst the triangular head-shape is obvious when the bird is excited and the bill often appears rather pale.

DISTRIBUTION Restricted to northwestern South America, where it is generally rather local. This remarkable bird is found on the west slope of the Andes in southwest Colombia (from Alto de Pisones, on the border between dptos. Risaralda and Antioquia, southwards) and in western Ecuador south to prov. Pichincha, with an apparently recently established, and isolated population in prov. El Oro, e.g. west of Piñas, and also known from a single specimen (taken in 1968) in western prov. Loja. There are no recent data from its former lowland sites in southern prov. Pichincha, at Río Palenque, or from prov. Los Ríos, near Quevedo. Mostly occurs at 400–1,550m, but recorded to 2,020m in southwest Colombia, in dpto. Cauca (Donegan and Dávalos 1999) and to 1,800m in northwest Ecuador (Solano-Ugalde in press).

MOVEMENTS Seems strongly sedentary in Colombia (e.g. Hilty 1997), but apparently is rather migratory in at least parts of Ecuador being regularly found down to 100m at one locality in the extreme north-west (Playa de Oro, prov. Esmeraldas) during the dry (non-breeding) season (Ridgely

and Greenfield 2001). Furthermore, the same authors suggest that the records from Río Palenque and Quevedo, also in Ecuador (see above) represented additional evidence of dispersal.

HABITAT Club-winged Manakin is found in the lower and middle levels of very humid premontane and foothill forests, but also frequently occurs in adjacent second growth and borders, with display areas ('arenas') frequently located in disturbed areas, such as an old treefall or ravines near pastures.

DESCRIPTION Sexes differ. Very short-tailed. The bill has an arched culmen and usually a hooked tip (sometimes pronounced, but occasionally entirely absent). The male has strongly modified secondaries, with the outermost to s7 being thickened, twisted and bent at the tip, forming a club shape that affords the species its name. The same modification is present but much reduced in ss8–10. Bend of wing yellow and the underwing-coverts are white in both sexes (both these features are conspicuous in the male's display). *Adult male.* – Forehead and forecrown scarlet, and often raised in excitement, with a dusky eye-stripe. Nape, mantle and most of the underparts are rufous-chestnut, albeit slightly paler over the face and throat. Rump, tail, lower belly and ventral region blackish, relieved by some white feathers on the flanks (only usually observed when the wings are raised) and the outer tail feathers. Scapulars and wings also black, the inner remiges strikingly fringed with white. *Adult female.* – Uniform olive-green above, the only relief provided by the contrasting white inner fringes to the inner remiges. Throat whitish with pale cinnamon face-sides, reaching onto the ear-coverts just below the eye. The rest of the underparts are pale olive, except the mid-belly, which is washed yellow. *Juvenile/Immature.* – Resembles the female, although young males start to show some cinnamon feathers on the body, and appear to gain adult wing feathers last of all. *Moult.* – Very few moult data are available, but females have been trapped in body moult in most months of the year, but the very few males captured in moult were all trapped in April/May. The rectrices are apparently replaced commencing with the central pair (F. A. Arango, H. D. Arias, C. Gomez, H. Loaiza, J. C. Luna, J. P. López and J. V. Sandoval/ProAves unpubl. data). *Bare parts.* – Males have the legs greyish-flesh to purplish-flesh, the irides deep red and the bill blackish, with a distinctly convex culmen. Females have the legs pale fleshy-horn, the irides dull brown and the bill is also usually described as being black, but can sometimes appear strikingly pale (see Fig. 7).

MEASUREMENTS (BMNH; RMNH: western Ecuador) Wing of male (n = 10) 61.5–66.0mm, wing of female (n = 4) 59–62mm; tail of male (n = 9) 21–26mm; tail of female (n = 4) 21–22mm; bill of male (n = 10) 10.49–11.52mm, bill of female (n = 4) 11–12mm; tarsus of male (n = 4) 15–17mm, tarsus of female (n = 3) 15–16mm. Data from live birds (variation in culmen-length suggests mix of measuring protocols): wing of male (n = 52) 57–64mm, wing of female (n = 144) 50–68mm; tail of male (n = 50) 17.5–26.5mm, tail of female (n = 139) 15.0–27.5mm; bill of male (n = 50) 7.4–13.4mm, bill of female (n = 139) 6.5–13.8mm; tarsus of male (n = 50) 16.1–21.2mm, tarsus of female (n = 138) 15.4–20.7mm (Colombia: F. A. Arango, H. D. Arias, C. Gomez, H. Loaiza, J. C. Luna, J. P. López and J. V. Sandoval/ProAves unpubl. data; T. M. Donegan and L. Dávalos unpubl. data). Weight (sexes combined): (7.3) 10.4–22.1g (Snow 2004b, Dunning 2008; F. A. Arango, H.

D. Arias, C. Gomez, H. Loaiza, J. C. Luna, J. P. López and J. V. Sandoval/ProAves unpubl. data; T. M. Donegan and L. Dávalos unpubl. data).

GEOGRAPHICAL VARIATION Monotypic.

VOICE Recordings have been published on the following compilations: Moore *et al.* (1999), Krabbe and Nilsson (2003) and Alvarez *et al.* (2007), and several recordings are also available online at www.xeno-canto.org. Up to four different mechanical sounds have been documented for this species, and their different usage appears exceptional within the entire Pipridae, especially as they have almost entirely replaced vocal communication in displays and because of the range of harmonics employed (Bostwick 2000). Males' main display (see below) is entirely produced by the modified secondaries, a dry electronic-sounding buzz that is preceded by one, three or most frequently two dry notes, *tip-tip buuuuuu* or *tip-tip-beeuwww* (the last part with a ringing quality) and which may be repeated 2–3 times per minute (Hilty and Brown 1986, Ridgely and Tudor 1994, Bostwick 2000, Ridgely and Greenfield 2001, Snow 2004b). Bostwick *et al.* (2010) found that the modified wing-feathers resonate at a frequency of 1,500Hz and possess exceptional harmonics, but that it is the quality of the resonance that is pre-selected by females (see also Bostwick 2010). Sometimes there is no introduction and on other occasions the *tip* notes may be interspersed by a lateral jump (Bostwick 2000). With each *tip* note (recalling the sound of wooden chopsticks being hit together) the bird flutters its wings to better expose the white feathering (a 'white flash'), followed by it raising its wings over the back, where they almost touch and the front edges are rotated downward, at the same time leaning slightly forward on the perch and making the *buuuuuu* sound (likened to a toy horn). Throughout each display, which lasts *c.*2 seconds, the tail is held slightly cocked and fanned. Mechanical sounds may continue almost from dawn to dusk, except for a brief hour-long break around midday (GG pers. obs.), although display generally declines from mid-morning onwards and is thereafter continued only sporadically throughout the rest of the day (Bostwick 2000). At leks, which at least in Colombia occur almost year-round (for at least eight months), males utter a high-pitched *seet* note, which may be doubled, and is followed by as many as eight loud *kee!* notes.

NATURAL HISTORY Retiring and difficult to observe, except at leks or when venturing to fruiting trees at the forest edge. Club-winged Manakin occasionally joins mixed-species foraging flocks.

FOOD AND FEEDING Diet is principally small berries (including melastomes) and insects, which are taken during short aerial sallies, or in the case of insects sometimes 'snapped' opportunistically whilst perched, but in general data on the species' feeding behaviour are very sparse.

DISPLAY The Club-winged Manakin's dispersed leks number up to seven or eight males, and each male occupies an area 10–40m in diameter. The male's extraordinary display (first described by Willis 1966, then by Orejuela *et al.* 1982) is given alone, but always in 'earshot' of other birds and generally in rather open forest. A display sequence was captured on film in the BBC's 'Trials of Life' video. Each male perches on an open branch 1–20m above the ground, the legs quite widely spread, to display, and is most impressive from behind. Bostwick (2000) remarked that at the lek site she studied in detail most displays occurred

above 15m, but at leks GMK has observed in Ecuador (and those watched by T. M. Donegan in Colombia) most activity has been much lower than this, usually within a couple of metres of the ground, and the same was apparently true of Willis's (1966) observations in Colombia. Bostwick (2000) identified six different display behaviours, namely (her terminology) the *wing-flash* (which is the most frequently given and is described above), the *backward wing-flash* (which is the most complex), the *crouch-call* (which is usually preceded by the *seet* call), the *wing-presentation* (which involves the bird crouching to display the white and black wing markings to best effect from the front), the *jump-turn* (in which the bird jumps up to 4cm into the air, turns 180° and lands up to 15cm away from the original perch) and the *lateral spring* (in which the bird leaps up to 30cm horizontally along the same branch, and which may be incorporated into the wing-flash display). Of these, the backward wing-flash and crouch-call displays appear to be given least frequently. Occasionally, 2–3 males may display rather closer together and Bostwick (2000) observed up to three males 'territory-invade' and display on the same perch. This comprised ritualised movements accompanied by mechanical, metallic sound produced by the males' highly modified secondaries (described under Voice). Between displays the bird may move rapidly (and silently) to another perch, or flip around to face in the other direction on the same perch; certain perches are obviously favoured above others, but some birds may change perches at a rate of almost once per minute (Bostwick 2000). Perches are usually narrow horizontal or slightly upward-inclined branches. Displays periodically intensify, suggesting the presence of females in the environs of the lek, but this is unclear and it is possible that other displays may be used in courtship (Bostwick 2000).

BREEDING Despite the interest in this species amongst birdwatchers, and the recent level of fieldwork in its range, the Club-winged Manakin's nest has been found only a few times. In southwest Colombia, in late March 1962, Willis (1966) found the nest of a Club-winged Manakin in dense undergrowth very close to a display site, sited in the small fork of a 1m-tall *Piper* sp. (Piperaceae) shrub and described by the observer as being *Vireo*-like. It was a small but deep pensile cup of vegetable fibres covered on the outside with moss, and contained two brownish-white eggs speckled with brown, which were being incubated by the female. Ramírez González and Arias García (1995) found four active nests between March and August 1992 at La Planada reserve, also in southwest Colombia. Nest and egg dimensions were presented by Ramírez González and Arias García (1995), whilst egg colour closely matched the description of Willis (1966), but no information is presented on clutch size. These same authors found an additional nine nests that were not in use. All of the nests were constructed in the same species of understorey tree, *Faramea affinis* (Rubiaceae), none of which was taller than 2m, whilst all of the nests were sited 51–120cm above the ground and were small cup-shaped structures of dark brown vegetable fibres, decorated on the outside with mosses, and placed in the horizontal forks. Elsewhere in western Colombia females with incubation patches have been captured in June, September and October, with males in breeding condition trapped in July (ProAves unpubl. data). In southwest Ecuador, H. F. Greeney (*in litt.* 2010) found ten active nests at the Buenaventura Reserve, El Oro, in February (cf. Fig. 8). All were within a very large lek area, *c.*600m long by 100m wide, 'populated' by perhaps as many as 100 males. All of the nests had copious green moss on the outside, representing a 'hybrid' appearance between 'tails' and 'skirts', and perhaps deeper than other genera, and certainly rather substantial in terms of their bulk. They were generally placed in more open areas of undergrowth, and females were extremely tame at their nests, permitting very close approach.

STATUS Treated as Least Concern by BirdLife International (2004, 2008). Anciães and Peterson (2006) predicted, using modelling techniques, that Club-winged Manakin could be moderately impacted by habitat modification in the face of potential climate change. Uncommon, and to some extent must be threatened by habitat destruction within its relatively limited range, despite the species' apparent persistence in second-growth localities. Club-winged Manakin was considered endemic to the Chocó Rainforest Centre of endemism (Cracraft 1985), but it has recently been found further south, e.g. at Buenaventura, near Piñas, in southern Ecuador (where it was discovered as recently as 1988 and, given previously intensive fieldwork at the same locality, the species seems to have colonised the area just recently). *M. deliciosus* is also relatively easy to see along the road above Junín, in western Nariño, Colombia. The

species is known from a reasonable number of protected areas, both privately and publicly owned throughout its range. These include the Tambito, Río Ñambí and La Planada reserves in southern Colombia, the newly created Fundación Jocotoco reserve at Buenaventura, in El Oro, and the Centro Científico Río Palenque, Reserva Maquipucuna and Reserva Milpe, all in Pichincha, Ecuador. At the last-named site, the species is often easily found by the car park!

REFERENCES Alvarez *et al.* (2007), Anciães and Peterson (2006, 2009), Best *et al.* (1993), BirdLife International (2004, 2008), Bostwick (2000, 2010), Bostwick *et al.* (2010), Boyla and Estrada (2005), Cisneros-Heredia (2009), Cracraft (1985), Cuervo *et al.* (2003), Donegan and Dávalos (1999), Dunning (2008), Haffer (1974), Hellmayr (1929b), Hilty (1997), Hilty and Brown (1986), Kirwan and Marlow (1996), Krabbe and Nilsson (2003), McKay *et al.* (2010), Moore *et al.* (1999), Orejuela *et al.* (1982), Prum (1990a, 1992, 1994a), Prum and Wilson (1987), Ramírez González and Arias García (1995), Restall *et al.* (2006), Ridgely and Greenfield (2001), Ridgely and Tudor (1994, 2009), Salaman *et al.* (2008, 2009), Solano-Ugalde (in press), Snow (2004b) Stotz *et al.* (1996), Willis (1966).

Club-winged Manakin *Machaeropterus deliciosus.* **Fig. 1**. Male, Milpe Bird Sanctuary, prov. Pichincha, northwest Ecuador, November (*Hadoram Shirihai / Photographic Handbook to Birds of the World*). **Fig. 2**. Male, El Pangan Bird Reserve, dpto. Nariño, southwest Colombia, February (*Hadoram Shirihai / Photographic Handbook to Birds of the World*). **Fig. 3**. Male, Milpe Bird Sanctuary, prov. Pichincha, northwest Ecuador, June (*Nick Athanas / Tropical Birding*). A displaying male.

Club-winged Manakin *Machaeropterus deliciosus*. **Figs. 4–6**. Male, Ecuador, February (*J. Jackson*). More images showing different aspects of the male's remarkable display. Recent research has demonstrated that females chose mates based on the quality of sound production. **Fig. 7**. Female, Buenaventura Reserve, prov. El Oro, near Piñas, southwest Ecuador, December (*Daniel J. Lebbin*). Note the buffy wash to the loral region and the pale bill. **Fig. 8**. Female, Buenaventura Reserve, prov. El Oro, near Piñas, southwest Ecuador, February (*Harold F. Greeney*). This female has an obviously dark bill, but brighter and more extensive colour on the face-sides.

Genus *Dixiphia*: White-crowned Manakin

Long treated as a member of the genus *Pipra* (see Systematics), and indeed it is maintained therein by the SACC (Remsen *et al.* 2009), we utilise *Dixiphia* for this largely black manakin based on multiple lines of evidence, including genetic, that demonstrate the species to be not closely related to *Pipra* species.

WHITE-CROWNED MANAKIN
Dixiphia pipra　　　　　　　　　　　　　Plate 5

Parus pipra **Linnaeus, 1758**, *Syst. Nat.*, 10th edn., 1: 190, based on the "Cacototl" of Seba, in Indiis [= Surinam]

This common and extremely widespread manakin is one of the most easily identified, even in female plumage. Detailed studies conducted largely in recent years have elucidated much of its natural history, but questions remain especially concerning its taxonomy. It seems likely that at least some described subspecies will, when subjected to closer scrutiny, be deemed synonyms, but there is yet the possibility that more than one species might be recognised among 'white-crowned' manakins.

IDENTIFICATION 8.5–11.8cm. An easily recognised manakin in all plumages and at all ages. The striking male White-crowned Manakin should prove immediately identifiable anywhere within its large range, due to it being the only member of the Pipridae to possess both an all-black body (with no blue elements) and a gleaming white crown. Male Blue-crowned Manakin *Lepidothrix coronata* is also all black but has a deep blue crown, whilst the obviously smaller-bodied Blue-rumped Manakin *L. isidorei* (limited overlap) has a pale blue rump and uppertail-coverts, which patch of colour is usually obvious. Even females (or young males) should prove readily attributable to species given their combination of dark red irides and a distinct grey cast to the crown and head-sides, which (with reasonable views) make this one of the most characteristic of the smaller manakins in non-adult male plumage.

DISTRIBUTION Widespread, with populations in southern Central America, parts of northern South America, and western and northern Amazonia, as well as an extremely isolated population in the Atlantic Forest of eastern Brazil. White-crowned Manakin reaches the northernmost extremity of its range in north-central Costa Rica, where it is found in the Cordilleras Central and Talamanca (Stiles and Skutch 1989), extending south and east almost to the western Canal Zone in Panama through eastern Chiriquí (in the Cordillera de Tolé) and Veraguas on the Pacific slope and in northern Veraguas and Coclé on the Caribbean slope (Wetmore 1972, Ridgely and Gwynne 1976, Angehr and Dean 2010). It is absent from Panama east of the Canal Zone, but reappears in northwest South America, in northern Colombia, and in northern Venezuela: in the latter region it occurs along the east base of the Andes from southeast Lara to southeast Táchira, as well as in the Sierra de Perijá, in Zulia (Hilty 2003). In Colombia it is found at the northern end of the West Andes, e.g. in southern Córdoba, the Serranía de San Lucas, the Magdalena Valley, from Caldas to Huila, and west of the Andes on the Pacific slope in dptos. Valle and Cauca (Hilty 1977), as well as throughout the east slope of the East Andes, from Norte to Santander to the Ecuadorian border, and across the

lowlands of Amazonia (Hilty and Brown 1986, Salaman *et al.* 2002a). Thereafter it occurs throughout most of eastern Ecuador (Ridgely and Greenfield 2001) and eastern Peru locally south to dpto. Cuzco (Schulenberg *et al.* 2007), thence east across Amazonian Brazil in Amazonas and Pará, as far east as Maranhão and Amapá, and south to northern Rondônia and northern Mato Grosso (Pinto 1944, Sick 1997). Elsewhere in Amazonia and northeast South America it also ranges across southern and eastern Venezuela, locally from southeast Sucre and the Delta Amacuro across most of Amazonas and Bolívar (Hilty 2003), and throughout all three of the Guianas (Ridgely and Tudor 1994, Restall *et al.* 2006). Finally, the extremely isolated population in the Atlantic Forest of eastern Brazil is confined to lowland and foothill forest between southern Bahia, e.g. around Ilhéus, south to northern Rio de Janeiro, as far as Nova Friburgo (Pinto 1944, Sick 1997). Principally found in lowland regions over much of its range, White-crowned Manakin has been recorded to 1,500m on the Brazilian side of the Cerro de la Neblina (Willard *et al.* 1991), to 1,700m in eastern Ecuador (J. F. Freile *in litt.* 2010), 1,570m in the Cerros del Sira, Peru (Mee *et al.* 2002), locally to 1,600m in the Colombian Andes (subspecies *D. p. unica* in Caldas: Hilty and Brown 1986) and elsewhere on the east slope of the Andes in Peru to 2,000m (Schulenberg *et al.* 2007). In Costa Rica the species is largely restricted to the subtropics, being found at 800–1,500m (Stiles and Skutch 1989). In the Colombian Andes it generally occurs at 600–1,200m, but lower, at 450–1,200m, in Panama (Angehr and Dean 2010) (Hilty and Brown 1986), although at their northernmost extremity, White-crowned Manakin has occurred as low as 100m (Salaman *et al.* 2002a).

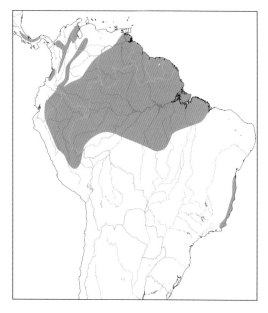

MOVEMENTS The species is generally considered to be resident and sedentary (Stiles and Skutch 1989, Snow 2004b). However, occasional movements to lower altitudes have been reported in the wet season in Costa Rica (Levey 1988, Blake and Loiselle 2001, 2002), and Hilty (1997) was unsure whether his occasional records in the Anchicayá Valley, in dpto. Valle, Colombia, were representative of a low-density resident population or occasional wandering 'vagrants'. Radio-tracking studies in French Guiana perhaps give the most accurate assessment of the species' capacity to move, at least in South America. Here, Théry (1990c) found that adults, especially males, are sedentary during the breeding season (with two territories of 2.1 and 2.3ha) but move over quite large areas, probably up to several hundred hectares, during the moulting period. During the breeding season, females wander rather more widely than males, with two individuals having home ranges of 8.8 and 9.2ha. Théry (1990c) also related how two immature males wandered over 18.7 and 20.9ha.

HABITAT Principally restricted to dense primary forest and tall second growth, *D. pipra* is also found in younger secondary forest, sandy-belt and isolated 'islands' of forest in savannas in the Orinoco and Rio Negro drainage, including Amazonian *caatingas* or *campinaranas* (Hilty and Brown 1986, Borges *et al.* 2001, Campos *et al.* 2010; MNRJ). In Ecuador it seems to be largely absent from level-ground *terra firme* forest, preferring hilly *terra firme* above 250m (Ridgely and Greenfield 2001). Also noted in palm-dominated *várzea* scrub including *igapós* on sandy soils (Borges *et al.* 2001, Hilty 2003).

DESCRIPTION The species' general structure recalls that of the members of the genus *Pipra*, especially the *P. erythrocephala* superspecies, in being small with a noticeably short tail. However, there is no modification to the wing feathers, which is reflected in the lack of mechanical sounds (see Voice), unlike in *Pipra* species. Bill structure is relatively similar to *Pipra*, with relatively large nostrils, a reasonably arched culmen and a slight hooked tip, perhaps especially in males. The nominate race is described here. *Adult male.* – As in all races, the bird's body and wings are all black (perhaps slightly browner over the wings and tail) with a slight violaceous or steel blue gloss and a strikingly contrasting snow white crown and nape, the long feathers of the latter forming a flattened crest. Most of these white feathers have grey bases, except over some of the forehead (Zimmer 1936). The belly and undertail-coverts are slightly less glossy black than the rest. The innermost axillaries are black, whilst the outer axillaries, underwing-coverts and tibial feathering are dark grey, and the undertail-coverts can be narrowly tipped dark grey. *Adult female.* – The upperparts are plain olive-green becoming greyer over the crown and head-sides, and rather paler grey-green on the underparts, especially pale on the throat and belly, and with most olive feathering on the breast and flanks. The wing-coverts, uppertail-coverts and central rectrices are slightly greyer than the rest, whilst the inner webs of the flight feathers are dull brownish-black. The axillaries and underwing-coverts are pale greyish-white, while the tibial feathering is dark brownish-grey. Females can occasionally show male plumage: Haverschmidt (1971) collected a female with well-developed ovaries that had several black wing-coverts and one black secondary, and Graves (1981) noted several female specimens with small white feathers in the crown. *Juvenile.* – Stiles and Skutch (1989) considered that young

birds are similar to adult females but are generally duller and darker, with a yellow tinge on the belly, and have brown irides. Zimmer (1936) postulated this plumage is marked by the more yellowish fringes to the remiges and browner wing-coverts; that the birds he was describing had softer-textured plumage appears to validate his assertion that these individuals do represent true juveniles. Wetmore (1972) noted that young males with the first white crown-feathers appearing on the forehead already have reddish irides (see also Castro-Astor *et al.* 2007). As in many manakins, males of *D. pipra* can be sexually mature prior to the acquisition of fully adult plumage (Haverschmidt 1971). Data concerning plumage maturation were recently supplied by Ryder and Durães (2005), who found that the first moult (body-feathers alone) occurs within two months of leaving the nest. During this moult, young males can acquire some signs of adult plumage but even if they do not, compared with adult males they will show moult limits in the wing-coverts (as do young females compared with adults). The second moult occurs *c.*1 year later and is typically complete: young males now acquire significant adult feathering on both the head and the body, but remarkably some apparently still show no signs of adult plumage. However, by the third moult full adult male plumage will be acquired. *Moult.* – Very little has been published concerning moult in this species, although Willard *et al.* (1991) noted that just one of five specimens taken in southern Venezuela in late February and early March showed any signs of feather replacement (light body moult). Another (a male) from February taken in northernmost Brazil was also replacing some feathers (Friedmann 1948). Beebe (1915) recorded that a bird taken in east Amazonian Brazil in early May had almost completed its moult, and that rectrices are replaced commencing with the central pair and proceeding outwards. *Hybrids.* – Graves (1993) identified a controversial male specimen held at MECN (2748) as a *D. pipra* × *Pipra filicauda* (Wire-tailed Manakin). It was collected at a locality in prov. Pastaza, eastern Ecuador. Photographs of the specimen have been published (Graves 1993: 437) illustrating its most striking (and diagnostic) characters, namely the golden-yellow crown and nape, the yellow-and-black mottled underparts, dark face patch, glossy black mantle, wings and tail, and shallowly forked tail (11mm). The bird has broadly rounded central rectrices with tapered outer ones, but no rachi extensions. We too have examined this specimen and concur with Graves' analysis. *Bare parts.* – The irides are generally amber or reddish-orange to ruby-red in males and dark brown to reddish-orange in females, although there is undoubtedly much overlap in iris colour between the sexes. Hilty (2003) considered that females might have more conspicuous eyes than males, perhaps because their irides are on average paler. The legs and feet are usually blackish to neutral grey, more occasionally purplish-red or brown, with plumbeous or grey-coloured soles and cream-coloured nails. The bill is generally dark, with a black or blackish maxilla and a greyer or bluish-grey mandible, sometimes with a whitish base or tip, very occasionally the entire mandible is very pale (Wetmore 1972, Novaes 1978, Willard *et al.* 1991, Hilty 2003, Snow 2004b; MNCR, MNRJ).

MEASUREMENTS *D. p. anthracina* (CUMZ; MNCR: Costa Rica and western Panama [males] and Wetmore 1972: Costa Rica and western Panama [females]): wing of male (*n* = 11) 57.0–63.5mm, wing of female (*n* = 5) 58–61mm; tail of male (*n* = 11) 25–32mm, tail of female (*n* = 5) 25.5–28.5mm; bill of male (*n* = 11) 9.45–11.15mm, bill of female (*n* = 5)

9.3–11.9mm; tarsus of male (*n* = 10) 13.60–15.28mm, tarsus of female (*n* = 5) 14.9–16.3mm. ***D. p. bolivari*** (live birds; C. Olaciregui/ProAves unpubl. data: northern Antioquia, Colombia): wing of male (*n* = 3) 59–66mm, wing of female (*n* = 4) 64–65mm. ***D. p. minima*** (Hellmayr 1929b: Cocal, dpto. Cauca, Colombia): wing of male (*n* = 2) 54–55mm; tail of male (*n* = 2) 24–25mm. ***D. p. discolor*** (Zimmer 1936: dpto. Loreto, northeast Peru): wing of male (*n* = 1) 67mm; tail of male (*n* = 1) 24mm; bill of male (*n* = 1) 11mm; tarsus of male (*n* = 1) 14mm. ***D. p. occulta*** (Zimmer 1936: upper Huallaga Valley, Peru): wing of male (*n* = 11) 63–68mm, wing of female (*n* = 4) 64–65mm; tail of male (*n* = 11) 30.5–32.0mm, tail of female (*n* = 4) 33–34mm; bill of male (*n* = 1) 11mm; tarsus of male (*n* = 1) 14.5mm. ***D. p. pygmaea*** (Zimmer 1936: lower Huallaga Valley, Peru): wing of male (*n* = 7) 58.0–61.5mm, wing of female (*n* = 8) 59.0–61.5mm; tail of male (*n* = 7) 24–25mm, tail of female (*n* = 8) 23.5–27.0mm. ***D. p. comata*** (FMNH: dptos. Huánuco, Junín, Loreto and Pasco, Peru): wing of male (*n* = 5) 62–69mm, wing of female (*n* = 3) 64.0–68.5mm; tail of male (*n* = 5) 29–34mm, tail of female (*n* = 3) 29.5–32.0mm; bill of male (*n* = 5) 10.20–11.51mm, bill of female (*n* = 3) 11.6–11.8mm; tarsus of male (*n* = 5) 11.25–14.98mm, tarsus of female (*n* = 3) 14.33–14.51mm. ***D. p. microlopha*** (Gyldenstolpe 1945: Amazonas, Brazil, and MNRJ: Rondônia, Brazil): wing of male (*n* = 3) 64–67mm, wing of female (*n* = 4) 63–65mm; tail of male (*n* = 3) 29–30mm, tail of female (*n* = 4) 28–32mm; bill of male (*n* = 3) 9.5mm, bill of female (*n* = 4) 9.50–12.04mm; tarsus of male (*n* = 3) 12.5mm, tarsus of female (*n* = 3) 12–13mm. ***D. p. pipra*** (CUMZ; MNRJ: Amapá and northern Amazonas, Brazil): wing of male (*n* = 18) 60.0–64.5mm, wing of female (*n* = 5) 62.5–65.5mm; tail of male (*n* = 18) 25–33mm, tail of female (*n* = 5) 26–31mm; bill of male (*n* = 18) 10.77–12.47mm, bill of female (*n* = 5) 10.92–12.47mm; tarsus of male (*n* = 14) 13.81–15.17mm, tarsus of female (*n* = 2) 14.69–15.27mm. ***D. p. separabilis*** (CUMZ; FMNH; MNRJ: Pará, Brazil): wing of male (*n* = 9) 61.5–67.0mm, wing of female (*n* = 4) 61.0–65.5mm; tail of male (*n* = 9) 27–34mm, tail of female (*n* = 4) 26–32mm; bill of male (*n* = 8) 10.86–11.72mm, bill of female (*n* = 4) 11.42–12.91mm; tarsus of male (*n* = 4) 13.51–14.33mm, tarsus of female (*n* = 1) 13.48mm. Additional morphometric data pertaining to this subspecies were presented by Gomes *et al.* (2009). ***D. p. cephaleucos*** (MNRJ: Bahia and Espírito Santo, Brazil): wing of male (*n* = 10) 62.5–67.0mm, wing of female (*n* = 2) 62.5–64.0mm; tail of male (*n* = 10) 26–28mm, tail of female (*n* = 2) 26–32mm; bill of male (*n* = 10) 11.56–12.79mm, bill of female (*n* = 2) 11.30–12.56mm; tarsus of male (*n* = 5) 14.23–14.86mm, tarsus of female (*n* = 1) 13.87mm. Chapman (1917) and Hellmayr (1929b) presented additional measurements for the subspecies *D. p. minima* and *D. p. microlopha*, respectively. Weight (subspecies combined): 9.1–15.5g (males), 9.6–17.0g (females) (Haverschmidt 1952, Dick *et al.* 1984, Stiles and Skutch 1989, Silva *et al.* 1990, King 1991, Willard *et al.* 1991, Snow 2004b, Dunning 2008, Gomes *et al.* 2009; FMNH; MNCR; MNRJ; C. Olaciregui/ProAves unpubl. data).

GEOGRAPHICAL VARIATION Polytypic with 13 subspecies recognised under most modern treatments (e.g. Dickinson 2003, Snow 2004b). Racial variation is unusual in manakins in being also detectable in the females of at least some forms. However, it is primarily expressed in the extent of the white on the crown and nape in males, with the extent of the grey on the head in females being another important feature. The gloss to the black of the male's

plumage also varies to some extent geographically, but is reported to become 'richer' with age (Restall *et al.* 2006). Unless otherwise stated differences cited below between the races refer to males alone. Wetmore (1972) considered that much of the recognised morphological variation could be regarded as 'minor', which seems true of many of the endemic Peruvian forms (several of which we would recommend might comfortably fall into synonymy), but recent authors have pointed to the potential to recognise some forms at species level, for instance Central American *anthracina* and east Andean *coracina* (AOU 1998, Ridgely and Greenfield 2001, Hilty 2003, Snow 2004b, Remsen *et al.* 2009). As a general rule, the white crown more frequently extends onto the nape in the Andean populations as opposed to Amazonian populations, in particular. There is also some geographical variation in voice (see below). Because the morphological and vocal data are still incomplete, we have elected to maintain one species for now. Furthermore, genetic sampling of this species has been very incomplete and extensive comparisons will be necessary to support or deny the multiple-species hypothesis. Tello *et al.* (2009) sampled nominate *pipra* and Rêgo *et al.* (2007) sampled three specimens of unstated provenance (but noted no intra-specific genetic structure). ***D. p. anthracina*** (Ridgway, 1906) occurs from Costa Rica to western Panama (i.e. west of the Canal Zone) and is sometimes known as Velvet or Zeledon's Manakin. It has black bases to the crown and nape feathers, but not those of the forehead, and has velvety black upperparts. ***D. p. bolivari*** (Meyer de Schauensee, 1950) occurs in northwest Colombia, from the upper Sinú Valley of dpto. Córdoba to dpto. Bolívar. This race basically recalls *anthracina* but for the slightly blue-glossed black upperparts. It has blackish bases to the white feathers of the crown, affording it a striated appearance (Restall *et al.* 2006). ***D. p. minima*** (Chapman, 1917) is found in dptos. Valle and Cauca, in southwest Colombia and was diagnosed on the basis of its smaller size and slightly more velvety black body-feathers than the previous subspecies. The undertail-coverts reportedly lack any grey tips. On the other hand, Restall *et al.* (2006) regarded it as being 'like *unica* but with shorter nape-feathers'. (Chapman had originally called this new subspecies '*minor*' but had overlooked the unavailability of that name due to the issue of homonymy with *Pipra mentalis minor*; this latter species might soon also be placed in *Dixiphia*: see Systematics, p. 40.) ***D. p. unica*** (Meyer de Schauensee, 1945) occurs through north-central to southern Colombia in the Magdalena Valley, from at least Caldas to Huila (Hilty and Brown 1986), and is differentiated by its longer white crest and entirely white bases to these feathers. Supposed differences in bare-parts coloration, seemingly postulated by Restall *et al.* (2006), are none. So-called Sclater's Manakin ***D. p. coracina*** (P. L. Sclater, 1856) is found in northwest Venezuela in the Sierra de Perijá and from southeast Lara to southeast Táchira, as well as on the east slope of the East Andes between Colombia (from Norte de Santander and including the outlying Sierra de Macarena) and north-central Peru north of the Río Marañón in northern San Martín (Schulenberg *et al.* 2007). Compared with the other western races, the white crown extends further back on the nape (with grey or black bases) in males, whilst females, in comparison with nominate *pipra*, have an entirely blue-grey head, brighter olive-green upperparts and are pale olive with a slight yellowish tinge below. Hellmayr (1929b) also considered that *coracina* is larger than nominate *pipra*, while

Zimmer (1936: 12) found the upperparts to be more velvety black than other Peruvian populations and females to be yellower on the belly than other taxa. **D. p. discolor** (J. T. Zimmer, 1936) occurs in northeast Peru (and perhaps neighbouring Ecuador as postulated by its describer), and is differentiated in being somewhat bluer on the body-feathers and upperparts than D. p. microlopha, with grey bases to the crown- and nape-feathers. Zimmer (1936: 12) considered this race to be nearest to nominate pipra, but it also seems hard to differentiate from microlopha, although its describer regarded the new taxon as 'glossier' with the 'crest usually broader at the posterior end'. Others, e.g. T. S. Schulenberg (pers. comm.), have also found males of D. p. discolor and D. p. microlopha almost if not actually indistinguishable. Compared with occulta, Zimmer (1936) described discolor as less violaceous and shorter-crested, and against comata 'much glossier … and crest shorter with darker bases'. The real question, however, seems to be whether it merits distinction from D. p. microlopha: Zimmer (1936) himself admitted that some discolor have the crest shape identical to microlopha. **D. p. occulta** (J. T. Zimmer, 1936) is found in north-central Peru east of the Andes; it rather resembles D. p. comata but has a less extensive white crown patch and these feathers have sooty-grey (rather than white) bases, as well as a shorter tail and wings, and females are almost whitish below, except for the yellowish breast and flanks. Compared with D. p. microlopha, Zimmer (1936) considered male occulta to have a longer crest and weaker bill, and females to be more yellowish-green above. **D. p. pygmaea** (J. T. Zimmer, 1936) is restricted to the lower Río Huallaga, and is thus also endemic to Peru. It resembles D. p. occulta and D. p. comata, but is smaller (unsurprisingly given its name) with grey bases to the nuchal-feathers (becoming white or slightly ashy on the crown), and the female is reportedly much paler (being more whitish on the throat and belly, and paler green on the back and breast). Females are, however, very similar to those of D. p. microlopha, except apparently in size and their marginally paler plumage on average (Zimmer 1936). **D. p. comata** (Berlepsch & Stolzmann, 1894) is found south of the last-named subspecies, across east-central Peru between dpto. Pasco and dpto. Cuzco. Compared with D. p. coracina (or D. p. pipra), this race is longer tailed, and the white on the head is the most extensive of any race (with white bases to these feathers). Zimmer (1936: 8) noted the existence of a male taken at the mouth of the Río Urubamba that appears intermediate between comata and the next subspecies. A female from the same locality, and therefore perhaps not referable to pure comata, was considered by Zimmer to have a whiter throat and belly and less distinctly greenish breast than average microlopha females. **D. p. microlopha** (J. T. Zimmer, 1929) has an extensive range from eastern Peru south of the Río Marañón through western Brazil. Compared with other races found in eastern Peru, it has shorter nape feathers and a slightly larger bill. The female is sometimes considered duller olive-green or greyish-green, with a pale grey nape washed green or olive, and sometimes there is very little contrast between the crown and the rest of the upperparts (Hellmayr 1929b, Schulenberg et al. 2007). However, Zimmer (1936) found no features to clearly delineate female microlopha from adjacent forms, and also noticed the existence of 'troublesome' specimens from the upper and lower Ucayali, i.e. well inside the range of the present subspecies, that are difficult to assign racially. **D. p. pipra** is also extensively distributed in northern Amazonia,

from southern and eastern Venezuela across the entire Guianas and lowland eastern Colombia (from Guainía south to northern Vaupés and northern Amazonas, at least) and all of Brazil north of the Amazon, although it reaches the south bank of the Solimões around Tefé, Amazonas. This race is described above under Description. **D. p. separabilis** (J. T. Zimmer, 1936) is endemic to the Pará centre of endemism in Brazil, where it ranges south of the Amazon from the Rio Tapajós to northern Maranhão. Compared with adjacent subspecies, this race is glossed violaceous above but is rather dull and brownish below, with narrow dusky bases to the crown feathers (forehead entirely white). Immature males are apparently unusually distinctive, having the top of the head entirely pale neutral grey, although Zimmer (1936: 15) did admit that some young males can have forehead and part of the crown whitish. Further work is therefore needed to definitely prove the distinctive features of separabilis. Finally, **D. p. cephaleucos** (Thunberg, 1822) is endemic to the Atlantic Forest of eastern Brazil, where it is found from southern Bahia to northern Rio de Janeiro. Adult males are identical to the previous subspecies, although Zimmer (1936: 14) speculated that Atlantic Forest birds might be duller on the belly, but immature males have a white (not a grey) crown, darker green upperparts and darker underparts, especially on the breast and flanks.

VOICE The most detailed description of the species' vocalisations pertains to the Atlantic Forest population (D. p. cephaleucos: Castro-Astor et al. 2007). These authors identified three main types of call and presented sonograms. That most frequently heard is the advertisement call, which as in the genus Pipra serves in male–male territorial defence and to attract females to the male's court. It commences with a buzz that lasts just over half a second and is principally at 4.5–2.5kHz and which is followed swiftly by an isolated, short, sharp note (e.g. tshrra-tewk). A partial version of this call, comprising the buzz alone (tsirrr), is sometimes given. Sick (1993, 1997) likened this to a locust and it seems rather similar to the advertisement call of D. p. pipra at least (see below concerning geographical variation in vocals). The advertisement call can be given on average every 16 seconds and neighbouring males frequently answer each other and will engage in vigorous bursts of counter-singing at boundaries of their territories. The whistle is mainly given at collective display sites, when up to six different birds may call at once, during both inter- and intra-specific interactions. Each whistle lasts c.0.25 seconds, and the call initially rises and then descends, although one variant documented by Castro-Astor et al. (2007) comprised a rapid, ascending modulation. It seems to be primarily uttered by female-plumage birds. Finally, the hover call was noted exclusively during inter-specific interactions, and was given by birds in all plumages while hovering. This vocalisation consists of a whistle similar to the whistle call, but preceded and followed by up to three short notes. Sick (1993, 1997) also mentioned a weak eh similar to a vocalisation given by Striped Manakin Machaeropterus regulus.

Schulenberg et al. (2007) described some of the geographical variation in this species' vocalisations. They considered that the song of D. p. coracina in northern Peru to be a hoarse pew … WURR'EEO, while in the central Andes (D. p. occulta) the analogous call is a ringing and ascending wurrrrb'TEE, and in the southern Andes in Pasco to Cuzco, D. p. comata gives a hoarse descending wur but this is not the song. In Amazonian Peru, the song of D. p. microlopha is a descending buzzy DZZEW, whilst the call is a mewing and descending *pew* or *weeo*. Further north, in Colombia, Hilty and Brown (1986) mentioned that birds on the Pacific slope (*D. p. minima*) utter a thin *shre-e-e-e-e* likened to a cicada, which is repeated at 15–20-second intervals; in Vaupés (*D. p. pipra*), the analogous vocalisation is given at *c*.30-second intervals. Oniki and Willis (1983) mentioned fledged juveniles giving a *few!* call. Examples of the species' vocalisations appear on the following commercially available audio compilations: Moore (1994), Ross and Whitney (1995), Boesman (1999, 2006b, 2009), Remold (2002), Krabbe and Nilsson (2003), Lysinger *et al.* (2005), Marantz and Zimmer (2006), Alvarez *et al.* (2007), Naka *et al.* (2008), Renaudier and Deroussen (2008) and Minns *et al.* (2009), and are also archived online at www.xeno-canto.org.

NATURAL HISTORY White-crowned Manakin has a liking for the dense understorey of humid forest, where it is generally found alone, except at leks or perhaps at fruiting trees (where female-plumaged birds are most frequently seen). Jullien and Thiollay (1998) and Hilty (2003) noted that White-crowned Manakin occasionally joins mixed-species flocks in the understorey and, especially in Amazonia, the species will share regular bathing sites with other manakins, e.g. at Cristalino Jungle Lodge, Brazil, with Snow-capped *Lepidothrix nattereri*, Red-headed *Pipra rubrocapilla* and Blue-backed Manakins *Chiroxiphia pareola* (GMK pers. obs.). At least in the breeding season, males seem to depend on a single bathing site, whereas the wider-ranging females (see Movements) may use several such sites (Théry 1990c). Males, especially, very frequently flick the wings, apparently nervously. Very few species-specific studies have been conducted on White-crowned Manakin, despite its abundance.

FOOD AND FEEDING Omnivorous like many manakins, taking both small fruits and insects although it presumably is largely frugivorous. Stiles and Skutch (1989) noted that White-crowned Manakin has a special liking for melastomes, for instance the fruits of the genera *Cephaelis*, *Psychotria* (both Rubiaceae) and *Phytolacca* (Phytolaccaceae). Blendinger *et al.* (2008) reported that *D. pipra* is one of the few species to take *Miconia fosteri* and *M. serrulata* (Melastomataceae) fruits in eastern Ecuador, in which region Loiselle *et al.* (2007b) recorded a total of 44 species in the bird's diet. In French Guiana, Théry (1990c) found that Melastomataceae and Rubiaceae are the two most important constituent families in its fruit diet, whilst Tostain (1988a) mentioned a *Norantea* sp. (Marcgraviaceae) in the species' diet. In eastern Amazonian Brazil, Gomes *et al.* (2008) and Marceliano *et al.* (2009) reported fruits of the following species in the bird's diet: *Miconia ciliata* (Melastomataceae), *Symphonia globulifera* (Clusiaceae), an *Inga* sp. and *Pterocarpus officinalis* (Fabaceae), *Piper aduncum* (Piperaceae), *Euterpe oleracea* (Arecaceae) and *Psidium guajava* (Myrtaceae). To that list, in northern Brazil, Silva *et al.* (2010) added *Heliconia acuminata* (Heliconiaceae). Willard *et al.* (1991) recorded *Pagamea plicata* (Rubiaceae) seeds in stomach contents. A young male collected in eastern Costa Rica had flower parts in the stomach contents (MNCR).

DISPLAY The first detailed observations on the species' displays were published by Snow (1961) based on his work in Guyana (subspecies *pipra*). White-crowned Manakin has a system of dispersed leks (cf. Théry 1992). Subsequently, Castro-Astor *et al.* (2007) presented a very detailed résumé of display behaviour (and vocalisations, see above) from southeast Brazil (subspecies *cephaleucos*). They found both

solitary display sites and dispersed leks, with mean distance between each display site (court) of 68m (range 41–113m) and relatively open areas being generally favoured, which was also Snow's experience in Guyana. Each male used many different perches (including vines) to display, all of them thin, horizontal and largely leafless. This too was Snow's experience in Guyana. This is quite unlike many (but not all) of the species placed in the genus *Pipra* in this book, which principally utilise a single favoured perch. Display-perches were generally 2–7m above the ground and usually close to wet ground, whilst each male occupied a territory of between 30 × 17m and 40 × 38m. As such most males were neither in visual nor in auditory contact, which is not the norm in dispersed lek species, wherein males are typically in vocal contact. Each territory (court) can be visited by adult males, young males and females. In southeast Brazil, display had 'tailed off' to basically nothing by 09.00 hrs. In eastern Ecuador (subspecies *coracina*), Loiselle *et al.* (2007a) found that the species appears to favour highly dissected drainages to site its leks, and that the number of males per lek varied from one to seven (versus three or four, plus the single display sites, noted in southeast Brazil by Castro-Astor *et al.* 2007). Castro-Astor *et al.* (2007), however, also discovered that males, especially in non-adult plumage, also visited what they termed 'collective display sites', 30m in diameter, around a centrally located curved vine situated close to individual display sites. Up to ten birds, most of them definitely males, were recorded visiting these sites during the course of a day.

Previous authors (e.g. Snow 1961, Prum 1994a) had considered the displays of White-crowned Manakin to be relatively simple, but Castro-Astor *et al.* (2007) described a more complex repertoire than hitherto believed, involving 11 different facets. These are as follows. The *turning-around display* is performed mainly by non-adult males both at individual display sites and at collective display sites. The male lands and immediately starts to repeatedly jump *c*.1cm, turning around rapidly on the perch, and raising its wings *c*.45° before flying away. *To-and-fro flights* are given commonly by males of all ages. The male flies between adjacent perches at the same level, repeating the sequence many times, and often performs the turning-around display on landing. The wings usually make a soft noise during these flights. *Swoop down below* display is given by males of all ages. In flying between perches, especially those that are further apart, the male sometimes comes into land by swooping down below the level of the perch, then up and down onto it, thus describing a shallow S-curve. *Butterfly flight*: if a female approaches a display site, the male often circles her using a slow flapping flight during which the wingbeats are audible. Should the female depart to another perch, the male follows still using the 'butterfly' flight. Again, males of all ages perform these flights. The *about-face* involves the male in a rapid 180° turn without lateral movement along the perch. As with *Pipra* species, about-faces are common in White-crowned Manakin. Castro-Astor *et al.* (2007) observed the *frenzied-flutter* just twice. It comprises a brief fluttering flight with the bird's feet sliding along the display perch, given immediately on landing, and as in Golden-headed Manakin *Pipra erythrocephala*, Round-tailed Manakin *P. chloromeros* and Red-headed Manakin *P. rubrocapilla* presumably simulates copulation. The *hover display* appears to signify agitation, as the male utters the whistle call (see Voice) while moving between adjacent perches, before hovering in front of another bird giving a trembling whistle. The remainder of the displays described by Castro-Astor *et al.* (2007) were observed only at collective display sites, and all but the jump display were only seen to be performed by non-adult males. In each of the following, one male displays on the central vine, surrounded by others performing turning-around or to-and-fro flight displays. Displays are performed asynchronously and each male's display on the central vine lasts just 9–40 seconds. *Jump display*: holding the body perpendicular to the perch the male performs a highly variable series of low jumps (a rapid lateral movement only slightly above the perch, with the wings opened 15°), high jumps (a high, almost looping movement with the wings opened 45°) and about-faces in various directions before flying away. In the *somersault* a male lands silently on the perch, then low jumps forward, high jumps backward, high jumps backward turning around in the air, then flies below the line of the perch prior to landing on it. *Step forward and high jump backward*: again, a male lands silently on the vine, is still for a few seconds then looks left, before low jumping backward, stepping forward, high jumping backward, looking left again, stepping forward, high jumping backward, looking left, low jumping forward and high jumping backward, before leaving the perch. *Clockwise and counter-clockwise high jump* displays commence as does the previous. The bird turns in the opposite direction, high jumps forward, high jumps anticlockwise and lands in the same place, high jumps three times forward in sequence, high jumps clockwise and lands in the same place, high jumps backward in a rapid swoop below the perch and then lands on it, i.e. performing an inverted S-curve, and then departs.

As with other Pipridae studied in eastern Ecuador, Loiselle *et al.* (2007c) found that males displaying at leks were not especially closely related, *contra* the suggestion by Castro-Astor *et al.* (2007). The latter authors observed White-crowned Manakins visiting the leks of other manakins, especially White-bearded *Manacus manacus*, and also observed *D. pipra* performing hover displays during interactions with Blue *Chiroxiphia caudata* and Red-headed Manakins *Pipra rubrocapilla*.

BREEDING The species' nest has been described from observations in French Guiana (Tostain 1988a), northern Amazonas, Brazil (Oniki and Willis 1982) and eastern Ecuador (Hidalgo *et al.* 2008). The nest is typical of manakins, being a small open cup placed 1.0–9.8m above the ground in the horizontal fork of an understorey tree or shrub, constructed of brownish-yellow or similarly coloured vegetable fibres and fungal hyphae (*Marasmius* sp.: Marasmiaceae), with the outer layer covered in dead leaves (cf. photograph in Tostain 1988a: 161, and Fig. 6). Fragments of palm fronds may also be incorporated and as usual among manakins, the nest is bound together and to the support plant using spiderwebs (Hidalgo *et al.* 2008). In eastern Ecuador, Hidalgo *et al.* (2008) found that *D. pipra* appears to prefer to nest in areas with a relatively dense understorey, but at the edges of treefall gaps or other openings. These authors found 13 nests, providing dimensions and other characteristics of their surroundings. A March nest containing one young in French Guiana was constructed in a *Qualea* sp. (Vochyliaceae) tree (Tostain 1988a), while in eastern Ecuador supporting plants have included *Miconia fosteri* (Melastomataceae) and *Rinorea viridifolia* (Violaceae) (Hidalgo *et al.* 2008). Dimensions of the French Guiana nest were also presented. Clutch size is two eggs, which were described by Velho (1932) and Pinto

(1953) as being dirty white and virtually covered in vinous-brown markings. However, there can be substantial variation even within the same clutch, in both background colour and depth and extent of markings (H. F. Greeney *in litt.* 2010). Pinto (1953) also presented the egg dimensions. Neither the fledging nor the incubation period is known (Snow 2004b), but Tostain (1988a) reported a nestling being fed on average every 40 minutes during wet weather. Concerning seasonality, Dick *et al.* (1984) reported examples of both sexes in breeding condition in February and Haverschmidt and Mees (1994) mentioned egg laying in October in Surinam, and in northern Pará, Brazil, Novaes (1980) took a male in breeding condition also in October. For Amapá, Brazil, Novaes (1978) mentioned birds in breeding condition between October and February, corresponding to the breeding period of many other species in this region (GMK pers. obs.). Around Belém, also in Pará, nesting occurs in June–October (Pinto 1953, Oniki and Willis 1983), and at Manaus, Amazonas, Oniki and Willis (1982) found a nest with a single well-grown young in the second week of December, with a bird taken in late August in breeding condition from the same region (MNRJ). In French Guiana, Tostain *et al.* (1992) reported a female nest building in early December, a female feeding two fledged juveniles in the middle of the same month, a nest at the end of August and another nest with a young in November. With respect to Colombia, M. A. Carriker (*in* Hilty and Brown 1986) collected 14 specimens in breeding condition between March and May in the Central Andes. In southernmost Venezuela, at the frontier with Brazil in Amazonas, Willard *et al.* (1991) recorded both sexes in breeding condition in February and March. Further south and east, birds are in breeding condition in October–December in Bahia, Brazil (MNRJ), while in eastern Ecuador, H. F. Greeney (*in litt.* 2010) photographed a nest with eggs in mid December.

STATUS Treated as Least Concern (BirdLife International 2004, 2008) based on its overall large population and very wide range (estimated at 4,950,000km²). Nonetheless, predicted levels of climate could have a near-catastrophic effect on this species' habitat and range (Anciães and Peterson 2006). Despite being generally abundant over Amazonia (Sick 1997, Schulenberg *et al.* 2007, Blake and Loiselle 2009) and the Guianan Shield (Blake 1950, Snyder 1966, Tostain *et al.* 1992, Cohn-Haft *et al.* 1997, Restall *et al.* 2006, Braun *et al.* 2007, Bernard 2008, Ottema *et al.* 2009), elsewhere it is less numerous, for instance being rather rare and poorly known in Panama (Wetmore 1972, Ridgely and Gwynne 1976, Angehr and Dean 2010) and rather local in Costa Rica (Stiles and Skutch 1989). White-crowned Manakin is known from many protected areas throughout its range. In Brazil, examples include Cabo Orange and Montanhas do Tumucumaque National Parks, Amapá (Bernard 2008, Souza *et al.* 2008), Jaú National Park (Borges *et al.* 2001) and the Reserva Ducke, both in Amazonas (Willis and Oniki 1982), FLONA de Tapajós (Henriques *et al.* 2003), Tapajós (Amazonia) National Park (Oren and Parker 1997) and the Carajás mosaic of protected areas (Pacheco *et al.* 2007), all in Pará, Sooretama Biological Reserve, Espírito Santo (Parker and Goerck 1997), and Poço das Antas Biological Reserve, Rio de Janeiro (Castro-Astor *et al.* 2007). Elsewhere, White-crowned Manakin is known from protected areas such as Braulio Carillo National Park (Blake and Loiselle 2001) and El Copal Biological Reserve, both in Costa Rica (Lawson 2010), Yasuní Biosphere Reserve, Ecuador (Hidalgo *et al.* 2008), and the following

ProAves-owned reserves in Colombia: El Pangan, Arrierito Antioqueña and Ranita Dorada (Salaman *et al.* 2009).

REFERENCES Alvarez *et al.* (2007), Alvarez-Alonso (2002), Alverson *et al.* (2001), Anciães and Peterson (2006, 2009), Angehr and Dean (2010), Antas *et al.* (2009), AOU (1998), Barnett *et al.* (2002), Beebe (1915), Bernard (2008), BirdLife International (2004, 2008), E. R. Blake (1950, 1962), Blake and Loiselle (2001, 2008, 2009), Blendinger *et al.* (2008), Boesman (1999, 2006b, 2009), Borges (2006), Borges *et al.* (2001), Braun *et al.* (2007), Brooks *et al.* (2009), Campos *et al.* (2010), Castro-Astor *et al.* (2007), Chapman (1917, 1921), Cherrie (1916), Chubb (1921), Cohn-Haft *et al.* (1997), Cracraft (1985), David and Gosselin (2002a), Dick *et al.* (1984), Dickinson (2003), Dunning (2008), Friedmann (1948), Garrigues and Dean (2007), Gomes and Marceliano (2009), Gomes *et al.* (2008, 2009), Graves (1981, 1993), Gyldenstolpe (1945), Haverschmidt (1952, 1971), Haverschmidt and Mees (1994), Heindl and Winkler (2003a), Hellmayr (1906d, 1929b), Henriques *et al.* (2003), Hidalgo *et al.* (2008), Hilty (1977, 1997, 2003), Hilty and Brown (1986), Jullien and Thiollay (1998), King (1991), Krabbe and Nilsson (2003), Lane *et al.* (2003), Lawson (2010), Levey (1988), Loiselle *et al.* (2007a, 2007b, 2007c), Lysinger *et al.* (2005), Marantz and Zimmer (2006), Marceliano *et al.* (2009), McKay *et al.* (2010), Mee *et al.* (2002), Minns *et al.* (2009), Moore (1994), Naka *et al.* (2006, 2008), Novaes (1957, 1970, 1978, 1980), Oniki and Willis (1982, 1983), Oren and Parker (1997), Ottema *et al.* (2009), Pacheco and Olmos (2005), Pacheco *et al.* (2007), Parker and Goerck (1997), Parker *et al.* (1982), Peres and Whittaker (1991), Pinto (1944, 1953, 1966), Pinto and Camargo (1957), Prum (1990a, 1990b, 1992, 1994a, 1997, 1998), Rêgo *et al.* (2007), Remold (2002), Remsen *et al.* (2009), Renaudier and Deroussen (2008), Restall *et al.* (2006), Reynaud (1998), Ridgely and Greenfield (2001), Ridgely and Gwynne (1976, 1989), Ridgely and Tudor (1994, 2009), Robbins *et al.* (2004, 2007, 2011), Ross and Whitney (1995), Ryder and Durães (2005), Salaman *et al.* (2002a, 2002b, 2008, 2009), Santos and Silva (2007), Schubart *et al.* (1965), Schulenberg *et al.* (2006, 2007), Sick (1993, 1997), Silva *et al.* (1990, 2010), Silveira *et al.* (2005), Simon (2009), Snethlage (1914), Snow (1961, 1975, 1979b, 2004b), Snyder (1966), Souza *et al.* (2008), Stiles and Skutch (1989), Stotz *et al.* (1996), Tello *et al.* (2009), Théry (1990c, 1992, 1997), Thiollay (1994), Tori *et al.* (2008), Tostain (1988a), Tostain *et al.* (1992), Velho (1932), Wetmore (1972), Whittaker (2009), J. T. Zimmer (1936), Zimmer and Hilty (1997), Zimmer *et al.* (1997), Zyskowski *et al.* (2011).

White-crowned Manakin *Dixiphia pipra*. **Fig. 1**. Male, *D. p. anthracina*, Rancho Naturalista, prov. Cartago, Costa Rica, March (*Steven Easley / Costa Rica Gateway*). The northernmost taxon is partially distinguished by the velvety-black upperparts. **Fig. 2**. Male, *D. p. cephaleucos*, Porto Seguro, Bahia, eastern Brazil, October (*Ciro Albano*). This taxon is restricted to the Atlantic Forest, once more demonstrating the former links between this zoogeographical region and Amazonia.

White-crowned Manakin *Dixiphia pipra*. **Fig. 3**. Male, *D. p. separabilis*, Cristalino Jungle Lodge, Alta Floresta, Mato Grosso, east Amazonian Brazil, November (*Hadoram Shirihai / Photographic Handbook to Birds of the World*). This race and *D. p. cephaleucos* are virtually identical (see text). **Fig. 4**. Male, *D. p. pipra*, Arrowpoint Nature Resort, northern Guyana, October (*Hadoram Shirihai / Photographic Handbook to Birds of the World*). **Fig. 5**. Female, *D. p. pipra*, Arrowpoint Nature Resort, northern Guyana, October (*Hadoram Shirihai / Photographic Handbook to Birds of the World*). This is surely one of the most distinctive of female manakins, and is usually easily identified on the basis of its strongly contrasting grey crown and nape, and the reddish irides. **Fig. 6.** Female, *D. p. pipra*, Biological Dynamics of Forest Fragments Project, north of Manaus, Amazonas, Brazil, January (*Gabriel Leite*). Note how the outer wall of the nest is extensively camouflaged by the use of dead leaves in the structure.

Genus *Xenopipo*: Black Manakin

This monospecific genus of manakins (as treated here) is obviously closely related to the four, largely non-Amazonian *Chloropipo* manakins, but is not monomorphic like those species. Nonetheless, and despite its also different and more frequently uttered calls, *Chloropipo* is frequently merged within *Xenopipo*, both historically and more recently following the work on syringeal morphology by Prum (1992). For a more detailed discussion of the question of whether these two genera should be merged see Systematics (p. 40).

BLACK MANAKIN
Xenopipo atronitens   Plate 9

Xenopipo atronitens **Cabanis, 1847**, *Archiv. Naturg.* 8(1): 235, Guyana

Despite being rather widespread and by no means rare, this somewhat dumpy and atypical manakin is poorly known; its nest has only recently been found and only in recent years have ornithologists begun to elucidate its, perhaps widespread, occurrence in sandy-soil forests of western Amazonia, well away from its 'main' range in northeast South America.

IDENTIFICATION 12.0–13.9cm. The male is unlikely to be confused with any other manakin (Jet Manakin *Chloropipo unicolor*, which has white underwing-coverts but is otherwise very similar, is entirely allopatric and not syntopic). Within Amazonia, the present species' combination of glossy blue-black plumage, rather long tail and pale greyish-blue bill is unique amongst the Pipridae. However, Amazonian Black Tyrant *Knipolegus poecilocercus* is a potential confusion species, and shares the glossy quality to its feathers (although the blue sheen is less obvious and it has a brown caste to the remiges). Black Manakin lacks the crested appearance of the Amazonian Black Tyrant, typically perches lower, squats on the branch, is more difficult to observe and is generally far less partial to flooded areas. Male Red-shouldered Tanager *Tachyphonus phoeniceus*, which also frequents savanna and sandy-soil woodlands, occurs sympatrically with Black Manakin. The red-and-white shoulder patch of the tanager can be difficult to see, but eliminates the possibility of confusion with the manakin as soon it does become visible. Female Black Manakin is very dark olive; its long- and notch-tailed appearance is rather atypical for a manakin, although the rounded head and lack of contrasting wing-feather fringes are characters typical of manakins, and should assist in 'nailing' the identification. In comparison, female White-bearded Manakin *Manacus manacus* has orange legs; and Golden-headed Manakin *Pipra erythrocephala* is smaller and markedly paler overall. Similar relatives – the *Chloropipo* manakins – are entirely allopatric (and not syntopic) and, once a correct family diagnosis is reached, identification becomes relatively straightforward, as the potentially similar female Blue-backed Manakin *Chiroxiphia pareola* has yellow (not dark) legs.

DISTRIBUTION The Black Manakin's range is principally confined to northeast South America, but it reaches south of the Amazon in eastern Amazonian Brazil, and spottily much further south and west, as far as Peru and Bolivia. These recently discovered populations suggest that the species might be decidedly more widespread than it is currently considered in western Amazonia. The species occurs in eastern Colombia, in northeast Guainía

and Vaupés, and west to central Meta (Hilty and Brown 1986), through southern and southeast Venezuela, in Amazonas and central and southern Bolívar north locally to the Orinoco River (Hilty 2003), virtually throughout the Guianas, except French Guiana where it is known from just three records, all since 1980 (Tostain *et al.* 1992), despite being locally common and reasonably widespread in neighbouring Surinam (Ottema *et al.* 2009), thence south through Amazonian Brazil, east of the Rio Negro as far as Amapá and, south of the Amazon, from the east bank of the Rio Araguaia south to the upper Rio Xingu in northern Mato Grosso (Sick 1997, Hidasi 1998, Pinheiro and Dornas 2009b), with potentially isolated populations in southwest Amazonia, in Parque Nacional da Serra da Cutia, and at Taquaras (Rondônia), Guajará, Marimoré, Rio Roosevelt and Tupana (all Amazonas, the first at the border with Acre), and at Porto Walter, Acre (Whittaker 2004, 2009, Aleixo and Poletto 2007, Guilherme and Borges 2008; GMK pers. obs.). There are also small populations in eastern Peru, in dptos. Loreto (at Jeberos) and Madre de Dios (on the Pampas del Heath and adjacent areas: Graham *et al.* 1980, Parker *et al.* 1994b, 1994c, Alvarez Alonso 2002). Black Manakin has also recently been discovered in northern and northeastern Bolivia, where it is locally common, on the Serranía de Huanchaca (Bates *et al.* 1992) and in Parque Nacional Noel Kempff Mercado and the nearby Estación Biológica Caparú, dpto. Santa Cruz (Bates *et al.* 1998, Vidoz *et al.* 2010), at Federico Román, dpto. Pando (Moskovits *et al.* 2003), and around Guayaramerin, dpto. Beni (Tobias and Seddon 2007). It has also been predicted to occur in extreme northwest dpto. La Paz (Remsen and Parker 1995). Regularly recorded to *c.*700m (below 300m in Colombia) and locally the species occurs to 1,200m in Venezuela.

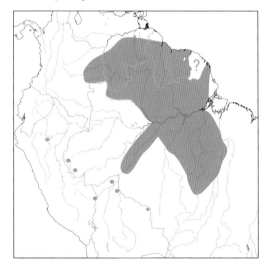

MOVEMENTS Resident and considered to be sedentary.

HABITAT Black Manakin favours slightly scrubby, low to some extent open, more frequently dense savanna, *campina* or *cerrado* forests, often on white-sand soils (and is restricted to such habitats in southern Venezuela), as well as gallery woodland and, locally, stunted *várzea* and *igapó* forests (e.g. in Jaú National Park, Amazonas, Brazil). The species generally shuns tall forest.

DESCRIPTION A somewhat flycatcher-like manakin, with a rather long, slightly cleft tail and a distinctly heavy, broad- and deep-based bill, which might even recall a finch, albeit usually with a sharply arched culmen and a rather strong hook tip (but some have no hook at the tip). The sexes differ. *Adult male.* – Glossy blue-black above and below, with slightly duller, browner remiges and rectrices. The underwing-coverts are black. *Adult female.* – Dull olive-green above, dappled darker, whilst the wings are contrastingly browner, with pale olive fringes to the secondaries, and the tail feathers are dull brownish-olive. Olive-green below, with a pale greyish chin and throat, a yellow-olive belly and lower flanks, and yellowish-white underwing coverts. The undertail is rather pale grey with duskier and browner outer webs to the feathers. *Juvenile.* – Appears to be undescribed (Snow 2004b), but young males are initially identical to females, before gaining the first black feathers on the crown and tertials, or on the lores, upper ear-coverts and forehead, and thereafter over the face, throat, scapulars and breast (INPA; MNRJ; RMNH). *Moult.* – No moult data have been published, but a male taken in the Rio Negro region in February was heavily worn and another of the same sex from this region, collected in July, was not replacing any feathers (MNRJ). Three collected in July in southern Amazonas, Brazil, were also not in moult (INPA). *Bare parts.* – Male has dark brown or chestnut irides and dark olive-grey or metallic grey legs; the bill is pale bluish-grey with a marginally darker tip, or black over the maxilla with a bluish-grey lower mandible (sometimes with the base palest of all). Female usually has the irides pale grey (a useful distinguishing field mark), but once black (see also Fig. 2), and the legs blackish or metallic grey; the bill is blackish or dark grey on the maxilla, with a blue-grey base to the lower mandible.

MEASUREMENTS (BMNH; INPA; MNRJ; RMNH: Amazonas, Mato Grosso and Pará, Brazil; Guyana; Surinam) Wing of male (*n* = 22) 67–74mm, wing of female (*n* = 22) 64.5–71.0mm; tail of male (*n* = 23) 42.0–52.5mm, tail of female (*n* = 22) 40–52mm; bill of male (*n* = 22) 12.08–14.2mm, bill of female (*n* = 22) 11.94–13.92mm; tarsus of male (*n* = 6) 12.69–16.64mm, tarsus of female (*n* = 6) 13.61–15.72mm. Weight (sexes combined, although females perhaps average slightly heavier): 12–18g (Fry 1970, Hilty 2003, Snow 2004b, Aleixo and Poletto 2007, Dunning 2008; FMNH; INPA; MNRJ; RMNH; ROM).

GEOGRAPHICAL VARIATION Monotypic.

VOICE Typically rather loud and sharp calls. A suddenly commenced *Skee skép, skép, skép* or longer with more, but similar, notes, or degenerating into a descending trill (Ridgely and Tudor 1994, 2009, Schulenberg *et al.* 2007) is given in display, often with long intervals between bouts of calling and sometimes with the first note omitted (Hilty 2003), whilst the warning or alarm-call is a loud *wet, wet, wet*, like the voice of some tree frogs (Sick 1993), and also gives a quiet groan or growl. All these calls are given from relatively low in the understorey (usually below 1.5m above

the ground). Hilty (2003) and Snow (2004b) mentioned a dry, rattling *trrrrrrup*. There do not seem to be any recordings published as part of commercial compilations as yet, but three recordings from east Amazonian Brazil are available online at www.xeno-canto.org.

NATURAL HISTORY Rather poorly known and begging detailed field study, in common with all of the species placed in the genus *Chloropipo* in this book. Often found alone or 2–3 males will occur in reasonably close (auditory) contact, and similar numbers might join groups of other birds at fruiting trees.

FOOD AND FEEDING The diet includes both small fruits and insects, which are taken during short aerial sallies (sally-strikes), but there is no further (or more detailed) published information. Black Manakin regularly joins mixed-species feeding flocks in scrub.

BREEDING Behaviour is virtually unknown, but the male display is distinctly unspectacular and undemonstrative by Pipridae standards, consisting solely of calls and chases amongst rival males, with no special display ground (see Sick 1959d, 1967). Photographs of a female on a nest, taken in late March 2006 at Zanderij savanna, northern Surinam (by F. C. Joe), appeared in Ottema (2009) and had previously been 'published' on the internet along with additional images of the nest (http://www1.nhl.nl/~ribot/php4/verspreiding.htm). The nest is an obviously flimsy and very small structure (the female's tail and ventral region protrude well outside it), constructed primarily of dead leaves (at least on the outside) and bound together and attached to three narrow supporting branches with spiderwebs. The base of the nest rests on a live leaf. In Surinam both sexes have been collected in breeding condition in May–June and September–December, and two very young males (no black feathers) in March and August (RMNH). Robbins *et al.* (2007) considered that the breeding season at Gunn's Strip, in southern Guyana (01°39′N, 58°37′W), is in February/March. Several males with enlarged testes were collected in southwest Amazonian Brazil in August (Aleixo and Poletto 2007), and another with moderately large gonads was collected from the Rio Negro, northwestern Brazil, in July (MNRJ).

STATUS Treated as Least Concern (BirdLife International 2004, 2008), and the species is generally fairly common locally, although see the comments under Distribution concerning its rather anomalous range in the Guianas. Despite this, based on modelling techniques Anciães and Peterson (2006) predicted that this species could be severely impacted by habitat modification in the face of potential climate change. Black Manakin seems inexplicably rare in northernmost Brazil, in Roraima, where it is known solely from an 1842 specimen collected by Johann Natterer (Pinto 1966, Naka *et al.* 2006). In Peru, the species is locally fairly common at one site in dpto. Loreto, but its status is unclear in the far south of the country (Schulenberg *et al.* 2007). Regular localities for Black Manakin that are frequently visited by birdwatchers include Junglaven, in Amazonas state, southern Venezuela, the INPA *campina* reserve north of Manaus, Amazonas, Brazil, and the so-called 'Mori scrub' south of Iwokrama Field Station in south-central Guyana, at all of which the species is easy to find. The species is known from relatively few protected areas including two in Bolivia (see 'Distribution') as well as, e.g., Cabo Orange National Park, Amapá, (Souza *et al.* 2008), and Sucunduri State Park, Amazonas, in Brazil (INPA), and in some where it is present the species seems rare, e.g. Tapajós National Park, Pará, Brazil (Oren and Parker 1997), and Cantão State Park, Tocantins, Brazil (Pinheiro and Dornas 2009a, 2009b).

REFERENCES Aleixo and Poletto (2007), Aleixo *et al.* (2011), Alvarez Alonso (2002), Anciães and Peterson (2006, 2009), Bates *et al.* (1992, 1998), BirdLife International (2004, 2008), Borges (2007), Borges *et al.* (2001), Braun *et al.* (2007), Campos *et al.* (2009), Chubb (1921), Crease (2009), Dunning (2008), Fry (1970), Graham *et al.* (1980), Guilherme and Borges (2008), Haffer (1974), Hellmayr (1910, 1929b), Hidasi (1998), Hilty (2003), Hilty and Brown (1986), Lees *et al.* (2008), Moskovits *et al.* (2003), Naka *et al.* (2006), Novaes (1960, 1980a), Oren and Parker (1997), Ottema (2009), Ottema *et al.* (2009), Pacheco and Olmos (2005), Parker *et al.* (1994b, 1994c), Pinheiro and Dornas (2009a, 2009b), Pinto (1944, 1966), Pinto and Camargo (1957), Prum (1992), Rêgo *et al.* (2007), Remsen and Parker (1995), Restall *et al.* (2006), Ridgely and Tudor (1994, 2009), Robbins *et al.* (2004, 2007), Salaman *et al.* (2008), Schulenberg *et al.* (2007), Sick (1959d, 1967, 1997), Snow (2004b), Snyder (1966), Souza *et al.* (2008), Stotz *et al.* (1996), Tello *et al.* (2007), Tobias and Seddon (2007), Tostain *et al.* (1992), Vidoz *et al.* (2010), Whittaker (2004, 2009), Zimmer and Hilty (1997), Zyskowski *et al.* (2011).

Black Manakin *Xenopipo atronitens*. **Fig. 1**. Male, Junglaven, Amazonas, southern Venezuela, December (*David J. Southall*). This white-sand scrub specialist should be easily identified by its glossy all-black plumage, relatively long tail and pale greyish-blue bill, provided it is realised to be a manakin. The most likely confusion risks are Amazonian Black Tyrant *Knipolegus poecilocercus* (which is, however, typically found in seasonally flooded habitats) and Red-shouldered Tanager *Tachyphonus phoeniceus*, which does occur sympatrically with the manakin. The species' behaviour and 'jizz' should distinguish it. **Fig. 2**. Female, Mori Scrub, Iwokrama, Guyana, October (*Hadoram Shirihai / Photographic Handbook to Birds of the World*). Note the atypical (for a manakin) relatively long tail and dark legs.

Genus *Chloropipo*

This genus is frequently merged within *Xenopipo* but irrespective of their generic assignment, this group of manakins (they were deemed to represent a superspecies by Snow 1979b) is one of the most poorly known amongst the Pipridae. As treated here, *Chloropipo* is a mainly Andean genus, although one species just reaches Central America, in eastern Panama, and another is restricted to the Pantepui. The nest of just one species, and that the most widespread, has been formally described, and our knowledge of their collective life histories is staggering only for the paucity of published information.

YELLOW-HEADED MANAKIN
Chloropipo flavicapilla   Plate 9

Pipra flavicapilla **P. L. Sclater, 1852**, *Rev. Mag. Zool.* (2)4: 9, Nouvelle Grenade [= Bogotá]

Undoubtedly the most attractive of the genus, the male Yellow-headed Manakin should prove unmistakable and only the female is likely to cause any identification problems. This is probably also the rarest of the genus and is practically endemic to Colombia, where its range is apparently rather fragmentary and has suffered local extinctions, although the species appears tolerant of second growth to some extent.

IDENTIFICATION 12–13cm. The handsome male is unlikely to be confused with any other member of the Pipridae. Females could be confused with the mainly lower elevation Green Manakin *Chloropipo holochlora*, but note Yellow-headed's orange eyes, white underwing-coverts and the brighter yellow crown than the mantle. Some individuals, probably immatures, lack the intense yellow tone to their plumage and the orange irides, and more closely resemble Green Manakin, which see for further discussion of the issue.

DISTRIBUTION Virtually endemic to Colombia, where its range is distinctly patchy on both slopes of the West Andes (in dptos. Valle and Cauca), on the west slope from the northernmost end of the Central Andes in dpto. Antioquia, on the east slope from dpto. Tolima (e.g. at the Río Combeima in the municipality of Ibague), and at the head of the Magdalena Valley in dpto. Huila southwards (Hilty and Brown 1986, Peña and Weber 2000, Cuervo *et al.* 2003, Boyla and Estrada 2005, Losada-Prado *et al.* 2005, Cuervo *et al.* 2008a, 2008b). Known from one 19th century record (at Hacienda Mapoto, Tungurahua, the southernmost locality) and the species has recently been rediscovered on the east

slope of the Andes in northern Ecuador, with records from the southern slope of the Cordillera de Huacamayos and the same slope of the Volcán Sumaco (Ridgely and Greenfield 2001, Boyla and Estrada 2005). Its altitudinal range spans 1,200–2,400 m, but the species has been found only at 1,500–2,100m in Ecuador.

MOVEMENTS None definitely known, although Cuervo *et al.* (2003) suspected that the species was perhaps only seasonally present at one of their study localities at the northern end of the Central Andes in Colombia.

HABITAT Prefers humid forest and tall second growth, but may regularly come to forest borders (Ridgely and Greenfield 2001), and seems particularly associated with drainages and shallow ravines (López-Lanús *et al.* 2000, Peña and Weber 2000; GMK pers. obs.).

DESCRIPTION A large, long-tailed 'typical' manakin with white underwing-coverts in both sexes. The culmen is reasonably well arched with a slightly hooked tip. *Adult male.* – The crown and hindneck are rich golden-yellow. The rest of the upperparts are fairly uniform, although the mantle has an 'oily' quality (M. Pearman pers. comm.). Ear-coverts olive dappled golden-yellow in some, but concolorous with the crown in others. Throat and breast yellowish-olive. The belly and ventral region is bright yellow. Remiges dull olive with brighter yellow fringes to the secondaries. *Adult female.* – More uniform olive above than the male. Crown slightly (sometimes obviously) brighter and more yellow than the mantle. Throat, breast and flanks dull olive; centre of belly yellow. *Moult.* – There are no published moult data, but one trapped in Colombia in February was in light body moult and others trapped in April were in body and wing moult, but one examined in November and another in February showed no evidence of feather renewal (D. Y. Ramírez, J. P. López, G. A. Suárez and D. A. Carantón/ProAves unpubl. data). *Bare parts.* – Iris reddish-orange (duller in the female); the bill and legs are pale horn to grey (the latter dull pinkish in the female).

MEASUREMENTS (BMNH; Peña and Weber 2000: Colombia) Wing of male ($n = 7$) 68–79mm, wing of female ($n = 2$) 73–74mm; tail of male ($n = 6$) 44–51mm, tail of female ($n = 2$) 41–55mm; bill of male ($n = 6$) 10–12mm, bill of female ($n = 2$) 11–12mm; tarsus of male ($n = 7$) 12.7–15.0mm, tarsus of female ($n = 2$) 14–15mm (<17.2mm in live birds). Weight (sexes combined): 15.3–19.5g (Snow 2004b, Dunning 2008; MVZ; D. Y. Ramírez, J. P. López, G. A. Suárez and D. A. Carantón/ProAves unpubl. data).

GEOGRAPHICAL VARIATION Monotypic.

VOICE Generally quiet and the species' vocalisations are poorly known. A short, single, downslurred whistle (not unlike other members of the genus) is given at slightly

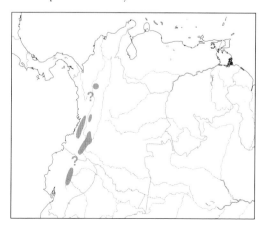

irregular intervals, sometimes slightly more prolonged, which might be rendered *hoeeet, whoit* or even *wheep*. In comparison with other *Chloropipo* species the voice sounds distinctly squeakier. Included on the commercial compilation of Alvarez *et al.* (2007), from where the transcription presented here is taken, but the vocalisations presented thereon were made by a bird that had been trapped and might not be entirely representative.

NATURAL HISTORY Essentially unknown, although probably its ecology is generally similar to congenerics (themselves not well known!). This species is not easily observed due to its quiet and usually solitary habits, although it at least occasionally joins mixed-species foraging flocks, including those with many tanagers (Hilty and Brown 1986, Ridgely and Greenfield 2001, Ridgely and Tudor 2009; GMK pers. obs.).

FOOD AND FEEDING Diet is probably mainly small fruits, with those of a *Palicourea* (Rubiaceae) recently mentioned (Peña and Weber 2000).

BREEDING Nesting until recently was basically unknown, although M. A. Carriker (*in* Hilty and Brown 1986) took a female in breeding condition in southwest dpto. Huila in March, whilst Miller (1963) observed a female feeding a still-dependent juvenile in May (now held in MVZ), and mist-netted another with a large brood patch in mid July (according to the label data), both in the West Andes near Cali. Peña and Weber (2000) mist-netted an adult male with large gonads in January. However, the nest of this species has been recently discovered, at La Romera Reserve, Sabaneta, dpto. Antioquia, Colombia, in January 2010 (Fig. 1). The nest was placed low down within the fork of a small shrub, above a narrow creek just a few metres from a road. It was principally constructed of strips of dry grass bound with spiderwebs, and lined with dry sticks. It held a single cream-coloured egg that was heavily marked. Two birds were seen carrying nesting material and foraging nearby, but it was impossible to know whether only one individual was incubating the egg. Indeed, once what was apparently a

third individual was observed foraging nearby. The nest was eventually predated (D. Calderón *et al.* in prep.).

STATUS Treated as Near Threatened (BirdLife International 2004, 2008) and considered to be uncommon and probably locally distributed in Colombia (Hilty and Brown 1986), and very rare in Ecuador (Ridgely and Greenfield 2001; see above). The latter authors suggested that it might really deserve upgrading to Vulnerable status, and at the time of writing (December 2010) BirdLife were actively considering the species' conservation listing. Regional extinctions are known to have occurred, which might help support such a hypothesis, e.g. in the vicinity of Santa Elena, dpto. Antioquia, in Colombia (Castaño-Villa and Patiño-Zabala 2008). There are records from three Endemic Bird Areas (EBAs): the Colombian Inter-Andean Slopes, Chocó and Ecuador–Peru East Andes EBAs (Stattersfield *et al.* 1998), as well as quite a number of Important Bird Areas in Colombia (Boyla and Estrada 2005). Deforestation has certainly been extensive throughout much of its known range, but this manakin occurs in at least eight protected areas: Reserva Florestal Yotoco, in the upper Pichindé Valley of dpto. Valle del Cauca, where the species is regularly seen, Farallones de Cali National Park, in the same department, Reserva Natural Merenberg, dpto. Huila, and San Sebastián Natural Reserve, dpto. Antioquia (Boyla and Estrada 2005), as well as Reserva Mirabilis Swarovksi, dpto. Cauca (Salaman *et al.* 2008), and Reserva San Miguel, dpto. Antioquia (Peña and Weber 2000). La Romera Reserve (see Breeding) is a regular locality for the species. In Ecuador, the species has been recorded within Sumaco-Napo Galeras National Park (Boyla and Estrada 2005).

REFERENCES Alvarez *et al.* (2007), Anciães and Peterson (2009), BirdLife International (2004, 2008), Boyla and Estrada (2005), Castaño-Villa and Patiño-Zabala (2008), Chapman (1917), Collar *et al.* (1992), Cuervo *et al.* (2003, 2008a, 2008b), Dunning (2008), Hellmayr (1929b), Hilty and Brown (1986), López-Lanús *et al.* (2000), Losada-Prado *et al.* (2005), Miller (1963), Peña and Weber (2000), Ridgely and Tudor (1994, 2009), Salaman *et al.* (2008), Snow (2004b), Stattersfield *et al.* (1998), Stotz *et al.* (1996).

Yellow-headed Manakin *Chloropipo flavicapilla.* **Fig. 1**. Female, La Romera Reserve, Saboneta, dpto. Antioquia, Central Andes, Colombia, January (*Juan David Ramírez*). The first nest to be found of this rare species (see text). In this photograph, the bird appears to be rather extensively yellow over the head and underparts, but this is an effect of the relative sunlight and shade; in other images of the same individual, it can be seen to have bright yellow more or less restricted to the crown. Note the striking orange-red irides.

GREEN MANAKIN
Chloropipo holochlora   Plate 9

Chloropipo holochlora **P. L. Sclater, 1888**, *Cat. Birds Brit. Mus.*
14: xvi, 281, 287, Bogotá [= east slope of the Andes in the
Bogotá area of Colombia]

Like all *Chloropipo* manakins, this species is rather poorly
known and comparatively infrequently seen. It is speculated
that two species might be involved, on the west and east
slopes of the Andes (Sibley 1996, R. O. Prum *in* Ridgely and
Greenfield 2001), but to date no ornithologist appears to
have followed up on this speculation.

IDENTIFICATION 11–13cm. This rather confusing
manakin is rather like a female *Lepidothrix* or *Pipra*, e.g.
Blue-crowned Manakin *L. coronata* (which west of the Andes
might be distinguished by the brighter upperparts and to
the east has a much brighter green breast). However, the
Green Manakin's dull bare-parts coloration, larger size and
longer tail should readily differentiate it as belonging to
a different genus, without recourse to plumage features.
Whilst Blue-crowned Manakin also occurs on both sides
of the Andes, Blue-backed Manakin *Chiroxiphia pareola* is
restricted to the east; females of the latter have dull orangey
legs (not greyish). Other potential confusion risks are
female White-crowned Manakin *Dixiphia pipra* (again most
useful are the structural features described above) and
female Golden-winged Manakin *Masius chrysopterus*, which
has a small but obvious forehead tuft and purplish legs (but
shares the longer tail). West of the Andes, the Broad-billed
Sapayoa *Sapayoa aenigma* is also very similar to this species,
but should appear noticeably larger than Green Manakin.
Female Yellow-headed Manakin *Chloropipo flavicapilla*,
which is usually found at higher elevations (exclusively so
in Ecuador to date), in most plumages shows a distinctly
yellower head than the rest of the upperparts, and the irides
are orange rather than dark as in Green Manakin. Yellow-
headed Manakin occurs in the subtropical zone, whereas
Green is found in the tropics, and this distinction may have
to serve in any circumstances in which the observer is faced
with an apparently immature-plumaged Yellow-headed
Manakin with duller irides and a much less obvious contrast
between the head and upperparts (see previous species).
Female Jet Manakin *Chloropipo unicolor* is a much duller olive
bird and, again, overlaps only to a very limited extent with
the present species (e.g. on the upper slopes of Palm Peak,
in eastern Ecuador: Ridgely and Greenfield 2001).

DISTRIBUTION Restricted to eastern Panama (in eastern
San Blas and eastern Darién), thence through Colombia
in the Macarena Mountains and south on the west slope
to prov. Esmeraldas and western Imbabura, occasionally
to southern Pichincha, exceptionally to provs. Los Ríos
(1950 record) and northwest Azuay (1991), all in Ecuador
(Ridgely and Greenfield 2001, but see Status), and via
virtually the entire east slope from western dpto. Meta
(at Villavicencio), Colombia, through Ecuador to eastern
Peru as far south as the Bolivian border (Schulenberg *et
al.* 2007). Predicted to occur in extreme northwest dpto.
La Paz, Bolivia (Remsen and Parker 1995), but the species
has not been found there to date. Recently recorded at one
locality at the north end of the Central Andes of Colombia
(Cuervo *et al.* 2008). Occurs to 1,275m in Panama (Wetmore
1972). In the west occurs from 100m to 900m in Colombia
(Hilty and Brown 1986) and to 1,100m in Ecuador (Ridgely

and Greenfield), whereas in the east it is found mainly at
300–1,200m in Ecuador (locally to 1,500m), to 1,425m in
the Central Andes of Colombia (Cuervo *et al.* 2008a) and
at 210–1,130m in Peru (Mee *et al.* 2002, Schulenberg *et al.*
2007, Brooks *et al.* 2009).

MOVEMENTS None known.

HABITAT Inhabits the undergrowth and lower midstorey
of humid, principally *terra firme* forest in the foothills
and lowlands. May regularly visit forest borders, at least
seasonally, in southeast Ecuador and presumably elsewhere,
especially where there are fruiting trees.

DESCRIPTION The sexes are similar. A rather large
and long-winged manakin with moss green upperparts.
Nominate *C. h. holochlora* is described here. The bill has a
reasonably well-arched culmen, sometimes a quite strongly
hooked tip and moderately large and prominent nostrils,
with a few to many rather long rictal bristles. *Adult.* – Remiges
are dusky or brownish with moss green outer fringes, whilst
the rest of the upperparts are bright grass green. The throat,
breast and flanks are olive; the chin and centre of the belly
are more pale yellowish. Underwing-coverts are greyish-olive
and undertail-coverts olive. *Juvenile/Immature.* – Described,
in reference to race *C. h. litae*, by Wetmore (1972) as
being 'duller colored'. See Christian (2001) for brief data
concerning a downy nestling. *Moult.* – Nothing has been
published concerning moult regime, but none of those
trapped in December, February and June was renewing its
plumage, but several (but not all) of those trapped in the
third and fourth weeks of March in Colombia were in light
to heavy wing and body moult, whilst one trapped in June
was in heavy body moult, and one (of several) examined
in August was in body moult (D. Y. Ramírez, F. Guerrero,
H. Loaiza and J. C. Luna/ProAves unpubl. data). Two
females collected in southeast Peru in late August and
early November were moulting the body-feathers and the
wing- and body-feathers, respectively, while three males from
the same region, all taken in November, were moulting the
body-feathers (FMNH). However, others of both sexes from
the same months (and, in some cases, identical localities)
showed no evidence of feather replacement. *Bare parts.* – All
comments refer to both sexes. Bill either black above and

dark grey on the lower mandible (sometimes confined to the base), or dark brown to black throughout (latter refers to race *C. h. viridior*). The irides are brown to dark brown with a pale eye-ring (data refer exclusively to *C. h. viridior* and *C. h. litae*). The legs and feet are dark grey, pinkish-grey or blackish to brown, once bluish-grey or greenish-grey (*C. h. litae*) and once dark pinkish (*C. h. viridior*) (Ridgely and Tudor 1994; FMNH).

MEASUREMENTS (BMNH; RMNH; Wetmore 1972: Colombia, Ecuador and Panama; see also Hellmayr 1906, 1929b for some additional mensural data) *C. h. litae/C. h. suffusa*: wing of male (*n* = 15) 69.0–74.5mm, wing of female (*n* = 15) 64–72mm; tail of male (*n* = 15) 39–49mm, tail of female (*n* = 15) 40–44mm; bill of male (*n* = 15) 12.5–14.0mm, bill of female (*n* = 15) 11.5–13.0mm; tarsus of male (*n* = 15) 13.8–16.0mm, tarsus of female (*n* = 14) 13.0–14.8mm (<17.2mm in live birds). *C. h. holochlora* (FMNH: eastern Colombia and Ecuador): wing of male (*n* = 10) 68.5–77.0mm, wing of female (*n* = 11) 66–73mm; tail of male (*n* = 10) 41–51mm, tail of female (*n* = 11) 40–47mm; bill of male (*n* = 10) 10.49–12.58mm, bill of female (*n* = 11) 12.01–13.06mm; tarsus of male (*n* = 8) 13.46–15.31mm, tarsus of female (*n* = 6) 14.34–15.26mm. *C. h. viridior* (FMNH: southeast Peru): wing of male (*n* = 15) 70.5–81.5mm, wing of female (*n* = 6) 69.0–75.5mm; tail of male (*n* = 15) 46–52mm, tail of female (*n* = 6) 43.0–48.5mm; bill of male (*n* = 15) 11.75–12.99mm, bill of female (*n* = 6) 12.02–13.08mm; tarsus of male (*n* = 8) 15.12–17.61mm, tarsus of female (*n* = 3) 15.02–16.77mm. Wing of *C. h. litae* (live birds) (*n* = 7 unsexed) 65–74mm (northwest Ecuador: J. Hornbuckle unpubl. data), tail (*n* = 3 both sexes) 43–46mm; bill (*n* = 3) 10.5–11.3mm (western Colombia: Hellmayr 1911). Other data from live birds, *C. h. holochlora*: wing of male (*n* = 2) 54–71mm, wing of female (*n* = 2) 72–74mm, wing (*n* = 12, unsexed) 60–76mm; tail of male (*n* = 1) 42.5mm, tail (*n* = 5, unsexed) 41.7–47.1mm; bill of male (*n* = 1) 11.4mm, bill (*n* = 4, unsexed) 9.5–12.3mm; tarsus of male (*n* = 1) 14.0mm, tarsus (*n* = 5, unsexed) 14.6–16.5mm (T. M. Donegan *et al.* unpubl. data). Weight: 10.5–21.0g (J. Hornbuckle unpubl. data from northwest Ecuador; King 1991, Snow 2004b, Dunning 2008; FMNH; MVZ; T. M. Donegan *et al.* unpubl. data; D. Y. Ramírez, F. Guerrero, H. Loaiza and J. C. Luna/ProAves unpubl. data).

GEOGRAPHICAL VARIATION Two to four subspecies are recognised on opposite sides of the Andes (all four were recognised by Dickinson 2003 and, more hesitantly, by Snow 2004a). We have examined too few specimens and possess insufficient field experience to comment knowledgeably on this issue, except to state that we feel reasonably confident that the poorly marked race *C. h. suffusa* might be comfortably subsumed within *C. h. litae*. The four described races are as follows. *C. h. litae* C. E. Hellmayr, 1906, of eastern Panama to northwest Ecuador is duller green above than the nominate race (not bright 'mossy'), with a dusky-olive breast and flanks that contrast much more obviously with the yellow centre to the lower breast and belly. This race was apparently recently recorded at the north end of the Central Andes in Colombia (Cuervo *et al.* 2008a, 2008b). (The latter almost certainly includes *C. h. suffusa* Griscom, 1932, of eastern Panama to northwest Colombia: see Wetmore 1972, Snow 2004a.) *C. h. litae* is sometimes speculated to represent a separate species, which might be named Chocó Manakin (cf. Ridgely and Greenfield 2001). *C. h. holochlora* (described above, and

perhaps includes *C. h. viridior* Chapman, 1924, described from the extreme south of the range, in southeast Peru, on the basis of it being on average larger, brighter above and with more extensive yellow underparts than the nominate) occurs over the rest of the species' range, east of the Andes in South America, from eastern Colombia to southeast Peru. Based on specimens at FMNH, there is much overlap in all of these features, although as average differences they perhaps hold true, especially in terms of size (see Measurements). The latter difference is, of course, unsurprising given that this is the more austral form, and it is perhaps worth noting that the smallest individual measured by us was also the northernmost specimen examined belonging to *C. h. viridior*. We would add that the nominate tends to have brighter yellow posterior underparts than *C. h. viridior* and that this seems to be a more consistent (but still not constant) difference than the extent of this coloration.

VOICE No vocal differences detected between populations on opposing sides of the Andes to date, but samples very small and wholly analogous vocalisations perhaps unavailable. Very quiet, although R. O. Prum (*in* Ridgely and Greenfield 2001) heard a harsh growling '*arrrn*' during agonistic encounters at a fruiting tree. Soft sputtering notes described from Ecuador for the western race *C. h. litae* (O. Jahn *in* Ridgely and Greenfield 2001), and a high, rising *tueee* for nominate *C. h. holochlora* in Peru (Schulenberg *et al.* 2007). Voice, from Ecuador, recently included in the commercial compilations presented by Jahn *et al.* (2002), Krabbe and Nilsson (2003), Lysinger *et al.* (2005), Alvarez *et al.* (2007) and Boesman (2009), and there is a recording from eastern Peru archived online at www.xeno-canto.org.

NATURAL HISTORY Solitary, but very poorly known due to the species' extremely secretive habits. It occasionally joins mixed-species foraging flocks and also visits fruiting trees, including at forest borders.

FOOD AND FEEDING Dietary information is more or less completely lacking, beyond that it principally takes small fruits, perhaps favouring *Anthurium* spp. (Araceae) (McMullan *et al.* 2010). Fruit is largely taken using typical short sally-hover movements, in which the bird either returns to the same or a different perch, which is marginally lower than the food source being visited (GMK pers. obs.). However, it has been speculated that Green Manakin might be more inclined to be insectivorous than many other small Pipridae (Snow 2004b) and insect remains have been found in the stomach contents of one female (FMNH).

BREEDING Nesting behaviour was basically unknown until very recently, although in Colombia a female in breeding condition was taken in northern Chocó in March (Haffer 1975), and M. A. Carriker (*in* Hilty and Brown 1986) took another in northern dpto. Antioquia in May, whilst there is a male in breeding condition from eastern Peru taken in late July (MVZ). In southeast Peru (dpto. Madre de Dios), three females were taken in breeding condition (one with an egg in the oviduct) in early August (*n* = 1) and early to mid November, while several males appeared to be in breeding condition during November in this region, but had already commenced their moult; see above (FMNH). Christian (2001) described the species' nest from observations at the Sierra de Jungurudó, eastern Panama, in mid August, and southeast Peru, in the first half of November. The first nest was in a small ravine with steep slopes and was sited 2m above a small stream in a small tree. It was a shallow cup nest constructed of rootlets and moss with a long 'tail' of moss, rootlets and dead leaves, suspended within a two-way fork and attached to the supporting branches using cobwebs, rootlets and moss (nest dimensions are presented in the paper). This Panamanian nest contained a single small nestling with dark greyish down that was brooded by a single adult (presumably the female). The Peruvian nest was similar and was suspended from the fork of a dead sapling, 1.6m above a very small drainage, and it contained a single egg (dimensions are presented in Christian 2001), dull olive in colour and speckled brown especially at the larger end. The nest was found empty but undamaged a few days later.

STATUS Treated as of Least Concern (BirdLife International 2004, 2008), but the species' range in western Ecuador appears to have contracted recently, due to extensive forest loss in this region, and it is now mainly known from prov. Esmeraldas on the west slope of the Andes in this country (Ridgely and Greenfield 2001). Furthermore, Green Manakin is still known from comparatively few records and localities in Colombia (Hilty and Brown 1986), but experience of mist-netting reveals the species to be far from rare, merely highly unobtrusive (Ridgely and Greenfield 2001), and it is considered locally fairly common in eastern Peru (Schulenberg *et al.* 2007). Nonetheless, Anciães and Peterson (2006) predicted that this species could be moderately to badly affected by habitat modification in

the face of potential climate change based on modelling techniques. Green Manakin is known to occur in several protected areas, e.g. Reserva El Pangán and Rio Ñambí Natural Reserve, both in dpto. Nariño, Tinigua National Park, dpto. Meta, and Reserva El Paujil, dpto. Boyacá, all in Colombia; Podocarpus National Park, in Ecuador; and Manu National Park and Biosphere Reserve, in Peru (Williams *et al.* 1997, Cadena *et al.* 2000, Snow 2004a, Walker *et al.* 2006, Salaman *et al.* 2008).

REFERENCES Alvarez *et al.* (2007), Alverson *et al.* (2001), Anciães and Peterson (2006, 2009), Angehr and Dean (2010), Angehr *et al.* (2004), AOU (1998), Balchin and Toyne (1998), BirdLife International (2004, 2008), Boesman (2009), Brooks *et al.* (2009), Cadena *et al.* (2000), Chapman (1917), Christian (2001), Cuervo *et al.* (2008a, 2008b), Dickinson (2003), Dunning (2008), Haffer (1975) Hellmayr (1906, 1911, 1929b), Hilty and Brown (1986), Jahn *et al.* (2002), King (1991), Krabbe and Nilsson (2003), Krabbe and Sornoza (1994), Lysinger *et al.* (2005), McMullan *et al.* (2010), Mee *et al.* (2002), Merkord *et al.* (2009), Parker and Wust (1994), Remsen and Parker (1995), Restall *et al.* (2006), Ridgely and Greenfield (2001), Ridgely and Gwynne (1989), Ridgely and Tudor (1994, 2009), Salaman *et al.* (1999, 2008), Schulenberg and Awbrey (1997), Schulenberg *et al.* (2007), Sibley (1996), Snow (2004b), Stotz *et al.* (1996), Walker *et al.* (2006), Wetmore (1972), Williams *et al.* (1997).

Green Manakin *Chloropipo holochlora*. **Fig. 1**. *C. h. litae*, Rio Canandé Reserve, Esmeraldas, northwest Ecuador, January (Dušan Brinkhuizen). The generally dull olive-green upperparts contrast rather well with the pale yellowish posterior underparts in this race, but none of the four subspecies described is particularly well marked.

OLIVE MANAKIN
Chloropipo uniformis   Plate 9

Chloropipo uniformis **Salvin & Godman, 1884**, *Ibis* (5)2: 447, Roraima

The only non-Andean representative of the genus *Chloropipo*, Olive Manakin is considered to possibly form a superspecies with Green Manakin *C. holochlora* (AOU 1983), although Mayr and Phelps (1967) thought that *C. uniformis* has no obvious close relative.

IDENTIFICATION 13.5–14.0cm. Restricted to the tepuis of southeastern Venezuela, northernmost Brazil and Guyana, this large, relatively long-tailed manakin should be readily identified within its limited range. The eye-ring, quite noticeable in the field, separates it from the drab female Black Manakin *Xenopipo atronitens*, which is unlikely to occur syntopically with the present species. Female Black is a slightly slimmer bird, prefers lower scrubby forest and is better described as dusky-green than olive. Female Scarlet-horned Manakin *Pipra cornuta*, another Pantepui endemic, is slightly smaller, has shorter wings, yellow tarsal feathering and brownish- or pinkish-orange legs, and a tufted appearance to the nape.

DISTRIBUTION A strict Pantepui endemic, Olive Manakin occurs across southern Venezuela, from the Cerro Sipapo in northwest Amazonas to the Sierra de Lema in Bolívar, thence south into extreme northern Brazil, where it is found only on the Serra Uei in Roraima (Phelps and Phelps 1962), and east into adjacent western Guyana, where the species is known solely from Mt Ayangganna (cf. Barnett *et al.* 2002) and Mt Twek-quay and the Ayangganna Mountains (Snyder 1966).

HABITAT The species prefers humid, wet and stunted, melastome-dominated second growth and mossy forest on tepui slopes, at 800–2,100m (perhaps once to 450m). It has been reported once in scrubby savanna in southern Venezuela (A. Renaudier *in* Kirwan *et al.* 2009).

MOVEMENTS Considered to be resident, but the species is perhaps not truly sedentary, as Hilty (2003) considered that seasonal elevational movements probably occur.

DESCRIPTION Sexes similar. Relatively typical of its genus, Olive Manakin is chunky and bull-necked with a broad-based bill, and relatively long wings and tail (which is also somewhat narrow proportionately). *Adult.* – Bright olive upperparts and outer fringes to the otherwise dark brownish remiges. The tail is rather dusky brown with broad olive fringes to the webs. Breast olive, slightly paler than the upperparts; the throat is yellow-olive. Centre of belly yellowish but with many greenish elements. Underwing-coverts and axillaries yellowish-white, but rarely seen in the field. Whitish to yellowish, rather faint, eye-ring. *Juvenile.* – Apparently resembles adult female (Snow 2004b). *Moult.* – The only published moult data involve the statement by Lentino *et al.* (1998) that eight of 23 birds of both sexes collected in February in southern Venezuela were in body moult. In addition, a female held at FMNH was replacing the primaries and some body feathers in mid November. *Bare parts.* – Few data. The irides are dark or brown in both sexes, while the short bill and legs and feet are dusky to dark grey or greyish-brown (FMNH).

MEASUREMENTS (BMNH; FMNH: Guyana and Venezuela; cf. Hellmayr 1929b and Chapman 1929b for additional mensural data) *C. u. uniformis*: wing of male (*n* = 4) 75–83mm, wing of female (*n* = 3) 75–77mm; tail of male (*n* = 4) 51–54mm, tail of female (*n* = 3) 50–51mm; bill of male (*n* = 3) 15mm, bill of female (*n* = 3) 13.96–15.01mm; tarsus of male (*n* = 4) 15–18mm, tarsus of female (*n* = 3) 14.02–17.09mm. *C. u. duidae*: wing of male (*n* = 5) 76–81mm, wing of female (*n* = 5) 75–77mm; tail of male (*n* = 5) 52–53mm, tail of female (*n* = 5) 49–51mm (Chapman 1929b). Weight: 18–21g (males) and 15–22g (females) (Dickerman and Phelps 1982, Lentino *et al.* 1998, Snow 2004b, Dunning 2008; FMNH).

GEOGRAPHICAL VARIATION Two races are traditionally recognised (Dickinson 2003, Snow 2004b). We have no experience of race *C. u. duidae*, and therefore cannot comment on this subspecies' validity, given that it is obviously only marginally distinguishable from the nominate race. *C. u. duidae* Chapman, 1929, occurs in southern Venezuela on the Cerros Duidae and Sipapo of central and northern Amazonas, and was described as being slightly smaller, brighter and more yellow, with a relatively narrower bill (breadth at base in males 5–6mm vs. 6.7mm, in females 5.6mm vs. 6.7mm) than nominate *C. u. uniformis*, which is found over the remainder of the species' range, from western Bolívar, Venezuela (on the Cerro Jaua, upper Río Caura), to western Guyana and northernmost Brazil.

VOICE Well described by Hilty (2003) and Restall *et al.* (2006), and presented on the compilations of Boesman (2006a, 2006b), with a single recording from southeast Venezuela archived online at www.xeno-canto.org. The male's advertising call is a penetrating but not loud *preeeeeeeEE*, clearly rising at the end; typically given at long intervals, this whistle is sometimes preceded by a stuttering series of low, rapidly delivered *stu-tu-tu-tu-tu* notes (e.g. D. Edwards recording XC20075), or a short *chip*. Also reported to frequently give a *zurrt!* (D. Ascanio *in* Restall *et al.* 2006). The species often reacts strongly to playback.

NATURAL HISTORY Very poorly known, like its congeners. The species is typically solitary, quiet, and most frequently encountered perched silently and inconspicuously at mid to lower levels inside shady forest.

FOOD AND FEEDING The species regularly visits forest edges with fruiting melastomes, where it joins other manakins, *Tangara* tanagers and thrushes in feeding melees

(Hilty 2003). Hilty suggested that the species might defend a resource-based territory.

BREEDING Nest undescribed, but Dickerman and Phelps (1982) reported that a juvenile has been collected in late March in southern Venezuela, already in light moult to adult plumage. Lentino *et al.* (1988) reported the availability of specimens of both sexes, also collected in southern Venezuela, which were in breeding condition in February. There are three specimens in breeding condition, also all collected in southern Venezuela, taken in November (*n* = 2) and late February in FMNH.

STATUS Treated as of Least Concern (BirdLife International 2004, 2008). Olive Manakin is considered generally fairly common in Venezuela (Hilty 2003), where it is known from Canaíma National Park, but is distinctly scarce in Guyana (Braun *et al.* 2007) and must be rare (as well as extremely local) in northernmost Brazil. The nominate race is considered to be endemic to the Gran Sabana subcentre of the Pantepui Centre of endemism, whilst the race *C. u.*

duidae is endemic to the Duida subcentre (Cracraft 1985). The species as a whole is considered to be restricted to the Tepuis Endemic Bird Area (Stattersfield *et al.* 1998). Anciães and Peterson (2006) predicted that this species could be very severely affected by habitat modification in the face of potential climate change based on modelling techniques.

REFERENCES Anciães and Peterson (2006, 2009), Barnett *et al.* (2002), Barrowclough *et al.* (1997), BirdLife International (2004, 2008), Boesman (2006a, 2006b), Braun *et al.* (2007), Chapman (1929b, 1931), Chubb (1921), Cracraft (1985), Dickerman and Phelps (1982), Dickinson (2003), Dunning (2008), Forrester (1993), Gilliard (1941), Hellmayr (1929b), Hilty (2003), Kirwan *et al.* (2009), Lentino *et al.* (1998), Meyer de Schauensee and Phelps (1978), Mayr and Phelps (1967), Mlíkovský (2009), Naka *et al.* (2006), Phelps and Phelps (1962), Pinto (1944), Restall *et al.* (2006), Ridgely and Tudor (1994, 2009), Rodner *et al.* (2000), Sick (1997), Snow (2004b), Snyder (1966), Stattersfield *et al.* (1998), Stotz *et al.* (1996).

Olive Manakin *Chloropipo uniformis.* **Fig. 1** *C. u. uniformis,* Sierra de Lema, Bolívar, southeast Venezuela, November (*Wim van der Schot*). Note the rather striking eye-ring, which readily separates this otherwise poorly marked species from the superficially similar female Black Manakin *Xenopipo atronitens,* although they also inhabit quite different habitats.

JET MANAKIN
Chloropipo unicolor   Plate 9

Chloropipo unicolor Taczanowski, 1884, *Orn. Pérou* 2: 335, Amable María, near Tulumayo River, dpto. Junín, Peru (cf. Mlíkovský 2009)

The southernmost-ranging of the *Chloropipo* manakins, and also the highest-ranging altitudinally, in parts of eastern Peru and Ecuador the Jet Manakin replaces the Green Manakin *C. holochlora* at around the 1,000m mark. For instance, in Manu National Park and Biosphere Reserve, Peru, the latter species reaches to 1,100m from the lowlands, whereas Jet Manakin is found only above 1,000 m.

IDENTIFICATION 11.5–14.0cm. Male quite unmistakable: the fundamentally identical Black Manakin *Xenopipo atronitens* is entirely allopatric and found in quite different (lowland) habitats. The sooty-olive female Jet Manakin resembles Green Manakin *C. holochlora* but the nominate race of Green Manakin on the east slope of the Andes (i.e. within the range of Jet) is brighter moss green on the upperparts, with a slightly yellowish belly. (Green Manakin of the race *C. h. litae* resembles female Jet more closely, but occurs in Panama and west of the Andes in Colombia south to northwest Ecuador.) The white underwing-coverts of this species are a helpful identification aid (although shared by Yellow-headed Manakin *C. flavicapilla*, their ranges only meet in prov. Napo, Ecuador).

DISTRIBUTION The Jet Manakin ranges in South America along the east slope of the Andes, from western prov. Napo, Ecuador, at the Volcán Sumaco (Robbins *et al.* 1987, Ridgely and Greenfield 2001), south very discontinuously through Peru, where even more local and less common in the south of the country (Schulenberg *et al.* 2007), and might be expected in northwest Bolivia (Remsen and Parker 1995), where currently unknown (Hennessey *et al.* 2003), given that in Peru it reaches south to dpto. Puno, e.g. at Abra Maruncunca, near Sandia (Valqui 2004). Elevational range is 1,450–1,700m in Ecuador, but mainly 790–2,225m in Peru (where substantially better known), and seemingly ranging higher, at least locally, with a specimen from 2,500m (dpto. Pasco) and sight record at 2,400m (dpto. Amazonas) (Mark *et al.* 2008).

MOVEMENTS None known, but is presumed to be resident, although arguably not sedentary given the occasional high-altitude records mentioned above, which might suggest some element of wandering.

HABITAT Jet Manakin inhabits the undergrowth and the lower midstorey of wet, humid subtropical and montane forest. It probably visits fruiting trees at forest borders, like others of the genus.

DESCRIPTION Sexes differ. The species is rather long-tailed with a small bill, like congenerics. *Adult male.* – Glossy black above with a bluish tint, duller black (with more of a 'matt' finish) over the underparts, relieved only by the white underwing-coverts. Sometimes appears greyer to browner black over the posterior underparts, the undertail and the flight feathers (perhaps when heavily worn). *Adult female.* – Uniform sooty to dark olive, becoming slightly greyer over the throat and belly, the whole relieved solely by an indistinct pale eye-ring and the rarely seen white underwing-coverts. *Juvenile.* – Undescribed (Snow 2004b), but young males initially gain black feathers on the crown, face-sides, tail and throat/upper breast. Thereafter the breast, head and crown can be extensively and solidly black before any black feathers have appeared on the rest of the underparts or much of the upperparts (FMNH). *Moult.* – Nothing is known, but none of four (of both sexes) collected in southeast Peru in October was replacing its feathers (FMNH). *Bare parts.* – Both sexes have dark brown or black irides, slate or dark olive-grey to pinkish-grey legs and feet, whilst the bill is either black becoming bluish-grey to grey over the basal third, or entirely black or grey (Ridgely and Tudor 1994, Schulenberg *et al.* 2007; FMNH).

MEASUREMENTS (FMNH: eastern Peru, supplemented with J. Hornbuckle unpubl. data, live birds: eastern Peru) Wing of male (*n* = 5) 72.5–79.0mm, wing of female (*n* = 2) 67.5–69.0mm; tail of male (*n* = 5) 45–50mm, tail of female (*n* = 2) 46–48mm; bill of male (*n* = 5) 9.2–12.38mm, bill of female (*n* = 2) 12.04–12.40mm; tarsus of male (*n* = 5) 14.31–16.50mm, tarsus of female (*n* = 2) 15.84–16.46mm. Weight (sexes combined): 15.2–16.5g (J. Hornbuckle unpubl. data; Snow 2004b, Dunning 2008; FMNH; MVZ).

GEOGRAPHICAL VARIATION Monotypic.

VOICE Gives a rough downslurred whistle, rendered *peeeeer* (T. J. Davis *in* Ridgely and Greenfield 2001), *dreee-ee-ee?* (J. Nilsson *in* Ridgely and Tudor 2009) or *queep* and sometimes slightly doubled (*que-eep*), or is more mechanical sounding. The species' voice was presented on the recently published commercial compilations of Krabbe and Nilsson (2003), Lysinger *et al.* (2005) and Boesman (2009).

NATURAL HISTORY As recently as the end of the 20th century the species was considered to be 'hardly known in life' (Ridgely and Greenfield 2001), but its natural history is presumably rather similar to those of the other *Chloropipo* manakins (although none can be described as well known). Encountered singly, or more rarely in pairs (Schulenberg *et al.* 2007) and Jet Manakin also joins mixed-species flocks (Mark *et al.* 2008), but the extent and regularity of such behaviour remain unknown.

FOOD AND FEEDING Feeds as low as just 1m above the ground, once on some unidentified white berries, taken via a short upward sally (Mark *et al.* 2008), but no other dietary information appears to have been published (Snow 2004b).

BREEDING The species' breeding biology is entirely unknown, although three (of both sexes) taken in August in southeast Peru had somewhat enlarged gonads (FMNH).

STATUS Treated as of Least Concern (BirdLife International 2004, 2008). The species is extremely poorly known (from just five localities) in eastern Ecuador, almost all of them based on mist-netted birds and it was discovered in this country as recently as 1979 (Ridgely and Greenfield 2001). Prior to this, Jet Manakin was considered endemic to the East Peruvian Andean subcentre of the Peruvian Andean Centre of endemism (Cracraft 1985). However, the species was described as 'often fairly common' in eastern Peru (Schulenberg *et al.* 2007), where it is known from the Manu National Park and Biosphere Reserve (Walker *et al.*

2006). Anciães and Peterson (2006) predicted that this species could be moderately to badly affected by habitat modification in the face of potential climate change based on modelling techniques.

REFERENCES Anciães and Peterson (2006, 2009), BirdLife International (2004, 2008), Boesman (2009), Brooks *et al.* (2009), Cracraft (1985), Dunning (2008), Hellmayr (1929b), Hennessey *et al.* (2003), Hornbuckle (1999), Krabbe and Nilsson (2003), Krabbe and Sornoza (1994), Lysinger *et al.* (2005), Mark *et al.* (2008), McKay *et al.* (2010), Mee *et al.* (2002), Merkord *et al.* (2009), Mlíkovský (2009), Parker and Parker (1982), Parker *et al.* (1982), Remsen and Parker (1995), Ridgely and Tudor (1994, 2009), Robbins *et al.* (1987, in press), Schulenberg *et al.* (2007), Snow (2004b), Stotz *et al.* (1996), Walker *et al.* (2006).

Jet Manakin *Chloropipo unicolor.* **Fig. 1.** Male, Abra Patricia, dpto. San Martín, northern Peru, November (*Jon Hornbuckle*). This species' life history is still very little known, doubtless because other than as mist-net captures it is so rarely recorded.

Genus *Ilicura*: Pin-tailed Manakin

The name of this genus, which was erected by Reichenbach without explanation as to its etymology, has attracted some recent attention in the literature. Jobling (1995) considered that it might derive from the Greek 'elix', a reference to a lock or curl of hair, or tendril, and thus alluding to the peculiar pin-tailed central rectrices. An alternative explanation, recently espoused (Straube 2008b), but also a reference to the tail feathers, is that the word derives from a popular old Latin word, ilex, which was first employed scientifically for a genus of oak trees with pin-shaped extensions to the leaves, derivations of which have thereafter been used many times in scientific nomenclature (which is perhaps unsurprising given that Reichenbach was also a botanist).

PIN-TAILED MANAKIN
Ilicura militaris   Plate 12

***Pipra militaris* G. Shaw, 1809**, *Natur. Misc.* 20, pl. 849, South America [= vicinity of Rio de Janeiro, Brazil, *fide* Hellmayr 1929a] [Date and authorship follow Dickinson *et al.* (2006).]

This beautiful and highly distinctive manakin is endemic to the Atlantic Forest of eastern Brazil, where it is not rare but is nonetheless highly prized by birdwatchers, especially as its quiet vocalisations can render it unobtrusive, making encounters much less frequent than with most other manakins that occur in the same region. Its systematic relationships have only recently been elucidated (see, in particular, Prum 1992 and Tello *et al.* 2009; summarised on p. 41), although its uniqueness has long been recognised by taxonomists. However, some facets of its life history, especially its breeding biology and diet, are still relatively poorly known.

IDENTIFICATION 11–14cm (males are on average slightly larger than females). The male is one of the most unmistakable and prettiest of the manakins, and even the female (or younger male) is difficult to confuse given that it shares the male's 'unusual' head shape and 'pin-tail' central rectrices (although the latter are, on average, much shorter than in males, whether adult or not). Aside from the very obvious plumage differences, other manakins that share the Atlantic Forest domain of this manakin are overall larger in size, e.g. Blue Manakin *Chiroxiphia caudata* and Greenish Schiffornis *Schiffornis virescens*, two species with which Pin-tailed Manakin is in more extensive sympatry, or smaller and squatter, e.g. White-bearded Manakin *Manacus manacus*, which is generally (but not exclusively) found at lower elevations than the present taxon. For instance, in Itatiaia National Park, Rio de Janeiro, *M. manacus* occurs to 1,200m and *I. militaris* between 800 and 1,600m (Pires *et al.* 1991).

DISTRIBUTION Endemic to eastern Brazil, Pin-tailed Manakin was until recently considered confined to the Serra do Mar centre of endemism (Cracraft 1985), where it occurs from Espírito Santo and southern Minas Gerais (locally north as far as the Serra do Cipó and the central Espinhaço range) south to western Paraná and eastern Santa Catarina, reaching not quite as far south as 28°S (Pinto 1944, Ridgely and Tudor 1994, Rosário 1996, Dornas *et al.* 2005, Bencke *et al.* 2006, Vasconcelos and D'Angelo Neto 2007). The species' southernmost limit appears to be around the Parque Estadual Serra do Tabuleiro (Bencke *et al.* 2006). It appears tolerant of relatively small, fragmented forests, e.g. in the municipality of Rio de Janeiro, where it

is known from several such areas (e.g. Pinto 1944, Mitchell 1957, Parker and Goerck 1997, Maciel 2009). In the last two decades, the species has been discovered at two well-surveyed localities in southernmost Bahia, Boa Nova and the Serra Bonita (Gonzaga *et al.* 1995, Souza 1999, Silveira *et al.* 2005), and subsequently Kirwan (2008) reported the existence of three specimens (two adults and one young male) from (Fazenda) Nova Veneza (16°23'S, 49°19'W), 38km southwest of Anápolis and 22km north of Goiâna, in south-central Goiás, which were collected in the late 1920s. However, the Pin-tailed Manakin has yet to be recorded in the well-studied Chapada Diamantina National Park, Bahia (Parrini *et al.* 1999), which marks the northernmost limit for a number of Atlantic Forest endemics. Furthermore, on the basis of modelling techniques, Anciães and Straube (1997) predicted that its distribution might prove to be considerably more widespread, even perhaps encompassing eastern Paraguay and northeast Argentina, but field evidence to support this hypothesis has yet to emerge. *Ilicura* occurs from sea level, e.g. at Ubatuba, São Paulo, to at least 1,370m in the interior of Minas Gerais (MNRJ specimen data), or 1,450/1,500m (Stotz *et al.* 1996, Anciães and Straube 1997, Vasconcelos and Melo Júnior 2001, Alves *et al.* 2009), but it is not generally found below 580m in the north of the species' range, or above 465m in the far south (Anciães and Straube 1997).

MOVEMENTS None known and the species is generally considered to be highly sedentary.

HABITAT The species prefers humid forest, woodlots and mature second growth, perhaps most frequently in valleys,

rather than on ridges (Snow and Snow 1985). Carrara *et al.* (2009) recently reported the species' presence in *Eucalyptus* plantations and at the ecotone between such plantations and natural vegetation, at least in Espírito Santo. *Ilicura* was recently recorded in July in an 'island' of *restinga* within an area of mangrove forest in coastal São Paulo (Silva e Silva and Olmos 2007), perhaps indicating some dispersal as this species had not previously been reported from this comparatively well-studied region.

DESCRIPTION *Ilicura* is a quite unique-looking manakin, being characterised by the elongated and sharply pointed central rectrices of the male (much shorter in the female), reasonably arched culmen, slender head shape, bristly forehead feathering and deeply striking plumage of the male. The adult male has structurally modified wing-feathers, most notably the outer primaries, which are broadest at the tips and narrow gradually towards the base, and the secondaries, which are stiffened and possess thick shafts. Both of these sets of feathers are instrumental in making various mechanical display sounds. The bill is relatively small and dainty, but it sometimes has a slightly hooked tip in both sexes. As already intimated, the sexes differ markedly in plumage. *Adult male.* – Crown, lores, nape, mantle, scapulars and wing-coverts are deep matt black, with a brilliant scarlet-red patch of feathers on the forehead and slightly more carmine-red (sometimes admixed bright orange) lower back, rump and somewhat elongated uppertail-coverts, and blackish tail (somewhat paler than the rest of the dark upperparts). Primaries dark brown, becoming blackish over the shaft region, but paler towards both edges and possess narrow almost greyish-white fringes, in fresh plumage, on the outer webs and broad, bright white fringes on the inner webs. The tertials are also dark brown with bright white inner webs and olive-green fringes to the outer webs, whilst the secondaries, especially the innermost, are more extensively olive-green with dark brown shaft-streaks. The entire underparts are variably pale, somewhat greyish over the ear-coverts and chin, becoming distinctly whiter over most of the ventral surface, from the throat and breast to the thighs and abdomen, although the abdomen has some very pale yellowish-green elements (undertail-coverts occasionally extensively pale olive-green), and there are usually some creamy or greyish elements scattered throughout, perhaps most especially on the body-sides and flanks (some, perhaps younger, males possess variable blackish or charcoal-grey streaking over these areas, which might occasionally reach sparsely across the abdomen). The area around the tibial feathering is frequently bright red, concolorous with the crown patch. The underwing is largely pale, off-white, with the primaries and some secondaries brownish-grey, and occasional creamy elements scattered throughout. *Adult female.* – Principally bright olive-green above, including the tail, with similar, peculiar (and distinctive) head shape as characterises the male, thereafter becoming dull grey over the face from eye-level (including the ear-coverts) and throat, pale greyish below with many pale olive-green elements, perhaps especially on the breast, body-sides and flanks. The primaries and some larger wing-coverts are principally dark brown, and many of the inner secondaries and tertials are also this colour, but have broad olive-green fringes and webs (though not the tips). Underwing is much as the male, but with some olive-green elements in the carpal region. *Juvenile.* – Initially female-like, as already noted by Snow (2004b), but thereafter acquires dark shaft-

streaks in the tail, the whitish belly (whilst retaining some olive-green elements in the breast) and whitish webs to the tertials (MNRJ specimen). Plumage maturation is thereafter unclear, but we have seen a Snethlage specimen from Goiás, in MNRJ, which has the plumage largely as fully adult male, except for scattered olive-green and greyish elements over the crown and nape, mantle, scapulars and wing-coverts (Kirwan 2008). Furthermore, this specimen also has by far the most extensive blackish feathering on the body-sides and flanks of any specimen we have examined, suggesting that this feature might also be to some extent indicative of immaturity. In some males, at least, the crimson forecrown is acquired well before the red rump-patch (M. Anciães *in* Marini and Hackett 2002). *Plumage aberration.* – Anciães *et al.* (2005) documented an aberrant male specimen of *I. militaris* from a locality in Minas Gerais. This bird had a yellow forecrown and rump patch, which the authors suggested had been caused by a genetic mutation wrought through dietary changes. *Hybridisation.* – At the same locality in Minas Gerais, Anciães *et al.* (2000) reported probable hybrids between this species and Blue Manakin *Chiroxiphia caudata*, and Marini and Hackett (2002) published full details of one of these. The bird was an apparent male hybrid collected at Barreiro reserve near Belo Horizonte in southern Minas Gerais, in March 1999, having been initially trapped in May 1997 when its plumage was entirely green. This bird was tested genetically, the results suggesting that its parents were a male *Ilicura* and female *Chiroxiphia*. It differed from adult male Pin-tailed Manakins in having the rump and uppertail-coverts grey basally, then green and black-tipped, a mostly dark back and the underparts a mix of green, grey and white feathers, and a reddish and more extensive forecrown, intermediate between *Ilicura* and *Chiroxiphia* (Marini and Hackett 2002). Iris and leg colours were unusual for *Ilicura*, the central tail feathers were shorter than either of the parental genera, and intermediate in their shape, whilst the head shape was more like *Chiroxiphia. Moult.* – Few moult data appear to have been published, but *Ilicura* almost certainly commences feather renewal immediately post-breeding (as would be expected), with males presumably preceding females in this respect, given that males take no part in parental care. Willis and Oniki (2002) reported two males completing their wing moult in March and a female similarly in April. *Bare parts.* – Irides are cream to orange or reddish-yellow in females, and usually orange to dark red in males (twice yellow), and often slightly paler in young birds of both sexes; the bill is blackish, with a greyish or reddish lower mandible (once whitish), upper mandible buff-coloured in some females, and has a strongly arched culmen, with pinkish, flesh- or ochre-brown-coloured legs and feet (sometimes tinged grey) with whitish to yellow soles (MNRJ; Snow 2004b, Anciães *et al.* 2005, Krabbe 2007).

MEASUREMENTS (MNRJ: Espírito Santo, Minas Gerais, Rio de Janeiro, São Paulo and Santa Catarina) Wing of male ($n = 20$) 60–65mm, wing of female ($n = 13$) 58–66mm; tail of male ($n = 20$) 32–41mm, tail of female ($n = 13$) 29–42mm, not including central rectrices, which protrude by up to 28mm in males, and exceptionally 11mm in females (cf. Snow and Snow 1985 for a more usual range of values in both sexes); bill of male ($n = 20$) 8.14–9.44mm, bill of female ($n = 13$) 8.15–9.95mm; tarsus of male ($n = 7$) 17.75–19.25mm, tarsus of female ($n = 7$) 17.28–18.78mm. See also Marini and Hackett (2002) and Anciães *et al.* (2005) for additional mensural data, including tarsus and bill (to nostrils), forecrown size and shortest rectrices. Weight (sexes combined): 10.5–15.0g, once 20.0g (Sick 1959d, Snow and Snow 1985, Anciães *et al.* 2000, 2005, Marini and Hackett 2002, Willis and Oniki 2002, Snow 2004b, Dunning 2008, Faria and Paula 2008; DZUFMG; MNRJ).

GEOGRAPHICAL VARIATION Monotypic.

VOICE In contrast to many species of manakins, the male's primary (advertising) vocalisation is easily overlooked at least by the less-experienced observer. It is an oft-repeated series of 5–8 rather soft, slightly 'squeaky', downward-inflected, plaintive and quite high-pitched notes, rendered *see-see-see-see-see* by Snow (2004b), on a slightly descending pitch, usually lasting *c.*1 second but sometimes fading away slowly, thus becoming fainter at the end and thus prolonged to *c.*2–3 seconds. This song covers a range of frequencies, the first note being usually between 7.8 and 6.7kHz and the last note between 6.6 and 5.6kHz (Snow and Snow 1985). The latter authors also reported that 'Occasionally, much longer songs [are] given ... the three recorded having 14–17 notes. In these longer songs, the pitch of successive notes [descends] in the usual way up to the fifth or sixth note, and then [rises], giving the impression that the bird [was singing] a second song before the first had ended.' Songs are frequently given in the morning during the early breeding season, but singing can continue virtually all day, with Snow and Snow (1985) speculating by extrapolation from timed counts that up to 1,400 songs might be given in a single day. While singing, the male makes his body very sleek, quite unlike many manakins, which rather expand the body plumage to appear plumper and larger. Sonograms were presented in the Snows' paper. In other contexts, away from the lek, both sexes give a very similar but shorter series of 3–4 notes, *swee-swee-swee*, lasting just 1 second. Males make 'mechanical' wing-whirring and snapping, double-snapping or clicking sounds, also all made using the wings, at the leks (see also Display). However, it is important to note that not all flights at the lek are accompanied by whirring sounds, indicating that *Ilicura* males are able to control their production of this sound (see Display). Snow and Snow (1985) found that snapping sounds were often immediately presaged by a special upward-inflected *weep* call, followed by a second call that is drowned-out by the snap in life (but is visible in sonograms). The energy associated with these noises is evenly distributed over a very wide range of frequencies, with the upper limits at 9.6–10.2kHz and the lower limits at 0.08–1.2kHz, and produces a rolling sound just detectable by the human ear. The *weep* call is occasionally given by males upon entering their territories, but without the wing-snap (Snow and Snow 1985). Vocalisations have been published on the following compilations: Remold (2002), Boesman (2006a) and Minns *et al.* (2009), and recordings are also available from several localities between Bahia and São Paulo online at www.xeno-canto.org.

NATURAL HISTORY Various aspects of this species' natural history remain rather poorly known, especially in comparison with many of the other species of manakins that occur in the Atlantic Forest region. Pin-tailed Manakin is occasionally inquisitive of playback of the voice of Ferruginous Pygmy Owl *Glaucidium brasilianum* (Specht *et al.* 2008). Anciães and Del Lama (2002) suggested that, as appears to be true of some other manakin species, females might have larger territorial ranges than adult or young males, based on their significantly higher recapture rates for males of any age versus females.

FOOD AND FEEDING *Ilicura* is normally encountered alone or sometimes in pairs, searching for small fruits (and their seeds) or insects (Formicidae and Araneae recorded by Durães and Marini 2005) in the midstorey or tall understorey. Food is usually snatched using a short flight of up to 30cm, but might also be plucked from a perch. The species most frequently feeds on *Rapanea* (Myrsinaceae), Loranthaceae and Melastomataceae, but no detailed studies of its diet have been published to date. However, Parrini and Pacheco (2011) reported three species of *Miconia* – *M. tristis*, *M. chartacea* and *M. budlejoides* – in this manakin's diet. Several individuals, especially females, can congregate at a fruiting tree. Pin-tailed Manakin has also recently been reported to occasionally follow *Labidus predator* and *Eciton burchelli* army ant swarms in search of insect prey disturbed by the ants (Faria and Rodrigues 2009). Both sexes regularly join mixed-species flocks, and will sometimes feed in the same trees as White-bearded Manakin *Manacus manacus*.

DISPLAY Although Sick (1967) mentioned observing two or three males displaying in adjacent trees, it seems to be more or less a strict rule that males display alone within a small (20–40m, exceptionally 60m) 'arena' replete with many slender stems, 4–10m (exceptionally 20m) above the ground (of which two to seven are preferred over the others), raising and fluffing-out the rump feathers while frequently singing and making short flights, sometimes producing a mechanical whirring sound in the presence of a female or a young male, at which point the male usually flies to the mating perch (see below). In the presence of a female or young male, the adult male will usually commence to display, of which single- and double-snap jumps, semicircular jumps and click displays have been described (cf. Snow and Snow 1985, Anciães and Prum 2008). However, occasionally a visiting female, for instance to a fruiting tree in the vicinity of a male's song perch, will not provoke any display behaviour by the male (GMK pers. obs.). Anciães and Prum (2008) tested whether males preferred to display in any particular ambient light conditions and whether females showed any mate selection based on this. Their study found strong individual male preference for either cloudy, shady or sunny light conditions, but no species-specific preference, and likewise females appeared not to visit male courts under any specific conditions (cf. also Tori *et al.* 2008). As revealed by Anciães and Del Lama (2002), not all green-plumaged individuals at display sites are females. Using molecular methods they found that the majority of female-like birds at leks are in fact pre-definitive plumaged males. Each male will leave the display region to feed for very brief bouts of 1.5–3.0 minutes, often very close by, and at the height of the breeding season the male spends up to 97% of each day in the immediate vicinity of the arena (Sick 1959d, 1967, Snow and Snow 1985). When a female has been attracted, the male makes low jumps above her as she crouches on the mating perch, which is a slightly thicker, horizontal branch than the other display perches, and is sometimes up to 13m above the ground. This branch will usually be free of emergent vegetation, and is maintained in this state through regular 'gardening' by the male, who will remove moss and surrounding leaves that might obscure his display. Other males (1–2 individuals) will display within earshot, *c.*40m apart, with each 'cluster' of territories being several hundred metres apart in one study in southern São Paulo (Snow and Snow 1985). Elements of the display and structural modifications of *Ilicura* recall those of *Manacus* and *Chiroxiphia* manakins, but there are also important differences (Snow and Snow 1985).

BREEDING Snow (2004b) recorded that the species probably lays eggs in the period November–February, but that very few nests have been found. The only specific details seem to be that the nest structure is a 'shallow basket' affair, constructed *c.*4m above the ground (Snow 2004b). There is a male-plumaged specimen (MNRJ 43565), collected in mid October in Minas Gerais, whose skull was not completely ossified but was apparently in breeding condition and was reported to possess a brood patch. As with other manakins, it is probable that some females acquire male-like plumage, rather than that males might occasionally undertake nesting duties. Specimen data indicate that males and females are in breeding condition between early August and February, whilst moult in adults occurs from April onwards (MNRJ; Krabbe 2007; see also Description). However, Anciães and Del Lama (2002) suggested that the breeding season might commence prior to August, at least in the interior of Minas Gerais.

STATUS Pin-tailed Manakin is currently regarded as of Least Concern (BirdLife International 2004, 2008), although Anciães and Peterson (2006) predicted that this species could be severely impacted by habitat modification in the face of potential climate change based on modelling techniques. Variously considered uncommon to fairly common across the species' wide range, Pin-tailed Manakin might not be threatened, but it appears relatively uncommon over much of its range, in part perhaps due to its easily overlooked (very quiet) vocalisations. *Ilicura* is known from 28 Brazilian Important Bird Areas (Bencke *et al.* 2006), many of them protected areas such as Serra do Mar, Carlos Botelho and Intervales State Parks (São Paulo), Tijuca and Itatiaia National Parks (where rare), Tinguá Biological Reserve and Serra dos Órgãos National Park (Rio de Janeiro), Mata do Cedro Ecological Station, Serra do Brigadeiro State Park, Serra do Cipó National Park and Serra da Canastra National Park (Minas Gerais), and Augusto Ruschi (formerly Nova Lombardia) Biological Reserve (Espírito Santo). It is also known from a considerable number of privately protected, forested areas.

REFERENCES Albano (2010b), Alves *et al.* (2009), Ames (1971), Anciães and Del Lama (2002), Anciães and Peterson (2006, 2009), Anciães and Prum (2008), Anciães and Straube (1997), Anciães *et al.* (2000, 2005), Bauer and Pacheco (2000), Bencke *et al.* (2006), BirdLife International (2004, 2008), Boesman (2006a), Buzzetti (2000), Carrara *et al.* (2009), Cracraft (1985), Dickinson *et al.* (2006), Dornas *et al.* (2005), Dunning (2008), Durães and Marini (2005), Faria and Paula (2008), Faria and Rodrigues (2009), Faria *et al.* (2006), Gonzaga *et al.* (1995), Hellmayr (1929a), Jobling (1995), Kirwan (2008), Krabbe (2007), Maciel (2009), Mallet-Rodrigues and Noronha (2003, 2009), Mallet-Rodrigues *et al.* (2007), Marini and Hackett (2002), McKay *et al.* (2010), Melo Júnior *et al.* (2001), Minns *et al.* (2009), Mitchell (1957), Parker and Goerck (1997), Parrini and Pacheco (2011), Parrini *et al.* (1999), Pimentel and Olmos (2011), Pinto (1944, 1951), Pires *et al.* (1991), Prum (1990a, 1992), Remold (2002), Ridgely and Tudor (1994, 2009), Rosário (1996), Scott and Brooke (1985), Sick (1959d, 1967, 1997), Silva e Silva and Olmos (2007), Silveira (1998), Silveira *et al.* (2005), Simon (2009), Snow (1975, 2004b), Snow and Snow (1985), Souza (1999), Specht *et al.* (2008), Stotz *et al.* (1996), Straube (2008b), Tello *et al.* (2009), Tori *et al.* (2008), Vasconcelos (2007), Vasconcelos and D'Angelo Neto (2007), Vasconcelos and Melo Júnior (2001), Vasconcelos *et al.* (2002), Willis (1992), Willis and Oniki (2002).

1

Pin-tailed Manakin *Ilicura militaris*. **Figs. 1–2**. Male, Boa Nova, Bahia, eastern Brazil, July (*Rafael Bessa*). One of the strangest and most beautiful of all manakins; instantly unmistakable. **Fig. 3**. Female, Camacã, Bahia, eastern Brazil, November (*Arthur Grosset / www.arthur-grosset.com*). **Fig. 4**. Female, Serra dos Órgãos National Park, Rio de Janeiro, November (*Hadoram Shirihai / Photographic Handbook to Birds of the World*). Females are also easily identified, based on the extensively grey-washed face and neck-sides, the unique head shape (with small frontal crest), slight 'pin' tail, and slim body.

Genus *Masius*: Golden-winged Manakin

The genus *Masius* is one of four monospecific genera recognised herein among the Pipridae, of which all but one are confined to the same subfamily, the Ilicurinae. The others are *Xenopipo* (Black Manakin), *Ilicura* (Pin-tailed Manakin) and *Dixiphia* (White-crowned Manakin). The last-named forms part of the subfamily Piprinae, whilst many authors subsume *Chloropipo* within *Xenopipo*, thereby removing its claim to be monospecific.

GOLDEN-WINGED MANAKIN
Masius chrysopterus   Plate 10

Pipra chrysoptera **Lafresnaye, 1843**, *Rev. Zool.* 6: 97, Santa Fé de Bogotá, Colombia

Masius is one of several strikingly beautiful manakins found in the northern Andes, where it is principally if not entirely restricted to the upper tropical and, especially, the subtropical zones. It is perhaps most frequently encountered within mixed-species foraging flocks, but like nearly all Pipridae the real treat is to observe a displaying male.

IDENTIFICATION 10.0–12.5cm. The principally black-and-yellow male is impossible to mistake if seen reasonably well, although the bird's ornate plumage is not always readily visible, whilst the female's yellow throat is also unique, albeit much less distinctively so. The relatively long tail, for a small manakin, also offers a useful field mark.

DISTRIBUTION Golden-winged Manakin is the only truly montane species of manakin. It is restricted to the Andes of northwest South America, where it occurs from western Venezuela as far south as northern Peru. In Venezuela, the species is found on the west slope of the Andes only in western Mérida (at La Azulita), and on the east slope of the Andes from southern Lara to northwest Barinas and southeast Táchira (Hilty 2003), thence it ranges south into Colombia, where it occurs over all three Andean ranges. In Ecuador, it ranges throughout the length of the east slope, thence south into northern Peru as far as northern San Martín, but in western Ecuador it ranges only as far south as El Oro (e.g. at Buenaventura) and western Loja (recently only at Vicentino) (Best *et al.* 1993), as well as in the coastal Cordillera de Mache, in dpto. Esmeraldas (Ridgely and Greenfield 2001).

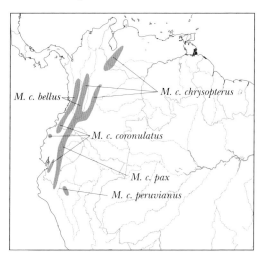

MOVEMENTS Generally considered to be resident (see, e.g., Hilty 1997).

HABITAT Prefers humid wet montane forest and tall second growth in the upper tropical and subtropical zones (principally the latter), including clearings and borders. In southwest Colombia, at least, the species prefers slopes with a moderate incline of 10–30° (C. Samper *in* Snow and Snow 1992). Overall altitudinal range 400–2,300m (Stotz *et al.* 1996, Ridgely and Greenfield 2001, Restall *et al.* 2006), but apparently not found below 600m in western Colombia (Hilty and Brown 1986), 700m in eastern Colombia (Salaman *et al.* 2002b, Salaman and Donegan 2007), 1,000m in Venezuela (Hilty 2003) or 1,200m in northern Peru (Schulenberg *et al.* 2007). In the Serranía de los Yariguíes, eastern Colombia, *Masius* occurs exclusively at 1,600–2,000m, and has not been found above or below this despite extensive fieldwork in the region during recent years (T. M. Donegan *in litt.* 2009). Golden-winged Manakin is largely found above 800m in Ecuador, but it ranges very locally down to 400m in the west (Ridgely and Greenfield 2001).

DESCRIPTION Sexes differ, and the male is highly distinctive and uniquely plumaged. Both sexes possess a relatively long tail. Nominate *M. c. chrysopterus* is described here. *Adult male.* – Largely has jet-black plumage, relieved by the golden yellow forecrown (with the feather tips orange, the feathers flattened and stiffened, and curled forwards over the bill). Elongated black feathers on the crown-sides form inconspicuous lateral horns, and the hindcrown and nape are broadly tipped orange-red. The small chin and large, almost crescent-shaped, lower-throat patches are yellow to bright yellow, respectively (but usually concealed except when displaying), as are most of the underwings (especially the coverts), the inner webs of the central remiges (particularly striking in flight) and the inner webs of the tail feathers (rarely visible in the field). *Adult female.* – The upperparts are olive, becoming paler olive on the underparts, with a pale yellow belly patch and pale yellow median and lower throat spots (the latter the larger of the two). *Juvenile.* – Unknown (Snow 2004b), but immature males are initially female-like, thereafter showing some yellow in the crest (and tiny patches of red on the hindcrown) and some (occasionally brighter) yellow on the throat, whilst subadults become mottled with black over the body plumage (Hilty 2003), at least in some initially on the upperparts and head (BMNH). *Moult.* – There are no published data on moult. *Bare parts.* – Irides dark brown or brown, whilst the bill is rather pale overall, being pale flesh-coloured to steel grey, and the legs and feet are strikingly coloured, being pinkish/flesh or raspberry red to purplish-brown (Hilty 2003, Snow 2004b; FMNH).

MEASUREMENTS *M. c. chrysopterus* (BMNH; ZMA: Colombia): wing of male (*n* = 7) 60.5–63.0mm, wing of female (*n* = 2) 63.5mm; tail of male (*n* = 7) 40.5–43.5mm, tail of female (*n* = 2) 39–41mm; bill of male (*n* = 7)

9.78–11.52mm, bill of female (*n* = 2) 9.26–10.32mm; tarsus of male (*n* = 5) 17.14–18.02mm, tarsus of female (*n* = 2) 16.47–17.00mm. *M. c. coronulatus* (western Ecuador): wing of male (*n* = 5) 57–60mm, wing of female (*n* = 1) 59mm (J. Hornbuckle unpubl. data from live birds). Same race (southwest Colombia): wing of female (*n* = 6) 54–61mm (T. M. Donegan and L. M. Dávalos unpubl. data from live birds). *M. c. pax* (southern Colombia): wing of male (*n* = 6) 63–67mm, wing of female (*n* = 11) 61–65mm; tail of male (*n* = 2) 42.0–43.7mm, tail of female (*n* = 2) 40.5–46.8mm; bill of male (*n* = 2) 8.3–9.3mm, bill of female (*n* = 2) 9–10mm; tarsus of male (*n* = 2) 16.5–17.9mm, tarsus of female (*n* = 2) 18.0–18.7mm (T. M. Donegan *et al.* unpubl. data from live birds). *M. c. peruvianus* (FMNH: dpto. Amazonas, Peru): wing of male (*n* = 2) 59.5–62.5mm; tail of male (*n* = 2) 42mm; bill of male (*n* = 2) 10.93–11.06mm; tarsus of male (*n* = 2) 16.49–18.12mm. Subspecies unknown (Serranía de los Yariguíes, eastern Colombia): wing of male (*n* = 34) 60–64mm, wing of female (*n* = 32) 58–65mm; tail of male (*n* = 34) 41–54mm, tail of female (*n* = 32) 38–46mm; tarsus of male (*n* = 34) 16.8–21.4mm, tarsus of female (*n* = 32) 16.5–21.1mm (J. C. Luna, E. Briceño and F. Guerrero/ ProAves unpubl. data from live birds). Weight: 6.1–14.8g (males) and 6.4–16.0g (females) (Rahbek *et al.* 1993, Snow 2004b, Dunning 2008; MVZ; J. Hornbuckle unpubl. data; T. M. Donegan *et al.* unpubl. data; N. Silva/J. P. López/J. C. Luna/C. Olaciregui/A. Tovar and R. Parra/ProAves unpubl. data; T. M. Donegan and L. Dávalos unpubl. data).

GEOGRAPHICAL VARIATION Polytypic, with five subspecies generally recognised by most modern literature (e.g. Dickinson 2003, Snow 2004b). Differences are only visible in males, and, considering variant claims in the literature concerning regional differences based on comparatively small series' of specimens, we speculate that at least some of the currently accepted named variation might be better classed as individual rather than geographical (see Hellmayr 1929b for some suggestions of this). Subspecific taxonomy of this species appears ripe for substantial revision, but has proved beyond the scope of the present work. *M. c. chrysopterus* (described above) is found in northwest Venezuela through the East Andes, apparently at least as far as dpto. Boyacá (Salaman *et al.* 2002b), and on the east slope of the Central Andes of Colombia, e.g. at the head of the Magdalena Valley in southern dpto. Huila (Chapman 1917, Hilty and Brown 1986). However, Salaman *et al.* (2002b) reported that specimens from the west slope of the East Andes in dptos. Boyacá and Santander have the nape patch orange-red, like males they ascribed to *M. c. pax* (see below), i.e. that the range of nominate *M. c. chrysopterus* appears curiously 'interrupted'. Treated as a synonym of *M. c. coronulatus* (see below) by Chapman (1917), *M. c. bellus* E. Hartert & Hellmayr, 1903, occurs in western Colombia from the west slope of the West Andes (north to the headwaters of the Río San Juan, in dptos. Chocó/ Risaralda) to the west slope of the Central Andes from dpto. Antioquia south at least as far as the Cauca Valley, and is characterised by having the hindcrown brown to reddish-brown. Race *M. c. bellus* is replaced in southwest Colombia (in dptos. Cauca and western Nariño) by *M. c. coronulatus* P. L. Sclater, 1860, which continues along the west slope of the Andes into western Ecuador (at least as far as El Oro and western Loja), and differs in having the central nape flame orange (Ridgely and Greenfield 2001; see photograph in Kirwan and Marlow 1996), whilst the hindcrown is also brown to reddish-brown (Restall *et al.* 2006). Chapman

(1917) considered that, on average, west Colombian specimens might have slightly deeper yellow on the wings than those from western Ecuador, but we doubt the utility of such claimed marginal differences in assigning birds to subspecies. Hellmayr (1929b) pointed to the availability of a series of males from dpto. Popayán containing birds typical of both *M. c. coronulatus* as well as of *M. c. bellus*, and to birds from dptos. Valle and Cauca more typical of *M. c. coronulatus*. *M. c. pax* Meyer de Schauensee, 1952, occurs in the East Andes of Colombia (certainly in southeast dpto. Nariño, but probably from as far north as dpto. Cundinamarca: Salaman *et al.* 2002b) and south on the east slope in Ecuador, and has the blunter mid-nape feathers scaly, brown and very shiny-looking (Ridgely and Greenfield 2001, Restall *et al.* 2006). Finally, it too is replaced further south by *M. c. peruvianus* Carriker, 1934, of southern Zamora-Chinchipe, in extreme southeast Ecuador (Ridgely and Greenfield 2001), and northern Peru south as far as northernmost San Martín (Schulenberg *et al.* 2007), which is reported to differ in having the hindcrown and nape orange-red (Restall *et al.* 2006). Both of these two latter-mentioned forms were not differentiated by Chapman (1926), who included all known east-slope populations south to Peru within nominate *M. c. chrysopterus*, and Ridgely and Greenfield (2001) stated simply that 'male *peruvianus* resemble male *pax*', which suggests to us that the validity of *M. c. peruvianus* at least requires more rigorous testing than appears to have been attempted to date. In addition, specimens taken further north in eastern Colombia, in the Serranía de los Yariguíes and at Charalá, both dpto. Santander, have been speculated to represent an undescribed subspecies closest to *M. c. pax* (Salaman *et al.* 2002b, Donegan *et al.* 2007).

VOICE Golden-winged Manakin is generally considered to be rather quiet (Ridgely and Tudor 1994, Hilty 2003). It might be noted that *Ilicura* is also a comparatively 'quiet' genus. The male advertisement call does not carry far and is a frog-like, nasal grunting *nurrt*, or *tseet-nurrt*, given four to six times per minute on the lek (Snow and Snow 1992). Also gives a thin, high-pitched *seee*, lasting 1–3 seconds during flights to and from the display ground log. At other times gives a slightly trilled *teeeeee* from a mid-level or canopy perch (Hilty 2003). Published recordings appear on the following audio compilations: Moore *et al.* (1999), Krabbe and Nilsson (2003), Lysinger *et al.* (2005), Boesman (2006b), Alvarez *et al.* (2007) and Boesman (2009), whilst recordings from Ecuador and Peru are available online at www.xeno-canto.org.

NATURAL HISTORY The species is easily overlooked. It forages alone or in small groups of 2–3 individuals, and regularly (but often briefly) with fast-moving mixed-species flocks, principally of tanagers (Prum and Johnson 1987, Hilty 2003), generally in the midstorey but also low and high into the subcanopy, and the species occasionally visits forest borders (Restall *et al.* 2006; GMK pers. obs.). However, it must be remarked that Bohórquez (2003) in her survey of such behaviour in southwest Colombia observed this species in fewer than 5% of mixed-species flocks.

FOOD AND FEEDING Golden-winged Manakin takes both small fruits and insects, using short upward sally-strikes, with a brief hover, usually to the underside of leaves. It returns to either the same or a different (lower) perch (GMK pers. obs.). In northwest Ecuador the main food plants were four *Miconia* spp. (Melastomataceae), but the manakin was also observed taking fruits of six other species belonging to the families Rubiaceae, Poaceae and Boraginaceae (Prum and Johnson 1992). In eastern Ecuador, at Wild Sumaco lodge, Napo province, *Masius* was observed visiting fruiting melastomes with four other piprid species (see Blue-rumped Manakin *Lepidothrix isidorei*: GMK pers. obs.).

DISPLAY The species' relative inconspicuous displays have been well described by Prum and Johnson (1987), based on observations in northwest Ecuador, and Snow and Snow (1992), in southwest Colombia. Hilty and Brown (1986) mentioned that males occasionally chase females through the understorey, flashing the yellow in the wings as they do so. Males display either alone or in 'exploded leks', the birds *c*.100m apart and spending much of their time within their territories, which measure up to 25 × 18m, and in southwest Colombia are centred on hillside gullies (Snow and Snow 1992). Display is focused on moss-covered fallen logs, 85–200cm in diameter in the Snows' Colombian study, with a small patch that is smooth and vegetation-free, and which the birds 'garden' to keep both the patch and the surrounding area free of moss, ferns and leaves. Each male probably uses 2–4 display logs situated 5–40m from each other (Prum and Johnson 1987). At the height of the breeding season, males spend much of their time singing (see Voice) in their territories (up to *c*.90% of the day), pausing for 1–3-minute-long feeding 'breaks' (Snow and Snow 1992). They use a variety of perches usually 2–4m above the ground (Prum and Johnson 1987) but in Colombia up to 11m high (Snow and Snow 1992) and the birds turn round frequently while perched. The birds also briefly expose the yellow throat patch while singing, by stretching the head slightly upwards and forward (Prum and Johnson 1987, Snow and Snow 1992). Periodically, the male visits one of his display logs, sometimes flying up to 15m (along a relatively clear flight path) to the log and uttering a high-pitched whistle as he does so. On landing from its oblique descent, the male gives a short two-note call, then immediately jumps back in the direction from which he arrived giving a call similar to the advertisement call (see Voice) and rotating in the air to perch again facing the original landing place. Snow and Snow (1992) described how males would often perform a series of such 'log-approach displays', each time departing the log to the side, but always arriving from upslope. Unlike 'log-approach displays', 'log-displays' are given silently and comprise two behaviours: the near-motionless 'chin-down display' and 'side-to-side bowing', the latter of which Snow and Snow (1992) witnessed most frequently. In the former display, often performed immediately after arriving at the log, the male lowers the head so that the chin is almost touching the log and raises the tail almost vertically whilst simultaneously sleeking the plumage, maintaining this position for up to 20 seconds (Prum and Johnson 1987). 'Side-to-side bowing' displays are performed both when the male is alone or in the presence of a female. The male faces downhill and bows alternately over each side of the log up to 34 times, sometimes giving 3–4 consecutive bows over the same side before increasing the speed of the display with single bows in each direction (Snow and Snow 1992), or the male might stand on one side of the log and bow towards either end of it (Prum and Johnson 1987). During this display the feathers are fluffed-out (covering the yellow in the wings), the back raised, the black horns erected and, sometimes, the orange hind crest raised (albeit inconspicuously). Between such display bouts, Snow and Snow (1992) occasionally witnessed males 'stamping' their feet on the log for <1 second, moving 2–3cm along the log in the process, these movements appearing to be ritualised. If a female is present, she generally perches just 7–15cm away, facing the male. Snow and Snow (1992) observed three copulation events, two of them involving the same 'pair' and occurring in relatively rapid succession with a bout of 'side-to-side bowing' between matings. On all three occasions the female appeared to initiate events by landing on the cleared area on the log, and in one instance the female fluttered back and forth over the male (which was displaying) up to ten times in the course of two minutes. The Snows also observed a female-plumaged bird, which they considered to be an immature male, visit a displaying adult male, flutter over him a couple of times and subsequently attempted to mount the male whilst the latter was performing a 'chin-down display', whereupon both birds departed the site.

BREEDING Concerning nesting, there is no information on incubation and fledging periods, or parental care (which is by the female alone). Interestingly, H. F. Greeney (*in litt.* 2010) reports that this species is much shyer in the vicinity of the nest than most manakins; females of many species (but not this one) will remain on the nest to within almost touching distance. Hilty and Brown (1986) mentioned the discovery of a nest with two eggs in late June, in Colombia's upper Anchieta Valley. It was described as a 'very thin-walled rootlet and moss cup suspended from [a] horizontal fork 2.3m up over [a] stream'. More recently, Greeney and Gelis (2007) found four active nests at Mushullacta reserve, in northeast Ecuador, in late March and early April, and Solano-Ugalde *et al.* (2007) found a nest above Mindo, Pichincha province, in the northwest of the same country in late January. All were shallow cups constructed of rootlets with an outside 'decoration' of pale green moss, which tended to form a 'tail' below the nest of up to 10.5cm, and the nests were attached to the supporting branches using spiderwebs. The nests were built in small saplings (two of Rubiaceae, one Solanaceae, one Chloranthaceae, one unidentified) and were placed 2.2 ± 1.9m above the ground, three of them immediately adjacent to streams, the fourth 40m from flowing water but sited within a depression in the ground, and the Mindo nest beside a well-used trail. Three of the nests contained two-egg clutches, which had been partially incubated, whilst the other two had single undeveloped eggs. In northeast Ecuador these were pale to dark olive-tan with heavy brown blotching usually forming a ring at the larger end (Fig. 3), whilst the eggs in the single nest at Mindo were pale salmon with red-brown maculations. The eggs in the Colombia nest were apparently more cream-coloured, also with brown markings, concentrated over the centre and larger end (Hilty and Brown 1986). Egg and nest dimensions were presented by Greeney and Gelis (2007) and Solano-Ugalde *et al.* (2007). In northwest Ecuador, Prum and Johnson (1987) mist-netted a female in late July with a well-developed brood patch, whilst in adjacent Colombia Snow and Snow (1992) witnessed three copulations also in late July. T. M. Donegan *et al.* (unpubl.) trapped three juveniles in southern Colombia between early July and mid August. Finally, two breeding-condition birds were collected in May and July in Colombia by M. A. Carriker (Hilty and Brown 1986).

STATUS Not globally threatened and currently treated as of Least Concern by BirdLife International (2004, 2008). The species' generally inconspicuous nature must mean that it is easily overlooked. Golden-winged Manakin is known from many protected areas across the species' range, including Guaramacal National Park, Trujillo (Hilty 2003), and Yacambú National Park, Lara (GMK pers. obs.), both in Venezuela; five ProAves-owned reserves, La Planada and Río Ñambí reserves, dpto. Nariño, Parque Nacional Natural Yariguíes, dpto. Santander, and Reserva Natural Tambito, dpto. Cauca, all in Colombia (Snow and Snow 1992, Donegan and Dávalos 1999, Snow 2004b, Donegan *et al.* 2007, Salaman *et al.* 2009), and Podocarpus National Park, in Ecuador (Bloch *et al.* 1991).

REFERENCES Alvarez *et al.* (2007), Anciães and Peterson (2009), Best *et al.* (1993), BirdLife International (2004, 2008), Bloch *et al.* (1991), Boesman (2006b, 2009), Bohórquez (2003), Chapman (1917, 1926), Donegan and Dávalos (1999), Dickinson (2003), Donegan *et al.* (2007, 2010), Greeney and Gelis (2007), Hellmayr (1911, 1929b), Hilty (1997, 2003), Hilty and Brown (1986), Hornbuckle (1999), Kirwan and Marlow (1996), Krabbe and Nilsson (2003), Krabbe and Sornoza (1994), Lysinger *et al.* (2005), McKay *et al.* (2010), Moore *et al.* (1999), Prum (1990a, 1992), Prum and Johnson (1987), Rahbek *et al.* (1993), Restall *et al.* (2006), Ridgely and Greenfield (2001), Ridgely and Tudor (1994, 2009), Salaman and Donegan (2007), Salaman *et al.* (1999, 2002b, 2008, 2009), Schulenberg *et al.* (2007), Snow (1975, 2004b), Snow and Snow (1992), Solano-Ugalde *et al.* (2007), Stotz *et al.* (1996), Tello *et al.* (2009), Tori *et al.* (2008).

Golden-winged Manakin *Masius chrysopterus.* **Fig. 1**. Male, *M. c. coronulatus*, Milpe Bird Sanctuary, prov. Pichincha, northwest Ecuador, June (*Nick Athanas / Tropical Birding*). **Fig. 2**. Female, *M. c. coronulatus*, El Carmen de Atrato, dpto. Chocó, western Colombia, February (*Hadoram Shirihai / Photographic Handbook to Birds of the World*). Note the unusual head shape, relatively long tail, bright legs, and yellow feathering around the fore face, all of which features identify females of this species. **Fig. 3**. Nest, Mushullacta Community Reserve, Loreto Road, prov. Napo, eastern Ecuador, April (*Harold F. Greeney*). Note how the nest is built over water. Unlike most species of manakins, this species is very shy when found on the nest.

Genus *Corapipo*: 'white-throated' manakins

The genus *Corapipo* comprises two or three wholly allopatric species (we prefer to take a conservative line and recognise just two), in which the males are beautifully and strikingly patterned glossy blue-black with startlingly white throats, in one species forming a ruff that is erected during some elements of its displays, whilst the other has white wing flashes, also important in display. Females (and young males) are, of course, typically much duller (and more difficult to identify), but typically possess whitish-grey throat patches, which if seen clearly should make them readily identifiable.

WHITE-RUFFED MANAKIN
Corapipo leucorrhoa   Plate 10

Pipra leucorrhoa **P. L. Sclater, 1863**, *Proc. Zool. Soc. Lond.* 1863: 63, pl. 10, Bogotá (type locality by subsequent designation: Bucaramanga, Santander, Colombia)

Contra several modern authorities, including the American Ornithologists' Union Checklist Committee, we have conservatively elected to consider the White-ruffed Manakin to represent a single species, rather than two species. The latter treatment, under which the two primarily Central American races are considered separately as *Corapipo altera*, has often been adopted in the non-periodical literature since the 1960s (e.g. Monroe 1968, Wetmore 1972, Ridgely and Gwynne 1976, Sibley and Monroe 1990, AOU 1998, Dickinson 2003, Restall *et al.* 2006, Remsen *et al.* 2009). Snow (1979b, 2004b) and Ridgely and Tudor (1994) were arguably the most notable opponents of this trend, and are followed here (and by Stiles and Skutch 1989 and Stotz *et al.* 1996) because the differences between the two groups of taxa are relatively slight and have to be formally documented and shown to be indicative of two species in the technical literature. On the other hand, Meyer de Schauensee (1966) considered that *C. leucorrhoa* (including *altera*) might be best treated as a subspecies of White-throated Manakin *Corapipo gutturalis*.

IDENTIFICATION 9.5–10.0cm. Largely glossy blue-black male with stunning white throat and ruff is unique in the species' range and should prove unmistakable given a reasonable view. Females are far less distinctive, but the pale (greyish) throat should serve as a useful distinguishing mark, once seen, from the same sex of Red-capped Manakin *Pipra mentalis*, which is also paler green above and has largely feathered tarsi in both sexes (unlike *Corapipo*), or White-crowned Manakin *Dixiphia pipra*, which has notably red irides and, even more importantly, an all-grey crown and nape. In the South American portion of the species' range, female Striped Manakin *Machaeropterus regulus* is similarly tiny and petite-looking, with a small bill, but is even shorter tailed, comparatively, and should always show some pinkish streaking on the flanks or more extensively over the underparts. In eastern Panama and northwest South America, female Golden-headed Manakin *Pipra erythrocephala* is also a potential confusion risk with female *C. leucorrhoa*, but the former has a pale (not a dark) bill and again lacks the obvious pale throat patch. Female *Manacus* manakins are slightly larger and have bright orange legs and feet, longer tails and no obvious throat contrast.

DISTRIBUTION White-ruffed Manakin ranges through much of Central America and the northwestern portion of South America. The species is found from southeast Honduras, e.g. at Arenal and San Esteban (Slud 1964, Monroe 1968), south over the Caribbean slope through eastern Nicaragua and Costa Rica, where *C. leucorrhoa* also appears on the Pacific slope in the extreme southwest of the country, around Guaitil, above the Río Pirrís and south through the Cordillera de Talamanca (Stiles and Skutch 1989), thence throughout much of Panama, including the highlands of the Darién and the Azuero Peninsula, although it is seemingly absent from the lowlands of the Canal Zone (Wetmore 1972, Ridgely and Gwynne 1976). Thereafter, it appears on the Colombia side of the border, in South America, south to the Serranía de Baudó, in Chocó, and east of the Atrato Valley in the Dagua Valley (in Valle), in the Central Andes south to the middle Magdalena Valley and northern Tolima (formerly Cali), and in the East Andes in Norte de Santander to northwest Arauca (Hilty and Brown 1983, 1986), as well as extremely locally in far-western Venezuela, in the Perijá Mts, in Zulia, and in southeastern Táchira on the Cerro El Teteo, both on the border with Colombia (where it occurs at Montes de Oca also in Perijá), as well as at Santa Elena on the west slope of the Andes in Mérida, and around Altamira in northwest Barinas (Hilty 2003). In terms of altitudinal range, White-ruffed Manakin ranges locally down to sea level, e.g. in Bocas del Toro and San Blas, in Panama (Ridgely and Gwynne 1976), but is generally more numerous above 200m throughout its range, and above 400m in South America. It also tends to breed at lower elevations on the Caribbean slope of Costa Rica (see Movements). In Venezuela it reaches 1,200m (Hilty 2003), but elsewhere *C. leucorrhoa* is found to 1,500m over much of its Colombian, Costa Rican and Panamanian range, with localised occurrence to 1,585m in Chiriquí, western Panama (Wetmore 1972), 1,524m in southwest Costa Rica (Skutch 1967) and 1,700m in the Serranía de los Yariguíes, Santander, Colombia (Donegan *et al.* 2010). In southwest

Costa Rica, Skutch considered the species to be largely restricted as a breeder to altitudes in excess of 1,000m, but it has recently been discovered probably breeding at lower elevations in western Costa Rica (MNCR specimen).

MOVEMENTS Although considered resident over much of the species' range, in southern Costa Rica the race *C. l. altera* descends to the lowlands and foothills during the non-breeding season, between July and December/January, with females apparently moving on average further downslope than males (Stiles and Skutch 1989). Sporadic movements to lower elevations are also reported at other seasons by the same authors, and Rosselli (1994) and Loiselle and Blake (1999) noted that White-ruffed Manakin is present only seasonally at La Selva Biological Station (for 4–6 months in the first half of the year). On the Caribbean slope in Costa Rica (nominate *leucorrhoa*), the species mainly breeds at 400–800m, being commonest at *c.*500m and locally occurs to 1,000m: the bird moves downslope in the non-breeding season, reaching 50m. In this region, males depart the breeding areas in July–October (mainly in August), but females slightly later, mainly in October, whilst males return in January–April (peaking February) and females in January–June (mostly March and April). Perhaps surprisingly, migration, at least in this region, does not appear to be related to fruit abundance (Rosselli 1994). Boyle *et al.* (2010) quantified these migrations in terms of their linear distance, *c.*20km, but also postulated that these downslope movements are related to storms and high rainfall at higher elevations, meaning that such altitudinal movements increase the birds' chances of survival. Similar altitudinal migrations might occur in parts of Panama (cf. Wetmore 1972, Ridgely and Gwynne 1976), but have not been documented with certainty to date. In eastern Costa Rica many males are in breeding condition in late June (MVZ). However, even in Costa Rica, within either the species' breeding or non-breeding areas this manakin is usually very faithful to its home range (Blake and Loiselle 2002).

HABITAT Like the next species, *C. leucorrhoa* has an obvious preference for humid primary forest, including gallery forest, and tall second growth, and comes to edges and clearings at least where there are fruiting trees. At La Selva Biological Station, Costa Rica, where the species is only a non-breeding visitor, White-ruffed Manakin appears to prefer valley bottoms (Loiselle *et al.* 2007b). Rosselli (1994) and Rosselli *et al.* (2002) provided a detailed characterisation of a study site on the Caribbean slope in Costa Rica at which White-ruffed Manakin is one of the most abundant understorey birds, especially during the breeding season.

DESCRIPTION A rather diminutive manakin (albeit slightly larger than the next species) with a tail that is relatively long for its body size. Both sexes can have a reasonably well-arched culmen, sometimes with a relatively striking hooked tip and quite large rounded nostrils. The nominate race is described here, in which the sixth primaries are the longest, whilst the seventh to ninth are each 3–5mm shorter than the preceding feather, and the tenth primary (the outermost) is very small and lanceolate (Hellmayr 1906c; see below). *Adult male.* – Virtually the entire plumage is glossy bluish-black (including the underwing-coverts), with the exception of the striking white chin, throat and most of the ear-coverts to the neck-sides (the feathers of which are long, silky and ruff-like), and the primaries and the inner

webs of the secondaries, which are dusky. The lores and forehead are slightly blacker and less bluish than the rest of the upperparts, but this is unlikely to be detectable in the field. The tail is also dusky, although the feather fringes are bluish-black, except those of the outer pair. The wing bend is white and the undertail-coverts sometimes possess scattered white tips to the feathers, or are even rather solidly white (Hilty and Brown 1986; CUMZ; MNCR). *Adult female.* – The upperparts are entirely olive-green, whilst below the chin and throat are pale grey to greyish olive-green, and the breast, breast-sides and flanks are pale olive-green, with a pale yellowish belly and undertail-coverts. The underwing-coverts are pale grey. *Juvenile.* – Stated to closely resemble the female plumage (Snow 2004b), but Stiles and Skutch (1989) considered it to be darker and more olive on the throat and belly. In young males the white throat feathers start to appear amongst the grey early on (Wetmore 1972) and Rosselli (1994) and Hilty (2003) remarked that males in their second year of life have a blackish mask over the face and a fully white throat (cf. BMNH 88.1.13.1299). There can be a striking dark lower border to the throat patch at this age. Some juvenile females can have surprisingly whitish throats (MNCR 27008). Young males of *C. l. heteroleuca* also possess the black mask but have the central throat dark grey, strongly contrasting with the white chin and cheeks. *Moult.* – The most robust data were gathered by Rosselli (1994) during her study on the Caribbean slope of Costa Rica. She found that the flight feathers are replaced between May and November (peaking in July) and in birds older than 1 year this is followed by a complete moult of the body feathers. This moult takes 2–3 months in a given individual. In the East Andes of Colombia, both sexes appear to be moulting both body and flight feathers in April–June, with one record of a male renewing some body feathers in September (J. C. Luna and D. M. Velasco/ProAves unpubl. data). *Bare parts.* – The irides are dark brown to chestnut or reddish-brown (black in one male *C. l. heteroleuca*), whilst the maxilla and bill tip is black with a neutral, plumbeous or bluish-grey mandible and cutting edges, and the tarsi and toes are very dark reddish-brown (occasionally dull reddish-pink), dark brown or dusky-grey, with black or blackish claws (Wetmore 1972, Robbins *et al.* 1985, Snow 2004b; FMNH).

MEASUREMENTS *C. l. leucorrhoa* (BMNH: Colombia): wing of male (*n* = 1) 59mm; tail of male (*n* = 1) 31mm; bill of male (*n* = 1) 9.89mm; tarsus of male (*n* = 1) 14.7mm. Live birds (East Andes of Colombia: J. C. Luna and D. M. Velasco/ProAves unpubl. data): wing of male (*n* = 35) 52–57mm, wing of female (*n* = 20) 53–57mm; tail of male (*n* = 31) 27.0–34.5mm, tail of female (*n* = 20) 22–35mm; tarsus of male (*n* = 31) 15.9–18.2mm, tarsus of female (*n* = 20) 15.7–18.2mm. *C. l. altera* (Wetmore 1972: Panama): wing of male (*n* = 10) 58.0–61.5mm, wing of female (*n* = 10) 59.0–61.5mm; tail of male (*n* = 10) 27–30mm, tail of female (*n* = 10) 28–32mm; bill of male (*n* = 10) 9.0–9.8mm, bill of female (*n* = 10) 10.1–11.1mm; tarsus of male (*n* = 10) 15.6–16.4mm, tarsus of female (*n* = 10) 15.9–16.6mm. *C. l. heteroleuca* (Wetmore 1972: southwest Costa Rica and western Panama): wing of male (*n* = 10) 58.0–60.5mm, wing of female (*n* = 10) 57.5–61.5mm; tail of male (*n* = 10) 29–31mm, tail of female (*n* = 10) 28–31mm; bill of male (*n* = 10) 9.2–10.3mm, bill of female (*n* = 10) 9.6–11.0mm; tarsus of male (*n* = 10) 15.5–16.5mm, tarsus of female (*n* = 10) 15.5–17.0mm. For additional measurements see Hellmayr (1906c, 1929b) and Chapman (1917). Weight (*C. l. altera* or *C. l. heteroleuca*): 9.0–12.8g (males) and 9.5–14.2g (females)

(Wetmore 1972, Burton 1975, Strauch 1977, Robbins *et al.* 1985, Snow 2004b, Dunning 2008; FMNH; MVZ). Rosselli (1994) and other authors have all found that females are, on average, heavier than males and young birds. Her study is also the only detailed work available concerning seasonal variation in the mass of a manakin species. She revealed that males have, on average, lowest body weights during the breeding period and are heaviest during the migration period. Female body weight varied similarly, being lowest during the moulting period, immediately following breeding (when they are still feeding dependent juveniles), and highest during the migration period. *C. l. leucorrhoa*: 8.6–12.5g (males) and 9.0–12.5g (females) (J. C. Luna and D. M. Velasco/ProAves unpubl. data). Dunning (2008) gave means of 10.7g (males) and 12.7g (females) for *C. l. leucorrhoa*, and 11.1g (males) and 12.5g (females) for *C. l. altera*.

GEOGRAPHICAL VARIATION As noted above, a number of authors, particularly since Blake (1958: 535), Monroe (1968) and Wetmore (1972), but even as early as Chapman (1917), have been content to recognise the three described taxa as belonging to two species, with the Middle American races, which just reach into northernmost South America, separated under *C. altera*, with South American *C. leucorrhoa* taking the English name White-bibbed Manakin, whereas *altera* retains the name White-ruffed Manakin. We continue to follow Snow (1979b, 2004b) and Ridgely and Tudor (1994) in recognising three subspecies of a single species, because the differences between them are generally very slight, principally involving the structure of the outermost primary and the wing formula, and have not been subject to a detailed review in the peer-reviewed literature. This seems to be the only appropriate course of action, until (or if) it can be shown that the differences in wing formula and modification to the primaries have led to the evolution of fundamentally different displays. Unfortunately, to date, the only detailed information on such behaviour relates to *C. l. altera* (Rosselli *et al.* 2002) and *C. l. heteroleuca* (Skutch 1967), with no detailed data available for *C. l. leucorrhoa*. **C. l. altera** Hellmayr, 1906, occurs on the Caribbean slope in Central America from Honduras to Costa Rica and through most of Panama to extreme northwest Colombia west of the Atrato Valley and south to the Serranía de Baudó (Wetmore 1972). It differs from the nominate race in having the outermost (tenth) primary broader and longer (25–30mm vs. 14–17mm in *C. l. leucorrhoa*: Hellmayr 1906c, Wetmore 1972), not shorter, as incorrectly stated by Snow (2004b). Compared with the nominate race (see Description), the wing formula is such that p7 is longest, p6 is *c.*2mm shorter, p8 is 1mm shorter, p9 is 2mm shorter and p10 is 12–14mm shorter; p10 is also somewhat narrower than the rest and slightly emarginated on the inner web (Hellmayr 1906c). Hellmayr (1906c) considered the female of this race to have the breast and flanks much duller green, and the mid-belly paler yellow than in *C. l. leucorrhoa*, but these differences seem very slight. This subspecies is replaced in southwest Costa Rica and westernmost Panama in western Chiriquí (as far as Boquete) by **C. l. heteroleuca** Hellmayr, 1910. However, it is unclear where the division between this race and the last lies, especially given that not all males from the core range of *C. l. heteroleuca* (at Las Cruces, San Vito, Puntarenas, Costa Rica) have really narrow throat patches, and that a tiny sample (*n* = 2) from Reserva Ríos Paraíso, Tarrazu, San José, closely approach this race in throat pattern. This race too differs from the nominate

in having a reduced outermost primary, but also in its less extensive white throat patch, being sometimes much narrower over the chin but equally broad and more flared over the rear ear-coverts. The indentation on the central throat is evident even in immature males (Wetmore 1972; MNCR). Females are by and large identical to those of the previous subspecies, although Wetmore (1972) considered that at least some are darker abdominally, but we have been unable to confirm this difference. Nominate **C. l. leucorrhoa** (described above) ranges from westernmost Venezuela, in the Perijá Mts and as far as Barinas, west and south to north-central and western Colombia.

VOICE The most commonly given vocal is the advertisement call, a high rolling or trilled, twanging *prreeet*, which is also given whilst birds are foraging (including by females) and covers frequencies between 3.7 and 6.2kHz (Rosselli *et al.* 2002). However, it is most frequently given from perches above the males' display logs, where rates of calling can reach up to 172 calls per hour or almost 1,400 per day. Rosselli *et al.* (2002) found some evidence that display logs with high rates of calling by resident males are visited more frequently by other males but conversely were subject to the lowest female visitation rates. Calling appears to generally peak between 06:00 and 08:00 hrs and again between 10:00 and 14:00 hrs. When additional males visit a male's display log, the advertisement call can become a several-second-long trilled *currrrtrrr*, delivered at lower frequencies on average, with the individual males perched within a few centimetres of one another. During the above-canopy portion of the species' main display, males sometimes (but not always) give a series of high-pitched *seeee* notes (termed canopy calls by Rosselli *et al.* 2002, who found that the incorporation of these calls into the display increased when females were present at the display log). In returning to the log during this same display, the male manakin produces a loud snapping sound apparently with the modified primaries (Prum 1998) and then one or two strident, high-pitched notes followed by a sharp buzzing note (see Display). 'Resident' males (see Display) produce a low *graaahh* or *cuaak* sound in defending their display area from other birds, e.g. thrushes and hummingbirds (Rosselli *et al.* 2002). The species' voice appears on the audio compilations of Ross and Whitney (1995), Boesman (1999) and Knapp and Will (2008), and recordings from Costa Rica, Nicaragua and Panama are archived at www.xeno-canto.org. Sonograms of the different calls were presented by Rosselli *et al.* (2002).

NATURAL HISTORY Like many other species of manakins, the White-ruffed Manakin is perhaps most likely to be seen visiting a fruiting tree at a forest edge to feed. Away from leks, the species is usually observed singly, but occasionally in 'couples' or small groups of both sexes (Stiles and Skutch 1989), which feed in the mid to lower storeys of forest (Hilty 2003). In southwest Costa Rica, Stiles and Skutch (1989) noted a propensity for White-ruffed Manakins to be less social with their own species in the lowlands, where they join mixed-species flocks with tanagers as their nucleus. Although Rosselli *et al.* (2002) noticed a marked imbalance in the ratio of males to females (in favour of the former), Ruiz-Gutiérrez *et al.* (2008) found no evidence for different survival rates between the sexes. The species' ecology and displays are generally rather similar to those of the next species, but some elements recall those of other genera of Pipridae.

FOOD AND FEEDING Comparatively well known due to several intensive studies in Costa Rica, supplemented by incidental observations from elsewhere. Wetmore (1972) found this species to often associate with honeycreepers at fruiting trees, but White-ruffed Manakin also joins mobile mixed-species foraging flocks (Stiles and Skutch 1989, Snow 2004b). Food is taken using short upward or more horizontal sallies (Moermond and Denslow 1985, Stiles and Skutch 1989). The diet is mainly small fruits and their seeds, with smaller but frequent proportions of insects and spiders (Rosselli 1994). Concerning the animal percentage of the species' diet, Rosselli (1994) found that females consume more insects than males and that while the latter sex takes more animal material during the moult period, consumption of insect prey by females peaks during the breeding season. To date, the most detailed study of this species' diet is the aforementioned work by Rosselli (1994), who found that 57 fruit species were consumed in a Costa Rican forest on the country's Caribbean slope, of which 70% were species of Melastomataceae (especially *Miconia smaragdina*, an *Oreopanax* sp., *Conostegia cooperi* and *Henriettea tuberculosa*) with a significant percentage of the rest being species of Rubiaceae. Species belonging to families such as Ericaceae and Gesneriaceae were consumed in very tiny percentages of the overall weight. Loiselle and Blake (1999) considered this species to be an important disperser of some seed species in lowland eastern Costa Rica, where White-ruffed Manakin regularly took the fruits of four species of Melastomataceae, namely *Clidemia densiflora*, *Henriettea tuberculosa*, *Miconia simplex* and *Ossaea macrophylla*, amongst a total of 39 plant species recorded in its diet at this site (Loiselle *et al.* 2007b).

DISPLAY Recorded in groups of up to a dozen at lekking arenas (Wetmore 1972), which like those of the next species are centred on moss-covered fallen logs, or live lianas, either on the ground or ≤40cm above the ground. In Costa Rica, these logs ranged in length from 3.8m to >50 m, but the manakins concentrated their displays on portions of the logs 0.5–1.3m long, which they attempt to keep clear of vegetation by 'gardening'; cf. Golden-winged Manakin *Masius chrysopterus* (Rosselli *et al.* 2002). Data from elsewhere are insufficiently robust to provide meaningful comparisons, but there is no suggestion of dramatic differences between other parts of the range and Costa Rican birds (in this case *C. l. altera*). Rosselli *et al.* (2002) found no other common characters at the display logs they observed. Accounts of the display behaviour were initially presented by Aldrich and Bole (1937), Slud (1964), J. A. Rowlett (*in* Davis 1982) and M. B. Robbins (*in* Prum 1986), but in most detail by Skutch (1967) and Rosselli *et al.* (2002). The authors of the last-named study found eight display logs within their study area, six of which were concentrated in two main areas and at least four of them had 'resident' banded males (and therefore individually identifiable) which spent between 41% and 94% of their time at the arena, although they leave the area immediately around the display log for periods of less than ten minutes, apparently to feed and/or bathe. These males probably have priority when it comes to mating with visiting females. Rosselli *et al.* (2002) also noted occasional display activity in two other areas where no logs were found, and even occasionally noted 'resident' males visiting adjacent display logs. However, in general, even 'non-resident' males tended to visit the same few, relatively adjacent logs, but Rosselli *et al.* (2002) found no evidence for the presence of coherent groups, which was

also the conclusion that Théry (1990) reached in respect of *C. gutturalis*. Mean distance between all of the logs was *c*.183m, but that between logs within the two clusters was *c*.27m. Rosselli *et al.* (2002) noted some degree of inter-annual faithfulness to display logs, but this was not entirely consistent. Despite the fact that each of the logs studied in greatest detail had a 'resident' male, all of them were visited on a daily basis by other males (including first- and second-years) and, of course, females, sometimes in 'groups' of up to six. Females tend to arrive more unobtrusively and remain only short periods, sometimes just a few seconds but up to ten minutes if visibly interested in the displays. Visiting and 'resident' males display and interact aggressively with one another (e.g. chases lasting up to one minute, or displacing each other on the log), but visitors appear nervous in their general behaviour.

Rosselli *et al.* (2002) observed and described the following different displays at their study site in eastern Costa Rica (schematic representations of some of these are presented in their paper). The most elaborate display termed the 'flap-chee-wah' by Rosselli *et al.* (2002) is, like the analogous behaviour in *C. gutturalis*, a log-approach display that contains a canopy or above-canopy element. Even immature (i.e. largely green-plumaged) males perform this display. The male initially flies towards the display log, but then proceeds steeply upwards, sometimes in a spiralling motion, to a point above the canopy (cf. J. A. Rowlett *in* Davis 1982, and M. B. Robbins *in* Prum 1986, both of whom observed only the above-canopy portion of these displays) giving 1–3 canopy calls (see Voice), before plummeting almost vertically downwards after 2–3 seconds back to the display log. On landing, whereupon the male is facing the opposite direction to his start position, the bird immediately 'rebounds' 10–90cm into the air and lands facing the original position again. The initial and second landings are accompanied by a loud explosive snap (the 'flap' sound), which is considered to be a mechanical sound (Prum 1998), followed by one or two high-pitched notes (*chee* or *chi-chi*) and then a sharp buzzing *waa* or *wheew* note (Rosselli *et al.* 2002). Following the second landing, the male either departs immediately, or crouches on the log flicking its wings and with the throat-feathers fluffed out (if another male is present, always facing him). Sometimes up to three different males give this display consecutively, either with each male appearing to 'dislodge' the one in front, or with all three males remaining on the log.

So-called butterfly flights also possess an analogous display in White-throated Manakin, and are given between low perches close to the display log or to and from the latter. As in *C. gutturalis*, the flight is slow and undulating, with the male also holding his body vertically, but unlike the other species, in White-ruffed Manakin the throat-feathers are completely fluffed-out. Rosselli *et al.* (2002) also observed undulating flights during which males oscillate up and down, but the throat-feathers are not inflated and the body is held normally, or what they termed rapid flights, between the display log and nearby perches, which would be preceded by or terminate with a non-vocal snap or plopping sound.

The only stereotyped display observed on the log itself was termed 'throat-flagging' by Rosselli *et al.* (2002), in which a male fully erects the throat-feathers into a 'beard' shape, faces the centre of the log and slowly rotates the head through 30–45° low over the flog, while flicking the wings open and closed just once. This display is then repeated but facing the opposite direction, and Rosselli *et al.* (2002) noted that it was given following either butterfly flights or 'flap-chee-wah' displays and usually, but not always, in the presence of other individuals (either male or female). The arrival of a potentially 'interested' female (see above) gives rise to more rapid movements amongst the males that are present, with both butterfly and rapid flights increasing, and each visit to the log being accompanied by the throat-flagging display. The female will sometimes start to follow or 'chase' a male.

Like Théry (1990) for White-throated Manakin, Rosselli *et al.* (2002) witnessed few actual copulation events, and these probably all involved 'resident' males. If a female lands on a log, the male (or males) will continue with butterfly and rapid flights to the log, performing the throat-flagging display following each landing, for up to 12 minutes. Finally, the male performs the 'flap-chee-wah' display, the termination of which involves 'rebounding' over her and then mounting the female for 2–3 seconds, whereupon she immediately departs. However, as Rosselli *et al.* (2002) found, the female can leave at any time during this series of displays', even during the culminating above-canopy display. Both copulations observed by Rosselli *et al.* (2002) occurred in the early afternoon and both occurred when just one male was present at the log.

BREEDING Skutch (1967) gave the most 'complete' account, based on his observations at Cañas Gordas in southwest Costa Rica (race *C. l. heteroleuca*), although the nest he found was apparently predated, meaning that we have no knowledge of the incubation or nestling periods (Snow 2004b). This nest was a shallow cup-shaped structure placed in the fork of a slender branch, placed 6.5m above the ground, and constructed of brown filaments and blackish fungal rhizomorphs, with leaf skeletons attached to the outside base to disguise its shape, as in many manakin nests. Two eggs were laid at the end of the first week of April (and the breeding season in this region at least is assumed to be March–June, especially from April: Skutch 1967, Rosselli 1994). These were dull white heavily marked with brown over the entire egg, but heaviest at the largest end. The nest's dimensions were presented by Skutch (1967). Males are capable of breeding in their second year of life, when still in non-adult plumage (Aldrich and Bole 1937). Other data are as follows. A female (race *C. l. altera*) collected on the Cerro Pirre, in eastern Panama, in the second week of March had an almost fully-formed egg in the oviduct (Burton 1975), and females collected in March on the Cerro Tacarcuna, in the same region, were ready to lay (Wetmore 1972). In Colombia, M. A. Carriker (*in* Hilty and Brown 1986) collected eight birds in breeding condition in the period May–October.

STATUS Given its wide range, White-ruffed Manakin is currently considered of Least Concern by BirdLife International (2004, 2008) and is generally fairly common (and locally very common) in Panama (Wetmore 1972,

Ridgely and Gwynne 1976, Angehr *et al.* 2004) and Costa Rica (Loiselle 1988, Stiles and Skutch 1989), but is considered rare and or very local at the northernmost and easternmost limits of its range, in Honduras (Monroe 1968) and Venezuela (Hilty 2003), respectively. *C. leucorrhoa* is also generally less common in Colombia (Hilty and Brown 1986) where, as in Venezuela, its range has been rather heavily fragmented due to ongoing forest destruction. Elsewhere, in Costa Rica, Ruiz-Gutiérrez *et al.* (2008) were able to confirm that survival rates amongst populations in forest fragments are significantly lower compared with figures for larger forest blocks, thereby suggesting that without conservation measures populations of this species are liable to local extinction in fragmented habitats. In eastern Costa Rica, Blake and Loiselle (2002) found evidence to suggest that survival rates for this species were better in old-growth forests and at higher altitudes. White-ruffed Manakin is known from a number of conservation units throughout most of the species' range, including Braulio Carrillo National Park, Rancho Naturalista, Monteverde Cloud Forest Reserve, Arenal Volcano National Park, Guayabo National Monument, La Selva OTS Biological Station, Carara National Park, Oro Verde Biological Reserve, Las Cruces Biological Station, El Copal Biological Reserve and the Río Negro Jaguar Preserve, all in Costa Rica (Cooper 1997, Loiselle and Blake 1999, Blake and Loiselle 2001, Wheatley and Brewer 2001, Rosselli *et al.* 2002, Lawson 2010), and Cerro Campana and General Omar Torrijos National Parks, Panama (Wheatley and Brewer 2001; R. Moore). In Colombia, the following ProAves reserves harbour *C. l. leucorrhoa*: El Paujil (Boyacá), Reinita Cielo Azul (Santander), Hormiguero de Torcoroma (Norte de Santander), Pauxi pauxi (Santander) and Reinita Dorada (Tolima) (Salaman *et al.* 2008, 2009, Donegan *et al.* 2010).

REFERENCES Aldrich and Bole (1937), Anciães and Peterson (2009), Angehr and Christian (2000), Angehr *et al.* (2004), AOU (1998), Barnett *et al.* (2008), BirdLife International (2004, 2008), Blake (1958), Blake and Loiselle (2001, 2002, 2009), Boesman (1999), Boyle *et al.* (2010), Chapman (1917), Cooper (1997), DaCosta *et al.* (2007), Davis (1982), Dickinson (2003), Donegan *et al.* (2010), Dunning (2008), Fierro-Calderón *et al.* (2006), Garrigues and Dean (2007), Hellmayr (1906c, 1929b), Hilty (2003), Hilty and Brown (1983, 1986), Kennard and Peters (1928), Knapp and Will (2008), Lawson (2010), Loiselle (1988), Loiselle and Blake (1999), Loiselle *et al.* (2007b), McKay *et al.* (2010), Meyer de Schauensee (1966), Meyer de Schauensee and Phelps (1978), Moermond and Denslow (1985), Monroe (1968, 1998), Prum (1986, 1998), Restall *et al.* (2006), Ridgely and Gwynne (1976, 1989), Ridgely and Tudor (1994, 2009), Robbins *et al.* (1985), Ross and Whitney (1995), Rosselli (1994), Rosselli *et al.* (2002), Ruiz-Gutiérrez *et al.* (2008), Salaman *et al.* (2008, 2009), Sibley and Monroe (1990), Slud (1964), Skutch (1967), Snow (1975, 2004b), Stiles and Skutch (1989), Stotz *et al.* (1996), Théry (1990), Wetmore (1972), Wheatley and Brewer (2001).

White-ruffed Manakin *Corapipo leucorrhoa*. **Fig. 1**. Male, *C. l. altera*, Arenal Observatory Lodge, La Fortuna, prov. Alajuela, Costa Rica, April (*Steven Easley / Costa Rica Gateway*). Note the slightly narrower 'ruff' compared to other taxa in this complex. **Fig. 2**. Male, *C. l. leucorrhoa*, Vereda El Llano, Falan, dpto. Tolima, Colombia, August (*Fundación ProAves / www.proaves.org*). The 'ruff' is broad and reaches well back on the neck-sides. **Fig. 3**. Female, *C. l. altera*, Cerro Azul, central Panama, December (*Nick Athanas / Tropical Birding*). **Fig. 4**. Female, *C. l. heteroleuca*, Las Brisas, prov. Guanacaste, Costa Rica, October (*Steven Easley / Costa Rica Gateway*). Compared to females, young males very quickly gain a few black feathers, usually around the lores and face-sides.

WHITE-THROATED MANAKIN
Corapipo gutturalis   Plate 10

Pipra gutturalis **Linnaeus, 1766**, *Syst. Nat.* 12th edn. 1: 340, based on 'Le manakin à gorge blanche' of Brisson, 1760, *Orn.* 4: 444, pl. 36, fig. 1, 'in America' = Cayenne (*fide* Berlepsch 1908)

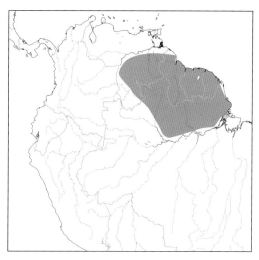

White-throated Manakin is considered to probably form a superspecies with White-ruffed Manakin *C. leucorrhoa* (Snow 1975); the two are entirely allopatric, with the latter species being primarily Central American in range.

IDENTIFICATION 8.5–9.5cm. Adult male White-throated Manakins should be easily identified throughout their range, as the nearly all-black plumage and highly contrasting white throat patch are entirely unique in the Guianan Shield. Females and younger males (with still largely green upperparts) should also be relatively easily identified, given reasonable views, based on the slim body shape and rather grey-whitish underparts (unlike sympatric *Pipra* or *Lepidothrix* species, which are overall similarly small sized). Also note the rather dull-coloured bare parts of *Corapipo*.

DISTRIBUTION White-throated Manakin is confined to the Guianan Shield, where it ranges from southern Venezuela, in northern Amazonas and Bolívar (Hilty 2003), thereafter across the Guianas, where it is widespread across Guyana (Snyder 1966) and is common in the forested interior of French Guiana (Tostain *et al.* 1992), and south across northern Brazil in northern Roraima (Phelps and Phelps 1948, Stotz 1997) east to Amapá, e.g. on the Serra do Navio (Sick 1993, Campos *et al.* 2009), and more locally south to around Manaus, Amazonas (Cohn-Haft *et al.* 1997). In Venezuela, the species is found mainly in hilly areas, from 200m to 1,100m (Hilty 2003), although Barnés (1955) apparently collected *C. gutturalis* at 1,500m on the Cerro Marahuaca (see below), but in Surinam it is found mainly at 400–700m (Snow 2004b), whilst in northern Brazil the species seems to be equally at home in lowland forest, although it has been recorded above 600m in Roraima (Naka *et al.* 2006).

MOVEMENTS The species is resident but not entirely sedentary; in French Guiana, adult males were found to wander over 2.0–2.5ha, whilst females moved much more widely, over 9–10ha.

HABITAT Principally found in tall humid forest but also in montane forest, and occasionally at borders and in clearings. In Surinam, Prum (1986) described the species' habitat as being characterised by a relatively open understorey and a canopy height of 20–35m.

DESCRIPTION A rather diminutive manakin with a very short tail. Both sexes can have a reasonably well-arched culmen, sometimes with a relatively striking hooked tip and quite large nostrils. There is no wing-feather specialisation in either sex, unlike in *Corapipo leucorrhoa*, but as noted by Prum (1986) the broad inner webs of the secondaries and the first six primaries overlap with the surfaces of the neighbouring feathers, and these are presumably used to create the mechanical *pop* sound in display. *Adult male.* – Stunningly beautiful, the petite male appears overall black set off by a strikingly clean white throat patch, which extends in a shallow V shape onto the upper breast, usually very cleanly (and clear-cut), but occasionally slightly more diffusely, and to the lower base of the rear ear-coverts. The underparts including the undertail are otherwise solid

black, whilst the lores and over the base of the bill back to the nape-sides are deep velvety black, but most of the rest of the upperparts possess a brilliant deep blue sheen, except on the flight feathers including the tail, and the rump. Rarely very visible in the field, the innermost primary and most of the secondaries have a very clean white outer web, which becomes steadily more extensive (including laterally) towards the innermost secondary. *Adult female.* – The upperparts are largely uniform moss-green, becoming dark grey on the flight feathers, larger wing-coverts and tail tip, with narrow pale green fringes to the wing feathers, and largely off-white upperparts, brightest and most contrasting (but still slightly greyish) on the chin and throat, with pale green body-sides and a slightly yellowish cast to the lower belly and undertail-coverts. *Juvenile.* – This plumage is said to resemble that of the female (Snow 2004b), but young males soon acquire a black mask over the forehead, lores and lower ear-coverts and some dark grey feathers on the flanks, breast-sides and flanks, whilst the white throat is already more striking and obvious than on adult females (BMNH; Prum 1986). Thereafter scattered black feathers usually appear first over the green dorsal surface. *Moult.* – No published data. *Bare parts.* – Males have dark irides, a pale greyish-horn or pale flesh-coloured bill, with purplish-coloured legs and feet. Females, by contrast, have lead-grey to greyish legs and feet (Snow 2004b).

MEASUREMENTS (BMNH; CUMZ; MNRJ; RMNH: Amapá, Brazil; Guyana; Surinam) Wing of male (*n* = 20) 55.0–58.5mm, wing of female (*n* = 8) 49.5–57.0mm; tail of male (*n* = 20) 27–32mm, tail of female (*n* = 7) 26–31mm; bill of male (*n* = 19) 8.14–10.54, bill of female (*n* = 1) 9.03–10.66mm; tarsus of male (*n* = 8) 13.45–16.20mm, tarsus of female (*n* = 5) 13.96–16.38mm. See also Geographical Variation. Weight: 7.7–8.1g (three males) and 8.8–9.5g (two females) (Snow 2004b, Dunning 2008; RMNH).

GEOGRAPHICAL VARIATION Monotypic as treated by most recent authors (Dickinson 2003, Snow 2004b). However, Barnés (1955) described a new subspecies, *C. g. carminae*, from the upper slopes of the Cerro Marahuaca, Amazonas, Venezuela, based on a single adult female, which had the 'entire dorsal surface, sides, and flanks darker, duller green; throat, breast, and abdomen clearer white', as well as an immature male. Measurements of the new form, wing 55.8mm, tail 27.6mm, culmen from base 8.9mm and tarsus 15.3mm, are well within the range of the nominate (see above). Meyer de Schauensee (1966) considered that White-ruffed Manakin *C. leucorrhoa* might be better treated as a subspecies of *C. gutturalis*, but this suggestion seems not to have been seriously entertained since.

VOICE Vocal elements in this species have been most fully described by Prum (1986). The advertisement call is a lengthened version of the foraging calls, namely a high-pitched *SEE-seee* or *SEE-seee-ee-e*, which is uttered by both sexes (Davis 1982). In advertisement, this becomes a *seeu-see-ee-ee-ee*, the latter part sounding somewhat slurred, and these calls punctuate courtship displays (Prum 1986). The latter observer also described the species' display-call, given during log displays (see Display), which is particularly complex and was rendered by Prum (1986) as *seee…seee-pop-tickee-yeah*. The introductory *seee* notes, which number anything between two and ten, resemble those of the advertisement call, and are given in flight in approach to the log. The muffled-sounding *pop* note (which is mechanical) is given on landing on the log, whilst the squeaky-sounding *tickee-yeah* (which consists of rising and falling harmonics and covers a wide range of frequencies) is given during the rebound off the log (see Display). Théry (1990) noted that the display-call is apparently never given in the presence of females, only between competitive males or by solitarily displaying males. Davis (1982) also described a flight song-display, from observations in Surinam (see Display, below). The flight song is a nine-set series of eight high-pitched, emphatic, insect-like, notes of slightly increasing intensity, terminating with a snap, e.g. *seee-seeee-seeee-seee-seeeee-seee-seeeee-seeee*-snap. Sonograms of the different vocalisations were published by Prum (1986). There is a single recording from southeast Venezuela archived at www.xeno-canto.org.

NATURAL HISTORY *C. gutturalis* is generally difficult to observe and is easily overlooked, in part because the species generally inhabits higher levels in the forest than most manakins in the same range. The species sometimes responds to playback of Amazonian Pygmy Owl *Glaucidium hardyi* (GMK pers. obs.).

FOOD AND FEEDING The diet of the White-throated Manakin generally comprises small fruits and insects, with the former perhaps dominated by Melastomataceae and Rubiaceae, at least in French Guiana. A *Goupia* sp. (Goupiaceae) has been noted in the species diet at Manaus, Brazil (http://www.wikiaves.com.br/222034&t=u&u=575&p=1). The species is considered to be a regular follower of mixed-species foraging flocks in the middle and upper storeys of the forest (Prum 1986, Jullien and Thiollay 1998, Snow 2004b), perhaps especially those of honeycreepers and tanagers (Snyder 1966, Davis 1982), but also warblers, other manakins and Sharpbill *Oxyruncus cristatus*, and occasionally low in the understorey with antbirds and furnariids (Prum 1986). Fruit and insects are taken using a short sally-hover (Prum 1986). 'Groups' of up to ten males have been observed congregating at a fruiting strangler fig in south-central Guyana, along with Golden-headed *Pipra erythrocephala* and White-crowned Manakins *Dixiphia pipra*, Spangled *Cotinga cayana*, Purple-breasted *C. cotinga* and Pompadour Cotingas *Xipholena punicea*, and a host of honeycreepers, dacnises and tanagers, amongst other frugivores (W. Prince pers. comm.).

DISPLAY The first published data concerning this species' unique displays were presented by Davis (1949a), who witnessed a group display around a fallen log. Prum (1986)

greatly expanded our knowledge of the White-throated Manakin's displays, not only describing their highly varied nature and how they interconnect, but also contextualising their performance within then-current knowledge of Pipridae displays. Finally, some additional observations from French Guiana were presented by Théry (1990), who concluded that territorial behaviour is more important in the White-throated Manakin's breeding system than mobile lekking, and that it is almost coincidental that males display at the same arenas, i.e. decaying logs on the ground. The displays of *C. gutturalis* are centred on a fallen log, which is moss-covered, up to 30m long and 1m wide, and usually free of obstructing vegetation. On this log, the birds generally prefer one small area, up to 1m long, on which to display, and on the largest logs several males sometimes display simultaneously but not synchronously or cooperatively. Prum (1986) considered the display logs he located in Surinam to be organised into two exploded leks of 250m in diameter and 350m apart, but Théry (1990) found them to be smaller, 120m in diameter, and closer spaced, 250m apart, in French Guiana. In the latter study, display logs within each exploded lek were on average 38m apart and Théry (1990) found that these benefited from better light conditions during the hours of peak display. Subsequently, Théry and Vehrencamp (1995) discovered that males occupying the brightest-lit display arenas tended to receive the greatest number of visits by females and be most successful at mating, provided that other males are not present to disrupt them. Théry (1990) banded up to ten individuals attending one of the six leks he observed, of which three were females, and Prum's data suggested that at least some males are faithful to a group display arena for an extended period, but that others are transient visitors, and these findings were common to both adults and immatures. Naturally, display is more intense during the breeding season (the wet season in French Guiana; October onwards: Théry 1990), but is also more frequent between 08:00 and 12:00 hrs, with display and singing sometimes continuing non-stop for up to 1.5 hours, but active display more usually lasting between 15 and 45 minutes, with each single log display lasting up to one minute but usually much less (Prum 1986). Group displays (involving up to seven adult and immature males) can last up to 70 minutes. Birds typically display at a single log for up to ten minutes before moving to another log, and display at up to five logs before departing the area (Prum 1986).

Displays commence in trees near the fallen logs on favoured perches 1–10m above the ground unobstructed by foliage. The males frequently adopt a bill-pointing posture, in which the bill is raised vertically to fully expose the white throat patch and erecting a small puff of feathers at the base of the throat (Fig. 2). Like many *Pipra* manakins, males frequently perform 180° about-faces with a quick hop, sometimes up to five times in succession, with to-and-fro displays between different perches 0.5–2.0m apart, occasionally performing up to 15 flights very rapidly between two perches. Advertisement calls sometimes punctuate these displays, but the displays themselves are performed silently, usually by groups of males. Thereafter, the male switches to making log-approach displays, which usually commence within 10m of the fallen log from a perch 1–4m off the ground. As in White-ruffed Manakin, this consists of a remarkable above-canopy flight-song display, which was initially described from a chance observation in Surinam by Davis (1982) and subsequently in more detail by Prum (1986) based on work in the same country. Davis (1982) described watching a male White-throated Manakin fly up from the crown of an isolated tree, then fly in a shallow arc above the canopy, its white throat puffed-out, wings beating 'furiously', calling all the time, then dive down into the crown of a tree at the edge of a clearing, the display ending with a wing snap (the mechanical *pop* sound, see Voice). The song flight was delivered back and forth between the same two trees four times in five minutes, before the bird disappeared for 15 minutes, then displayed again. Five minutes later, a male reappeared chasing a female through the forest *c.*10m above the ground. However, the more detailed work of Prum (1986) revealed that this above-canopy display serves as either an elaborate log-approach or an independent flight-song display, in which the male does not visit the display log (which was the case in Davis's observation). Sometimes two males will perform similar displays in close spatial and temporal proximity, and they terminate in the mechanical sound on *c.*50% of occasions. The birds can reach between 10 and 25m above the forest canopy, the male adopting the bill-pointing posture in flight, before plummeting back to the trees and, in the case of a log-approach display, to the fallen log itself. Non-aerial approaches are frequently repeated and involve the bird gradually getting closer to the display log. Some log-approach displays, as documented by Prum (1986) and Théry (1990), involve the male in a moth-like, slow and undulating flight, during which the white wing flashes are prominent, with the body held vertically and the wings beating rapidly, and is performed either solitarily or in response to a visit by a neighbouring male. As noted by Théry (1990), this display echoes a similar behaviour in White-crowned Manakin.

The culmination of the log-approach display is marked by the bird stalling in mid-air, dropping to the log, then rebounding into the air and landing again 30–40cm further down the log but facing the original landing point, all of this accompanied by the display-call (see Voice) (Prum 1986). During the rebound movement, the male often jumps over a subordinate individual, fluffing out the throat feathers during the process (Théry 1990). Once a male has arrived at the focal log, three different types of stereotypical display are given: bill-pointing but with the throat almost touching the log with abrupt 90° or 180° turns (which is the commonest display posture); the hunched posture, in which the male lowers his head and raises the bend of the closed wing, which is usually given in the presence of an intruding male; and the wing-shiver display, wherein the male lowers the head and opens the wings to expose the white flashes, while strutting backwards jerkily along the log like a wind-up toy (Fig. 3; Prum 1986). Prum considered the last-mentioned display to serve as a solicitation to females. Males also perform to-and-fro displays on the log, the bird initially flying forwards, then turns in mid-air, lands in the bill-pointing posture 20–40cm away from the starting point and facing in the opposite direction. This display can be performed up to ten times in quick succession and has a machine-like quality, with the flash of the white wing marking one of its most conspicuous features. Males compete for the ability to control the display log, with more than one male often landing there simultaneously. Should a female land on the display log, a male will move backwards towards her, i.e. maintaining his eyes on any rival males on the log (Prum 1986), but Théry (1990) described the complete courtship display (which he observed over 100 times, although only three ended in copulation) as follows. Initially the male performs a stereotyped display-flight with display-calls, before landing

facing away from the female (in such approaches when no female is present, the birds land facing inward), then flaps his wings noisily and rebounds directly backwards over the female. The male thereafter rebounds back to his original position, facing outwards and adopting the bill-pointing posture, while creeping backwards toward the female, his throat lowered onto the log, rapidly flapping his wings and flashing the white wing-patches. Finally, the female either touches the male's primaries with her bill (which happened in all three instances that led to copulation) or departs. In the former case, the male then returns to a perch away from the log, before recommencing the display flight and landing on the log again. Immediately after snapping his wings on landing, the male jumps onto the female's back for copulation. Although Davis (1949a) observed copulation following a group display, all of the mating events witnessed by Théry (1990) followed single male displays.

BREEDING Tostain (1988c) described and illustrated the nest based on observations in French Guiana, in the fourth week of October. It was a very small cup, the outer layer constructed of moss and lined with a thin layer of black fungal rhizomorphs (*Marasmius* sp.), sited 8.3m above the ground in the horizontal fork of an understorey *Sloanea* sp. (Elaeocarpaceae) tree, and bound to the supporting twigs with spiderwebs. Dimensions of the nest and eggs were published by Tostain (1988c). The eggs are pinkish-white with scattered brown markings densest at the large end. Clutch size is two eggs (Tostain 1988c), and only the female incubated (as in all manakins) with off-bouts lasting up to 20 minutes, but there is no information on incubation or fledging periods (Snow 2004b). Birds (both sexes) have been collected in breeding condition in Surinam in January and October (RMNH).

STATUS *C. gutturalis* is currently considered Least Concern by BirdLife International (2004, 2008). In French Guiana, Thiollay (1994) estimated the species' density at 2.5 pairs per 100ha at one study site. It is generally uncommon to locally fairly common in southern Venezuela (Hilty 2003), common north of Manaus, Brazil (Cohn-Haft *et al.* 1997), and widespread and at least locally common across the Guianas (Snyder 1966, Tostain *et al.* 1992, Ottema *et al.* 2009). White-throated Manakin is known from a number of protected areas, including three conservation units in the Serra do Navio, and Parque Nacional Montanhas do Tumucumaque, Amapá, Brazil (Bernard 2008, Campos *et al.* 2009), Réserve Naturelle de Trésor, French Guiana (Renaudier 2009), and Brownsberg Nature Park, Surinam (Ottema 2009).

REFERENCES Anciães and Peterson (2009), Barnés (1955), Bernard (2008), BirdLife International (2004, 2008), Blake (1950), Braun *et al.* (2007), Campos *et al.* (2009), Chubb (1921), Cohn-Haft *et al.* (1997), Davis, T. A. W. (1949a), Davis, T. H. (1982), Dickinson (2003), Dunning (2008), Haverschmidt and Mees (1994), Hellmayr (1929b), Hilty (2003), Ingels (1981), Jullien and Thiollay (1998), Meyer de Schauensee (1966), Meyer de Schauensee and Phelps (1978), Naka *et al.* (2006), Novaes (1978), Ottema (2009), Ottema *et al.* (2009), Phelps and Phelps (1948), Prum (1986, 1990a), Renaudier (2009), Restall *et al.* (2006), Reynaud (1998), Ridgely and Tudor (1994, 2009), Sick (1993, 1997), Snow (1975, 2004b), Snyder (1966), Stotz (1997), Stotz *et al.* (1996), Théry (1990, 1992, 1997), Théry and Vehrencamp (1995), Thiollay (1994), Tostain (1988c), Tostain *et al.* (1992), Zyskowski *et al.* (2011).

White-throated Manakin *Corapipo gutturalis*. **Fig. 1**. Male, Montagne de Kaw, French Guiana, December (*Maxime Dechelle*). **Fig. 2**. Male, Saül, French Guiana, August (*Thierry Nogaro*). Male displaying on his log, adopting the bill-pointing posture (see text). **Figs. 3–4**. Male displaying on his log, Biological Dynamics of Forest Fragments Project, north of Manaus, Amazonas, Brazil, January (*Gabriel Leite*). **Fig. 5**. Female, Saül, French Guiana, August (*Thierry Nogaro*).

Genus *Chiroxiphia*: 'blue' manakins

The genus *Chiroxiphia* comprises five species (one of them only comparatively recently recognised, Yungas Manakin *C. boliviana*) whose males exhibit varying combinations of blue, black and red. Females, like those of so many manakins, are almost exclusively olive-green. *Chiroxiphia* can be regarded as forming a superspecies whose members range from southeast Mexico to northeast Argentina, replacing one another geographically. That Blue Manakin *C. caudata* is less closely related to the other species of the genus (Snow 1975) is further supported by the findings that there is some limited geographical sympatry between this species and Blue-backed Manakin *C. pareola*. Indeed, Long-tailed *C. linearis*, Lance-tailed *C. lanceolata* and Blue-backed Manakins have been considered as conspecific. Their displays are spectacular, relatively complex and well known for four of the five species, with males performing highly coordinated courtship manoeuvres. 'Alpha' males are highly dominant at the leks. Because of their abundance and the interest of their displays for elucidating wider biological problems, these rituals have been well studied, especially those of Long-tailed Manakin.

LONG-TAILED MANAKIN
Chiroxiphia linearis   Plate 11

Pipra linearis **C. L. Bonaparte, 1838**, *Proc. Zool. Soc. Lond.* 5: 113, [Santa Efigenia, Oaxaca,] Mexico

This, the northernmost representative of the genus *Chiroxiphia*, is also the most flamboyant, on account of the male's remarkable tail. It has in the past sometimes been considered conspecific with both Lance-tailed *C. lanceolata* and Blue-backed Manakins *C. pareola*, these species being entirely allopatric (cf. Hellmayr 1929b, Monroe 1968, AOU 1998); and these three perhaps form a superspecies. In Costa Rica, the species' local name is el Toledo because of its onomatopoeic song.

IDENTIFICATION 11.0–11.5cm; the extraordinary tail extensions reach 10–17cm in males and 2–4cm in females. Male Long-tailed Manakins can scarcely be mistaken for any other species, as this is the only blue-backed manakin in its range (there is no overlap with the geographically most proximate species, Lance-tailed Manakin) and even females should prove immediately recognisable given their obviously elongated central tail feathers. In many areas of its range this is the *only* species of manakin.

DISTRIBUTION Long-tailed Manakin is restricted to the Pacific slope of Middle America, where it occurs from southern Mexico, in easternmost Oaxaca west as far as

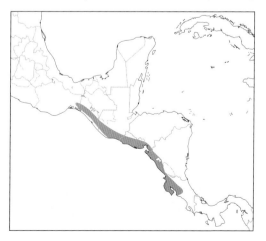

Chivela (16°42'N, 95°00'W: Bangs and Peters 1928, Binford 1989), south through Guatemala, El Salvador, southwestern and southern Honduras and western Nicaragua to northwest Costa Rica, in the last-named country extending south as far as the Carara and Dota regions, including the Valle Central (Monroe 1968, Stiles and Skutch 1989, Howell and Webb 1995, AOU 1998). It locally reaches the Caribbean slope in Costa Rica from Ochomongo to Juan Viñas (perhaps only formerly) and in the Cordillera de Guanacaste (Stiles and Skutch 1989). Its elevational range ascends to *c*.1,500m in Costa Rica (Stiles and Skutch 1989), but is confined to elevations below 900m in Guatemala (Eisenmann and Avendaño 2007).

MOVEMENTS The species is usually considered to be sedentary.

HABITAT Principally inhabits both dry and, more locally, humid lowland and foothill forests, usually but not always with a dense understorey (Foster 1976, Howell and Webb 1995). Long-tailed Manakin is also found in gallery woodland (perhaps especially in northwest Costa Rica), at borders with mangrove swamp, old secondary forest (Slud 1957, Binford 1989, Stiles and Skutch 1989), and even scrubby and regenerating wooded agricultural areas (Eisenmann and Avendaño 2007) and young second growth (MNCR).

DESCRIPTION A relatively bulky-bodied Pipridae, typical of the genus *Chiroxiphia*. The feathers on the forehead are stiffened and slightly erect, forming a tuft-like patch, and extend forward to the base of the nostrils. Culmen reasonably well arched, sometimes with a strikingly hooked tip. The following applies to nominate *C. l. linearis. Adult male.* – Virtually the entire plumage is black, including all of the rectrices, relieved only by the crimson-red crown patch which does not reach the forehead or far to the rear, and the pale blue mantle and scapulars (the latter tract slightly elongated). The crown appears extraordinarily flat, like a cartoon character hit by a hammer! The sky-blue back often has a narrow upper border of white, which can appear more greyish in some individuals, although this is not always visible in the field, if present. The underwing is entirely black. Male tail-length apparently decreases with age once they have achieved fully adult plumage (Arévalo and Heeb 2005). Note that the two elongated rectrices rarely seem to be the same length. *Adult female.* – The entire upperparts are solid uniform green with browner wings (especially the primaries and secondaries) and a slightly duskier tail, whilst the underparts are distinctly paler green, in some becoming slightly yellower ventrally, in others marginally greyer or even whiter, and usually with a slightly paler throat. The underwing-coverts are off-white with some yellow on the wing-bend. Some females (very rarely) show some red in the crown (Stiles and Skutch 1989) and this state appears to become commoner with age and might represent a by-product of sexual selection for brighter plumage (Doucet *et al.* 2007). *Juvenile.* – This plumage is reported to closely resemble that of the adult female, except for having a somewhat paler belly (Stiles and Skutch 1989, Howell and Webb 1995, Snow 2004b). The nestling, which has greyish-tan natal down and a golden-yellow gape, was described by Foster (1976), who also presented some details concerning the chick's development. Young males can be accurately aged despite their prolonged maturation, permitting status-signalling in these plumages (Doucet *et al.* 2007). Acquisition of adult plumage in males takes five moults (usually undertaken in June–November), with partial red on the crown (which often takes the form of two parallel strips of feathers) being acquired between four and 15 months of age. Thereafter, some black on the face becomes evident and the crown more solidly red. Between 27 and 39 months black feathers start to grow on the body and blue feathers appear on the otherwise green mantle. Some individuals at this stage might easily be mistaken for full-adult males in the field, because of the extent of their black and blue feathering. Full plumage is achieved at any time beyond 39 months, which was termed the fifth calendar year by Doucet *et al.* (2007). Statements by other authors (e.g. Howell and Webb 1995, Arévalo and Heeb 2005) that adulthood is reached after 3–4 years merely reflect differing terminologies. Arévalo and Heeb (2005) found that young males invest disproportionately in tail length relative to their body size, presumably to signal competitive ability. In contrast, young females can breed in the year following hatching (Foster 1976). *Moult.* – According to Doucet *et al.* (2007) female moult activity shows an initial peak during February–April, then little activity between May and July, but a pronounced peak in October. In contrast, the same authors found that males in definitive (adult) plumage showed a single peak in moult activity, commencing in June and continuing until October. *Bare parts.* – The irides are dark reddish-brown, the bill is black, and the legs and feet are dull yellow-orange to orange, sometimes even pinkish-red.

MEASUREMENTS *C. l. linearis* (BMNH; CUMZ; FMNH: Mexico and Guatemala): wing of male (*n* = 20) 67–74mm, wing of female (*n* = 6) 68–72mm; tail of male (*n* = 12) 27–35mm, tail of female (*n* = 6) 30.5–36.0mm; bill of male (*n* = 20) 10.56–12.43mm, bill of female (*n* = 5) 11.47–12.44mm; tarsus of male (*n* = 12) 17.78–19.67mm, tarsus of female (*n* = 6) 15.91–18.36mm. *C. l. fastuosa* (BMNH; CUMZ; FMNH; MNCR: Costa Rica, El Salvador and Nicaragua): wing of male (*n* = 37) 68–74mm, wing of female (*n* = 6) 62.5–72.0mm; tail of male (*n* = 13) 29–34mm, tail of female (*n* = 6) 30.5–37.0mm; bill of male (*n* = 37) 10.04–12.01mm, bill of female (*n* = 8) 10.75–11.80mm; tarsus of male (*n* = 12) 16.48–19.14mm, tarsus of female (*n* = 6) 16.84–18.18mm. Females apparently have on average longer wings than males (Arévalo and Heeb 2005). Weight: 14.3–21.2g (males) and 15.0–22.5g (one of 25.0g and another of 23.9g had single eggs in their oviducts) (females) (FMNH; MNCR; MVZ; Snow 2004b). Dunning (2008) records a maximum weight of 26g for males and minima of 11g and 9g for males and females, respectively.

GEOGRAPHICAL VARIATION Polytypic, with two subspecies generally recognised (Dickinson 2003, Snow 2004b), although Ridgway (1907) and Hellmayr (1929b) had treated Long-tailed Manakin as monotypic, and it was only with the publication of Bangs and Peters (1928) that two subspecies were generally recognised, based on the length of the central rectrices (shorter in northern populations) and the larger and relatively broader bill of *C. l. linearis*. However, this suggestion was refuted by Monroe (1968). We trepidatiously maintain two subspecies here, but acknowledge that Monroe's (1968) recommendation to return the species to monotypy requires further investigation, especially given that for adult males held in BMNH we can find no obvious difference in bill length whilst in respect of the length of the central rectrices in *C. l. linearis* (125–161mm; *n* = 10) versus *C. l. fastuosa* (129–156mm; *n* = 10), the purported difference appears easily refutable (see also Kirwan 2011). Nominate *C. l. linearis* (described above) occurs in the north of the species' range, from southern Mexico to Guatemala, whilst *C. l. fastuosa* (Lesson, 1842) is found from El Salvador south to Costa Rica. The latter race is also purported to differ from *C. l. linearis* in being brighter overall, with the red hindcrown feathers forming a short crest (Snow 2004b), which our examination of BMNH and MNCR material again suggests might be impossible to validate (Kirwan 2011). McDonald (2003) found evidence for asymmetric gene flow between two populations of Long-tailed Manakins in northwest Costa Rica.

VOICE Male Long-tailed Manakins possess an unusually rich vocal repertoire among Pipridae involving 13 distinct vocalisations (Trainer and McDonald 1993) and females appear to use song in their choosing of a mate (Trainer and McDonald 1995). Slud (1957) had already pointed to the virtuosity of this manakin. Sonograms of most of the vocalisations were published by Trainer and McDonald (1993) and these authors speculated that the rise of such vocal diversity in this species (which is unmatched within Pipridae) must be related to the complex cooperative social system that has evolved amongst males (see Natural History).

The vocalisations and their functions are as follows. The loud *toledo* song (audible over 250m and also transcribed as *too-lay-do* or *to dee oh*) is the most frequently given vocalisation, lasting *c.*0.60 seconds, and serves to attract females to the lek. This vocalisation can have a slightly metallic quality. It is only very rarely uttered by a lone male, instead being given by two male partners, usually an alpha and beta pairing (see Natural History) perched 4–15m above the ground in the subcanopy, with their songs overlapping, as the second male commences to sing *c.*0.1 seconds after the first male. In one two-hour period, Trainer and McDonald (1993) heard a 'pair' of males utter 1,919 songs!

Four calls are also given during song bouts. First is a soft *wit*, also given very frequently, which acts to synchronise male partners into commencing a song bout, with a slower version of the *wit* call given prior to any interaction with affiliate males at the same lek (see Natural History) or females. Secondly, an infrequently uttered soft *owng* has also been heard during bouts of *toledo* songs, and this note seeks to stimulate the female to move to the dance perch (and probably signals excitement in the male uttering it). During male display dances, both partners frequently utter the nasal-sounding *nyanyownh* call, but only the alpha male (see Natural History) gives a loud *buzz-weent*. The latter is given much less frequently and serves to signal dominance following a series of leapfrog displays, after which the subordinate (beta) male will leave the perch-zone and the alpha male will perform a solo butterfly flight-display (see Natural History).

Non-courtship vocalisations identified by Trainer and McDonald (1993) include a loud but intermittently given *c.*1-second-long *teeamoo*, given by an alpha male to attract its partner to commence a song-bout, and a loud *weet* in mild distress between all males at a lek (e.g. indicating human presence). Other calls are all generally given rather infrequently and include a loud *squawk*, which is also a distress call (given by both sexes when caught in mist-nets) and a loud *wheeoo*, used in chorus by three or more males at a lek to mob predators (e.g. owls) or unknown males that range into a new territory (this call is also sometimes given by females). The *wheeoo* is also frequently given in response to playback (along with, to a lesser extent, the *wit* and *teeamoo* calls).

The remainder of the repertoire consists of quieter notes: a *waanh* that serves as a contact call between males at a lek (perhaps especially immatures), the so-called *doodoodoo* and *toodleloo* calls, both of which are of uncertain function but uttered by males towards other males at the same lek (the former if imitated often causes the male to approach), and a trilled *chitter*, sometimes given by a subordinate male to an alpha male at the same lek, as a signal of submissiveness.

Nestlings are known to utter soft *cheep* notes if handled in the nest, and this may also serve as a begging call (Foster 1976, wherein a sonogram of this was presented). Trainer and Parsons (2001) tested for evidence of geographical variation in vocalisations at three localities in Costa Rica, but found no evidence of any differentiation. Recordings are available on the audio compilations of Ross (2000) and Knapp and Will (2008), whilst others from Costa Rica and Nicaragua are available online at www.xeno-canto.org.

NATURAL HISTORY Found in the middle and upper understorey, the life history of this species shares many similarities with that of the Lance-tailed Manakin.

FOOD AND FEEDING Long-tailed Manakin's diet is principally frugivorous, although some insects are also taken. In Costa Rica, Vallely (2001) noted *C. linearis* attending army ant swarms, presumably feeding on arthropods disturbed by their passage. However, this manakin does not customarily join mixed-species foraging flocks. There are relatively few specific data concerning its feeding preferences, but Wheelwright *et al.* (1984) and Moermond and Denslow (1985) reported 37 species of fruit in this manakin's diet, of which plant species belonging to the families Araceae, Caprifoliaceae, Flacourtiaceae and Solanaceae were deemed the most important. Stiles and Skutch (1989) mentioned its liking for fruits of the understorey *Ardisia revoluta* (Myrsinaceae) tree, and Foster (1976) reported that both adults and young consumed *Trichilia cuneata* (Meliaceae) fruits. Foster (1977) found that during periods of depressed fruit production, Long-tailed Manakin takes unripe fruits. Foster (1976), who attempted, unsuccessfully, to raise a chick in captivity, fed the bird on both fruits and a smaller quantity of insects.

DISPLAY Male courtship displays are unusual among manakins (but common to *Chiroxiphia*) in that they are performed cooperatively between males and are highly coordinated, and are focused on a traditional area known as

the perch-zone (Foster 1977b, 1981, Snow 1977b, McDonald 1989b). Displays were first described as early as the late 19th century (Nutting 1884), then in more detail by Slud (1957). Trainer and McDonald (1995) found that displays showed no clear peaks associated with early morning or late afternoon. Perch-zones are separated by 75–300m, each arena being occupied by a different alpha male, together with a beta male and up to 11 affiliate males, some of which are immatures (McDonald 1989b), including very young birds with just a trace of red on the crown (GMK pers. obs.). These relationships develop over considerable periods of time, and because McDonald (1993b) has found that males can live for more than 13 years, this hierarchical system means that some alpha males can remain dominant at a lek for almost a decade. Interestingly, McDonald (2007) found that relationships between males at a lek often could be predicted based on their interactions as immatures.

Males sing for long periods in the subcanopy within the environs of the perch-zone, as well as on the display perch itself (see Snow 2004b: 132). When a female appears in the vicinity, two males, usually the alpha and beta individuals (McDonald 1989b) perform what is known as the 'cartwheel dance'. As with song bouts, other affiliations (partnerships) between males occur. However, immature males dance with one another but never seem to form partnerships with an adult male, and have not been witnessed performing the 'cartwheel dance' (Slud 1957). The dance always commences on the same branch or vine (the display perch) within 1.5m of the ground, from which each male in turn flutters upwards calling and then 'falls' backwards (the leapfrog), landing on the spot from where the next male has moved forward by hopping (whilst giving the *nyanyownh* call) to perform his 'cartwheel', like a clockwork cyclical motion. Sometimes the tempo increases during the performance, which always ends suddenly and can include up to 100 different leapfrogs. The leapfrogs are interspersed by up to ten butterfly flights, in which the male performs a special radial slow-motion fluttering flight on deep wingbeats, each of which can last up to *c.*1 minute. The female often lands on the same display branch as that used by the males, effectively intruding on the dance. Only the alpha male will successfully mate with any females (McDonald 1989a; see Snow 2004b: 133) and such displays that precede copulation always include a solo butterfly flight by the alpha male.

In a second type of display, at which females are never observed, the males congregate in either pairs or, more occasionally, trios (usually involving one immature male) perching *c.*20–30cm (or less) apart on the display perch. They take turns to make fluttering upward leaps (known as 'popcorns'), seeming to hang suspended at the top of the jump but returning to the display perch each time. The jumps become progressively lower, but the tempo and frequency of the leaps, and the pitch of the calls all increase. Each fluttering jump is preceded by the bird lowering its head, showing off its red crown, with the blue mantle-feathers loosely fluffed out and the long tail held arched (see photograph in Snow 2004b: 132). Finally, the birds seem hardly to rise off their perches at all and 'almost bump each other as they flop about like helpless victims of an internal disorder' (Slud 1957: 337).

David McDonald and Jill Trainer have found that learning plays a role in the development of these displays and the accompanying vocalisations, and it appears that males fine-tune the frequencies of their songs to match their male partners, whilst subadult males seem to perfect the consistency of their songs and frequency matching with time (Trainer and McDonald 1995, Trainer and Parsons 2001, Trainer *et al.* 2002).

BREEDING The breeding season is mainly April–July in Costa Rica, spanning the wet and dry seasons in this region (Slud 1957, Foster 1976, Stiles and Skutch 1989), and May in southwest Oaxaca, Mexico (Binford 1989). In Nicaragua a male was collected in breeding condition in May (MVZ). However, male displays commence in late February and continue until the start of September in Costa Rica, as noted by Foster (1976), who also presented other evidence of a more prolonged season, at least in this region, during her detailed study of this manakin's breeding ecology. Furthermore, Slud (1980) reported a tail-less fledgling being tended by a female in northwest Costa Rica in September.

Nest building (described in detail by Foster 1976) is undertaken by the female alone and takes approximately three days (but can be completely interrupted for several days). Even during periods when the female is actively building, she may spend up to 30–60 minutes away from the nest, and then visit it at *c.*5-minute intervals. The nest is a shallow, flimsy-looking circular cup, placed 0.6–2.0m above the ground in the horizontal fork of a small tree or less often a shrub, often at or near the end of a small branch (Foster 1976, Stiles and Skutch 1989). In her northwest Costa Rican study, Foster (1976) noted that Long-tailed Manakin shows a predilection for nesting in certain species of trees, principally a *Eugenia* sp. (Myrtaceae), *Terminalia lucida* (Combretaceae), *Ardisia revoluta* and *Psychotria* sp. (Rubiaceae), in descending order of importance, and that the individual trees chosen were not in fruit. The outer two layers of the nest are constructed of leaves, blades of grass (*Panicum fasciculatum*, Poaceae), moss (Leskeaceae) and fern (*Lygodium venustum*, Lygodiaceae, and *Adiantum* sp., Pteridaceae) fragments and petioles, and strips of bark, with quite large dead leaves hanging from the rim and forming a 'tail' below the nest of up to 8.5cm to disguise or camouflage its shape. The nest is often sited over a streambed or other slightly open space (Foster 1976, Stiles and Skutch 1989). Overhanging leaves always provide some shade, from indirect sunlight, and shelter, from rain, from above (see black-and-white photograph in Foster 1976: 402). Outside and inside, the nest is lined with leaf midribs and fungal hyphae, and typically of manakins it is attached to the tree fork at two points using sticky, elastic spiderwebs, *Marasmius* sp. (Marasmiaceae) fungal rhizomorphs or insect cocoon threads. Nest dimensions and further details were presented by Foster (1976).

Clutch size is usually two eggs, coloured buffy with chocolate-brown spots, which can be either heavy or light, always heaviest at the larger end and sometimes solely concentrated there (Foster 1976, Binford 1989, Stiles and Skutch 1989). Dimensions and mass of eggs from both Costa Rica and Mexico were presented by Foster (1976). Single-egg clutches have been recorded, but these might be due to predation events (Foster 1976). The first egg is laid two days after the nest is completed, and the second egg the following day, but the female might not commence incubating them until 24 hours (or more) later (Foster 1976). To date, there has been no information concerning incubation or fledging periods, although Foster (1976) provided some information concerning incubation rhythms. She found that females appear to spend less time incubating in the morning, although the birds usually remain nearby in the vicinity of the nest. Feeding bouts by the female during this period are generally short.

Once the young hatch, the female removes their faecal sacs and regurgitated seeds from the vicinity of the nest. The results of Foster's (1976) Costa Rican study suggested that predation rates can be high, as of 15 eggs just one hatched and the young did not fledge. Snakes, birds, large lizards and mammals, e.g. opossums (Didelphidae), were all considered probable predators. Three nests of Long-tailed Manakin in Chiapas, Mexico, reported by Wagner (1945), appear almost certainly to have been misidentified (cf. Foster 1976).

STATUS Long-tailed Manakin is currently listed as Least Concern (BirdLife International 2004, 2008) based on on its wide geographical range and degree of habitat tolerance. Anciães and Peterson (2006) suggested that it might only be moderately affected by currently predicted levels of global climate change in the future. The species is generally considered fairly common or common in northwest Costa Rica (Stiles and Skutch 1989), El Salvador (Monroe 1968), Guatemala (Griscom 1932) and southernmost Mexico (Howell and Webb 1995). However, more recently, Komar (1998) regarded Long-tailed Manakin as threatened in El Salvador. Protected areas that harbour populations include El Triunfo in Mexico (Howell 1999), El Imposible National Park in El Salvador (Fagan 2009), and Río Negro Jaguar Reserve (Cooper 1997), Santa Rosa National Park, Lomas Barbudal National Park, Carara Biological Reserve and the Monteverde system of reserves, all in Costa Rica (e.g. Wheatley and Brewer 2001, Lawson 2010).

REFERENCES Anciães and Peterson (2006, 2009), AOU (1998), Arévalo and Heeb (2005), Bangs and Peters (1928), Binford (1989), BirdLife International (2004, 2008), Boesman (2006c), Cooper (1997), Dickey and van Rossem (1938), Dickinson (2003), Doucet and Hill (2009), Doucet *et al.* (2007a), Dunning (2008), Eisenmann and Avendaño (2007), Fagan (2009), Foster (1976, 1977a, 1977b, 1981), Garrigues and Dean (2007), Griscom (1932), Haffer (1985), Hellmayr (1929b), Howell (1999), Howell and Webb (1995), Kirwan (2011), Knapp and Will (2008), Komar (1998), Lawson (2010), McDonald (1989a,b, 1993a,b, 2003, 2007), McKay *et al.* (2010), Moermond and Denslow (1985), Monroe (1968), Nutting (1884), Ridgway (1907), Ross (2000), Slud (1957, 1964, 1980), Snow (1973c, 1977b, 2004b), Stiles and Skutch (1989), Stotz *et al.* (1996), Trainer and McDonald (1993, 1995), Trainer and Parsons (2001), Trainer *et al.* (2002), Vallely (2001), Wagner (1945), Wheatley and Brewer (2001), Wheelwright *et al.* (1984).

Long-tailed Manakin *Chiroxiphia linearis*. **Fig. 1**. Male, *C. l. fastuosa*, Rincón de la Vieja National Park, Guanacaste, northwest Costa Rica, July (*Steve Garvie / www.pbase.com/rainbirder*). **Fig. 2**. Male, *C. l. fastuosa*, Santuario Ecológico, Monteverde, prov. Alajuela, northwest Costa Rica, February (*Steven Easley / Costa Rica Gateway*). The northern representative of this superspecies is often considered to comprise two subspecies, but the validity of *C. l. fastuosa* seems doubtful (see text). **Fig. 3**. Incubating female, *C. l. fastuosa*, Guanacaste, northwest Costa Rica, June (*Harold F. Greeney*). Like females of several manakins, this Long-tailed Manakin has gained a partially male-like crown plumage.

LANCE-TAILED MANAKIN
Chiroxiphia lanceolata   Plate 11

Pipra lanceolata **Wagler, 1830**, *Isis* 1830: 931, Guiana sive Cajenna [= Cerro Turumiquire, Sucre, northeast Venezuela]

This species, the other 'northern' representative of the genus, also has modified central tail feathers, in both sexes, but these are distinctly less remarkable than those of the allopatric Long-tailed Manakin *C. linearis*. However, males at least are equally unmistakable given the lack of geographical overlap with any of the other blue-backed manakins. Like all of its congenerics, with the exception of Yungas Manakin *C. boliviana*, Lance-tailed Manakin is a relatively well-studied bird, at least within the Central American portion of the species' range.

IDENTIFICATION 11.5–14.5cm; males are probably on average slightly larger than females, in part because of the marginally more elongated central rectrices (which might only protrude by 5mm in females). There is no overlap with the even longer-tailed Long-tailed Manakin, or indeed with any other congeneric manakin, as for instance Blue-backed Manakin *C. pareola* only comes relatively close in range in Venezuela, and even here they are separated by several hundred kilometres. All other manakins in range are decidedly less chunky birds and none of them possesses the longer central rectrices that are usually an easily noted feature of both sexes of Lance-tailed Manakin. For females, the most likely confusion is probably with White-bearded Manakin *Manacus manacus*, but the latter species is obviously smaller, darker and longer tailed, with brighter (orange) legs on average.

DISTRIBUTION Lance-tailed Manakin ranges from southern Central America to northern South America, from southwest Costa Rica (in the Coto Brus Valley, e.g. at Rio Negro and La Amistad Lodge, from Las Alturas to La Sabanilla, with an old report from Golfito: Stiles and Skutch 1989, Lawson 2010) through Panama, from east-central Chiriquí east and south, including more patchily on the Caribbean slope, and very locally as far as the Darién (Wetmore 1972, Ridgely and Gwynne 1989), thence into northern Colombia, eastwards along the entire Caribbean coast and south discontinuously to Tolima in the Central Andes and the northern tip of the East Andes in Norte de Santander (Hilty and Brown 1983, 1986, Pacheco and Laverde 2002), as well as across northern Venezuela, from Zulia, in the Sierra de Perijá (Phelps 1944) and the Maracaibo basin, as far east as the Paria Peninsula, Sucre, and northern Monagas, as well as reaching south to northwest Táchira, southern Cojedes and Portuguesa (Hilty 2003). The species also occurs on several offshore islands, namely Margarita, off northeast Venezuela (Meyer de Schauensee and Phelps 1978, Hilty 2003), and Parida, Coiba, Canal de Afuera, Afuerita, Gobernadora and Cébaco, off the Pacific coast of Panama (Hellmayr 1929b, Wetmore 1972). Generally recorded from sea level, the species' elevational range principally reaches 1,500m (e.g. in Costa Rica, where *C. lanceolata* mainly occurs above 1,000m) but locally the species is apparently found to 1,650–1,700m, e.g. near Boquete, in Panama, and on the Sierra de Aroa, Yaracuy, Venezuela (Wetmore 1972, Meyer de Schauensee and Phelps 1978). There is a single record from 1,860m in northern Venezuela (Verea 2004; see Movements). On Isla

Margarita it occurs to 900m (Hilty 2003) and in Colombia only to *c.*850m (Hilty and Brown 1986).

MOVEMENTS Like the previous species, Lance-tailed Manakin is usually reported to be resident and sedentary (Snow 2004b). However, Verea (2004) trapped a female in a cloud forest in northern Venezuela well above the usual altitudinal range of the species, hinting at the possibility of occasional wandering movements.

HABITAT Lance-tailed Manakin inhabits all types of woodland with a reasonably open understorey, and both dry and more humid semi-deciduous forest. It is also able to tolerate scrubby patches of secondary woodland in semi-open country surrounded by fields and open stands of trees, or overgrown areas near or within old cocoa and coffee plantations (Wetmore 1972, Jones *et al.* 2002, Hilty 2003, Snow 2004b, Verea and Solórzano 2005, Restall *et al.* 2006). The major constituent understorey trees within a second-growth forest utilised by Lance-tailed Manakins in western Panama were characterised by DuVal (2007c).

DESCRIPTION A relatively bulky-bodied Pipridae, like all of the *Chiroxiphia* species. The feathers on the forehead are stiffened and slightly erect, forming a tuft-like patch, and extend forward to the base of the nostrils (which are rather large like those of the entire genus). The outer primaries in males appear to have slightly stiffer rachi than those of females and might be used in the production of mechanical sounds during displays (DuVal 2007c). *Adult male.* – The head, except the central crown, as well as the neck, entire underparts tail, wings and underwing-coverts are velvety black, albeit often with a dull grey-green tinge (Stiles and Skutch 1989). The central crown patch consists of a flattened group of glossy crimson-red feathers with tiny black bases, whilst the mantle and scapulars are a somewhat greyish-blue to bright sky blue, and these feathers are slightly elongated. The rump and uppertail-coverts are slate-coloured with a slightly olive cast. The central pair of rectrices is 1.1–1.8cm longer than the rest (Wetmore 1972). Compared with males of the previous species, in addition to lacking the highly modified central rectrices, Lance-tailed Manakin males are duller black on the face and underparts. *Adult female.* – Upperparts are olive-green, with shorter but still slightly erect tuft-like feathers on the forehead, becoming paler and greyer on the underparts. However, the breast and foreneck are generally somewhat darker than the rest of the ventral surface, especially the central belly, which is olive-yellow to greyish-white. The axillaries and underwing-coverts are greyish-white, becoming greyish olive-green over the outermost of the coverts. Some individuals, presumably older birds (see Long-tailed Manakin), exhibit a flattened but narrower red crest (Wetmore 1972). DuVal (2005) found that *c.*5% of females might achieve such plumage, but that an additional 17% had at least a few orangey feathers in the crown. *Juvenile.* – This plumage closely resembles that of the adult female, although males quickly acquire a tawny cap, distinguishing them from females (Snow 2004b, DuVal 2005). Plumage maturation of males has only recently been subject to the detailed study afforded to Long-tailed Manakin, but occupies one year less, with three distinct sequence changes (or moults). The elongated central rectrices are swiftly acquired whilst the red cap appears after about six months (Snow 2004b, DuVal 2005). In younger males, the red of the crown is paler and more scarlet than in the adult (Stiles and Skutch 1989), and the crest initially grows in the form of a V (DuVal 2005). The black lores and or face are acquired at the end of the first year, when 10–12 months old, whilst the second moult, following which the birds possess a partially blue mantle and mottled green-and-black body plumage, occurs at 13–15 months. The third moult, to adult plumage, occurs at 26 months old, but males may still have greenish-black body feathers at this stage (although these will probably be impossible to observe in the field). *Moult.* – In western Panama, DuVal (2005) found that moult generally commences towards the end of the breeding season, in June and July. Young moult their body feathers 2–3 months after fledging, but apparently retain their flight feathers. Thereafter, annual moult is complete (DuVal 2005). A subadult male collected in northern Colombia in early September was actively moulting (Todd and Carriker 1922). *Bare parts.* – The irides are dark brown to dark red, or varying shades of reddish-brown (usually the latter in females), the bill is fuscous-black to black (perhaps more dusky in females, sometimes with a dull brown base to the mandible), and the legs and feet are yellowish to yellow-orange (females and young) or orange to orange-red (males), with mouse brown, fuscous-brown or black claws (Wetmore 1941, Friedmann and Smith 1950, Wetmore 1972, Stiles and Skutch 1989, Hilty 2003, Restall *et al.* 2006, Snow 2004b).

MEASUREMENTS (Wetmore 1972: Panama, except bill taken at BMNH: Colombia, Panama and Venezuela). Wing of male (*n* = 10) 70.5–73.5mm, wing of female (*n* = 10) 68–74mm; tail of male (*n* = 10) 47.0–52.5mm, tail of female (*n* = 10) 42.0–45.5mm; bill of male (*n* = 9) 10.40–12.62mm, bill of female (*n* = 2) 12.20–12.54mm; tarsus of male (*n* = 10) 18.2–19.7mm, tarsus of female (*n* = 10) 17.9–18.9mm. DuVal (2005) found that the length of both the central rectrices and the wing-chord vary to some extent with age. Weight: 14.0–20.5g (males) and 14.1–22.3g (females) (Burton 1975, Strauch 1977, Thomas 1982, 1990, Verea *et al.* 1999, Snow 2004b, Dunning 2008; MVZ).

GEOGRAPHICAL VARIATION Monotypic, but in the past Lance-tailed Manakin has been sometimes speculated to be a subspecies of Blue-backed Manakin, along with Long-tailed Manakin. Hellmayr (1929b) noted an insignificant tendency for adult males from Venezuela to average slightly duller and less blackish below than those from elsewhere.

VOICE Broadly similar to that of the previous species. Lance-tailed Manakin's vocalisations have been described in most detail by DuVal (2007c), who also presented sonograms, based on her observations in western Panama. Additional sonograms were presented by Pacheco and Laverde (2004). The song, which is most usually (but not invariably) given as a duet between two males at a lek, is a loud and musical-sounding *to-wit-doo* (Snow 2004b), *toe-LEE-dough* (Hilty 2003) or *kay-REE-ko* or *querico* (DuVal 2007c), sometimes varied as *curry-ho*, or a mellower-sounding *toe-curry-ho* (Hilty 2003). Solo singing is generally less sustained than duets (DuVal 2007c). Compared with the similar advertising song of Long-tailed Manakin, they are scratchier, with a shorter second syllable and are frequently interspersed with ascending whistled (*salir*) notes, e.g. *querico salir-querico querico*, or (in separate duets) growling *graaw* notes (DuVal 2007c). The whistled interventions are, however, usually only given by one male at a time, whilst both males may utter the growling calls, which give rise to its local name in Venezuela, the Benitaro (Wetmore 1939).

Males sing in unison at a lek, perched in the subcanopy and *c.*10cm apart, like Long-tailed and Blue-backed Manakins. Either member of the male 'pair' (usually an alpha and beta partnership) may commence the duet. Vocalisations uttered during courtship displays also recall those of Long-tailed Manakin, and include a nasal, snarling *tuuuoo*, a buzzy, repeated, frog-like *na-a-a-a-a-a-a* or twanging *nraawnraawnraaw* during their leaping bouts, and a *pip* note on landing following a flight display (Hilty 2003, Snow 2004b, DuVal 2007c). Two mechanical sounds are also made during these displays, wing-clicks (7–30 in quick succession), which are given more commonly when a female is present, and a low-frequency *whoosh* (DuVal 2007c). For further details concerning the contexts in which these vocalisations are given see the next section. Hilty (2003) also reports a mellow *kow* note given singly. Recordings are available on the Boesman (1999, 2006b) compilations of Venezuelan bird sounds, and the species is also said to react strongly to the song of a Ferruginous Pygmy Owl *Glaucidium brasilianum* (Restall *et al.* 2006). Recordings from Colombia, Panama and Venezuela are archived online at www.xeno-canto.org.

NATURAL HISTORY Found in the middle and upper understorey, the life history of this species shares many similarities with that of the Long-tailed Manakin. For Blue Manakin *C. caudata*, it has been speculated that there is strong male bias to the population, but this does not seem to be the case in the present species, where in Panama, Laucht *et al.* (2008) found an overall slight bias in favour of females and also noted that the proportion of male offspring varied significantly between years.

FOOD AND FEEDING There are few specific details concerning the species' diet beyond that it takes small fruits, swallowed whole, using a brief sally-hover to small trees and shrubs, and that some insects are also taken (Hallinan 1924, Stiles and Skutch 1989, Snow 2004b). Up to ten individuals may assemble at a rich food resource (Friedmann and Smith 1950). Males will break off from displaying to visit nearby fruiting melastomes (Melastomaceae) or *Trema* (Cannabaceae) trees (Hilty 2003). *Davilla kunthii* (Dilleniaceae) seeds have been reported as stomach contents in Panama (MVZ).

DISPLAY Male displays (involving two, more occasionally three, individuals) to some extent recall those of *C. linearis* and *C. pareola*, insomuch as the birds, usually an alpha and beta male, gather on low (<2m above the ground), generally horizontal, slender branches or vines, sometimes over a fallen log, and surrounded by dense cover. (Gilliard 1959a reported seeing males displaying well above the ground, but this seems erroneous or at least inaccurately reported.) Displays continue virtually throughout the day, with alpha males spending particularly large percentages of the diurnal hours at the lek (although mid morning marks the period of least activity and copulation apparently peaks in early afternoon: DuVal 2007c). Each display ground (lek) contains up to four display perches, is spaced *c*.100m from the next display ground, averages *c*.2,500m² in size (range 525–4,500m²) and is used for several years by the same males (DuVal 2007c). The most detailed characterisation of lekking behaviour, based on work in Panama, has been provided by DuVal (2007c), with less detailed information, from Colombia, being presented by Pacheco and Laverde (2002, 2004). Males clean the area around the display perches and the perches themselves, tearing at leaves or scratching at the branches, but never when females are present. During the courtship display, the alpha male is usually joined by a subordinate male in alternately making fluttering upward leaps and short to-and-fro flights, with 11 different display elements identified by DuVal (2007c), which are summarised below. Some of these displays can be performed by lone males, including by immatures.

(1) *Pip* flight – a circular display flight around the perch area, with the birds calling *pip* on landing. (2) Paired slow flight – flying on slow wingbeats around the display perch, calling on landing, with this display given between bouts of leapfrog dancing or preceding such displays. (3) Up-and-down – two males alight close together on the display perch and make alternate leaps, hovering briefly before landing, calling, and flicking their wings and flaring their crests while perched. (4) Leapfrog dance – two males perch close to the female, who generally remains near-motionless, and the male closest to her leaps up, calls, hovers and then descends back to perch slightly behind his starting point, while the second male shuffles forward, ducking under the leaping male, before repeating the performance. The entire dance lasts <45 seconds, becoming increasingly frenzied with time, and sometimes terminates in the *eek* display. (5) Back-and-forth – a crouched male splays his crest and darts rapidly in a series of single low leaps back and forth along the display perch, sometimes flapping one wing, with the female terminating the performance by flying to the perch and displacing the male. (6) *Eek* display – used to complete the leapfrog dance, with one male turning to face the other, with his back to the female, and uttering an *eek* call and flying off in an arc, followed soon after by the silent second male, which performance may or may not serve to terminate cooperative male displays. (7) Solo slow flight – as in (2) but performed by one male alone and always as a prelude to copulation with the female. (8) Quick-turn – during slow-flight displays, a male may execute a 180° turn on the branch, before continuing the flights. (9) Swoop – one male ascends to the subcanopy up to 20m from the display perch, giving the *pip* call on landing, before making a rapid dive back to the display perch, which ends with an upward swoop to land (and sometimes is accompanied by the *whoosh* noise). (10) Bounce – the displaying male flies vertically down to the display perch but touches it only briefly before flying back to another perch close to his starting point, thus appearing to bounce off the display perch. This display is often given several times in rapid succession but never in dual-male displays. (11) Bow – following (10) the male lands on the display perch beside the female but facing in the opposite direction, peering down below the branch and fully spreading the long red crown-feathers. Following this, the male leaps into the air, reverses direction and lands on the female to copulate. Throughout such displays where they were present, females would usually remain attentive to the males' movements.

Like other *Chiroxiphia*, in general (see below) only the dominant (alpha) male will mate with females that visit the display ground (or perch-zone). Subordinate (apprentice or beta) males must generally wait several years to have any chance of succeeding to the top of the hierarchy as alpha males can maintain such status for at least 2–5 years, but do not seem to achieve such status earlier than six years of age. Beta males are generally younger than the alpha male (DuVal 2007b). In contrast, females are capable of breeding in their second year (Laucht *et al.* 2008). Social structure in Lance-tailed Manakins has been intensively studied by DuVal (2005, 2007a, 2007b) and her co-workers (DuVal and Kempenaers 2008, Laucht *et al.* 2008), based on their fieldwork on Isla Boca Brava, a *c*.3,000ha island off Chiriquí, Panama. This research has revealed that alpha males rarely interact with one another and their display areas are dispersed through available habitat in an exploded lek of dominant individuals, who are never in visual contact with one another (DuVal and Kempenaers 2008). Occasionally, some alpha males form multiple alliances at the lek, 'pairing off' with several high-ranking subordinate males to display, whereas others are solitary, whilst such partnerships or lack of them seems to be determined opportunistically and varies between years (DuVal 2007b). Females will often visit several alpha males at different leks to observe their displays, regardless of whether they are solitary (DuVal 2007b), but alpha status has been conferred prior to female mate selection and thus females rarely mate with non-alpha individuals. However, beta males (which are rarely closely related to alpha males) do derive benefits from cooperation, principal being that their chances of becoming dominant appear higher than random (DuVal 2007a). Alpha males probably sire over 90% of young, with beta males accounting for less than 1% in DuVal and Kempenaer's (2008) study. The remainder is mainly sired by soon-to-be alpha males (be they beta or not), but probably never by males in non-adult plumage. On average *c*.60% of alpha males produced young per annum, but never more than four chicks annually, and it is seemingly very rare for an alpha male to fail to copulate with one female in any given year (DuVal and Kempenaer 2008).

BREEDING In southwest Costa Rica, display apparently peaks between July and September (Lawson 2010), which presumably coincides with the local breeding season. On Isla Boca Brava, Panama, the peak breeding season appears to last from early March to late June at least, with nests still being initiated in July and displays persisting until November, thus spanning the late dry season and into the wet season in this region (DuVal 2007c; MVZ). Elsewhere in Panama, e.g. in the Canal Zone, the season is reported as being August–September (Hallinan 1924) and May (Strauch 1977), but these are based on 'snapshots' rather than intensive studies. In northern Colombia, Carriker collected breeding-condition birds in June, H. H. Smith (*in* Allen 1905 and Todd and Carriker 1922) collected nests during the middle two weeks of May in the Santa Marta region, and nearby a female building a nest was observed in early March (Hilty and Brown 1986). In northeast Venezuela the breeding season is suspected to be in May–June (Friedmann and Smith 1955) and in north-central Venezuela, near Caracas, the species nests in May and June (Thomas 1993). Much like the previous species, the nest (which was first described by Hallinan 1924) is a compact, shallow cup-like affair, slung in the low fork between two branches, and constructed of dried grasses, twigs and leaf fibres, and slender petioles, with dead leaves hung from the sides and below used to camouflage the nest (as in Long-tailed Manakin). The nest is bound to the supporting branches using spiderwebs (and perhaps also saliva: Todd and Carriker 1922), and one nest was placed *c*.1m above the ground. DuVal and Kempenaers (2008) found that the female may construct her nest anything from just *c*.30m to almost 1km from the lek site where she mated. Lance-tailed Manakin generally lays two eggs (mean 1.88 of 170 nests in Panama: DuVal 2007a), which are creamy white to brownish-white with reddish or chocolate-brown and lilac spotting generally concentrated 'wreath-like' at the larger end, but sometimes covering virtually the entire egg (Hallinan 1924, Todd and Carriker 1922, Hilty and Brown 1986). Egg dimensions were presented by Hallinan (1924) and repeated by Wetmore (1972), and nest dimensions by Allen (1905) and Todd and Carriker (1922). Concerning incubation and fledging periods, DuVal (2007c) mentioned that incubation occupies 18 days and that chicks fledge at 16 days old. Just as Foster (1976) uncovered apparently high rates of nest predation on Long-tailed Manakin, Reidy (2009) in her study on Isla Boca Brava noted that six of seven nests of Lance-tailed Manakin failed. Four were predated by other birds, namely Crested Oropendolas *Psarocolius decumanus* (two nests), Roadside Hawk *Buteo magnirostris* and Black-chested Jay *Cyanocorax affinis* (one each), by day, whilst a fifth was predated, nocturnally, by a Common Opossum *Didelphis marsupialis*. On the same island, DuVal and Kempenaers (2008) mentioned that between 33% and 63% of nests that they located failed prior to the chicks fledging.

STATUS Lance-tailed Manakin is currently listed as Least Concern by BirdLife International (2004, 2008) given its relatively wide range and degree of habitat tolerance (much like other *Chiroxiphia*). Anciães and Peterson (2006) speculated that Lance-tailed Manakin might be moderately to badly affected by predicted levels of climate change on its habitat in coming decades. The species is known from a number of protected areas in most range states, including Tayrona National Park, Colombia (Hilty and Brown 1986), and Guatopo (Wheatley 1994), Paria (Sharpe 1997) and Henri Pittier National Parks, Venezuela (Verea and Solórzano 1998, Hilty 2003).

REFERENCES Allen (1905), Anciães and Peterson (2006, 2009), Angehr and Dean (2010), AOU (1998), BirdLife International (2004, 2008), Boesman (1999, 2006b), Burton (1975), Dunning (2008), DuVal (2005, 2007a, 2007b, 2007c), DuVal and Kempenaers (2008), DuVal and Nutt (2008), DuVal *et al.* (2007), Friedmann and Smith (1950, 1955), Garrigues and Dean (2007), Gilliard (1959a), Haffer (1975, 1985), Hallinan (1924), Hellmayr (1929b), Hilty (2003), Hilty and Brown (1983, 1986), Jones *et al.* (2002), Laucht *et al.* (2008), Lawson (2010), Meyer de Schauensee and Phelps (1978), Moermond and Denslow (1985), Pacheco and Laverde (2002, 2004), Phelps (1944), Reidy (2009), Restall *et al.* (2006), Ridgely and Gwynne (1976, 1989), Ridgely and Tudor (1994, 2009), Salaman *et al.* (2008, 2009), Sharpe (1997), Slud (1964), Snow (1977b, 2004b), Stiles and Skutch (1989), Stotz *et al.* (1996), Strauch (1977), Thomas (1982, 1990, 1993), Todd and Carriker (1922), Verea (2004), Verea and Solórzano (1998, 2001, 2005), Wetmore (1939, 1941, 1972), Wheatley (1994).

1

Lance-tailed Manakin *Chiroxiphia lanceolata*. **Fig. 1**. Male, Cotumbo Road, Aragua, northern Venezuela, October (*Nick Athanas / Tropical Birding*). **Fig. 2**. Male, La Lucha, prov. Puntarenas, southwest Costa Rica, October (*Steven Easley / Costa Rica Gateway*). Much shorter-tailed than Long-tailed Manakin *C. linearis*, but in any case there is no geographical overlap between the two species. **Fig. 3**. Female, Tayrona National Park, dpto. Magdalena, northeast Colombia, January (*Hadoram Shirihai / Photographic Handbook to Birds of the World*).

BLUE-BACKED MANAKIN
Chiroxiphia pareola   Plate 11

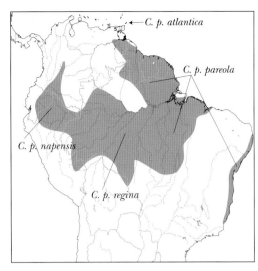

Pipra pareola **Linnaeus, 1766**, *Syst. Nat.*, 12th edn., 1: 339 [based on Brisson, 'Le Manakin de noir huppé', and Edwards and Marcgrave, 'Brasilia et Cayana' = Cayenne, designated by Pinto 1944]

Blue-backed Manakin is the most widespread of the genus and the only species of *Chiroxiphia* to exhibit any geographical variation, albeit this is only visible in males and is, with the exception of one subspecies, restricted to size.

IDENTIFICATION 11.5–13.5cm. Males of this entire genus are generally easily identified due to the lack of sympatry with most of their congenerics. Blue-backed Manakin does overlap marginally in geographical range with the extremely similar Yungas Manakin *C. boliviana* (which was previously treated as a subspecies of *C. pareola*), but the two are entirely separated altitudinally, with the present species found at much lower elevations and in different habitat; as such there should be no potential for confusion (for more details see Yungas Manakin). There is no overlap with the Lance-tailed Manakin *C. lanceolata* of northernmost South America, as the latter species is only found north of the Orinoco River, whereas the present species is only found south of that river. Male (and female) Blue-backed Manakins, in any case, lack the elongated central rectrices common to both sexes of Lance-tailed Manakin. In the Atlantic Forest region, in eastern Brazil, there is a limited area of overlap with the Blue Manakin *C. caudata* over parts of southern Bahia and northern Espírito Santo states. However, in this region, these two species are elevationally parapatric, with *C. pareola* in the lowlands (below 500m) and Blue Manakin above this, negating any real risk of confusion. However, at Camacan, in southern Bahia, there is a record of the two species together, with a male of the present species visiting a Blue Manakin display arena (Sick 1997: 638) and J. F. Pacheco (*in litt.* 2010) found the two species together in Parque Estadual do Desengano, in northern Rio de Janeiro, in the 1980s. Males of the latter species are easily distinguished, given a reasonable view, by their all-blue underparts, more extensive red crown patch and 'swallow' tail, the last of these features also shared, to a lesser extent, by females, which should offer a relatively readily used distinguishing mark from female Blue-backed Manakin. Female Blue-backed Manakin could be mistaken for female White-bearded Manakin *Manacus manacus*, throughout most of its range, but note the larger size of *C. pareola*, as well as the more olive-coloured belly and perhaps usually marginally paler tarsi. In certain *campinas* in Amazonia, this sex might also be confused with female Black Manakin *Xenopipo atronitens*, but the *Chiroxiphia* is still chunkier and shorter tailed, as well as having obviously much brighter coloured legs and feet (dusky-coloured in Black Manakin). Female Golden-winged Manakin *Masius chrysopterus* (again limited geographical sympatry, in northern Peru, and possibly no elevational overlap) is considerably smaller than females of the present species and also appear much more yellow below; their behaviour is also very different.

DISTRIBUTION Blue-backed Manakin occurs throughout much of the northern half of South America, east of the Andes and south of the Orinoco River, as well as the northern half of the Atlantic Forest region of coastal Brazil, with an isolated insular population on Tobago. It occurs from northeast Bolívar, in southeast Venezuela, from the Río Candelarita, near Ciudad Bolívar (Hilty 2003) and across the Guianas to northern Brazil in Roraima, Pará and Amapá south to Mato Grosso and the lower Rio Tapajós, as well as northern and central Tocantins (Hidasi 1998, Diniz *et al.* 2009, Pinheiro and Dornas 2009a), and east as far as Maranhão, e.g. at São Luís (Hellmayr 1929a; J. F. Pacheco *in litt.* 2010), and thence west across southern Amazonia to eastern Peru and northernmost Bolivia, where it is known from five localities in Pando, La Paz and Santa Cruz departments (Parker and Remsen 1987, Bates *et al.* 1989, Remsen and Traylor 1989, Maillard *et al.* 2007), and then north virtually throughout the lowlands of eastern Ecuador, although there is only one record from the extreme southeast (Schulenberg and Awbrey 1997, Ridgely and Greenfield 2001) and southeast Colombia, in southeast Nariño, western Putumayo and Amazonas, reaching north to southern Meta, in the Macarena Mts (Hilty and Brown 1986). There is a widely disjunct population in the northern and central Atlantic Forest of eastern Brazil, from Rio Grande do Norte south to northern Espírito Santo (Snow 2004b) and also very locally south as far as northern Rio de Janeiro (Meyer de Schauensee 1966, Sick 1997; J. F. Pacheco *in litt.* 2010), with another population apparently confined to the island of Tobago, off extreme northeastern South America (but see next section). Blue-backed Manakin is largely found below 500m, but in eastern Ecuador and eastern Peru it occurs locally to 750m (Ridgely and Greenfield 2001, Schulenberg *et al.* 2007) and once at 900m (Schulenberg and Awbrey 1997, Balchin and Toyne 1998). In east Amazonian Brazil, Blue-backed Manakin is found at only marginally lower altitudes (*c.*800 m) in the Serra dos Carajás, Pará (Pacheco *et al.* 2007).

MOVEMENTS None known. The species is widely considered to be resident and sedentary like the other members of the genus (Snow 2004b). However, recent unconfirmed sight records of this species from Trinidad, if proven correct, would presumably indicate dispersal (or vagrancy) from neighbouring Tobago (Kenefick *et al.* 2007).

HABITAT Blue-backed Manakin occurs in humid forest, albeit not throughout its range, e.g. in Venezuela (Hilty 2003), including tall-canopy *terra firme* across Amazonia, *campinas* and *campinaranas* in northern Brazil (Naka *et al.* 2006), swampy woodlands in Surinam (Ottema *et al.* 2009), mangrove in at least one area in northeast Brazil (Araujo *et al.* 2006), gallery woodland, drier secondary woodland (e.g. on Tobago, but also elsewhere) and islands of lower-stature forest in savanna in the southern Guianas and northernmost Brazil (see, e.g., Santos and Silva 2007), in particular, provided there is a reasonably dense understorey. It is known from some small islands offshore in the Baia de Todos os Santos, near Salvador, Bahia (Freitas 2008), and has recently been recorded in *igapó* (albeit perhaps transitorily) in easternmost Amazonian Brazil (Hohnwald 2009).

DESCRIPTION A typical member of the genus *Chiroxiphia*, being a bulky, short-tailed manakin, with a combination of blue, black and some red feathering on the crown in adult males. Like most others of the genus, both sexes (especially males) possess a short tuft of stiffened, erect feathers on the forehead. Females can have a striking hooked tip to the mandible, but this character is usually far more evident in males (MNRJ), the culmen is rather well arched, and the nostrils are rather large and prominent. The three outermost primaries of the adult male are slightly modified in having thickened shafts and reduced barbs (Snow 2004b). The following description refers to nominate *C. p. pareola. Adult male.* – Principally black with a relatively small red crown patch that extends neither to the nape nor to the forehead, and a striking pale blue patch on the back, comprising the feathers of the mantle and scapulars (which are slightly elongate), often with a narrow, pale white upper rim where it borders the neck. The underwing-coverts are charcoal black. *Adult female.* – The plumage is generally very nondescript: the entire upperparts are olive-green with browner flight feathers and wing-coverts, whilst the underparts are somewhat paler green, becoming greyer over the chin, throat and face-sides, and appearing marginally paler abdominally. Some females have off-white outer webs to the tertials and some of the inner secondaries. *Juvenile.* – Reportedly this plumage resembles that of the adult female, as in other *Chiroxiphia* (Snethlage 1914, Gilliard 1959b, Snow 2004b). Plumage maturation in males is prolonged, as in other *Chiroxiphia*, but is much less well known than in, for example, Long-tailed Manakin *C. linearis*. Young males acquire the red (or yellow in *C. p. regina*) cap, at least partially, during the first complete post-juvenile moult, as well as sometimes some blue feathers on the mantle. In the final stage, males possess a few green feathers in the blue mantle and on the rump/tail-coverts, whilst the red (or yellow) cap is not quite full, the black face and underparts are slightly duller than in adult males, and they may also show greenish fringes to the wing- and tail feathers. *Moult.* – Few moult data appear to have been published, but in the northeast Brazilian Atlantic Forest a female was moulting the outermost primaries, some inner secondaries and body feathers in April, but others of the same sex taken in March and July showed no evidence of moult (MNRJ), whilst in Roraima a male taken in September was replacing some wing feathers (INPA). *Hybridisation.* – There are recent records of intergeneric Helmeted Manakin *Antilophia galeata* × Blue-backed Manakin hybrids from the Chapada Diamantina, Bahia (Gatto 2005), and the Serra da Ibiapaba, Ceará (C. Albano *in litt.* 2009; Fig. 5, p. 330; vocalisations from this bird are available online, cf. XC33391). *Bare parts.* – The irides are amber, or brown to varying shades of chestnut or reddish-brown, and once orange in a male (perhaps more usually brown in females and paler in young)

with dark grey pupils, the bill is black or blackish (especially over the maxilla), sometimes with a pale grey, whitish-grey or even rose-grey base to the mandible, and the legs and feet are orange through reddish-orange to bright red (with no sexual dimorphism apparent) (Hellmayr 1910, Novaes 1978, Hilty 2003, Snow 2004b; MNRJ; INPA).

MEASUREMENTS *C. p. pareola* (CUMZ; FMNH; MNRJ: Alagoas, Bahia, Maranhão, Mato Grosso, Pará, Paraíba, Pernambuco, Roraima, Tocantins, all in Brazil): wing of male (*n* = 29) 68–79mm, wing of female (*n* = 15) 65.0–71.5mm; tail of male (*n* = 29) 29–43mm, tail of female (*n* = 15) 33–43mm; bill of male (*n* = 29) 10.35–12.45mm, bill of female (*n* = 15) 11.88–13.27mm; tarsus of male (*n* = 6) 18.91–21.35mm, tarsus of female (*n* = 6) 18.69–20.12mm. Females have on average longer culmens than males, but shorter wings. *C. p. regina* (Hellmayr and Gyldenstolpe 1937; BMNH; FMNH; INPA; MNRJ: Amazonas and Rondônia, Brazil): wing of male (*n* = 13) 70.5–74.0mm, wing of female (*n* = 6) 68–72mm; tail of male (*n* = 13) 32–36mm, tail of female (*n* = 6) 34.5–37.0mm; bill of male (*n* = 5) 10.40–12.37mm, bill of female (*n* = 2) 11.35–11.90mm; tarsus of male (*n* = 5) 17.64–20.05mm, tarsus of female (*n* = 2) 17.70–20.95mm. Some additional measurements from Amazonian Brazil were presented by Hellmayr (1910) and Gyldenstolpe (1945, 1951), and from the Guianas by Berlepsch (1908). *C. p. napensis* (BMNH; FMNH: Colombia, Ecuador and Peru): wing of male (*n* = 5) 69.0–70.5mm, wing of female (*n* = 4) 65.0–72.5mm; tail of male (*n* = 5) 28.0–34.5mm, tail of female (*n* = 4) 30.5–35.0mm; bill of male (*n* = 5) 10.15–11.67mm, bill of female (*n* = 4) 11.06–12.37mm; tarsus of male (*n* = 5) 19.01–21.62mm; tarsus of female (*n* = 4) 16.27–18.82mm. Hellmayr (1929b) presented additional wing and tail measurements for males. *C. p. atlantica* (BMNH: Tobago): wing of male (*n* = 8) 78.0–80.5mm, wing of female (*n* = 5) 73–78mm; tail of male (*n* = 8) 37–42mm, tail of female (*n* = 5) 36–42mm; bill of male (*n* = 8) 11.66–12.61mm, bill of female (*n* = 5) 12.47–13.59mm. Hellmayr (1929b) also presented wing and tail measurements for both sexes of this race, and additional measurements of males were published by Junge and Mees (1958). Weight: 15.0–21.8g (males, one young male 11g) and 18–22g (females; races *C. p. pareola* and *C. p. regina*), whilst for the first-named Magalhães *et al.* (2007) noted a range of 17.5–23.5g but provided no breakdown by sex; males (subspecies *C. p. atlantica*) 20.0–24.5g (Junge and Mees 1958, Fry 1970, Novaes 1976, Bates *et al.* 1989, Silva *et al.* 1990, Snow 2004b, Dunning 2008; FMNH; INPA; MNRJ).

GEOGRAPHICAL VARIATION Polytypic, with four subspecies widely recognised (Dickinson 2003, Snow 2004b). Yungas Manakin was until comparatively recently considered to represent a fifth subspecies of the present species, but following the brief recommendation of Parker and Remsen (1987) has been generally regarded as a separate species (including here), based primarily on differences in ecology and voice. Hilty (2003) speculated that more than one species might still be involved, presumably in reference to the position of *C. p. regina* (see below). The northern species of the genus, Long-tailed Manakin and *C. lanceolata*, have sometimes been suggested to be mere subspecies of *C. pareola*. The following subspecies differ only in size and, to a lesser extent, in male coloration. Females of the different subspecies are probably largely indistinguishable. *C. p. pareola* (described above) occurs in southeast Venezuela, the Guianas and northern and eastern Amazonian Brazil, as well as in the Atlantic Forest, but is replaced by **C. p. regina** P. L. Sclater, 1856, in Brazil south of the Amazon west of the lower Rio Tapajós, e.g. in Amazônia National Park (Haffer 1985, Oren and Parker 1997) and, at three localities, north of the Amazon, west of the lower Rio Negro, where it is uncommon (Hellmayr and Gyldenstolpe 1937, Borges *et al.* 2001, Borges 2007). However, the situation seems more complex and decidedly less clear-cut than this in the headwaters of the Tapajós (Gyldenstolpe 1945, Lees *et al.* 2008). The first-named examined *C. p. pareola* specimens from both banks of the lower Rio Tapajós. The latter found red-crowned birds in the Serra dos Caiabis, in northern Mato Grosso, albeit perhaps with vocal differences from typical *C. p. pareola* (see XC9407, 9522, 9523), betwixt populations of yellow-crowned *C. p. regina*, e.g. to the northeast in *terra firme* on the west bank of the Rio Cristalino, a tributary of the Rio Teles Pires (Lees *et al.* in prep.; GMK pers. obs.) and to the east at Dardanelos, on the Rio Aripuanã (Novaes 1976). Further east of the Rio Teles Pires, H. Sick collected only red-crowned *C. p. pareola* in the region of the upper Rio Xingu, also in northern Mato Grosso (MNRJ). Thereafter, *C. p. regina* extends across Amazonia to eastern Peru south of the Río Marañón and east of the Río Ucayali, e.g. on the Río Yavarí (Lane *et al.* 2003, Schulenberg *et al.* 2007), and to northern Bolivia. It is the most easily separated of the races, being easily distinguished by the golden-yellow, rather than red, crown patch, whilst Hellmayr (1910, 1929b) reported that females possess brighter upperparts and are much darker and more uniform oil green below compared with the same sex of nominate *C. p. pareola* and *C. p. atlantica*. Like most authors, we treat *C. p. aliceae*, Hellmayr & Gyldenstolpe, 1937, described from Codajás (03°50'N, 62°05'W), on the north bank of the lower Rio Solimões, as a synonym of *C. p. regina*. It was stated to have a paler mantle and scapulars than the latter race, whilst its describers considered that the yellow crown patch might be more restricted than in birds from south of the Amazon, but we are unable to detect such differences. **C. p. napensis** W. de W. Miller, 1908, occupies the rest of the species' mainland South American range, in eastern Peru mainly north of the Río Marañón and west of the Río Ucayali (Schulenberg *et al.* 2007), and north to southeastern Colombia. This subspecies is generally rather smaller than the rest, albeit with a reportedly larger bill (Hellmayr 1929b), with a marginally brighter red crown patch, and somewhat darker duller blue on the mantle and scapulars (Restall *et al.* 2006). **C. p. atlantica** Dalmas, 1900, is confined to the island of Tobago, and is frequently reported to be relatively distinct in size, being the largest race, although this only seems particularly obvious *vis-à-vis* the nominate race in respect of female wing-length (see Measurements). It also has a slightly more extensive red crown patch than other subspecies and larger and more turquoise blue mantle patch, whilst females are reportedly overall paler with a yellower abdominal line (Hellmayr 1929b, Restall *et al.* 2006).

VOICE Vocalisations are generally considered similar to some of those given by *C. linearis*. They were described in some detail by Gilliard (1959b). The male song is a drawn-out, ascending *wwwrrr*, considered to be wren-like by Gilliard, which can be immediately followed by an explosive *churr*, *chow* or *chup* note, sometimes doubled. The dominant male in summoning subordinate males to the display perch (see Natural History) will utter a *chew-wheat*, also rendered *joy-ee*, the first part of which is descending, the second part

an ascending, ringing whistle, and which is sometimes varied with a similar *chaa-chew chew*. As the males gather at the perch-zone (see Natural History), they issue a series of whistled *kii* notes, followed by a series of *chu* notes, likened to the clicking of billiard balls (Gilliard 1959b), e.g. *clock-clock-clock* (Hilty 2003), or a mellower *whee-whew*. In contrast the male duet consists of an almost perfectly synchronised series of *chup* notes, but with the arrival of a female these change to what Snow (2004b) described as loud twanging notes, and Gilliard (1959b) considered to be insect-like buzzes or scraping sounds, which increase in tempo with the display itself. At the close of this, the dominant male asserts his authority and utters a very loud *swee- eeék*, described by Gilliard (1959b) thus: 'two to four rapid choking noises, with its mouth wide open and directed towards its dance partner'. Sound-recordings are available on the following commercial compilations: White (1977), Murphy (1991), Moore (1994), Connop (1996), Schulenberg *et al.* (2000), Remold (2002), Krabbe and Nilsson (2003), Hammick (2004), Boesman (2006a, 2006b, 2009), Marantz and Zimmer (2006), Renaudier and Deroussen (2008) and Minns *et al.* (2009). Recordings from Brazil (both Atlantic Forest and Amazonia; probably all *C. p. pareola*), Ecuador, Peru (*C. p. napensis* and *C. p. regina*) and Surinam are available online at www.xeno-canto-org.

NATURAL HISTORY The species' ecology is generally similar to those of its congenerics. Blue-backed Manakin is usually found in the understorey and midstorey.

FOOD AND FEEDING Its diet has not been documented in detail, but like other *Chiroxiphia* it sally-hovers or gleans to take small fruits and an unknown, but presumably smaller, proportion of insects (Berla 1946). In eastern Ecuador, Loiselle *et al.* (2007b) found Araceae fruits were an important dietary constituent. Elsewhere there are few specific data, but Gomes *et al.* (2008) and Marceliano *et al.* (2009) reported *Miconia ciliata* (Melastomataceae) and *Ficus maxima* (Moraceae) berries in the Blue-backed Manakin's diet in eastern Amazonia. Beebe (1915) mentioned the species visiting a fruiting Lauraceae tree. Fruits are also gleaned from a perched position. The species probably does not join mixed-species foraging flocks (GMK pers. obs.).

DISPLAY Male displays are cooperative as in *C. linearis* and *C. lanceolata*, although the Blue-backed Manakin's vocal repertoire is not known to be as diverse as in Long-tailed Manakin (see above). Circumstantial evidence suggests that the lek arenas may be used for up to decades, provided that the habitat is not changed. These displays were studied on Tobago by Gilliard (1959b) and then Snow (1956, 1963b, 1971b, 1977b), who also presented data in his later paper from observations in Guyana. Males call together in the subcanopy from adjacent perches in near-unison. Two (rarely three or four) males display together on low (*c*.0.75–1.0m above the ground), slender, horizontal stems, with the dominant (alpha) male responsible for uttering a 'summoning' call that serves to bring the other males together at the lek arena, which is usually sited within particularly dense undergrowth. Each group of males including the subordinates (*c*.5) usually has up to four different display perches sited 30–40m apart within an area of *c*.100 × 50m (based on observations in southern Guyana, by Snow 1971b). Males (especially alpha and beta individuals) periodically appear to remove leaves from perches within the display area itself. If disturbed at one display site, the displaying birds will usually move to another, and the presence of a third male sometimes also causes the display to 'break down' and the birds to revert to mere calling. A strict hierarchy exists insomuch as older subordinate (including beta) males are dominant over immature males (still green-plumaged except for some red on the crown), but the group of display perches is the common property of the entire group of males. On Tobago, Snow (1963b) observed pairs of males displaying simultaneously at neighbouring perches, whereas in Guyana, subordinate males never displayed with each other, only with the dominant male (Snow 1971b).

In terms of the display itself, each male makes alternate upward-fluttering leaps (of <20cm), accompanied by the nasal twanging note (see Voice). It is only in such displays that more than two birds participate. Should a female arrive in the perch-zone, the alpha and beta males face her and continue to display, and call, but the leaps change to short jumps, followed by a hover and a cartwheel motion, after which they land back on the same perch. The two males are now perfectly coordinated for, meanwhile, the beta male hitches along the branch to perform the same display as soon as the alpha has landed again (see illustration in Junge and Mees 1958). This continues 'in a dizzying but spectacular vortex of activity' (Hilty 2003) until the dominant male utters the loud *swee-eeék* call (rendered *tic-tic* by Sick 1997) in hovering flight, which serves as a signal for any subordinate males to depart, although A. C. Lees (*in litt.* 2010) once observed the female depart the lek with the dominant male at this moment, leaving a subordinate male crouched on the display branch. The same observer has also observed a female appearing to mimic the males' display, performing three short leaps into the air while they are displaying (A. C. Lees *in litt.* 2010). Thereafter, just as in *C. linearis*, the alpha male will perform a silent butterfly (floating) dancing flight, punctuated by brief pauses, during which the male performs a bowing movement with red crest fully flared facing the female, as a prelude to copulation on the display branch (Snow 1963b). It seems likely that subordinate males must wait several years to succeed to the pinnacle of the local hierarchy. Blake and Loiselle's (2008) eastern Ecuador study provides additional support for the hypothesis that these manakins are relatively long-lived, and they also found that lek members are frequently not closely related, suggesting that males join leks more or less randomly (Loiselle *et al.* 2007c). The same seems to be true of Blue Manakin (which see).

BREEDING The breeding season is March–July on Tobago (ffrench and Kenefick 2003), March/April in the Rupununi of southern Guyana (Schomburgk *in* Chubb 1921, Robbins *et al.* 2004), September–April at Belém, Pará, east Amazonian Brazil (Snethlage 1935, Pinto 1953), and November in Bahia (Snow 2004b), with copulation observed in late January in Pernambuco (Lamm 1948). Other data from the Atlantic Forest suggest that the breeding period might commence earlier and finish later (MNRJ). A female collected in Amazonas, Brazil, was in breeding condition in November (INPA). In southeast Venezuela, Blue-backed Manakin is considered to be most vocal during the rainy season (October–February), and this presumably coincides with the breeding season (Hilty 2003). Nest and eggs were initially described by Snethlage (1935) and subsequently by Pinto (1953). The nest is a comparatively deep but typically flimsy-looking cup-shaped affair of dark rootlets on a base of dead leaves, with leaves and fibres hanging below the

nest to disguise its shape. It is sited in a two-way fork of an understorey tree or tall shrub, usually 1–2m above the ground, once in the leaf base of a palm tree (see photographs in Snow 2004b: 138). The clutch is two eggs, which are pale yellowish-brown with blackish streaks and flecks (Snethlage 1935) or dirty white with variable markings both in colour (chocolate-brown, reddish-brown, vinaceous-brown to grey) and in density (Velho 1932, Pinto 1953). Dimensions and mass of the eggs were presented by Burmeister (1856), Velho (1932) and Pinto (1953) and were repeated by Foster (1976). Incubation and fledging periods are unknown in the wild, but Olney (1973, 1974) described breeding the species in captivity: the eggs were incubated for 17 days, and the young left the nest after another 15 days but they continued to be fed by the female for several weeks. There are no data concerning predation rates in this species.

STATUS *C. pareola* is currently listed as Least Concern by BirdLife International (2004, 2008). Blue-backed Manakin is locally common on Tobago (Kenefick *et al.* 2007) and in northeast and Amazonian Brazil (Stotz *et al.* 1997, Silveira *et al.* 2003a; GMK pers. obs.), Ecuador (Ridgely and Greenfield 2001), Guyana (Braun *et al.* 2007) and Venezuela (Hilty 2003), whilst its degree of habitat tolerance and amount of available suitable habitat should make it relatively secure from most threats, as was noted by Snow (2004b). Nonetheless, Blue-backed Manakin is rare locally, even being considered Endangered in the southeast Brazilian state of Espírito Santo (Passamani and Mendes 2007, Simon 2009), and it is local and uncommon in east-central and southeast Peru (Schulenberg *et al.* 2007), generally local in Colombia (Hilty and Brown 1986), rare in the interior but reasonably common in the littoral of French Guiana (Tostain *et al.* 1992) and generally uncommon in Surinam (Ottema *et al.* 2009). Using modelling techniques, Anciães and Peterson (2006) predicted a perilous future for Blue-backed Manakin should predicted levels of climate change and their effects on forest habitat actually occur. Blue-backed Manakin is known from many protected areas throughout the species' range, including, for instance, Noel Kempff Mercado National Park (Bates *et al.* 1989, 1998), Reserva Natural Federico Román (Stotz *et al.* 2003) and Reserva de Vida Silvestre Tahuamanu (Schulenberg *et al.* 2000), all in Bolivia; Cabo Orange and Montanhas do Tumucumaque National Parks, Amapá (Bernard 2008, Souza *et al.* 2008), Murici Ecological Station, Alagoas (Nunes *et al.* 2010), Chapada Diamantina National Park, Bahia (Parrini *et al.* 1999), Jaú National Park, Amazonas (Borges *et al.* 2001), Reserva Particular do Patrimonio Natural Senador Antonio Farias, Mata Estrela, Rio Grande do Norte (Olmos 2003, Freitas *et al.* 2005), FLONA do Tapajós, Pará (Henriques *et al.* 2003), Tapajós (Amazônia) National Park, Pará/Amazonas (Oren and Parker 1997), and Una Biological Reserve, Bahia, all in Brazil; and Manu Biosphere Reserve, Peru (Walker *et al.* 2006).

REFERENCES Almeida *et al.* (2003), Anciães and Peterson (2006, 2009), Araujo *et al.* (2006), Balchin and Toyne (1998), Barnett *et al.* (2002), Bates *et al.* (1989, 1998), Beebe (1915), Berla (1946), Berlepsch (1908), Bernard (2008), BirdLife International (2004, 2008), Blake and Loiselle (2008), Boesman (2006a, 2006b, 2009), Borges (2007), Borges *et al.* (2001), Braun *et al.* (2007), Brooks *et al.* (2009), Burmeister (1856), Campos *et al.* (2009), Chubb (1921), Connop (1996), Dickinson (2003), Diniz *et al.* (2009), Dunning (2008), ffrench (1991), ffrench and

Kenefick (2003), Foster (1976), Freitas (2008), Freitas *et al.* (2005), Gatto (2005), Gilliard (1959b), Gomes *et al.* (2008), Gyldenstolpe (1945, 1951), Haffer (1985), Hammick (2004), Haverschmidt and Mees (1994), Hellmayr (1906b, 1910, 1929a, 1929b), Hellmayr and Gyldenstolpe (1937), Henriques *et al.* (2003), Hidasi (1998), Hilty (2003), Hilty and Brown (1986), Junge and Mees (1958), Kenefick *et al.* (2007), Lamm (1948), Lane *et al.* (2003), Lees *et al.* (2008, in prep.), Loiselle *et al.* (2007b, 2007c), Magalhães *et al.* (2007), Maillard *et al.* (2007), Marantz and Zimmer (2006), Marceliano *et al.* (2009), Mestre *et al.* (2010), Meyer de Schauensee (1966), Minns *et al.* (2009), Mittermeier *et al.* (2010), Moore (1994), Murphy (1991), Naka *et al.* (2006), Novaes (1960, 1976, 1978), Nunes *et al.* (2010), Olmos (2003), Olney (1973, 1974), Oren and Parker (1997), Ottema *et al.* (2009), Pacheco and Olmos (2005), Pacheco *et al.* (2007), Parker and Remsen (1987), Parker *et al.* (1982), Parrini *et al.* (1999), Passamani and Mendes (2007), Pereira *et al.* (2005), Peres and Whittaker (1991), Pinheiro and Dornas (2009a), Pinto (1944, 1953, 1966), Prum (1990a), Remold (2002), Remsen and Traylor (1989), Renaudier and Deroussen (2008), Restall *et al.* (2006), Ridgely and Greenfield (2001), Ridgely and Tudor (1994, 2009), Robbins *et al.* (2004), Salaman *et al.* (2008, 2009), Santos and Silva (2007), Schulenberg and Awbrey (1997), Schulenberg *et al.* (2000, 2006, 2007), Sick (1960, 1993, 1997), Silva *et al.* (1990), Silveira *et al.* (2003a), Simon (2009), Snethlage (1907, 1914, 1935), Snow (1956, 1963b, 1971b, 1977b, 2004b), Snyder (1966), Souza *et al.* (2008), Stotz *et al.* (1996, 1997, 2003), Thiollay (1994), Tostain *et al.* (1992), Velho (1932), Walker *et al.* (2006), White (1977), Whittaker (2009), Wiley (2010), Zimmer *et al.* (1997).

Blue-backed Manakin *Chiroxiphia pareola*. **Fig. 1**. Males, *C. p. pareola*, Ibiapaba, Ceará, eastern Brazil, December (*Ciro Albano*). **Fig. 2**. Male, *C. p. pareola*, Moco Moco, near Lethem, southern Guyana, October (*Hadoram Shirihai / Photographic Handbook to Birds of the World*). **Fig. 3**. Male, *C. p. napensis*, Shiripuno Lodge, prov. Pastaza, eastern Ecuador, November (*Hadoram Shirihai / Photographic Handbook to Birds of the World*). Compared to those of the nominate race, *C. p. napensis* males are generally considered to be smaller, with a darker blue back and marginally brighter red crown patch. As can be seen in these photos, the two plumage characters are not easy to judge, although they are detectable. **Fig. 4**. Male, *C. p. regina*, Cristalino Jungle Lodge, Alta Floresta, eastern Amazonian Brazil, December (*Arthur Grosset / www.arthurgrosset.com*). The yellow-crowned race sometimes is suggested to represent a separate species, but more research is required, and its range still requires additional elucidation (see text). **Fig. 5**. Male, *C. p. regina*, Los Amigos, dpto. Madre de Dios, southeast Peru, October (*Hadoram Shirihai / Photographic Handbook to Birds of the World*). In this region, the potential for confusion between the present species and Yungas Manakin *C. boliviana* is precluded by the fact that the subspecies of Blue-backed Manakin present is yellow-crowned *regina*. **Fig. 6**. Subadult male, *C. p. atlantica*, Grafton House Estate, Tobago, July 2006 (*Steve Garvie / www.pbase.com/rainbirder*). Frequently reported to be the largest race, and also stated to possess a slightly more extensive red crown patch than other subspecies and a larger and more turquoise blue mantle patch. However, none of these differences is easily assessed outside of museum series'. The olive-green fringes to the wing and tail feathers indicate that this individual is not an adult. **Fig. 7**. Female, *C. p. pareola*, Karanambu Ranch, southern Guyana, October (*Hadoram Shirihai / Photographic Handbook to Birds of the World*).

YUNGAS MANAKIN
Chiroxiphia boliviana   **Plate 11**

Chiroxiphia pareola boliviana **J. A. Allen, 1889**, *Bull. Amer. Mus. Nat. Hist.* 2: 87, Yungas, Bolivia [subsequently restricted to Apolo, La Paz, Bolivia]

Restricted to the highlands of southeast Peru south to central Bolivia, Yungas Manakin is a recently advocated split from the wide-ranging and principally Amazonian Blue-backed Manakin *C. pareola*.

IDENTIFICATION 10.7–13.0cm. Although they are very similar to same-sex Blue-backed Manakins, males can be separated based on their red crown patch (as the subspecies of *C. pareola* found in the same region, *regina*, has a yellow crown), the obviously longer tail and darker (more reddish or purplish) leg colour. Subsidiary features include the marginally duller blue mantle, the smaller and slenderer bill, and longer tarsal feathering. Females of the two species, however, would be much harder to separate, except on leg colour but, fortunately, there is no overlap in elevational range with Blue-backed Manakin, e.g. in Manu National Park and Biosphere Reserve, in southeast Peru. Blue-backed Manakin occurs exclusively below 450m, whereas Yungas Manakin does not replace it until *c*.950m (Walker *et al.* 2006). In southeast Peru, observers might also need to preclude the possibility of confusing female-plumaged Yungas Manakin with Green Manakin *Chloropipo holochlora* (limited altitudinal overlap), but the latter species always has dark (typically greyish) legs and feet, and also has brighter green upperparts.

DISTRIBUTION Restricted to the east slope of the southern Andes, where it replaces Blue-backed Manakin elevationally (see also Identification). Yungas Manakin occurs in southeast Peru, from northern dpto. Cuzco, southern Madre de Dios and Puno, south as far as south central Bolivia in northern dpto. Chuquisaca, where it was initially found by Remsen *et al.* (1987) but the species was subsequently located at several additional localities (Fjeldså and Mayer 1996). It is also known in Bolivia from dptos. La Paz, Beni, Cochabamba and Santa Cruz (Remsen and Traylor 1989, Hennessey *et al.* 2003a).

MOVEMENTS Presumed resident (Snow 2004b), although Tobias and Seddon (2007) trapped a female-plumaged bird at 3,200m, in dpto. La Paz in December, which given the lack of any other reports above 2,600m (Hennessey *et al.*

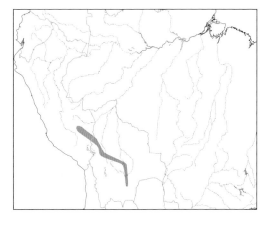

2003b) or even generally above 2,200m (see below) suggests that the species might at least occasionally make significant altitudinal movements in the non-breeding season. Graves *et al.* (1983) noted that females are considerably more dispersive than adult males, whilst immature males show dispersal abilities somewhat intermediate between adults of the two sexes.

HABITAT The species inhabits humid hill forest, especially at lower altitudes, being most easily found at edges and in clearings. At least occasionally it is found in bamboo. Canopy height at one Bolivian study site was 15–30m (Graves *et al.* 1983). Yungas Manakin occurs at 600–2,200m, although it is occasionally recorded to 2,600m (Herzog *et al.* 1999, Hennessey *et al.* 2003b) and once at 3,200m (trapped and photographed; Tobias and Seddon 2007), perhaps suggesting that the species might periodically perform altitudinal migrations (see above). ROM has a specimen from dpto. Santa Cruz, Bolivia, which was apparently collected at 500m. Tobias and Seddon (2007) reported that they have never heard birds vocalising above 2,300m, and that in Bolivia the species is generally commonest at 1,500–2,000m. In Peru it usually occurs above 900m and it is probably only infrequently recorded below this altitude throughout its range (Stotz *et al.* 1996).

DESCRIPTION A typical member of the genus *Chiroxiphia*. Both sexes closely recall those of Blue-backed Manakin, other than males of the subspecies *C. p. regina*. Compared with males of other subspecies of *C. pareola* (none of which is sympatric), males have a slightly darker crimson-red crown and broader black forehead patch. Like most others of the genus, both sexes (especially males) possess a short tuft of stiffened, erect feathers on the forehead. The culmen is rather well arched, with a slight hooked tip, and the nostrils are rather large and prominent. The three outermost primaries of the adult male are slightly modified in having thickened shafts and reduced barbs (Snow 2004b). *Adult male.* – Principally black with a relatively small red crown patch that extends just to the nape from above the eye, and a striking pale blue patch on the back, comprising the feathers of the mantle and scapulars (which are slightly elongate), often with a narrow, pale greyish upper rim where it borders the neck. *Adult female.* – The plumage is generally very nondescript: the entire upperparts are olive-green with browner flight feathers and wing-coverts, whilst the underparts are somewhat paler green, with virtually no contrast, except for a tendency to become marginally paler still towards the lower belly and undertail-coverts. Some females have narrow off-white outer webs to the tertials and some of the inner secondaries. Females can, at least occasionally, show a tiny number of red feathers in the crown (e.g. FMNH 364361). *Juvenile.* – This plumage presumably resembles that of the adult female, as in other *Chiroxiphia* but has not been formally described (Snow 2004b). Plumage maturation in males is doubtless prolonged, as in other *Chiroxiphia*, but is undescribed in the literature. We have examined a young male from Bolivia at BMNH that has the blue upperparts patch still admixed with some green feathers, largely green wing-coverts, still many green feathers admixed with the black below, and a more or less complete red crown patch. Another male lacks any trace of blue on the back, but has acquired a near-full red crown patch and many traces of black around the head, neck and upper breast (BMNH). *Moult.* – Nothing has been published, but none of those collected in southeast Peru between late July and November was replacing its feathers (FMNH). *Bare* *parts.* – The irides are brown, grey-brown or reddish-brown, the bill is black or blackish (especially over the maxilla), and the legs and feet are purplish-brown to pale yellowish flesh, with yellow soles (no sexual dimorphism apparent) (BMNH; FMNH; Snow 2004b).

MEASUREMENTS (BMNH; FMNH; ROM; Fjeldså and Mayer 1996: dptos. Santa Cruz, La Paz and Cochabamba, Bolivia, and dptos. Cuzco and Madre de Dios, Peru) Wing of male (*n* = 24) 66.5–73.5mm, wing of female (*n* = 14) 65.0–69.5mm; tail of male (*n* = 11) 42–48mm, wing of female (*n* = 14) 42–47mm; bill of male (*n* = 11) 9.48–11.93mm, bill of female (*n* = 14) 10.33–12.02mm; tarsus of male (*n* = 10) 18.46–20.76mm, tarsus of female (*n* = 14) 16.95–18.99mm. Hellmayr (1929b) presented some additional mensural data. Weight: 14.9–18.0g (males) and 14.0–21.8g (females) (Snow 2004b, Dunning 2008; FMNH; MVZ).

GEOGRAPHICAL VARIATION Monotypic, although Fjeldså and Mayer (1996) mentioned that a male collected in dpto. Chuquisaca was larger (wing 76.5mm), with a clearer sky blue mantle and longer red crest-feathers (17–18mm versus 12–16mm) than birds from dptos. La Paz and Cochabamba, suggesting to them the existence of subspecific differentiation. Additional work is clearly required to support or reject their hypothesis. Until recently, Yungas Manakin was considered to be a subspecies of *C. pareola*, but the split is now widely accepted (following the brief recommendation of Parker and Remsen 1987).

VOICE Typical of the genus, but clearly differs from that of *C. pareola*. Displaying males utter a fast-paced and variable *wheeyr-wheeyr-wheeyr-wheeyr* (Ridgely and Tudor 2009). Also gives a higher pitched and less husky *chereeo* than Blue-backed Manakin. Males give a nasal frog-like call when a female approaches the lek (S. K. Herzog recording; XC3593). The species' vocalisations were published recently for the first time on the compilation of Boesman (2009) and recordings from Bolivia and Peru are available online at www.xeno-canto-org.

NATURAL HISTORY Mainly found at forest edges, especially where there are fruiting melastomes, including *Miconia* sp. (Melastomataceae) or *Rubus* spp. (Rubiaceae) trees (Fjeldså and Mayer 1996; FMNH). Males have apparently been observed displaying alone (Ridgely and

Tudor 1994), but this does seem to be the norm, and at least in southeast Peru 'pairs' of males (presumably alpha and beta) customarily display together (H. Lloyd *in litt.* 2010). Display behaviour has yet to be described in detail and this aspect of the species' life history demands investigation.

BREEDING The species' nesting biology is unknown to date (Snow 2004b), although four males were collected in breeding condition, in Cochabamba, Bolivia, in the second to third weeks of November (MVZ) and Graves *et al.* (1983) considered that just over one-third of females trapped in La Paz, Bolivia, in July, were breeding. In southeast Peru (dptos. Cuzco and Madre de Dios), females have been collected with eggs forming in the oviduct in late August, October and November (FMNH).

STATUS Yungas Manakin is generally common, at least locally, within its elevational range, and is currently treated as Least Concern by BirdLife International (2004, 2008). Nonetheless, using modelling techniques, Anciães and Peterson (2006) predicted the species could still be moderately affected by the effects of predicted levels of climate change on its forest habitat. The species occurs in two Endemic Bird Areas (EBAs), namely the Peruvian East Andean Foothills EBA and Bolivian and Peruvian Lower Yungas EBA, this region being considered a conservation priority within the Neotropics as a whole (Stattersfield *et al.* 1998). Yungas Manakin occurs at various localities in Madidi National Park, dpto. La Paz (Perry *et al.* 1997, Hennessey and Gomez 2003), and in Pilón Lajas Biosphere Reserve, dpto. Beni (Hennessey *et al.* 2003a), both in Bolivia, as well as in Manu National Park and Biosphere Reserve, Peru (Walker *et al.* 2006).

REFERENCES Anciães and Peterson (2006, 2009), BirdLife International (2004, 2008), Boesman (2009), Dunning (2008), Fjeldså and Mayer (1996), Graves *et al.* (1983), Hellmayr (1929b), Hennessey (2004), Hennessey and Gomez (2003), Hennessey *et al.* (2003a, 2003b), Herzog *et al.* (1999), Parker and Remsen (1987), Parker and Wust (1994), Perry *et al.* (1997), Remsen and Traylor (1989), Remsen *et al.* (1987), Ridgely and Tudor (1994, 2009), Robbins *et al.* (2011), Schulenberg *et al.* (2007), Snow (2004b), Stattersfield *et al.* (1998), Stotz *et al.* (1996), Tobias and Seddon (2007), Walker (2001), Walker *et al.* (2006).

Yungas Manakin *Chiroxiphia boliviana*. **Fig. 1**. Male, Cock-of-the-Rock Lodge, Manu Road, dpto. Cuzco, southeast Peru, December (*Roger Ahlman / www.pbase.com/ahlman*). **Fig. 2**. Male, Chulumani, dpto. La Paz, Bolivia, October (*Ron Hoff*). This species was long treated as a race of Blue-backed Manakin *C. pareola*. It is altitudinally parapatric with the yellow-crowned *C. p. regina* in southeast Peru. Compared to red-crowned races of Blue-backed Manakin, none of which occurs nearby, Yungas Manakin is slightly longer tailed with a darker red crown and darker legs.

BLUE MANAKIN
Chiroxiphia caudata   Plate 11

Pipra caudata **G. Shaw, 1793**, *Natur. Misc.* 5: pl. 153, 'in the warmer parts of South America' [Rio de Janeiro, Brazil, following Pinto (1944)]. [Date and authorship follow Dickinson *et al.* (2006).]

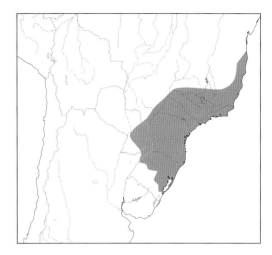

Known locally as the Tangará or Dançador, this is one of the most immediately recognisable and beautiful species found in the Atlantic Forest. Furthermore, the Blue (or Swallow-tailed) Manakin is also pleasingly common and easily observed, making it a perennial favourite amongst birdwatchers, especially given its spectacular and noisy displays. Pacheco (2001) discussed the history of the name Tangará, which has been in centuries-old use for this species (and Blue-backed Manakin *C. pareola*) in Brazil, yet seems to have directly given rise to the scientific name for a colourful genus of tanagers. Pacheco found that the first mention of Tangará in natural history literature dates from 1584, and that it was only with the publication of Georg Marcgrave's *Historia Naturalis Brasiliae*, in 1648, that the name was associated with the *Tangara* tanagers. Because this famous work was well distributed in Europe, the name stuck. Blue Manakin is virtually endemic to the Serra do Mar and Paraná centres of endemism (Cracraft 1985).

IDENTIFICATION 11.7–17.3cm (including the central rectrices, which project *c.*11–20mm in males, but usually <10mm in females; the female is on average slightly smaller than the male). Both sexes are chunky manakins, significantly larger than any other 'true' manakins in most of the species' range, e.g. White-bearded Manakin *Manacus manacus* and Pin-tailed Manakin *Ilicura militaris*. There is some very limited overlap in the interior of Brazil with the equally bulky-bodied Helmeted Manakin *Antilophia galeata*, but the males of the two species are completely different and the characteristic head shape of the female *Antilophia* should serve to distinguish it readily from female *Chiroxiphia* even if given only a brief view. In the vast majority of instances, the male should be immediately recognised by its predominantly blue body, red crown and black on the wings, with slightly elongated central rectrices, except in that region of southern Bahia and northern Espírito Santo where this species overlaps but is almost entirely elevationally parapatric with Blue-backed Manakin *C. pareola*. Readers are referred to the latter species' account for a discussion of the problem, but the elongated central tail feathers should always serve to identify both sexes of Blue Manakin.

DISTRIBUTION Blue Manakin is endemic to the Atlantic Forest region. The species occurs in southern Bahia, e.g. at Boa Nova (Gonzaga *et al.* 1995) and north as far as the Serra das Lontras–Javi complex (Silveira *et al.* 2005), south to western Paraná, Santa Catarina, where it is restricted to the eastern third and the extreme west of the state (do Rosário 1996), and Rio Grande do Sul, where it is widespread across the northern half of the state and the species is uncommon as far south as Pelotas and Porto Alegre in the southern hills (Belton 1985, Efe *et al.* 2001, Accordi and Barcellos 2006), in Brazil. In Minas Gerais it ranges north as far as the Rio Doce State Park (Pinto 1944), the Serra do Cipó (Melo Júnior *et al.* 2001) and the Chapada de Sao Domingos (Vasconcelos and D'Angelo Neto 2007). At least formerly, the species probably ranged into extreme southeastern Mato Grosso

do Sul (Straube *et al.* 1996, Straube and Urben-Filho 2008) and there is a recent record from the same state at Fazenda Caiman (19°56'N, 56°20'W), just inside the boundaries of the Pantanal wetland (Tubelis and Tomas 2003). Blue Manakin is also present on many near-shore islands, e.g. from north to south, Ilha Grande, off Rio de Janeiro state, Ilha do Cardoso, off São Paulo, Ilha do Mel, off Paraná, and Santa Catarina Island, where it is sometimes amongst the most abundant bird species (Naka *et al.* 2002, Marsden *et al.* 2003, Clausi 2005, Alves and Vecchi 2009). Sclater (1888) mentioned occurrence in southern Goiás, at Rio Claro, but there have been no subsequent records and Hellmayr (1929b) had already questioned the provenance of this record, although the state was, undoubtedly on the same basis, readmitted to the species' range by Snow (2004b). There are relatively small extensions of its range into northeast Argentina, where Blue Manakin is found in Misiones and northeast Corrientes, along the Río Uruguay (Short 1971, de la Peña 1989), and southeastern Paraguay, where *C. caudata* occurs commonly in the country's Orient, with two old (specimen) records from the west bank of the Paraguay River, in dpto. Presidente Hayes (Hayes 1995). The elevational range generally spans the region from sea level to 1,550m, but locally the species reaches even higher, e.g. to 1,700m in the littoral of southwestern Rio de Janeiro (Buzzetti 2000), and to 1,950m on the Serra do Papagaio and at similar altitudes elsewhere in the Serra da Mantiqueira, in extreme southeastern Minas Gerais (Vasconcelos 2008, Vasconcelos *et al.* 2009).

MOVEMENTS Presumed to be resident and sedentary, like most of its congenerics (Snow 2004b).

HABITAT *C. caudata* inhabits humid mid-elevation and lowland forest with a dense understorey, including montane areas and locally in *Araucaria* (Araucariaceae) forests (Schlichting and Bispo 2009, Vasconcelos *et al.* 2009), and secondary woodland, including at the borders of clearings and tracks, and in relatively close proximity to urban areas. Recently published radio-tracking data suggest that the species generally avoids forest edges (Hansbauer *et al.* 2008, 2010) and Cândido (2000) had already demonstrated that *C. caudata* is notably more abundant away from edges, although it is willing to cross roads between forest patches (Awade *et al.* 2003). Hansbauer *et al.* (2010) further studied the microhabitat preferences of Blue Manakin.

DESCRIPTION The most radically 'different' of the *Chiroxiphia* manakins. Males have predominantly blue rather than mainly black plumage and a much more extensive red crown patch. Females share the 'swallow' tail (see Identification for the relative lengths of these feathers). The bill has a well-arched culmen and marked hook tip in most males, but females only rarely show a hooked tip and this is usually much less noticeable. *Adult male.* – Bright pale red crown and forehead extend well onto the nape, and contrast strongly with the solid black face, throat and ear-coverts, which reaches onto the lores, above the eyes and the head-sides. The lower border of the black face is very straight and neat. The entire underparts and the majority of the upperparts including the tail are pale ultramarine blue, contrasting with the generally black wings (the flight feathers become browner with wear). The central rectrices (also blue) are slightly but obviously elongate and spatulate. *Adult female.* – Virtually the entire plumage is mid olive-green becoming marginally paler over the posterior underparts, with overall browner wings, especially the primaries and secondaries (although the fringes are pale olive-green and the tertials are predominantly green). Like males, the female's central rectrices project to form a slight 'swallow' tail. Females occasionally show a few or even many red feathers in the crown, most typically at the front (e.g. MNRJ 10591, from Minas Gerais, and MNRJ 38431, from São Paulo; see also Willis and Oniki 2002), but certainly brighter than the orange-yellow forehead mentioned by Snow (2004b; see also Willis and Oniki 1988b). Clay (1995) speculated, probably correctly, that this feature (its relative extent and brightness) is undoubtedly age-related, with older birds probably acquiring more and brighter red feathers. *Juvenile.* – Resembles the female as in other *Chiroxiphia* (Snow 2004b). The nestling seems to be undescribed beyond the extremely brief notes given by Marini *et al.* (2007). Plumage maturation in males is prolonged as in congenerics, and probably takes *c.*3–4 years (Sick 1997, Snow 2004b). Following the first post-juvenile moult, they gradually acquire a red crown (starting with a few scattered orange feathers on the forehead) but the central tail projection usually remains very short (although in some individuals it is near full). Sick (1997) reported that it can take six months for the red crown-patch to be fully attained. The skull's ossification seems to be variable at this stage; in many the skull is not fully ossified, but in some (probably a minority) it is. Following this, the next moult sees the acquisition of the black face, throat, wings and tail, and thereafter the blue feathering gradually replaces the green (Clay 1995; MNRJ). In the final stage, subadult males are much as adults except for the presence of a few scattered green feathers in the mantle and wings (MNRJ). *Moult.* – There are relatively few published moult data, but in southern Rio Grande do Sul, Bugoni *et al.* (2002) captured birds that were moulting their body, wing and tail feathers in February–April and October and November. At least some of these birds were apparently breeding (indicated by the presence of brood-patches) at the same time as engaged in feather renewal, and the same is true of some specimens held in MNRJ. In Rio de Janeiro state Mallet-Rodrigues (2005) found that, in common with other passerines, Blue Manakin's moult largely occurred post-breeding (as would be expected) and that flight feathers and body feathers were usually moulted concurrently, mainly in the first five months of the year. Further north again, in Espírito Santo, Willis and Oniki (2002) reported two males in wing moult in April. *Hybridisation.* – Hybrids are known with both

Helmeted Manakin *Antilophia galeata* (Sick 1979b, Pacheco and Parrini 1995, 1996, Gussoni *et al.* 2005, Vasconcelos *et al.* 2005, Guaraldo *et al.* 2008), thereby providing additional confirmation of the close relationship between these two genera, and, also, Pin-tailed Manakin *Ilicura militaris* (Anciães *et al.* 2000, Marini and Hackett 2002). *Chiroxiphia* × *Antilophia* hybrids apparently vocalise strangely, not sounding exactly like either parent but as a cross between them (Sick 1979b). For more information concerning hybridisation with *A. galeata* and *I. militaris* see those species. *Bare parts.* – Sexual and age-related dimorphism in bare-parts colours seems limited, but individual variation is relatively pronounced. The irides are dark brown to varying shades of chestnut or reddish-brown, occasionally red in males and once black in a female (perhaps more frequently brown in females and in young) with pale to dark grey pupils. The bill varies from amber to reddish-brown or olive-brown (especially over the maxilla) to pearl or dark grey, often with slightly darker or black cutting edges and tip to the mandible (once yellow-buff in a female). The legs and feet are greyish purplish-red or dark violet to brighter rose-red or dark red (with yellow or ochre soles), but tarsi once described as lemon-coloured in a subadult male (Belton 1985, Snow 2004b; MNRJ).

MEASUREMENTS (CUMZ; MNRJ: Espírito Santo, Minas Gerais, Paraná, Rio de Janeiro, Santa Catarina, São Paulo, all Brazil): wing of male ($n = 41$) 69.5–80.5mm, wing of female ($n = 31$) 70–77mm; tail of male ($n = 41$) 40–56mm, tail of female ($n = 31$) 35–45mm; bill of male ($n = 40$) 10.51–14.50mm, bill of female ($n = 30$) 11.31–14.14mm; tarsus of male ($n = 5$) 20.33–21.71mm, tarsus of female ($n = 2$) 18.91–19.17mm. Additional mensural data were presented by Bugoni *et al.* (2002). Weight: 21.0–29.8g (males) and 20–28g (females) (Short 1971, Belton 1985, Bugoni *et al.* 2002, Willis and Oniki 2002, Snow 2004b, Faria and Paula 2008; DZUFMG; MNRJ). Marini *et al.* (2007) presented mass data for nestlings.

GEOGRAPHICAL VARIATION Monotypic (cf. Hellmayr 1929b), with no evidence for any genetic structure between populations (Silva-Ribeiro *et al.* 2010).

VOICE One of the most distinctive and frequently heard species in the Atlantic Forest. Like other *Chiroxiphia*, its vocal repertoire is surprisingly diverse. The male's main call is a doubled *ptuwa, ptuwa* or *dwewt dwewot* in warning, which can be heard at just about any time of day, but in contrast to some other *Chiroxiphia* this vocalisation when given in male duets is not particularly well synchronised, and as noted by Snow (2004b) sounds gabbled. During courtship dances the males utter a loud and guttural *kwa-a-a-a* or *qua-a-a-a*, these calls possessing a curiously non-avian, almost cat-like whining quality (rendered *tiOO-oo, oo, oo tiOO-oo, oo, oo...* by Sick 1997), whilst such displays are terminated, as in other *Chiroxiphia*, by the alpha male uttering a very sharp series of *eek* or *tic* notes, up to three (Sick 1942, Clay 1995). Both sexes give a far-carrying *chorreeo* or *chorreeo cho-cho-cho*, which seems to serve in a variety of contexts, including the alpha male's summons to the lek; it is also occasionally given by two males in duet (Clay 1995). In chasing the female, either prior to or following the display (see Natural History), a male utters a series of *trrrr* calls. Sick (1997) reported that the nestling's vocalisation, which is unsurprisingly audible only when close to, recalled to him that of the song of Pin-tailed Manakin. The species' vocalisations have appeared on the following sound-recording compilations: Gonzaga and Castiglioni (2001), Remold (2002), Boesman (2006a) and

Minns *et al.* (2009). There are also numerous recordings of the species archived online at www.xeno-canto-org.

NATURAL HISTORY Comparatively well known, based principally on many studies in Brazil and to a lesser extent in Paraguay. Blue Manakin is usually found in the upper understorey or midstorey of forest. There has been speculated to be a sexual imbalance in the species' population, in favour of males, at least in southeast Brazil (Sick 1979b, 1997). The species does not customarily join mixed-species foraging flocks, but birds might be 'stirred up' into activity when such a band passes through their territory.

FOOD AND FEEDING Diet is mainly small fruits including those of the following 31 species: *Melia azedarach* (Meliaceae) (Voss and Sander 1981), *Rapanea acuminata*, *R. ferruginea*, *R. guyanensis* and *R. schwackeana* (Myrsinaceae) (Pineschi 1990), *Trema micrantha* (Ulmaceae), *Ixora venulosa* (Rubiaceae), *Cabralea canjerana* and *Trichilia clausenii* (Meliaceae), *Protium heptaphyllum* (Burseraceae) and *Chamissoa altissima* (Amaranthaceae) (Galetti and Pizo 1996, Gondim 2001), *Miconia prasina* (Melastomataceae) (Antonini *et al.* 2000), *Ilex* sp. (Aquifoliaceae), *Nectandra* sp. (Lauraceae), *Miconia cinnamomifolia*, *M. tristis*, *M. tentaticulifera*, *M. chartacea* and *M. budlejoides* (Melastomataceae), *Guarea macrophylla* (Meliaceae), *Guapira opposita* (Nyctaginaceae), *Psychotria sessilis* and *Psychotria* sp. (Rubiaceae), *Allophyllus edulis* and *Paullinia* sp. (Sapindaceae) (Fadini and Marco 2004, Parrini and Pacheco 2011), *Euterpe edulis* (Arecaceae) and the exotic *Eriobotrya japonica* (Rosaceae) (Fonseca and Antunes 2007), *Symplocos uniflora* (Symplocaceae) (Carrano and Marins 2008), *Psychotria suterella* (Rubiaceae) (Manhães and Dias 2009), *Miconia dodecandra* (Melastomataceae) (Campos and Varassin 2009), and *Coussapoa microcarpa* (Cecropiaceae) (Parrini and Pacheco 2010). Fruit is usually taken using a short sally-hover movement (especially, apparently, *Psychotria*: Della-Flora *et al.* 2010), but Blue Manakins also take berries by perch-gleaning, including bromeliad fruits (GMK pers. obs.). Berries are swallowed whole. Some insects are also taken (Lopes *et al.* 2005, MNRJ) but the approximate percentage of non-fruit items in the diet is unknown. Blue Manakin has recently been reported to occasionally follow *Labidus* predator and *Eciton burchelli* army ant swarms in search of insect prey disturbed by the ants (Faria and Rodrigues 2009). However, insects are probably a major dietary constituent for nestlings within the first few days after hatching (Clay 1995). Hasui *et al.* (2009) attempted to identify whether this species and Greenish Schiffornis *Schiffornis virescens* partitioned food resources. During periods of high fruit availability, they found no evidence of fruit trait selection. In contrast, during periods of fruit scarcity in primary forests, there was evidence of niche partitioning, with *C. caudata* foraging for larger fruits in the canopy and *S. virescens* searching for understorey plants. The niche overlap was higher in secondary forest during periods of scarcity, when both species fed on small understorey fruits. Sick (1997) recorded Blue Manakins 'anting', in which the birds rubbed the ants against the wings and the base of the tail.

DISPLAY Holt (1925) was the first observer to describe the male displays in the English language, but there are earlier references, even dating back to the 16th century (Sick 1997). The male displays are in some respects rather similar to those of Blue-backed Manakin and were described in detail by Sick (1942, 1959d) in Brazil, and by Foster (1981) and Clay (1995), who also studied *C. caudata* in eastern

Paraguay. As in *C. pareola*, groups of males communally own a series of perch-zones at which they display, and, of the group, there is always a dominant (alpha) male. During intervals between displays the different males at the lek perch some little distance from one another, calling occasionally. Periodically, however, the dominant bird summons the subordinate males, and females, to the perch-zone from a calling perch in the subcanopy (uttering the *chorreeo* call). Like the other *Chiroxiphia* species, different groups of males are never within more than auditory distance of one another (Sick 1997; pers. obs.). With the arrival of a female at the lek, one or two, occasionally up to five, subordinate males (along with the alpha bird) will descend to the dance perch (with two or more additional subordinates often present in the near environs watching on). Sometimes a male, presumably the alpha bird, may even chase the female prior to the display (Sick 1997). The female positions herself at one end of the same branch, and remains immobile and somewhat erect (especially the head and neck) throughout the following display (see Sick 1959d: 11, Sick 1997), which can last up to two minutes. In situations where more than two or three males gather, the 'suitors' will position themselves either side of the female, and the display may become confused due to multiple males attempting to hover in front of her at the same time (Sick 1997). In a traditional display involving a smaller number of birds, all of the males face the female and the bird nearest her (not necessarily the alpha male) jumps upwards towards her, hovers in front of the female (see photograph in *Neotrop. Birding* 6: 54), and then performs a backwards cartwheel, ending up at the back of the line of males, which shuffles (or tap-dances: Sick 1997) forward along the perch. Meanwhile the other males squat on the perch and quiver their bodies and appear to stomp on the branch. Each male takes his turn performing for the female, the birds all the time uttering twanging, purring calls (see Voice). After a while the males start to approach the female more closely whilst their jumps become concurrently flatter and lower (Snow 1976b). At this point, the alpha male will assert his premier position, by turning to face the other males at the termination of a higher and longer leap, vibrating the tail and giving the shrill *eek* call, which serves to disperse the subordinate males. Following this, the dominant male performs his solo floating, butterfly-like flight, a laboured circular display on slow-beating wings, much like that of other *Chiroxiphia*, after which he may mate with the female, although apparently not at the court itself. Gatto and Roper (2004) found that copulation was most likely to occur when fewer males were present, thus enabling the alpha male to control the lek more successfully. The males may reconvene to display again after just a few minutes, and Sick (1959d) reported that it will sometimes be the last male in line that commences the dance anew. Occasionally a second female may appear simultaneously at the display arena, provoking a fight between them (Sick 1997). Subordinate (but not immature) males do rarely manage to copulate with females that visit the perch-zone (Foster 1981, Clay 1995) and dances also occur without a female being present but in such instances are apparently less organised (Sick 1997). Sometimes just two (alpha and beta) males dance together, more or less in the manner of *C. pareola*. Furthermore, Sick (1942) reported that immature males (with or without the red cap) might sometimes serve as surrogate females in such displays, which behaviour is apparently unique among all birds. As in others of the genus, dominance is strictly age-based and the bird's lifespan is probably unusually long to counter for the fact that relatively few males acquire the chance to breed in any given season. Blue Manakins can survive to at least 16 years old in captivity (Low 2009: 234). A recent study by Francisco *et al.* (2009) found that leks consist of both related and unrelated males, and that close male relatives were present at only half of the leks examined, suggesting limited dispersal in this species, rather than a direct selection process.

BREEDING The nest is loosely and sometimes 'untidily' constructed of dry plant fibres, fungal rhizomorphs (*Marasmius*: Marasmiaceae) and occasionally moss, with dry leaves camouflaging the sides and hanging below the nest, further disguising its outline. It is usually placed, like those of other *Chiroxiphia*, in the low fork of a small understorey tree or shrub, and attached to the branches using plentiful spiderwebs, but plant fibres and rhizomorphs may also be used to hold the nest in place. However, GMK (pers. obs.) found a nest in January in the Augusto Ruschi (Nova Lombardia) Biological Reserve that was placed *c*.2.5m above the ground. In captivity, A. Assumpção (1985 and in Sick 1997) reported that the female manakin would test the gap in a suitable tree fork for size prior to building, by suspending herself between the branches resting her body on her tail and feet, and rotating her body. The clutch is usually two eggs, but perhaps occasionally just one (Sick 1997, Marini *et al.* 2007) and these are off-white to yellowish-white in colour with brown or reddish-brown lines and spots concentrated at the larger end (de la Peña 1989; GMK pers. obs.). Dimensions of the eggs were presented by Burmeister (1856), Euler (1900), Ihering (1900, 1902), Chubb (1910), Foster (1976) and de la Peña (1989). Concerning seasonality of nesting, Snow (2004b) noted that egg laying occurs mainly in August–February. Breeding has been noted in October/November in southeast Paraguay (Madroño *et al.* 1997b) and Short (1971) collected males in breeding condition in northeast Argentina in late September. In Brazil, males have been collected or trapped in breeding condition in Rio Grande do Sul in late September to late November and in February–April (Belton 1985, Bugoni *et al.* 2002), whilst Marini *et al.* (2007) found four nests with either eggs or young in November/December in southeast Minas Gerais, and in Rio de Janeiro and Espírito Santo birds show varying evidence of breeding condition (including brood patches) between at least July and April, indicating a longer breeding period than reported in Snow (MNRJ). In the last-mentioned state, Willis and Oniki (2002) mentioned a nest with eggs collected in mid December. Despite the Blue Manakin's abundance, there seem to be no precise data concerning either incubation or fledging periods, although Marini *et al.* (2007) found an empty (but presumably completed) nest on 11 November, which had two eggs six days later and these were still being incubated on 2 December. Nestlings were observed on 9 and 14 December, but the nest was empty (and presumed successful) on 22 December.

STATUS Unsurprisingly, given its obvious abundance in all three range states, Blue Manakin is treated as of Least Concern by BirdLife International (2004, 2008). However, density estimates appear to be generally lacking. Not only is its range relatively wide but the species is protected within numerous national parks and reserves, both privately and publicly owned, especially but far from exclusively in Brazil (see, e.g., Belton 1985, Hayes and Scharf 1995a, 1995b,

Saibene *et al.* 1996, Aleixo and Galetti 1997, Madroño *et al.* 1997a, 1997b, Parker and Goerck 1997, Chebez *et al.* 1999, Melo Júnior *et al.* 2001, Vasconcelos and Melo Júnior 2001, Bencke *et al.* 2006, Mallet-Rodrigues *et al.* 2008, Pacheco *et al.* 2008, Maciel 2009, Mallet-Rodrigues and Noronha 2009, Bodrati *et al.* 2010, Pimentel and Olmos 2011). The species is also known from a great many Important Bird Areas in southeastern Brazil (Bencke *et al.* 2006). Furthermore, Francisco *et al.* (2006) discovered that genetic diversity within isolated populations of this species appeared to remain largely intact, at least within forest fragments of a reasonable size, suggesting that fragmentation might have less effect on *C. caudata* than on some birds. Nonetheless, local extinctions have been reported, even in recent years, with, for instance, Mendonça *et al.* (2009) speculating that *C. caudata* had become extinct in the valley of the upper Rio Paraná, on the Paraná/Mato Grosso do Sul border. Furthermore, based on modelling techniques, Anciães and Peterson (2006) predicted that this species could be moderately affected by habitat modification in the face of potential climate changes.

REFERENCES Accordi and Barcellos (2006), Aleixo and Galetti (1997), Alves and Vecchi (2009), Alves *et al.* (2009), Anciães and Peterson (2006, 2009), Anciães *et al.* (2000) Anjos *et al.* (1997), Antonini and Piratelli (2005), Antonini *et al.* (2000), Assumpção (1985), Awade *et al.* (2003), Bauer and Pacheco (2000), Belton (1985), Bencke (2001), Bencke and Kindel (1999), Bencke *et al.* (2006), BirdLife International (2004, 2008), Bodrati *et al.* (2010), Boesman (2006a), Browne (2005), Bugoni *et al.* (2002), Burmeister (1856), Buzzetti (2000), Campos and Varassin (2009), Carrano and Marins (2008), Clausi (2005), Clay (1995), Cracraft (1985), Della-Flora *et al.* (2010), Dickinson *et al.* (2006), Donatelli and Ferreira (2009), Efe *et al.* (2001), Faria and Paula (2008), Faria and Rodrigues (2009), Fonseca and Antunes (2007), Foster (1976, 1981), Francisco *et al.* (2004, 2006, 2007, 2008b, 2009), Galetti and Pizo (1996), Gatto and Roper (2004), Goerck (1999), Gondim (2001), Gonzaga and Castiglioni (2001), Gonzaga *et al.* (1995), Guaraldo *et al.* (2008), Gussoni *et al.* (2005), Haffer (1985), Hansbauer *et al.* (2008, 2010), Hasui *et al.* (2009), Hayes (1995), Hayes and Scharf (1995a, 1995b), Hellmayr (1929b), Holt (1925), Ihering (1900), Krabbe (2007), Lima *et al.* (2010), Lopes *et al.* (2005), Low (2009), Maciel (2009), Madroño *et al.* (1997a, 1997b), Mallet-Rodrigues (2005), Mallet-Rodrigues and Noronha (2003, 2009), Mallet-Rodrigues *et al.* (2007, 2008), Manhães and Dias (2009), Marini and Hackett (2002), Marini *et al.* (2007), Mazar Barnett and Pearman (2001), Melo Júnior *et al.* (2001), Mendonça *et al.* (2009), Minns *et al.* (2009), Mitchell (1957), Naka *et al.* (2002), Pacheco (2001), Pacheco and Parrini (1995, 1996), Pacheco *et al.* (2008), Parker and Goerck (1997), Parrini and Pacheco (2010, 2011), de la Peña (1989), Pimentel and Olmos (2011), Pineschi (1990), Pinto (1944), Piratelli *et al.* (2010), Prum (1990a), Remold (2002), Ridgely and Tudor (1994, 2009), do Rosário (1996), Scherer-Neto and Straube (1995), Schlichting and Bispo (2009), Sclater (1888), Short (1971), Sick (1942, 1957, 1959d, 1979b, 1993, 1997), Silva-Ribeiro *et al.* (2010), Silveira *et al.* (2005), Simon (2009), Snow (1976b, 2004b), Stotz *et al.* (1996), Straube (2008a), Straube and Urben-Filho (2008), Straube *et al.* (1996), Tubelis and Tomas (2003), Vasconcelos (2008), Vasconcelos and D'Angelo Neto (2007), Vasconcelos and Melo Júnior (2001), Vasconcelos *et al.* (2002, 2005, 2009), Voss and Sander (1981), Willis (1992), Willis and Oniki (1988b, 2002).

Blue Manakin *Chiroxiphia caudata.* **Fig. 1**. Male, Boa Nova, Bahia, eastern Brazil, July (*Rafael Bessa*). **Fig. 2**. Male, Reserva Ecológica de Guapiaçu, near Cachoeiras de Macacu, Rio de Janeiro, southeast Brazil, October (*Lee Dingain*). There is almost no overlap with Blue-backed Manakin *C. pareola*, but in any case the two are easily separated in males. Identification of females will largely depend on gaining views of the tail. **Figs. 3–4**. Males displaying to a female, Puerto Bemberg, prov. Misiones, northeast Argentina, September (*Emilio White*). *Chiroxiphia* manakins possess some of the most highly developed displays of all Pipridae (see text). **Fig. 5**. Female, Guapimirim, Rio de Janeiro, southeast Brazil, August (*Rafael Bessa*).

Genus *Antilophia*: 'helmeted' manakins

This genus, long thought to be monospecific, was recently shown to comprise two species, in which both sexes of the two species possess a prominent, forward-protruding crest. The species-pair consists of the Helmeted Manakin *A. galeata*, of gallery forest in the Brazilian *Cerrado* and adjacent Paraguay and Bolivia, and the recently described Araripe Manakin *A. bokermanni*, which is endemic to a tiny area of humid foothill forest in the generally arid Brazilian northeast. Snow (1975) had already drawn attention to the possibility that *Antilophia* represented a 'primitive' form within the manakins, given that its range is centred on the geologically very old Brazilian Planalto (tableland), where a number of basal plant and animals appear to have evolved prior to the formation of lowland Amazonia (Haffer 1974).

HELMETED MANAKIN
Antilophia galeata   Plate 12

Pipra galeata **M. H. C. Lichtenstein, 1823**, *Verz. Dubl. Berlin. Mus.*: 28, São Paulo, Brazil

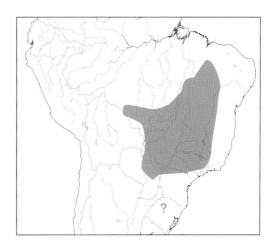

A large, spectacular manakin, which is near-endemic to interior Brazil and is probably most closely related to the *Chiroxiphia* manakins (it occasionally interbreeds with Blue Manakin *C. caudata*, producing a striking hybrid form known as the Rei-dos-tangarás, or King-of-the-Manakins), although their displays are quite different. These hybrids, apparently produced by pairs formed by male *Chiroxiphia* and female *Antilophia* (Sari *et al.* 2006), are known from southern Minas Gerais and the interior of São Paulo (Sick 1979b, Pacheco and Parrini 1995, 1996, Gussoni *et al.* 2005, Vasconcelos *et al.* 2005, Guaraldo *et al.* 2008). There are also recent records of Helmeted Manakin × Blue-backed Manakin *C. pareola* hybrids from the Chapada Diamantina, Bahia (Gatto 2005), and the Serra da Ibiapaba, Ceará, the latter involving two birds with similar but not identical plumage, which displayed alone but in the manner of *Chiroxiphia* (C. Albano *in litt.* 2009; Fig. 5). Helmeted Manakin is confined to the Campo Cerrado Centre of endemism (Cracraft 1985).

IDENTIFICATION 13.9–17.5cm. Adult males are both quite unmistakable and stunningly beautiful birds. The less-distinctive (but still easily identified) females can be recognised by their frontal crest and comparatively long tail. The only truly similar species that might be found in (parts of) the same range are female Blue (Swallow-tailed) Manakin and Greenish Schiffornis *Schiffornis virescens*. Compared with female Helmeted Manakin, the former is much deeper green, especially over the underparts, has no frontal crest and possesses a slight 'swallow' tail, whilst the *Schiffornis* is on average slightly larger, has obviously contrasting brown wing and tail feathers, strikingly pale lores and eye-ring (compared with the rest of the head), and again lacks any trace of a frontal crest. There is no overlap with the recently described Araripe Manakin *A. bokermanni* (which see), the female of which is very similar to that of the present species.

DISTRIBUTION Confined to the interior of southeastern South America, where it is practically confined to the *Cerrado* region and must be one of the most widespread *Cerrado* endemics. In Brazil it occurs from central Maranhão, southern Piauí and the southern half of Tocantins (certainly as far north as the vicinity of Palmas), in the north, and western Bahia south to the interior of São Paulo (where included on the state's Red Data list), western Paraná

(where rare), Rio Grande Sul (where known only from one site in the environs of Santa Maria in the centre of the state (Reis *et al.* 1997) but these birds were speculated to be escapes from captivity by Bencke 2001), and northern and eastern Mato Grosso do Sul. In this western portion of its range, the Helmeted Manakin ranges at least as far north as the Serra dos Parecis, in Mato Grosso (Mello *et al.* 2008). In northeastern Bolivia, it occurs solely on the Serranía de Huanchaca in northeast Santa Cruz, where it was only recently rediscovered (Bates *et al.* 1992), despite two century-old references to its occurrence in the country, a female-plumaged specimen having been collected by Clarence Buckley near Simacu (Ihering 1898, Hellmayr 1908), an untraced locality apparently in dpto. La Paz (Paynter 1992). The species is also known from northeastern Paraguay (in Concepción, Canindeyú and probably Amambay).

MOVEMENTS None known.

HABITAT Mainly found in the lower to middle strata of woodland in the tropical lowlands and foothills at 500–1,100m, in particular in gallery forests along watercourses and in larger forest 'islands' (for instance *Mauritia vinifera* [Arecaceae] 'veredas' in Brazil).

DESCRIPTION Sexes differ. Large and long-tailed, both sexes possess the erect frontal crest, which covers the bill base and nostrils, although it is less pronounced in the female. Bill has a strongly arched culmen and a well-hooked tip (less well developed, if at all, in young birds). Female is overall smaller, on average, in most measurements. *Adult male.* – Very attractive and highly distinctive; its plumage recalls a 'velvet brush'. Head (including crest) and mantle is bright crimson-red or scarlet, the feathers becoming deep yellow apically and then pure white basally, and the patch of red terminating in a point on the lower back. Rest of plumage black, with a navy-blue sheen, although this is unlikely to be evident in the field. *Adult female.* – Not as spectacular as the male, with only a suggestion of a frontal crest. Body plumage completely olive- or yellow-green, with greyer wing and tail feathers. *Juvenile.* – Closely resembles female (Snow 2004b). Probably only achieves adult plumage in third year of life. Subadult males gradually gain the black and red feathers, with the first red feathers usually appearing on the forecrown and above the eye or elsewhere on the superciliary region, whilst the first black feathers typically are the smallest tertial, or on the tail or breast. However, sometimes red feathers are evident on the mantle before any elsewhere or before any black feathers have appeared. Thereafter, the males acquire very spotty chestnut-red feathers over the mantle, whilst there are still very few on the crown, as well as a black undertail and uppertail-coverts (GMK pers. obs.). Allen (1893) recorded that of the upperparts, the greater coverts were one of the last tracts to acquire fully black feathering, with the uppertail becoming black only in the second year of life. *Moult.* – Antas (2004) reported that moult occurs mainly during the first five months of the year in the northern Pantanal (Mato Grosso). Moult data were also presented by Marini (1992b) based on fieldwork in central Brazil. He recorded body moult throughout the year, but especially between December and February, whilst the remiges were replaced between September and March, peaking in December–March, and the rectrices between December and April, reaching a peak in February. Thus moult is concentrated in the post-breeding period in this region. Although based on many fewer data, Allen (1893) recorded a similar pattern at the Chapada dos Guiramães, Mato Grosso. *Hybridisation.* – See the introduction to the species account for information and references to hybrids with Blue-backed (rare, with single records in Bahia and Ceará) and Blue Manakins (more frequent, with records from Minas Gerais and São Paulo). *Bare parts.* – Irides reddish, chestnut or dark brown, bill dark brown or bluish to almost black, sometimes with a slightly paler base, and the legs are violet or pinkish with dark ochre soles. All bare-parts colorations are generally duller in the female (MNRJ).

MEASUREMENTS (BMNH; MNRJ: Bahia, Distrito Federal, Goiás, Mato Grosso, Minas Gerais, all in Brazil; see also Hellmayr 1908, Coelho and Silva 1998 and Marini and Hackett 2002 for a wider range of measurements) Wing of male (*n* = 16) 75.0–82.5mm, wing of female (*n* = 10) 74–77mm; tail of male (*n* = 16) 60–68mm, tail of female (*n* = 10) 54.0–64.5mm; bill of male (*n* = 16) 10.86–13.13mm, bill of female (*n* = 10) 11.49–13.17mm; tarsus of male (*n* = 4) 17–19mm, tarsus of female (*n* = 4) 17–19mm. Oliveira Rodrigues *et al.* (2009) found no statistically significant differences between adult males and female-plumaged birds (i.e. adult females and young males) in wing and tarsus lengths. Weight (sexes combined): 16.0–26.5g (Sick 1958, Fry 1970, Cavalcanti and Marini 1993, Marini *et al.* 1997b, Snow 2004a, Dunning 2008; DZUFMG; MNRJ). Oliveira Rodrigues *et al.* (2009) reported mean weights of 21.1g for adult males and 21.09g for female-plumaged birds at a study site in Minas Gerais. (For a breakdown by age and sex, see Cavalcanti and Marini 1993.)

GEOGRAPHICAL VARIATION Monotypic.

VOICE An oft-repeated *wee-ur* or *wreee pur* is given in contact by either sex. The male's song is a surprisingly musical, fast and rich *whip-dip*, *wih-deh-deh-dehdidip* (Ridgely and Tudor 1994) or variants; striking and easily learnt, it has a distinctly 'rollicking' cadence, as noted by Snow (2004b) and is audible up to 100m away (Marini 1992b). A female at a nest gave several *qua* notes (Marini 1992b). In the Pantanal mainly vocal in January to April or May (Antas 2004), but will sing during other months and responds to playback at all times, whilst in central Brazil vocalisations appear to peak in July–November (Marini 1992b; GMK pers. obs.). Usually selects song perches in the midstorey, but in lower-stature vegetation will also sing from the subcanopy. Although subadult males also sing, chases between rival males are confined to adult on adult (Marini 1992b). Published recordings are available on the following compilations: Vielliard (1999), Remold (2002), Boesman (2006a) and Minns *et al.* (2009), and there are recordings from Bolivia and a great many states across the species' Brazilian range archived online at www.xeno-canto.org.

NATURAL HISTORY Usually found singly or in pairs, with 'rival' males rarely closer than within 'earshot'. Not particularly shy, although can be difficult to see in the dense foliage that often characterises its habitat.

FOOD AND FEEDING Regularly joins understorey or midstorey mixed-species foraging flocks, including those containing various tanagers, flycatchers, warblers, piculets, etc. but largely or exclusively when not breeding, and sometimes venturing out into more open savannas away from gallery forests in their company (Silva and Oniki 1988, Tubelis 2004, 2007; GMK pers. obs.). Once, in southern Piauí, reported to follow army ants with other species, including Spotted Puffbird *Bucco tamatia*, Straight-billed Woodcreeper *Xiphorhynchus picus*, Rusty-backed Spinetail *Cranioleuca vulpina*, Squirrel Cuckoo *Piaya cayana* and Grey Elaenia *Myiopagis caniceps* (Silveira *et al.* 2001). Research in central Brazil suggests that males and females select slightly different areas of the midstorey in which to forage, with females generally slightly higher than males (Ferreira and Cavalcanti 1997). Helmeted Manakin is primarily frugivorous, although arthropods are regularly taken in small quantities (see especially Marini 1992a): recorded food species and families include *Rapanea lancifolia* (Myrsinaceae), *Davilla rugosa* (Dilleniaceae), *Nectandra oppositifolia* (Lauraceae), *Miconia* spp. (Melastomataceae), as well as unknown species of Aquifoliaceae, Rubiaceae and Myrtaceae. Two more recent studies in central Brazil found *A. galeata* to take fruits of 41 species belonging to 20 families, namely Burseraceae and Rubiaceae (five species each), Chrysobalanaceae and Melastomataceae (four each), Annonaceae and Boragineae (three each), Anacardiaceae, Myrtaceae and Euphorbiaceae (two each) and Cecropiaceae, Eleaocarpaceae, Ericaeae, Flacourtiaceae, Lacistemaceae, Lauraceae, Caesalpinioideae, Meliaceae, Monimiaceae, Myrsinaceae and Ochnaceae (one each). Amongst the Lacistemaceae, Melo and Oliveira (2009) found Helmeted Manakin to be the most frequent visitor to a *Lacistema hasslerianum* tree. Most fruit is taken using a short-range sally-hover, but perch-gleaning is also used (Silva and Melo 2011).

BREEDING Interestingly, not only is this the only manakin with sexual plumage dichromatism to be found in the *Cerrado* region, it seems to be the only dichromatic manakin with a non-promiscuous mating system. This might be a consequence of reduced fruit availability within the gallery forests of the *Cerrado* allowing less time for lekking or other sexual posturing (Marini 1992b). The nest and eggs were first described by Ihering (1900, 1902), then by Marini (1992b) and a colour photograph of a female tending a nest appears in Snow (2004b: 137). Assumed to breed principally in August–December, especially September–November (based on females trapped with brood patches or eggs in the oviduct, and male testis size), and clutch size is probably always two. Specific nesting data as follows, all from central Brazil, in the Distrito Federal and Minas Gerais (Marini 1992b, Marini *et al.* 1997a): in August (*n* = 1, in construction), September (*n* = 2, one in construction, the other with two young), October (*n* = 2, nest with two eggs, the other with two young) and November (*n* = 1, with eggs). Ihering (1902) also found a nest with eggs in December. The eggs are either beige or yellowish-white with dark stripes and spots concentrated at the larger end. All of the well-described nests were similarly positioned and open-cup structures, and were sited 0.5–10.0m above the ground in a range of different species of trees and shrubs; nest dimensions and egg weights were presented by Marini (1992b) and Marini *et al.* (1997a). Nests are bowl-shaped, suspended between two twigs, constructed of small rootlets and twigs, and lined with fungal hyphae, with leaves camouflaging the outside (see photograph in Snow 2004a: 137). However, incubation and fledging periods are still unknown (Snow 2004b). Only females are assumed to undertake nesting duties, although P. T. Z. Antas (*in* Marini 1992b) observed a male following a female that was building a nest, and males regularly sing within close proximity of nests. Other breeding data are scattered and scanty. Sick (1958) found an abandoned nest of this species 2.5m above the ground on a small branch. A female collected in Bolivia in late September had an egg in the oviduct (Bates *et al.* 1992), whilst another from central Brazil taken in mid December had active ovaries (MNRJ).

STATUS Fairly common to common, being relatively easy to see in areas such as Lajeado State Park (Tocantins), Serra da Canastra National Park (Minas Gerais), Brasília National Park (Distrito Federal), Chapada dos Veadeiros National Park (Goiás), Chapada dos Guiramães National Park (Mato Grosso) and Nascentes do Rio Taquari State Park (Mato Grosso do Sul), as well as at many localities in the Pantanal (Lowen and Bernardon 2010 list some of the best), all in the interior of Brazil. Known from a large number of protected areas, virtually throughout its wide range. Has been observed flying between stands of gallery woodland (Sick 1997) and genetic testing of different populations in such fragments in the Distrito Federal and Goiás has revealed them to be heterogeneous (Ferreira *et al.* 2001a, 2001b). However, increasing fragmentation and habitat alteration is likely to compromise the species' survival at local levels in the longer term (Ferreira and Cavalcanti 2000, 2001), although it appears to persist in fragmented habitats (Marini 2001) and might even locally increase in such areas under certain circumstances (Willis 2006). Anciães and Peterson (2006) predicted that this species could be moderately to badly affected by habitat modification in the face of potential climate change based on modelling techniques. At the state level it is considered to be threatened and declining in São Paulo and the species has become locally extinct in northwest Paraná (Straube and Bornschein 1995). Males of this species can be difficult to locate at times (GG pers. obs.) and this could be related to the species' desirability as a cagebird, for which presumably showy males will be more sought after than duller females (see also Sick 1997).

REFERENCES Abreu and Mattos (2004), Aires *et al.* (2008), Allen (1893), Anciães and Peterson (2006, 2009), Antas (2004), Bates *et al.* (1992), Bencke (2001), Berg and Abreu (2004), BirdLife International (2004, 2008), Boesman (2006a), Braz and Cavalcanti (2001), Cavalcanti and Marini (1993), Coelho and Silva (1998), Cracraft (1985), Diniz *et al.* (2009), Donatelli and Ferreira (2009), Dunning (2008), Ferreira and Cavalcanti (1997, 2000, 2001), Ferreira *et al.* (2001a, 2001b, 2009), Franchin and Marçal Júnior (2003), Franchin *et al.* (2001, 2007, 2009), Francisco and Galetti (2001, 2002), Fry (1970), Gatto (2005), Guaraldo *et al.* (2008), Guimarães *et al.* (2009), Gussoni *et al.* (2005), Hass *et al.* (2001), Hellmayr (1908, 1929a, 1929b), Hidasi (1998, 2007), Ihering (1898, 1900, 1902), Krabbe (2007), Laranjeiras *et al.* (2004), Lima *et al.* (2010), Lopes and Braz (2007), Lopes *et al.* (2005, 2008, 2009), Lowen and Bernardon (2010), Marçal Júnior *et al.* (2004), Marini (1992a, 1992b), Marini *et al.* (1997a, 1997b, 2001), Marini and Hackett (2002), McKay *et al.* (2010), Mello *et al.* (2008), Melo and Oliveira (2009), Melo Júnior *et al.* (2001), Mendonça-Lima and Fontana (2000), Minns *et al.* (2009), Oliveira *et al.* (2003), Oliveira Rodrigues *et al.* (2009), Pacheco and Olmos (2006, 2010), Pacheco and Parrini (1995, 1996), Paynter (1992), Pina *et al.* (2005), Pinho and Marini (2005), Pinto (1944), Posso *et al.* (2009), Pozza (2002), Prado *et al.* (2005), Ramos *et al.* (2003), Reis *et al.* (1997), Remold (2002), Ridgely and Tudor (1994, 2009), Sari *et al.* (2006), Sick (1958, 1979b, 1997), Silva and Melo (2011), Silva and Oniki (1988), Silveira (1998), Silveira *et al.* (2001), Snow (2004b), Stotz *et al.* (1996), Straube and Bornschein (1995), Tubelis (2004, 2007), Tubelis and Tomas (2003), Ubaid *et al.* (2005), Valle and Silva (2003), Vasconcelos and D'Angelo Neto (2007), Vasconcelos *et al.* (2002, 2005), Vasques *et al.* (2001), Vielliard (1999), Willis (2006), Willis and Oniki (1990).

1

Helmeted Manakin *Antilophia galeata*. **Fig. 1**. Male, Transpantaneira, Pantanal, southern Mato Grosso, Brazil, September (*James Lowen / www. pbase/james_lowen*). One of the most easily identified manakins. **Figs. 2–3**. Male, Brasília, Distrito Federal, central Brazil, July (*Ciro Albano*). **Fig. 4**. Female, Serra da Canastra National Park, Minas Gerais, southeast Brazil, July (*Rafael Bessa*). Females too are highly distinctive due to their comparatively large size, long tail and distinct forehead 'tuft'. **Fig. 5**. Hybrid with Blue-backed Manakin *Chiroxiphia pareola*, Tianguá, Serra da Ibiapaba, Ceará, northeast Brazil, December (*Ciro Albano*). Hybrids, known as the 'King of the Manakins' (rei-dos-tangarás), between Helmeted Manakin and Blue Manakin *Chiroxiphia caudata* are quite well known, but have only been recorded twice between Helmeted and Blue-backed Manakins (see text).

ARARIPE MANAKIN
Antilophia bokermanni   **Plate 12**

Antilophia bokermanni **Coelho and Girão e Silva, 1998**, *Ararajuba* 6: 81, Nascente do Farias, Chapada do Araripe, Arajara district, Barbalha municipality, Ceará, Brazil

The revelation of the Araripe Manakin in the mid 1990s represented just one in a series of amazing discoveries (and equally dramatic rediscoveries) in Brazil during that decade, although the possibility of a hybrid origin for such a morphologically unique manakin had to be eliminated prior to publication. The discovery also made the ornithological news because the new species' scientific name was published in a Recife newspaper, the *Jornal do Commercio* (along with photographs of collected birds), on 15 June 1997, well before the formal description had appeared in the Brazilian journal *Ararajuba*. The manakin was discovered literally during the final moments of an excursion to the Chapada do Araripe from the Federal University of Pernambuco in December 1996, and is named for the Brazilian zoologist Werner Carlos Augusto Bokermann, who died in 1995. Although the species' date of publication is given as 1998, there is some doubt concerning the dates of publication of many of the earlier issues of the journal *Ararajuba* (Kirwan and Pacheco in press). However, without definitive proof that the relevant issue was published in 1999, the year 1998 must stand.

IDENTIFICATION 13.9–16.5cm. A large, long-tailed manakin with a frontal crest, the male Araripe Manakin is startlingly distinctive due to its mainly white plumage (not unknown amongst cotingas, but unique within the manakins). The female has no similar confusion species within the range, and the frontal crest is easy to see in both species' of *Antilophia*. Hybrid origin can be discounted because the only vaguely close relative of *A. bokermanni* in this region is the Pale-bellied Tyrant-Manakin *Neopelma pallescens*, which is totally different morphologically. Furthermore, Helmeted Manakin *A. galeata* is unknown to occur closer to the Chapada do Araripe than central west Piauí.

DISTRIBUTION Endemic to a region of 28km² on the north flank of the Chapada do Araripe, in southern Ceará, northeast Brazil, where it is found at just a few localities,

in the municipalities of Barbalha, Crato and Missão Velha, on the slopes of this range, being entirely absent from the plateau on its top, whereon there is a government-protected area (the Araripe-Apodi National Forest, of 39,262ha, created in 1946). Those studying the bird have speculated that the species' range was formerly more widespread across the Cariri Valley, but has been restricted to the slopes of the Chapada as a result of agricultural expansion decimating habitat for the manakin. This immaculate bird is also confined to the Caatinga Centre of endemism (Cracraft 1985).

MOVEMENTS Resident and sedentary.

HABITAT Restricted to primary and secondary humid foothill forest on the slopes of the Chapada do Araripe, at *c*.800m, where Araripe Manakin shows a strong preference for valleys with small streams or springs.

DESCRIPTION Sexes differ. The bill has a well-arched culmen and slightly hooked tip in both sexes. The bushy crest extends forward slightly beyond the tip of the bill. *Adult male.* – Principally gleaming white over the body, face, throat and entire underparts, and rump and uppertail-coverts, relieved only by the brilliant carmine-red frontal crest (erected shield-like and the forehead feathers pointing slightly forward over the bill) that extends over the crown, the nape and much of the mantle, where it narrows almost to a point (exactly as in Helmeted Manakin), as well as the glistening black tail (often extensively obscured by the long white uppertail-coverts) and flight feathers. The wing-coverts are frequently obscured by the somewhat long white scapulars, but have black inner webs to at least some of the feathers. The wing bend, and undertail- and underwing-coverts are white, whilst the underside of the flight feathers is black, but these feathers have somewhat greyish webs and bases. *Adult female.* – Fundamentally very similar to the same sex of Helmeted Manakin, although the underparts are on average paler and distinctly greyer, especially over the chin, throat, ear-coverts, belly and undertail-coverts. As with the previous species, the upperparts are principally greenish-olive, whilst the belly is greyish-olive, the wings brownish-olive with slightly greyer fringes, and the tail brownish-olive with greener fringes. *Juvenile.* – Undescribed but unlikely to differ from that of its sister species. The nestling was illustrated (photographically) in a popular article (Ribeiro 2009). *Immature.* – Young males appear to develop patchy white feathers on the breast and elements of the (initially yellow-orange) red crest and mantle in much the same way as do individuals of the same sex in Helmeted Manakin (GMK pers. obs.; see also Fig. 6 in Albano and Girão 2009). The colour of the crest seems to be gained first, at least in some birds (Azevedo Júnior *et al.* 2000). *Moult.* – There are very few published moult data, but two adult females trapped in late July were not renewing any of the feathers (Azevedo Júnior *et al.* 2000). Two birds were replacing their head feathers in July and two in late December were renewing their wing and tail feathers (W. Girão *et al.* unpubl.). *Bare parts.* – Both sexes have the irides russet or brown (the latter in young), the bill generally dark (cinnamon-brown to blackish) and the legs and feet are dusky to blackish-brown.

MEASUREMENTS (taken from Coelho and Silva 1998, Azevedo Júnior *et al.* 2000; W. Girão *et al.* unpubl.) Wing of male (*n* = 21) 73–80mm, wing of female (*n* = 5) 73–79mm, unsexed (*n* = 14) 72–78mm; tail of male (*n* = 21) 58–70mm, tail of female (*n* = 5) 59–65mm, unsexed (*n* = 14) 60.0–

69.5mm; bill of male (*n* = 1) 13.3mm (*n* = 16, to nostrils) 6.9–8.5mm, bill of female (*n* = 1) 13.6mm (*n* = 2, to nostrils) 7.8–8.2mm, unsexed (*n* = 10) 7.4–8.85mm; tarsus of male (*n* = 3) 18.0–18.8mm, tarsus of female (*n* = 3) 18.6–19.6mm. Weight (sexes and ages combined): 19–23g (Azevedo Júnior *et al.* 2000, Snow 2004b, Dunning 2008).

GEOGRAPHICAL VARIATION Monotypic. A recently published genetic study (Rêgo *et al.* 2010) found evidence to suggest that the two species of *Antilophia* manakins have only diverged comparatively recently, and that the genetic variability of Araripe Manakin is only slightly less than that within Helmeted Manakin.

VOICE The male advertisement is similar to that of *A. galeata*, but with a distinct difference in the cadence of the first three notes (rising in *galeata*, falling in *bokermanni*), and rendered *guru-ui*; this voice is given by both adult and young (non-white) males. Both sexes utter a throaty *wreee pur*, the first note ascending, very similar to the corresponding vocalisation of Helmeted Manakin (which see for further details). Easily attracted using playback, but given the extreme rarity of this species, such use should be minimised. In any case, the bird is easily seen without recourse to broadcasting its song. Published recordings are only available on the recently published compilations of Boesman (2006) and Minns *et al.* (2009) but are also available online at www.xeno-canto.org.

NATURAL HISTORY Detailed studies are in progress, but considered to be generally similar to those of its commoner congener. Generally found in pairs in the forest under- to midstorey, at or near the forest edge, as well as in bushes within adjacent clearings; several females and young males can occur in close proximity (GMK pers. obs.).

FOOD AND FEEDING Recorded feeding on the fruits of *Cordia* spp. (Boraginaceae) and a *Cecropia* sp. (Coelho and Silva 1998, Azevedo Júnior *et al.* 2000). Ribeiro (2009) stated that the species takes principally small fruits, but that the diet is supplemented during the dry periods of the year, when fruit productivity is lower, with arthropods. It is possible that, as is suspected in Helmeted Manakin, females might be more reliant on the extra protein offered by insect prey during the breeding season.

BREEDING As with other manakins, males take no part in the nesting duties but remain on and defend a territory, selecting a single female to mate with (Ribeiro 2009). Display not yet formally described in the literature, but Albano and Girão (2009) depict a displaying male raising the wings almost vertically and the tail less prominently while on a song perch, as well as illustrating copulation. Nest and eggs undescribed in the technical literature, but two females had the early signs of brood patches in July (Azevedo Júnior *et al.* 2000), and four other females had brood patches in late December (W. Girão *et al.* unpubl.). The nest, eggs and nestlings were recently depicted in two popular articles (Ribeiro 2009, Albano and Girão 2009), in the first of which it was mentioned that the female alone is responsible for nest building, placing the nest within the three-way fork of an understorey tree and usually in close proximity to water. The detailed study of Linhares *et al.* (2010), which found a total of 28 nests, revealed that at least 11 different plant species belonging to eight families were selected, Melastomataceae, Rubiaceae and Piperaceae being the commonest. These nest support plants were also used by the manakins to feed. From the photographs presented in the articles mentioned above and our own observations (GMK pers. obs.), the open-cup nest appears to be comparatively deep, principally constructed of small dry twigs and dark rootlets, with some dead leaves at least on the outside of the nest, presumably to aid its 'disguise. The nest is strongly attached to the branches of the tree fork with many spiderwebs in multiple places. Nests are typically sited within 2m of the ground, but have been rarely recorded up to 5m above the ground (Linhares *et al.* 2010). In general two eggs (which appear whitish with reddish-brown blotches and more linear markings concentrated in a ring towards the larger end) are apparently laid and the eggs hatch in three weeks, with the young leaving the nest following a further three weeks. In the same article by Ribeiro, the breeding season was stated to be November–March, coinciding with the wet season in this region (leading to some variation in accordance with the rains: Albano and Girão 2009). Earlier, based on vocal activity, Girão and Souto (2004) suggested that breeding might commence in August, reach a peak in September/October, and continue until February, thereby overlapping to some degree with the main rainfall and fruiting seasons for trees in the region. This is further supported by the fact the holotype, collected in mid May, had only small testes.

STATUS Critically Endangered both globally and nationally (BirdLife International 2000, 2004, 2008) and highly range-restricted, this species' population had been suggested to number as few as 50–249 individuals, but surveys in 2005–2006 revealed perhaps as many as 800 birds (*World Birdwatch* 30(2): 22; Albano and Girão 2009). Rêgo *et al.*'s (2005) molecular study uncovered low genetic diversity in the species' population and suggested that it had recently passed through a reduction in its numbers. The *c.*11 or more specific localities (e.g. Nascente do Sítio Melo, Barbalha, and Nascente da AABEC, Crato) are nearly all threatened by agricultural development, selective logging and the construction of small dams. Linhares *et al.* (2010) specifically reported the removal of woody plants along watercourses by humans as an important threat to the Araripe Manakin's survival. Fortunately, local farmers are now more interested in habitat recovery, especially around springs (Langley 2010). Lowland forest below the known range of the Araripe Manakin has almost entirely been destroyed due to rapid development of the surrounding area, for farming and housing developments. Nonetheless, the type locality, the Nascente do Farias, Barbalha, which has since been converted to a theme park and a privately owned conservation unit (Park Arajara, 27.81 ha; www. arajarapark.com.br), still harbours the species (and is arguably still the best site for it), demonstrating that Araripe Manakin might prove resilient to some degree of habitat change and modification. The Chapada do Araripe was identified as a Key Area (Wege and Long 1995) and thereafter an Important Bird Area (Bencke *et al.* 2006), but the only government protected area within the region (the Floresta Nacional do Araripe-Apodi) lacks the legal basis to prevent future exploitation and, in any case, does not cover the habitat occupied by the manakin (Coelho and Silva 1998). However, more recently, in addition to Park Arajara, the 1,000,000ha APA da Chapada do Araripe has been established, and at least four other conservation areas, including the RPPN da Fazenda Serra do Mato, in Missão Velho, are in the process of being created (cf. Langley 2010). A conservation action plan for the species was drawn up in 2006 (and more recently updated), which aims (among other things) to combat habitat fragmentation by promoting the recuperation of marginal areas that are currently somewhat degraded. The manakin (known locally as the 'soldadinho-do-Araripe' or 'língua-de-tamanduá', the latter because of the species' vocalisation) has been successfully used as a symbol for the region's conservation by the organisations SAVE Brasil (the BirdLife partner in Brazil) and the Associação de Pesquisa e Preservação de Ecossistemas Aquáticos (Aquasis; www.aquasis.org), and was adopted as the municipal symbol in the town of Barbalha in June 2009. Aquasis has established a local birdwatching club (Langley 2010) and has been responsible for producing a DVD entitled *Língua de tamanduá: a verdadeira historia do soldadinho do Araripe*, which tells the story of this remarkable bird and is especially aimed at young people and schoolchildren. The manakin even featured on an item of woman's clothing in a collection featured as part of Vogue Fashion's Night Out, in September 2009, which ran simultaneously in 14 cities around the world, including São Paulo (www.birdlife.org/news/news/2009/09/araripe_mannequin.html). Local people

have been successfully drawn into the project to conserve the manakin, including José Cirilo Barbosa, who for seven years has been monitoring and protecting the species' nests (Ribeiro 2009). As of 2010, Aquasis was also involved in creating a database of the 130 or so springs within the manakin's range and is organising a survey of these localities to more accurately establish relative presence and absence (Langley 2010). The bird has also given its name to a local award, whose recipients have contributed significantly to nature conservation. *Antilophia bokermanni* is considered to be most easily seen in July–November, with September being the best month to find the species (Ribeiro 2009).

REFERENCES Albano (2010), Albano and Girão (2009), Azevedo Júnior *et al.* (2000), Bencke *et al.* (2006), BirdLife International (2000, 2004, 2008), Boesman (2006), Coelho and Silva (1998), Cracraft (1985), Dunning (2008), Girão and Souto (2004), Kirwan and Pacheco (in press), Langley (2010), Linhares *et al.* (2010), Minns *et al.* (2009), Rêgo *et al.* (2005, 2010), Ribeiro (2009), Ridgely and Tudor (2009), Snow (2004b), Wege and Long (1995).

Araripe Manakin *Antilophia bokermanni*. All photographs taken at Arajara, Chapada do Araripe, Ceará, northeast Brazil. **Fig. 1**. Male, December (*Pete Morris*). **Fig. 2**. Male, July (*Rafael Bessa*). **Fig. 3**. Singing male, January (*Ciro Albano*). **Fig. 4**. Female, July (*Rafael Bessa*). **Fig. 5**. Female on nest, January (*Ciro Albano*). One of the most remarkable avian discoveries in the Neotropics in recent decades was this fantastic manakin. Sadly, it is ranked as being Critically Endangered, with a small population confined to the lower, largely denuded slopes of a single massif in northeast Brazil.

FAMILY OXYRUNCIDAE

Genus *Oxyruncus*: Sharpbill

Of all those Neotropical birds that have been described as enigmatic this surely is the one to which the adjective is most appropriately applied. The problems of the Sharpbill's classification within the suboscine passerines are almost legion and have baffled ornithologists for as long as the species has been known to scientists (see below), but its natural history and range are also sufficiently poorly known as to attract the status of enigma.

SHARPBILL
Oxyruncus cristatus   Plate 15

Oxyrhynchus [*sic*] *cristatus* **Swainson, 1821**, *Zool. Illus.* 1(9): pl. 49, Brazil [Rio de Janeiro, suggested by Pinto (1944)]

If any species exemplifies the notion that the 'cotingas' represent an assemblage of unrelated taxa derived from the Tyrannidae, then it must be the Sharpbill *O. cristatus*. Frequently placed in its own monotypic family (Oxyruncidae) and still relatively little known, the Sharpbill with its unique pointed bill, concealed crown patch (shared with some true cotingas) and modified outermost primary might seem better suited to placement within the tyrant flycatchers (to where it was removed by Lanyon 1985). At least for the purposes of this compendium, we have decided to remove *Oxyruncus* to its own family, rather than retaining it within the Cotingidae (as did Sibley *et al.* 1984, Prum 1990b) based on its general structure, singing behaviour (possibly at an exploded lek) and because the young are fed by regurgitation (although not all cotingas do so), unlike the Tyrannidae. The AOU also maintains a separate family for the species (AOU 1998, Remsen *et al.* 2009).

IDENTIFICATION 15–19cm. In Amazonia this uniquely plumaged bird is perhaps most likely to be confused with one of the spotted, green-plumaged *Tangara* tanagers, e.g. Spotted *T. punctata* or Speckled Tanagers *T. guttata*; the quite long and definitely pointed, never blunt-looking bill, orange eyes, crest (if seen; it is usually only raised during agonistic encounters with its own or other species) and spotted underparts are the best features. Sharpbill is also an upright-perching bird, not horizontal as in these tanagers. In southeast Brazil, and elsewhere, it might initially be confused with a female or immature male bellbird *Procnias* sp., but the latter are always much larger and bulkier than the lean-looking (only slightly plump) *Oxyruncus*, and they possess a heavier bill, streaked, rather than spotted, underparts, a darker head and no crest, amongst many other separating features.

DISTRIBUTION Widespread, but nearly always local and the species' range is extremely disjunct. The Sharpbill occurs from southern Central America, on the Caribbean slope of Costa Rica (from the Cordillera de Guanacaste) and western Panama to Bocas del Toro and Veraguas, in which country it reappears on the slopes of several mountains in the Darién (e.g. on the Cerro Pirre). Records in the western third of Panama seem to be very few, especially in recent decades, and an old specimen labelled as being from Chiriquí is variously disputed (Wetmore 1972) or accepted (Ridgely and Gwynne 1989, Angehr and Dean 2010). Thereafter, it occurs extremely patchily over western South America,

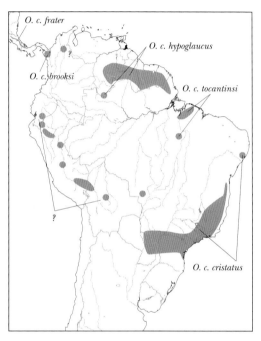

O. c. frater

O. c. hypoglaucus

O. c. brooksi

O. c. tocantinsi

O. c. cristatus

most continuously in the north and east. Only recently confirmed to occur in Colombia, from a bird trapped at 1,300m in the Serranía de San Lucas, dpto. Bolívar, at the north end of the Central Andes, in 2001 (Salaman *et al.* 2002a, Alvarez *et al.* 2007), and a bird collected nearby at San Gertrudis, in Antioquia, at 1,475m, in 2002 (Cuervo *et al.* 2008a), although its occurrence had long been suspected in Colombia's Darién (Hilty and Brown 1986). In Ecuador it is known solely from the lower slopes of the Cordillera del Cóndor, in southeast prov. Zamora-Chinchipe, in the extreme south of the country (Balchin and Toyne 1998, Ridgely and Greenfield 2001, Boyla and Estrada 2005), and in Peru it is restricted to a relatively small number of outlying ridges on the east slope of the Andes, in dptos. San Martín/Amazonas, e.g. above Jesús del Monte and in the Cordillera Azul, the southern Cerros del Sira, and disjunctly in dptos. Junín, Cuzco and Puno (Davis 1986, Parker and Wust 1994, Alverson *et al.* 2001, Schulenberg *et al.* 2007, Merkord *et al.* 2009, , Harvey *et al.* 2011). Further south, in Bolivia it was recently discovered southwest of Apolo (Parker *et al.* 1991), at the Río Tuichi (Perry *et al.* 1997), and commonly to 700m in the Serranía Sadiri, all in dpto. Paz (Hosner *et al.* 2009). In the northeast of the continent, the Sharpbill is restricted to southern Venezuela in dptos. Bolívar and Amazonas (Hilty 2003), and is also known from a very few localities in the Guianas, e.g. just five highland sites in Surinam and the species was only discovered in French Guiana as recently as 1984, where it is now known from six localities (Mees 1974, Davis 1979, Tostain *et al.* 1992, Claessens 1997, Ottema *et al.* 2009, Zyskowski *et al.* 2011). From there, it occurs patchily southwards through east Amazonian Brazil, north of the Amazon in Roraima, northernmost Pará (Aleixo *et al.* 2011) and Amapá, and south of that river in south-central Pará (e.g. in the Serra dos Carajás) and extreme northern Tocantins (Hidasi 1998). Discovered recently in the remnant hill forests of Murici, Alagoas, in northeast Brazil (Teixeira *et al.* 1986), it probably also occurs in the Pedra Talhada Biological Reserve in the same state, as it was recently discovered in adjoining Pernambuco, as well as at Usina Serra Grande, also in the latter state (Pereira *et al.* 2008). The main range is centred on the southern Atlantic Forest of Brazil, south from southern Goiás, Minas Gerais and southern Bahia (e.g. at Boa Nova, and Camacã) to Santa Catarina, and perhaps even northernmost Rio Grande do Sul, from where well-documented reports are still lacking (Bencke 2001, Mazar Barnett *et al.* 2004a), as well as in easternmost Paraguay and northeasternmost Argentina (where the species is restricted to Iguazú National Park and another nearby locality, and was first found as recently as 1986/87: Finch 1991, Ridgely and Tudor 1994, Bodrati and Cockle 2006a). The species also occurs on at least some of the larger but close inshore islands, e.g. Ilha Grande, off eastern Brazil (Marsden *et al.* 2003, Alves and Vecchi 2009), as well as at various localities within the city limits of Rio de Janeiro (Maciel 2009). Further afield, it was reported from the Serra das Araras, in south-central Mato Grosso, by Willis and Oniki (1990). Published altitudinal information is as follows. In Venezuela the Sharpbill is found at 500–1,800m (Hilty 2003), in Panama at 750–1,500m (Angehr and Dean 2010), in Costa Rica and Ecuador to 1,400m (Stiles and Skutch 1989; MECN), in Peru at 750–1,750m (Schulenberg *et al.* 2007), in Bolivia to 1,600m, and elsewhere, to *c.*800m in east Amazonian Brazil (in the Serra dos Carajás: Pacheco *et al.* 2007), and to at least 1,300m in the Serra do Mar of southeast Brazil (Brooke *et al.* 1983; GMK pers. obs.). In the last-named region it ranges down to sea level at least in the non-breeding season, e.g. at Ubatuba, and on Ilha Comprida, both in the state of São Paulo (GMK pers. obs.).

MOVEMENTS Probably resident in many parts of its range, but at least in the Atlantic Forest of southeast Brazil, and in Costa Rica, it seems likely that Sharpbills move to lower altitudes during the non-breeding season (see also above). Silva (1993) postulated that the *O. cristatus* population in the Serra dos Carajás, Pará, migrates altitudinally, moving to the lower Amazon (e.g. at Belém) in the non-breeding season, based on his lack of records from the highlands outside the period July–December. Further data are required to adequately prove or disprove this theory, as there are records of Sharpbill from the Serra dos Carajás until at least early February (GMK unpubl.). However, there are few, if any, concrete published data on this phenomenon from anywhere in the species' range (cf. Stiles and Skutch 1989) and this would make a useful (but difficult) future research project.

HABITAT Sharpbill prefers humid and wet forests throughout its range, being most often found in tall *terra firme* in Amazonia, but is regularly recorded at man-made edges and in the Atlantic Forest will even visit clearings, old coffee plantations and other secondary situations

(GMK pers. obs.). Sometimes found in stunted forest on sandy soil (Davis 1986, Parker *et al.* 1991) and the species has been reported once from mixed *Araucaria* forest in southern Brazil (Mazar Barnett *et al.* 2004a). In Colombia, the species has been recorded at two sites in premontane forest, below the cloud belt, where it occurs in forest edge and forest habitats at 1,300–1,400m.

DESCRIPTION Sturdy, with a comparatively short, square-ended tail (consisting of ten rectrices), a rather plump body, a small head and a sharply pointed, conical bill. The legs are relatively short. Outermost primary (p10) modified in males (possesses hooked barbs) and recalls that of many flycatchers. Reasonably well-developed rictal bristles (*c.*5mm). *Adult.* – The crown is black admixed olive-green (creating a spotted or barred effect). The scarlet-red erectile crest (traditionally considered to be brighter in males, more orange-coloured in females, but Restall *et al.* (2006) found no evidence for this in Venezuelan specimens), and bordered by black, is normally flattened and invisible under normal viewing conditions (except in agonistic behaviour, e.g. when mobbing a perceived owl with other birds, or in confrontations with members of the same species). Head and neck mainly whitish covered with narrow black crescents. The upperparts are bright olive with pale yellowish-olive fringes to the median and greater coverts, which form indistinct wingbars. Secondaries olive-green with broad yellow fringes to the tertials. Primaries blackish, the outermost having a serrated outer web in the male (see above), and the square-ended rectrices are blackish with olive webs. Face and throat whitish-grey with black scales and spots. Rest of underparts yellowish (nominate *cristatus*) or whitish (see Geographical Variation), heavily marked with black spots and scallops, these becoming chevron-shaped on the undertail-coverts. *Immature.* – Following is based on a single female taken in northern Costa Rica (*O .c. frater*). Reddish feathering on the head is restricted to the rear crown, whilst rest of crown is covered by dark brown crescentic markings. However, rest of plumage is much as adult, although the underparts markings are perhaps slightly less blackish and less extensive. *Juvenile.* – Apparently differs solely in lacking any red on the crown, or this is heavily reduced, as well as having less heavy black markings below, and brighter and broader wingbars (Wetmore 1972, Stiles and Skutch 1989). Also has white spots on the longer tail-coverts, white tail tips, and more prominent white markings on the forehead and head-sides (Restall *et al.* 2006). Immediately after leaving the nest on fledging, the two chicks in Costa Rica (see below) had the appearance of a pale eye-ring with a slightly droop-shaped rear border, whilst the underparts and mantle were both paler than in adult plumage (Camacho *et al.* 2010). The nestling was briefly described in Brooke *et al.* (1983), and Ortega (2008) published photographs of downy young and chicks close to fledging. Note that the downy young are apparently dark yellow in southeast Brazil, but white in Costa Rica, with a shorter, slightly pink-toned bill that had a dark tip (Brooke *et al.* 1983, Ortega 2008, Camacho *et al.* 2010). Some details of chick development were presented by Camacho *et al.* (2010). *Moult.* – No published moult data, but two specimens from southeast Brazil were renewing the body, head and tail feathers, and wing-coverts in April, and some body feathers in May (MNRJ). A male collected in southeast Brazil in March was completing wing moult (Willis and Oniki 2002). Of those collected in southeast Ecuador, one from November is not moulting, but the two individuals taken in late January are moulting the body and wing feathers, respectively (MECN). *Bare parts.* – Irides generally red to creamy yellow (often redder in males, but once described as bright white, and occasionally brown or greyish-brown in females, and buff in immatures), bill plumbeous to black over the maxilla with a greyer lower mandible (sometimes paler flesh or pinkish-grey at the base), and the legs and feet are grey (described as being blue-grey in single Ecuadorian and Peruvian specimens, and pale bluish-slate in some Paraguayan specimens) with ochre soles (cf. Davis 1986) or plumbeous soles in immatures (MNCR 24429).

MEASUREMENTS *O. c. cristatus* (BMNH; CUMZ; FMNH; MNRJ; RMNH: Espírito Santo and Rio de Janeiro, southeast Brazil; and Paraguay): wing of male (*n* = 24) 89.5–99.0mm, wing of female (*n* = 21) 90.0–98.5mm; tail of male (*n* = 23) 59–73mm, tail of female (*n* = 21) 59.0–67.5mm; bill of male (*n* = 24) 14.31–18.82mm, bill of female (*n* = 21) 12.30–18.86mm; tarsus of male (*n* = 6) 20.67–22.93mm, tarsus of female (*n* = 5) 20.46–23.92mm. *O. c. frater* (BMNH; FMNH; Wetmore 1972: Costa Rica and western Panama): wing of male (*n* = 11) 88.5–97.0mm, wing of female (*n* = 9) 88.5–93.0mm; tail of male (*n* = 11) 53.5–59.0mm, tail of female (*n* = 9) 51.5–56.5mm; bill of male (*n* = 11) 16.8–19.5mm, bill of female (*n* = 9) 17.60–19.72mm; tarsus of male (*n* = 7) 18.7–20.4mm, tarsus of female (*n* = 5) 19.6–20.6mm. *O. c. brooksi* (Wetmore 1972: eastern Panama; see also Wetmore 1929b for mensural data): wing of male (*n* = 3) 90.0–93.5mm, wing of female (*n* = 2) 86.5–88.5mm; tail of male (*n* = 3) 55.0–59.5mm, tail of female (*n* = 2) 54.5–57.5mm; bill of male (*n* = 3) 16.1–17.6mm, bill of female (*n* = 1) 18.2mm; tarsus of male (*n* = 3) 18.8–20.6mm, tarsus of female (*n* = 2) 19.0–19.8mm. *O. c. phelpsi* (FMNH: Venezuela, Guyana): wing of male (*n* = 1) 88mm, wing of female (3) 90–93mm; tail of male (*n* = 1) 58mm, tail of female (*n* = 3) 60–63mm; bill of male (*n* = 1) 13.29mm, bill of female (*n* = 3) 13.20–13.31mm; tarsus of male (*n* = 1) 24.13mm, tarsus of female (*n* = 3) 20.36–21.64mm. *O. c. hypoglaucus* (Novaes 1978, Silva 1993; BMNH; RMNH: Guyana, Surinam and Brazil): wing of both sexes combined (*n* = 22) 83–94mm; tail of both sexes combined (*n* = 22) 56.0–64.5mm; bill of both sexes combined (*n* = 20) 16.0–20.5mm; tarsus of both sexes combined (*n* = 17) 16.5–20.19mm. *O. c. tocantinsi* (Silva 1993; FMNH: Goiás, Brazil): wing of both sexes combined (*n* = 6) 85.5–90.0mm; tail of both sexes combined (*n* = 6) 55.5–60.0mm; bill of both sexes combined (*n* = 6) 13.03–18.0mm; tarsus of both sexes combined (*n* = 5) 15.5–18.0mm. *Subspecies unknown* (Ecuador): wing of male (*n* = 3) 90.0–92.5mm; tail of male (*n* = 3) 56–63mm; bill of male (*n* = 3) 16.3–17.7mm (MECN); and Colombia: wing of male (*n* = 1, live bird) 94mm, wing of female (*n* = 1, specimen, ICN) 88mm; tail of male (*n* = 1) 53mm, tail of female (*n* = 1) 57mm; bill of male (*n* = 1) 17.3mm, bill of female (*n* = 1) 17.5mm; tarsus of male (*n* = 1) 18mm, tarsus of female (*n* = 1) 19.5mm (T. M. Donegan). Weight (sexes and races combined): 34–60g (Phelps 1973, Robbins *et al.* 1985, Davis 1986, Dickerman and Phelps 1982, Stiles and Skutch 1989, Hilty 2003, Snow 2004a, Dunning 2008; T. M. Donegan *in litt.* 2010; DZUFMG; ICN; MECN; MNCR; MNRJ; RMNH).

GEOGRAPHICAL VARIATION There is some variation in the intensity of the yellow on the underparts between the races. For instance, *O. c. frater* is a paler yellow below than nominate *cristatus*, whereas in *O. c. brooksi* the yellowish-white hue is restricted (being almost absent on the neck) and reduced on the breast; *O. c. hypoglaucus*, *O. c. phelpsi*

and *O. c. tocantinsi* are whiter below, lacking the yellowish wash, but not all of these populations seem very distinct. For instance, *phelpsi* and *hypoglaucus* are obviously very similar, and the purportedly more extensively whitish underparts of the former were regarded as being an artefact of specimen preparation by Dickerman and Phelps (1982). Furthermore, *O. c. tocantinsi*, which was described as being slightly smaller, with the ground colour of the underparts paler, and the breast spotting less pronounced and rounder, was regarded as a synonym of *hypoglaucus* by both Mees (1974) and Silva (1993). Populations in northern Colombia (speculated to involve *brooksi*: Alvarez *et al.* 2007, or 'tacarcunae' [a *nomen nudum*]: Salaman *et al.* 2008; the latter authors also suggest that the race *phelpsi* might occur in eastern Colombia; see Donegan *et al.* 2009, for further discussion of subspecies in this country), southeast Ecuador (measurements presented above), eastern Peru, northwest Bolivia, and southern (southeast Mato Grosso do Sul and southern Mato Grosso) and northeast Brazil (in Pernambuco, Alagoas and southern Bahia) (all of which are generally poorly known) have not been definitively assigned to subspecies, and may well represent undescribed taxa (cf. also Cuervo *et al.* 2008a, Donegan *et al.* 2009).

The ranges and diagnoses of the described taxa are as follows: *O. c. frater* (P. L. Sclater & Salvin, 1868) occurs in Costa Rica and western Panama east, perhaps discontinuously, as far as Veraguas. Compared with the nominate, it differs in having much brighter (fresher) green upperparts, relieved by rather broader yellow fringes to the wing-coverts and tertials. *O. c. brooksi* Bangs & Barbour, 1922, is probably restricted to eastern Panama and perhaps north-central Colombia. Unsurprisingly, it is similar to the previous subspecies, but this subspecies has largely white underparts (inclining to yellow only on the flanks and undertail-coverts) with fewer black spots, and differs from *O. c. hypoglaucus* in having broader fringes to the wing-coverts and tertials, and brighter, more yellowish-green upperparts. Snow (2004a), but not Dickinson (2003), continued to uphold *O. c. phelpsi* Chapman, 1939, which is found in the mountains of southern and eastern Venezuela (in northern and southern Amazonas, and more commonly in southeast Bolívar), and adjacent northernmost Brazil (on the Serra Urutaní, in Roraima) and southern Guyana (in the Acari Mountains). However, we concur with the well-supported rationale put forward by Mees (1974) and Dickerman and Phelps (1982) for subsuming *phelpsi* within the next subspecies. The latter authors did find evidence to suggest that those Sharpbills on the Gran Sabana have longer bills than those from elsewhere in the Venezuelan Pantepui (to nostrils, 10.4–11.7mm vs. 11.3–13.1mm; wing-chord 88–92mm vs. 85–96mm: Dickerman and Phelps 1982). Greenway (1987) also remarked that *phelpsi* is only 'very slightly differentiated'. *O. c. hypoglaucus* (Salvin & Godman, 1883) occurs at one locality in extreme southeast Venezuela (on the Cerro Roraima), as well as elsewhere in the Guianas and in extreme northeast Brazil in Amapá (Novaes 1978). The subspecies in northernmost Pará has not been identified (Aleixo *et al.* 2011). It, too, is generally similar to nominate *cristatus*, but has white underparts (but becoming greenish-yellow on the sides and undertail-coverts), white (rather than pale yellow) lores and cheeks, a slightly brighter green mantle and broader yellow fringes to the median coverts. Chapman (1931) considered *O. c. hypoglaucus* to be fundamentally identical to *O. c. brooksi*, but of course the two are widely separated geographically, although this hints at the possibility of validating just one taxon for all

Sharpbill populations across northernmost South America. *O. c. tocantinsi* Chapman, 1939, is restricted to southern Pará, in east Amazonian Brazil, from the east bank of the lower Rio Tocantins, south to the Serra dos Carajás, but perhaps also as far south as Goiás (FMNH 344720). Both Mees (1974) and Silva (1993) recommended that *tocantinsi* should be considered a synonym of *hypoglaucus*, with which opinion we concur. *O. c. cristatus* (including *O. c. paraguayensis* Chubb, 1910) is endemic to the Atlantic Forest of southeast Brazil, eastern Paraguay (wherein it reaches to within 50–60km to the east of the río Paraguay: Hayes 1995) and extreme northeast Argentina (in northern Misiones). At least some of the Andean populations might represent undescribed subspecies (see above).

VOICE Generally unmistakable and rather far-carrying, and frequently likened to the sound of a falling bomb, although this analogy only appears really true of nominate *cristatus*. In Venezuela, Hilty (2003) described the song as a 'long-drawn, buzzy trill that descends and fades slightly, *bzeeeeee uuuuu'u'u'a'a'a.*' In Costa Rica, Ecuador, southern Venezuela, Peru and east Amazonian Brazil the primary vocalisation is a descending 'screech', with a slightly mechanical or electrical quality especially at its terminus, likened to a cicada by Stiles and Whitney (1983), and sometimes presaged by a lower, flatter whistle, like something falling to the ground. The whole sound lasts *c.*2.5 seconds. However, in southern Brazil, as already noted by Ridgely and Tudor (1994), it is this descending whistle, the falling bomb (without the explosion), that is the song and it seems to almost wholly lack any sensation of the electrical quality that is so characteristic of Amazonian birds in particular. Clearly, more work is required on the vocalisations of this mysterious species. In southern Brazil, observers (especially inexperienced ones) should beware the possibility of confusion, especially if the sound heard is distant, with the voices of two Thamnophilidae, Spot-backed Antshrike *Hypoedaleus guttatus* and Large-tailed Antshrike *Mackenziaena leachii*, and here and elsewhere Short-tailed Hawk *Buteo brachyurus* has a similar vocalisation (Mazar Barnett *et al.* 2004a). Throughout its range the Sharpbill appears to form small, loose ('exploded') leks of 2–5 calling males, which sing from the subcanopy and more occasionally occur in close proximity, closer than the *c.*200m territories mentioned by Snow (2004a, and once, at *c.*1,300m in southeast Brazil, with a singing Elegant Mourner *Laniisoma elegans* nearby: GMK pers. obs.). In Costa Rica such leks can also be dispersed over some distance, with each male 100–300m apart and each using several perches within a 50–100m radius (Stiles and Whitney 1983). However, also sings alone, sometimes from the highest point of a leafless tree. The song is generally only given at rather long intervals, except at leks or in response to playback, when may be uttered 2–3 times per minute, although even then the bird rarely approaches the observer. When singing, the male stretches the neck forwards, fluffs out of the head feathers and opens the bill very wide (Stiles and Whitney 1983). Song is mainly given March–June in Costa Rica (Stiles and Whitney 1983) and September–January in southeast Brazil (Snow 2004a; GMK pers. obs.). Camacho *et al.* (2010) reported that juveniles just out of the nest vocalised much like the adults, but that their calls were shorter and even higher pitched. Published recordings of the song are available on the following compilations: Ross and Whitney (1995), Boesman (1999), Mayer (2000), Schulenberg (2000a), Remold (2002), Krabbe and Nilsson

(2003), Moore *et al.* (2005), Boesman (2006), Marantz and Zimmer (2006), Alvarez *et al.* (2007), Boesman (2009) and Minns *et al.* (2009). In addition, vocalisations from Bolivia (unknown taxon), Brazil and Paraguay (nominate), French Guiana (*hypoglaucus*) and Peru (unknown taxon) are presented online at www.xeno-canto.org. Other reported vocalisations include a weak *tet*, a high tremulous *tsirrr* (both of unknown context) and a weak, descending, 6–10-syllable, chattering phrase given during apparent courtship (Stiles and Whitney 1983, Sick 1997, Snow 2004a). Stiles and Whitney (1983) observed a striking flight-display whose precise purpose is to date unexplained:

> After giving a song, the bird sat silently on its perch for 3–4 minutes, then suddenly launched into a strange, rapid, fluttery flight in which the wings quivered while the tail pumped sharply downward as the bird flew directly across the clearing. While in mid-flight, the bird jerked its head up slightly, opened its bill wide, delivered one song, and continued flying until lost from view behind a tree, after which it could not be relocated. The song given in flight sounded exactly like that which the bird had just given from a perch. No possible mechanically produced sounds were heard during this peculiar flight, so the function of the serrations of the male's outer primary remains unknown.

NATURAL HISTORY Movements are generally slow and deliberate, the bird inquisitively and somewhat methodically inspecting its surroundings and searching for food. Seen alone, occasionally in pairs, but is perhaps most frequently observed accompanying large mixed-species foraging flocks in the canopy and subcanopy, as well as with groups of birds mobbing owls, e.g. Brazilian Pygmy Owl *Glaucidium minutissimum* in southeast Brazil (GMK pers. obs.). In Amazonia, these flocks typically comprise woodpeckers, various foliage-gleaners, tanagers *Tangara*, *Lanio* and *Tachyphonus* spp., and Red-billed Pied Tanager *Lamprospiza melanoleuca*, *Tityra* spp., flycatchers, warblers, and greenlets *Hylophilus* spp. (Parker *et al.* 1991, Silva 1993, Hilty 2003; GMK pers. obs.). In the Atlantic Forest it also joins groups of tanagers *Tangara*, *Tachyphonus* and *Hemithraupis* spp., flycatchers, becards *Pachyramphus* spp., Buff-fronted Foliage-gleaner *Philydor rufus*, etc. (cf. Venturini *et al.* 2005; GMK pers. obs.). Sharpbill has also been observed with a flock of antwrens and antshrikes (Thamnophilidae) in northeast Argentina (Bodrati and Cockle 2006a), tanagers in Costa Rica (Stiles and Whitney 1983) and Slaty-winged *Philydor fuscipenne* and Buff-fronted Foliage-gleaners, Rufous-naped Greenlet *Hylophilus semibrunneus*, Red-rumped Woodpecker *Veniliornis kirkii*, Yellow-throated Vireo *Vireo flavifrons* and Olivaceous Woodcreeper *Sittasomus griseicapillus* (T. M. Donegan *in litt.* 2010). In such situations, its frequent habit of hanging upside-down (like a giant piculet *Picumnus* sp.), e.g. to access fruits, or to seize insects from the underside of leaves, draws the observers' attention. The incidence of flock-joining behaviour is difficult to establish and the available data are too few to conclude firmly that Sharpbills more commonly join less-mobile flocks, or that they mainly join flocks in the non-breeding season, although both possibilities seem at least partially (but not wholly) true from our own observations. Other topics worthy of further investigation include the possibility that Sharpbills might show some seasonal preferences in diet, perhaps exhibiting a greater reliance on fruit in the non-breeding season.

Singing males stretch the neck forwards and fluff out the same feathers, but (perhaps surprisingly) do not appear to raise the red crown-feathers.

FOOD AND FEEDING Diet includes substantial fruit intake, perhaps especially in winter in southeast Brazil, where Pizo *et al.* (2002) identified berries of nine small species, including one parasitic plant, namely *Peschiera catharinensis* (Apocynaceae), *Euterpe edulis* (Arecaceae), *Psittacanthus* sp. and *Struthanthus vulgaris* (Loranthaceae), *Cabralea canjerana* (Meliaceae), *Myrsine coriacea* (Myrsinaceae), *Paulinia* sp. (Sapindaceae) and *Trema micrantha* (Ulmaceae), to which list Parrini and Pacheco (2010) added *Coussapoa microcarpa* (Cecropiaceae), but also includes comparatively large items, all taken from a perch. In Costa Rica, birds particularly visited two species of fruiting trees: *Hampea appendiculata* (Tiliaceae) and *Clusia oblanceolata* (Guttiferae) (Stiles and Whitney 1983). Gleans insects such as arthropods from leaves and branches, again from a perch, by inspecting rolled-up leaves and tufts of moss (Stiles and Whitney 1983), flowers (Perry *et al.* 1997; GMK pers. obs.), or by gleaning from both surfaces of green foliage. Willis (2002) speculated that the Sharpbill might occasionally search flowers, such as *Clusia*, for nectar. Wetmore (1972) recorded spiders and their eggs, as well as a large ant in the stomach contents, and Davis (1986) mentioned caterpillars and vegetable matter in the stomachs of two birds in Peru.

BREEDING Data are comparatively few and the eggs are apparently still undescribed. As noted by Brooke *et al.* (1983) and Sick (1997) the nest's shape, construction and positioning recall those of the genus *Iodopleura*, but also some flycatchers such as *Suiriri*. Hilty (2003) mentioned a February nest, found in the Sierra de Lema, southern Venezuela, as being a 'hummingbird-like [which description also serves for *Iodopleura*] open cup of plant down molded into feltlike consistency; in open at tip of high, exposed *Cecropia* branch.' A nest in the state of Rio de Janeiro, southeast Brazil, found in the early stages of construction on 9 October, almost 30m above the ground in a tall tree (Clusiaceae?), was followed (albeit not continuously) to completion. The nest was constructed of leguminous petioles and a few dry leaves, coated over the outside with mosses, liverworts and spiderwebs, and was saddled over a slender horizontal branch, but further supported by another. Brooke *et al.* (1983) also postulated that saliva was used to bind the nest together, although this was doubted by Camacho *et al.* (2010), who did not observe this or any similar substance in the Costa Rican nest (see below). At the Brazilian nest only the female participated in nest building, which continued until at least 20 October, and thereafter the female was incubating by 29 October and the (presumed to be two) eggs hatched on 13 November. The two chicks that were visible by 18 November were fed both small fruits and invertebrates, and were seemingly close to fledging by the time observations ceased on 7 December (Brooke *et al.* 1983). Approximate nest dimensions and some details of nestling care are presented in the original paper. In the same general region, Sick (1997) found another nest 10m above the ground at the top of a damaged tree in the middle of the forest, still being built at the end of September. The first nest to be discovered in the Central American portion of the species' range was described recently by both Ortega (2008), which contribution contains colour photographs of the adults, chicks and nest, and Camacho *et al.* (2010). It was found in Tapantí National Park, on the Caribbean

slope in Costa Rica, on 3 June 2008, and was sited *c.*8m above the ground in the horizontal three-way fork of a *Wercklea insignis* (Malvaceae) tree, shaded from above and at an altitude of 1,280m. Dimensions of the nest were presented by Camacho *et al.* (2010). The nest itself closely matched that described by Brooke *et al.* (1983) from eastern Brazil; seeds regurgitated by the chicks were observed on the nest walls. The two chicks were initially covered in white down (dark yellow in Brazil), but as at the latter only one adult (reported to be the female) was ever seen visiting the Costa Rican nest. The young were apparently entirely fed a diet of small fruits, including those of *Clusia* and *Miconia* spp., (Melastomataceae) and fledged in *c.*27–28 days (Ortega 2008). Camacho *et al.* (2010) gave further details, reporting that the chicks were fed by the female while she was perched outside the nest, and that her approaches to the nest were made cautiously: fruits fed to the chicks observed by these authors included a *Coupania* sp. (Sapindaceae), a *Diphembachia* sp. (Araceae), a *Saphium* sp. (Euphorbiaceae), an unknown Fabaceae and a *Cavendishia* sp. (Ericaceae). Droppings were swallowed by the female, which carefully checked the nest for these after each feeding session. After the chicks fledged, they were observed being fed caterpillars (Camacho *et al.* 2010). Each time the female left the nest, following a feeding visit, she would dive directly towards the ground and only commence to fly horizontally away through the dense understorey when *c.*1m above the ground (Camacho *et al.* 2010). The latter authors considered that overhead predators (e.g. various raptor species) might be a significant risk to Sharpbills, based on the behaviour of the female and young at the Costa Rican nest, although the position of the Brazilian nest does not suggest this. Other relevant data from southeast Brazil involve specimens in or coming into breeding condition taken in most months between early July and April (MNRJ). Two males taken in southeast Ecuador in late January have enlarged gonads (MECN), a male collected in Amapá, Brazil, in late May is apparently in breeding condition (Novaes 1978), whilst a male and female collected in Surinam in the second half of August are both in breeding condition (RMNH).

STATUS Categorised as of Least Concern by BirdLife International (2004, 2008). As with many species covered in this book, there are very few robust measures of abundance, but Thiollay (1994) estimated there to be 0.75 pairs of Sharpbills per 100ha at a study site in French Guiana. The race *O. c. frater* is considered rare in western Panama (Wetmore 1972, Ridgely and Gwynne 1989) and is also uncommon and local in Costa Rica (Stiles and Skutch 1989), where one of the best sites to find this species is Silent Mountain (Lawson 2010). Wetmore (1972) also described race *O. c. brooksi* as being rare in eastern Panama. Sharpbill appears to be localised in Venezuela, where the species is apparently most frequently seen on the slopes of the Sierra de Lema at 800–1,200m (Hilty 2003; GMK pers. obs.), and it is restricted to a single locality (at 900m) in Ecuador, and likewise, in Argentina the species is almost entirely known from the environs of Iguazú National Park and Establecimiento San Jorge, with rather few records in total (see Distribution; Finch 1991, Canevari 1992, Pearman 1994a, Ridgely and Tudor 1994, Bodrati and Cockle 2006a, Kirwan *et al.* 2008). Within Argentina, the species is perhaps most regularly seen at a *Euterpe edulis* forest located north of Posada Puerto Bemberg, Misiones (Lowen 2010). Also uncommon or rare and poorly known in Guyana (Braun *et al.* 2007), French Guiana (Tostain *et al.* 1992) and Surinam

(Mees 1974, Davis 1979, Ottema *et al.* 2009), but in contrast Sharpbill seems locally common in the Atlantic Forest, e.g. at several sites in São Paulo, Rio de Janeiro and Espírito Santo states of Brazil (Brooke *et al.* 1983, Goerck 1999; GMK pers. obs.). Known from many protected areas across the species' very broad but patchy range (although neither of the localities in Colombia is protected), including Carajás National Forest, Ibitipoca State Park, Itatiaia, Tijuca and Serra dos Órgãos National Parks in Brazil, Braulio Carrillo National Park, El Copal Biological Reserve and Tapantí National Park in Costa Rica, Serranía San Luis, San Rafael and Cerro Corá National Parks in Paraguay, Manu National Park and Biosphere Reserve in Peru, and Brownsberg National Park in Surinam.

REFERENCES Aleixo *et al.* (2011), Alvarez *et al.* (2007), Alverson *et al.* (2001), Alves and Vecchi (2009), Ames (1971), Angehr and Dean (2010), AOU (1998), Balchin and Toyne (1998), Bauer and Pacheco (2000), Bencke (2001), BirdLife International (2004, 2008), Blake (1950), Bodrati and Cockle (2006a), Boesman (1999, 2009), Boyla and Estrada (2005), Brandt *et al.* (2005), Braun *et al.* (2007), Brooke *et al.* (1983), Browne (2005), Camacho *et al.* (2010), Canevari (1992), Chapman (1931, 1939), Chesser (2004), Chubb (1921), Cuervo *et al.* (2008a, 2008b), Davis (1979, 1986), Dekker (2003), Dickerman and Phelps (1982), Dickinson (2003), Donatelli and Ferreira (2009), Donegan *et al.* (2009), Dunning (2008), Ericson *et al.* (2006), Finch (1991), Garrigues and Dean (2007), Gilliard (1941), Goerck (1999), Gonzaga *et al.* (1995), Greenway (1987), Harvey *et al.* (2011), Haverschmidt and Mees (1994), Hayes (1995), Hayes and Scharf (1995b), Hellmayr (1929b), Hidasi (1998, 2007), Hilty (2003), Hilty and Brown (1986), Hinkelmann and Fiebig (2001), Hosner *et al.* (2009), Johansson *et al.* (2002), Kirwan *et al.* (2008), Krabbe (2007), Krabbe and Nilsson (2003), Lanyon (1985), Lawson (2010), Lowen (2010), Lowen *et al.* (1996), Maciel (2009), Madroño *et al.* (1997a), Mallet-Rodrigues and Noronha (2009), Mallet-Rodrigues *et al.* (2007), Marantz and Zimmer (2006), Marsden *et al.* (2003), Mayer (2000), Mayr and Amadon (1951), Mayr and Phelps (1967), Mazar Barnett and Pearman (2001), Mazar Barnett *et al.* (2004a), Mees (1974), Merkord *et al.* (2009), Minns *et al.* (2009), Moore *et al.* (2005), Naka *et al.* (2006), Novaes (1978), Ohlson *et al.* (2008), Ortega (2008), Ottema (2009), Ottema *et al.* (2009), Pacheco *et al.* (2007), Parker and Goerck (1997), Parker and Wust (1994), Parker *et al.* (1991), Parrini and Pacheco (2010), Pearman (1994a), Pereira *et al.* (2008), Perry *et al.* (1997), Phelps (1973), Pimentel and Olmos (2011), Pinto (1944), Pizo *et al.* (2002), Prum (1990b), Remold (2002), Remsen *et al.* (2009), Restall *et al.* (2006), Ridgely and Greenfield (2001), Ridgely and Gwynne (1989), Ridgely and Tudor (1994, 2009), Robbins *et al.* (1985, 1999), Ross and Whitney (1995), Salaman *et al.* (2002a, 2008, 2009), Schulenberg (2000a), Schulenberg *et al.* (2007), Sclater (1888), Sibley and Ahlquist (1985, 1990), Sibley *et al.* (1984), Sick (1971, 1997), Silva (1993, 1996), Silveira *et al.* (2005), Snow (2004a), Stiles and Skutch (1989), Stiles and Whitney (1983), Stotz *et al.* (1996), Teixeira *et al.* (1986), Tello *et al.* (2009), Thiollay (1994), Tostain *et al.* (1992), Venturini *et al.* (2005), Walker *et al.* (2006), Wetmore (1960, 1972), Willis (2002), Willis and Oniki (1990, 2002), Zyskowski *et al.* (2011).

Sharpbill *Oxyruncus cristatus*. **Figs. 1–2**. Male, *O. c. cristatus*, Reserva Ecológica de Guapiaçu, near Cachoeiras de Macacu, Rio de Janeiro, southeast Brazil, August (*William Price / www.pbase/tereksandpiper*). The bird is singing in Fig. 2. **Fig. 3**. Sex unknown, *O. c. cristatus*, Ubatuba, São Paulo, southeast Brazil, July (*David Fisher*). Movements in this species are poorly known, but there is at least some evidence that in southeast Brazil birds descend to lower elevations in the austral winter. **Fig. 4**. Perhaps female or juvenile, *O. c. cristatus*, Parque do Zizo, São Paulo, southeast Brazil, November (*Arthur Grosset / www.arthurgrosset.com*). Identification as a female based on orange irides. No reddish or orange is visible in the central crown, even at such an advantageous angle, although it is usually at least partially concealed in both sexes. Juveniles show no reddish in the crown at all, but this bird's worn wing and tail feathers suggest that it is an adult.

Genus *Schiffornis*: mourners

This aberrant genus of three species, one of them extremely widespread almost throughout the Neotropics, is chiefly characterised as follows (*sensu* Snow 1975): its compressed and laterally notched upper mandible, rather long and strong tarsi, the longish tail and sexually monomorphic plumages. Ames (1971) added that its syringeal structure (at least that of *S. turdina*) is closest to *Lipaugus*, of those species he studied. Furthermore, our knowledge of its nesting behaviour also sets *Schiffornis* apart from manakins, as was first commented on by Skutch (1969) and Wetmore (1972). Snow (1975, 1979b) elected, obviously with some reluctance, to maintain *Schiffornis* within Pipridae, although he speculated that it might prove to nestle within Cotingidae. Subsequently, with the heavyweight techniques now open to researchers to resolve phylogenetic relationships, it has emerged that *Schiffornis* lies outwith both families (see Systematics, p. 42).

VÁRZEA SCHIFFORNIS
Schiffornis major   Plate 13

Schiffornis major **Des Murs** *in* **Castelnau, 1856**, *Expéd. Amér. Sud. Oiseaux* 18: 66, pl. 18, fig. 2, Sarayacu, Peru

Formerly known, rather inappropriately, as the Greater Manakin, Prum and Lanyon (1989) recommended adopting the name Várzea Mourner, to better reflect both its habitat preferences and its relationships. *S. major* was formerly (e.g. Hellmayr 1929b) placed in the monotypic genus *Massornis*, but soon thereafter it was removed to *Schiffornis* by Zimmer (1936a). Barber and Rice (2007) showed that it is the sister to *S. turdina* and *S. virescens*.

IDENTIFICATION 15–16cm. Várzea Schiffornis is almost entirely cinnamon, but is paler below and on the rump. A feature not correlated with age, sex or race is the individual variation in the amount of grey on the face. Although usually restricted to the ocular region, the grey can also be present on the head-sides and the crown, or even extend over the entire head and throat. Similar in shape to its congener, Thrush-like Schiffornis *Schiffornis turdina*, the present species should prove readily separable by its much more brightly coloured plumage and its strict habitat preferences. The syntopic Cinnamon Attila *Attila cinnamomeus* is of similar coloration, but is generally found in the subcanopy, and is also larger, longer tailed and has the hook-tipped bill typical of *Attila*. The same holds true of the similar Citron-bellied Attila *A. citriniventris*, but this species is almost entirely restricted to tall *terra firme*, and is thus extremely unlikely to enter into the same areas inhabited by *S. major*.

DISTRIBUTION Principally restricted to western Amazonia, from southern and southeast Colombia (at Leticia, dpto. Amazonas, and Parque Nacional Natural La Paya, dpto. Putumayo) and in southern Venezuela (from Caño Capuana south to the Brazilian border), thence south across western and central Amazonian Brazil, south of the Amazon River east as far as the mouth of the Rio Tapajós, at Santarém. The precise extent of its range north of the Amazon is still unclear, but it occurs east at least as far as Itacoatiara, Amazonas (GMK pers. obs.). Also found in northeast Ecuador (where principally restricted to the environs of the Río Napo and its immediately adjacent tributaries, and further south at Kapawi Lodge), and through eastern Peru to northern Bolivia (e.g. in dpto. La Paz). Várzea Schiffornis has recently been discovered at several localities in southern Roraima state, Brazil (Naka *et al.* 2006). There is also a recent sight record of a bird

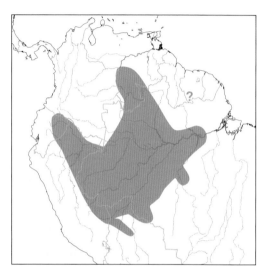

considered to be race *S. m. duidae* in Surinam (O. Ottema) although to date the species has not been officially admitted to that country's bird list (Ottema *et al.* 2009). The species is generally found below 300m, but is known to 500m in Manu National Park (Walker *et al.* 2006) and has apparently been recorded to 1,000m in southeast Peru (Ridgely and Tudor 2009).

MOVEMENTS None known and the species is presumed to be resident and almost certainly strongly sedentary (Snow 2004a).

HABITAT Restricted to the understorey of *várzea* forest including that associated with *igapó* (black-water rivers), Várzea Schiffornis favours densely wooded creeks and stream banks, including on river islands, and swampy, low-lying forest that is regularly (or seasonally) inundated. The species is rarely found far from water; it is also sometimes recorded in bamboo (Willard *et al.* 1991).

DESCRIPTION The sexes are alike, but the male appears to be, on average, larger (see below). Well-developed, but usually has rather few, rictal bristles. The bill is slightly blunt and heavy, with a strongly arched culmen and slightly hooked tip. Bill, tail and tarsi are all, on average, shorter than in *S. turdina*, and the bill appears notably short in the field on account of the forecrown feathers lying flat over the culmen. *Adult.* – Head colour very variable (see also above), but is mostly cinnamon-rufous or reddish-brown with a grey area on the face, surrounding the eye, and often with the central crown brightest. However, some (e.g. a female from João Pessoa, on the Rio Juruá, western Brazil) have virtually the entire head as far as the upper mantle, most of the ear-coverts and even some of the throat-feathers grey (with evidence of a restricted cinnamon central coronal stripe; rather more extensive than depicted in Snow 2004a: Plate 15). At the Río Yanayacu, dpto. Loreto, Peru, D. Beadle, GMK and H. Shirihai observed and photographed different territorial males ranging from those with just a tiny area of grey over the ocular region to those with a completely grey head. (See also Zimmer 1936a and Gyldenstolpe 1945, 1951, for further discussion of variation in head coloration.) Lores paler cinnamon, and the mantle and tail are usually concolorous with the crown (although some have the mantle more olive: Gyldenstolpe 1945, 1951), but the rump and uppertail-coverts are noticeably brighter cinnamon than the rest of the upperparts. The wing-coverts are dark brown with slightly paler fringes (though the contrast is not obvious), whilst the wing bend and underwing-coverts are pale or bright cinnamon, respectively. Flight feathers (especially the primaries) are contrastingly dusky to dark brown, especially on the outer webs, but with contrastingly pale buff fringes. The underparts are cinnamon with a paler throat and belly, thus leaving something of a slight breast-band effect. *Juvenile.* – Apparently undescribed (Snow 2004a), but this plumage is considered to resemble the adult. A photograph of a bird from central Amazonia in Snow (2004a: 120) appears to show drop-shaped bluish-grey tips to the median coverts, which is perhaps a feature of immature plumage? *Moult.* – No data have been published, but two from the Rio Juruá, western Brazil, were very heavily worn and were moulting the tail feathers and tertials, at least, in January (MNRJ). *Bare parts.* – Bill dark grey to blackish, at least sometimes with a pale base, and legs dark grey to blackish; the irides are large and dark brownish with a pale cinnamon orbital ring.

MEASUREMENTS (from Hellmayr 1910, Gyldenstolpe 1945, 1951, Romero-Zambrano 1978, Delgado 2000; BMNH; MNRJ: Brazil, Colombia) *S. m. major*: wing of male (*n* = 15) 77–89mm, wing of female (*n* = 11) 77–87mm; tail of male (*n* = 15) 56–65mm, tail of female (*n* = 11) 53.5–63.0mm; bill of male (*n* = 3) 16.17–18.00mm, bill of female (*n* = 2) 14.00–16.14mm; tarsus of male (*n* = 12) 18–21mm, tarsus of female (*n* = 6) 18.4–21.0mm. Weight (sexes combined): 29.1–31.0g (Willard *et al.* 1991, Hilty 2003, Snow 2004a).

GEOGRAPHICAL VARIATION Two subspecies are generally recognised, but it seems possible that individual variation might account for the described differences between the races and that the species might be better treated as monotypic. *S. m. major* (most of species' range, through southeast Colombia, northeast Ecuador, eastern Peru, northern Bolivia, and western and central Amazonian Brazil; described above); and *S. m. duidae* J. T. Zimmer, 1936 (in southwest Venezuela, and perhaps this subspecies recently seen in Surinam), which purportedly differs from the nominate race by virtue of its clearer grey crown extending over the hindneck and that the mantle also has a more olive-brown cast than in the nominate race. However, Gyldenstolpe (1945, 1951) already reported the existence of specimens from the Rios Juruá and Purus, in western Brazil, with either or both the head and upperparts colorations tending well towards the characters of *S. m. duidae*. Subsequent authors have added to Zimmer's diagnosis the greyish-olive throat, which grades into the

yellowish-cinnamon breast. However, Zimmer (1936a) declined to definitively cite this character in his diagnosis because Taczanowski in his type description of *S. major* had mentioned a grey throat; see Description above for other evidence that *S. m. major* can exhibit grey on the throat.

VOICE Várzea Schiffornis principally vocalises at dawn and dusk, and often responds aggressively to playback at these periods but much less so at other times of day, although the species sings even during the hottest hours (GMK pers. obs.). It sometimes comes to investigate playback of Amazonian Pygmy Owl *Glaucidium hardyi* (GMK pers. obs.). The advertising song is a slow, leisurely but complex series of slurred whistles, which becomes more drawn-out as it progresses (the final notes being interspersed by gaps of 2–3 seconds) and recalls, to some extent, that of Thrush-like Schiffornis (albeit it is distinctly longer). The song was rendered by Hilty (2003) as: *twoweeo, tweeEET, teeu-dewEE, tweeEET…teeu…dewEET…teeu…dewEET* (see also Schulenberg *et al.* 2007 and Ridgely and Tudor 2009 for alternative transliterations). Also utters a musical chatter or rattle, usually when excited: *chew trr'rr'rr'rr* (Ridgely and Greenfield 2001, Schulenberg *et al.* 2007). The species' voice was presented on the following audio compilations: Moore (1993, 1997), Boesman (1999, 2006a, 2006b, 2009), Schulenberg *et al.* (2000), Krabbe and Nilsson (2003) and Marantz and Zimmer (2006), and several recordings from Brazil and Peru are available online at www.xeno-canto.org.

NATURAL HISTORY Typically stolid and sluggish, and Várzea Schiffornis is usually encountered alone or in pairs (Thrush-like Schiffornis is very seldom observed in pairs). This species is extremely difficult to observe except when singing. Generally the species stays within *c.*4m of the ground, and typically flies some distance (even across 100m-wide rivers) in response to playback, before landing and remaining quiet and still for up to several minutes before switching to a new perch. The species' habits are generally considered similar to those of *S. turdina*.

FOOD AND FEEDING No data seem to have been specifically recorded.

BREEDING Nesting is completely unknown (Snow 2004a), although two males with large gonads were collected in extreme southern Venezuela, beside the Río Baría, in February and March (Willard *et al.* 1991).

STATUS Várzea Schiffornis is currently treated as of Least Concern (BirdLife International 2004, 2008). The species is known from just five localities in southernmost Venezuela, where suitable habitat is apparently restricted and sparsely distributed (Hilty 2003), but *S. major* is reasonably widespread (but still uncommon) in eastern Peru (Schulenberg *et al.* 2007), where densities of just one bird per 100ha of suitable habitat have been reported (Terborgh *et al.* 1990). It is also considered to be uncommon in southern and southeast Colombia, where the species' range is largely restricted to the region around Leticia (Hilty and Brown 1986). Further south, Várzea Schiffornis is principally known from the Río Napo in eastern Ecuador (Ridgely and Greenfield 2001), where it is found at quite a number of the regularly visited ecotourism lodges (e.g. Napo Wildlife Center, Sani and Yuturi), but was first recorded only in the mid 1970s (Ridgely 1980). *S. major* is found in Viruá National Park, Roraima (Naka *et al.* 2007), and Jaú National Park, Amazonas, northern Brazil (Borges *et al.* 2001), whilst one of the most accessible sites for this species is the nearby Anavilhanas archipelago (Cintra *et al.* 2007), Manu National Park and Biosphere Reserve, Peru (Robinson 1997, Walker *et al.* 2006), the Tambopata-Candamo Reserved Zone, Peru (Parker *et al.* 1994), the Río Yanuyacu at Muyuna Lodge, dpto. Loreto, Peru (GMK pers. obs.), and Parque Nacional Natural La Paya, southeast Colombia (Delgado 2000).

REFERENCES Barber and Rice (2007), van den Berg and Bosman (1984), BirdLife International (2004, 2008), Boesman (1999, 2006a, 2006b, 2009), Borges (2007), Borges *et al.* (2001), Cintra *et al.* (2007), Delgado (2000), Guilherme and Santos (2009), Gyldenstolpe (1945, 1951), Hellmayr (1910, 1929b), Hilty (2003), Hilty and Brown (1986), Krabbe and Nilsson (2003), Lane *et al.* (2003), Maillard *et al.* (2007), Marantz and Zimmer (2006), Meyer de Schauensee and Phelps (1987), Moore (1993, 1997), Naka *et al.* (2006, 2007), Novaes (1957), Ottema *et al.* (2009), Parker *et al.* (1994b, 1994c), Pinto (1944), Prum and Lanyon (1989), Remsen and Parker (1995), Restall *et al.* (2006), Ridgely (1980), Ridgely and Greenfield (2001), Ridgely and Tudor (1994, 2009), Robinson (1997), Robinson and Terborgh (1997), Romero-Zambrano (1978), Rosenberg (1990), Salaman *et al.* (2008), Schulenberg *et al.* (2007), Snethlage (1908a, 1914), Snow (2004b), Stotz *et al.* (1996, 1997), Terborgh *et al.* (1990), Walker *et al.* (2006), Willard *et al.* (1991), J. T. Zimmer (1936a), Zimmer *et al.* (1997).

Várzea Schiffornis *Schiffornis major.* **Fig. 1.** Presumed male, *S. m. major,* Muyuna Lodge, dpto. Loreto, northeast Peru, September (*Hadoram Shirihai / Photographic Handbook to Birds of the World*). This individual has a rather extensively grey head, and thus arguably is closer morphologically to *S. m. duidae* of northern Amazonia, although the throat seems to be solely buff-coloured (see Description, and Geographical Variation). Note the rather short-looking bill, in part because of the relatively long forehead feathers.

GREENISH SCHIFFORNIS
Schiffornis virescens   **Plate 13**

Ptil[ochloris] virescens **Lafresnaye, 1838**, *Rev. Zool.* 1: 238, Brazil [= Rio de Janeiro]

Considered to form a superspecies with the Thrush-like Schiffornis *Schiffornis turdina* (Snow 1975, Sibley and Monroe 1990), the Greenish Schiffornis is restricted to southeastern South America, where it is generally still common in what remains of the Atlantic Forest. That *S. virescens* and *S. turdina* are sister species was recently confirmed (Barber and Rice 2007), although they have been separated by *c.*4.2 million years according to the results of an even more recent molecular study (G. Cabanne *per* F. M. D'Horta pers. comm.), which also found no evidence of any genetic structuring within *S. virescens.*

IDENTIFICATION 15.3–18.0cm. This strange 'manakin' is most likely to be mistaken for one or other of two species in its range. Thrush-like Schiffornis, vaguely similar in its more olivaceous forms (which are not sympatric with *S. virescens*), has a less distinct eye-ring and lacks the greener body plumage contrasting with the rufescent wings and tail. These two *Schiffornis* species are altitudinally separated in their zone of sympatry in southeast Brazil, where Thrush-like generally occurs below 500m, and also note their quite different vocalisations. However, both species can occur at the same locality, e.g. RPPN REGUA, near Cachoeiras de Macacu, Rio de Janeiro (Pimentel and Olmos 2011). Female Blue Manakin *Chiroxiphia caudata* is of similar size to Greenish Schiffornis and frequently occurs alongside it in humid montane forest. At times the elongated central tail feathers of the female Blue Manakin can be difficult to see, but the latter species has brighter green plumage, no rufous in the wings and its legs are reddish, whilst their vocalisations are again quite different.

DISTRIBUTION Endemic to southeastern South America, where it is largely restricted to eastern Brazil, from central and even northern Goiás (e.g. around Anápolis and the Parque Nacional da Chapada dos Veadeiros), the Distrito

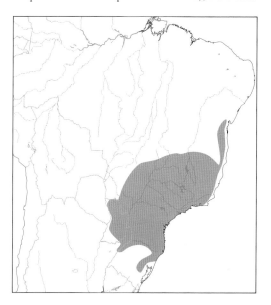

Federal and extreme northwest Minas Gerais along the middle Rio Preto, east to southern and central Bahia (e.g. at Boa Nova and in the Chapada Diamantina) and south to eastern Mato Grosso do Sul and northern Rio Grande do Sul, to just north of Pelotas and around Porto Alegre, with small extensions of its range into eastern Paraguay (to within 50–60km of the río Paraguay), and northeastern Argentina (in Misiones and northeast Corrientes). Greenish Schiffornis is generally recorded from sea level to *c.*1,300m (or to 1,800m in southern Minas Gerais: Vasconcelos 2008, and even 2,000m in Itatiaia National Park: Pires *et al.* 1991).

MOVEMENTS None definitely recorded, but Iartelli (2004) recorded unspecified local movements within a 350ha protected area in São Paulo, hinting that the species is not entirely sedentary.

HABITAT Greenish Schiffornis inhabits the understorey and midstorey of humid forest including mature secondary woodland, *Araucaria* forest and well-wooded borders, as well as gallery forests in the *Cerrado.* Carrara *et al.* (2009) reported the species' presence in *Eucalyptus* (Myrtaceae) plantations and at the interface between such woodlands and natural vegetation, at least in Espírito Santo. In areas of overlap with Thrush-like Schiffornis, the present species tends to replace the latter at higher elevations (see above), but elsewhere *S. virescens* occurs to sea level and it is even found in low, stunted, *restinga* forests on inshore islands such as Ilha Comprida, in southern São Paulo.

DESCRIPTION Sexes alike, with extensive overlap in size (see Measurements), although Snow's (2004b) summary of mass data suggests that females are on average heavier than males. Greenish Schiffornis possesses very long rictal bristles, but only comparatively small nostrils. *Adult.* – The head, mantle, rump and underparts are olive-green, although the bird is generally paler below than on the upperparts. There is a chestnut tone to the wings (including the wing-coverts and tertials) and tail feathers. This contrast is especially evident when the wings are flicked and the tail is spread. The narrow but relatively conspicuous eye-ring is whitish. *Juvenile.* – Undescribed (Snow 2004b). *Moult.* – The only published moult data involve a male in wing moult in November and a female moulting the rectrices in April, both from Espírito Santo (Willis and Oniki 2002), while a female collected in São Paulo state in February was replacing the body feathers (FMNH). *Bare parts.* – The bill has a blackish or, less usually, a dark plumbeous-grey maxilla, with a dark grey, plumbeous or horn brown base (sometimes tinged bluish or bluish-white); the irides are usually dark brown or chestnut; and the legs and feet are grey or plumbeous, or brown (once bright pale blue), with ochre-coloured soles (Belton 1985, Krabbe 2007; MNRJ).

MEASUREMENTS (BMNH; CUMZ; MNRJ: Goiás, Minas Gerais, Rio de Janeiro and São Paulo, Brazil) Wing of male (*n* = 19) 77–83mm, wing of female (*n* = 9) 71–80mm; tail of male (*n* = 19) 60–73mm, tail of female (*n* = 9) 58–70mm; bill of male (*n* = 19) 12.95–15.14mm, bill of female (*n* = 9) 13.24–16.06mm; tarsus of male (*n* = 14) 18.40–21.01mm, tarsus of female (*n* = 6) 20.0–22.29mm. Weight (sexes combined): 21.5–29.0g (Belton 1985, Marini *et al.* 1997b, Blamires *et al.* 2002, Snow 2004b; FMNH; DZUFMG; MNRJ).

GEOGRAPHICAL VARIATION Monotypic and a recent molecular study found no evidence of any genetic structuring between populations of this species from across its geographical range (G. Cabanne *per* F. M. D'Horta pers. comm.).

VOICE Described in some detail by Belton (1985) and Sick (1997). Advertisement, presumably by male alone, is given at infrequent intervals and comprises a series of two to five clear whistled notes, e.g. *tzu-tzuit-tzu-tzu*, or *choo-wEEt towit-towit-towEEt*, sometimes with the emphasis on the final two, but equally, if not more often on the first. Once learnt, this vocalisation is highly distinctive and will vastly increase an observer's contacts with this species. It can be highly responsive to playback, when typically gives a loud *choo-wEEt* (Belton 1985). Published recordings are available on the following compilations: Straneck (1990), Gonzaga and Castiglioni (2001), Remold (2002), Boesman (2006a) and Minns *et al.* (2009), and recordings from Argentina, Brazil and Paraguay are available online at www.xeno-canto.org.

NATURAL HISTORY Behaviour is much like that of the next species. Greenish Schiffornis is principally found alone, perched quietly in the lower midstorey or understorey, often on a near-vertical branch.

FOOD AND FEEDING Greenish Schiffornis joins mixed-species flocks, but is not one of the most frequent constituents of such feeding bands in southeast Brazil (see Aleixo 1997; GMK pers. obs.). Feeds on insects and their larvae, spiders and vegetable matter including berries (e.g. of at least one species of *Rapanea*, Myrsinaceae, *Symplocos uniflora*, Symplocaceae, and *Psychotria suterella*, Rubiaceae) and seeds, perhaps in broadly equal proportions (Belton 1985, Pineschi 1990, Gomes and Silva 2002, Clausi 2005, Lopes *et al.* 2005, Krabbe 2007, Carrano and Marins 2008, Manhães and Dias 2009; MNRJ). Lima *et al.* (2010) reported the following insect prey in the species' diet: Coleoptera (beetles), Lepidoptera (butterflies) and Orthoptera (grasshoppers etc.). It has recently been reported to occasionally follow *Labidus predator* and *Eciton burchelli* army ant swarms in search of insect prey disturbed by the ants (Faria and Rodrigues 2009). Diet also includes exotic plant species (Scheibler and Melo-Júnior 2003). Hasui *et al.* (2009) attempted to identify whether this species and *Chiroxiphia caudata* partitioned food resources. During periods of high fruit availability, these authors found no evidence of fruit trait selection. In contrast, during periods of fruit scarcity in primary forests, there was evidence of niche partitioning, with *C. caudata* foraging for larger fruits in the canopy and *S. virescens* searching for understorey plants. The niche overlap was greatest in secondary forest during periods of scarcity, when both species fed on small understorey fruits.

BREEDING Sick (1997) appeared to consider the species' breeding behaviour to be much like *S. turdina*, but apparently only one nest has ever been found, despite the species' unquestionable abundance, on 19 December, in Brasília (Distrito Federal). This was a large cup of leaves placed 3m above the ground in the upright fork of an understorey plant, and contained two eggs (Snow 2004b). A full description of the species' nest and eggs, as well, of course, as other aspects of its breeding behaviour is eagerly awaited. Otherwise, all that is known concerning seasonality of breeding is that Belton (1985) collected two males in mid September with enlarged testes, while FMNH has a female that already had slightly enlarged gonads in mid July.

STATUS Greenish Schiffornis is treated as of Least Concern (BirdLife International 2004, 2008), and is known from a great many protected areas, both privately and publicly owned, as well as many Important Bird Areas throughout its wide range (e.g. Madroño *et al.* 1997a, Parker and Goerck 1997, Chebez *et al.* 1999, Mazar Barnett and Kirwan 1999,

Parrini *et al.* 1999, Braz and Cavalcanti 2001, Vasconcelos and Melo Júnior 2001, Bencke *et al.* 2006, Pacheco *et al.* 2009, Bodrati *et al.* 2010).

REFERENCES Accordi and Barcellos (2006), Aleixo (1997), Alves *et al.* (2009), Anjos and Boçon (1999), Barber and Rice (2007), Bauer and Pacheco (2000), Belton (1985), Bencke and Kindel (1999), Bencke *et al.* (2006), BirdLife International (2004, 2008), Blamires *et al.* (2002), Bodrati *et al.* (2010), Boesman (2006a), Braz and Cavalcanti (2001), Browne (2005), Carrara *et al.* (2009), Carrano and Marins (2008), Chebez *et al.* (1999), Clausi (2005), Corrêa *et al.* (2008), Donatelli and Ferreira (2009), Faria and Rodrigues (2009), Goerck (1999), Gomes and Silva (2002), Gonzaga and Castiglioni (2001), Gonzaga *et al.* (1995), Hasui *et al.* (2009), Hayes (1995), Hellmayr (1929b), Iartelli (2004), Krabbe (2007), Lopes *et al.* (2005, 2008), Maciel (2009), Maciel *et al.* (2009), Madroño *et al.* (1997a, 1997b), Mallet-Rodrigues and Noronha (2009), Mallet-Rodrigues *et al.* (2007), Manhães and Dias (2009), Marini *et al.* (1997b), Maurício and Dias (1998), Mazar Barnett and Kirwan (1999), Mestre (2004), Minns *et al.* (2009), Naka *et al.* (2002), Ohlson *et al.* (2008), Oliveira *et al.* (2009), Pacheco *et al.* (2009), Parker and Goerck (1997), Parrini *et al.* (1999), de la Peña (1989), Pineschi (1990), Pinto (1944), Pimentel and Olmos (2011), Pires *et al.* (1991), Remold (2002), Ridgely and Tudor (1994, 2009), do Rosário (1996), Scheibler and Melo-Júnior (2003), Sick (1993, 1997), Silva (1996), Snow (1975, 2004b), Stotz *et al.* (1996), Straneck (1990), Straube (2008a), Straube and Urben-Filho (2008), Vasconcelos (2008), Vasconcelos and D'Angelo Neto (2007, 2009), Vasconcelos and Melo Júnior (2001), Vasconcelos *et al.* (2002, 2003), Venturini *et al.* (2001), Willis (1992), Willis and Oniki (2002).

Greenish Schiffornis *Schiffornis virescens.* **Fig. 1**. Ilha Comprida, São Paulo, southeast Brazil, October (*Hadoram Shirihai / Photographic Handbook to Birds of the World*). This species and Thrush Schiffornis *S. turdina* are altitudinally segregated in the Atlantic Forest of eastern Brazil, with the *S. virescens* at higher elevations where the two co-occur. However, Greenish Schiffornis is more widespread in this region than *S. turdina* and where the latter is absent the present species can be found down to sea level, like the bird in the photograph.

THRUSH-LIKE SCHIFFORNIS
Schiffornis turdina   Plate 13

Muscicapa turdina Wied, 1831, *Beitr. Naturg. Bras.* 3(2): 817, [Bahia,] Brazil

As its name suggests, to the uninitiated this species might briefly recall a small and very poorly marked thrush, although its short tail, different bill shape, specific lack of obvious markings and generally 'manakin'-like behaviour should swiftly enable its identification, at least to genus.

IDENTIFICATION 14.5–19.5cm. This geographically variable species is the largest of the genus *Schiffornis* (it was formerly placed in the monotypic genus *Herteropelma* by some authorities, e.g. by Sclater 1888). All subspecies are essentially brown or olive-brown, being paler on the underparts, with prominent large dark eyes (described as 'dreamy-looking' by Hilty 2003) and an indistinct pale eye-ring. Thrush-like Schiffornis can be recognised by its rather stocky proportions, relatively long tail (for a 'manakin'), rounded head and 'wide-eyed stare' (Griscom 1932). The lack of bright cinnamon tones and a grey ocular area separate it from Várzea Schiffornis *Schiffornis major*, from which it is likely to be almost entirely separated by habitat. In the Atlantic Forest, *S. turdina* is never so olive as to raise the real possibility of confusion with the generally much more ubiquitous Greenish Schiffornis *Schiffornis virescens*. Several rather nondescript female manakins overlap with *S. turdina* across its extremely broad range, but all are much greener and, if its colour can not be readily appreciated, much smaller. In Panama, western Colombia and extreme northwest Ecuador, Broad-billed Sapayoa *Sapayoa aenigma* must be considered. However, the schiffornis is less pure olive and lacks the yellow tones to the belly of the *Sapayoa*. Brownish Twistwing *Cnipodectes subbrunneus*, a tyrannid of Panama and western South America, is slimmer and longer tailed than Thrush-like Schiffornis, and has a larger mandible with a paler base and obvious rictal bristles. Furthermore, it has buff fringes to the wing feathers and fairly distinct wingbars (Thrush-like's wings are relatively plain), and the twistwing habitually raises its wings.

DISTRIBUTION Thrush-like Schiffornis has a broad range across all of Central America, and north into Mexico, as well as over much of northern and central South America, south to Bolivia and southeastern Brazil. West of the Andes, Thrush-like Schiffornis ranges from the Pacific lowlands of Colombia, through Ecuador to Tumbes, in extreme northwest Peru, where it was discovered as recently as 1979 (Wiedenfeld *et al.* 1985), and north through the Caribbean lowlands to northwest Venezuela, in Zulia to Aragua, thereafter reappearing in southern Venezuela and across the Guianas. The species then occurs south and west across most of Amazonia, from Maranhão and northern Tocantins in northeast Brazil to northern Bolivia (south to dptos. Santa Cruz and Cochabamba) and southeastern Peru. There is a quite separate population in the Atlantic Forest of eastern Brazil, which is found from Paraíba south to Espírito Santo and locally into northern Rio de Janeiro as far south as the Serra dos Órgãos region (Mallet-Rodrigues *et al.* 2007, Pimentel and Olmos 2011). In Venezuela this schiffornis reaches to 1,800m north of the Orinoco, but rarely above 800m to the south of the river (although it has been noted to 1,450m on the Sierra de Lema: Hilty 2003). In Peru it ascends the foothills east of the Andes to

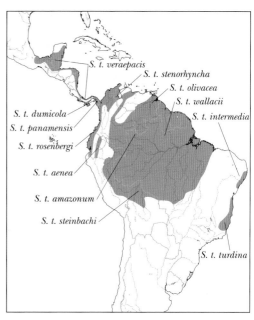

1,800m (Robbins *et al.* 2011), and reaches 1,700m in Bolivia (Hennessey 2004b), whilst in Panama the species occurs to at least 1,400m (Wetmore 1972). Thrush-like Schiffornis has recently been observed in the East Andes of Colombia at 1,000m (Salaman *et al.* 2002b), but it is generally found below 800m in Amazonian Brazil and the Atlantic Forest.

HABITAT Thrush-like Schiffornis is found in many types of humid and wet forest, as well as in tall second growth and wooded *campina* in Brazil, semi-deciduous forest in Tumbes, Peru, *garúa* forest in Ecuador (Becker and Agreda 2005) and deciduous forest in northern Venezuela (in Henri Pittier National Park).

MOVEMENTS None definitely known; e.g. the species was resident at Hilty's (1997) study site in the Pacific Andes. However, in northern Venezuela at a study locality in deciduous forest, Verea and Solórzano (2001) recorded this species only in the dry season, indicating that some kind of, as yet poorly understood, movements are performed at least in some parts of the species' range.

DESCRIPTION Sexes are alike, although Wetmore (1972) considered females to be usually somewhat duller. Generally, the species' structural attributes are much like those of its congenerics (which see). *Adult.* – Variable, but most are rather dingy brown with some rufous, grey or olive according to race (see Geographical Variation). Typical birds (including the nominate race) are uniform dingy brown above with slightly more rufescent fringes to the wing feathers. The underparts are dull olive-brown, becoming slightly more cinnamon on the throat. Paler mid belly. *Juvenile.* – For Panama, Wetmore (1972) described this age as being largely rather dull reddish-brown on the upper- and underparts, becoming even brighter on the crown, and greyer on the throat and ventral region. Skutch (1969) reported the nestling to have 'copious long brownish grey down, more abundant than that on the nestlings of the majority of passerine birds.' This contrasts with the rather minimal amount of natal down in 'true' Pipridae (Skutch 1969, Foster 1976, Collins 1982, Christian 2001). *Moult.* –

335

There are few published moult data. Willard *et al.* (1991) reported that two collected in southern Venezuela (race *S. t. amazonum*) were replacing the tail- and wing feathers, and another taken in March was in body moult, but still others from the same locality in the same months showed no evidence of feather replacement. In eastern Ecuador birds (race *S. t. aenea*) collected in June–September were evidently moulting (variably) wing-, tail- and body feathers, whilst those taken in March and April showed no evidence of feather replacement (MECN). In northwest Ecuador (race *S. t. rosenbergi*) one taken in late May was replacing some body feathers, whilst another, collected in July, was moulting both the body- and wing feathers (MECN). *Bare parts.* – Bill black or blackish, occasionally dark brown and sometimes with a paler (flesh-coloured) base to the lower mandible; the legs, feet and soles are blackish to grey or even blue-grey; and the irides are whitish-brown, brown, coffee-coloured or greyish-brown, with a narrow pale eye-ring (data pertain to *S. t. veraepacis*, *S. t. acrolophites*, *S. t. amazonum*, *S. t. rosenbergi*, *S. t. wallacii* and *S. t. aenea*: Hartert 1898, Novaes 1978, Robbins *et al.* 1985, Wiedenfeld *et al.* 1985; MECN; MNCR).

MEASUREMENTS Data for all races are presented with the sexes combined. *S. t. turdina* (BMNH; MNRJ: Espírito Santo and Bahia, eastern Brazil): wing ($n = 9$) 93.5–102.0mm; tail ($n = 14$) 65–76mm; bill ($n = 9$) 17.61–18.55mm; tarsus ($n = 6$) 22–23mm. *S. t. veraepacis* (FMNH; MNCR; RMNH: Costa Rica, Guatemala, Honduras and Mexico): wing ($n = 17$) 86–92mm; tail ($n = 17$) 60.5–73.5mm; bill ($n = 17$) 16.22–17.91mm; tarsus ($n = 17$) 17.52–22.53mm. Data from a live bird (Jenkins 1982: Belize): wing ($n = 1$) 85mm; bill ($n = 1$) 14.4mm; tarsus ($n = 1$) 21.6mm. *S. t. dumicola* (Wetmore 1972: western and central Panama): wing ($n = 18$) 85–92mm; tail ($n = 18$) 58.5–68.5mm; bill ($n = 18$) 15.8–18.6mm; tarsus ($n = 18$) 20.6–23.6mm. *S. t. panamensis* (Wetmore 1972: eastern Panama): wing ($n = 20$) 87–93mm; tail ($n = 20$) 57.0–66.5mm; bill ($n = 20$) 15.3–17.7mm; tarsus ($n = 20$) 21.0–22.9mm. *S. t. acrolophites* (Wetmore 1972: eastern Panamanian highlands): wing ($n = 13$) 85.0–93.5mm; tail ($n = 13$) 59–70mm; bill ($n = 13$) 16.6–19.5mm; tarsus ($n = 13$) 21.3–23.3mm (cf. also Zimmer 1936a). *S. t. aenea* (MECN: eastern Ecuador): wing ($n = 7$) 87–96mm; tail ($n = 7$) 62–73mm; bill ($n = 7$) 15.3–17.0mm. *S. t. rosenbergi* (BMNH; MECN; Hartert 1898; J. Hornbuckle unpubl. of live birds: Colombia and west Ecuador): wing ($n = 10$) 83–89mm; tail ($n = 9$) 59–67mm; bill ($n = 4$) 15.20–17.67mm; tarsus ($n = 7$) 20.86–23.00mm. *S. t. stenorhyncha* (Blake 1950; BMNH; FMNH: Colombia): wing ($n = 9$) 88–94mm; tail ($n = 10$) 59–68mm; bill ($n = 9$) 15.54–17.82mm; tarsus ($n = 9$) 21.65–24.00mm. *S. t. olivacea* (BMNH; FMNH: Brazil, Guyana): wing ($n = 11$) 84–94mm; tail ($n = 11$) 59–70mm; bill ($n = 11$) 14.69–16.81mm; tarsus ($n = 10$) 21–24mm. *S. t. wallacii* (MNRJ; RMNH: Amapá and Pará, Brazil, and Surinam): wing ($n = 21$) 82–95mm; tail ($n = 21$) 62–74mm; bill ($n = 21$) 14.67–16.93mm; tarsus ($n = 3$) 18.75–23.33mm. Additional measurements were presented by Hellmayr (1906b). *S. t. amazonum* (BMNH: Ecuador and Peru; Hellmayr 1910: Amazonas; MNRJ: Mato Grosso, both Brazil): wing ($n = 11$) 86–91mm; tail ($n = 16$) 58–70mm; bill ($n = 7$) 15.71–17.08mm; tarsus ($n = 3$) 17.74–18.34mm. *S. t. steinbachi* (J. Hornbuckle unpubl. of live birds: Beni, Bolivia, for wing only; other measurements BMNH: Peru and Bolivia): wing ($n = 29$) 83–91mm; tail ($n = 3$) 60–65mm; tarsus ($n = 3$) 21–22mm. Weight (sexes combined): 39–43g (*S. t. turdina*; two unsexed: MNRJ); 30.2–35.5g (*S. t.*

veraepacis; five males and one female: Binford 1989; MNCR; ROM); 33.1g (*S. t. dumicola*; one female: Strauch 1977); 32–40g (*S. t. acrolophites*; $n = 15$: Robbins *et al.* 1985); 28–32g (*S. t. olivacea*; three males and one female: Pérez-Emán *et al.* 2003; FMNH; ROM); 28.5–31.0g (*S. t. aenea*; $n = 7$: MECN); 21–35g (*S. t. rosenbergi*; $n = 9$: King 1991; J. Hornbuckle unpubl.; FMNH; MECN); 30–34g (*S. t. stenorhyncha*; $n = 3$: Verea *et al.* 1999); 22–37g (*S. t. wallacii*; $n = 27$: Haverschmidt 1952, Fry 1970, Novaes 1976, Dick *et al.* 1984, Silva *et al.* 1990; MVZ; RMNH; ROM); 28.3–34.0g (*S. t. amazonum*; $n = 12$: Willard *et al.* 1991); 22.0–38.4g (*S. t. steinbachi*; $n = 45$: Bates *et al.* 1989; J. Hornbuckle unpubl.).

GEOGRAPHICAL VARIATION Deeply complex, but never very marked or striking. Thirteen races are currently recognised (Dickinson 2003, Snow 2004b), although some rationalisation might be advisable. Their traditionally ascribed ranges are delimited below. *S. t. turdina* in eastern Brazil, from southern Bahia to Espírito Santo, is described above; typical plumage, and distinctly larger than the other races, which from north to south are as follows. *S. t. veraepacis* (P. L. Sclater & Salvin, 1860) of southeastern Mexico to western Panama is more olivaceous overall than the nominate race, and has the throat brighter olive; the fringes to the wing feathers are contrastingly warm brown. *S. t. dumicola* (Bangs, 1903, including *S. t. furva* Ridgway, 1906, which race was recognised well into the 20th century and even ascribed a rather wide range) of western and central Panama is darker above than the nominate race, and is dark olive-grey below (duller than *S. t. veraepacis*). The wing feathers have contrastingly browner fringes. (See also Wetmore 1972.) Hellmayr (1929b) and Monroe (1968) considered this race to be invalid. *S. t. panamensis* C. E. Hellmayr, 1929, in the lowlands (below *c.*600m) of eastern Panama and the northern Chocó of Colombia (as far as the Ríos Sinú and Cauca) has a brighter rufous crown, wings and tail, and the throat and upper breast are cinnamon-rufous, contrasting with the greyish-olive lower breast and belly (cf. Wetmore 1972). *S. t. acrolophites* Wetmore, 1972, in the highlands of eastern Panama (where it is common on the Serranía de Jungurudó) and northwest Colombia (at least as far as the Serranía de Baudó) is generally darker and more olive-brown than the last, and is uniform brownish-olive below, lacking any greyish tones (becoming chestnut-brown on the chin and throat). *S. t. rosenbergi* (E. Hartert, 1898) is found in southwestern Colombia and western Ecuador as far south as northwest Peru, and closely resembles *S. t. acrolophites*, but was considered by Wetmore (1972) to have the wings and tail more olive-grey (with fewer rufous tones), the throat paler and also less rufescent, and to be somewhat smaller in size. *S. t. stenorhyncha* (P. L. Sclater & Salvin, 1869) of western Venezuela (at the base of the Andes, from Táchira and Barinas to Lara, and eastern Falcón to Aragua and perhaps Miranda) and eastern Colombia is markedly more rufous (like *S. t. panamensis*), especially on the wings, whilst the throat and breast are tinged yellowish, offering some contrast with the rest of the greyish-olive rear underparts. However, Blake (1950) felt unable to assign a female from the Sierra Macarena to this or any other known race, illustrating again the difficulties posed by this species. *S. t. aenea* J. T. Zimmer, 1936, occurs on the east slope of the Andes in Ecuador and northern Peru. It is more uniform, as in *S. t. acrolophites*, and was described as being nearest to *S. t. rosenbergi* but having the upperparts browner and less greenish, with a more rufescent crown, more brownish breast, more greenish belly and the outer wings warmer brown. Compared with *S. t. amazonum*, Zimmer (1936a) felt that *S. t. aenea* was overall brighter and more greenish, especially on the belly, the back more bronzy and the breast more golden-brown. **S. t. amazonum** (P. L. Sclater, 1860, including *S. t. intercedens* Todd, 1928) is widespread across southern Venezuela (in Amazonas), southeast Colombia (see Dugand and Phelps 1948), eastern Peru and western Brazil east as far as northwestern Mato Grosso, and is similar to the nominate race, albeit the crown is slightly more cinnamon and it lacks the distinct cinnamon-brown wash to the upper breast of *S. t. turdina*. But, based on specimen material in MNRJ, in morphology it clearly grades closely into *S. t. wallacii* in the region of the central Rio Teles Pires. Gyldenstolpe (1945) considered that *S. t. wallacii* and *S. t. amazonum* might intergrade between the lower Rio Tapajós and lower Rio Madeira, but earlier Zimmer (1936a) had considered that *S. t. wallacii* reaches much further west than currently agreed subspecific limits, as far as the Rio Madeira, graphically illustrating the difficulties of assigning such very similar birds to one subspecies or another. Four specimens from Beni, Bolivia, were also considered by Gyldenstolpe to be somewhat intermediate between *S. t. wallacii* and *S. t. amazonum*. Such difficulties in racial assignation are clearly compounded by the existence of not inconsiderable individual variation amongst birds from the same locality (Gyldenstolpe 1945). The spelling of this race has been modified in line with the correction made by David and Gosselin (2011) to their earlier paper (David and Gosselin 2002b). *S. t. intercedens* was described from the Rio Purus, Amazonas, Brazil, but is clearly invalid (Gyldenstolpe 1951). **S. t. olivacea** (Ridgway, 1906) of eastern Venezuela (in dptos. Bolívar and Delta Amacuro) and Guyana has dull olive tones and uniform plumage as in *S. t. acrolophites*. Gyldenstolpe (1945) considered that it might be separable from *S. t. wallacii* in being more brownish-olive above with a browner throat, and from *S. t. amazonum* in its slightly paler upperparts, less reddish cast to the crown and greyer belly. **S. t. wallacii** (P. L. Sclater & Salvin, 1867) occurs in northern Brazil (as far south as the lower Rio Teles Pires and the Serra do Roncador, Mato Grosso, and east to Maranhão), French Guiana and Surinam, and resembles the nominate race (its type locality is not known beyond Pará, which may present future nomenclatural problems should revised species limits be accepted, see below); it was considered to be paler throughout than *S. t. amazonum* by Zimmer (1936a). Also extremely similar to the nominate are **S. t. steinbachi** Todd, 1928, of southeast Peru and northern Bolivia, and **S. t. intermedia** Pinto, 1954, of eastern Brazil, in Paraíba, Pernambuco and Alagoas.

Following the suggestions of Meyer de Schauensee (1966), Stiles and Skutch (1989), Ridgely and Tudor (1994) and the AOU (1998) that multiple species might be involved in this complex, a more recent attempt to reconstruct the phylogeography of *S. turdina*, coupled with a partial vocal analysis of the group, revealed seven lineages, and recommended that five parapatric and vocally distinct forms should be recognised as species under the Biological Species Concept (Nyári 2007). The latter author found evidence of vocal (note structure, number of notes, note frequency range) and mitochondrial molecular characters to justify recommending the recognition of several species. These are as follows: *S. veraepacis* (Brown Schiffornis) from Mexico to northwest Peru (including the following taxa, *S. t. dumicola*, *S. t. acrolophites* and *S. t. rosenbergi*), *S. stenorhyncha* (Slender-billed Schiffornis) in the lowlands of eastern

Panama to northern Colombia and northwest Venezuela (thus including *S. t. panamensis*, which was not directly sampled by the study), *S. olivacea* (Olivaceous Schiffornis) from southeast Venezuela and the Guianas south across northern Amazonia (including *S. t. wallacii* and part of the range formerly attributed to *S. t. amazonum*), *S. aenea* (Foothill Schiffornis) in the east-slope foothills of the Andes in Ecuador and northern Peru (monotypic), *S. amazonum* (Amazonian Schiffornis) over western Amazonia (including *S. t. steinbachi*) and *S. turdina* (Thrush-like Schiffornis) in southeast Amazonia and the Atlantic Forest of eastern Brazil (including part of the range formerly attributed to *S. t. amazonum*, and *S. t. intermedia*). Peterson and Nyári (2008) found evidence, using niche modelling, to suggest that most of these phylogroups correspond to particular putative Pleistocene refugia. Nyári's (2007) arrangement follows to some extent the species limits adopted by Ridgway (1907), albeit with significant differences. Remsen *et al.* (2009) rejected this proposal, principally due to the large geographical gaps in Nyári's sample and the fact that there was to some extent a lack of congruence between the vocal and genetic data used, and we concur with the latter decision for now. In fact, as also noted by Remsen *et al.* (2009), the species limits proposed by Nyári (2007) might even prove too conservative, especially as the latter author uncovered large genetic differences between populations that he assigned to the same species, and the advertisement vocalisation of southeast Amazonian birds differs to some extent from that in the Atlantic Forest. Whilst playback experiments do not necessarily provide strong evidence of species limits, in our experience (GMK pers. obs.), birds from within the range of *S. t. wallacii* (in northern Brazil) respond swiftly to the voices of Peruvian (*S. t. amazonum*) and eastern Brazilian (*S. t. turdina*), and birds from various localities in Brazil south of the Amazon will respond equally well to the voice of other populations of *S. t. amazonum*, or even *S. t. turdina*. Nonetheless, it is hard to deny that, for instance, *S. t. amazonum* and *S. t. turdina* have easily identifiably different advertisements, but equally there seems to be some evidence of dialects or perhaps even a cline in vocalisations of *S. t. amazonum*. EB has found that *S. aenea* only responds very weakly to the voice of *S. t. amazonum* in northeast Peru. Furthermore, Pacheco and Cohn-Haft (2010) found that the young of *S. turdina sensu lato* shows only very limited ability to 'learn' its song, further hinting that variation in the song across the range might be considered indicative of multiple species-level units. Clearly more work is required, but for now we retain the traditional taxonomy.

VOICE Commercial recordings are available on the following compilations: Delaney (1992), Moore (1992, 1994), Ross and Whitney (1995), Boesman (1999, 2006a, 2006b, 2006c, 2009), Mayer (2000), Ross (2000), Schulenberg *et al.* (2000), Jahn *et al.* (2002), Krabbe and Nilsson (2003), Lysinger *et al.* (2005), Marantz and Zimmer (2006), Alvarez *et al.* (2007), Knapp and Will (2008), Renaudier and Deroussen (2008), Naka *et al.* (2008) and Minns *et al.* (2009). Sound-recordings are also available online at www.xeno-canto.org from the following countries: Belize and Nicaragua (*S. t. veraepacis*), Bolivia (*S. t. steinbachi*), Brazil (nominate, *S. t. amazonum*, *S. t. intermedia* and *S. t. wallacii*), Ecuador (*S. t. aenea* and *S. t. rosenbergi*), Panama (*S. t. dumicola* and *S. t. panamensis*), Peru (*S. t. amazonum*), and Surinam and Venezuela (*S. t. olivacea*). The song, which is highly distinctive once learnt, exhibits some geographical variation (see Nyári 2007, Ridgely and Tudor 2009) but is rarely sufficient to be confusing and playback experiments (see above) suggest that many subspecies recognise and respond vigorously to the song of geographically far removed taxa. The basic song is a 3–4-note series of clear whistles, often with a brief pause after the first note, the second usually high-pitched, and the final note inflected sharply upwards, e.g. *weeeeee...PREE, a-weET* in Amazonas, Venezuela (race *S. t. amazonum*: Hilty 2003), and this is similar in the same race in eastern Peru (Schulenberg *et al.* 2007), the whole sounding rather like the tune to a 'football chant'. To our ear, the southern Venezuelan 'rendition' generally closely recalls the typical song given in northern and central Amazonas, and in northern Mato Grosso, Brazil (all referable to *S. t. wallacii*) (pers. obs.). In contrast the song of *S. t. rosenbergi* (in northwest Peru) is considered thinner and rendered *teeeeeew tui-chuEEE?*, whilst in the foothills on the east slope in the same country, *S. t. aenea* sings a simpler *hew EeuEE TU-hew* (Schulenberg *et al.* 2007), which is considered much faster than the song of *S. t. rosenbergi* (Ridgely and Greenfield 2001). In Mexico (*S. t. veraepacis*) the song is rendered *djeeeeu whee-chee* or *dweeeer weet* (Howell and Webb 1995), whilst in eastern Brazil the song is described as sluggish and can be rendered *teeeu, yoowee tu, tu-wee* (cf. Snow 2004b). Thrush-like Schiffornis sings somewhat irregularly, at more or less any time of day but most frequently in the early morning hours, at intervals of one to several minutes.

NATURAL HISTORY Thrush-like Schiffornis is usually encountered alone and apparently rarely joins mixed-species foraging flocks. Generally retiring and secretive, and usually seen rather infrequently, unless specifically 'called' using playback, when the bird normally bursts back and forth rapidly past the observer, perching in heavy cover some distance from the recording, or may arrive quietly and perch close by, but unobtrusively. Typically perches at 1–3m in an understorey tree, and may cling to vertical stems (like the previous species), as well as perching more conventionally, but often obscured by leaves. Radio-tracking (this is one of the few species treated herein for which such studies have been attempted) has revealed that in French Guiana two males had home ranges of 14.3 and 16.5ha, whilst that of a female was 20.1ha (Théry 1990c *in* Snow 2004b).

FOOD AND FEEDING The species' diet comprises fruit, spiders and insects (including caterpillars, larvae and cicadas) taken using short sallies to leaves and stems. Thrush-like Schiffornis takes larger fruits than true manakins, including those of the following families in French Guiana: Myristicaceae, Burseraceae, Meliaceae, Annonaceae, Lauraceae and Moraceae (Théry 1990c in Snow 2004b). In central Panama, Poulin *et al.* (1999) found that *S. turdina* takes at least ten species of the genera *Miconia* (Melastomataceae) and *Psychotria* (Rubiaceae) alone. In addition, males and females apparently consume approximately equal proportions of melastomes (Melastomataceae) in their diet, at just over 25% (Théry 1990c).

BREEDING Concrete nesting data are distinctly few, especially considering the species' broad geographical range. Females alone are responsible for nest building, incubation and nestling care. Nests found in Costa Rica (*S. t. veraepacis*) were bulky cups lined with fine rootlets and skeletal leaves, and sited 0.5–1.8m above the ground. The nests were sited in a palm stump or lodged against a palm trunk, and contained two pale buff eggs heavily marked with black, dark brown and lilac-grey, especially at the larger end (Skutch 1969). Egg dimensions are given in the latter

publication, and repeated in Wetmore (1972, along with those for Guyana). Seasonality suggested as February in northern and eastern Brazil (Snethlage 1935, Snow 2004b), August/September in southern Guyana (Robbins *et al.* 2007) and January–June in northern Colombia (Hilty and Brown 1986). Other specific breeding data are as follows. Smithe (1966) mentioned a couple of nests in Guatemala and Belize, both with two eggs, although the whitish colour of the first clutch suggests that the identification might be erroneous. Alvarez del Toro's (1952) description of a nest and eggs in Chiapas, Mexico, match well with those of Skutch (1969), as does the description (in Wetmore 1972) of a clutch taken in Guyana in late April and held in the Natural History Museum, Tring (race *S. t. olivacea*). From Oaxaca, Mexico, Binford (1989) reported a male specimen with enlarged testes taken in late May, whilst in Nicaragua, Howell (1957) mentioned a male with slightly enlarged testes in August, and there are specimens in breeding condition collected in Belize in March and July (ROM) and in Costa Rica in January, September and November (FMNH, MNCR). In French Guiana an adult was feeding young (number unspecified) in early December (Tostain *et al.* 1992) and both sexes have been collected in breeding condition in neighbouring Surinam in January–February (RMNH). A fledgling was observed in early October in Bolivia (Hennessey *et al.* 2003a). In eastern Guatemala, both sexes have been collected in breeding condition in mid March (Land 1963) and a female in late January (FMNH); in Ecuador birds in breeding condition have been collected in March (east of the Andes) and July (west slope) (MECN).

STATUS Thrush-like Schiffornis is treated as Least Concern (BirdLife International 2004, 2008) and even if the revised species limits (mentioned above) were to be adopted it seems unlikely that any of the taxa concerned would trigger international-level concern for their conservation. The species is generally fairly common to uncommon across much of its range, especially in Amazonia, but it seems rather local and has almost certainly declined in eastern Brazil due to habitat destruction, where *S. turdina* is mainly confined to the lowlands and lower foothills (Snow 2004b; GMK pers. obs.), as well as in western and northern Venezuela (Hilty 2003). Mist-netting studies have revealed it to be one of the ten most numerous constituents of the understorey avifauna at study sites in southern Venezuela and at Manaus, Brazil, but to be far less common during another, similar study in eastern lowland Ecuador (Blake and Loiselle 2009) and another intensive study in French Guiana also considered the species to be rather uncommon, with just 1.5 pairs per 100ha (Thiollay 1994). However, in Bocas del Toro (Panama), Robinson *et al.* (2000a) estimated the density of subspecies *S. t. panamensis* at four pairs per 100ha. Subspecies *S. t. rosenbergi* is considered rare in northwest Peru (Schulenberg *et al.* 2007) and subspecies *S. t. veraepacis* was regarded as uncommon in Oaxaca, Mexico (Binford 1989). Overall, Thrush-like Schiffornis is known from a large number of protected areas across the species' extremely broad range. The nominate form is confined to the Serra do Mar Centre of endemism (Cracraft 1985).

REFERENCES Almeida *et al.* (2003), Alvarez *et al.* (2007), Alvarez del Toro (1952), Anderson *et al.* (2004), Angehr and Dean (2010), Angehr *et al.* (2004), AOU (1998), Balchin and Toyne (1998), Barnett *et al.* (2002), Bates *et al.* (1989), Becker and Agreda (2005), Becker and López Lanús (1997), Bernard (2008), Binford (1989), BirdLife

International (2004, 2008), Blake (1950), Blake and Loiselle (2009), Boesman (1999, 2006a, 2006b, 2006c, 2009), Borges (2007), Borges *et al.* (2001), Brooks *et al.* (2009), Cadena *et al.* (2000), Chapman (1931), Cohn-Haft *et al.* (1997), Cooper (1997), Cracraft (1985), David and Gosselin (2002b, 2011), Delaney (1992), Dickinson (2003), Donegan and Dávalos (1999), Dugand and Phelps (1948), England (2000), Fry (1970), Garrigues and Dean (2007), Gilliard (1941), González (1998), Griscom (1932), Gyldenstolpe (1945, 1951), Hartert (1898), Haverschmidt (1952, 1968), Hellmayr (1929a, 1929b), Hennessey (2004b), Henriques *et al.* (2003), Hidasi (1998, 2007), Hilty (1997, 2003), Hilty and Brown (1986), Howell and Webb (1995), Jones (2004), Hellmayr (1906b, 1910, 1929b), Hennessey *et al.* (2003a, 2003b), Hornbuckle (1999), Hosner *et al.* (2009), Howell (1957), Jahn *et al.* (2002), Jenkins (1982), King (1991), Kirwan and Marlow (1996), Knapp and Will (2008), Krabbe (2007), Krabbe and Nilsson (2003), Krabbe and Sornoza (1994), Lane *et al.* (2003), Lawson (2010), Lysinger *et al.* (2005), MacLeod *et al.* (2005), Maillard *et al.* (2007), Mallet-Rodrigues *et al.* (2007), Marantz and Zimmer (2006), Mee *et al.* (2002), Merkord *et al.* (2009), Meyer de Schauensee (1966), Meyer de Schauensee and Phelps (1978), Minns *et al.* (2009), Monroe (1968), Moore (1992, 1994), Naka *et al.* (2006, 2008), Novaes (1976, 1978), Nyári (2007), Ohlson *et al.* (2008), Oren and Parker (1997), Ottema *et al.* (2009), Pacheco and Cohn-Haft (2010), Pacheco and Olmos (2005), Pacheco *et al.* (2007), Parker and Goerck (1997), Parker and Parker (1982), Parker and Wust (1994), Parker *et al.* (1994b, 1994c), Pérez-Emán *et al.* (2003), Perry *et al.* (1997), Peterson and Nyári (2008), Pinto (1944, 1953), Pimentel and Olmos (2011), Poulin *et al.* (1999), Puebla-Olivares *et al.* (2002), Peres and Whittaker (1991), Piaskowski *et al.* (2006), Quevedo *et al.* (2006), Remsen *et al.* (2009), Renaudier and Deroussen (2008), Restall *et al.* (2006), Reynaud (1998), Ridgely and Greenfield (2001), Ridgely and Gwynne (1989), Ridgely and Tudor (1994, 2009), Ridgway (1907), Robbins *et al.* (1985, 2004, 2007, 2011), Robinson *et al.* (2000a), Ross (2000), Ross and Whitney (1995), Salaman *et al.* (2002b, 2008), Schulenberg *et al.* (2006, 2007), Sclater (1888), Sick (1993, 1997), Silva (1996), Silva *et al.* (1990), Silveira *et al.* (2005), Skutch (1969, 1981), Smithe (1966), Snethlage (1907, 1908a, 1914, 1935), Snow (2004b), Snyder (1966), Souza *et al.* (2008), Stiles and Skutch (1989), Stone (1928), Stotz *et al.* (1996, 1997), Strauch (1977), Strewe and Navarro (2004a), Théry (1990b, 1990c), Thiollay (1994), Todd and Carriker (1922), Tostain *et al.* (1992), Vallely and Whitman (1997), Verea and Solórzano (2001), Verea *et al.* (1999), Vidoz *et al.* (2010), Wetmore (1972), Wiedenfeld *et al.* (1985), Willard *et al.* (1991), Willis (1992), Willis and Oniki (1990), Winker *et al.* (1992), J. T. Zimmer (1930, 1936a), Zimmer and Hilty (1997), Zimmer *et al.* (1997), Zyskowski *et al.* (2011).

1

Thrush-like Schiffornis *Schiffornis turdina.* **Fig. 1**. *S. t. veraepacis*, Laguna del Lagarto Lodge, prov. Heredia, northeast Costa Rica, September (*Kevin Easley / Costa Rica Gateway*). **Fig. 2**. *S. t. rosenbergi*, Milpe Bird Sanctuary, prov. Pichincha, northwest Ecuador, June (*Nick Athanas / Tropical Birding*). **Fig. 3**. *S. t. wallacii*, INPA Campina Reserve, north of Manaus, Amazonas, northern Amazonian Brazil, September (*Hadoram Shirihai / Photographic Handbook to Birds of the World*). **Fig. 4**. *S. t. wallacii*, near Senhor do Bonfim, Tocantins, east Amazonian Brazil, January (*William Price / www.pbase/tereksandpiper*). **Fig. 5**. *S. t. turdina*, Porto Seguro, Bahia, eastern Brazil, April (*Ciro Albano*). Thirteen subspecies are generally recognised in this very widespread species, but morphological variation between them proves to be very slight, as these photographs prove. Nonetheless, vocalisations and genetic data suggest that as many as five species might be recognised within this complex.

Genus *Laniocera*: mourners

In terms of their relationships, the two species of *Laniocera* mourners have been a most unsatisfactorily known pair of taxa. Sclater (1888) considered them Cotingidae, as did Hellmayr (1929b), whereas Ridgway (1907) preferred to place them (and *Schiffornis*) within the Pipridae. In total contrast, Ames (1971) recommended that *Laniocera* be removed to the Tyrannidae based on the musculature of the syrinx resembling that in *Attila*, *Casiornis* and *Rhytipterna*, which was followed by Wetmore (1972), Traylor (1979) and the AOU (1983). Lanyon (1985), however, disagreed with Ames's syringeal analysis and stated confidently that *Laniocera* could not be a near relative of *Myiarchus* and should not be placed within the Tyranninae. Seemingly, there is now some certainty that they belong, with several other species treated in this book, outwith both the Cotingidae and the Pipridae, amongst the so-called Schiffornis assemblage, for which the family Tityridae has recently been resurrected for most constituents (Ericson *et al.* 2006, Remsen *et al.* 2009). Genetic data reveal *Laniocera* and *Laniisoma* to be close relatives, and arguably more circumstantial evidence of this close relationship has become available recently, with the discovery of the chick of the Cinereous Mourner *Laniocera hypopyrra* (d'Horta *et al.* in prep.).

CINEREOUS MOURNER
Laniocera hypopyrra   Plate 20

Ampelis hypopyrra **Vieillot 1817**, *Nouv. Dict. Hist. Nat.*, nouv. édn. 8: 164, La Guyane (= Cayenne)

A widespread but generally uncommon and rather inconspicuous inhabitant of Amazonian forests, Cinereous Mourner is one of those many species which will be encountered rather more frequently once its quite easily overlooked vocalisations are learnt.

IDENTIFICATION 20–21cm. The present species is readily separated from the wholly allopatric Speckled Mourner *Laniocera rufescens* based on its largely grey plumage. The most significant confusion risks are almost certainly Screaming Piha *Lipaugus vociferans* and Greyish Mourner *Rhytipterna simplex*, both of which widely overlap in geographical and altitudinal range with the present species, and all three can be found syntopically. Neither the piha nor the *Rhytipterna* possess any rufous spotting in the wing-coverts or on the tail tip, or on the underparts, and both of these potential confusion species lack the yellow or orange pectoral tufts of the present species, whilst the piha is also marginally larger and the Greyish Mourner slightly smaller than this species. Furthermore, *R. simplex* has a much 'fiercer' facial expression, created by its flatter crown, which is less rounded and dove-like than that of Cinereous Mourner.

DISTRIBUTION The Cinereous Mourner is widely distributed virtually throughout Amazonia and the Guianan Shield, with an isolated population in a relatively small part of eastern Brazil again affirming the close relationship between the Atlantic and Amazonian forests (Willis 1992). It is found from northeast Venezuela, where the species reaches its northernmost extent in southeast Sucre, at Caño La Brea, south and east through the remainder of easternmost Venezuela and locally over the entire country south of the Río Orinoco (Hilty 2003), and the Guianas, where it is widespread but uncommon in Guyana (Braun *et al.* 2007), rare to uncommon in Surinam (Ottema *et al.* 2009) and rare in French Guiana (Tostain *et al.* 1992), southeast Colombia, in extreme southwest Casanare and northeast Guainía southward (Hilty and Brown 1986), throughout most of lowland eastern Ecuador (Ridgely and Greenfield 2001) and eastern Peru (Schulenberg *et al.* 2007) to northern Bolivia as far south as dptos. La Paz,

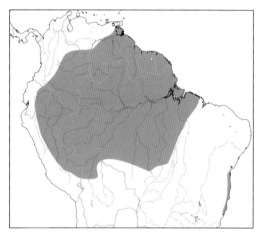

Cochabamba and Santa Cruz (Remsen *et al.* 1987, Remsen and Traylor 1989), and across the vast swathe of Amazonian Brazil, east as far as Belém, in eastern Pará, and western Maranhão, and south in the east of its Amazonian range to the headwaters of the Tapajós and Xingu, in northern Mato Grosso (Sick 1997, Zimmer *et al.* 1997). There is a quite separate, but not morphologically distinct, population in the Atlantic Forest of eastern Brazil, which is apparently confined to northern Espírito Santo and southeastern Bahia, where the species is known from comparatively few sites, among them Sooretama Biological Reserve, Espírito Santo (Parker and Goerck 1997, Passamani *et al.* 2009), the Serra das Lontras, Bahia (Silveira *et al.* 2005) and Barrolândia (16°04'N, 39°11'W), Bahia (GMK pers. obs.). It reaches north in Bahia as far as the environs of Ituberá (13°44'S, 39°09'W: XC15693). Cinereous Mourner is generally found below 500m, e.g. in the Atlantic Forest of Brazil, as well as in Bolivia, Colombia, Ecuador and Venezuela (Hilty and Brown 1986, Ridgely and Greenfield 2001, Hennessey *et al.* 2003b, Hilty 2003), but has recently been found at *c.*800m in the Serra dos Carajás, Pará, Brazil (Pacheco *et al.* 2007), at 830m in southernmost Venezuela (Crease 2009), to 850m in southeastern Ecuador (Schulenberg and Awbrey 1997) and the species occurs irregularly to 900m in eastern Peru, e.g. on the Cerros del Sira (Terborgh and Weske 1975, Schulenberg *et al.* 2007). There is an unpublished record from southern Venezuela, west of Santa Elena de Uairén, Bolívar, from 1,010m (C. Parrish; XC6176).

MOVEMENTS The species is considered to be probably sedentary (Walther 2004).

HABITAT This mourner principally inhabits relatively tall-canopy *terra firme* forest, perhaps most especially on sloping ground or near wet ravines (Peres and Whittaker 1991, Hilty 2003), but is also found in seasonally flooded *igapó* and swampy forests (Zimmer and Hilty 1997, Borges *et al.* 2001, Schulenberg *et al.* 2007) as well as in humid sandy-belt woodland, more extensive savanna forests (e.g. in the Guianas, northernmost Brazil, southern Venezuela and eastern Colombia) and wooded sand-ridges (Hilty and Brown 1986, Zimmer and Hilty 1997, Robbins *et al.* 2004, Santos and Silva 2007).

DESCRIPTION The sexes are usually considered to be identical in plumage (e.g. Walther 2004, Restall *et al.* 2006), but Hilty and Brown (1986) and Hilty (2003), amongst others, state that they differ in the colour of the pectoral tufts, as apparently does the next species. However, the evidence for this statement is unclear and seems not compelling (see below). There appears to be quite extensive individual variation, at all ages, in the amount and brightness of rufous spotting in the plumage and this has undoubtedly led to the ongoing controversy concerning sex- and age-related plumage variation. The bill is rounded and only slightly hooked at the tip (both sexes) and the rictal bristles are well developed being up to 12mm long. *Adult.* – Primarily grey with slightly darker wings and tail than the rest of the upperparts, and, on the underparts, the throat and upper breast are slightly paler than the remainder, which in turn are marginally lighter than the entire dorsal surface. Some adults have pale outer fringes to the tertials. There are faint pale bars across the lower breast and belly, and a tuft of bright orange-cinnamon feathers on the body-sides, which is usually obscured by the wings. The female is sometimes stated to be differentiated by having paler, lemon-yellow pectoral tufts (Snyder 1966, Hilty and Brown 1986, Hilty 2003). However, Friedmann (1948) reported female specimens with both yellow and orange-tawny tufts on the body-sides, and considered that this variation was individual (as had Zimmer 1936b), and we have seen Brazilian specimens labelled as being females with bright orange pectoral tufts (e.g. BMNH 88.1.13.1539) or a mix of pale yellow and bright tawny feathers in this region (e.g. BMNH 88.1.13.1536) and a male from Guyana also has mixed feathers (e.g. BMNH 88.1.20.603). Note that in *L. rufescens*, it is apparently the male that has the paler-coloured pectoral tufts. Zimmer (1936b) added that females (and young) have more pronounced dusky barring than adult males on the feathers of the shoulder patch and pectoral tuft. The most obvious feature of the adult plumage is the pale cinnamon spots that adorn the tips of the median and greater wing-coverts, which create two discontinuous wingbars, and on the tertials. *Juvenile/ Immature.* – Restall *et al.* (2006) considered that juveniles are highly distinct in having bright cinnamon and rufous spots with black subterminal margins on the wing-coverts, secondaries and tertials, cinnamon-rufous tips to the rectrices and uppertail-coverts, and a V-shaped pattern of rufous-and-black spots across the belly and undertail-coverts, whilst immature or subadult birds have just a few random rufous spots on the lower body and retain the black frames to the wing-covert spots. Hilty (2003) and Schulenberg *et al.* (2007), respectively, described and illustrated this species as having inconspicuous pale rufous tips to the tail feathers,

the implication being that this character is not shown by adults. In contrast to Restall *et al.* (2006), the immature plumage has generally been considered since the work of Zimmer (1936b) to be differentiated by having highly variable rufous feathering intermixed with black terminal spotting to the feathers of the belly and undertail-coverts, and sometimes also variously over the uppertail-coverts, breast, interscapular region and superciliary, the last named without any black tips. Pinto (1947), in contrast, considered that the rufous pattern is highly inconstant in immatures. Further, Zimmer (1936b) also remarked that immatures seem to have brighter spotting on the wing-coverts with strong terminal black bars to these feathers, but again noted that these spots can be variable (as indeed they are to some extent in adults), and that juveniles can have rufous spotting at the tips of the rectrices (with which Restall *et al.* 2006 agreed). The pectoral tufts are usually even less conspicuous at this age, and can be mixed tawny and yellow. Although we lack sufficiently detailed field or museum experience to comment extensively on this issue, it seems likely to us that, given the recent (to date unpublished) discovery that the nestling of *L. hypopyrra* closely resembles that of Elegant Mourner *Laniisoma elegans* (which see; d'Horta *et al.* in prep.), plumage maturation is probably much as suggested by Restall *et al.* (2006), i.e. the birds progressively shed their rufous feathering with age, just as in *L. elegans*. *Moult.* – Almost nothing is known concerning moult in this species, but Zimmer (1936b) suggested that the post-juvenile moult must be partial and that the immature/subadult plumage must be relatively short-lived, with a complete moult to adult plumage following shortly afterwards. One mid-March specimen taken in southern Venezuela was renewing the rectrices; however, others taken during the same period showed no evidence of moult (Willard *et al.* 1991). Females collected in southeast Peru in August and Bolivia in October were not moulting (FMNH). *Bare parts.* – The irides are dark brown or grey-brown to black (once purple) surrounded by a narrow yellow to orange eye-ring, with a largely dark brown to blackish bill relieved by a greyish base to the mandible and maxilla, and the legs and feet are grey, brown or greenish-grey (Snethlage 1908b, Novaes 1978, Willard *et al.* 1991, Ridgely and Greenfield 2001, Walther 2004; FMNH).

MEASUREMENTS (CUMZ; BMNH: Brazil, Colombia, Guyana, Peru, Surinam) Wing of male (n = 9) 106.5– 112.0mm, wing of female (n = 19) 104.0–114.5mm; tail of male (n = 9) 82–98mm, tail of female (n = 18) 81.0–97.5mm; bill of male (n = 7) 17.71–21.87mm, bill of female (n = 9) 18.01–21.35mm; tarsus of male (n = 6) 17.72–21.95mm, tarsus of female (n = 7) 18.36–24.06mm. Some additional mensural data were presented by Hellmayr (1929b) and Pinto (1966). Specimens from north of the Amazon appear to be, on average, slightly shorter winged and shorter tailed than those populations from further south, including those in the Atlantic Forest. Weight (sexes combined): 36.0–58.5g (Haverschmidt 1952, Bates *et al.* 1989, Willard *et al.* 1991, Walther 2004, Dunning 2008; FMNH).

GEOGRAPHICAL VARIATION Monotypic, although the name *L. h. sibilatrix*, Wied, 1831, is available for the eastern Brazil population should it, for instance, prove to be genetically distinct. Zimmer (1936b) found no evidence to recognise it on morphological pretexts and there is no reason to suppose that the Atlantic Forest birds differ vocally.

VOICE The species' ventriloquial and far-carrying song is easily passed off as belonging to an insect or an amphibian, especially at any distance. The song is a series of up to 10–15 very high-pitched, somewhat squeaky, slurred *eww-EE*, or *seea-weh* or *tee-o-weeét* phrases, which sounds not unlike that of *L. rufescens*. The first whistle can be more prolonged, e.g. *cheeeeee-a-wee*, perhaps somewhat recalling the song of Sharpbill *Oxyruncus cristatus*, which is also on a descending scale but sounds fuller and is repeated more frequently (Sick 1997), and thereafter the bird enters what has been described as a singsong rhythm (Hilty 2003). Like the next species, the Cinereous Mourner probably operates an exploded lek system, with 2–4 males singing over a relatively large area of several hundred metres, with each bird only just in earshot of the next. Also in common with Speckled Mourner, the species can sing for long periods, albeit with considerable pauses between songs, even during the hottest part of the day. Individuals sing from comparatively open perches in the midstorey, but nonetheless they can still be difficult to spot in relatively dense forest. Other reported vocalisations are broadly similar to the song and include a plaintive *teeéuw* whistle, given 3–4 times (Ridgely and Greenfield 2001) and a shrieking *weet-jeh* (P. Coopmans *in* Ridgely and Greenfield 2001). Cinereous Mourner can be responsive to playback, often approaching the observer at around eye level. The vocalisations of this species appear on the following audio compilations: Moore (1993), Boesman (1999), Mayer (2000), Schulenberg *et al.* (2000), Krabbe and Nilsson (2003), Boesman (2006a, 2006b, 2009), Marantz and Zimmer (2006), Naka *et al.* (2008) and Renaudier and Deroussen (2008). Recordings from Bolivia, Brazil, French Guiana, Peru and Venezuela are also available online at www.xeno-canto.org.

NATURAL HISTORY Easily overlooked and the species is generally encountered rather infrequently (Ridgely and Tudor 2009). Cinereous Mourner principally inhabits the midstorey and upper understorey, where it at least occasionally joins mixed-species flocks, e.g. of antbirds and woodcreepers (Hilty 2003) but also of flycatchers, woodpeckers and tanagers, etc. (GMK pers. obs.). However, such behaviour is considered uncommon, at least in Peru (Schulenberg *et al.* 2007). In the Peruvian Amazon, Brooks *et al.* (1999) observed a male Spangled Cotinga *Cotinga cayana* and a Cinereous Mourner mobbing a female Bare-necked Fruitcrow *Gymnoderus foetidus* in the canopy of primary forest, which they swiftly chased off.

FOOD AND FEEDING Diet is rather imprecisely known, beyond that it sally-hovers to glean arthropods (including dipterans and lepidopterans) and their larvae from either bark or foliage, more occasionally taking airborne insects (flies and wasps), and pluck fruits (Walther 2004, Restall *et al.* 2006).

BREEDING The only nest details to have been published were based on observations in southeast Peru in late September (matching the general breeding season for birds in lowland forests of this region). This nest was a bulky unlined cup of dry leaves (the upper part of the nest consisting of just a single layer of leaves) concealed within the branches of an epiphytic fern on a tree trunk 1.8m above the ground. The tree itself was 4m tall and sited in floodplain forest with a relatively open understorey and no other tall woody plants within 2m of the nest tree (Londoño and Cadena 2003, wherein colour photographs of the nest and eggs are presented). The clutch is two buff-coloured eggs marked with small brown spots throughout and heavier elongate chocolate-brown blotches at the larger end. Only one adult, presumed to be the female, was seen tending the nest, which was apparently predated just over a week after it was initially found (Londoño and Cadena 2003). Dimensions of the nest and eggs were also presented by the latter authors. Breeding is otherwise very poorly known, although birds with moderate to large gonads and, in one case, a shelled egg in the oviduct have been trapped in September–November in Bolivia and Peru (FMNH), April and May in northern Brazil (Novaes 1978) and Venezuela in March (Willard *et al.* 1991). Snethlage (1908b) collected a juvenile in mid January in east Amazonian Brazil.

STATUS The species is not globally threatened (BirdLife International 2004, 2008) given its wide range, much of it still relatively unspoilt. Nonetheless, its status in the Atlantic Forest seems likely to be quite imperiled, given the small number of suitable localities from which the species is apparently known in this region. Perhaps unsurprisingly, *L. hypopyrra* is listed as Critically Endangered in the state of Espírito Santo (Passamani and Mendes 2007, Simon 2009). Elsewhere, Cinereous Mourner is generally uncommon to rare over most of Amazonia (densities of 1–2 individuals per 100ha, reported in southeast Peru, are probably typical elsewhere too: Terborgh *et al.* 1990, Robinson and Terborgh 1997), but the species is known from a fair number of protected areas across much of its range, including, for example, Pilón Lajas Biosphere Reserve, Bolivia (Hennessey *et al.* 2003a); Cabo Orange and Montanhas do Tumucumaque National Parks, Amapá (Bernard 2008, Souza *et al.* 2008), Reserva Florestal Adolpho Ducke (XC 14612) and Jaú National Park, both Amazonas (Borges *et al.* 2001), Reserva Florestal Michelin, Ituberá (N. Athanas), and Monte Pascoal National Park, both Bahia (GMK pers. obs.), Sooretama Biological Reserve, Espírito Santo (Parker and Goerck 1997, Passamani *et al.* 2009), Tapajós National Park, Pará/Amazonas (Oren and Parker 1997), FLONA de Tapajós, Pará (Henriques *et al.* 2003), Una Biological Reserve (Forrester 1993), RPPN Estação Veracel, Porto Seguro, Bahia (D. A. Scott *et al.*), Reserva Natural de Xixuaú, Roraima (Trolle and Walther 2004), all in Brazil; Tinigua National Park, Colombia (Cadena *et al.* 2000), Yasuni National Park and Biosphere Reserve, and Cuyabeno Faunistic Production Reserve, Ecuador (Williams *et al.* 1997, Ridgely and Greenfield 2001); Manu National Park and Biosphere Reserve (Terborgh *et al.* 1984, Walker *et al.* 2006) and the Tambopata-Candamo Reserved Zone, Peru (Parker and Wust 1994, Parker *et al.* 1994a, 1994b); and the Alto Orinoco-Casiquiare Biosphere Reserve, Bolívar, Venezuela (Walther 2004).

REFERENCES Alverson *et al.* (2001), Balchin and Toyne (1998), Bates *et al.* (1989), Berlepsch and Hartert (1902), Bernard (2008), BirdLife International (2004, 2008), Blake (1962), Boesman (1995, 1999, 2006a, 2006b, 2009), Borges (2007), Borges *et al.* (2001), Brace *et al.* (1997), Braun *et al.* (2007), Brooks *et al.* (1999, 2009), Cadena *et al.* (2000), Cherrie (1916), Cohn-Haft *et al.* (1997), Crease (2009), Dick *et al.* (1984), Forrester (1993), Friedmann (1948), Gilliard (1941), Gyldenstolpe (1945), Haverschmidt (1952), Haverschmidt and Mees (1994), Hellmayr (1929b), Hennessey *et al.* (2003a, 2003b), Henriques *et al.* (2003), Hilty (2003), Hilty and Brown (1986), d'Horta *et al.* (in prep.), Krabbe and Nilsson (2003), Lane *et al.* (2003), Londoño and Cadena (2003), Marantz and Zimmer (2006),

Mayer (2000), Mee *et al.* (2002), Merkord *et al.* (2009), Meyer de Schauensee and Phelps (1978), Moore (1993), Naka *et al.* (2006, 2008), Novaes (1957, 1978), Oren and Parker (1997), Ottema *et al.* (2009), Pacheco *et al.* (2007), Parker and Goerck (1997), Parker and Wust (1994), Parker *et al.* (1982, 1994a, 1994b), Passamani and Mendes (2007), Passamani *et al.* (2009), Peres and Whittaker (1991), Pinto (1944, 1947, 1966), Remsen and Parker (1995), Remsen and Traylor (1989), Remsen *et al.* (1987), Renaudier and Deroussen (2008), Restall *et al.* (2006), Ridgely and Greenfield (2001), Ridgely and Tudor (1994, 2009), Robbins *et al.* (2004, 2007), Robinson and Terborgh (1997), Salaman *et al.* (2008, 2009), Santos and Silva (2007), Schulenberg and Awbrey (1997), Schulenberg *et al.* (2000, 2006, 2007), Sick (1993, 1997), Silva (1996), Silveira *et al.* (2005), Snethlage (1907, 1908b, 1914), Snyder (1966), Souza *et al.* (2008), Stotz *et al.* (1996), Terborgh and Weske (1975), Terborgh *et al.* (1984, 1990), Tostain *et al.* (1992), Trolle and Walther (2004), Walker *et al.* (2006), Walther (2004), Whittaker (2009), Willard *et al.* (1991), Williams *et al.* (1997), Willis (1992), J. T. Zimmer (1930, 1936b), Zimmer and Hilty (1997), Zimmer *et al.* (1997).

Cinereous Mourner *Laniocera hypopyrra*. **Fig. 1**. Junglaven, Amazonas, southern Venezuela, February (*Pete Morris*). **Fig. 2**. Presumed male, Explornapo Lodge, dpto. Loreto, northeast Peru, September (*Hadoram Shirihai / Photographic Handbook to Birds of the World*). The boldly rufous-spotted wing-coverts, which are shared not only with its sole congener, but also with younger *Laniisoma* provide a morphological clue to the close relationship between these two genera, which has been confirmed recently through molecular research.

SPECKLED MOURNER
Laniocera rufescens   **Plate 20**

Lipaugus rufescens **P. L. Sclater, 1858**, *Proc. Zool. Soc. Lond.* 1857: 276, Cobán, Alta Verapaz, Guatemala

This species, which forms a superspecies with Cinereous Mourner *Laniocera hypopyrra*, has a wide range, but is rather infrequently seen over most of it. As long ago as the first third of the 19th century, the Speckled Mourner was described as one of the scarcest of Middle American birds, suggesting that modern-day rates of deforestation are not solely to blame for its perceived rarity. Nonetheless, *L. rufescens* seems tolerably common in parts of eastern Panama, this region being probably the best area to find the species.

IDENTIFICATION 19.0–21.5cm. Although superficially similar to several other largely rufous-plumaged tyrannids or tyrannid-like birds, given a reasonable view this species should be relatively easily identified. There is no overlap with the previous species, but in any case its sole congeneric has quite different, principally grey, rather than rufous plumage. Remember that in most regions, the two principal confusion species are undoubtedly much more likely to be encountered than is *L. rufescens*. Speckled Mourner is probably most likely to be confused with the slightly larger Rufous Piha *Lipaugus unirufus*, which has a heavier (deeper based) bill, no markings on the breast, lacks the pectoral tufts of the present species and shows no obvious wing markings, unlike this mourner. Despite its name, the wholly unrelated Rufous Mourner *Rhytipterna holerythra* is almost identically sized, but it too has unmarked underparts, no obvious spotting on the wing-coverts, and has a slightly smaller bill, a less rounded head shape and no pectoral tufts. The *Laniocera* also has an obvious yellow eye-ring, which feature is lacking in both the *Lipaugus* and the *Rhytipterna*. The voices of all three species, which will usually serve as the first notice of their presence, are quite different. The overall smaller-bodied Cinnamon Becard *Pachyramphus cinnamomeus* has an obviously smaller, more compact bill typical of becards, without a paler base, and is further distinguished by many of the same features useful in separating the previously mentioned potential confusion species.

DISTRIBUTION The Speckled Mourner ranges from northern Middle America south to northwest South America. It occurs from the Caribbean slope in southeast Mexico, where it is known from just one record in northern Oaxaca (Binford 1989) and very few in northern Chiapas, e.g. Bonampak (Howell and Webb 1995, Howell 1999), through Belize, where it occurs in western and southeast Orange Walk District and the Maya Mts (Vallely and Whitman 1997, Jones 2004), northern Guatemala, where until the early 1990s it was known only from three old trade skins (Griscom 1932, Howell and Webb 1992, Seavy *et al.* 1997, Eisermann and Avendaño 2007) and northern Honduras (Monroe 1968, Howell and Webb 1992, Anderson *et al.* 2004), eastern Nicaragua (Hellmayr 1929b, AOU 1998), and over the length of the Caribbean slope in Costa Rica but only very locally in the west of the country (in the Golfo Dulce region north to Quepos: Slud 1964, Stiles and Skutch 1989, AOU 1998), to Panama, where it occurs throughout much of the country from Veraguas (and probably Bocas del Toro) on the Caribbean slope east

through the Canal Zone, from where it also appears on the Pacific slope, thence south to San Blas and Darién (Wetmore 1972, Ridgely and Gwynne 1976). In South America, it occurs throughout the Pacific lowlands of Colombia as well as north of the Andes to the middle Magdalena Valley in eastern Antioquia (Hilty and Brown 1986), and in northwest Ecuador the Speckled Mourner is principally known from Esmeraldas province, as far south as the Río Verde and Bilsa, and there is just a couple of definite records from Pichincha, with the southernmost at Río Palenque (Ridgely and Greenfield 2001). The species' elevational range reaches to 1,350/1,400m, e.g. on the Cerro Tacarcuna, in eastern Panama (Wetmore 1972, Stotz *et al.* 1996), but in Ecuador it has not been found above 500m (Ridgely and Greenfield 2001) whilst in Colombia the species is mainly found in the foothills to 1,000m (Hilty and Brown 1986).

MOVEMENTS Speckled Mourner is considered to be probably sedentary (AOU 1998, Walther 2004).

HABITAT Humid to very humid evergreen or broadleaved forest and mature second growth with a relatively tall canopy, including edges, and is often found near swampy places, in shady ravines and along well-forested streams (Ridgely and Gwynne 1976, Stiles and Skutch 1989, Vallely and Whitman 1997). Seavy *et al.* (1997) provided a more detailed characterisation of one locality for the species in Guatemala. It very much seems to prefer large, relatively undisturbed tracts of forest (Ridgely and Greenfield 2001).

DESCRIPTION Differences between the sexes are not well marked. The bill is slightly hooked at the tip. The nominate subspecies is described here. *Adult male.* – Entirely dull cinnamon-rufous on the upperparts, including the head, although the crown-feathers are narrowly fringed with dark grey, the rump and uppertail-coverts are narrowly and indistinctly barred dusky, and the tail is more russet-coloured. The throat is obviously paler than the rest of the underparts, which are largely ochraceous to cinnamon-rufous (including the underwing-coverts), with the exception of the upper breast and breast-sides, which are indistinctly barred greyish-brown. The barring continues more indistinctly and less closely packed over the belly and flanks, but not apparently onto the lower belly or undertail-coverts. There are small, and generally concealed, lemon-yellow pectoral tufts at the sides. The primaries and coverts are generally dusky, but the latter have broad cinnamon-rufous spots at their tips forming 2–3 broken wingbars, which can be overlain by the scapulars to some extent, and the primaries and secondaries have cinnamon-rufous fringes to both webs. *Adult female.* – Not well differentiated from the male, but usually lacks the latter's pectoral tufts (although it should be clearly stated that, even in males, these are usually hidden by the wing-bend anyway) and if present they are usually orange ochraceous, rather than yellow (Ridgely and Gwynne 1976, Hilty and Brown 1986). *Juvenile/Immature.* – The juvenile is stated to be greyer on the head, with black fringes to the greater and median wing-coverts and randomly black-spotted body-sides (Restall *et al.* 2004), whilst the immature is reported to resemble the female, albeit with more prominent wing and underparts markings, a greyish wash to the crown, foreneck, lower back and rump, and sometimes with some sparse black spotting on the breast, whilst dull grey bands extend from the neck-sides to the undertail-coverts (Wetmore 1972, Hilty and Brown 1986, Walther 2004). However, it is unclear whether these descriptions refer to separate plumages, and indeed whether the species has a distinctive second non-adult plumage, or if Speckled Mourner moults directly from juvenile to adult garb. However, it can be added that birds in non-adult plumage are also characterised by having grey-barred upperparts, extending from the mantle and scapulars to the rump and uppertail-coverts. *Moult.* – There seems to be no published data concerning moult in this species. *Bare parts.* – The irides are dark brown to grey-brown surrounded by a narrow orange or golden-yellow eye-ring, with a largely dark brown to blackish bill relieved by a greyish-flesh or brownish-white base to the mandible and a dull honey-yellow gape, and the legs and feet are brownish-grey with dark grey claws (Wetmore 1972, Robbins *et al.* 1985, Ridgely and Greenfield 2001, Walther 2004).

MEASUREMENTS *L. r. rufescens* (Wetmore 1972: Nicaragua and Panama): wing of male (n = 10) 111.5–116.5mm, wing of female (n = 10) 112.5–118.0mm; tail of male (n = 10) 78.0–88.5mm, tail of female (n = 10) 78–86mm; bill of male (n = 10) 18–20mm, bill of female (n = 10) 18–22mm; tarsus of male (n = 10) 19.1–20.9mm, tarsus of female (n = 10) 20.0–22.5mm. *L. r. griseigula* (BMNH: Colombia): wing of male (n = 2) 107.5–108.0mm; tail of male (n = 2) 73–80mm; bill of male (n = 1) 19.77mm; tarsus of male (n = 2) 19.72–20.47mm. Weight (sexes combined): 38.6–56.0g (Strauch 1977, Robbins *et al.* 1985, Stiles and Skutch 1989, Walther 2004, Dunning 2008).

GEOGRAPHICAL VARIATION Polytypic, with three subspecies generally recognised (Dickinson 2003, Walther 2004). Note that Restall *et al.* (2006) erroneously transposed the South American ranges of the nominate race and *L. r. griseigula*. A revision of the taxonomy of this species appears warranted, given that none of the three races is very well marked, that the variation involved seems at least in part clinal (see below) and that as long ago as Hellmayr (1929b) it was questioned whether Ecuadorian birds were really distinct from Middle American populations. Nominate *L. r. rufescens* (described above) ranges from southeast Mexico to coastal northwest Colombia. Wetmore (1972) noted that there seemed to be some signs of intermediacy (e.g. a slightly grey-washed throat) in birds from eastern Darién towards characters associated with the next race. *L. r. griseigula* Meyer de Schauensee, 1950, occurs from northern Chocó and northern Antioquia to Santander in

the middle Magdalena Valley, in north-central Colombia, and is considered to be slightly smaller and darker (duller) cinnamon- and rufous-brown than nominate *L. r. rufescens*, with the central foreneck and upper breast grey. This taxon was considered endemic to the Nechí Rainforest Centre of endemism by Cracraft (1985). *L. r. tertia* E. Hartert, 1902, is found in southwest Colombia (from Cauca southwards) to northwest Ecuador (in Esmeraldas and Pichincha), which is darker and more chestnut, especially on the upperparts than the nominate.

VOICE Often quiet, but the loud, ventriloquial song is noticeable and is apparently given at exploded leks, with each bird 50–150m apart (Stiles and Skutch 1989, Seavy *et al.* 1997). Alternatively, it has been considered that this simply represents several males singing within earshot of one another (Ridgely and Greenfield 2001). Perches inconspicuously in the same place, usually 3–20m above the ground, sometimes calling monotonously for long periods throughout the day, including the hottest hours (R. S. Ridgely *in* Hilty and Brown 1986, Stiles and Skutch 1989, Walther 2004) and the species is reported to use the same sites from which to sing for many years, at least in Panama (Willis and Eisenmann 1979). The song, a series of up to 12–15 high-pitched *tlee-yeei* whistles, preceded by a single *tleeyr* note, is considered to recall one of the principal vocalisations of the White-breasted Wood Wren *Henicorhina leucosticta* or Thrush-like Schiffornis *Schiffornis turdina* (Stiles and Skutch 1989, Howell and Webb 1995, Jones 2004) as well as that of Cinereous Mourner (Hilty and Brown 1986). Lengthy pauses may punctuate bouts of singing. Also gives a drawn-out, slightly mewing and plaintive-sounding *peeeeeeeu*, which ends abruptly. The species' voice appears on the audio compilations by Jahn *et al.* (2002) and Boesman (2006c), and recordings from Colombia and Panama are also available online at www.xeno-canto.org.

NATURAL HISTORY Not very well known and never studied intensively. Speckled Mourner is usually found singly in the midstorey to subcanopy of forest, although it also ventures into the upper understorey (Stiles and Skutch 1989, Ridgely and Greenfield 2001). *L. rufescens* appears to spend long periods in one place (see Voice), peering sluggishly, even morosely, at its surroundings, by twisting its neck into strange positions (Hilty and Brown 1986, Stiles and Skutch 1989, Restall *et al.* 2006). Flight is swift and direct.

FOOD AND FEEDING Although it usually forages singly, lone individuals have also been observed within mixed-species foraging flocks, including those of antwrens, furnariids and tanagers (Stiles and Skutch 1989), as is true of *L. hypopyrra*. Food is taken using short-range sally-hovers to leaves or branches, or occasionally airborne insects. Arthropods (e.g. lepidopterans, including caterpillars and pupae), small lizards and fruit have all been mentioned in this species' diet, but there are few specific data (Wetmore 1972, Walther 2004).

BREEDING As noted under Voice, Stiles and Skutch (1989) speculated that the Speckled Mourner might form exploded leks. There is no information on nesting, other than that birds in breeding condition have been collected in southern Bolívar, Colombia, in May (M. A. Carriker *in* Hilty and Brown 1986), in Panama in June–July (FMNH) and in southeast Mexico in late June (Binford 1989).

STATUS The species is not globally threatened (BirdLife

International 2004, 2008), in large part due to its broad range, but Speckled Mourner seems rare over the greater part of its Middle American distribution (Griscom 1932 described the species as one of the rarest Central American birds) and it is considered Near Threatened at national level in Ecuador (Granizo *et al.* 2002). Extensive deforestation, especially in lowland regions, has unquestionably led to local extinctions (Walther 2004). For instance, *L. rufescens* is considered to be scarce in Belize (Jones 2004), rare and local in Oaxaca, Mexico (Binford 1989), rare in Guatemala (Eisermann and Avendaño 2007), exceedingly scarce in Honduras (Monroe 1968), although very recently the species has proved to be fairly common at one locality, in the upper Río Platano (Vallely *et al.* 2010), and it also appears to be extremely difficult to find in Costa Rica, where there are fewer than a handful of reports per annum (K. Easley *in litt.* 2009) and where it is reportedly best searched for at La Selva OTS Biological Station and Laguna del Lagarto Lodge (Lawson 2010). Speckled Mourner is known from a number of protected areas throughout its wide range, including the Columbia River Forest Reserve (Parker *et al.* 1993) and Río Bravo Conservation and Management Area (Kricher and Davis 1992), both in Belize, the Maya Biosphere Reserve, Guatemala (Seavy *et al.* 1997), Río Plátano Biosphere Reserve, Honduras (Vallely *et al.* 2010), the Río Negro Jaguar Preserve, Costa Rica (Cooper 1997), Reserva Natural de las Aves Arrierito Antioqueño and Reserva Natural de las Aves Pauxi pauxi, in Colombia (Salaman *et al.* 2009),

and Awá Forest Reserve and Cotacachi-Cayapas Ecological Reserve, both in Ecuador (Ridgely and Greenfield 2001). It is considered fairly common in eastern Panama (Ridgely and Gwynne 1976) and is perhaps most easily found at Cana, in the Darién, eastern Panama (K. Easley *in litt.* 2009). The statement by Walther (2004) that the species is commonest in Panama in Bocas del Toro is perhaps erroneous, although Robinson *et al.* (2000a) found a density of 12 individuals per 100ha at a study site there.

REFERENCES Ames (1971), Anderson *et al.* (2004), Angehr and Dean (2010), AOU (1998), Binford (1989), BirdLife International (2004, 2008), Boesman (2006c), Cooper (1997), Cracraft (1985), Dickinson (2003), Dunning (2008), Eisermann and Avendaño (2007), Garrigues and Dean (2007), Granizo *et al.* (2002), Griscom (1932), Hellmayr (1929b), Hilty and Brown (1986), Howell (1999), Howell and Webb (1992, 1995), Jahn *et al.* (2002), Jones (2004), Kricher and Davis (1992), Lanyon (1985), Lawson (2010), Monroe (1968), Parker *et al.* (1993), Peters (1929), Restall *et al.* (2006), Ridgely and Greenfield (2001), Ridgely and Gwynne (1976, 1989), Ridgely and Tudor (1994, 2009), Ridgway (1907), Robbins *et al.* (1985), Robinson *et al.* (2000a), Salaman *et al.* (2008, 2009), Seavy *et al.* (1997), Slud (1964), Stiles and Skutch (1989), Stotz *et al.* (1996), Strauch (1977), Vallely and Whitman (1997), Vallely *et al.* (2010), Walther (2004), Wetmore (1972), Willis and Eisenmann (1979).

Speckled Mourner *Laniocera rufescens*. **Figs. 1–2**. Adult, Pipeline Road, Canal Zone, central Panama, November (*Jim Swalwell*). Although the bold rufous spotting on the wing-coverts is only just visible in these images, the bird is still clearly identifiable, *vis-à-vis* the superficially similar Rufous Mourner *Rhytipterna holerythra* and Rufous Piha *Lipaugus unirufus*, both of which overlap extensively in range with this species. Note, in particular, the grey vermiculations on the breast, flanks and upper belly, the bold yellow orbital ring, and the heavier bill (compared to Rufous Mourner). This bird might be a female based on the lack of visible pectoral tufts, but as these are often very difficult to see, even on males, sexual identification is impossible. Although Speckled Mourner has a comparatively wide range, from southeast Mexico to northwest Ecuador, it is rare and difficult to find over the vast majority of its distribution. **Figs. 3–5**. Adult male, Pipeline Road, Canal Zone, central Panama, November (*Steven Easley / Costa Rica Gateway*). These images, all of the same bird, show the remainder of the species' features, especially the boldly rufous-spotted dusky wing-coverts. The lemon-yellow pectoral tufts, well displayed in Fig. 4, identify the bird as a male (if present in females, they are usually more ochraceous).

Genus *Laniisoma*: Elegant Mourner

Despite considerable fieldwork in all parts of this lovely bird's range during the intervening decades, David Snow's words, from over 25 years ago, still strike a resonant chord. He wrote that the Shrike-like Cotinga, as it was then usually known, 'is in every way an unsatisfactorily known genus…and indeed it has in the past been placed in the related family Pipridae (manakins) based on the basis of its foot structure', although therein it had been presciently clumped in a subfamily with the three *Schiffornis* and other enigmatic taxa (Sclater 1888). It is true that we now appear to have reached some certainty that it belongs, with several other species and genera covered in this book, outwith both the Cotingidae and the Pipridae, amongst the so-called *Schiffornis* assemblage, for which the family Tityridae has recently been resurrected for most of its constituents (Ericson *et al.* 2006, Remsen *et al.* 2009).

ELEGANT MOURNER
Laniisoma elegans   Plate 15

Ampelis elegans Thunberg, 1823, *Dissert. Tullberg., Nov. Spec. Ampelis*: 2, [mountains of Rio de Janeiro,] Brazil

Previously known by the inappropriate but alluring name Shrike-like Cotinga, this species represents one of the most mysterious of the cotingas, at least to field observers. Firstly, it is probably not a true cotinga, but is a member of the *Schiffornis* assemblage, as initially proposed by Prum and Lanyon (1989), and subsequently confirmed by additional work (Irestedt *et al.* 2002, Chesser 2004, Ericson *et al.* 2006, Barber and Rice 2007, Ohlson *et al.* 2007, 2008, Tello *et al.* 2008; see above). This finding has proved the final 'nail in the coffin' of the Shrike-like Cotinga; as Snow (1982) and Ridgely and Tudor (1994) had already noted, this species possesses no 'shrike-like' characters, and now it seems not to be a cotinga either! (cf. also Restall *et al.* 2006). Secondly, in Brazil its vocalisation sounds very similar (to human ears) to a monkey, the Buffy-tufted Marmoset *Callithrix aurita* (see below). Thirdly, it is possibly one of the more difficult 'cotingas' to observe in the field, especially the Andean population, although the nominate taxon *L. e. elegans* has become much better known within its Brazilian range in the last two decades. Fourth, the nestlings of the species are wonderfully bizarre, as referral to Plate 13 demonstrates. The taxonomic status of the two widely separated populations is not entirely clear. Although the possibility that the *L. e. elegans* and *L. e. buckleyi* groups comprise two species has been highlighted, based on perceived differences in female plumage and vocalisations (foremost by Collar *et al.* 1992, Sibley and Monroe 1993, Ridgely and Tudor 1994, 2009), such a 'split' has yet to be formally approved (e.g. by the American Ornithologists' Union South American Checklist Committee: Remsen *et al.* 2009). However, it was adopted by Gill and Wright (2006) in the IOC list of global bird names wherein the English names Andean Laniisoma and Brazilian Laniisoma were adopted. Alternatively, the Andean bird might be called Buckley's Mourner, with nominate *L. e. elegans* retaining the Elegant modifier. This effectively marked a return to the taxonomy adopted by Hellmayr (1929b), although given the extreme paucity of material then to hand, even of *L. e. elegans*, this was (as the author himself noted) a strictly provisional classification. Whilst the two 'groups' are treated separately in some sections below, no inference should be drawn from this concerning our own view as to their taxonomic status. Indeed, given that their plumage (including the remarkable nestling and juvenile garb) and vocalisations are obviously extremely similar (the former

already noted by Snow 1982), it seems to us that such a 'split' is both premature (in the absence of a detailed, published analysis) and heavily reliant on the geographical distance between the taxa, which is not a 'character' in itself that should inform taxonomy. The same conclusion seems also to have been reached by Restall *et al.* (2006).

IDENTIFICATION 19.5–20.5cm (*L. e. buckleyi* is apparently smaller, at 17.3–18.0cm, but there are still relatively few data). In southeast Brazil, this species is not easily confused. Both of the *Carpornis* berryeaters are larger (especially Hooded *C. cucullata*) and have quite different voices, amongst many other distinguishing features, whilst Swallow-tailed Cotinga *Phibalura flavirostris* (with which *L. elegans* is occasionally found in the same flocks in the austral winter) bears only a superficial resemblance to the Elegant Mourner, possessing much heavier barred underparts, a much smaller bill and, of course, a totally different tail shape. Sharpbill *Oxyruncus cristatus* might also require elimination under unfavourable viewing conditions (and this also applies to the *L. e. buckleyi* group), but this species is spotted (not barred) and generally much paler below, has a distinctly bare-faced expression (lacking the solid dark cap of *Laniisoma*) and behaves rather differently. Females (especially) of the *L. e. buckleyi* group might be confused with any one of several fruiteaters within their broad Andean range. Barred Fruiteater *Pipreola arcuata* is found at much higher elevations and is even more barred on the underparts. Scaled Fruiteater *Ampelioides tschudii* (whose altitudinal range overlaps extensively with *Laniisoma*, at least in Peru and Ecuador) is rather dumpier, has a more complex head pattern and is much more densely marked below, amongst many other separating features. Both Green-and-black *Pipreola riefferii* and Golden-breasted Fruiteaters *P. aureopectus* are larger and generally occur at higher elevations, as well as lacking barring below. Other, more similar-sized and altitudinally allopatric *Pipreola* generally show some orange or red on the underparts, a much smaller and brightly coloured bill, and no barring on the underside. Remember also that the *Laniisoma* is probably far rarer than virtually any of the sympatric *Pipreola*. Hilty and Brown (1986) and Hilty (2003) also highlight the possibility of confusion with females of the smaller and dumpier Barred Becard *Pachyramphus versicolor*, but the latter is paler yellow below and has a rufous patch in the wings, as well as being found at generally higher elevations.

DISTRIBUTION The *L. e. buckleyi* group occurs on the east slope of the Andes in Venezuela (race *L. e. venezuelense*), where it is known solely on the basis of six specimens (none recent) from southwestern Barinas and southeastern Táchira (Hilty 2003), and Colombia (where it was for long known from merely a single record, involving a 'pair'

L. e. venezuelense

L. e. buckleyi

L. e. cadwaladeri

L. e. elegans

of specimens taken in April 1959), in northern Boyacá, with 'nominate' *L. e. buckleyi* from southeast Colombia, in western Meta, through eastern Ecuador (probably patchily throughout, although there are relatively few records; Ridgely and Greenfield 2001), and eastern Peru (where first recorded as recently as 1961), extremely locally in dptos. Amazonas to Pasco, and recently recorded in the upper Urubamba Valley in dpto. Cuzco (Thoresen 1974, Snow 1975, Schulenberg *et al.* 2007, Robbins *et al.* 2011). In northwest Bolivia the weakly differentiated subspecies *L. e. cadwaladeri* is found in dptos. La Paz and Beni (Carriker 1935, Remsen and Traylor 1989), based on Carriker's specimen from Santa Ana on the Río Coroico, and a recent sight record on the northern side of Serranía Beu, in Pilón Lajas Biosphere Reserve in September 1999 (Hinojosa *et al.* 1998, Hennessey *et al.* 2003a, Snow 2004a). There is a recording on Alvarez *et al.* (2007) of this species, apparently made at Ipiales, between the Ríos Rumiyaco and Ranchería, in dpto. Nariño, in southernmost Colombia, providing the first documentation of the species in that country for many years; this record might be inferred to pertain to *L. e. buckleyi* on distributional grounds alone. Nominate *L. e. elegans* (monotypic if treated as a separate species) is endemic to Brazil, where it principally occurs from southern Bahia, in the environs of Boa Nova (Gonzaga *et al.* 1995, Souza 1999, Silveira *et al.* 2005; GMK pers. obs., where also reported historically but records were previously considered doubtful), south in the Atlantic Forest biome to Espírito Santo, through southeastern and south-central Minas Gerais (e.g. Torga *et al.* 2007, in press), Rio de Janeiro and São Paulo, to eastern Paraná (cf. Pinto 1944, Scherer-Neto and Straube 1995, Wege and Long 1995, Bencke *et al.* 2006). Also found in drier woodlots in the interior of Minas Gerais, as far inland as Belo Horizonte (e.g. Anciães *et al.* 2001), and there is one (sight) record from much further northeast, at Murici, Alagoas, in October 2004 (Freiberg 2005). The species was also recently reported in the state of Goiás, a single bird mist-netted in a secondary forest fragment at Quirinópolis (18°22'S, 50°47'W) in the extreme south of the state (Ferreira *et al.* 2010). An adult female was trapped and ringed near Blumenau, in eastern Santa Catarina, in July 2003, the southernmost record in Brazil

(Borchardt-Junior *et al.* 2004). The species is also recorded from at least one inshore island, the Ilha do Cardoso, São Paulo, but whether only as a migrant is unknown (Collar *et al.* 1992). The *L. e. buckleyi* group occurs in foothill forests from 200m (more usually 700m) to 1,830m in the Andes (though found exclusively below 530m in Venezuela: Hilty 2003), whereas *L. e. elegans* is restricted to the Atlantic Forest biome of Brazil, from sea level (perhaps mainly in winter) to *c.*1,300m (GMK pers. obs.), and even more exceptionally reported to 2,000m (Anciães *et al.* 2001; principally or solely in the austral summer?). (See also Movements.)

MOVEMENTS Nominate *L. e. elegans* is suspected to make (probably limited) altitudinal movements, as suggested as long ago as the 1940s (Davis 1945) and amplified subsequently by Willis (1979), Gonzaga (1986) and Willis and Oniki (2002), but Mallet-Rodrigues *et al.* (2007) remarked that greater confirmation of such movements was required. In our view, at least some probably do ascend higher into the foothills during the early austral summer (it certainly seems absent, or silent, at certain 'regular' sites at higher elevations [i.e. above 800m] in western and central Rio de Janeiro, and southern Espírito Santo states, Brazil, at this season: GMK pers. obs.). Nonetheless, there are records from the austral winter as high as *c.*900m in some of the same areas, which suggests that either not all of the population performs such movements, or that their extent is determined by climatic events, or that winter absence is merely apparent (a function of the birds generally falling silent at this season). Recent evidence suggests that some lowland localities, e.g. around Cachoeiras do Macucu, Rio de Janeiro state, are occupied nearly year-round. Nonetheless, in the latter region Pimentel and Olmos (2011) found that between February and August the species generally occurs below 300m, but that during the rest of the year it is found at elevations of 500–800m. Furthermore, May and October records, such as that by Lo (1994) of a bird in a small park close to the city of São Paulo, surely represent wandering birds or migrants, as probably does the recent record in August (2005) from southern Goiás of a single immature male (Ferreira *et al.* 2010). The same might not be true of the occasional records from within the municipality of Rio de Janeiro (Maciel 2009). Snow (1982) speculated on the possibility that Andean populations might move to subtropical elevations from lower (or true lowland) regions, but this hypothesis has yet to be confirmed or refuted with published evidence, although presence is reportedly seasonal at some localities on the east slope in Ecuador, e.g. at Wild Sumaco Lodge. Given the strong possibility that nominate *L. e. elegans* does indeed perform altitudinal migrations, and the otherwise strong similarities between the two groups, this facet of the Andean birds' life history merits additional attention.

HABITAT *L. elegans* prefers tall humid forest from the lowlands to the lower subtropics in both the Andes and southeast Brazil, and in the former region Ridgely and Greenfield (2001) noted a preference for streamside areas. The latter microhabitat association does not appear especially true of nominate *L. e. elegans* (GMK pers. obs.), which also seems tolerant, to some extent, of smaller and drier woodlots in the interior (Anciães *et al.* 2001). Certainly tolerates dense and older, but fragmented, secondary habitats in southeast Brazil, albeit perhaps principally during the austral winter or on 'migration'. Within forest, both groups are found at virtually all levels, from the taller understorey to the subcanopy (Ridgely and Greenfield 2001, Hilty 2003; GMK pers. obs.).

DESCRIPTION The sexes differ. Bill is long, straight over the culmen and has a slightly but abruptly hooked tip. The well-developed rictal bristles partially obscure the nostrils. For a description of the curiously un-cotinga-like foot structure see Snow (1982: 38). The seventh primary has an attenuated and elongated tip (adult male only). The following refers to the nominate race from southeast Brazil. *Adult male.* – Strikingly plumaged, with a deep black crown, and otherwise mid to bright olive-green upperparts, relieved by the dusky alula, fringes to the flight feathers and outer webs to the tertials. Rather bright golden-yellow underparts from the throat to the undertail-coverts. Coarse black vermiculations provide further contrast, being scattered irregularly (varying individually) over the throat-sides, breast, flanks, body-sides and ventral region. *Adult female.* – Recalls the male, but is easily separated (given reasonable views) by the much more extensively scaled and vermiculated underparts (virtually the entire ventral surface is so marked, with the exception of the chin and central belly), and the crown appears marginally duskier and less blackish, being more dark olive-green on the sides and the superciliary. *Immature.* – Plumage much as adult of the respective sex or is more female-like, although at least some males partially develop the black crown, and all birds have some ventral scaling (perhaps narrower in *L. e. buckleyi*), but also retains (from juvenile plumage) large and irregular rufous-chestnut spots near the tips of the larger, duskier, wing-coverts (making ageing straightforward). Norton *et al.* (1972) suggested that *L. e. buckleyi* and *L. e. elegans* differ at this age in that the former has black tips to the wing-coverts, whereas the latter has black fringes to the same feathers. The confusion expressed by Restall *et al.* (2006) concerning the appearance of immature plumage arose due to imprecise ageing terminology in some earlier publications. *Juvenile.* – The only true description we have of a juvenile (i.e. a young bird recently out of the nest) comes from J. C. Minns (*in litt.* 2008) who described a bird in the company of an adult, in southeast Brazil, thus: 'Same size [as adult], body mottled dark greenish-brown, almost black, and rufous, in large asymmetric patches—feathers on head and around beak erect and spiky, like Struwwelpeter'. The extraordinary nestling's plumage is apparently soon replaced (Snow 1982), being mostly cinnamon over the upperparts, head and throat, with black subterminal bars and small white tips to the feathers, whilst the rest of the underparts are primarily dark grey to blackish barred off-white, especially broadly on the breast, with cinnamon-orange fluffy feathers on the flanks and ventral region. The wing-coverts are olive-green, but would be difficult to see in the field. However, the truly remarkable feature is the filamentous down feathers that sprout 20–26mm from the head and body like a 'pin cushion', and are variously black with white tips on the head or cinnamon with white tips on the back. For a fuller description see d'Horta *et al.* (in prep.). Snow (1982) speculated that the nestling had evolved to appear like a moss covered by fruits, but it might equally be a broken-off stump or similar. The only specimens are syntypes of *L. e. buckleyi* and are held in The Natural History Museum, Tring (1888.20.1.337 and 1888.20.1.338). (For further information the reader is referred to Sclater and Salvin 1880, Snow 1982, and Hilty 2003.) Snow (2004a) noted that this remarkable plumage presumably represented an adaptation to the species using an exposed

nest-site. *Moult.* – There are few published data concerning moult (see Snow 1976a, Mallet-Rodrigues 2005), but Anciães *et al.* (2001) noted that singles mist-netted in Brazil in June and July were not moulting, whilst one trapped in April was replacing the head-, body- and tail feathers. Snow (1982) considered that moult may commence as early as August or September in southeast Brazil. Three Ecuadorian specimens (*L. e. buckleyi*), taken in August and September, had all finished their moults (MECN), whilst approximately half of those taken in Táchira, Venezuela (*L. e. venezuelense*), collected in July–November were in either wing or tail moult (COP; FMNH). *Bare parts.* – Sexes probably similar: the bill is blackish or dark steel grey above, and greenish, horn or grey-green (*L. e. buckleyi* group) or pale horn (*L. e. elegans* alone?) on the lower mandible; the legs and feet are olive-green or plumbeous (*L. e. buckleyi* group), bluish-grey or steel grey (*L. e. elegans*), but overlap in all bare-parts colorations between the different taxa has not been eliminated; and the irides are dark red to blackish (seemingly no difference between taxa, but probably generally darker in females), with a narrow pale greenish-yellow or fleshy green eye-ring (*L. e. elegans* and *L. e. buckleyi*; both sexes).

MEASUREMENTS (For some additional measurements not included here see Hellmayr 1929b, Blake 1961, Norton *et al.* 1972 and Snow 1975, 1982.) *L. e. elegans* (Anciães *et al.* 2001; CUMZ; FMNH; MNRJ; RMNH; ZMA; ZISP: Minas Gerais and Rio de Janeiro, southeast Brazil): wing of male (*n* = 8) 99–105mm, wing of female (*n* = 10) 99–108mm; tail of male (*n* = 8) 56–69mm, tail of female (*n* = 8) 60–64mm; bill of male (*n* = 6) 18.12–19.39mm, bill of female (*n* = 9) 14.92–21.35mm; tarsus of male (*n* = 3) 21.69–26.50mm, tarsus of female (*n* = 2) 21.35mm. *L. e. buckleyi* (BMNH; FMNH; MECN: southeast Ecuador and Peru): wing of male (*n* = 5) 97.5–101.0mm, wing of female (*n* = 4) 102–104mm; tail of male (*n* = 5) 59.0–64.5mm, tail of female (*n* = 4) 60–63mm; bill of male (*n* = 3) 16.0–18.82mm, bill of female (*n* = 3) 14.92–20.03mm. *L. e. venezuelense* (Phelps and Gilliard 1941; COP; FMNH: Colombia and Venezuela): wing of male (*n* = 5) 90.0–96.5mm, wing of female (*n* = 1) 93mm; tail of male (*n* = 5) 54.5–61.0mm, tail of female (*n* = 1) 60mm; bill of male (*n* = 5) 15.9–19.0mm, bill of female (*n* = 1) 18.24mm. *L. e. cadwaladeri* (from Snow 1982): wing of male (*n* = 1) 102mm; tail of male (*n* = 1) 65mm. Weight. – *L. e. buckleyi*: 40–48g (males) and 45.8–59.8g (females; Snow 1975, 2004a; BMNH; FMNH; MECN); *L. e. elegans*: 41–48g (three males; Anciães *et al.* 2001, Willis and Oniki 2002) and 44.2 and 51.3g (two females; MNRJ).

GEOGRAPHICAL VARIATION The two subspecies groups, nominate *L. e. elegans* in eastern Brazil (described above) and *L. e. buckleyi* (three subspecies) in the Andes, differ rather marginally, in the smaller size of the *L. e. buckleyi* group, with fewer dark vermiculations on the underparts in either sex and the much paler crown in the female (almost concolorous with the rest of the upperparts). As noted in the introduction to this account, *L. e. elegans* and the *L. e. buckleyi* group were considered species by Hellmayr (1929b) and, again, by several recent authors (e.g. Collar *et al.* 1992, Sibley and Monroe 1993), despite the lack of a peer-reviewed publication to support such treatment. Indeed, BirdLife's own taxonomic working group has now rejected the earlier proposal of Collar *et al.* (1992). Within the *L. e. buckleyi* group three subspecies are recognised as follows (from north to south). *L. e. venezuelense* W. L. Phelps, Sr, & Gilliard, 1941, is, as its name suggests, restricted to southwestern Venezuela, with a single record from dpto. Boyacá, Colombia (FMNH 261458–59; see Distribution); **L. e. buckleyi** (P. L. Sclater & Salvin, 1880) was described from eastern Ecuador, and has since been found from southeast Colombia to Peru (see Distribution), whilst the main differences between this form and *L. e. elegans* (see Description) are described above; and the extremely slightly differentiated **L. e. cadwaladeri** Carriker, 1935, in northwest Bolivia. The last was named for Charles Cadwalader, Director of the Academy of Natural Sciences at Philadelphia, which financed Carriker's Bolivian expeditions. Ironically, at the time of the description Cadwalader was already taking up arms against Carriker, on behalf of one of the Academy's curators, on quite obviously false pretences (Olson 2007). Snow (1982) suggested that some size differences might occur through the Andes, but highlighted the lack of material on which to base any assumptions (or descriptions). Indeed, *L. e. cadwaladeri* was described on the basis of just a single male with almost immaculate yellow underparts, and *L. e. venezuelense* was described (also from a single specimen) as differing from *L. e. buckleyi* only in its slightly yellower green upperparts with less heavily barred flanks, body-sides and undertail-coverts, more slender bill, and paler sides to the forehead. FMNH 285113, a male from dpto. Pasco, Peru, also has almost immaculate yellow underparts, with dark barring confined to the breast-sides (little) and flanks (most), and very faint barring on the lower throat-sides and undertail-coverts, which might suggest that *L. e. cadwaladeri* occurs into Peru, or can be taken as additional evidence against recognising the latter. Purported differences in tail- and wing-lengths can be dismissed on the sample sizes available (see Measurements). We have examined a reasonable sample of *L. e. venezuelense* but none of *L. e. cadwaladeri*, but would never feel confident in recognising, much less describing, comparatively subtle forms on the basis of such a paucity of material. Even Phelps and Gilliard (1941), in describing *L. e. venezuelense*, admitted that both *L. e. cadwaladeri* and their new form might well prove to be synonyms of *L. e. buckleyi*. Subject to further investigation, we would recommend that recognition of a single form in the Andes, namely *L. e. buckleyi*, is probably sufficient to encompass the currently known levels of variation found therein (this arrangement appears also to have been Snow's unstated preference, given his guarded comments over the lack of obvious variation). It is worth noting that Bond and Meyer de Schauensee (1942) also expressed reservations about recognising more than one form in the Andes, but decided to maintain the status quo. They also noted the existence of a specimen of unknown origin that seems to have since fallen from view, described as *Ptilochloris remigialis* Lafresnaye, 1838, which J. L. Peters (*in* Bond and Meyer de Schauensee 1942: 356) considered very close in appearance in size to Andean birds, especially Bolivian *cadwaladeri*. Hellmayr (1929b: 96) had placed *P. remigialis* in the synonymy of *L. e. elegans*, but it might equally be of Andean origin and perhaps therefore an older name for *L. e. buckleyi*. This question might usefully be revisited. The type of *remigialis* is in Philadelphia.

VOICE Throughout the species' wide range, the primary vocalisation is a slightly piercing, very high-pitched, sibilant and far-carrying *psieeeeeeee, psieeeeeeee, psieeeeeeee* (transcription from our own recordings of nominate *elegans*, and very similar to that of T. A. Parker *in* Snow 1982), or *SEEeeweeEEE, SEEeeweeEEE, SEEeeweeEEE,* … (Schulenberg *et al.* 2007). Each phrase falls slightly and ends in a slight crescendo,

with the relative strength of the vocal almost certainly increasing, but the overall length shortening, in response to playback (GMK pers. obs.). The whole sounds almost as if being slightly 'squeezed out'. The song is presumably given solely by the male, uttered with the mandibles wide open, the tail depressed and the throat-feathers puffed out, and serves mainly to advertise the territory. In Ecuador, the song of *L. e. buckleyi* is considered to recall that of Black-streaked Puffbird *Malacoptila fulvogularis* (Ridgely and Greenfield 2001), which is especially relevant given that both species can be encountered (the puffbird commonly) along the Río Bombuscaro, in Podocarpus National Park, southern Ecuador (Ridgely and Greenfield 2001; GMK pers. obs.). Although Collar *et al.* (1992), citing a personal communication from B. M. Whitney, alleged that vocal differences supported separate treatment of *L. e. buckleyi* and *L. e. elegans*, our own field experience of both groups suggests no such thing. Parker and Parker (1982) considered that vocalisations of the *L. e. buckleyi* group peak in the late morning/early afternoon, but in Brazil this does not appear especially true, and birds can be attracted using playback at most hours of the day during the breeding and immediate post-breeding seasons at least. Response to playback, indeed, can be dramatic in both groups (GMK pers. obs.). However, the birds often cease vocalising whilst moving towards the observer, and often perch extremely unobtrusively within dense foliage, usually without making 'a pass' first, and furthermore almost motionlessly (only occasionally moving the head and puffing out the throat-feathers: as first noted by T. A. Parker *in* Snow 1982). Furthermore, they often move on relatively quickly and soon lose 'interest' in the source of the sound. Schulenberg *et al.* (2007) also mentioned a squeaky rattle and similarly toned, descending *ki-ki-ki*, as calls, and J. C. Minns (*in litt.* 2008; Minns *et al.* 2009) has sound-recorded a very similar and presumably analogous vocalisation to the latter in southeast Brazil, which was given in flight, prior to the bird giving the usual advertisement. Alvarez *et al.* (2007) presents the song of *L. e. buckleyi* (presumably; see Distribution) from southernmost Colombia, Krabbe and Nilsson (2003) and Lysinger *et al.* (2005) from southeast Ecuador, and Schulenberg (2000a) from Peru, whilst Vielliard (1995), Boesman (2006a) and Minns *et al.* (2009) present that of *L. e. elegans* from southeast Brazil. Recordings of subspecies *L. e. buckleyi* (from Ecuador) and *L. e. elegans* (from southeast Brazil) are also archived online at www.xeno-canto.org. For Brazil, Sick (1997) pointed out the remarkable similarity of the vocalisation to Buffy-tufted Marmoset and this may prove something of a pitfall to the uninitiated. However, bear in mind (a) that the monkey is very vocal (far more so than *Laniisoma*) and is much commoner than the bird (e.g. it can be heard in virtually any wooded area of southeast Brazil, including even built-up areas of Rio de Janeiro); (b) its vocalisation is generally louder and less insistent; and (c) the monkey's calls lack any trace of a crescendo, are rather more formless and of longer duration than *Laniisoma* (GMK pers. obs.).

NATURAL HISTORY Our knowledge of the natural history of *L. elegans* is almost entirely confined to nominate *L. e. elegans*. Easily overlooked and poorly known, this is a shy, retiring and generally lethargic species, which is not readily observed (and, if so, usually alone), although it will respond to playback and even whistled imitations of its vocalisations. Rarely observed by chance, the Elegant Mourner is one of the real prizes for lovers of Neotropical birds. Behaviour is very poorly known, despite the increasing number of observations throughout the species' range in recent decades.

FOOD AND FEEDING Diet comprises principally fruits of various melastomes (which are abundant, even in fragmented secondary woodlands, in southeast Brazil: Anciães *et al.* 2001), and which are probably mainly taken in a typical 'snatch and grab' operation via a short upward sally (GMK pers. obs.). The only fruit identified for this species by Pizo *et al.* (2002) in their study of cotingid diet at Intervales State Park was a species of *Miconia* (Melastomataceae), but Pineschi (1990) also witnessed the species taking a species of *Rapanea* (Myrsinaceae). It is also known to take insects including Lepidoptera larvae, especially 'hairy' caterpillars (Lo 1994, Pimentel and Olmos 2011; W. Price pers. obs.), but there is no further information on this. It occasionally joins mixed-species foraging flocks, including of tanagers, both in the Atlantic Forest (Aleixo 1997) and in the Andean foothills (J. & B. Olsen pers. comm.), but we have never observed such behaviour.

DISPLAY N. Krabbe and J. Nilsson (pers. comm.) have reported apparent lekking behaviour for *L. e. buckleyi*, from the west slope of the Cordillera de Cutucú, Morona-Santiago, Ecuador, in August 2002, where 4–5 males were singing less than 100m apart from moss-covered horizontal vines and branches at 6–8m up in wet primary forest with several, rather steep, small ravines.

BREEDING This facet of the species' life history is basically unknown, although in Brazil, at least, vocalisations appear to peak in September–December, i.e. the austral spring and early summer when many species in this region are nesting. J. C. Minns (*in litt.* 2008) observed the juvenile described above (Description) at the end of December, in the Serra do Mar State Park, São Paulo, Brazil. T. A. Parker's observations in Peru involved birds vocalising frequently in late August to mid September, and a female collected in late August in southeast Peru had a brood patch and two yolking eggs (FMNH 322417). In contrast, two taken in southeast Peru in April were not breeding (Robbins *et al.* 2011). Nestlings, acquiring their juvenile plumage, were collected in eastern Ecuador as long ago as the 19th century, but unfortunately no data accompany them, although C. Buckley apparently took an adult female in their company (i.e. the clutch is two); they reside in The Natural History Museum, Tring, and anyone with more than a passing interest in Neotropical birds visiting that institution is encouraged to see them for him- or herself.

STATUS Currently treated as a single species by BirdLife International, who presently rate its conservation status as of Least Concern (2008), but this organisation formerly regarded *L. e. elegans* and *L. e. buckleyi* as separate species, treating *L. e. elegans* as Vulnerable (Collar *et al.* 1992, BirdLife International 2000). Collar *et al.* (1992) thought that *L. e. buckleyi*, when treated separately, might qualify for Near Threatened status but it has not subsequently appeared in lists of globally threatened species. Considered Near Threatened in Ecuador (Granizo *et al.* 2002), *L. e. buckleyi* within its vast range is patchily recorded (although this may as much reflect the difficulties in locating this species as its true status), with recent records from various foothill sites in Ecuador and Peru, such as the Río Bombuscaro in Podocarpus National Park, and Wild Sumaco lodge, both in Ecuador, and in the vicinity of Abra Patricia, dpto. San Martín, Peru. *L. e. venezuelense* is apparently extremely rare, being known solely from six specimens and a single sight record (see Hilty 2003, and above), and has not been recorded in Venezuela for almost 60 years. *L. e. cadwaladeri* is confined to Bolivia, where it is known from just one specimen and one sight record. Nominate *L. e. elegans* is confined to the foothill Atlantic Forests and some interior woodlots of Brazil, where its distribution is patchy, but has been elucidated significantly recently. For a full inventory of museum and field records up to *c.*1990, Collar *et al.* (1992) is an admirable reference. It is known from at least 20 Important Bird Areas in Brazil (including at least three national parks), as follows (after Bencke *et al.* 2006): one in Bahia (Boa Nova), two in Minas Gerais (where treated as Vulnerable), three in Espírito Santo (in which state it is also considered Vulnerable to extinction), nine in Rio de Janeiro, four in São Paulo and one in Paraná, but in most of these states it is known from at least several other localities. Although this taxon can be difficult to observe, knowledge of its vocalisations has meant the discovery of several new localities in the last 10–15 years. Nominate *L. e. elegans* is regularly recorded in Itatiaia National Park, especially at lower elevations around the museum, but also higher, for instance on the Três Picos trail, at least in the austral summer. Nevertheless, relative densities always seem low (GMK pers. obs.). One of the best localities to find this species is currently the RPPN REGUA, near Cachoeiras de Macacu, Rio de Janeiro state (Pimentel and Olmos 2011; GMK pers. obs.). Thus *L. e. elegans* is almost certainly more secure than *L. e. buckleyi*, and its range more widely understood. Paradoxically, many of the known sites for *L. e. elegans* enjoy some degree of protection under different Brazilian federal or state statutes, although those populations in Bahia are threatened by clearance of the humid forests both within and outside designated protected areas.

REFERENCES Aleixo (1997), Alvarez *et al.* (2007), Anciães *et al.* (2001), Balchin and Toyne (1998), Barber and Rice (2007), Bencke *et al.* (2006), BirdLife International (2004), Blake (1961), Boesman (2006a), Bond and Meyer de Schauensee (1942), Borchardt-Junior *et al.* (2004), Brooks *et al.* (2009), Browne (2005), Carriker (1935), Chesser (2004), Collar *et al.* (1992), Cracraft (1985), David and Gosselin (2002b), Davis (1945), Ericson *et al.* (2006), Ferreira *et al.* (2010), Freiberg (2005), Gill and Wright (2006), Goerck (1999), Gonzaga (1986), Gonzaga *et al.* (1995), Granizo *et al.* (2002), Hellmayr (1929b), Hennessey *et al.* (2003a, 2003b), Hilty (2003), Hilty and Brown (1986), Hinojosa *et al.* (1998), Hornbuckle (1999), Irestedt *et al.* (2002), Krabbe and Nilsson (2003), Lo (1994), Lysinger *et al.* (2005), Maciel (2009), Mallet-Rodrigues (2005), Mallet-Rodrigues and Noronha (2003, 2009), Mallet-Rodrigues *et al.* (2007), Minns *et al.* (2009), Norton *et al.* (1972), Ohlson *et al.* (2007, 2008), Parker and Goerck (1997), Parker and Parker (1982), Passamani and Mendes (2007), Phelps and Gilliard (1941), Pimentel and Olmos (2011), Pineschi (1990), Pinto (1944), Pizo *et al.* (2002), Prum and Lanyon (1989), Remsen and Traylor (1989), Remsen *et al.* (2009), Restall *et al.* (2006), Ridgely and Greenfield (2001), Ridgely and Tudor (1994, 2009), Robbins *et al.* (2011), Salaman *et al.* (2008), Scherer-Neto and Straube (1995), Schulenberg (2000a), Schulenberg *et al.* (2007), Schunck and Silveira (2010), Sibley and Monroe (1993), Sick (1997), Silva (2000), Silveira *et al.* (2005), Souza (1999), Snow (1975, 1976, 1982, 2004a), Stotz *et al.* (1996), Tello *et al.* (2009), Thoresen (1974), Torga *et al.* (2007, in press), Vasconcelos and Melo Júnior (2001), Vielliard (1995), Wege and Long (1995), Willis (1979), Willis and Oniki (2002).

Elegant Mourner *Laniisoma elegans*. **Figs. 1–3**. All photographs are of male *L. e. elegans* and were taken at Reserva Ecológica de Guapiaçu, near Cachoeiras de Macacu, Rio de Janeiro, southeast Brazil. Figs. 1 and 3, August (*William Price / www.pbase/tereksandpiper*), Fig. 2, November (*Lee Dingain*). Note how wide the bill is opened when singing.

Genus *Iodopleura*: purpletufts

The purpletufts, *Iodopleura*, comprise a group of miniature 'cotingas' (see below) that inhabit the canopy of low-land or foothill forest, and which are most likely to be encountered perched high on a tall, bare, forest emergent. Purpletufts are compact birds with a stubby bill, long wings and a short tail. Undoubtedly, the most efficient way of observing these tiny (and thus easily overlooked) birds is from a clearing, forest road or canopy observation platform. The three currently recognised species appear to be entirely allopatric, as far as is known, although there is an area in northernmost Brazil, southern Venezuela and parts of the southernmost Guianas where no *Iodopleura* has been found to date, and more fieldwork in this region may yield fresh clues as to the true status of two members of the group.

WHITE-BROWED PURPLETUFT
Iodopleura isabellae   Plate 14

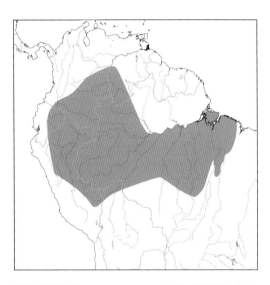

Iodopleurus isabellae **Parzudaki, 1847**, *Rev. Zool.* 10: 186, [San Carlos, Amazonas] Venezuela

Unquestionably the commonest and most widespread of its genus, the White-browed Purpletuft is, nonetheless, not so easily encountered in the majority of its Amazonian range, and its biology, like those of its congeners, remains comparatively poorly known. J. Moojen (*in* Descourtilz 1944 reprint of 1854–56) regarded the present species as a race of the Buff-throated Purpletuft *Iodopleura pipra*.

IDENTIFICATION 11–13cm. Males average smaller than females by *c.*10% (Brooks *et al.* 1999). There is no known overlap with either of this species' two congenerics. Observers must beware of the pitfall of identifying any small, cotinga-like bird, perched high on an emergent tree in Amazonia as a purpletuft. The Swallow-wing *Chelidoptera tenebrosa* is a bird of lowland forests of South America, commonly seen sallying from high, exposed perches. Swallow-wings are rather dumpy birds, being obviously larger, far more squat and 'hunched' than a purpletuft. The white loral area and postocular stripe of the purpletuft is lacking in the Swallow-wing, although they share a white rump. Furthermore, Swallow-wing sometimes sallies to the ground, quite unlike any purpletuft, and has rufous undertail-coverts, another character that separates it from all species of *Iodopleura*. Where it occurs, the Swallow-wing is also a far commoner bird than any of the purpletuft species.

DISTRIBUTION White-browed Purpletuft is widespread in Amazonia, from the mouth of the Amazon in eastern Brazil to the west of the basin in Peru, north to Colombia and the upper Orinoco drainage in Venezuela, and south to northern and northeast Bolivia. Found in southwest Venezuela (in Amazonas, north to Puerto Ayacucho on the Río Orinoco), southeast Colombia (north to western Meta and eastern Guainía), eastern Ecuador (Sucumbíos south to Zamora-Chinchipe), eastern Peru (e.g. in Amazonas, Huánuco, Cuzco and Madre de Dios), extreme northern Bolivia (dptos. Pando, La Paz and Santa Cruz, in Noel Kempff Mercado National Park, and recently found at one locality in dpto. Beni, unsurprisingly, as known from Guajará-Mirim, on the right bank of the Rio Mamoré, in adjacent Brazil), Amazonian Brazil, east to the Rio Negro north of the Amazon, and south of the river east to Pará, northwest Maranhão (e.g. at Imperatriz), and south to Rondônia, northern Mato Grosso (e.g. at Alta Floresta, the Serra dos Caiabis and Parque Indígena do Xingu), and northernmost Tocantins (Araguatins: LSUMZ specimen;

Hidasi 1997). However, more recently (in 2010) *I. isabellae* has been collected in central Tocantins, around Presidente Kennedy (M. A. Raposo *et al.*). It has also been predicted to occur in Roraima, in northernmost Brazil (Naka *et al.* 2007). Reaches to 1,200m (at Wawa Sumaco, Napo, Ecuador: Guevara *et al.* 2008), and to 950m (Tono, Madre de Dios) and 850m (Manu National Park), Peru (Walker *et al.* 2007), but throughout its range White-browed Purpletuft is commonest below 500m, although it remains numerous to 700m in the Serra dos Carajás, Pará, Brazil (Pacheco *et al.* 2007). Not known above 200m in southern Venezuela.

MOVEMENTS None recorded, but birds probably wander quite widely (like many Amazonian cotingas) in search of food (see Natural History).

HABITAT Tall rainforest, river-bluff, *várzea* and *terra firme*, in the canopy and at borders; the species is also occasionally observed in isolated trees within adjacent clearings.

DESCRIPTION All purpletufts are diminutive passerines, with a short bill and short legs. The culmen is broad-based, slightly arched and slightly hook-tipped, whilst the nostrils are concealed by feathering. Sexual dimorphism in plumage is weakly expressed. The flight feathers are unmodified and the birds lack any rictal bristles. *Adult male.* – The crown, nape, mantle and tail are dark chocolate-brown, being marginally darkest over the cap. Rump is white. Wings are dark chocolate-brown and the flight feathers slightly darker; when very fresh may show slight, off-white, tips to all three tertials, especially the largest. Sides of head strikingly patterned: large white loral area (bordered by a brown malar stripe) and white postocular stripe. Rear ear-coverts dark brown. Throat and majority of rest of central underparts white. Breast-sides solid brown, breaking into dusky-brown mottling and barring on the lower flanks, with long white undertail-coverts. The silky purple upper-flank 'tufts' from which the genus acquires its name are difficult to see in the field, but become extremely obvious in display (either aggressive, distress or in courtship, prior to copulation), during which these feathers are flared out across two-thirds of the breast, leaving only a small white centre, and can even be curled round over the bird's nape, forming a purple-collared effect. This function has only definitely been observed in the present species, but is presumably common to all purpletufts (see Descourtilz 1854–1856, Camargo and Camargo 1964, Snow 1982, Whittaker and Kirwan 2008). In flight, the underwing-coverts and basal primaries are white. *Adult female.* – Resembles the male in all respects, except that the purple flank tufts are replaced by white. *Juvenile.* – Snow (1982) reported that juveniles of all purpletufts have conspicuously white-tipped feathers. After the first moult, they become indistinguishable (or nearly so) from the adult. *Moult.* – There are very few published data concerning moult, but one collected in eastern Ecuador in late September was replacing the body feathers (MECN) and Snow (1982) calculated the onset of moult as June, November and December in the Belém area of east Amazonian Brazil and October–November in southern Peru, and moult is calculated to last *c.*100 days (Snow 1976a). *Bare parts.* – Irides dark brown (dark coffee); the bill is black (slightly broader at the base and hooked at the tip), leaden below; the tarsi are dark leaden to black.

MEASUREMENTS (from Snow 1982; MECN; MNRJ; RMNH: Brazil, Ecuador and Peru) Wing of male (*n* = 15) 75–81mm, wing of female (*n* = 11) 71.5–79.0mm; tail of male (*n* = 15) 35–40mm, tail of female (*n* = 11) 28–40mm; bill of male (*n* = 15) 7.00–9.32mm, bill of female (*n* = 11) 7.0–10.6mm; tarsus of male (*n* = 14) 13–15mm, tarsus of female (*n* = 8) 14mm. Females average longer in tail-length than males, but wing-chord averages shorter in females (Brooks *et al.* 1999). Weight: 17.0–20.2g (Brooks *et al.* 1999, Snow 2004a, Dunning 2008; FMNH; MECN; MNRJ). Females can average up to 20% heavier than males (Brooks *et al.* 1999).

GEOGRAPHICAL VARIATION Best considered monotypic on present evidence. The rarely recognised *I. i. paraensis* Todd, 1950, was described from near Belém, Pará, and seems to occupy all of the species' eastern range, in Pará, Tocantins and Maranhão. It is only rather marginally differentiated from nominate *isabellae*, it having a less-obvious (and partially interrupted) white mesial line, but stronger pale (brownish-white) barring and mottling on the flanks, and perhaps has the upperparts darker than *I. i. isabellae*. Although Gyldenstolpe (1951) considered himself unable to comment on the validity of *paraensis*, he already noted that birds from Bolivia appeared to agree better with Todd's form than with the nominate, which hints at the difficulties associated in trying to recognise any geographical variation within this species. Measurements (from Camargo and Camargo 1964) as follows: wing of male (*n* = 11) 74–82mm, of female (*n* = 2) 75–79mm; tail of male (*n* = 11) 39–46mm, of female (*n* = 2) 40–41mm; and bill of male (*n* = 11) 5–8mm, of female (*n* = 2) 6–7mm. Its validity appears questionable and demands further work.

VOICE Rarely heard, but a variety of vocalisations have been described in the literature, all of them fine, rather shrill and thin-sounding, including soft trills, a weak *jee-jee—jee* (the display-song), a very thin rattle (apparently in greeting or as a threat) and a rather plaintive *wheeee*, the length of which perhaps varies slightly (undoubtedly given by both races), and which is occasionally doubled or tripled (see Hilty and Brown 1986, Moore 1994, Boesman 1999, Ridgely and Greenfield 2001, Hilty 2003, Krabbe and Nilsson 2003, Snow 2004a, Boesman 2006, Marantz and Zimmer 2006, Guevara *et al.* 2008, Boesman 2009). Several recordings from Peru and Brazil are archived online at www.xeno-canto.org.

NATURAL HISTORY Like other purpletufts, this species typically perches above the canopy on tiny bare twigs or small branches, although occasionally it comes lower, usually at the edges of forest. Generally difficult to observe from the ground, the White-browed Purpletuft is relatively easily seen, with patience, from one of the many canopy platforms in Amazonia, such as at Sacha Lodge in eastern Ecuador. Here, and elsewhere, the sporadic sightings over several days imply that individuals wander quite widely in search of fruit and small berries including mistletoes.

FOOD AND FEEDING Usually seen alone or in small parties of up to six individuals, but this purpletuft rarely appears to join cotingas, and other frugivores, at fruiting trees, including once a *Ficus pertusa* (Moraceae) tree in southeast Peru (Tello 2003). However, Walther (2004) mentioned seeing the species, and Purple-breasted Cotinga *Cotinga cotinga*, within a foraging canopy flock also containing many tanagers and allies, as well as Gilded Barbet *Capito auratus* and Spot-backed Antwren *Herpsilochmus dorsimaculatus* in Amazonas, Venezuela. It is unclear if his observations pertained to a mobile flock or birds visiting a particular fruiting tree. White-browed Purpletuft also performs vertical and horizontal sallies for flying insects. Fruit is taken either during a brief hovering flight or when perched.

DISPLAY The function of the purple pectoral tufts has only recently been elucidated (Whittaker and Kirwan 2008), when A. Whittaker observed a group of three at a nest in construction chase away two additional individuals, after which the male of the original group displayed by flaring the pectoral tufts in the manner described under Description. Aggressive interactions (undescribed) between individuals of this species were also noted by Guevara *et al.* (2008). Subsequent field observations made by GMK, D. Beadle and H. Shirihai also throw further light on this behaviour. At *c.*08.30 hours on 3 October 2008, in the Allpahuayo-Mishana Reserved Zone, dpto. Loreto, Peru, these observers discovered a male White-browed Purpletuft *c.*20m above the ground in the canopy of a forest-edge tree. In response to playback, the bird commenced to dramatically flare out the purple pectoral tufts, before flying to another tree, whereupon a second bird, apparently a female, joined it. With continued playback, the male returned to the original tree and continued to flare the pectoral tufts, before launching into an apparent display-flight, in which the bird flew at a low angle from its treetop perch, and proceeded in tight zigzags to a new perch *c.*15m from the first tree. Strong reaction to playback ceased thereafter.

BREEDING Previously unpublished nesting data are from eastern Ecuador, where EB observed a pair at Sani Lodge on 10–12 January 2008, from the canopy tower, attending a nest with a well-grown young (*c.*40% of adult size). The nest was in a *Cecropia* (Urticaceae) and *c.*20m above the ground on a slender, angled branch, below the canopy of an adjacent emergent (*c.*35m). It was constructed of lichens and fine mosses and coated with spiderwebs. As is typical of the genus, the nest was a tiny cup-shaped structure that exactly matched the colour and texture of the branch. Both adults tended and fed the nestling throughout the morning and late afternoon, but only the female was noted brooding during the heat of the day and at dusk. Published data concern single nests in southern Venezuela, in March, and northeastern Peru, in January, with birds collected in breeding condition in Colombia in August–September, and Amazonas, Brazil, in early October (see Whittaker and Kirwan 2008 for fuller details). It breeds principally in September–December in northeast Brazil, based on observations of dependent juveniles and a single nest near Belém, Pará, which was a minute, cylindrical, hummingbird-like cup, with the appearance of papier mâché (and made of vegetable horsehair and Cyanophyceae and Chlorophyceae algae), coated with spiderwebs, and sited at 18–19m in the crown of a dead tree (Sick 1979a, Snow 1982, Oniki and Willis 1983). The other nests were either slightly lower or considerably higher (up to 30m above the ground) and were usually sited on horizontal or near-horizontal branches. Saliva as well as regurgitated sticky seeds or fruits, and/or excrement is used to bind the nest together, so thickly that the underlying nest materials can be invisible, and is worked into the structure with either the bird's bill or feet. At both the Brazilian and the Peruvian nests, three birds were present during the nest-building phase, but one bird merely observed the activity by the other two (the presumed pair) (Sick 1979a, Snow 1982, Whittaker and Kirwan 2008). As mentioned by Snow (1982), the egg description and clutch size (three) of Schönwetter (1969) appear to be unquestionably erroneous.

STATUS Treated as Least Concern by BirdLife International (2008). Considered generally uncommon by Ridgely and Tudor (1994), or even scarce in eastern Ecuador (Ridgely and Greenfield 2001) and western Acre, Brazil (Whittaker and Oren 1999), this widespread bird presumably has a healthy overall population, given the species' vast range, and it appears even to be locally common in parts of east Amazonian Brazil. It is known from several protected areas (some mentioned under Distribution), in all range states, e.g. the Serra dos Carajás mosiac of conservation units in Pará, Brazil, where the species seems to be particularly numerous (Pacheco *et al.* 2007).

REFERENCES Almeida (2005), Awbrey and Schulenberg (1992), Balchin and Toyne (1998), BirdLife International (2008), Boesman (1999, 2006b, 2009), Brooks *et al.* (1999, 2009), Cadena *et al.* (2000), Camargo and Camargo (1964), Cohn-Haft *et al.* (1997), Descourtilz (1854–56), Dugand and Phelps (1948), Dunning (2008), Guevara *et al.* (2008), Gyldenstolpe (1951), Haffer (1974), Hellmayr (1929b), Henriques *et al.* (2003), Hidasi (1997), Hilty (2003), Hilty and Brown (1986), Krabbe and Nilsson (2003), Lane *et al.* (2003), Maillard *et al.* (2007), Marantz and Zimmer (2006), Mazar Barnett *et al.* (1998), Mestre *et al.* (2010), Moore (1994), Naka *et al.* (2007), Novaes (1960), Ohlson *et al.* (2008), Oniki and Willis (1983), Oren and Parker (1997), Pacheco and Olmos (2005), Pacheco *et al.* (2007), Parker *et al.* (1994b, 1994c), Peres and Whittaker (1991), Pinto (1944), Poulsen (1992), Ridgely and Greenfield (2001), Ridgely and Tudor (1994, 2009), Sick (1979a, 1997), Salaman *et al.* (2008), Schönwetter (1969), Schulenberg *et al.* (2006, 2007), Snethlage (1907), Snow (1976a, 1982, 2004a), Stone (1928), Stotz *et al.* (1996, 1997), Tello (2003), Tobias and Seddon (2007), Todd (1950), Walker *et al.* (2007), Walther (2004), Whittaker and Kirwan (2008), Whittaker and Oren (1999), Willard *et al.* (1991), Zimmer and Hilty (1997), Zimmer *et al.* (1997).

1

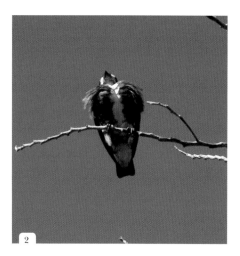

White-browed Purpletuft *Iodopleura isabellae*. **Fig. 1**. Male, Yasuní Research Station, prov. Orellana, eastern Ecuador, August (*Nick Athanas / Tropical Birding*). Purple pectoral tufts raised and 'flared' in response to playback. **Figs. 2–3**. Male, Reserva Nacional Allpahuayo-Mishana, dpto. Loreto, northeast Peru, October (*Hadoram Shirihai / Photographic Handbook to Birds of the World*). The same bird 'relaxed' and in display. The purple pectoral tufts are only flared in display (either aggressive or sexual), but can almost completely encircle the neck. **Fig. 4**. Female, near Mazuco, dpto. Madre de Dios, southeast Peru, October (*Hadoram Shirihai / Photographic Handbook to Birds of the World*). This bird appears to definitively lack the purple pectoral tufts and therefore can be confidently sexed as a female.

DUSKY PURPLETUFT
Iodopleura fusca   Plate 14

Ampelis fusca **Vieillot, 1817**, *Nouv. Dict. Hist. Nat.*, new edn., 8: 162, [Cayenne]

The type is illustrated in Dekker (2003).

Whilst not the rarest of its genus, Dusky Purpletuft is a very poorly known and infrequently observed species, principally restricted to the Guianas, where the first observations of its breeding biology were made recently. Hellmayr (1929b) and Meyer de Schauensee (1966) opined that Dusky and White-browed Purpletufts *Iodopleura isabellae* might prove to be conspecifics, a suggestion most recently repeated by Hilty (2003).

IDENTIFICATION 11–12cm. Unmistakable if seen well. This species retains the typical purpletuft shape of the apparently wholly allopatric White-browed Purpletuft, but is far less ornately plumaged. As its name suggests, *I. fusca* is the darker of the two species, it having chocolate-brown underparts from the throat to the lower flanks, apart from a whitish median line and mottled undertail-coverts, and lacks any white markings on the head. As noted for the previous species as well, a potential confusion risk for inexperienced observers is the much larger Swallow-wing *Chelidoptera tenebrosa*; they share broad-based wings and a very short tail. However, the rufous belly of the puffbird, the narrower white rump band of the purpletuft (which does not extend to the lower back, albeit which is still obvious even at a relatively long distance in suitable light) and their totally different flight patterns should preclude confusion.

DISTRIBUTION Restricted to extreme northeast South America and the Guianan Centre of endemism (Cracraft 1985), its range being centred on the Guianas: from southeast Venezuela, where known from just four localities in eastern Bolívar, north as far as the Sierra de Imataca Forest Reserve, and southeast Delta Amacuro (Restall *et al.* 2006); throughout the Guianas, where considered uncommon in Guyana (Snyder 1966), rare to uncommon in Surinam (at least six widespread localities) and uncommon in French Guiana (where known from sites such as Saül, Apatou and Mana and, most recently, the Montagne de Kaw; see also Tostain *et al.* 1992, Ingels and Vinot 2010, J. Ingels *in litt.* 2010); and Brazil, where first discovered as recently as the 1980s, in Roraima (Estação Ecológica de Maracá, Colônia de Apaiú, and the environs of Boa Vista: Sick 1997), in Amazonas, 80–130km north of Manaus (as far as Balbina), in northern Pará at the FLONA Trombetas (Aleixo *et al.* 2011) and in Amapá (where observed, by J. F. Pacheco and F. Olmos, at Laranjal do Jari, in the extreme southwest of the state, in October 2006; and already listed or mapped for Amapá by Snow 2004a and Ridgely and Tudor 2009 on an unknown basis), and presumably elsewhere in the country north of the Amazon. Recently reported for the first time (surprisingly) from the ZF2 tower north of Manaus (*per* A. Whittaker pers. comm.). Never listed or reported from the state of Pará, although it surely occurs there, at least in the extreme north (an extremely inaccessible region). The species' range comes close to that of the White-browed Purpletuft in southeast Venezuela/northern Brazil, where Dusky is known from as far west as the Río Icabarú (Venezuela) and northern Roraima, and White-browed east to north-central Amazonas (Hilty 2003); and, in northwest and central Amazonian Brazil, *fusca* occurs

as close to *isabellae* as *c.*150km distant, with *isabellae* known from localities such as São Gabriel da Cachoeira, on the east bank of the Rio Negro (A. Whittaker *in litt.* 2007), and Borba (many observers). Dusky Purpletuft occurs to at least 500m, and has recently been recorded to at least *c.*920m in southernmost Bolívar, Venezuela (Whittaker and Kirwan 2008, Crease 2009).

MOVEMENTS None certainly recorded, but Cohn-Haft *et al.* (1997) suggested that Dusky Purpletuft might perform as yet unspecified movements in northern Brazil, presumably in an effort to explain the relative lack of observations from a comparatively well-watched region in which the species is certainly present.

HABITAT Like White-browed Purpletuft, this species is found almost entirely in the canopy and at borders of tall lowland *terra firme* forest.

DESCRIPTION Dusky Purpletuft possesses a typical purpletuft's shape and size. The culmen is broad-based, slightly arched and slightly hook-tipped, whilst the nostrils are concealed by feathering. The flight feathers are unmodified and the species has no rictal bristles. No sex- or age-related, or geographical, plumage variation recorded (but see below). The species is distinctly rare in collections. *Adult male.* – Resembles White-browed Purpletuft, but lacks the white facial markings of the latter. Upperparts dark chocolate-brown to blackish, even darker on the crown, producing a slightly capped appearance, and relieved only by the white rump band. Wings brown, the flight feathers slightly darker, with a white patch at the base of the primaries on the underwing (Hilty 2003), whilst the wing-coverts have very slightly paler brown narrow fringes and tips to many feathers. From below, the species appears much darker than White-browed Purpletuft. Ear-coverts are solid dark chocolate-brown with no white markings, the throat is brown, and the breast and flanks are also brown, barred blackish-brown. There is a white median line from the centre of the breast to the very long undertail-coverts (dark undertail just visible), the latter white with very diffuse barring. Purple flank tufts present, appearing under most conditions as a purple triangle at the wing-bend, but these are difficult to detect in the field without the aid of a telescope. One of two males observed in Amazonas, Brazil, had heavier horizontal flanks barring and more pronounced scaling on the upper breast (Whittaker and

Kirwan 2008). The underwing-coverts and axillaries are extensively white-tipped. *Adult female.* – Slightly duller overall and lacks the purple flank tufts (this area being silky white). A female (based on the lack of purple flank tufts) observed in Amazonas, Brazil, had distinct, symmetrical white lateral throat-stripes either side of the bill base, and an indistinct small white smudge on the lores (Whittaker and Kirwan 2008). *Juvenile.* – Snow (1982) reported that juveniles have conspicuously white-tipped feathers. After the first moult, they are indistinguishable (or nearly so) from adults. *Moult.* – There are no published data concerning the annual moult cycle, but feather renewal might be expected to last *c.*100 days as in White-browed Purpletuft (which see). *Bare parts.* – Irides brown; the slightly hooked, broad-based bill is black (darker on the upper mandible) and the tarsi (and presumably the feet) are lead-coloured.

MEASUREMENTS (from Snow 1982; CUMZ; RMNH: Guianas) Wing of male ($n = 5$) 73–77mm, wing of female ($n = 5$) 76.0–80.5mm; tail of male ($n = 5$) 36–39mm, tail of female ($n = 5$) 37–40mm; bill of male ($n = 5$) 7.00–8.95mm, bill of female ($n = 5$) 7.00–9.55mm; tarsus of male ($n = 5$) 13.50–14.17mm, tarsus of female ($n = 5$) 14.00–16.31mm. Weight: 15.3g (one male: Dunning 2008; RMNH).

GEOGRAPHICAL VARIATION None recorded, but see Description.

VOICE Song similar to White-browed's, a thin but shrill *seeee* (Naka *et al.* 2008, Whittaker and Kirwan 2008) or *peeee* (R. A. De By recording; XC9942), slightly plaintive, generally rather short and usually uttered singly, but repeated after a short period. Naka *et al.* (2008) published a fast, almost rollicking series of much deeper notes, *prrrr, prrrr-up.* Hilty (2003) and Snow (2004a) also mention soft trills, which might refer to the same calls described here. Response to playback is not usually very marked, but the birds can circle the source of the sound albeit keeping their overall distance from it (GMK pers. obs.).

NATURAL HISTORY The species' biology is almost entirely unknown, due principally to its small size and canopy-dwelling habits, but perhaps also because the species' range is still relatively little visited by ornithologists. Furthermore, throughout most of the Dusky Purpletuft's range, canopy observation towers are lacking, the only exceptions being the Iwokrama Canopy Walkway in Guyana and the ZF2 tower north of Manaus, Brazil, at the latter of which the species has been observed just once to date. Like Buff-throated Purpletuft *Iodopleura pipra*, it often perches (or is most easily detected) in largely leafless legumes or other open emergent trees in the canopy, and the species can also select such sites for roosting, the birds remaining in relatively close proximity to one another; Dusky Purpletuft exhibits extraordinarily long-lived faithfulness to roost sites, a characteristic not yet recorded in other *Iodopleura* (cf. Whittaker and Kirwan 2008).

FOOD AND FEEDING Dusky Purpletuft is usually encountered singly, in pairs or occasionally in small groups of 3–5 individuals. It performs (usually short, vertical and horizontal) aerial sallies for winged insects, e.g. at hatching events of Isoptera or Hymenoptera, or Lepidoptera, or also to take small fruits. J. Ingels (*in litt.* 2007) and C. F. Collins (*in litt.* 2008) record that, like other purpletufts, *I. fusca* appears to be a mistletoe (Loranthaceae) specialist based on observations around Saül, in the interior of French Guiana, and in central southern Guyana, respectively.

BREEDING Data were virtually non-existent, until very recently, when a nest under construction was discovered in the Forêt de Tamanoir, near the Counamama River, in southeast French Guiana (05°17'N, 53°17'W), in late December 2008 (P. Ingremeau, R. Monchâtre & A. Vinot; Ingels and Vinot 2010). From the photographs and description, the nest appeared typical of the genus, and was sited on a near-horizontal bare branch high in the outer crown of a *c.*20m-tall roadside tree that was rather bereft of leaves. The approximate dimensions of the tiny, open-cup nest, which appeared to be largely constructed of spiderwebs, were *c.*30mm (diameter at cup), *c.*45mm (diameter at the base) and *c.*25mm (height) (Ingels and Vinot 2010). These are similar to the dimensions of nests of *I. isabellae*, although the latter species might construct nests that are less than half the height of that of Dusky Purpletuft (see Snow 1982). By 19 January the *I. fusca* nest was apparently complete, but was subsequently destroyed during storms shortly afterwards. The female immediately commenced building another nest, but heavy rains prevented further access to the area; by April, when the site was next visited, the upper part of the tree had been destroyed. The male remained in the vicinity as the female constructed the nest, but was not observed to actually engage in its construction, although it was observed to vocalise relatively frequently. Elsewhere, a pair with a single fledgling was observed in February in Venezuela (Hilty 2003); there are no other details.

STATUS Not considered globally threatened (Least Concern) by BirdLife International (2008); indeed, its range still comprises vast areas of unaltered habitat, including almost 60,000ha of the Guianan Shield, which was recently declared a protected area by the Brazilian government, as well as the 370,000ha Iwokrama reserve in Guyana. Known from several protected areas in French Guiana, including the Réserve Naturelle des Nouragues, Réserve Naturelle de Kaw-Roura and Réserve Naturelle de la Trinité (Tostain *et al.* 1992, Ingels and Vinot 2010; J. Ingels *in litt.* 2010). Nonetheless, logging and mining concessions are ever-present threats in some areas, and it should be remarked that all purpletufts can be curiously local, even within vast areas of apparently uniformly appropriate habitat. Considered commoner in French Guiana than elsewhere by Tostain *et al.* (1992, followed by Ridgely and Tudor 1994), but even there the species is never abundant and, in general, it appears to be rarer than White-browed Purpletuft. At his study site in French Guiana, Thiollay (1994) estimated the density of *I. fusca* as just one pair per 100ha. Ottema *et al.* (2009) listed it as rare in Surinam. The species appears to be especially local and uncommon in Brazil around Manaus, and in southeast Venezuela, although Crease (2009) considered it to be reasonably common in the El Paují region close to the border with Brazil. It is regularly encountered from the canopy walkway and camp clearing at Atta Rainforest Lodge in central Guyana (Collins 2007; GMK pers. obs.), and Dusky Purpletuft is also known from several other areas within the Iwokrama reserve (C. F. Collins *in litt.* 2008; GMK pers. obs.), suggesting that the species' relative abundance in this area is reasonably high.

REFERENCES Aleixo *et al.* (2011), BirdLife International (2008), Borges (1994), Cohn-Haft *et al.* (1997), Collins (2007), Cracraft (1985), Crease (2009), Dekker (2003), Dunning (2008), Haffer (1974), Hellmayr (1929b), Hilty

(2003), Ingels and Vinot (2010), Naka *et al.* (2006, 2008), Ottema *et al.* (2009), Renaudier (2009), Restall *et al.* (2006), Ridgely and Tudor (1994, 2009), Sick (1997), Snow (1982, 2004a), Snyder (1966), Stotz and Bierregaard (1989), Stotz *et al.* (1996), Thiollay (1994), Tostain *et al.* (1992), Whittaker and Kirwan (2008), Willis and Oniki (1988c).

Dusky Purpletuft *Iodopleura fusca*. **Fig. 1**. Female, Polo Road, El Paují, Bolívar, southern Venezuela, October (*Tony Crease*). The white pectoral tufts identify this bird as a female. **Fig. 2**. Male, Paracou, Sinnamary, French Guiana, February (*Alexandre Vinot*). Apparent male given the lack of any visible white feathers on the upper flanks. **Fig. 3**. Female, nest building, Piste de Counamama, French Guiana, December (*Alexandre Vinot*). The white upper-flank feathers are just visible. This was the first nest to be discovered and described by ornithologists.

BUFF-THROATED PURPLETUFT
Iodopleura pipra   Plate 14

Pardalotus pipra Lesson, 1831, *Cent. Zool.*: 81, pl. 26, [Rio de Janeiro, Brazil]

The rarest of the purpletufts, this species is restricted to the ever-dwindling lowland forests of eastern Brazil; however, modern-day fieldwork has expanded its range somewhat, resulting in it being recently downgraded from Endangered to Near Threatened by BirdLife International.

IDENTIFICATION 8.7–10.5cm. The rare and, until recently, little-known Buff-throated Purpletuft is restricted to low- and mid-elevation Atlantic Forest, in eastern Brazil. If seen well, there is little likelihood of confusing this bird, it being even smaller than other purpletufts and records of Swallow-wing *Chelidoptera tenebrosa* at the same sites are nearly all purely historical, except in Bahia. Although an even smaller bird, it retains the comparatively long-winged and short-tailed appearance of its congeners.

DISTRIBUTION Buff-throated Purpletuft is endemic to eastern Brazil, where it is entirely restricted to the humid Atlantic Forest biome and the Serra do Mar Centre of endemism (Cracraft 1985), with perhaps three disjunct subpopulations. In the far northeast the species occurs in eastern Paraíba (at Mamanguape, and the campus of the Universidade Federal da Paraíba, João Pessoa, but probably also at other localities: Almeida and Teixeira 1997), in eastern Pernambuco (Garanhuns, Charles Darwin Ecological Reserve, Gurjaú and Timbaúba) and in Alagoas (at Murici and Engenho Coimbra). Further south, *I. pipra* is known also from southern Bahia (in the Serra do Javi and Serra do Ouricana, near Boa Nova) and extreme northeastern Minas Gerais (at Bandeira). Thereafter there is a considerable gap to records in southern Espírito Santo, e.g. around Santa Teresa and Augusto Ruschi Ecological Station (the former Nova Lombardia Biological Reserve), thence south, apparently very discontinuously, to São Paulo, where it is best known in the lowlands around Ubatuba, in the extreme east of the state, but has even been recorded in the Greater São Paulo metropolitan area in the relatively recent past, and at least formerly (there are no recent records) from the lowlands of the extreme south of the

state (see Camargo and Camargo 1964, Collar *et al.* 1992). It is known from four Important Bird Areas in the state of Rio de Janeiro, one of them, Itatiaia National Park, on the border with Minas Gerais, although there is apparently only one record (in 1988) from there (Wege and Long 1995). The species ranges to *c.*900m in Espírito Santo and 1,000m in northeast Brazil. Buff-throated Purpletuft's reported occurrence in Guyana (e.g. Snyder 1966) is in error, based on two (with hindsight obviously) mislabelled specimens, apparently of the race *I. p. leucopygia* (Snow 1982), whilst the single record well inland in southeast Brazil, from Lagoa Santa, Minas Gerais, reported by Burmeister (1856) appears highly unlikely on the basis of our present knowledge of the species and is generally ignored in the modern literature (see Hellmayr 1929b, Collar *et al.* 1992).

MOVEMENTS Sick (1993) reported the existence of altitudinal movements, based on the observation of small flocks 'migrating' at 900m in Espírito Santo, but available data suggest that subspecies *I. p. leucopygia* is resident at highland localities, and even in the range of nominate *I. p. pipra*, recent observations in the lowlands of São Paulo, at Ubatuba, are available from nearly all months, whilst records from highland localities between São Paulo and Espírito Santo at seasons other than summer (Camargo and Camargo 1964, Collar *et al.* 1992, Willis and Oniki 2002) cast further doubt on the migration theory. Only in the upper part of the Serra dos Órgãos, in the environs of Teresópolis, Rio de Janeiro, are some data available that lend any support to the migration hypothesis (and even here the species is apparently resident at lower elevations), but until more accurate information concerning the species' overall range becomes available, these might just as easily signal that the species is more widespread than generally appreciated, or that, like other purpletufts, they wander widely in search of food at certain times (see discussion in Whittaker and Kirwan 2008).

HABITAT Humid Atlantic Forest and associated second growth and adjacent clearings, and at least locally the species is found in cacao and abandoned banana plantations with shade trees.

DESCRIPTION Typical purpletuft size and shape. The culmen is broad-based, slightly arched and slightly hook-tipped, whilst the nostrils are concealed by feathering. Sexual dimorphism in plumage is weakly expressed. The flight feathers are unmodified and, like the other *Iodopleura*, this species lacks rictal bristles. The nominate subspecies is described here. *Adult male.* – Paler than other purpletufts; the plumage is ash-grey above with an obviously darker crown (which is sometimes raised in a crest, especially in agonistic display), and darker and browner grey wings and stubby tail. The throat and upper breast are cinnamon-buff, the belly barred dark grey and white, with buff undertail-coverts. The upper-flank tufts are lilac-coloured (very hard to see under most conditions, but can be erected and spread slightly when excited, when the wings may also be raised: Descourtilz 1854–56, Snow 1982, Sick 1997). In worn or abraded plumage, the tertials can show somewhat browner fringes. Some *I. p. pipra* in southeast Brazil show traces of a white or whitish-buff rump band (GG and GMK pers. obs., Hellmayr 1929b, Collar *et al.* 1992). Underwing-coverts and axillaries are extensively tipped very clean white. *Adult female.* – Resembles the male, except in having vestigial lilac or white flank tufts, and can also have conspicuously whiter underparts due to it having less heavy barring. *Juvenile.* – Snow (1982) reported

that juveniles have conspicuously white-tipped feathers, but we have examined a young bird (ZISP 117196) with pale buffy-cinnamon tips to some feathers of the forehead to nape, mantle and lesser coverts, and more extensively on the median and greater coverts, tertials, primaries and rectrices. After the first moult, indistinguishable (or nearly so) from the adult. *Moult.* – Very few published moult data, but Snow (1982) mentioned that two specimens from São Paulo state had commenced feather renewal in August–September, and moult might be expected to last *c*.100 days as in White-browed Purpletuft *Iodopleura isabellae* (which see). *Bare parts.* – Irides are dark brown, the bill is black (like other purpletufts with a slightly expanded base and fractionally hooked tip) and the tarsi are lead-coloured.

MEASUREMENTS (from Snow 1982; CUMZ; RMNH; ZISP; ZMA; subspecies combined: eastern Brazil) Wing of male (*n* = 20) 54–60mm, wing of female (*n* = 10) 55–62mm; tail of male (*n* = 20) 29–35mm, tail of female (*n* = 9) 22.0–33.5mm; bill of male (*n* = 16) 5–6mm (*n* = 4, to skull 8.45–8.61mm), bill of female (*n* = 5) 5–6mm (*n* = 4, to skull 7.54–9.43mm); tarsus of male (*n* = 17) 13.0–15.5mm, tarsus of female (*n* = 6) 14.00–15.12mm. For mensural data separated according to subspecies see Snow (1982). Weight (sexes combined): 9.6–10.5g (*n* = 2; Teixeira *et al.* 1993, Almeida and Teixeira 1997, Dunning 2008).

GEOGRAPHICAL VARIATION Polytypic with two subspecies being generally recognised (Snow 1982, 2004a). *I. p. pipra*, which occurs in southeast Brazil (São Paulo, Rio de Janeiro and Espírito Santo) is described above. *I. p. leucopygia* Salvin, 1885, of northeast Brazil (Paraíba, Pernambuco, Alagoas and Bahia) resembles the nominate but generally has a better-developed white rump band (5–6mm wide), a purer, less greyish, buff throat patch, more striking superciliary, narrower sooty fringes to the underparts and paler undertail-coverts (*sensu* Hellmayr 1929b and Teixeira *et al.* 1993). *I. p. leucopygia* is sometimes known as the White-rumped or Alagoas Purpletuft, and has even been postulated to warrant species status (see Ridgely and Tudor 1994, Sibley 1996), seemingly based as much on geography as features that separate them, but this view lacks much credibility, especially given that gap in the distributions may not be real, or is perhaps merely a function of the loss of forest cover in recent centuries. Furthermore, concerning the most obvious feature purported to separate the two species, namely the presence of a broad white rump-band in *leucopygia*, a photograph of a male from Bahia (in Snow 2004a: 39) clearly lacks this feature completely, which either calls into question the validity of the name *leucopygia* (given that its other separating features are all very marginal), or suggests that the range of nominate *pipra* reaches much further north than currently believed.

VOICE The most commonly heard vocalisation (apparently in contact) is a bisyllabic and slightly descending *si-si*, or *swee-yee*, sometimes trebled and somewhat reminiscent of a Purple-throated Euphonia *Euphonia chlorotica*, but finer, and can be lengthened to become a short trill in flight (Remold 2002). The extremely high-pitched song is easily (and was long) overlooked, but was described by Sick (1997) as a short sequence of clear chirps, repeated readily (GMK pers. obs.). Buff-throated Purpletufts may even sing at midday (Mallet-Rodrigues and Marinho de Noronha 2003). It readily responds to playback of its own voice, or imitations of Brazilian Pygmy Owl *Glaucidium minutissimum* (Whittaker and Kirwan 2008). Recordings of both subspecies (no

obvious differences are audible between them) are available online at www.xeno-canto.org.

NATURAL HISTORY Phlegmatic, like all purpletufts, perching relatively bolt upright on the highest branches or twigs of tall trees, but the species also regularly descends to smaller trees, especially in clearings, and will even feed in close proximity to, but apparently not in direct association with, mixed-species feeding flocks of insectivores.

FOOD AND FEEDING Another mistletoe (Loranthaceae) specialist, its diet of small fruits and berries is, like other purpletufts, supplemented with arthropods caught in flight and taken from the vegetation while perched. Mendoça and Gonzaga (2000) reported that a nestling in Rio de Janeiro was fed principally on green fruits of *Struthanthus* (Loranthaceae), supplemented by small arthropods, spiders, tiny lizards, wasps and small gastropods, amongst others. Buff-throated Purpletuft appears to perch-glean more frequently than its congenerics, with apparently few observations of fruits being taken in hovering flight, and these are usually of very short distance (<50cm: GMK pers. obs.). A study in extreme northeast Brazil identified fruits of seven species of tree, belonging to three families, namely Loranthaceae (*n* = 4), Cambretaceae (*n* = 1) and Leguminoseae (*n* = 2) (Almeida and Teixeira 1997).

BREEDING This purpletuft's breeding biology is, in comparison with other *Iodopleura*, rather well studied (many published and previously unpublished data were summarised by Whittaker and Kirwan 2008). Song is heard from June (until at least December in the southeast) and nests have been recorded between midwinter and early spring (July–October in south of range, May in north). Buff-throated Purpletuft perhaps commences nesting even earlier in southeast Brazil, as suggested by a female watched apparently prospecting for suitable nest-sites in the third week of June (GMK pers. obs.). As in *I. isabellae*, the species constructs a tiny open cup nest, very much reminiscent of a hummingbird's, generally placed 10–25m above the ground, often in a practically leafless legume, e.g. *Citharexylum myrianthum* (Verbenaceae) or *Dimorphandra mollis* (Fabaceae), or a *Cecropia* sp. (Urticaceae), either on a horizontal branch or in a tree fork, much like other purpletufts as far as we can ascertain. Nest dimensions and constituents used in construction are detailed in Mendoça and Gonzaga (2000). In nests constructed on grey tree bark the species uses grey-green lichens, but on somewhat mossy trunks the female selects many fresh green lichens to adorn the outside of the nest (GMK pers. obs.). Males have often been observed 'standing guard' while females incubate the egg or construct the nest (sometimes descending almost to the ground to collect materials), but do not seem to actively assist; however, both sexes do appear to provision the chicks (Whittaker and Kirwan 2008). Lays a single egg, but there are no data concerning the incubation period, although the nestling, whose grey down closely matches the colour of many nests, fledges in *c*.11 days (see Willis and Oniki 1988a, Teixeira *et al.* 1990, Mendoça and Gonzaga 2000, Whittaker and Kirwan 2008). Both sexes defend the nest and its immediate environs, belligerently chasing away much larger tanagers (*Tachyphonus*), thrushes (*Turdus*) and becards, although one nest was built in very close proximity to a nest of Crested Becard *Pachyramphus validus* (Whittaker and Kirwan 2008), but purpletufts apparently evacuate the nest on approach by a toucan or a Buff-bellied Puffbird *Notharchus macrorhynchus* (Mendoça and Gonzaga 2000).

STATUS Until recently, considered Endangered by BirdLife International (2000), but since downlisted to Near Threatened (BirdLife International 2004, 2008). Buff-throated Purpletuft is undoubtedly rare and local, and its populations have been highly fragmented by the severe reduction in extent of lowland and foothill forest in southeast and, especially, northeast Brazil, where only tiny remnants of Atlantic Forest are still extant. Nonetheless, like other purpletufts, its diminutive appearance and, until recently, our complete lack of knowledge of the species' voice will have almost certainly masked our conception of its true abundance. For instance, it was not until the early 1990s that the species was discovered in southern coastal Bahia, where it is now known from at least two localities. Buff-throated Purpletuft occurs in several protected areas, particularly the extensive Serra do Mar State Park, in São Paulo, which is largely impossible to access by road, as well as in at least two privately protected areas (within the umbrella of the Ubatuba Experimental Station), and the Serra dos Órgãos National Park and Desengano State Park (both Rio de Janeiro), as well as Augusto Ruschi Ecological Station, Forno Grande and Pedra Azul State Parks (Espírito Santo). Ongoing deforestation in the extreme northeast of the species' range, where the overall population appears tiny, e.g. at Murici (Alagoas), gives cause for considerable concern at a more local level.

REFERENCES Albano (2010a, 2010b), Almeida and Teixeira (1997), Bencke *et al.* (2006), BirdLife International (2000, 2004, 2007, 2008), Browne (2005), Camargo and Camargo (1964), Collar *et al.* (1992), Cracraft (1985), Descourtilz (1854–56), Dunning (2008), Goerck (1999), Gonzaga *et al.* (1995), Hellmayr (1929b), Knox and Walters (1994), Magalhães *et al.* (2007), Mallet-Rodrigues and Marinho de Noronha (2003), Mendoça and Gonzaga (2000), Pinto (1944), Remold (2002), Ribon *et al.* (2004), Ridgely and Tudor (1994, 2009), Sibley (1996), Sick (1993, 1997), Silveira *et al.* (2005), Snow (1982, 2004a), Stotz *et al.* (1996), Teixeira *et al.* (1987, 1990, 1993), Wege and Long (1995), Whitehouse and Ribon (2010), Whittaker and Kirwan (2008), Willis (1992), Willis and Oniki (1988a, 2002).

Buff-throated Purpletuft *Iodopleura pipra*. **Fig. 1**. Female, *I. p. pipra*, on nest, Fazenda Angelim, Ubatuba, São Paulo, southeast Brazil, October (*Hadoram Shirihai / Photographic Handbook to Birds of the World*). **Figs. 2–3**. Male, *I. p. leucopygia*, RPPN Frei Caneca (Jaqueira), Pernambuco, northeast Brazil, December (*Pete Morris*). Note the obvious white rump band on this male, which is the principal feature of the northern subspecies. However, this character is perhaps not as reliable as sometimes quoted in the literature (see text).

Genus *Pipreola*: fruiteaters

Most of the 11 species of *Pipreola* (the largest single genus of Cotingidae) are Andean in distribution, where they encompass all elevational gradients from the treeline to the foothills, and all are essentially green-coloured, forest-based species that are easily overlooked unless you are familiar with their typical high-pitched songs or their even quieter and even more inaudible calls.

The first four species treated here, Golden-breasted Fruiteater *Pipreola aureopectus*, Orange-breasted Fruiteater *P. jucunda*, Masked Fruiteater *P. pulchra* and Black-chested Fruiteater *P. lubomirskii*, are generally considered to form a superspecies (Sibley and Monroe 1990). These four have been considered conspecific (Snow 1973, 1979a), but most authors since have treated them as separate species (including Remsen *et al.* 2009).

GOLDEN-BREASTED FRUITEATER
Pipreola aureopectus   Plate 16

Ampelis aureopectus **Lafresnaye, 1843**, *Rev. Zool.* 6: 68, 'Santa Fé de Bogotá', Colombia

Golden-breasted Fruiteater is endemic to northern Vene-zuela and western Colombia, where it is generally tolerably common and the simplest fruiteater in plumage, with the male lacking the black head of several sympatric species.

IDENTIFICATION 16.5–17.5cm. The male of this species is unlikely to be confused with any sympatric congener, as in Venezuela male Green-and-black Fruiteater *P. riefferii* has a black hood and both sexes of Handsome Fruiteater *P. formosa* exhibit much larger white tertial spots. Bright grass green upperparts and flanks, with yellow underparts, facilitate straightforward identification given reasonable views. The drabber female, however, is essentially green and yellow with no distinctive field characters, and it could be mistaken for females of three other species. Indeed, as noted in the introduction, it has been suggested that the three other members of the *P. aureopectus* superspecies – *P. jucunda* (Orange-breasted Fruiteater), *P. pulchra* (Masked Fruiteater) and *P. lubomirskii* (Black-chested Fruiteater) – are in fact well-marked subspecies of Golden-breasted Fruiteater. Certainly, females of all four forms are rather similar, but female Golden-breasted is separated from all of the others by virtue of the yellow throat streaking and white tertial fringes, and there is only any known range overlap with *P. jucunda*, in the Andes of southwest Colombia, where the two are not syntopic and there is no evidence of intergradation, further supporting their specific status. Black-chested Fruiteater, which does not overlap in range with any other member of the superspecies, occurs on the east slope of the Andes in southern Colombia to northern Peru, whilst Masked is confined to the east Peruvian Andes.

DISTRIBUTION Golden-breasted Fruiteater is confined to extreme northwestern South America, in the Coastal Cordillera, Sierra de Perijá and Andes of northwest Venezuela (Hilty 2003), and the Sierra de Nevada de Santa Marta and Andean foothills of northern and western Colombia, thence spottily through the West Andes from Antioquia south to Nariño, and at the northern end of the Central and East Andes south at least to Valdivia and southern Norte de Santander, respectively (Chapman 1917, Hilty and Brown 1986). For further details of the range see Geographical Variation. Elevational range is 600–3,100m, but this fruiteater usually occurs above 1,700m in Colombia (Hilty and Brown 1986) and is mainly found above 1,000m in Venezuela (Hilty 2003).

MOVEMENTS None recorded and the species is considered resident.

HABITAT The species occurs at lower and mid elevations of humid premontane and montane forest, including borders, shade-coffee plantations (Jones *et al.* 2002) and taller second growth. In Henri Pittier National Park, Venezuela, at least, it appears to avoid the most humid areas, and is found at intermediate and drier levels between the ranges of Handsome (lowest) and Green-and-black Fruiteaters (highest), usually on the south side of the north-facing mountains in the Coastal Cordillera of Venezuela. Golden-breasted Fruiteater generally inhabits the midstorey.

DESCRIPTION A typical 'dumpy', sluggish and 'clumsy'-looking fruiteater. The sexes differ. The bill has a slightly arched culmen and hooked tip, with exposed nostrils and weak rictal bristles. The flight feathers are not modified (as in all fruiteaters, including *Ampelioides*). The nominate race is described here. *Adult male.* – Upperparts bright grass green (sometimes faintly tinged bluish), including the ear-coverts and wing-coverts, becoming darker over the lores which may even appear black in the field. The remiges are grey-brown with grass green outer webs to the secondaries. Narrow white fringes to the tertials, which darken distally, but these are rather indistinct, and broadest at the tip. Chin dark green, concolorous with the forehead. Throat and upper breast golden-yellow, becoming paler, lemon-yellow on the belly and palest on the undertail-coverts, where sullied with green. Breast-sides and flanks same colour as the upperparts, reaching to feathering just above the tarsi. This solid green area breaks into streaks as it meets the yellow of the belly and on the rear flanks.

Adult female. – The upperparts are also grass green, as in the male, but the female lacks darker lores. Tertial fringes are also white, but smaller. Throat evenly streaked lemon-yellow and green directly below the bill. Rest of underparts mainly green, with pale yellow flammulations in the centre of the breast, becoming heavier on the belly and the rear flanks. Undertail-coverts pale yellow streaked lightly with green. *Juvenile.* – Duller overall and lacks the pale tips to the tertials, with brown irides and is even more heavily flammulated on the throat and breast (Restall *et al.* 2006). *Moult.* – There are no published data on moult, but in northern Colombia, principally in the Sierra Nevada de Santa Marta (race *P. a. decora*), birds have been examined in various stages of feather renewal between March and August at least, but no clear pattern is evident (J. C. Luna and C. A. Páez O./ ProAves unpubl. data). *Bare parts.* – Male has the bill orange or orange-red, the legs are grey-green and the irides are orange-yellow to yellow-white. The female has the bill dusky-grey, the legs grey-green and the irides yellow-white.

MEASUREMENTS (from Snow 1982, except bill; BMNH: Venezuela and Colombia) *P. a. festiva*: wing of male ($n = 10$) 89–95mm, wing of female ($n = 7$) 90–94mm; tail of male ($n = 10$) 65–71mm, tail of female ($n = 7$) 64–71mm; bill of male ($n = 4$) 14–15mm, bill of female ($n = 4$) 15–16mm; tarsus of male ($n = 10$) 20.5–23.0mm, tarsus of female ($n = 7$) 20.5–23.0mm. *P. a. aureopectus*: wing of male ($n = 14$) 88–96mm (Hellmayr 1929b). *P. a. decora*: wing of male ($n = 5$) 83–88mm, wing of female ($n = 1$) 84mm; tail ($n = 6$, sexes combined) 63–67mm (Hellmayr 1929b). Weight: 34.0–46.5g (11 males) and 34–60g (five females) (Dunning 2008; J. C. Luna and C. A. Páez O./ProAves unpubl. data).

GEOGRAPHICAL VARIATION Polytypic; three races are currently recognised. *P. a. aureopectus* (described above) occurs in western Venezuela from southern Táchira north and east to Lara (1,000–2,300m), the Sierra de Perijá (1,700–3,100m), and through the Andes of north and west Colombia (600–2,300m). *P. a. festiva* (Todd, 1912) occurs in the Coastal Cordillera (800–2,050m) of northern Venezuela, from Carabobo east to Aragua (and perhaps Miranda, where the species is unrecorded to date), and differs from the nominate race solely in the male, which has more extensive yellow on the underparts (reaching to the anal region) and better-streaked and spotted body-sides and flanks (although the last feature is occasionally apparent, to a lesser extent, in nominate *P. a. aureopectus*: Hellmayr 1929b). Male *P. a. decora* Bangs, 1899, of the Santa Marta Mountains of northern Colombia (from 600m to at least 2,100m), is considered to be smaller than the nominate race and has a yellow post-auricular band (although, as noted by Hellmayr 1929, some nominate *P. a. aureopectus*, e.g. from Caracas, Venezuela, also show this feature).

VOICE Similar in quality to others of the genus, e.g. Orange-breasted Fruiteater, the primary vocalisation being a high-pitched *pseEEEE-e-e-e-ee-e-e* of *c.*3-seconds duration, which initially rises quickly, then descends and finally ascends again, and may then be followed after a brief pause by two short notes *tic, tic* (Boesman 1999, Hilty 2003, Alvarez *et al.* 2007, Krabbe 2008). In addition to the published recordings just mentioned, recordings from Colombia (*P. a. decora*) and Venezuela (*P. a. festiva*) are available online at www.xeno-canto.org. Occasionally gives a briefer *seeeeeEEE* as a song (shorter and more forceful in conclusion than other fruiteaters) and a short *pseeeéé* in contact (D. Ascanio *in* Restall *et al.* 2006).

NATURAL HISTORY Virtually all of the *Pipreola* species are relatively poorly known in terms of their natural history, although there is probably also a great deal of similarity in terms of their behaviour. Solitary or in pairs, this species is usually located in the midstorey to the canopy. Golden-breasted Fruiteater is often encountered within mixed-species flocks, although it is perhaps the case that the species is simply more easily located when such a mobile flock is present in the vicinity. Can be confiding, and like all fruiteaters typically perches near-motionless for long periods, permitting close scrutiny.

FOOD AND FEEDING Diet is solely small fruit, plucked whilst the bird is perched, but there seems to be no information on preferred species etc.

BREEDING There are no data on breeding, other than that 18 breeding-condition birds were collected in Colombia in January–June, and one in September (Hilty and Brown 1986), and Schaefer and Phelps (1954) considered the nesting period to be centred on May in northern Venezuela.

STATUS Golden-breasted Fruiteater is considered Least Concern (BirdLife International 2004, 2008). Very few concrete data, although it is considered to be reasonably common in the Santa Marta Mountains (where it is the only fruiteater present) and in the Sierra de Perijá, but the species is generally rare in the Colombian Andes (Hilty and Brown 1986). In slight contrast *P. aureopectus* is generally somewhat local but fairly common in northern Venezuela (Hilty 2003). The Choroni Road, in Henri Pittier National Park, Venezuela, is a particularly good site to see this species, which is protected within a number of reserves and national parks (e.g. Sierra Nevada National Park, Mérida, Venezuela) in both countries, including several recently declared ProAves-owned reserves in Colombia (cf. Hilty 2003, Salaman *et al.* 2008, 2009).

REFERENCES Alvarez *et al.* (2007), Boesman (1999), Chapman (1917), Cuervo *et al.* (2008b), David and Gosselin (2002), Hellmayr (1929b), Hilty (2003), Hilty and Brown (1983, 1986), Jones *et al.* (2002), Krabbe (2008), Meyer de Schauensee and Phelps (1987), Olson (1971), Restall *et al.* (2006), Ridgely and Tudor (1994, 2009), Schaefer and Phelps (1954), Salaman *et al.* (2008, 2009), Snow (1982, 2004a), Stotz *et al.* (1996), Strewe and Navarro (2004b), Todd and Carriker (1922).

Golden-breasted Fruiteater *Pipreola aureopectus*. **Fig. 1**. Male, *P. a. decora*, Sierra Nevada de Santa Marta, northern Colombia, March (*Pete Morris*). The pale yellow band on the neck-sides generally distinguishes this race (but see text). **Fig. 2**. Male, *P. a. festiva*, Colonia Tovar, Aragua, north-coastal Venezuela, October (*Nick Athanas / Tropical Birding*). Note the extensive yellow on the central underparts and the well-spotted and green-streaked breast-sides and flanks.

367

ORANGE-BREASTED FRUITEATER
Pipreola jucunda   Plate 16

Pipreola jucunda **P. L. Sclater, 1860**, *Proc. Zool. Soc. Lond.* 28: 89, pl. 160, Cachillacta, near Nanegal, Pichincha, Ecuador

Formerly considered a race of the previous species, the range of this fruiteater is restricted to the western Andes of southern Colombia and northwestern Ecuador, and it is completely allopatric with *P. aureopectus*.

IDENTIFICATION 18cm. The male most resembles the allopatric male Masked Fruiteater *P. pulchra*, but has the entire head glossy black (rather than mainly olive) as well as a fiery orange breast. Male Golden-breasted Fruiteater *P. aureopectus*, which occurs sympatrically with Orange-breasted in parts of western Colombia, but has not yet proven to be syntopic, also lacks black on the head and the underparts are almost entirely golden-yellow. Females of these two species are more similar, but the throat is a more uniform olive in Orange-breasted (rather than streaked yellow), and it lacks the faint pale tertial tips of Golden-breasted. The present species perhaps marginally overlaps with the larger Green-and-black Fruiteater *P. riefferii*, but note the different head and upper-breast pattern of males of the two species, and in females the different underparts patterns, lack of white tertial tips in the present species and the grey-green (not orange) legs of Orange-breasted.

DISTRIBUTION Orange-breasted Fruiteater has a comparatively limited range in the Chocó region of western South America, on the west slope of the West Andes north to southern Chocó in Colombia, and south to Pichincha in Ecuador, although it formerly occurred as far south as eastern Guayas. Elevational range is 600–2,300m, but the species is mainly recorded at 1,100–1,850m.

MOVEMENTS None recorded, although Hilty (1997) considered Orange-breasted Fruiteater to be a vagrant or short-distance migrant at a study site in the West Andes of Colombia.

HABITAT The species inhabits the lower and middle elevations of submontane cloud forests, including forest borders, particularly the super-humid 'moss forests'.

DESCRIPTION A typical 'dumpy' fruiteater. The sexes

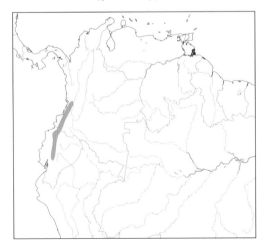

differ. The bill has a reasonably arched culmen and a hooked tip, with exposed nostrils and weak rictal bristles. The flight feathers are not modified (as in all fruiteaters, including *Ampelioides*). *Adult male.* – Head and throat glossy black, forming a hood that reaches to the lower nape at the back, and bright grass green from the hind-collar to tail, with somewhat darker primaries. Upper breast is fiery orange, extending narrowly as a paler half-collar to below the ear-coverts, and bordered below by black. Rest of underparts lemon-yellow with a grass green intrusion on the 'shoulders' (almost forming a pectoral band) and flanks where it breaks into streaks, thus the division of yellow and green does not appear sharply defined. Underwing-coverts bright yellow. *Adult female.* – The entire upperparts are grass green, whilst the throat appears uniform olive in the field; the rest of the underparts are streaked green and yellow. *Juvenile.* – Apparently undescribed (Snow 2004a). *Moult.* – There are no published data on moult, but a male collected in August in Ecuador was replacing a moderate number of body feathers (MECN), whilst in Colombia birds have been trapped in light body moult in October (male), heavy wing moult and light body moult in July (sex not stated), but others in February and August were not replacing any of their feathers (J. C. Luna and H. Loaiza/ ProAves unpubl. data). Snow (1982) reported that feather replacement may commence virtually year-round in *Pipreola* in southern Colombia and Ecuador. *Bare parts.* – Bill red to yellow (and all variations between these two colours, with no apparent sexual dimorphism), legs greyish-olive to orange (again no sexual dimorphism is evident), and the irides pale yellowish-white to orange with a black pupil, but generally duller in the female.

MEASUREMENTS (BMNH; MECN; except tarsus, from Snow 1982: Ecuador) Wing of male ($n = 6$) 92–96mm, wing of female ($n = 4$) 93–96mm; tail of male ($n = 6$) 55–68mm, tail of female ($n = 4$) 59–65mm; bill of male ($n = 6$) 16.7–20.0mm, bill of female ($n = 4$) 17.7–20.0mm; tarsus of male ($n = 11$) 21.0–23.5mm, tarsus of female ($n = 4$) 21.5–23.0mm. Weight: 52–65g (three males) and 54–62g (two females) (MECN; J. C. Luna and H. Loaiza/ProAves unpubl. data).

GEOGRAPHICAL VARIATION Monotypic.

VOICE Utters a typical *Pipreola* hissing whistle, a very high, ascending *se-e-e-e-e-e-EEEE* that lasts 2–3 seconds, but is sometimes prolonged to *c.*5 seconds (A. Spencer recording, XC22190) and generally recalls that of Black-chested Fruiteater *P. lubomirskii*. There is a pronounced upslurred ending to this call, which is presumed to be the song (A. Solano-Ugalde pers. comm.). A pair has been recorded calling together (S. Olmstead recording, XC37024), with the male giving slightly louder and shorter upslurred notes, *sweeep*, and the female uttering quieter, higher pitched *seee* calls. Also recorded is an infrequently given, sharp and piercing *psii* or *eeest* with variations given by both sexes (Connop 1996, Moore *et al.* 1999, Snow 2004a, Restall *et al.* 2006). GMK and A. Solano-Ugalde (pers. obs.) witnessed a male give a short hissing-like vocalisation in apparent threat during an interaction with a party of Moss-backed Tanagers *Bangsia edwardsi*. Recordings from Colombia and Ecuador are archived online at www.xeno-canto.org.

NATURAL HISTORY A typical fruiteater. The species is usually found in pairs or alone, and it appears only occasionally to join mixed-species flocks.

FOOD AND FEEDING The diet is exclusively fruit but again there are no published data concerning any preferences (as per *P. aureopectus*). However, A. Solano-Ugalde (pers. comm.) has noted 15 food plant species in the bird's diet. Food is either plucked whilst perched (with a rapid twist and pull movement) or taken during a brief and rather clumsy-looking hover-sally. The male offers the female fruit in courtship, including immediately prior to copulation (and *Pipreola* is one of the very few genera of cotingas in which such behaviour is known or suspected: Snow 1982, Samper 1992).

DISPLAY Ritualised displays are basically unknown in this genus, but in mid-August 2010, GMK, A. Solano-Ugalde and N. Blackwood observed two males engaged in a previously unrecorded behaviour at the so-called Mashpi Road, in Pichincha, northwest Ecuador. The two birds were watched for *c*.3 minutes perched at less than 1m distance on the same branch, one slightly above the other, calling regularly and performing near-synchronised movements, which consisted of inflating the chest feathers, tipping the head slightly backwards simultaneously, and various bobbing and swaying movements with the body, accompanied by short, high-pitched calls. One of the two individuals remained completely stationary, but the other occasionally made very short sideways movements on the branch between performances. The behaviour ceased when one bird flew from sight and the other flew to a branch *c*.2m away a few seconds later. No females were seen in the direct vicinity, but there was at least one female within the general area.

BREEDING There are very few breeding data, but our knowledge is perhaps surprisingly greater than that for the previous species. Lint and Dolan (1966) observed captive male Orange-breasted Fruiteater feed the female on the nest (and prior to laying), and noted that the clutch consisted of two eggs, which were light tan with fine brown flecking, were laid on consecutive days and incubated for 16 or 17 days. Only one young successfully fledged, at 25 days, and thereafter it was provisioned by both adults, as had been the case prior to fledging. In the wild, Samper (1992) found a nest in southwest Colombia at the start of August (1988), but was unable to observe it closely, as the structure was concealed within a mass of epiphytes on a large trunk *c*.5m above the ground, to which the female brought moss. Another nest, found by Strewe (2001) in mid-April 1998, also in southwest Colombia, apparently had young, as both adults were visiting the clump of vines in which it was concealed, and the female was observed food-carrying. More recently, in northwest Ecuador, Solano-Ugalde (in press) described a nest, found in mid November, at Refugio Paz de las Aves, which contained a dead chick that was infested with fly larvae. The outside of the nest was composed of dead and live mosses, while internally the materials were bound to a network of interwoven fine twigs and fern fibres. Nest dimensions are presented by Solano-Ugalde (in press). Additionally, a pair with nesting material was observed briefly in the second week of December, in old second growth at Reserva Inti Llacta. There is also a photograph of a female at a nest, apparently taken in Ecuador, online at http://www.glennbartley.com/naturephotography/Ecuador/Birds/ORANGE-BREASTED%20FRUITEATER.html. As can be seen therein, the species builds a reasonably substantial nest, like most fruiteaters, in the fork of a tree, heavily surrounded and partially concealed by moss and epiphytes.

STATUS Orange-breasted Fruiteater is treated as Least Concern by BirdLife International (2004, 2008). The species is uncommon in Ecuador, but almost certainly more frequently encountered in Colombia, where it is known from the La Planada, Río Ñambí and El Pangán reserves in the extreme south. Extremely difficult to find in most of its Ecuadorian range, where the patchy Chocó forests around Puerto Maldonado, northwest of Mindo, and the 'cloud forests' on the old Chiriboga–Santo Domingo road offer some of the best bets for finding one of these fruiteaters. There are also several recent records from the Reserva Las Gralarias near Mindo, close to the capital, Quito, and the species also seems to be common and easily found between La Delicia and Mashpi, also in Pichincha province (A. Solano-Ugalde pers. comm.; GMK pers. obs.). The species has also been recently recorded around Toisán, Imbabura, also in northern Ecuador (Boyla and Estrada 2005). The species is endemic to the Chocó Rainforest Centre of endemism (Cracraft 1985).

REFERENCES BirdLife International (2004, 2008), Boyla and Estrada (2005), Connop (1996), Cracraft (1985), Hellmayr (1929b), Hilty (1997), Hilty and Brown (1986), Kirwan and Marlow (1996), Lint and Dolan (1966), Moore *et al*. (1999), Restall *et al*. (2006), Ridgely and Greenfield (2001), Ridgely and Tudor (1994, 2009), Salaman *et al*. (2008), Samper (1992), Snow (1982, 2004a), Solano-Ugalde (in press), Stotz *et al*. (1996), Strewe (2001).

Orange-breasted Fruiteater *Pipreola jucunda.* **Fig. 1.** Female, Mashpi Road, prov. Pichincha, northwest Ecuador, October (*János Oláh*). **Fig. 2.** Male, Mashpi Road, prov. Pichincha, northwest Ecuador, October (*János Oláh*). Orange-breasted Fruiteater is common at this site. **Figs. 3–4.** Male, Refugio Paz de las Antpittas, prov. Pichincha, northwest Ecuador, April, May (*Roger Ahlman / www.pbase.com/ahlman*). Another regular locality for the species, with birds occasionally visiting feeders with tanagers and other frugivores.

MASKED FRUITEATER
Pipreola pulchra   **Plate 16**

Euchlornis pulchra **C. E. Hellmayr, 1917**, *Verh. Orn. Ges. Bayern* 13: 199 [new name for *Ampelis elegans*, Tschudi, 1843, *Archiv. Naturg.* 9(1): 385], River Tullumayo, Junín, Peru

Restricted to Peru, this striking fruiteater is relatively easily identified, but it is one of the most poorly known members of its genus. Almost nothing has been published concerning many aspects of its natural history.

IDENTIFICATION 18–19cm. Unlikely to be confused with other fruiteaters, as *P. pulchra* does not overlap in range with any other member of the *P. aureopectus* superspecies (see Introduction). The male's head is olive but can appear darker in the field, especially around the throat, forehead and ear-coverts. Compared with Orange-breasted Fruiteater *P. jucunda* (no overlap) the present species has a much greener tone to the head (being less solid black) and the breast is less fiery orange (more golden in colour). Females resemble those of other members of the superspecies, but may be separated from female Scarlet-breasted Fruiteater *P. frontalis*, which has a similar geographical and partially overlapping elevational range, by having streaked (not scaled) underparts, olive tarsi (red in Scarlet-breasted) and no pale spots on the tips of the tertials.

DISTRIBUTION Endemic to Peru, where Masked Fruit-eater is restricted to the east slope of the Andes from central west dpto. Amazonas south to southern dpto. Cuzco, in the Cordillera Vilcabamba, and is found exclusively at 1,500–2,400m. The species is endemic to the East Peruvian Andean subcentre of the Peruvian Andean Centre of endemism (Cracraft 1985) and to the Ecuador–Peru East Andes Endemic Bird Area (Stattersfield *et al.* 1998).

MOVEMENTS None recorded.

HABITAT Masked Fruiteater is found in the interior and at the borders of humid mid-elevation cloud forest and associated mature second growth.

DESCRIPTION A typical 'dumpy' and sluggish-looking fruiteater. The sexes differ. The bill has a slightly arched culmen and hooked tip, with exposed nostrils and weak rictal bristles. The flight feathers are not modified (just like

all fruiteaters, including *Ampelioides*). *Adult male.* – Head and upperparts grass green, becoming slightly darker on the head-sides and throat, and the primaries are also darker; the lower throat and breast are orange-yellow (brightest in the centre), and this colour continues as a post-auricular band around the rear of the ear-coverts. The throat and breast patch are bordered with a narrow black line at the sides. Lemon-yellow belly and undertail-coverts (the latter slightly scaled with olive); the shoulders (almost joining across the breast) are green, breaking into streaks lower on the flanks. *Adult female.* – Similar to female Orange-breasted Fruiteater. The entire upperparts are bright green as in the male, whilst the throat appears uniform olive in the field; the rest of the underparts are streaked green and yellow. *Moult.* – No published data concerning moult, but Snow (1982) recorded that feather renewal in the relevant part of Peru amongst *Pipreola* in general appears to be in October–March. *Juvenile.* – This plumage is apparently undescribed (Snow 2004a). *Bare parts.* – Bill coral-red to orange, irides yellowish-white to dark brown and legs dark greenish to grey (Snow 2004a; FMNH).

MEASUREMENTS (from Snow 1982, 2004a: eastern Peru) Wing of male (*n* = 4) 93–101mm, wing of female (*n* = 2) 92–93mm; tail of male (*n* = 4) 65–78mm; bill of male (*n* = 4) 10.5mm; tarsus of male (*n* = 4) 23mm. Weight: 51.2–63g (males) and 42–63g (two females) (Dunning 2008).

GEOGRAPHICAL VARIATION Monotypic.

VOICE The song is a typical fruiteater sibilant, drawn-out whistle, rendered *psee-pseee* (Walker 2002) or *tseeeeeeeweee* (Schulenberg *et al.* (2007), and lasting *c*.3 seconds. The call is a shorter rising *tsweet?* of similar quality and with a duration lasting approximately one-third that of the song, most often given in contact between members of a pair while foraging. Recordings of the species' voice appear on Schulenberg (2000b) and Boesman (2009) and both the song and the contact calls are archived online at www. xeno-canto.org. In southern Peru, playback of the song of Masked Fruiteater to other Andean species (e.g. Barred *P. arcuata* and Band-tailed Fruiteaters *P. intermedia*) usually provokes a highly aggressive response by those species (H. Lloyd *in litt.* 2010).

NATURAL HISTORY Mainly a canopy and subcanopy species, natural history information concerning the Masked Fruiteater is incredibly spartan. The species' habits recall those of other Andean fruiteaters, it being a lethargic bird typically found alone or in pairs and most usually encountered at fruiting trees.

FOOD AND FEEDING The diet is apparently exclusively frugivorous, but no details concerning species composition or even foraging techniques are available

BREEDING To date nothing is known concerning the species' breeding biology, although doubtless in most aspects this will be similar to other *Pipreola*.

STATUS Currently treated as Least Concern by BirdLife International (2004, 2008). Masked Fruiteater is generally rare to uncommon, but is almost certainly easily overlooked without knowledge of its vocalisations. However, *P. pulchra* was recently discovered to be unusually common in the Gran Pajonal, Ucayali (http://www.allaboutbirds.org/netcommunity/page.aspx?pid=1788#top). Perhaps the most spectacular area to search for this species is the footpath and along the road downhill from the Macchu

Picchu archaeological site in northern Cuzco toward the bridge (Puente Ruinas), near Aguas Calientes. It can also be found fairly easily along the Paty Trail/Carpish Tunnel, in central Peru.

REFERENCES BirdLife International (2004, 2008), Boesman (2009), Cracraft (1985), Dunning (2008), Hellmayr (1929b), Ridgely and Tudor (1994, 2009), Robbins *et al.* (2011), Schulenberg (2000b), Schulenberg *et al.* (2007), Snow (1982, 2004a), Stattersfield *et al.* (1998), Stotz *et al.* (1996), Walker (2002).

Masked Fruiteater *Pipreola pulchra.* **Fig. 1**. Male, Machu Picchu, dpto. Cuzco, southeast Peru, December (*Fábio Olmos*). **Fig. 2**. Female, Machu Picchu, dpto. Cuzco, southeast Peru, November (*Hadoram Shirihai / Photographic Handbook to Birds of the World*).

BLACK-CHESTED FRUITEATER
Pipreola lubomirskii   Plate 16

Pipreola lubomirskii **Taczanowski, 1879**, *Proc. Zool. Soc. Lond.* 1879: 236, pl. 22, Tambillo, dpto. Cajamarca, Peru

The fourth member of the *P. aureopectus* superspecies is largely distributed along the humid east Andean slope from southern Colombia to northeast Peru, although it has recently been discovered at one locality on the west slope in northern Peru (Salinas *et al.* 2003). Furthermore, comparatively recently Black-chested Fruiteater has also been found at a single site south of the Marañón River, suggesting that it and Masked Fruiteater *P. pulchra* might come into contact (or almost so) in this region.

IDENTIFICATION 17–18cm. The male Black-chested Fruiteater superficially resembles the commoner Green-and-black Fruiteater *P. riefferii*, but does not certainly occur alongside any other member of the *P. aureopectus* group (see above), thus making the larger Green-and-black Fruiteater the most likely pitfall. Separation of these two species is reasonably straightforward, given a decent view, as both sexes of Green-and-black Fruiteater exhibit pale tertial tips, orange-red legs and dark irides, whilst male Black-chested also lacks the yellow border to the black hood of male *P. riefferii* and has unmarked central underparts.

DISTRIBUTION Black-chested Fruiteater occurs in the Andes of western South America, principally being known from the eastern Andean slope of Ecuador, extending marginally north into southern Colombia (at the head of the Magdalena Valley in Huila and in southeastern Nariño, and has been speculated to occur also in western Caquetá and Putumayo), as well as just south into northern Peru, principally north and west of the Marañón, south to northern Cajamarca, including on the west slope of the Andes, at two sites in the Zaña Valley (Salinas *et al.* 2003), and in central Amazonas reaching just south of the Marañón, in the Cordillera de Colán (Barnes *et al.* 1997). Elevational range is 1,200–2,300m, but in Ecuador the species is known solely from 1,500 to 2,100m; in Peru at 1,600–2,300m.

MOVEMENTS None known.

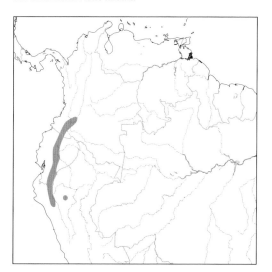

HABITAT Black-chested Fruiteater is an inhabitant of the lower and mid levels of mid-elevation cloud forest and their borders.

DESCRIPTION A typical 'dumpy' and sluggish-looking fruiteater. The sexes differ. The bill has a slightly arched culmen with a moderately hooked tip, as well as exposed nostrils and weak rictal bristles. The flight feathers are not modified (as in all fruiteaters, including *Ampelioides*). *Adult male.* – The head and throat to the central breast are black, with rather uniform grass green upperparts and breast-sides, except the somewhat darker primaries. Flanks lightly scaled with green and there are a few black spots where the green meets the yellow. Rest of underparts lemon-yellow, with faint olive scaling on the undertail-coverts. *Adult female.* – Entirely bright green above. The throat and upper breast are solid green, whilst the rest of the underparts are streaked green and yellow. *Juvenile.* – This plumage is apparently undescribed (Snow 2004a). *Moult.* – There are no published data concerning moult, but a male collected in June in southeast Ecuador showed some body moult (MECN), and Snow (1982) recorded that feather renewal in the relevant regions of the Andes amongst *Pipreola* in general appears to be virtually year-round. *Bare parts.* – Orange-red to yellowish-red bill (duller in the female), greyish-green legs with olive feet and orange to yellow irides.

MEASUREMENTS (from Snow 1982, 2004a; MECN: Napo and Zamora-Chinchipe, eastern Ecuador) Wing of male (n = 9) 90–97mm, wing of female (n = 5) 88.5–94.0mm; tail of male (n = 9) 62–68mm, tail of female (n = 5) 59–67mm; bill of male (n = 7) 9.5–10.5mm (n = 2, to skull, 14.6–16.8mm); bill of female (n = 4) 9.5–10.5mm (n = 1, to skull, 15.4mm); tarsus of male (n = 7) 20.5–23.0mm, tarsus of female (n = 4) 21.0–22.5mm. Weight: 55.5–64.0g (two males; MECN).

GEOGRAPHICAL VARIATION Monotypic.

VOICE The voice is typical of the *Pipreola* fruiteaters, a thin and slightly protracted *pseeeeeeet* (lasting just *c.*2 seconds), becoming emphatic in the finale, as well as a shorter, much weaker and less easily noticed *pseet* (see Moore and Lysinger 1997, Krabbe and Nilsson 2003). An example of this species' vocalisations from Ecuador is archived at www.xeno-canto.org.

NATURAL HISTORY Like its congenerics, Black-chested Fruiteater is usually encountered alone or in pairs. Its behaviour is probably typical of all the Andean fruiteaters but, like the previous species, *P. lubomirskii* is especially poorly known.

FOOD AND FEEDING Its diet is apparently exclusively fruit, but there are no details of species taken, any preferences or even foraging behaviour.

BREEDING The species' breeding biology is also completely unknown, although a breeding-condition male was collected in dpto. Huila, Colombia, in late March (Hilty and Brown 1986) and two males collected in southeast Ecuador in June and September had enlarged testes (MECN).

STATUS Formerly afforded Near Threatened status (Collar *et al.* 1994), but the species has subsequently been listed as Least Concern (BirdLife International 2004, 2008), although Snow (2004a) speculated that its previous listing might be more appropriate. Black-chested Fruiteater is endemic to the North Andean Centre of endemism (Cracraft 1985). It is apparently rare and local throughout its range (Hilty and Brown 1986, Ridgely and Greenfield 2001, Schulenberg *et* al. 2007), and is generally infrequently seen. Black-chested Fruiteater is particularly difficult to encounter, at least in Ecuador, it being recorded far less frequently than the much commoner sympatric Green-and-black Fruiteater. The species is perhaps best looked for in the forests around the Cordillera de Guacamayos, on the road between Baeza and Tena, in eastern Ecuador (cf. Cisneros-Heredia 2009). It is also known from the upper Saña Valley in Cajamarca, northern Peru (Boyla and Estrada 2005). Much suitable montane habitat still remains, some protected, at least in Ecuador, but further habitat destruction in parts of the species' range, such as the Cordillera de Colán in northern Peru, could render it more at risk.

REFERENCES Barnes *et al.* (1997), BirdLife International (2004, 2008), Cisneros-Heredia (2009), Collar *et al.* (1994), Cracraft (1985), Davies *et al.* (1994), Hellmayr (1929b), Hilty and Brown (1986), Krabbe and Nilsson (2003), Krabbe and Sornoza (1994), Mlíkovský (2009), Moore and Lysinger (1997), Parker *et al.* (1982, 1985), Ridgely and Greenfield (2001), Ridgely and Tudor (1994, 2009), Salinas *et al.* (2003), Schulenberg *et al.* (2007), Snow (1982, 2004a), Stotz *et al.* (1996).

Black-chested Fruiteater *Pipreola lubomirskii*. **Fig. 1**. Male, Cabañas San Isidro, prov. Napo, eastern Ecuador, January (*Roger Ahlman / www. pbase.com/ahlman*). **Fig. 2**. Male, Baeza, prov. Napo, eastern Ecuador, June (*Dušan M. Brinkhuizen*). Note the pale irides, which provide a ready distinguishing feature from the much commoner Green-and-black Fruiteater *Pipreola riefferii*. This species is rarely photographed.

SCARLET-BREASTED FRUITEATER
Pipreola frontalis   **Plate 17**

Euchlornis frontalis **P. L. Sclater, 1858**, *Proc. Zool. Soc. Lond.* 26: 446, [Samaipata, Santa Cruz,] Bolivia

This beautiful and distinctive smaller fruiteater appears to be most closely related to the Fiery-throated Fruiteater *P. chlorolepidota*, and previous authorities have speculated that their speciation might have been a comparatively recent event. Scarlet-breasted and Fiery-throated Fruiteaters still exhibit rather extensive geographical overlap, although their altitudinal ranges are largely parapatric. Even more interesting is that the two subspecies of *P. frontalis* would appear to merit specific status, as already speculated by, for example, Ridgely and Greenfield (2001) and Snow (2004a), given that their females are as different as any two recognised species within the *P. aureopectus* superspecies, and the males only slightly less so. The two subspecies' primary vocalisations also appear to differ as much as between other species of *Pipreola*.

IDENTIFICATION 15.5–16.5cm. The male of this small fruiteater should be easily identified if seen well: the red bill and scarlet wash to the throat, otherwise yellow underparts and grass green upperparts should leave little doubt as to this bird's identity. The female is less distinct, but still attractive and offers just reward for any lengthy search. The bright green upperparts and breast, lower underparts scaled green and yellow, yellow chin, throat and forehead make identification as a *Pipreola* easy. Female Fiery-throated Fruiteater, which generally occurs at lower altitudes, is superficially similar but lacks any yellow on the forehead (although see the description of female *P. f. squamipectus*), is more uniformly and densely scaled below, has a white (rather than yellow) iris and is also obviously smaller. Male Fiery-throated Fruiteater represents much less of a confusion risk as it has largely green underparts, with almost no yellow, and exhibits no contrast between the crown and nape and the rest of the upperparts. Female Masked Fruiteater *P. pulchra*, which also occurs in Peru, is larger and streaked (rather than scaled) yellow and green below.

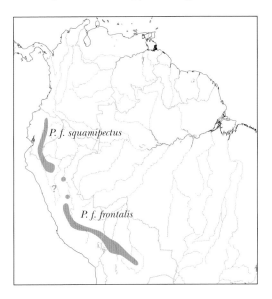

DISTRIBUTION Scarlet-breasted Fruiteater is comparatively wide-ranging in the Andes but is entirely confined to the east slope, from northern Ecuador (around Volcán Sumaco, in western Napo) locally south to northern Peru (in dpto. San Martín, e.g. at Abra Patricia and on the northern Cordillera Azul), and then reappears in central Peru (from the Cordillera Azul and Cerros del Sira, in dptos. Huánuco/Ucayali) and continues south to central Bolivia, reaching its southernmost extent in western dpto. Santa Cruz. Elevational range is 670–2,300m, but the species is probably very rare below 900m (and Ridgely and Greenfield 2001 thought any such low-elevation records might be in error) and is uncommon above 1,700m.

MOVEMENTS Like most other fruiteaters, none known, but the possibility that the species makes comparatively short-range movements in response to fruiting events cannot be discounted.

HABITAT Principally recorded in foothill, premontane and montane forests, more rarely at borders.

DESCRIPTION A typical 'dumpy' and sluggish-looking fruiteater. The sexes differ. Bill has a moderately arched culmen and hooked tip, with exposed nostrils and weak rictal bristles. The flight feathers are not modified (as in all fruiteaters, including *Ampelioides*). The nominate race is described here. *Adult male.* – Bright grass green above, with a somewhat darker bluish-green face, especially over the loral region, whitish tips to the tertials and somewhat darker primaries. The chin is yellow, becoming vivid red over the centre of the throat and breast. The rest of the underparts are mainly yellow, but are streaked and mottled with green on the flanks. *Adult female.* – Upperparts grass green, as in the male, with a narrow yellow band on the forehead immediately above the bill and reaching towards the eyes, and a much less obviously darker face, whilst the white tertial tips are probably on average smaller. Underparts: the yellow throat is clearly demarcated by a green pectoral band, below which the remaining underparts are scaled yellow and green (appearing barred in the field). *Juvenile.* – This plumage is apparently undescribed (Snow 2004a). *Moult.* – There are no published data on moult, but in Ecuadorian specimens birds (both sexes) in June were variably replacing the wing, tail and body feathers, but none of those examined in September–October was in moult (MECN). Snow (1982) noted that moult amongst *Pipreola* in general might be expected to commence virtually year-round in the north of this species' range, but to be distinctly concentrated in September–March in the south. *Bare parts.* – Irides yellow to yellowish-white (both sexes). The bill and legs are orange-red to scarlet or dark reddish in the male, but some females have the bill dusky with a yellow base to the lower mandible (others dark red), and the legs are orange, yellowish-red or brownish-yellow in both sexes.

MEASUREMENTS *P. f. frontalis* (BMNH; FMNH: Bolivia and eastern Peru): wing of male ($n = 7$) 84.0–89.5mm, wing of female ($n = 3$) 85–88mm; tail of male ($n = 7$) 64–74mm, tail of female ($n = 3$) 61–67mm; bill of male ($n = 7$) 13.27–15.18mm, bill of female ($n = 3$) 12.04–14.19mm; tarsus of male ($n = 6$) 17.80–21.11mm, tarsus of female ($n = 2$) 16.49–19.82mm. *P. f. squamipectus* (from Snow 1982; BMNH; FMNH; MECN: Morona-Santiago, Napo and Zamora-Chinchipe, eastern Ecuador, and Amazonas, northern Peru) wing of male ($n = 8$) 81.5–88.0mm, wing of female ($n = 8$) 80.5–88.5mm; tail of male ($n = 8$) 54–66mm, tail of female ($n = 10$) 54–63mm; bill of male ($n = 8$) 12.5–13.6mm, bill of female ($n = 10$) 12.74–13.71mm; tarsus of male ($n = 3$) 18.69–19.50mm, tarsus of female ($n = 7$) 17.76–19.90mm. Weight: 38.5–45.8g (males) and 39.5–47.0g (females) (*P. f. squamipectus*: Snow 1982, Dunning 2008; MECN), and 42.5–44.3g (three males) and 38.0g (one female) (*P. f. frontalis*: FMNH).

GEOGRAPHICAL VARIATION Two subspecies are recognised, separated by a substantial gap in northern Peru, which when taken together with the plumage differences elucidated below led Ridgely and Greenfield (2001) to postulate that two species might be involved. We, like other recent authors, maintain the traditional arrangement for the moment, until such time as a robust study, using any one or several of morphology, vocalisations, mensural characters or molecular data, becomes available. However, we do admit the strong possibility that two species-level taxa are involved. *P. f. frontalis* of central Peru to Bolivia is described above, whilst *P. f. squamipectus* (Chapman, 1925) (Bluish-fronted Fruiteater) of eastern Ecuador to northeast Peru is slightly smaller, with a longer and broader bill. The male *P. f. squamipectus* has the scarlet on the underparts restricted to the lower throat and chest, and the patch on the face is darker, glossier and distinctly more extensive, thereafter becoming bluish-green over much of the crown. Furthermore, it has some white on the tips to the greater coverts and secondaries (illustration in Schulenberg *et al.* 2007). Compared with female *P. f. frontalis*, female *P. f. squamipectus* is generally scaled yellow and green from the throat to belly (i.e. it lacks a distinct throat patch), with more solidly green flanks and patchy yellow undertail-coverts (versus more solidly yellow in *P. f. frontalis*). The forehead is only lightly spotted with yellow above the base of the bill, which would be difficult to detect in the field. (See also Hellmayr 1929b.)

VOICE Schulenberg *et al.* (2007) described apparent geographical variation in songs between the two subspecies, with that of *P. f. frontalis* being a rising, high-pitched, thin, somewhat stuttering trill that descends over its final part, *ti, ti, ti, ti, ti, ti tseeeeeeeeer* (cf. S. K. Herzog recording; XC3423). In contrast, the presumed song of *P. f. squamipectus* is a short rising *tsweeet*. This form also gives a very high, short *pseet*, and both calls are scarcely one second in duration (see also Schulenberg 2000b, Krabbe and Nilsson 2003, Lysinger *et al.* 2005). Recordings from Bolivia are archived online at www.xeno-canto.org.

NATURAL HISTORY An inhabitant of the midstorey and subcanopy, *P. frontalis* represents another chronically poorly known fruiteater taxon. It joins mixed-species flocks (including those principally comprising tanagers: GMK pers. obs.) and is usually found in pairs or alone, just like others of the genus.

FOOD AND FEEDING Like its congeners, Scarlet-breasted Fruiteater appears to be exclusively frugivorous, but as with many other *Pipreola* details are incredibly sparse concerning this and all other aspects of its natural history.

BREEDING Poorly known, although both adults incubate the eggs, as in other fruiteaters, and the changeover at the nest is very rapid. The first nest was found rather recently (in January 1998) in eastern Ecuador, and was placed 15m above the ground on a horizontal branch (close to its broken end), in the subcanopy of an unidentified forest edge tree. It was a small (*c.*18cm in diameter) bowl-shaped structure, externally comprising moss and lichens which matched the surrounding epiphytes in coloration. The female was present at the nest, but the finders speculated that it contained neither eggs nor young because the nest was left unattended during a heavy shower, whilst the male always remained close by (Aversa and Vallely 1999). Two other nests have been found even more recently, also in eastern Ecuador, at Wild Sumaco Lodge Sanctuary, Napo province, in mid-February 2009 and late December 2009, at which both adults were seen incubating (S. Woods: www.samwoodsbirding.blogspot.com; N. Athanas: www.antpitta.com). It is hoped that full details of this latter nest will be published in due course. However, specimen data suggest that birds are already in breeding condition (e.g. males with large testes: MECN) by late September.

STATUS Very little known. Scarlet-breasted Fruiteater is currently listed as of Least Concern by BirdLife International (2004, 2008), although it was formerly considered Near Threatened (Collar *et al.* 1994). The species is generally considered uncommon to locally fairly common in both range states (Ridgely and Greenfield 2001, Schulenberg *et al.* 2007). It is known from a number of protected areas, including Podocarpus National Park (southern Ecuador; *P. f. squamipectus*), Manu National Park and Biosphere Reserve (southern Peru) and Madidi National Park (Bolivia; both *P. f. frontalis*). The species was treated as endemic to the Peruvian Andean Centre of endemism (Cracraft 1985), but its true range is more extensive than the confines of this unit.

REFERENCES Alverson *et al.* (2001), Aversa and Vallely (1999), BirdLife International (2004, 2008), Brooks *et al.* (2009), Chapman (1925), Collar *et al.* (1994), Cracraft (1985), Dunning (2008), Hellmayr (1929b), Hennessey (2004b), Hornbuckle (1999), Krabbe and Nilsson (2003), Krabbe and Sornoza (1994), Lysinger *et al.* (2005), Mazar Barnett and Kirwan (2000b), Mee *et al.* (2002), Merkord *et al.* (2009), Parker and Parker (1982), Perry *et al.* (1997), Ridgely and Greenfield (2001), Ridgely and Tudor (1994, 2009), Schulenberg (2000b), Schulenberg *et al.* (2001), Snow (1982, 2004a), Stotz *et al.* (1996), Walker *et al.* (2006).

Scarlet-breasted Fruiteater *Pipreola frontalis*. **Fig. 1**. Singing male, *P. f. squamipectus*, Afluente, below Abra Patricia, dpto. San Martín, northern Peru; all fruiteaters possess very high-pitched songs. Note that the red is restricted to the throat and the upper breast, while the forehead is very dark, both of which features distinguish males of this subspecies from the more southerly ranging *P. f. frontalis*. More work is required, but it seems quite probable that two species-level taxa might be involved in Scarlet-breasted Fruiteater. **Fig. 2**. Male, *P. f. squamipectus*, Wild Sumaco Lodge, prov. Napo, eastern Ecuador, December (*Tim Mitzen*). **Fig. 3**. Incubating male, *P. f. squamipectus*, Wild Sumaco Lodge, prov. Napo, eastern Ecuador, February (*Nick Athanas / Tropical Birding*). **Fig. 4**. Incubating female, *P. f. squamipectus*, Wild Sumaco Lodge, prov. Napo, eastern Ecuador, February (*Nick Athanas / Tropical Birding*). These photographs depict a pair at one of the few nests to have been found of this uncommon species. Unusually for cotingas, in fruiteaters both sexes participate in breeding activities.

FIERY-THROATED FRUITEATER
Pipreola chlorolepidota   Plate 17

Pipreola chlorolepidota **Swainson, 1837**, *Anim. Menag.*: 357, Moyobamba, Peru

Fiery-throated Fruiteater is the smallest of the genus *Pipreola*, and appears to be most closely related to the Scarlet-breasted Fruiteater *P. frontalis*. These two species are largely elevationally parapatric, but they occur syntopically at a number of localities, such as along the road north to Loreto from Archidona, in eastern Ecuador, but also in eastern Peru. Fiery-throated Fruiteater was, until the second third of the 20th century, known as *Euchlornis sclateri* (e.g. in Hellmayr 1929b), but its nomenclature was resolved by Zimmer (1930), who through collecting new material established that Swainson's name was the oldest valid name for this taxon.

IDENTIFICATION 12.0–13.3cm. This small fruiteater of the east Andean foothills of southern Colombia to northern Peru is perhaps just as likely to be mistaken for a manakin (Pipridae) than another fruiteater. The female, in particular, resembles one of the female *Chiroxiphia* manakins because of the colour of its legs, but should be swiftly separated by virtue of its white tertial tips, green and yellow-barred underparts, and its more upright stance. The male with its orange-red throat could be mistaken for the larger Scarlet-breasted Fruiteater, which usually occurs at higher elevations and has the remaining underparts yellow rather than green. (For further discussion see the previous species.)

DISTRIBUTION Its geographical range extensively overlaps with that of the Scarlet-breasted Fruiteater, albeit weighted slightly further north, over the east slope of the Andes and its outlying ridges, from southern Colombia, in western dptos. Caquetá and Putumayo, and eastern dptos. Cauca and Huila (in which country it was only discovered as recently as 1962), south to dptos. Nariño and Huila (Hilty and Brown 1986, Willis 1988, Salaman *et al.* 1999, 2002b), and through eastern Ecuador, where it is generally rather rare (Ridgely and Greenfield 2001), to central Peru (in Pasco), with single records further south, in Cuzco, and in Puno, in the extreme southeast (Schulenberg *et al.* 2007). It is predicted to occur in extreme northwest Bolivia, in dpto. La Paz (Remsen and Parker 1995). Elevational range

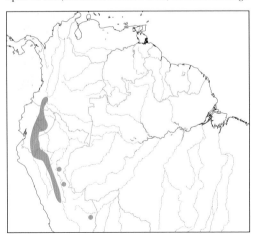

is centred on 500–1,200m, but the species was recently recorded to 1,500m in the Cerros del Sira, Peru (Mee *et al.* 2002) and to 1,600m in the Serranía de los Churumbelos, southern Colombia (Salaman *et al.* 2002b). The species has also been observed down to 300m in southeast Ecuador (Ridgely and Tudor 1994) and to 210m in Peru (Schulenberg *et al.* 2007, Brooks *et al.* 2009).

MOVEMENTS None known, but the species is speculated to perform short-range movements in response to fruiting events (H. Lloyd *in litt.* 2010).

HABITAT Fiery-throated Fruiteater inhabits humid foothill forest including tall (mature) second growth, at least locally.

DESCRIPTION Diminutive; the smallest fruiteater. The sexes differ. The bill has an arched culmen often with a slightly hooked tip, with exposed nostrils and weak rictal bristles. The flight feathers are not modified (as in all fruiteaters, including *Ampelioides*). *Adult male.* – Entirely bright grass green above, with tertials tipped white and slightly darker remiges. The throat and upper breast are scarlet, becoming more orange towards their edges (used in aggressive displays when humans visited the only known nest, see below, and perhaps in courtship). Rest of underparts green (slightly duller than above), but more yellow towards the undertail-coverts. *Adult female.* – From above it resembles the male, but the female lacks the red throat/upper breast, and has the entire underparts coarsely barred green and yellowish. There is an unmarked yellow chin spot, which is quite variable, some having the throat virtually lacking any yellow, but in others it is extensive with an orange-red centre (based on specimens of known sex). If seen poorly, the female often appears almost entirely green below. We have seen one female with a yellow forecrown, the feathers fringed greenish (MECN). *Juvenile.* – On fledging, green above like the adults with creamy white tips to the remiges and creamy-tipped tertials, some fine creamy streaks on the nape, ear-coverts and forehead, dull yellowish legs and more greyish irides (Gelis *et al.* 2006). *Moult.* – There are no published data on moult, but two specimens from Ecuador were renewing some body feathers in July and February; however, most others (from July to September) were apparently not replacing any feathers (MECN). Snow (1982) noted that moult amongst *Pipreola* in general might be expected to commence virtually year-round in this species' range. *Bare parts.* – The male has orange to slightly reddish legs, a salmon-pink or red bill with a dusky or blackish tip, and pale grey-green to greyish-white irides. Females have the legs and bill dull or dark orange-red (occasionally brown or blackish with a pale base to the lower mandible), with a blackish tip, whilst Snow (2004a) reported that the irides are duller than in males, but well-labelled specimens from Ecuador at MECN belie this (some even have yellow irides).

GEOGRAPHICAL VARIATION Monotypic.

MEASUREMENTS (from Snow 1982; MECN; RMNH: Morona-Santiago, Pastaza and Zamora-Chinchipe, eastern Ecuador) Wing of male (*n* = 13) 73–78mm, wing of female (*n* = 10) 73–85mm; tail of male (*n* = 13) 42.5–51.0mm, tail of female (*n* = 9) 42–48mm; bill of male (*n* = 9) 7.5–9.5mm (*n* = 4, to skull, 12.1–12.6mm), bill of female (*n* = 3) 8.0–8.5mm (*n* = 7, to skull, 11.8–12.7mm); tarsus of male (*n* = 10) 16.65–19.0mm, tarsus of female (*n* = 3) 17.5–18.0mm. Weight: 28.0–36.5g (three males) and 26.75–37.00g (females) (Snow 2004a, Dunning 2008; MECN; MVZ).

VOICE The song is typical of *Pipreola* fruiteaters, a thin, high-pitched *pseeew* (recordings on Krabbe and Nilsson 2003, Alvarez *et al.* 2007). The call is a shorter *tsi* or *tsit*, which may be given with particular frequency around the nest, serving as cues for adults to switch during the nestling stage or for the male to 'stand guard' at the nest during a female off-bout during the incubation period (Gelis *et al.* 2006). Salaman *et al.* (2002b) mentioned a male giving a high-pitched *pitch* note.

NATURAL HISTORY Fiery-throated Fruiteater is generally found alone or in pairs, like congenerics, and is sometimes observed following mixed-species flocks, e.g. a bird in the Cerros del Sira was seen to be associating with Yellow-throated Tanagers *Iridosornis analis* (Mee *et al.* 2002), and in Colombia the species has been watched feeding with Orange-bellied Euphonia *Euphonia xanthogaster*, Golden Tanager *Tangara arthus* and White-winged Tanager *Piranga leucoptera*, and other frugivores, at virtually all levels from the understorey to the canopy (Salaman *et al.* 2002b, Restrepo *et al.* 2002; see also Zimmer 1930). The species has also been recorded in small groups of up to four individuals at a small fruiting tree above Jesús del Monte, dpto. San Martín, Peru, in September (D. Beadle pers. obs.). Generally, the species has been seen feeding at 1–5m above the ground, once at the edge of a landslide (Salaman *et al.* 2002b) and on other occasion at the forest border in a remote clearing (T. M. Donegan pers. obs.).

FOOD AND FEEDING Like its congeners, it is perhaps most frequently recorded at fruiting trees, and is entirely frugivorous or almost so (including seeds), but specific information on diet is sadly lacking.

BREEDING The nest (found in April–May) was recently described from observations in northeastern Ecuador (Gelis *et al.* 2006). This was a flat, saucer-shaped structure placed in the three-way fork of a horizontal branch, 8m above the ground and 5m from the main trunk, in tall primary forest on a gentle slope. It was tiny and heavily obscured from all angles by vines, the outside being constructed of moss and liverworts and the inside lined with roots and rootlets. Nest construction was apparently entirely the responsibility of the female, but the male remained close by and performed distraction flights in front of the nest to obscure the female's destination. The two eggs, creamy white with dark brown spotting (concentrated at the larger end), were incubated solely by the female (for 17–22 days), but the male sometimes fed his mate on the nest (as has been reported for other fruiteaters). Only the female brooded the young, but both adults, especially the male, brought food (fruit and their seeds) and the young fledged in 20 days. Two females and a male, all from July, and all taken in Ecuador were in breeding condition (MECN), and MVZ has two females in breeding condition taken in August and September from eastern Peru.

STATUS Fiery-throated Fruiteater is currently listed as Near Threatened (BirdLife International 2004, 2008). Forest habitat within the species' elevational band throughout its range is being converted to cattle pastures and for agriculture, as well as for mining, oil exploration, timber extraction, and tea and coffee farms. The species is generally considered rare throughout its range, e.g. being known from just *c*.10 localities in Colombia (in which country it is treated as Vulnerable: Restrepo *et al.* 2002), where at best Fiery-throated Fruiteater can be described as locally uncommon, although its small size and typically inconspicuous behaviour, and the general inaccessibility of foothill forest on the East Andean 'wall', unquestionably mean that the species is under-recorded. *P. chlorolepidota* is regarded as the least common *Pipreola* in Peru (Schulenberg *et al.* 2007). It is known from several protected areas through its range, including Cordillera Azul National Park, in Peru, Bosque Protector Alto Nangaritza, and Sumaco-Napo Galeras and Sangay National Parks, in eastern Ecuador, and the Parque Nacional Natural Cueva de lo Guácharos, dpto. Huila, Colombia, as well as from several Important Bird Areas (Boyla and Estrada 2005).

REFERENCES Alvarez *et al.* (2007), Balchin and Toyne (1998), BirdLife International (2004, 2008), Boyla and Estrada (2005), Brooks *et al.* (2009), Dunning (2008), Gelis *et al.* (2006), Hellmayr (1929b), Hilty and Brown (1986), Krabbe and Nilsson (2003), Mee *et al.* (2002), Merkord *et al.* (2009), Parker and Wust (1994), Pearman (1994a), Remsen and Parker (1995), Restall *et al.* (2006), Restrepo *et al.* (2002), Ridgely and Greenfield (2001), Ridgely and Tudor (1994, 2009), Salaman *et al.* (1999, 2002b), Schulenberg *et al.* (2007), Snow (1982, 2004a), Stotz *et al.* (1996), Willis (1988), Zimmer (1930).

Fiery-throated Fruiteater *Pipreola chlorolepidota*. **Fig. 1**. Male, Mushullacta Community Reserve, Loreto Road, prov. Napo, eastern Ecuador, May (*Rudy Gelis*). **Figs. 2–3**. Male, Loreto Road, prov. Napo, eastern Ecuador, March (*Roger Ahlman / www.pbase.com/ahlman*). On average the most diminutive of the genus, the male is also one of the beautiful fruiteaters. Confusion with Scarlet-breasted Fruiteater *P. frontalis* might be possible given a poor view, but note the distinctive head shape of the present species and the different underparts pattern. **Fig. 4**. Female, Mushullacta Community Reserve, Loreto Road, prov. Napo, eastern Ecuador, May (*Rudy Gelis*). This female was incubating eggs at the first-ever nest of the species to be discovered (see Breeding).

HANDSOME FRUITEATER
Pipreola formosa   **Plate 17**

Ampelis formosa **Hartlaub, 1849**, *Rev. Mag. Zool.* (2)1: 275, 439, pl. 14, fig. 2, Caracas, Venezuela

This species, endemic to the coastal and interior cordilleras of northern Venezuela, inhabits the mist-laden cloud forests of the upper tropical and subtropical zones. Snow (1982, 2004a) considered Handsome Fruiteater to be the sister taxon of Fiery-throated Fruiteater *P. chlorolepidota*. The beautiful male can be difficult to see when perched in the dense foliage of these forests, but a patient wait beside a suitable fruiting tree, for instance, near Rancho Grande, in Henri Pittier National Park, or on the Paria Peninsula, should reward the would-be observer. The species is often remarkably tame.

IDENTIFICATION 16–18cm. Although Handsome Fruiteater occurs sympatrically with two other *Pipreola* species (Green-and-black *P. riefferii* and Golden-breasted Fruiteaters *P. aureopectus*), the identification of either sex of this species should usually prove to be a straightforward matter. The black hood of the male immediately excludes Golden-breasted, and the splash of orange across the breast readily separates Handsome from Green-and-black Fruiteater. The female's barred underparts and yellow breast patch (which can be difficult to see) are diagnostic, whilst the particularly bold white tertial spots in both sexes of this truly 'handsome' fruiteater offers another useful feature.

DISTRIBUTION Confined to northern Venezuela, where it occurs in the Sierra de San Lucas, in Falcón, thence through the mountains of Yaracuy and the Coastal Cordillera as far as Miranda, as well as the Interior Cordillera in southern Aragua, Miranda and northern Anzoátegui (as far as the Cerro Tucusito), to northern Monagas, on the Cerro Negro, as well as the Cerros Humo and Azul, on the Paria Peninsula (Sucre). Altitudinal range is 800–2,200m (Hilty 2003).

MOVEMENTS The species is considered to be resident and sedentary (Hilty 2003).

HABITAT Handsome Fruiteater's preference is for moderately humid to wet mossy premontane and montane cloud forests, where it inhabits the undergrowth to midstorey.

DESCRIPTION The sexes differ. The bill has a slightly

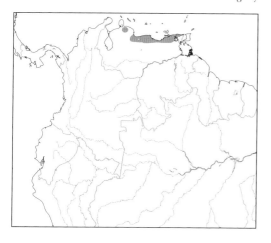

arched culmen and hooked tip, with exposed nostrils and weak rictal bristles. The flight feathers are not modified (as in all fruiteaters, including *Ampelioides*). Nominate *P. f. formosa* is described here. *Adult male.* – The hood and throat are glossy black, whilst the upperparts and tail are bright grass green. Proximal two tertials are grass green over their outer webs with a large white tip; blackish inner web with reduced white tip. The distal tertial is fringed white. Tips to secondaries also white. Underparts are bright lemon-yellow with a fiery orange suffusion to the breast, just below the black throat. Flanks pale green. *Adult female.* – Uniform grass green above with broad white tertial tips as in the male. White tips to secondaries. From below, the throat is green with a hint of yellow and there is a small transverse golden-yellow patch on the breast just below the throat. The rest of the underparts are generally barred green and yellow, the green barring being slightly heavier across the breast, where it forms an indistinct pectoral band. Undertail-coverts yellow. *Juvenile.* – Undescribed, but Restall *et al.* (2006) mentioned that juveniles of the nominate race have dark yellow irides (brown in same-age *P. f. rubidior* and brown to orange in juvenile *P. f. pariae*) without describing their plumage in detail, although for *P. f. pariae* and *P. f. rubidior* they noted simply that juveniles are all green. As with other *Pipreola* plumage maturation in this species is effectively unknown, but for other races Restall *et al.* (2006) again reported that immature males have the throat orange (*P. f. pariae*). *Moult.* – Snow (1982) noted that moult amongst *Pipreola* in general commences in April–August in this species' range. *Bare parts.* – Both sexes have the bill orange-red, the legs olive-grey and the irides orange to orange-yellow (records of birds with dark eyes presumably relate to young birds, see above; and there might be some very marginal and doubtfully consistent geographical differences in the colour of the irides: Restall *et al.* 2006).

MEASUREMENTS (from Snow 1982; except bill, BMNH: northern Venezuela) *P. f. formosa*: wing of male (*n* = 10) 84–90mm, wing of female (*n* = 6) 85–89mm; tail of male (*n* = 10) 55–65mm, tail of female (*n* = 6) 63–64mm; bill of male (*n* = 4) 12–15mm, bill of female (*n* = 5) 12–15mm; tarsus of male (*n* = 10) 19–21mm, tarsus of female (*n* = 6) 20.0–20.5mm. *P. f. rubidior* (sexes combined): wing (*n* = 7) 87–90mm; tail (*n* = 7) 65–68mm (Hellmayr 1929b). Weight: 39–56g (males) and 41–49g (six females) (Collins 1972, Snow 1982, Verea *et al.* 1999, Snow 2004a, Dunning 2008).

GEOGRAPHICAL VARIATION Three subspecies are generally recognised, which perhaps form two groups (nominate *P. f. formosa*, and the *P. f. rubidior*/*P. f. pariae* group) and these, in turn, have been speculated to represent separate species (D. Ascanio *et al. in* Restall *et al.* 2006), but the evidence to date for such a treatment seems to hinge on relatively marginal differences in the form of the red breast-patch, tertial pattern (both of which characters vary clinally to some extent) and voice (see below). *P. f. formosa* (described above) occurs in the Coastal Cordillera of northern Venezuela, with *P. f. rubidior* (Chapman, 1925) in the Coastal Cordillera of northeast Venezuela, which in both sexes is somewhat intermediate between the nominate and the next race in the intensity of the breast coloration (in both sexes) and the amount of white on the tertials, whilst the female has the yellow throat distinctly spotted or barred dusky-green, and *P. f. pariae* Phelps & Phelps, 1949, in the coastal mountains of extreme northeast Venezuela, on the Paria Peninsula. The form *P. f. dilutior*, Todd, 1950, described from two localities in the states of Lara and Carabobo, based on the reduced orange area on the breast of males, is not generally recognised (cf. Snow 1982, 2004a, Dickinson 2003, Hilty 2003, Restall *et al.* 2006). In *P. f. pariae* the male has the upper breast scarlet in the centre fading to orange on the breast sides, and this patch of colour is more extensive than in *P. f. formosa*. There are broad white fringes to the tertials, the proximal end of the fringe having a black border. The throat colour in the female is yellow, evenly barred with dusky-green and the small breast patch is more orange, or even scarlet, in tone than the nominate race. The female displays the male's tertial pattern, and similarly the secondaries are tipped white (the four outer primaries are tipped white in *P. f. rubidior*).

VOICE Described in Hilty (2003) and Restall *et al.* (2006): *P. f. formosa* gives a high, thin *pik* note and a *ti-ti-ti-ti-ti-ti...*; elsewhere, the song is either a high-pitched *ti'ti'ti'ti'ti'ti'ti'ti'ti'ti't...*, *peeééé-eeeeeee-e-e-e-e* (Cerro Negro; *P. f. pariae*) or *peeEEEeeeeeee'e'e'e'e* (*P. f. pariae* and *P. f. rubidior*), which is louder at the start and slows at the end, but does not vary much in pitch. The song of nominate *P. f. formosa* is reputedly at a higher pitch than the medium-frequency songs of *P. f. rubidior* and *P. f. pariae* (Restall *et al.* 2006). A recording attributable to the subspecies *P. f. pariae* is archived online at www.xeno-canto.org.

NATURAL HISTORY Natural history information was summarised by Hilty (2003) and Restall *et al.* (2006). The species is usually found alone or in pairs, less frequently in groups of three. Like other fruiteaters, Handsome Fruiteater typically peers around for 20–30 seconds before switching perches, and will regularly join mixed-species canopy flocks, for instance of tanagers and warblers, but probably only for a short duration as the foraging birds move through the fruiteater's territory. Lentino *et al.* (2003) twice retrapped a female Handsome Fruiteater in Henri Pittier National Park that was at least six years old when last caught.

FOOD AND FEEDING Diet, as with other fruiteaters, is either wholly or largely fruit and berries, taken either whilst perched or via a short upward sally-hover movement.

BREEDING Schaefer and Phelps (1954) considered the nesting period to be centred on April–June in northern Venezuela, but there seems to be an acute lack of specific data concerning breeding.

STATUS Handsome Fruiteater is treated as Least Concern by BirdLife International (2004, 2008) and the species is generally considered to be fairly common, it being particularly numerous on the Paria Peninsula, Sucre, and on the Cerro Negro, Monagas (Hilty 2003). The species is known from several protected areas including Henri Pittier National Park, Aragua/Carabobo, Macarao National Park and El Ávila National Park, both in Distrito Federal/Miranda (subspecies *P. f. formosa*), and the Península de Paria National Park, Sucre (subspecies *P. f. pariae*), the last being considered a potential stronghold for the species (Sharpe 1997, Boyla and Estrada 2005). The subspecies *P. f. rubidior* and *P. f. pariae* are endemic to the Parian Montane Centre of endemism, whilst the nominate race is endemic to the Venezuelan Montane Centre (Cracraft 1985).

REFERENCES BirdLife International (2004, 2008), Boyla and Estrada (2005), Chapman (1925), Collins (1972), Cracraft (1985), Dickinson (2003), Dunning (2008), Hellmayr (1929b), Hilty (2003), Lentino *et al.* (2003), Meyer de Schauensee and Phelps (1978), Olson (1971), Restall *et al.* (2006), Ridgely and Tudor (1994, 2009), Schaefer and Phelps (1954), Sharpe (1997), Snow (1982, 2004a), Stotz *et al.* (1996), Todd (1950), Verea *et al.* (1999), Wetmore (1939).

Handsome Fruiteater *Pipreola formosa*. **Fig. 1**. Male, *P. f. formosa*, Rancho Grande Biological Station, Henri Pittier National Park, Aragua, north coastal Venezuela, March (*David Fisher*). **Fig. 2**. Female, *P. f. formosa*, Rancho Grande Biological Station, Henri Pittier National Park, Aragua, north coastal Venezuela, June (*Ron Hoff*). This Venezuelan endemic is not easily confused with any other *Pipreola* given that it overlaps only with Golden-breasted *P. aureopectus* and Green-and-black Fruiteaters *P. riefferii*, both of which are quite different in plumage.

RED-BANDED FRUITEATER
Pipreola whitelyi   **Plate 16**

Pipreola whitelyi **Salvin & Godman, 1884**, *Ibis* (5)2: 449, Cerro Roraima, Venezuela

This much sought-after bird, by observers visiting the Pantepui region of South America, is one of the most spectacular endemics of the region. Red-banded Fruiteater is perhaps most easily encountered along the Escalera Road, on the Sierra de Lema, in Bolívar, Venezuela, where lush subtropical forest abuts the roadside. The origin and relationships of this remarkable species, which exhibits a plumage quite unlike any of its congeners, have baffled biogeographers (Mayr and Phelps 1967).

IDENTIFICATION 16.0–17.5cm. Easily identified in its restricted range; the male Red-banded Fruiteater has basically dull moss green upperparts and greyish underparts, with a contrasting orangey-red breast-band and bronze wash to the flight feathers. The female is much duller; greenish on the upperparts, with heavily streaked underparts from the throat to the vent. There are, however, no sympatric congeners in the Pantepui, and the female should not present any identification difficulties once the two superficially similar, but rather larger female bellbirds (*Procnias* spp.) are eliminated. The overall dark slate-grey Rose-collared Piha *Lipaugus streptophorus* is rather larger, longer tailed and heavier (and darker) billed than the fruiteater, but both these Pantepui endemics possess a red collar (complete in the piha), which might momentarily lead to confusion. Sharpbill *Oxyruncus cristatus* too might be confused with the female Red-banded Fruiteater, but is plumper with a different facial pattern and streaked underparts.

DISTRIBUTION Red-banded Fruiteater has a tiny range in the eastern Pantepui of extreme southeast Venezuela, where it is known from about seven tepuis on the Gran Sabana (Hilty 2003), and three adjacent peaks in Guyana (Mts Roraima, Twek-quay and Kowa), but the species seems to be absent from other, drier peaks further east such as Mt Kopinang (O'Shea *et al.* 2007). *P. whitelyi* is apparently recorded exclusively at 1,300–2,250m. Two sightings of males from the Manaus areas, Amazonas, Brazil, lack documentation (Cohn-Haft *et al.* 1997) and seem incredible; the species is otherwise unknown from the country (Sick

1997), though Red-banded Fruiteater has been predicted to occur in Roraima, northernmost Brazil (Naka *et al.* 2007).

MOVEMENTS None recorded and the species is considered resident.

HABITAT Red-banded Fruiteater inhabits wet montane mossy and cloud forest, as well as more stunted, dense secondary forest, but always with a predominance of melastomes.

DESCRIPTION The sexes differ. As with other *Pipreola*, the bill has a slightly arched culmen and hooked tip, with exposed nostrils and weak rictal bristles. The flight feathers are not modified (as in all fruiteaters, including *Ampelioides*). *P. w. whitelyi* is described here. *Adult male.* – The forecrown, supercilia, ear-coverts and nuchal collar are all tawny-gold (although the ear-coverts become mossy green distally), brightest and richest on the collar, and rustier on the cheeks. The rest of the upperparts are dull moss green, with a grey cast to the crown. The wing-coverts and remiges are rufescent brown, conspicuously fringed orange-brown, in contrast to the moss green scapulars. Rectrices brown with bright tawny fringes. Throat, lower breast and belly are ash-grey, broken by a vermilion or coral-red pectoral band that becomes progressively more orange on the lower neck-sides where it meets the nuchal collar. Undertail-coverts dull orange. *Adult female.* – Slightly brighter moss green above, with a rather inconspicuous pale green forehead, supercilia and short nuchal collar. Fringes of secondary-coverts and remiges olive-yellow. Underparts are basally whitish but heavily streaked dark to blackish, from the chin to the undertail-coverts, with a yellowish-white wash that is most intense on the breast-sides, where the streaking is also at its most intense. Contrasting whitish throat. *Juvenile.* – Dark olive-green above, with large and broad buff-coloured spots, replete with a blackish terminal fringe, over the mantle, lower back, rump and wing-coverts, but becoming sparser distally, and pale, yellow-streaked below; crown also streaked yellow. Spots and streaks are lost distally, and the forecrown and breast are the first parts to acquire brighter colours in the males (see Restall *et al.* 2006). As in other fruiteaters, this plumage is swiftly lost, with the birds rapidly assuming adult plumage. *Moult.* – There are virtually no published moult data, but Snow (1982) noted that feather renewal commences in January–July, with a peak in March–May. *Bare parts.* – Male has the bill dark red (more ochre-red in *P. w. kathleenae*), the irides reddish-hazel, and the legs are red. Females have the bill and legs dark to paler brown, or the bill yellow-orange (*P. w. kathleenae*), and the irides pale ochre to yellowish.

MEASUREMENTS (from Snow 1982; except bill in both sexes, and tail and tarsus of female; BMNH: Guyana, Venezuela) *P. w. whitelyi:* wing of male (*n* = 9) 89–95mm, wing of female (*n* = 7) 88–94mm; tail of male (*n* = 9) 59–66mm, tail of female (*n* = 2) 65–67mm; bill of male (*n* = 2) 16–17mm, bill of female (*n* = 2) 15–16mm; tarsus of male (*n* = 9) 21–22mm, tarsus of female (*n* = 2) 23–25mm. Weight: 50.0–52.5g (two males) (*P. w. kathleenae:* Dunning 2008; FMNH).

GEOGRAPHICAL VARIATION Two races are recognised, both of which are endemic to the Gran Sabana subcentre of the Pantepui Centre of endemism (Cracraft 1985). *P. w. whitelyi* (described above) is restricted to extreme southeast Venezuela, at 1,800–2,250m on the Cerro Roraima, and in adjacent Guyana, and *P. w. kathleenae* J. T. Zimmer & W. L. Phelps, Sr, 1944, is found solely on those tepuis west of the

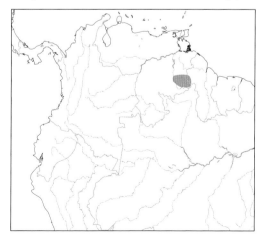

Cerro Roraima, also in southeast Venezuela (i.e. that part of its range most frequently visited by ornithologists and birdwatchers). Male *P. w. kathleenae* is separated from the nominate race by the more extensive tawny-gold on the forehead, paler streaks on the crown, paler grey underparts, the other head markings are yellower, with the breast-band reduced to heavy spots and streaks of bright orange (rather than a continuous, solid band), and the female by the blacker streaks on whiter underparts, with any yellowish wash confined to the vent and undertail-coverts (Restall *et al.* 2006).

VOICE Like all fruiteaters, the species' insect-like song is very high-pitched and easily overlooked, it being a thin, almost hissing *pss-ee-ee-ee-ee-ee-ee* or *tseeaaaaeeeeeeeeee* with a very slightly undulating quality and lasting *c.*2–3 seconds, which is given at rather long intervals. In duet, both members of the pair produce a short, initially even-pitched call that rises at the end, *peeeu-ééu* (D. Ascanio *in* Restall *et al.* 2006). The pattern most closely resembles Golden-breasted Fruiteater *P. aureopectus.* In excitement/alarm, Red-banded Fruiteater gives high thin *ti* notes, often in a short (4–6-note) series, but the species is reported to generally vocalise rather infrequently (Hilty 2003, Snow 2004a, Boesman 2006b, Restall *et al.* 2006). Two recordings of the subspecies *P. w. kathleenae* are archived online at www.xeno-canto.org.

NATURAL HISTORY Surprisingly poorly known, presumably in large part due to its inconspicuousness. Most behavioural observations reveal a life history apparently very similar to its congeners. Its movements are typically slow and deliberate, and the species is generally found at low to mid levels inside forest, sometimes near streams, but Red-banded Fruiteater is also occasionally found at edges and even in the canopy (perhaps most frequently with flocks).

FOOD AND FEEDING Diet appears to be entirely frugivorous, but like most congenerics its preferences are almost entirely unknown. Singles regularly accompany mixed-species flocks, especially with tanagers and warblers, but perhaps like other fruiteaters it does not follow them far or for long. The species is usually noted in pairs.

BREEDING Data are completely lacking.

STATUS Red-banded Fruiteater is categorised as Least Concern (BirdLife International 2004, 2008), despite its tiny range and generally low-density population. The species is known from at least one protected area (Canaíma National Park, Venezuela) and is considered to be endemic to the Tepuis Endemic Bird Area (Stattersfield *et al.* 1998). Generally considered rare to uncommon and never numerous in Venezuela, but like all other *Pipreola*, Red-banded Fruiteater is easily overlooked and much of this species' small range is difficult of access (e.g. the Sierra de Lema is probably generally too low for this species, although it is regularly seen there). Perhaps most numerous on Ptari-tepui and Auyán-tepui (race *P. w. kathleenae*). It seems rare on Mt Kowa, Guyana (Barnett *et al.* 2002), but the species is considered generally common in the extreme west of this country by Braun *et al.* (2007).

REFERENCES Barnett *et al.* (2002), BirdLife International (2004, 2008), Boesman (2006b), Braun *et al.* (2007), Chapman (1931), Cohn-Haft *et al.* (1997), Cracraft (1985), Dunning (2008), Hellmayr (1929b), Hilty (2003), Mayr and Phelps (1967), Meyer de Schauensee and Phelps (1978), Naka *et al.* (2007), O'Shea *et al.* (2007), Restall *et al.* (2006), Ridgely and Tudor (1994, 2009), Sick (1997), Snow (1982, 2004a), Snyder (1966), Stattersfield *et al.* (1998), Stotz *et al.* (1996).

Red-banded Fruiteater *Pipreola whitelyi.* **Fig. 1**. Male, *P. w. kathleenae,* Sierra de Lema, Bolívar, southeast Venezuela, October (*Nick Athanas / Tropical Birding*). **Fig. 2**. Male, *P. w. kathleenae,* Sierra de Lema, Bolívar, southeast Venezuela, March (*Pete Morris*). The 'oddball' of the genus *Pipreola.* Ironically, the range of nominate *P. w. whitelyi* is rarely visited by ornithologists and birdwatchers. Male *P. w. kathleenae* is separated from the nominate race by the more extensive tawny-gold on the forehead, paler streaks on the crown, paler grey underparts, the other head markings are yellower, with the breast-band reduced to heavy spots and streaks of bright orange (rather than a continuous, solid band).

BARRED FRUITEATER
Pipreola arcuata   **Plate 18**

Ampelis arcuata **Lafresnaye, 1843**, *Rev. Zool.* 6: 98, Bogotá, Colombia

A large and easily identified fruiteater of higher elevation cloud forest habitats, Barred Fruiteater is generally common throughout its range from Venezuela to Bolivia.

IDENTIFICATION 22.0–23.8cm. A bird of the elfin forest treeline to the interior of upper elevational cloud forests, and the most commonly encountered high-elevation fruiteater. Band-tailed Fruiteater *P. intermedia* is found at similar elevations but is rather smaller, and both sexes lack the coarse barring on the underparts so obvious in *P. arcuata*. Green-and-black Fruiteater *P. riefferii*, which shares the wide geographical range and overlaps at the lower elevation limits of the present species, is smaller, with unbarred underparts, a different pattern to the wing-coverts, no black band towards the tail tip and paler red legs.

DISTRIBUTION Barred Fruiteater has the most extensive range of any of the *Pipreola* species. It is found in the Andes of western Venezuela, north to southwest Lara at the Páramo de Cendé; in Colombia, only from dpto. Cauca in the western Andes and south to Cundinamarca in the eastern Andes (Salaman *et al.* 2002b), both Andean slopes of Ecuador, but only south to prov. Bolívar (at Salinas) on the western slope; and throughout eastern Peru to western Bolivia in dptos. La Paz, Santa Cruz and Cochabamba. It is also found on the Sierra de Perijá on the Colombia/Venezuela border.

MOVEMENTS None recorded. This species appears resident throughout its range, although Hilty (2003) hints at local movements to slightly lower elevations in the wet season in parts of the Venezuelan Andes.

HABITAT Barred Fruiteater inhabits upper subtropical and temperate montane forest and borders, mainly above 1,800m (higher in Peru), but down to 1,500m (and exceptionally 900m) in Colombia, to at least 3,500m, e.g. at Bosque Unchog, in Peru (Schulenberg *et al.* 2007) and Ecuador (A. T. Chartier recording, XC9854).

DESCRIPTION The sexes differ. The bill has a slightly arched culmen and hooked tip, with exposed nostrils and weak rictal bristles. The flight feathers are not modified (as in all fruiteaters, including *Ampelioides*). Nominate *P. a. arcuata* is described here. *Adult male.* – The crown, throat, upper chest and ear-coverts are glossy black. Underparts barred black and yellow. The upperparts are bright moss green with some black barring on the uppertail-coverts, these feathers being tipped with bright yellowish-olive. There is a black subterminal band to the green tail, with neat white tips to the rectrices. Wings mainly appear green at rest in the field, but the pattern is quite complex on closer inspection. The lesser and median coverts are green, and the greater coverts are green with bright yellowish-olive distal fringes (appearing as pale streaks in the field) and large black tips. The remiges are mainly green, brightly fringed with yellow-olive and blacker tips to the outer flight feathers. Tertials centred black with pale yellowish-olive spots distally. Tips of primary wing-coverts black. *Adult female.* – Lacks the black-'hooded' appearance of the male and the entire underparts from the chin to the undertail-coverts (with the exception of the throat, which is more or less solidly green and concolorous with the rest of the head) are more or less evenly barred pale blackish and pale yellow. The wing pattern resembles that of males. *Juvenile.* – Undescribed (Snow 2004a). *Moult.* – There are no published data on moult, but feather renewal is probably virtually year-round through much of the Andes, albeit probably more seasonal (concentrated in September–March) in southern Peru and Bolivia, based on general moult data for the genus *Pipreola* (Snow 1982). Previously unpublished mist-net data from Colombia of birds trapped in virtually all months of the year reveal no obvious pattern to feather renewal, not even of any differences between the sexes, with moult seemingly likely to be initiated at almost any time (D. Carantón, J. Castaño, F. Guzman, J. P. López, G. A. Suárez and J. P. Varona/ProAves unpubl. data). *Bare parts.* – Both sexes have the bill, legs and feet crimson; the bill tip may be dark grey or blackish, at least in females. The colour of the irides is variable (see Geographical Variation below), but juveniles perhaps incline to have duller, dark brown or dark greyish irides (A. M. Cuervo).

MEASUREMENTS (Snow 1982; ROM, except culmen to skull and tarsus: ProAves unpubl. data) *P. a. arcuata*: wing of male (*n* = 13) 120–131mm, wing of female (*n* = 8) 114–127mm; tail of male (*n* = 13) 75–93mm, tail of female (*n* = 8) 72–95mm; bill of male (*n* = 13) 19.3–24.2mm, bill of female (*n* = 4) 22.7–24.1mm; tarsus of male (*n* = 13) 23.1–32.7mm, tarsus of female (*n* = 4) 23.9–29.2mm. Weight: 84.1–120.0g (males) and 100–128g (females) (Rahbek *et al.* 1993, Snow 2004a; FMNH; MVZ; D. Carantón, J. Castaño, F. Guzman, J. P. López, G. A. Suárez and J. P. Varona/ProAves unpubl. data).

GEOGRAPHICAL VARIATION Two subspecies are recognised. *P. a. arcuata* (in the north of the species' range, in Venezuela to northern Peru) is described above, but shows some variation in the colour of the irides, although this seems to be some extent individual. On specimen labels this is noted as red or yellow in Venezuela, bright red to orange-red in Colombia and Ecuador, and chestnut in northern Peru. Field observations and photographs reveal that iris colour can be dark orange or scarlet in the West Andes of Colombia (D. Calderón), or yellow in Cuzco, Peru (C. Merkord). Ridgely and Tudor (2009) stated that 'iris varies from orange red (northward) to greyish olive, or even whitish (southward)', whilst Schulenberg *et al.* (2007) note that 'iris color [is] variable, but usually dark in north ... iris pale from Junín south'. However, we have seen photographs of birds in eastern Ecuador with greyish-blue irides (at least in females), and A. T. Chartier (*in litt.* 2009) reports birds at Yanacocha with yellowish eyes. *P. a. viridicauda* Meyer de Schauensee, 1953 (of central Peru, from Junín, to northern Bolivia), has the irides pale yellow to creamy white and has considerably more green on the four outermost tail feathers.

VOICE Barred Fruiteater gives the usual *Pipreola*-type eerie sibilant whistle, with a duration of *c.*2.5 seconds, rendered as *s-seeeeeeeeeeeeeaaaaaaee* by Hilty (2003), which descends throughout, but sometimes rises slightly in the finale. Alternatively, the species gives a hissing *si-si-si-iiiiEEEseeeeeeeeeeeeett* that rises slightly, then descends, before closing with a slight upturn, but is considered shorter in Peru than in Colombia (T. A. Parker *in* Snow 1982). The song lacks many of the introductory notes of Green-and-black Fruiteater. Commercial recordings are available on the following compilations: Boesman (1999, 2006b, 2009), Mayer (2000), Krabbe *et al.* (2001), Álvarez-Rebolledo and Córdoba-Córdoba (2002), Krabbe and Nilsson (2003) and Alvarez *et al.* (2007), whilst recordings from Bolivia, Ecuador and Peru are available online at www.xeno-canto.org.

NATURAL HISTORY This is a particularly bulky and sluggish fruiteater, usually found singly or in pairs, but occasionally as groups of 3–4, sometimes with Green-and-black Fruiteaters, and it seems to join mixed-species flocks (especially other frugivores) reasonably regularly in some areas (Poulsen 1996). Often the presence of an individual is betrayed by the wing-whirring noise of a bird plucking fruit on the wing (and the fact it regularly sings). Particularly stolid, even for this undemonstrative genus, Barred Fruiteater spends long periods largely inactive, especially following an early-morning foraging period.

FOOD AND FEEDING Doubtless the species is principally frugivorous and mainly takes its food using techniques common to the genus, but very few data on this facet of its life history have been recorded.

BREEDING Surprisingly, despite this being one of the most commonly encountered *Pipreola* species, the species' nest remains unknown. Most breeding data were summarised by Fjeldså and Krabbe (1990): fledglings have been noted in western Ecuador in July and Cochabamba, Bolivia, in January, and juveniles or immatures in dptos. Ayacucho and Pasco (both Peru), in July and March, respectively. A juvenile, accompanied by both adults, was seen in northwest Peru in July (Vellinga *et al.* 2004). A male and female collected in western Colombia in August had enlarged and active gonads, and the female a visible brood patch (Echeverry-Galvis and Córdoba-Córdoba 2007), whilst M. A. Carriker (*in* Hilty and Brown 1986) collected a male in breeding condition in the Sierra de Perijá in early May, and A. Pazos collected a female with enlarged ovaries in dpto. Cauca in the fourth week of January (ROM).

STATUS Barred Fruiteater is listed as of Least Concern by BirdLife International (2004, 2008). Uncommon, but relatively frequently observed in various localities, such as the Cajanuma area of Podocarpus National Park, southern Ecuador, Bosque Unchog, in central Peru, or at higher elevations (>2,500m) on the Manu road, near Pillhuata, in Peru. It is also known from many protected areas within its large range (e.g. see Echeverri 1986, Hilty and Brown 1986, Cresswell *et al.* 1999, Donegan and Dávalos 1999, Ocampo 2002, Hilty 2003, Echeverry-Galvis and Córdoba-Córdoba 2007, Salaman *et al.* 2008).

REFERENCES Álvarez-Rebolledo and Córdoba-Córdoba (2002), Alvarez *et al.* (2007), BirdLife International (2004, 2008), Boesman (1999, 2006b, 2009), Cresswell *et al.* (1999), Donegan and Dávalos (1999), Echeverri (1986), Echeverry-Galvis and Córdoba-Córdoba (2007), Fjeldså and Krabbe (1990), Hellmayr (1929b), Hennessey and Gomez (2003), Hilty (2003), Hilty and Brown (1986), Krabbe *et al.* (1997, 2001), Krabbe and Nilsson (2003), MacLeod *et al.* (2005), Mark *et al.* (2008), Mayer (2000), Ocampo (2002), Parker *et al.* (1982, 1985), Poulsen (1996), Rahbek *et al.* (1993), Ridgely and Greenfield (2001), Ridgely and Tudor (1994, 2009), Salaman *et al.* (2002b, 2008, 2009), Schulenberg *et al.* (2007), Snow (1982, 2004a), Stotz *et al.* (1996), Vellinga *et al.* (2004), Whitney *et al.* (1994).

Barred Fruiteater *Pipreola arcuata*. **Fig. 1**. Male, *P. a. arcuata*, Tapichalaca Reserve, prov. Zamora-Chinchipe, southern Ecuador, December (*Dušan Brinkhuizen*). **Fig. 2**. Female, *P. a. arcuata*, Tapichalaca Reserve, prov. Zamora-Chinchipe, southern Ecuador, November (*Hadoram Shirihai / Photographic Handbook to Birds of the World*). The large Barred Fruiteater frequently occurs at higher altitudes than other fruiteaters and is well named for its underparts pattern; confusion with other species is difficult given a reasonable view.

GREEN-AND-BLACK FRUITEATER
Pipreola riefferii   Plate 18

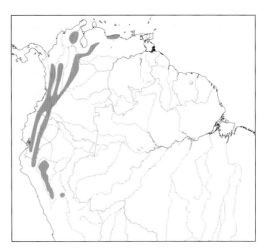

Ampelis riefferii **Boissonneau, 1840**, *Rev. Zool.* 3: 3, Santa Fé de Bogotá, Colombia

The lovely Green-and-black Fruiteater is arguably the most frequently encountered of the genus *Pipreola* virtually throughout its very broad range, and for many observers this species will be the first of this almost exclusively Andean genus that they come across. Like most of the genus it was formerly placed in *Euchlornis* (e.g. in Hellmayr 1929b), until Zimmer (1930) removed it to *Pipreola*, where it has remained until the present.

IDENTIFICATION 16–20cm. Observers in the northern Andes will probably encounter this fruiteater before any of its congenerics. An inhabitant of forests in the upper subtropical and lower temperate zones, from Venezuela to central Peru, the range of Green-and-black Fruiteater overlaps in part with that of nine other species of *Pipreola*. Of these nine, Band-tailed Fruiteater *P. intermedia* and Black-chested Fruiteater *P. lubomirskii* are perhaps the most likely candidates for confusion; in both these species, however, the males possess black chests and the females are essentially green above and yellow below with some olive. Other sympatric *Pipreola* are much easier to differentiate from Green-and-black Fruiteater, by virtue of their more decorative plumage (usually having red or orange breasts in males), and bare-part colours (females). Note, also, that in many areas the different species rarely occupy the same elevational ecotones, e.g. in central Peru, the rather larger, heavily barred and longer tailed Barred Fruiteater *P. arcuata* occurs at higher elevations than Green-and-black, while the also quite different Masked Fruiteater *P. pulchra* occurs mainly at lower elevations (O'Neill and Parker 1981). In Venezuela's Coastal Cordillera, Handsome Fruiteater *P. formosa* is mostly found below the elevational range of Green-and-black Fruiteater, with Golden-breasted Fruiteater *P. aureopectus* in wetter forests at higher elevations (Hilty 2003). Band-tailed overlaps with Green-and-black in central Peru, e.g. in the departments of La Libertad and Huánuco (and the two have been considered conspecifics), but elsewhere in Peru *P. intermedia* generally occurs at higher elevations (above 2,300m) and, in the relevant area of complete syntopy in Peru, is larger than the sympatric races (*P. r. tallmanorum* and *P. r. chachapoyas*) of Green-and-black Fruiteater. Furthermore, male Band-tailed Fruiteater has obvious blackish chevrons on the flanks admixed with some green mottling, as well as a much less obvious yellow collar line. In addition, both sexes of Band-tailed Fruiteater possess a broad subterminal tail-band and whitish tail tips, although these are rarely conspicuous. Male Black-chested Fruiteater *P. lubomirskii* (which is far more localised than Green-and-black, on the east slope of the Andes from southern Colombia to northern Peru) also has a black hood, but this lacks the bright yellow lower border present in Green-and-black. Black-chested Fruiteaters also differ in bare-part coloration compared with Green-and-black in the same regions: pale yellowish irides and greenish-grey legs in Black-chested; dark irides in Green-and-black with coral-red legs.

DISTRIBUTION Green-and-black Fruiteater is widespread through the Andes and some outlying ranges, from the Coastal Cordillera in northern Venezuela, in Miranda to Aragua, thence through the Andes of southeast Lara (e.g. in

Yacambú National Park) to southern Táchira. In Colombia, it occurs more or less continuously over all three Andean ranges, from Norte de Santander in the east, and in the Sierra de Perijá on the Venezuelan border, to Ecuador, south along the entire length of the east slope to northernmost Peru in western dpto. Amazonas, then discontinuously south through the eastern Andes elsewhere in dpto. Amazonas and dptos. San Martín to Huánuco, in central Peru. In western Ecuador, in the modern day, it is known only to as far south as western Cotopaxi, but at least formerly the species reached El Oro. Its elevational range is principally 1,100–2,900m, but Green-and-black Fruiteater is recorded locally to 3,050m in the Venezuelan Andes, to 3,200m in Colombia (Donegan *et al.* 2007) and even to 3,300m further south (Cerro Mongus, Ecuador). The species is recorded from as low as 900m on the Pacific slope of Colombia.

MOVEMENTS None noted, although short-range seasonal movements following fruiting events are suspected, as with other fruiteaters.

HABITAT Green-and-black Fruiteater inhabits premontane to montane forest, and sub-páramo, including cloud forest, disturbed areas, second growth and borders, but may also visit fruiting trees away from forest. It ranges from the lower midstorey to the subcanopy and canopy.

DESCRIPTION Typical fruiteater; dumpy, sluggish-looking and stolid. The bill has the slightly arched culmen and hooked tip, with exposed nostrils and weak rictal bristles typical of all *Pipreola*. The flight feathers are not modified (as in all fruiteaters, including *Ampelioides*). The nominate race is described here. *Adult male.* – Black hood reaching to the nape and upper breast, mottled dark olive on the lower throat and bordered by a yellow collar (which fades on the nape). Mantle, scapulars, secondary wing-coverts, rump and tail bright moss green, and the remiges are blackish-brown; broad moss green distal fringes to the tertials, with a white tip to each feather. Fringes to secondaries moss green. The underparts are bright yellow, irregularly streaked with olive, mainly below the black bib and on the breast-sides and flanks, but extending onto the undertail-coverts. *Adult female.* – Bright moss green above, lacking black hood of male; wing pattern as male but the white tertial tips are smaller. Moss green throat and breast, breaking into broad streaks on the flanks and these appear somewhat diffuse against the yellow background. Undertail-coverts yellow, streaked olive. *Juvenile.* – Dark olive-green above, with yellow terminal spots to the smaller wing-coverts and crown feathers, and dull olive streaked greenish-yellow below, but this plumage is replaced after 3–12 weeks by adult plumage (Fjeldså and Krabbe 1990). *Moult.* – There are few published moult data: in Ecuador birds were replacing their body feathers in June–July, as well as November and March (MECN), and in northern Venezuela the onset of moult is in April–August (especially May–July), however elsewhere it is probably year-round, e.g. in Colombia, with no evidence of obvious differences in timing between the sexes, but wing feathers might be moulted symmetrically, unlike the rectrices (Snow 1982; L. F. Barrera, A. Bermúdez, J. V. Sandoval, J. P. López, C. A. Páez O., D. Y. Ramírez, G. A. Suárez, A. Tovar, J. P. Varona and D. M. Velasco/ProAves unpubl. data; T. M. Donegan and L. Dávalos unpubl. data). *Bare parts.* – The irides are very dark reddish-brown (brown in one female specimen); and the bill and legs are bright red to orange-red, with the lower mandible sometimes having a black tip.

MEASUREMENTS (mainly from Snow 1982; with additional J. Hornbuckle unpubl. data for *P. r. occidentalis* and *P. r. chachapoyas*) *P. r. riefferii*: wing of male (*n* = 5) 91–95mm, wing of female (*n* = 4) 89–94mm; tail of male (*n* = 5) 67–75mm, tail of female (*n* = 4) 68–73mm; bill of male (*n* = 5) 8.5–9.5mm, bill of female (*n* = 4) 8.5–9.0mm; tarsus of male (*n* = 5) 22–24mm, tarsus of female (*n* = 4) 22.0–22.5mm. *P. r. melanolaema*: wing of male (*n* = 5) 90–97mm, wing of female (*n* = 4) 84–92mm; tail of male (*n* = 5) 74–80mm, tail of female (*n* = 4) 69–75mm; bill of male (*n* = 5) 8.5–9.5mm, bill of female (4) 8–10mm; tarsus of male (*n* = 5) 23.0–23.5mm, tarsus of female (*n* = 4) 23–24mm. *P. r. confusa*: wing of male (*n* = 1) 90.25mm; tail of male (*n* = 1) 73mm; bill of male (*n* = 1) 12mm; tarsus of male (*n* = 1) 23mm (Zimmer 1936a). *P. r. occidentalis*: wing of male (*n* = 10) 90–96mm, wing of female (*n* = 1) 93mm; tail of male (*n* = 8) 66–74mm; bill of male (*n* = 8) 9.5–11.0mm; tarsus of male (*n* = 8) 22.0–24.5mm (cf. also Hellmayr 1929b). *P. r. chachapoyas*: wing of male (*n* = 22) 86.5–92.0mm, wing of female (*n* = 2) 92mm; tail of male (*n* = 22) 60–75mm, tail of female (*n* = 2) 65–70mm; bill of male (*n* = 14) 7.2–9.0mm (*n* = 7, to skull, 12.0–14.7mm), bill of female (*n* = 2) 7.0–7.7mm (*n* = 2, to skull, 14.3–14.7mm); tarsus of male (*n* = 12) 19.3–24.5mm, tarsus of female (*n* = 2) 23.3–23.6mm (J. Hornbuckle unpubl., with additional wing and tail data from Hellmayr 1929b; and bill to feathers, and tarsus also from Snow 1982). *P. r. tallmanorum*: mean (*n* = 14) wing of male 84mm, of tail 68.6mm (O'Neill and Parker 1981). Other data from live birds, pertaining to *P. r. occidentalis*: wing of male (*n* = 95) 84–98mm, wing of female (*n* = 55) 82–95mm; tail of male (*n* = 45) 60–82mm, tail of female (*n* = 40) 57–76mm; bill of male (*n* = 68) 11.9–17.8mm, bill of female (*n* = 41) 10.9–17.3mm; tarsus of male (*n* = 69) 19.7–27.7mm, tarsus of female (*n* = 41) 18.8–26.9mm (L. F. Barrera, Bermúdez, A., J. V. Sandoval, J. P. López, C. A. Páez O., D. Y. Ramírez, G. A. Suárez, A. Tovar, J. P. Varona and D. M. Velasco/ProAves unpubl. data). Weight (races and sexes combined): 30.4–62.0g; for *P. r. occidentalis* (western Colombia): 30.7–59.5g (males) and 30.4–63.5g (females) (Hilty 2003, Rahbek *et al.* 1993, Snow 2004a, Echeverry-Galvis *et al.* 2006, Dunning 2008; MECN; MVZ; ROM; J. Hornbuckle unpubl.; L. F. Barrera, A. Bermúdez, J. V. Sandoval, J. P. López, C. A. Páez O., D. Y. Ramírez, G. A. Suárez, A. Tovar, J. P. Varona and D. M. Velasco/ProAves unpubl. data; T. M. Donegan and L. Dávalos unpubl. data).

GEOGRAPHICAL VARIATION Six subspecies generally recognised, although one, *P. r. confusa*, is probably best synonymised, and another, *P. r. tallmanorum*, could merit specific status. *P. r. melanolaema* P. L. Sclater, 1856 (in north and northwest Venezuela, as far as central Táchira), is smaller than the nominate. The male resembles *P. r. riefferii* (see above) but lacks the dull olive wash to the hood, has obviously unmarked yellow central underparts and the pale tips to the tertials are more conspicuous (though see Hellmayr 1929b) because these feathers (and the coverts) are dark-centred; the greater coverts have yellowish fringes and tips forming a slight wingbar. Female appears less streaked below than *P. r. riefferii*, the feathers of the rear underparts are yellow with olive fringes, producing a more scaled (less streaked) effect on the belly and flanks, and some exhibit an ill-defined yellow collar. *P. r. riefferii* (of southern Táchira, Venezuela, and the Central and East Andes, in Colombia) is described above; those in Venezuela, e.g. from the Páramo de Tamá, clearly present plumage transitional to *P. r. melanolaema* (Hellmayr 1929b). *P. r. occidentalis* (Chapman, 1914) occurs in the West, and perhaps the southernmost Central, Andes of Colombia south to El Oro, western Ecuador. Males are heavily streaked and mottled olive on the central belly and the inner greater wing-coverts are lightly tipped yellowish when fresh (cf. also Hellmayr 1929b). In *P. r. confusa* J. T. Zimmer, 1936 (of eastern Ecuador and the northern tip of the central Andes in northern Peru), the black on the upper breast of males is washed mossy green and the yellow underparts are heavily marked with olive, whilst the mantle and neck are virtually concolorous. *P. r. chachapoyas* (C. E. Hellmayr, 1915) occurs in northern Peru on the east side of the central Andes in dpto. San Martín, and resembles *P. r. confusa* but is generally less heavily marked below. Females are identical to others from as far afield as the range of *P. r. occidentalis*, albeit perhaps on average marginally smaller. *P. r. chachapoyas* and *P. r. confusa* intergrade in northern Peru and it was suggested that birds from eastern Ecuador south to at least eastern La Libertad, Peru, should all be considered under the name *P. r. chachapoyas* (O'Neill and Parker 1981), which possibility was further mooted by Ridgely and Greenfield (2001) and Snow (2004a). Plumage differences between them are very obscure and in a sample from the Cordillera de Colán, dpto. Amazonas, Peru, there was sufficient variation amongst males to suggest the presence of both forms there. *P. r. tallmanorum* O'Neill & Parker, 1981, occurs on the east slope of the Carpish Mountains and Cerros del Sira, dpto. Huánuco, central Peru, and is most similar to the nominate in plumage, but significantly smaller. The male has the head and upper breast shiny black, the underparts mainly lemon-yellow and less streaked, except on the vent and flanks. In contrast to other populations, the irides are bright red. Females differ from those of all other subspecies in their small size, darker, more bluish-green upperparts and more golden-yellow underparts. This form has been speculated to deserve specific status (O'Neill and Parker 1981, Sibley and Monroe 1990, Snow 2004a), but as in the case of *P. s. squamipectus* versus *P. s. frontalis* (Scarlet-breasted Fruiteater), we prefer to await the results of a robust analysis of these taxa before changing the status quo.

VOICE Like most fruiteaters, the vocalisations of this species are easily overlooked by inexperienced observers as insects, but (like other fruiteaters) it tends to respond well to playback (both sexes). The primary song (given by both sexes) recalls that of Band-tailed Fruiteater, and comprises several very soft, slightly drawn and high-pitched notes, followed by a very thin *seeee*, e.g. *ti-ti-ti-s-s-s-s-s-seeee*, or hissing *tic-tic-ti-ti-ti-tiseeeeeeeeeeeeeeeeeeaa* that descends and fades away. The song of *P. r. tallmanorum* recalls that of *P. r. chachapoyas* (cf. H. Lloyd recording, XC 36784), but there is perhaps some variation across the range as in Ecuador the song, which may or may not fade or slow at end, usually lasts 2–3 seconds, but in Colombia and Venezuela it may last *c*.5–6 seconds (Hilty and Brown 1986, Boesman 2006b). Outside of central Peru the song apparently lacks the terminating *seeee*. The species is also known to utter a sharp *tsip* in contact (Ridgely and Greenfield 2001) and *char-a-a-a-a* during copulation (Fjeldså and Krabbe 1990). Another call (context unknown) is a single, high whistle, initially ascending then descending, recalling a similar call of Barred Fruiteater, whilst that of Black-chested ascends (Ridgely and Greenfield 2001). The wings produce a mechanical rattling sound in flight. A high-pitched chatter was given by a female flushed from a nest with eggs (Miller 1963; see below). In northwest Ecuador, in alarm or agitation gives a *skree-chup!* (GMK pers. obs.). Published recordings are available on the following audio compilations: Moore and Lysinger (1997), Boesman (1999, 2006b, 2009), Moore *et al.* (1999), Álvarez-Rebolledo and Córdoba-Córdoba (2003), Krabbe and Nilsson (2003), Connop (2004) and Alvarez *et al.* (2007). In addition, recordings from Colombia (nominate), Ecuador (*P. r. occidentalis*), Peru (*P. r. tallmanorum*) and Venezuela (*P. r. melanolaema*) are archived online at www.xeno-canto.org.

NATURAL HISTORY Typically lethargic, like the majority of fruiteaters. Unhurried and stoic, rarely appearing 'phased' by human presence and generally the species is confiding and unsuspicious. Found at virtually all heights in the vegetation, from the understorey to relatively high in the canopy, but Green-and-black Fruiteater is typically found at mid levels and generally remains within a comparatively small home range. The species is most frequently noted in pairs but occasionally in groups of up to four, more occasionally as many as six birds, and often briefly accompanying mixed-species flocks but rarely for long. However, in her study of cloud forest flocks, based in southwest Colombia, Bohórquez (2003) observed the species in less than 2% of mixed flocks.

FOOD AND FEEDING Diet is apparently exclusively fruits (particularly melastomes) of understorey trees and vines, e.g. *Hedyosum* (Chloranthaceae), taken either whilst perched or, less frequently, during a short, clumsy sally-hover typical of all fruiteaters. Fjeldså and Krabbe (1990) also reported that it takes small quantities of insects.

BREEDING Everitt (1963) observed a captive male Green-and-black Fruiteater feed the female on the nest, and he was able to follow nesting attempts by two different females. Both females were solely responsible for nest construction and incubation, and all clutches were of two eggs, laid either on consecutive days or 2–3 days apart. Evidence both from captivity and the wild suggests that males may to some extent 'stand guard' near the nest. The eggs are pale brown spotted sepia, especially at the larger end (dimensions were presented in Everitt 1963). Incubation lasted 19–20 days in two breeding attempts and both adults fed the nestlings, one of which successfully fledged at 21 days and was thereafter fed solely by the male. In the wild, breeding-condition birds have been taken in February–July in western and central Colombia and two mossy cup nests lined with black rootlets

were found in the West Andes in the same country in March and mid September. Both were placed just 1–2m above the ground, and the first contained two cream-coloured eggs with fine red-brown dots principally at the larger end, whilst the second had two young 3–4 days old when discovered; pin feathers had started to emerge two days later (Miller 1963, where nest and egg dimensions were presented). Miller's data further suggested breeding attempts in southwest Colombia in February, March, May and August (and MVZ has males collected in breeding condition from February, March and July, and a females with eggs or otherwise in breeding condition in March). Females (and one male) have been trapped in western Colombia with brood patches in several months between June and December (L. F. Barrera, A. Bermúdez, J. V. Sandoval, J. P. López, C. A. Páez O., D. Y. Ramírez, G. A. Suárez, A. Tovar, J. P. Varona and D. M. Velasco/ProAves unpubl. data). In the north of Colombia five eggs were collected by T. K. Salmon and described by Sclater and Salvin (1879) as being pale salmon-coloured with a few dark red-brown spots (for dimensions and mass see Schönwetter 1969). Further north, the breeding period is considered to be centred on June in northern Venezuela (Schaefer and Phelps 1954). Females have been collected with active ovaries in Ecuador in September and January (MECN). In north-central Venezuela, at Colonia Tovar, GMK found an active nest attended by both adults on 7 March 1995. In northwest Ecuador an active nest at an unknown stage has been reported in early September and an adult building in early October (Greeney and Nunnery 2006). Greeney *et al.* (2010) observed nest building in late April and a nestling in late June in southeast Ecuador. Fledglings have been noted in January (Colombia), March (western Venezuela), and March, June and August (northwest Ecuador), and moult data indicate that the species may well nest year-round (Fjeldså and Krabbe 1990, Greeney and Nunnery 2006; see above).

STATUS Green-and-black Fruiteater is categorised as of Least Concern (BirdLife International 2004, 2008) and the species is generally one of the commonest fruiteaters throughout its range, being ecologically the most tolerant of the *Pipreola*, even utilising small patches of trees away from forest blocks within fragmented landscapes. However, there are local variations; for instance, in the Coastal Cordillera of Venezuela Hilty (2003) considered it to be less common than the Handsome Fruiteater, and there have been local extinctions due to deforestation, e.g. around Santa Elena, Antioquia, Colombia (Castaño-Villa and Patiño-Zabala (2008). Nonetheless, Green-and-black Fruiteater has been recorded from numerous reserves and other protected areas throughout its widespread distribution (e.g. for Colombia, see Ocampo 2002, Salaman *et al.* 2009).

REFERENCES Álvarez-Rebolledo and Córdoba-Córdoba (2003), Alvarez *et al.* (2007), BirdLife International (2004, 2008), Boesman (1999, 2006b, 2009), Bohórquez (2003), Castaño-Villa and Patiño-Zabala (2008), Connop (2004), Donegan and Dávalos (1999), Donegan *et al.* (2007, 2010), Dunning (2008), Echeverry-Galvis *et al.* (2006), Everitt (1963), Fjeldså and Krabbe (1990), Freile and Chaves (2004), Hellmayr (1929b), Greeney and Nunnery (2006), Greeney *et al.* (2010), Hilty (2003), Hilty and Brown (1986), Hornbuckle (1999), Kirwan and Marlow (1996), Krabbe and Nilsson (2003), Krabbe and Sornoza (1994), Krabbe *et al.* (2006), López-Lanús *et al.* (2000), Mark *et al.* (2008), Mee *et al.* (2002), Miller (1963), Mlíkovský (2009), Moore *et al.*

(1999), Moore and Lysinger (1997), Ocampo (2002), Olson (1971), O'Neill and Parker (1981), Parker *et al.* (1982, 1985), Rahbek *et al.* (1993), Ridgely and Gaulin (1980), Ridgely and Greenfield (2001), Ridgely and Tudor (1994, 2009), Salaman *et al.* (1999, 2008, 2009), Schaefer and Phelps (1954), Sclater and Salvin (1879), Schönwetter (1969), Schulenberg *et al.* (2007), Sibley and Monroe (1990), Snow (1982, 2004a), Stotz *et al.* (1996), Zimmer (1930).

Green-and-black Fruiteater *Pipreola riefferii.* **Fig. 1**. Male, *P. r. occidentalis*, Bellavista Lodge, prov. Pichincha, October (*János Oláh*). **Fig. 2**. Female, *P. r. chachapoyas*, Abra Patricia, dpto. San Martín, northern Peru, November (*Hadoram Shirihai / Photographic Handbook to Birds of the World*). **Fig. 3**. Male, *P. r. occidentalis*, Jardín, dpto. Antioquia, western Colombia, January (*Joe Tobias / Edward Grey Institute, Oxford University*). Some of the inner greater wing-coverts still possess small yellow tips in this individual, but neither this or the bird in Fig. 1 appears to be extensively green-mottled over the central underparts, which is considered to be another feature of this subspecies. **Figs. 4–5**. Male and female, *P. r. tallmanorum*, Paty trail, dpto. Huánuco, Peru, November (*Hadoram Shirihai / Photographic Handbook to Birds of the World*). Subspecies *tallmanorum* is sometimes suggested to be a possible 'split'. In addition to being smaller than other subspecies, the male has the head and upper breast shiny black, the underparts mainly lemon-yellow and less streaked, and the irides are bright red. Females differ from those of all other subspecies in their darker, more bluish-green upperparts, and more golden-yellow underparts, as well as also having red irides.

BAND-TAILED FRUITEATER
Pipreola intermedia   **Plate 18**

Pipreola intermedia **Taczanowski, 1884**, *Orn. Pérou* 2: 376, Maraynioc, dpto. Junín, Peru

Previously considered conspecific with Green-and-black Fruiteater *P. riefferii*, the Band-tailed Fruiteater has since found to be sympatric, although usually elevationally parapatric, with the former species in central Peru (as was early realised by Zimmer 1936b). Sibley and Monroe (1990) considered these two species to form a superspecies, whilst Snow (2004a) treated them as sister species. Like many fruiteaters, our knowledge of the Band-tailed Fruiteater's natural history is still very basic.

IDENTIFICATION 18.5–19.5cm. Either sex is only really likely to be mistaken for a Green-and-black Fruiteater, but the sympatric races of Green-and-black (*P. r. chachapoyas* and *P. r. tallmanorum*) are appreciably smaller than Band-tailed, and furthermore lack the subterminal tail-band with whitish tips and densely variegated underparts of *P. intermedia*. In addition, Band-tailed generally occurs at higher elevations than Green-and-black Fruiteater, although there is some limited elevational overlap in dptos. La Libertad and Huánuco, Peru. Many of the same features that distinguish Green-and-black Fruiteater, as well as the present species' tail markings, will be useful in separating Band-tailed Fruiteater from other *Pipreola* species.

DISTRIBUTION Band-tailed Fruiteater is found in the eastern Andes, from central Peru, in eastern dpto. La Libertad, to western Bolivia, in dptos. La Paz, Cochabamba and Santa Cruz, where it reaches its southernmost terminus on the Serranía de Siberia (Whitney *et al.* 1994). Found at 1,500–3,300m in Peru, but recorded down to 1,100m in Bolivia. The species is principally found above 2,300m in both countries.

MOVEMENTS None definitely known, but a single low-altitude record in Bolivia (see Distribution) might indicate at least periodic or seasonal dispersal to lower elevations.

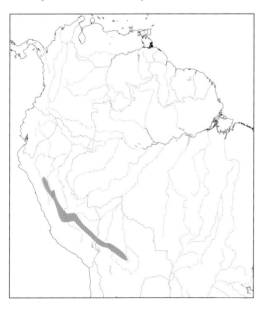

HABITAT Preferences very similar to those of the previous species, but Band-tailed is generally found at higher elevations to Green-and-black Fruiteater, especially in the area of overlap between the two, although they have been observed feeding together at the same fruiting tree.

DESCRIPTION Sexes differ. The bill has a slightly arched culmen and hooked tip, with exposed nostrils and weak rictal bristles. The flight feathers are not modified (as in all fruiteaters, including *Ampelioides*). Nominate *P. i. intermedia* is described here. *Adult male.* – The black hood and bib are bordered by a broken yellow half-collar. Moss green upperparts; the tertials are blackish with moss green outer webs and conspicuous white tips. Outer remiges blackish with the distal fringes of the secondaries moss green. The rather long tail is also moss green but with a blackish subterminal band, and each feather is tipped white. Below yellow with scattered blackish-olive crescents. Undertail greyish-brown, darker distally with white tips. Undertail-coverts blotchy yellow-olive. *Adult female.* – Very bright moss green above, and lacks black hood of male but retains the striking tertial pattern. It has an inconspicuous yellowish eye-ring. The tail pattern resembles that of the male, but is somewhat less striking, and the subterminal band may even be absent (Schulenberg *et al.* 2007). The throat and breast are moss green with slight yellow barring on the chin. Rest of underparts yellow, with blackish-olive crescents. *Juvenile.* – Undescribed (Snow 2004a). *Moult.* – There are no detailed moult data for this species (although see Fjeldså and Krabbe 1990), but general information concerning the onset of moult in *Pipreola* would suggest that it is seasonal (September–March) in southern Peru and Bolivia, but virtually year-round further north (Snow 1982). *Bare parts.* – Irides brown or pale green (perhaps occasionally grey); the bill is crimson to reddish-orange (and the culmen ridge sometimes black); and the legs and feet are red or orange-red (FMNH; Snow 2004b).

MEASUREMENTS (from Hellmayr 1929b, Snow 1982) *P. i. intermedia*: wing of male (*n* = 5) 87.5–99.0mm, wing of female (*n* = 3) 87–89mm [95mm: Hellmayr 1929b]; tail of male (*n* = 5) 68.0–75.5mm [87mm: Hellmayr 1929b], tail of female (*n* = 3) 72.5–77.0mm [81mm: Hellmayr 1929b]; tarsus of male (*n* = 5) 21.4–23.8mm, tarsus of female (*n* = 3) 21.2–24.5mm. *P. i. signata* (data from large sample [*n* = 29] of Hellmayr incorporated directly, but he did not state separate totals by sex, so totals for males are only from Snow 1982): wing of male (*n* = 4) 92–100mm, wing of female 91–98mm; tail of male (*n* = 4) 73–87mm, tail of female 80–87mm; bill of male (*n* = 4) 9–10mm; tarsus of male (*n* = 4) 23.0–24.5mm. Weight (races combined): 44.0–58.9g (males) and 43–56g (females) (Snow 1982, 2004a, Dunning 2008; FMNH).

GEOGRAPHICAL VARIATION Polytypic with two well-recognised subspecies. *P. i. intermedia* (central Peru, from dptos. La Libertad to southern San Martín and Junín), is described above. *P. i. signata* (C. E. Hellmayr, 1917) (dpto. Cuzco in southeast Peru, to dptos. La Paz and Cochabamba, northwestern Bolivia) differs in that males are cleaner yellow on the central underparts (lacking the crescents of nominate *P. i. intermedia*) and have the flanks scalloped dark olive, with a more noticeable chrome yellow half-collar. Female *P. i. signata* has a yellower throat and lores than the nominate race, and an appreciably more noticeable yellowish-white eye-ring.

VOICE The song typically consists of a very high-pitched trill, rendered *tsi-tsi-tsi-tsiiii* and rather similar to that of

Green-and-black Fruiteater, and lasting 4–5 seconds (Walker 2001). What are perhaps calls, or an alternate song, consist of 5–6 *tsi* notes, at first on an even pitch, then falling and rising at the end. Also gives long, rising, whistles at a very high-pitched frequency, each whistle lasting up to 3.5 seconds (Mayer 2000, Boesman 2009). Recordings of this species are also available online at www.xeno-canto.org.

NATURAL HISTORY In many respects, probably a typically undemonstrative *Pipreola* fruiteater, generally appearing very staid and sluggish, and is certainly unobtrusive. Fjeldså and Krabbe (1990) considered its habits to be much like those of *P. riefferii*.

FOOD AND FEEDING Unstudied: Band-tailed Fruiteater typically perches alone or in pairs from the understorey to mid canopy, and it appears to have a wholly frugivorous diet.

BREEDING There is no information concerning the species' breeding biology, although moult data (peak December–January in Peru and November–December in Bolivia) suggest breeding occurs year-round.

STATUS Currently categorised as Least Concern (BirdLife International 2004, 2008), Band-tailed Fruiteater seems fairly common, at least locally. The species is endemic to the Peruvian Andean Centre of endemism (Cracraft 1985). Band-tailed Fruiteater is apparently observed frequently at the Carpish pass in Huánuco, Peru (Snow 2004a), and also between Rocotal and San Pedro on the Manu Road (H. Lloyd *in litt.* 2010). It is known from several protected areas in both range countries, e.g. Madidi National Park, in Bolivia, and Manu National Park Biosphere Reserve, and Macchu Picchu Historical Sanctuary, in Peru.

REFERENCES Alarcón and Vidoz (2010), BirdLife International (2004, 2008), Boesman (2009), Cracraft (1985), Dunning (2008), Fjeldså and Krabbe (1990), Hellmayr (1929b), Hennessey and Gomez (2003), MacLeod *et al.* (2005), Mayer (2000), Mlíkovský (2009), Ridgely and Tudor (1994, 2009), Schulenberg *et al.* (2007), Sibley and Monroe (1990), Snow (1982, 2004a), Stotz *et al.* (1996), Walker and Fjeldså (2001), Walker *et al.* (2006), Whitney *et al.* (1994), Zimmer (1936b).

Band-tailed Fruiteater *Pipreola intermedia*. **Fig. 1**. Male, *P. i. intermedia*, Oxapampa, dpto. Pasco, central Peru, September (*Alejandro Tabini*). **Fig. 2**. Male, *P. i. signata*, Carrasco National Park, dpto. Cochabamba, Bolivia (*Daniel Alarcón*). Males of the southern race *P. i. signata* lack the black crescents on the central underparts. **Fig. 3**. Female, *P. i. signata*, Tunquini, dpto. La Paz, northwest Bolivia, January (*Joe Tobias / Edward Grey Institute, Oxford University*). Note the obvious yellow-white eye-ring, as well as the striking tail pattern when seen well from behind.

Genus *Ampelioides*: Scaled Fruiteater

The Scaled Fruiteater is a relatively large, sluggish fruiteater of submontane forests in the Andes. *Ampelioides* shares certain morphological characters with *Pipreola*, which is presumably its closest relative, and is very similar to the largest of the latter genus, *P. arcuata*, particularly in its tail morphology.

SCALED FRUITEATER
Ampelioides tschudii   Plate 15

Cotinga tschudii **G. R. Gray, 1846**, *Genera Birds* 1: 279 (new name for *Ampelis cincta* Tschudi, 1843), Pangos, east of Tarma, dpto. Junín, Peru

This species and the tepui endemic Red-banded Fruiteater *Pipreola whitelyi* are the 'oddballs' of the fruiteater group of taxa. Described from Peru, the Scaled Fruiteater has a range that encompasses most of the Andes, from western Venezuela to western Bolivia, but it is only in recent decades that a better knowledge of this somewhat wary species has been gained, and there are still many gaps in our understanding.

IDENTIFICATION 19.0–20.5cm. Given a reasonable view, it is unlikely that either sex of this attractive cotinga could be mistaken for any other species. The combination of chunky, fruiteater shape, heavy dark bill, scaled underparts (more boldly marked in the female) and dark crown (in the male) makes this species easily identified. All those *Pipreola* fruiteaters that overlap in range with *Ampelioides* have full black hoods (males) or lack the scalloped effect on the underparts (females).

DISTRIBUTION The Scaled Fruiteater ranges through the subtropical Andes, in Colombia mainly on the west slope north to dpto. Antioquia, but also on the east slope in dptos. Norte de Santander, Cauca and Nariño, in the Magdalena Valley, and the Sierra de Macarena and Serranía de los Churumbelos, all in the East Andes (Hilty and Brown 1986, Salaman *et al.* 2002b); on both slopes in Ecuador, on the west side south to western Loja and the outlying coastal cordillera in Esmeraldas and Guayas, in the east to Zamora-Chinchipe (Ridgely and Greenfield 2001); in

eastern Peru south to southern dptos. Madre de Dios and Cuzco; and to westernmost Bolivia in La Paz (Serranías Bellavista and Sadiri, and the middle Tuichi Valley) and Beni (Pilón Lajas Biosphere Reserve, Serranía Cuchilla: *Cotinga* 13: 75; Hennessey, Herzog *et al.* 2003, Hosner *et al.* 2009; see also XC3137). Also, the Sierra de Perijá on the border of Colombia and Venezuela, and in the latter country on the Cerro El Teteo, southeast Táchira. Recently recorded further west in Venezuela, in Yacambú National Park, Lara, in January (Hilty 2003) and July 1999 (Ryan 2000), a northeastwards range extension of *c.*350km. Elevational range mainly 800–2,000m (to 1,900m in Ecuador), but exceptionally occurs to 750m in the coastal cordillera of western Ecuador (Becker and López Lanús 1997; GMK pers. obs.), to 700m in Manu National Park, Peru (Walker *et al.* 2006), and (perhaps doubtfully) at 2,400–2,700m in the Perijá range, and 650m in Norte de Santander, Colombia (Hilty and Brown 1986).

MOVEMENTS None recorded, although Hilty (1997) considered it was perhaps a short-distance migrant at a study site in Valle, southwest Colombia, and Restall *et al.* (2006) also considered there to be possible evidence for short-range altitudinal movements.

HABITAT Humid submontane forest and its borders, in the subcanopy and at mid levels, but the species is occasionally recorded low in the understorey (Salaman *et al.* 2002b).

DESCRIPTION An extremely chunky and unusually well-patterned cotinga (especially the underparts). Sexes differ. Primaries unmodified. Nostrils are large, oval-shaped and well exposed. See below for bill structure. *Adult male.* – Distinctive, with a black crown, nape and ear-coverts creating a hooded appearance. Lores yellowish-white. Throat and collar white, the latter with an olive-yellow hue. Throat bordered below by black, with a broken malar stripe. Mantle and scapulars mixed dull moss green and black (large black centres and broad moss-green fringes). The lesser and median wing-coverts are also black with the feathers fringed moss green. Greater coverts moss green, with or without black tips (individually variable: see Chapman 1926a). Remiges (and tertials) black; the outermost and innermost flight-feathers fringed moss green. Rump and uppertail-coverts moss green (more yellowish-green distally), with blackish feather centres. Short tail with black subterminal band and whitish or buffish tips to the feathers. Breast, belly and vent olive-yellow, scaled broadly olive (each feather with a neat 'stained glass window' effect), the whole becoming less yellowish and more olive distally, with brighter yellow undertail-coverts, broadly barred blackish. *Adult female.* – Plumage generally mirrors that of the male, except that the crown patch is less distinct, being olive rather than black, and this sex lacks the hind-collar. Conversely, the malar is more obvious, albeit olive rather than black, and the underparts pattern is bolder: the scaling is black (breast) or darker green (lower belly and vent) than in the male. *Immature.* – Upperparts feathers are extensively pale-tipped, with yellow-green subterminal spots on the crown and the same colour tips to the back, wing-coverts and inner secondaries (Snow 1982). There is no information on younger birds. *Moult.* – In the north of the species' range (Colombia/Ecuador) feather renewal commences December–April, and may persist until June–August (Ecuador; MECN), whilst in Peru recorded start dates are in January and June. There seems to be no difference between males and females in moult timing (Snow 1982), doubtless because both sexes appear to share nesting duties (based on the limited information available to date; see below). *Bare parts.* – Irides golden-yellow, yellow-green, yellow-red or orange-red (with black pupils), sometimes with a red inner ring (slightly duller, more olive-green in females); legs and feet olive-grey or bluish-grey (male), or bluish-grey or grey-green (female); bill broad-based and rather swollen laterally, with a strongly arched culmen and at most a slightly hooked tip: upper mandible black, lower mandible paler, olive or olive-horn (male), or grey with a greenish base, sometimes becoming black distally only on upper mandible (female). Young perhaps have browner irides (Snow 1982).

MEASUREMENTS (from Snow 1982; MECN; RMNH: Azuay, El Oro, Pichincha and Zamora-Chinchipe, Ecuador) Wing of male (*n* = 17) 98–108mm, wing of female (*n* = 7) 95–104mm; tail of male (*n* = 17) 57–65mm, tail of female (*n* = 7) 58–66mm; bill of male (*n* = 14) 12.0–13.5mm (*n* = 4 to skull, 20.00–20.81mm), bill of female (*n* = 7) 12.0–12.5mm (*n* = 2 to skull, 18.80–20.62mm); tarsus of male (*n* = 14) 21–23mm, tarsus of female (*n* = 7) 20.5–22.0mm. Weight: 74–95g (males) and 71.5–84.5g (females) (Snow 2004a, Salaman and Donegan 2007, Dunning 2008; FMNH; MECN).

GEOGRAPHICAL VARIATION Monotypic.

VOICE Resembles that of a raptor, and is much lower pitched and louder than that of *Pipreola* species, the song (given by the male alone) being a series of loud, downward-inflected whistles, each note at first rising then dropping slightly in pitch, transcribed as *wheeeeeéééeeur*, and repeated at 3–10-second intervals, sometimes extremely repetitively but in some areas only given seasonally, e.g. December to early April in Valle, Colombia (Hilty and Brown 1986, Hilty 1997, 2003, Ridgely and Greenfield 2001, Snow 2004a). May recall Dusky-capped Flycatcher *Myiarchus tuberculifer*. Female noted to give a soft chatter that is scarcely audible, resembling the calls of some orioles *Icterus* spp. or Squirrel Cuckoo *Piaya cayana* (Parker *et al.* 1980). Mechanical wing noise given in flight (perhaps only by males). Published recordings of the species' voice exist on the following audio compilations: Moore *et al.* (1999), Mayer (2000), Schulenberg (2000a), Krabbe and Nilsson (2003), Connop (2004), Alvarez *et al.* (2007) and Boesman (2009). There are also many recordings from across much of the species' range (namely from Bolivia, Colombia and Ecuador) archived at www.xeno-canto.org.

NATURAL HISTORY Much remains to be elucidated concerning this species' ecology. Normally appears extremely sluggish, hopping deliberately along moss-covered limbs, and is generally found alone or in pairs (occasionally small groups of 3–4, which presumably constitute family parties), and sometimes in association with mixed-species feeding flocks in the canopy, up to 10–20m above the ground, but occasionally much lower in cloud or elfin forest (Barnes *et al.* 1994). Perches quietly for long periods and is frequently hard to see, being generally a more wary species than most *Pipreola* (Hilty 2003). Video footage of a bird near Mindo, Ecuador, by C. F. Collins demonstrates the slow, almost myopic manner in which the species often peers at its surroundings, only sallying for fruit very occasionally.

FOOD AND FEEDING Mainly takes larger fruits, but very few data on species composition; Salaman *et al.* (2002b) mentioned a bird feeding on a *Ficus* sp. A pair observed by GG, also near Mindo, was accompanying a mixed-species flock at the forest edge near a main road. They perched horizontally on horizontal branches, moving fairly quickly along these, presumably searching for insects, there being no fruit evident in the surroundings. Consumption of arboreal snails was reported by Williams (2002), taken in an upward sally to the underside of a branch and then beaten against the branch, from his observations made in northwest Ecuador.

BREEDING Almost nothing is known concerning breeding, although S. Bird *et al.* (unpubl.; see photographs currently archived at www.birdseekers.co.uk) discovered and photographed both members of a pair attending a nest at Buenaventura, prov. El Oro, southwest Ecuador, in the fourth week of February. From the photographs, the nest appears to be a relatively large open cup of lichens, liverworts, moss and rootlets placed in a crotch on a heavily epiphyte-encrusted branch adjacent to a near-vertical trunk (*c.*10cm depth at breast height). It was unclear what stage the nesting cycle had reached. Other breeding data concern a male that was observed feeding fruit to a juvenile in mid November, in Bolivia (Hennessey, Herzog *et al.* 2003); three breeding-condition birds have been collected in July in Colombia, where an immature was taken in August (Hilty and Brown 1986), but in northwest Ecuador birds (both sexes) were still moulting and males had small testes in June–August (MECN).

STATUS Not considered globally threatened (Least Concern), but Scaled Fruiteater was formerly treated as Near Threatened (Collar *et al.* 1992). Seems distinctly local and uncommon in Venezuela and Colombia (Hilty and Brown 1986, Hilty 2003, Restall *et al.* 2006). This fruiteater's distribution along a large section of the Andes affords some protection from loss of forest cover in parts of its range, and it is also known from a number of protected areas in all range states (see, for instance, Hilty and Brown 1986, Collar *et al.* 1992, Hilty 2003, Boyla and Estrada 2005, Walker *et al.* 2006, Salaman *et al.* 2008).

REFERENCES Alvarez *et al.* (2007), Alverson *et al.* (2001), Becker and López Lanús (1997), van den Berg and Bosman (1984), Best *et al.* (1993), BirdLife International (2004, 2008), Boesman (2009), Boyla and Estrada (2005), Chapman (1926a), Collar *et al.* (1992), Connop (2004), Davies *et al.* (1994), Dunning (2008), Fjeldså and Krabbe (1990), Hellmayr (1929b), Hennessey *et al.* (2003b), Hilty (1997, 2003), Hilty and Brown (1986), Hornbuckle (1999), Hosner *et al.* (2009), Kirwan and Marlow (1996), Krabbe and Nilsson (2003), Mayer (2000), Mazar Barnett and Kirwan (2000a), Moore *et al.* (1999), Ohlson *et al.* (2007, 2008), Parker and Parker (1982), Parker *et al.* (1980), Perry *et al.* (1997), Prum *et al.* (2000), Restall *et al.* (2006), Ridgely and Greenfield (2001), Ridgely and Tudor (1994, 2009), Ryan (2000), Salaman *et al.* (1999, 2002b, 2008), Salaman and Donegan (2007), Schulenberg (2000a), Schulenberg *et al.* (2007), Snow (2004a), Stotz *et al.* (1996), Tello *et al.* (2009), Walker *et al.* (2006), Williams (2002), Zimmer (1930).

Scaled Fruiteater *Ampelioides tschudii*. **Fig. 1**. Male, Buenaventura Reserve, prov. El Oro, southwest Ecuador, July (*Hadoram Shirihai / Photographic Handbook to Birds of the World*). **Fig. 2**. Female, Buenaventura Reserve, prov. El Oro, southwest Ecuador, July and August (*Hadoram Shirihai / Photographic Handbook to Birds of the World*). The plumage of both sexes is very distinctive compared to any of the *Pipreola* fruiteaters.

Genus *Lipaugus*: pihas

The pihas represent the antithesis of everyone's typical cotinga: drab, unspectacular and, at face value, unexciting. Representatives of *Lipaugus* are found from Middle America, in the northern Neotropics, to the Atlantic Forest biome of southeast South America via the Andes and the Amazonian lowlands; it is thus virtually a pan-Neotropical genus. *Lipaugus* contains one of the species most characteristic of South America, the Screaming Piha *L. vociferans*, as well as some extremely rare and restricted-range species.

One species, Scimitar-winged Piha *L. uropygialis* was formerly afforded its own genus, *Chirocylla*, but we follow Remsen *et al.* (1982), and all subsequent authors, in subsuming this within *Lipaugus* (for further discussion see the relevant species account). Their drabness is belied by their extremely demonstrative and loud whistling vocalisations, with the three-phase call of the Screaming Piha among one of the best-known voices of the tropics. The preferred habitat of many species is almost exclusively submontane and montane forest, from the upper tropical foothills to temperate elfin forests; Screaming Piha and Rufous Piha *L. unirufus* are the only exclusively lowland species.

Except Screaming Piha, Rufous Piha and Rose-collared Piha *L. streptophorus*, the other *Lipaugus* (and the green pihas *Snowornis*) possess specialised modified primary barbules used in a wing-whirring display and probably constitute a superspecies. Most *Lipaugus* display at 'exploded leks' where individuals gather in a defined but relatively large area to vocalise and 'wing-whirr', although the display arena of Dusky Piha *L. fuscocinereus* is relatively compact.

DUSKY PIHA
Lipaugus fuscocinereus   Plate 19

Querula fusco-cinerea **Lafresnaye, 1843**, *Rev. Zool.* 6: 291, Colombie [= Santa Fé de Bogotá, Colombia]

The Dusky Piha is generally presumed to form a superspecies with Scimitar-winged Piha *L. uropygialis* (Remsen 1984), whilst Cuervo *et al.* (2001) and Snow (2004a) suggested that the Chestnut-capped Piha *L. weberi* might well also form part of this grouping.

IDENTIFICATION 31–33cm. A large, long-tailed piha with a short, thick bill that is slightly decurved. Dusky Piha superficially resembles Screaming Piha *L. vociferans* of the Amazonian lowlands, but Dusky occurs in subtropical and temperate forests of the Andes, and is also much larger. Olivaceous Piha *Snowornis cryptolophus*, which generally occurs just below the range of the present species, is smaller and olive-green above and below, and is therefore unlikely to be confused with it. Note that the silhouette of Dusky Piha differs subtly from those of potential confusion species; it has a relatively small, slightly flattened head, narrow 'shoulders', a long but relatively narrow body and a very substantial, long tail.

DISTRIBUTION Dusky Piha is restricted to northwestern South America, in the Andes of Colombia (in the East Andes, from dpto. Norte de Santander south to dpto. Cauca; throughout the Central Andes except the low-elevation section, where it is replaced by Chestnut-capped Piha; and the West Andes, at their northern end on the Cordillera de Paramillo and Páramo de Frontino, dpto. Antioquia: Chapman 1917, Hilty and Brown 1986, Salaman *et al.* 1999, Cuervo *et al.* 2001, Krabbe *et al.* 2006, Donegan *et al.* 2007), thence south along the entire east slope of Ecuador (Ridgely and Greenfield 2001) to extreme northern Peru in the Cordillera de Chinguela at 2,125–2,250m, where the species was only discovered in 1980 (Parker *et al.* 1985, Schulenberg *et al.* 2007). Dusky Piha has also been speculated to occur in southwest Táchira, Venezuela, given its presence in virtually adjacent Colombia (Hilty 2003).

MOVEMENTS None recorded to date.

HABITAT Dusky Piha is found in upper levels of montane forest between 1,700 and 3,200m, but the species is probably most frequent above 2,200m and can sometimes occur in mature secondary growth.

DESCRIPTION The sexes are similar, but males average larger in wing- and tail-length (Cuervo *et al.* 2001). This is the largest *Lipaugus*, with a conspicuously long tail, and pp5–7 are modified in the male alone, the barbs over the middle part of the outer webs being non-interlocking, elongated and somewhat stiffened. The rather deep- and broad-based bill has a well-arched culmen and a prominently hooked tip (see photograph in Greeney *et al.* 2009). Dusky Piha has short rictal bristles but relatively obvious nostrils. *Adult.* – Slate or dark grey above, with a slightly browner cast to the remiges and the rectrices. Paler below, being pale grey on the throat, and the breast and belly are faintly tinged brownish, becoming even warmer (cinnamon-grey) on the undertail-coverts. Underwing grey. *Immature.* – Differs from the adult in having broad rusty-rufous tips and fringes to the wing feathers, especially the greater coverts (which are thought to be a vestigial character of a rufous juvenile plumage), but some doubt exists as to whether this plumage is truly immature or that of the juvenile (see Cuervo *et al.* 2001, who suggest that this plumage is that presented on fledging and that it is probably moulted rapidly to full adult plumage). *Juvenile.* – Described as cinnamon to cinnamon-rufous throughout (Fjeldså and Krabbe 1990), but it has been suggested that this reference is probably to a pullus (T. M. Donegan *in litt.* 2009). *Moult.* – There are no published moult data, but birds taken in Ecuador in November showed evidence of body, wing and tail moult; however, one collected in October was not replacing any feathers (MECN). The wing-coverts and secondaries can sometimes be retained (G. A. Suárez/ProAves unpubl. data). *Bare parts.* – Irides dark brown to blackish, the legs and feet are grey to dark grey, and the bill is black or blackish-grey to dark brown, sometimes with a paler base to the lower mandible or marginally paler cutting edges (MECN).

MEASUREMENTS (from Cuervo *et al.* 2001: geographical spread of sample unknown) Wing of male (n = 23) 168–177mm, wing of female (n = 26) 175–188mm; tail of male (n = 22) 156–160mm, tail of female (n = 28) 154–168mm; bill of male (n = 24) 27–30mm, bill of female (n = 22) 29–30mm; tarsus of male (n = 24) 29–32mm, tarsus of female (n = 25) 28–32mm. Weight (sexes combined): 120–156g (once 80.0g) (MECN; Parker *et al.* 1985, Cuervo *et al.* 2001, Snow 2004a, Dunning 2008; T. M. Donegan *et al.* unpubl. data; G. A. Suárez/ProAves unpubl. data).

GEOGRAPHICAL VARIATION Monotypic.

VOICE Recalls that of other members of the genus, especially that of the Screaming Piha. The song is a high, piercing whistle that initially rises, then falls, rises and falls again, and reaches its highest pitch in the finale: *wee'uWEEER*, sometimes given every 3–4 minutes but also occasionally at much shorter intervals. A 'modified' song has also been recorded (T. M. Donegan recording, XC 29815) in which the latter part of the phrase appears to glide downwards on a slightly glistening scale. Two birds have also been recorded apparently producing a duet (T. M. Donegan recording, XC25527). Dusky Piha produces a series of loud, low-frequency 'puffs' with the wings, recalling the mechanical sound produced by the flight feathers of Sickle-winged Guan *Chamaepetes goudotii*, during its recently described flight-display (López-Lanús 2000). Like the newly described Chestnut-capped Piha, the Dusky Piha sings in flight during these displays. Commercial recordings are available on the following compilations: Moore and Lysinger (1997), Krabbe and Nilsson (2003), Alvarez *et al.* (2007) and Boesman (2009). There are also many recordings, from Colombia, Ecuador and Peru, archived online at www. xeno-canto.org.

NATURAL HISTORY Generally solitary, or in small groups of up to 2–5 (mainly at leks), but the species sometimes joins mixed-species flocks including groups of Turquoise Jays *Cyanolyca turcosa*, Hooded Mountain Tanagers *Buthraupis montana* and Northern Mountain Caciques *Cacicus leucoramphus* (Fjeldså and Krabbe 1990, Schulenberg *et al.* 2007). The species is regularly observed in such groups at Guango Lodge, below Papallacta pass, in eastern Ecuador (M. Lysinger). Sometimes observed feeding alone in 'groups' of two close to the ground, almost like large thrushes, at the edge of regenerating landslides (H. F. Greeney *in litt.* 2010).

FOOD AND FEEDING Diet is not well known, but in eastern Colombia fruits of eight different families, especially Chloranthaceae, have been recorded as taken (Renjifo 1991), and the presumed female that tended the nest recently found in eastern Ecuador (see below) was observed to feed on small *Hyeronima* (Euphorbiaceae) fruits (Greeney *et al.* 2009). Also recorded taking unidentified Malphigiaceae and *Hediosynum* (Chloranthaceae) fruits in eastern Ecuador (H. F. Greeney *in litt.* 2010). Like most pihas, fruits are taken using a short sally and brief hover-glean method.

DISPLAY This species is one of the more demonstrative of pihas, and indeed cotingas, and can be relatively easy to see in the canopy of montane forest within its range, especially whilst lekking (e.g. in June in the Central Andes of Colombia). One seen (by GG) near the entrance to the Cordillera de Guacamayos trail in eastern Ecuador was easy to observe in its dashing flights from one perch to another, once settling on a conspicuous snag affording a vista over the local area. This is a regular site for the species (Cisneros-Heredia 2009). S. L. Hilty (*in* Snow 1982) was the first to observe the lek of the Dusky Piha, in northern Colombia, where he watched several individuals singing from the treetops or high, exposed branches, with much toing and froing between perches. As such the lek is similar to that of Screaming Piha, but differs in being sited in the subcanopy and canopy (rather than the midstorey, albeit usually in shorter-stature forest) and that the birds fly back and forth frequently (rather than remaining largely on one perch). López-Lanús (2000) described a flight-display observed in June in central Colombia, wherein a bird flew almost directly downwards from a *c.*10m-high branch, folding and unfolding its wings during the descent (as if trying to stall its fall) up to 12 times, before returning to an adjacent tree when *c.*5m above the ground. Undulating whistles were heard from other birds in the vicinity during this display, as well as the mechanical wing sounds described under Voice by the bird performing the display. The species is now also observed readily at another lek site, near the settlement of Cuyuja in eastern Ecuador.

BREEDING The nest and egg were recently described by Greeney *et al.* (2009), from observations at Yanayacu Biological Station in prov. Napo, northeast Ecuador. The nest was discovered in late March within an area of selectively logged forest with a relatively sparse understorey but well-developed canopy (including many *Miconia*, Melastomataceae), and was sited in the horizontal fork of a *c.*10m-tall *Vismia tomentosa* (Clusiaceae) tree, *c.*8.5m above the ground, sheltered from above by dense foliage. The nest contained a single egg (described as being 'pale beige with coarse brown and lavender flecking and splotching, heaviest at the largest end') and was a flattened and rather substantial cup constructed mostly of tightly curled, dried vine tendrils, atop a sparse platform of long sticks (dimensions of both the nest and the egg were presented in Greeney *et al.* 2009). Only a single adult, presumably the female, was observed in the vicinity of the nest, and it would approach cautiously and yet quickly depart if disturbed, although it would otherwise remain on the nest if the observers remained quiet, despite the bird being obviously aware of their presence (Greeney *et al.* 2009). Unfortunately, the finders were unable to follow the nest to completion. The only other breeding data concern two males collected in Ecuador that had enlarged testes in August and November, four juveniles collected in July and September (Cuervo *et al.* 2001), and Fjeldså and Krabbe (1990) suggested that breeding might occur year-round (based on unpublished moult data), as well as reporting juveniles collected in November and January in northeast Ecuador, and immatures in November and March from the same region.

STATUS Dusky Piha is not globally threatened and is currently treated as Least Concern (BirdLife International 2004, 2008). However, the species is local and has doubtless decreased in numbers through loss of montane forest within its extensive range, but it remains common in some areas, e.g. at several sites and on both slopes of the Serranía de los Yariguíes, in the East Andes of Colombia, which area has recently been declared a national park (Donegan *et al.* 2007), the Reserva Florestal Río Blanco, Manizales (Ocampo 2002), and Dusky Piha is also known from several other privately protected areas in the same country, e.g. all three Fundación ProAves reserves in dpto. Antioquia, Serranía de los Churumbelos National Park, dpto. Cauca (Salaman *et*

al. 2008, 2009), and in various government-protected areas in the Central Andes of Colombia (T. M. Donegan *in litt.* 2009). The species is more or less endemic to the North Andean Centre of endemism (Cracraft 1985).

REFERENCES Alvarez *et al.* (2007), BirdLife International (2004, 2008), Boesman (2009), Chapman (1917), Cisneros-Heredia (2009), Cracraft (1985), Cuervo *et al.* (2001), Donegan *et al.* (2007, 2009), Fjeldså and Krabbe (1990), Greeney *et al.* (2009), Hellmayr (1929b), Hilty (2003), Hilty and Brown (1986), Krabbe and Nilsson (2003), Krabbe *et al.* (2006), López-Lanús (2000), López-Lanús *et al.* (2000), Moore and Lysinger (1997), Ocampo (2002), Parker *et al.* (1982, 1985), Remsen (1984), Remsen *et al.* (1982), Renjifo (1991), Restall *et al.* (2006), Ridgely and Greenfield (2001), Ridgely and Tudor (1994, 2009), Salaman *et al.* (1999, 2008, 2009), Schulenberg *et al.* (2007), Snow (1982, 2004a), Stotz *et al.* (1996).

Dusky Piha *Lipaugus fuscocinereus.* **Fig. 1**. Adult, Guacamayos Ridge, prov. Napo, eastern Ecuador, October (*János Oláh*). **Fig. 2**. Adult, Guacamayos Ridge, prov. Napo, eastern Ecuador, October (*Leif Gabrielsen*). This is a large piha and should prove easily identified within its range, despite the lack of any striking plumage features.

CHESTNUT-CAPPED PIHA
Lipaugus weberi   Plate 19

Lipaugus weberi **Cuervo, Salaman, Donegan & Ochoa,** *Ibis* 143: 354, Reserva La Forzosa, Vereda Roble Arriba, *c.*10km southwest of Anorí, dpto. Antioquia, Colombia

The discovery of this new species of cotingid in 1999 represents one of the most intriguing in recent Neotropical ornithology. Intriguing because the species was discovered in what is now a relatively accessible (although at the time it was politically unstable), but still largely ornithologically unexplored area of Colombia, offering the possibility of still more undiscovered species many decades after the main thrust of new species documentation. The following is based principally on the main available literature sources at the time of writing (Cuervo *et al.* 2001, Cuervo and Renjifo 2002a).

IDENTIFICATION 22.0–24.8cm. Closely related and morphologically similar to Dusky Piha *L. fuscocinereus*, but it is much smaller and greyer overall, with a distinctive chestnut-brown crown, yellow orbital ring and very different vocalisations. Note, however, that in poor light both the crown colour and that of the orbital ring can prove difficult to discern. Confusion with the similar-sized Rufous Piha *L. unirufus* is effectively impossible due to the entirely different plumage colour, whilst the much more similar, in both plumage and size, Screaming Piha *L. vociferans* is found entirely below the new species' elevational range and east of the Andes (indeed, to date, no other congeneric has been found in sympatry with the present species). Cuervo *et al.* (2001) recorded that Chestnut-capped Piha appears to have the propensity to perch more horizontally than some other *Lipaugus*, which typically perch very upright.

DISTRIBUTION Endemic to Colombia, where it is highly localised, being restricted to the northern slope of the Cordillera Central, in dpto. Antioquia, where the species is known from 16 discrete localities east of the Nechí Valley in the municipalities of Amalfi and Anorí, principally in the latter (Cuervo *et al.* 2001, 2008b; *Cotinga* 19: 10). Chestnut-capped Piha is also confined to the North Andean Centre of endemism and the Central Andes Endemic Bird Area, respectively (Cracraft 1985, Stattersfield *et al.* 1998).

MOVEMENTS None recorded.

HABITAT Chestnut-capped Piha is restricted to a narrow belt of ultra-humid premontane 'cloud forest', at 1,500–1,820m, although it is suspected to range as low as 1,200m and perhaps higher, to 2,000m by Cuervo *et al.* (2001) and Cuervo and Renjifo (2002a), wherein detailed habitat descriptions are presented. The species favours pristine forest and its borders, but tolerates some selective logging, although Chestnut-capped Piha is apparently much less common in more fragmented areas.

DESCRIPTION The sexes are similar, but males probably average marginally larger (as in Dusky Piha). This is a relatively small *Lipaugus*, albeit with a conspicuously long and forked tail, whilst pp6–7 are modified, in the male alone, the barbs over the entire length of the outer webs being non-interlocking, elongated and somewhat stiffened. The rather deep- and broad-based bill has a well-arched culmen and a prominently hooked tip (see photographs in Cuervo *et al.* 2001; *Cotinga* 18: 6; *Neotropical Birding* 1: 36). Chestnut-capped Piha has short rictal bristles but relatively obvious nostrils. *Adult.* – Lead or dark grey above, with an obvious chestnut-brown, or rusty, crown to upper nape patch, with slightly paler (grey to olivaceous) fringes to the feathers of many of the upperparts, and a dark greyish-brown tail. The wing-coverts are dark grey with slightly paler tips and fringes, and the remiges are dark brownish-grey with cinnamon-brown fringes to the tertials and secondaries. Paler on the underparts, especially on the throat, but becoming slightly darker on the breast and belly (some feathers possess olivaceous-brown fringes), with a pale cinnamon-brown vent and undertail-coverts. With wear, many of these fringes are lost, and the plumage becomes even more uniform in appearance. The underwing is pale silver-grey. *Immature.* – Undescribed, but there is apparently no distinctive plumage intermediate between that of the adult and juvenile (T. M. Donegan *in litt.* 2009). *Juvenile.* – Described (by Cuervo *et al.* 2001) as differing from the adult in having a less obvious rusty crown patch, lacking the primary-feather modifications, and having brighter and broader rufous fringes to the tertials and secondaries. *Moult.* – The only published moult data come from Cuervo *et al.* (2001) who recorded that a female collected in late August was undertaking a full body, wing and tail moult; the adult male holotype, also collected in late August, had apparently recently completed its moult, thereby suggesting that feather renewal commences earlier in males than females, as is typical of many cotingas (as females are presumably solely responsible for tending the nest and young). One bird trapped in April showed heavy abrasion to many of the upperparts feathers (see photograph in *Neotropical Birding* 1: 36), and another trapped in mid August was in active moult of both the body and flight feathers (A. Tovar/ ProAves unpubl. data). *Bare parts.* – Irides dark brown (dark brownish-grey in the juvenile) with a bright yellow but rather narrow orbital ring, the legs and feet are dark grey with yellow soles, and the bill is blackish.

MEASUREMENTS (from Cuervo *et al.* 2001/A. Tovar and C. Olaciregui/ProAves unpubl. data: Central Andes of Colombia) Sexes/ages combined: wing (*n* = 7) 123–131mm; tail (*n* = 5) 102–110mm; bill (*n* = 5) 20.0–22.9mm; tarsus (*n* = 5) 20.0–23.5mm. Weight (sexes combined): 69.4–72.2g (Cuervo *et al.* 2001; A. Tovar/ProAves unpubl. data).

GEOGRAPHICAL VARIATION Monotypic.

VOICE Recordings were presented on the recent compilation of Alvarez *et al.* (2007), on which the following, along with the description in Cuervo *et al.* (2001), is entirely based. Several recordings are also available online at www.xeno-canto.org. Songs are given throughout the day and year-round, albeit as in most pihas somewhat sporadically, and consist of a loud piercing *screek* audible over 100m distance. Each song bout commences with a brief slightly rising introductory note. The main phrase is a brief rising scream that abruptly descends, repeated at one-second intervals, except when the bird is agitated, when the interval is reduced to 0.36 seconds. Compared with the somewhat similar primary vocalisation of Dusky Piha, the present species' song terminates more abruptly and is usually of shorter duration. Three other calls have been documented. Non-singing birds have uttered a 'low-pitched, relatively quiet nasal *gluck-gluck*, apparently a contact or alarm call' (Cuervo *et al.* 2001). A probable contact call *cu-whee* or *chew-wit* was also heard and 'on landing at a perch, a distinctive, nasal chirpy call of short duration' was sometimes uttered (Cuervo *et al.* 2001). Perhaps only when particularly excited or agitated males produce a mechanical wing-whirring sound in flight, considered to be reminiscent of that produced in flight by Sickle-winged Guan *Chamaepetes goudotii* and also to the corresponding display of Dusky Piha. Cuervo *et al.* (2001) considered that, compared with the latter, the wing-whirring of *L. weberi* is less strident, perhaps due to the fewer wingbeats but at a more rapid rate of movement, the smaller number of modified primaries and the species' overall smaller size. Chestnut-capped Piha sings in flight during such displays. The species responds strongly to playback or imitations of the male advertisement (song).

NATURAL HISTORY Conspicuous by voice in the remaining forest fragments in the region, the Chestnut-capped Piha has yet to be recorded in secondary forest, although it will cross smaller gaps between forested areas. Typically sluggish and generally inactive, this piha is usually found alone, perched in the midstorey to lower canopy, and occasionally flicking the tail upwards and raising the crown-feathers (apparently when agitated).

FOOD AND FEEDING *L. weberi* occasionally joins mixed-species foraging flocks in the upper strata of its forest haunts, albeit perhaps usually only for the relatively short period in which the birds pass through the piha's territory, and the species equally infrequently takes large invertebrates. The diet, as described by Cuervo *et al.* (2001), principally comprises small to medium-sized fruits of the following families: Myrsinaceae, Euphorbiaceae, Caprifoliaceae, Linnaceae, Lauraceae, Aquifoliaceae and Melastomataceae. Food is taken in a short sally and hover-glean typical of the genus, or, less commonly, from a perched position. Fruits may sometimes be removed from the pedicel by an acrobatic pirouetting movement, and larger fruits may be bashed against a perch prior to consumption.

DISPLAY Lekking behaviour is poorly known to date, but a possible lek involving three individuals (two chasing one another) was observed in July, and might closely mirror that of Dusky Piha.

BREEDING Nesting biology is undescribed, but the female paratype, taken in late August, was considered to have probably recently bred, whilst the other paratype, a juvenile, collected in early June, was considered, based on skull ossification, to be 'several months' old (Cuervo *et al.* 2001, Cuervo and Renjifo 2002a). In March 2000, the species was found mainly in pairs and vocalising frequently (Cuervo and Renjifo 2002a) suggesting that the breeding season was about to commence. Another juvenile (precise age unknown) was recently trapped in early December (www.proaves.org).

STATUS Treated as Endangered at the global level (BirdLife International 2004, 2008), but Critically Endangered in the Colombian Red Data list (Cuervo and Renjifo 2002a). Chestnut-capped Piha is relatively common within its small range, although the Cordillera Central is heavily deforested and the remaining forest is severely fragmented, due to palm extraction, erosion, mining, clearance for coffee, etc., thereby rendering the new species of particular conservation concern (Cuervo and Renjifo 2002a). Cuervo *et al.* (2001) estimated that just 130km^2 of forest might remain to it, within the species' known altitudinal and geographical range, and speculated that this piha had probably been extirpated from much of its range prior to discovery. The population is postulated to number fewer than 2,500 individuals (BirdLife International 2004), with the largest numbers at sites within the municipality of Anorí (Cuervo and Renjifo 2002a); and the latter authors alarmingly considered that the entire population might not be just one-tenth of that estimated by BirdLife. Chestnut-capped Piha has been found in the Reserva Municipal La Serrana (07°05'N, 75°07'W), although it is unclear whether this locality can be effectively protected. In addition, the type locality, La Forzosa (06°59'N, 75°08'W), had already been declared a reserve (of 450ha) by the local landowner before the discovery of the piha, and is important for its populations of several other threatened birds, e.g. Black Tinamou *Tinamus osgoodi*, Parker's Antbird *Cercomacra parkeri*, Red-bellied Grackle *Hypopyrrhus pyrohypogaster*, Purplish-mantled Tanager *Iridosornis porphyrocephala*, Multicoloured Tanager *Chlorochrysa nitidissima* and Black-and-gold Tanager *Bangsia melanochlamys*. Another recently declared protected area, Reserva Arrierito Antioqueño, also harbours the piha (Salaman *et al.* 2008).

REFERENCES Alvarez *et al.* (2007), Boyla and Estrada (2005), Cuervo and Renjifo (2002a), Cuervo *et al.* (2001, 2008b), BirdLife International (2004, 2008), Cracraft (1985), Restall *et al.* (2006), Ridgely and Tudor (2009), Salaman *et al.* (2008), Stattersfield *et al.* (1998).

Chestnut-capped Piha *Lipaugus weberi*. **Fig. 1**. Male, Bodega Vieja, Amalfi, dpto. Antioquia, Central Andes, Colombia, April (*Diego Calderón-Franco / Colombia Birding*). The chestnut crown patch is just visible in this photograph. **Fig. 2**. Sex unknown, Arrierito Antioqueño Bird Reserve, Anorí, dpto. Antioquia, Central Andes, Colombia, April (*Fundación ProAves / www.proaves.org*). Note the narrow but clear yellow orbital ring. At this angle, the crown colour is not visible. Confined to a small area of the Colombian Central Andes, this piha was the most recent species of cotinga to be described, in the final years of the 20th century.

SCREAMING PIHA
Lipaugus vociferans   Plate 19

Muscicapa vociferans **Wied, 1820**, *Reise Brasilien* 1: 242 (replacement name for *Ampelis cinerea* Vieillot, 1817), Fazenda Pindoba, north of Caravellas [= Caravelas], Bahia, Brazil [cf. Gyldenstolpe (1951)]

Although this drab cotinga is unquestionably one of the least eye-catching of this spectacular family, its call when heard during a frantic period of lekking is one of the most memorable sounds of the Amazonian forests. Formerly known as *Lipaugus cineraceus* (Vieillot, 1817), Snow (1979) postulated that the Screaming Piha might prove to be conspecific with Rufous Piha *L. unirufus*, but he subsequently suggested that it might be rather more closely related to the genus *Tijuca* (especially Black-and-gold Cotinga *T. atra*) than might ostensibly appear likely (Snow 1980, 2004a). Molecular work has recently provided some support for the latter relationship (see Systematics, p. 43).

IDENTIFICATION 24–28cm; the female averages very fractionally longer in total length (Brooks *et al.* 1999). When located by its distinctive calls this species will present no identification problems, although the rather nondescript plumage may otherwise lead to confusion with the almost equally uniform Greyish Mourner *Rhytipterna simplex*. A member of the Tyrannidae whose range mirrors that of the Screaming Piha almost exactly, the Greyish Mourner is sometimes illustrated as being virtually identical to Screaming Piha. The mourner is however smaller (20cm) and slimmer, and has a very different song. Furthermore, its plumage shows a strong hint of olive below, especially if viewed in good light, and the mourner has an obvious reddish iris, which is easy to see. The slight risk of confusion with the Brazilian endemic Cinnamon-vented Piha *L. lanioides* is covered under the latter species; these two species overlap, both altitudinally and geographically, at a very small number of localities in the north of the range of *L. lanioides* (Silveira *et al.* 2005).

DISTRIBUTION Very much a bird of extreme lowland rainforest in the Orinoco and Amazon drainages, throughout

the Guianas, southern and eastern Venezuela (eastern dptos. Sucre, Delta Amacuro, Amazonas and Bolívar), eastern Colombia (north to dptos. Meta and Guainía, and west to the east slope of the Andes), throughout the lowlands and foothills of eastern Ecuador and eastern Peru, northern Bolivia (as far south as dptos. La Paz, Cochabamba and northern Santa Cruz) and across Amazonian Brazil, as far south as southern Mato Grosso, and northern Tocantins, and as far east as northern Maranhão (Hilty and Brown 1986, Ridgely and Tudor 1994, 2009, Hidasi 1997, Sick 1997, Hilty 2003, Restall *et al.* 2006, Snow 2004a). Note that reference to Goiás in Ridgely and Tudor (1994) concerns occurrence in Tocantins, and that the species has yet to be recorded in the former state (Hidasi 2007). There is a separate population in the Atlantic Forest biome of coastal Brazil, from Pernambuco south to central Espírito Santo (Sick 1997). Screaming Piha is recorded to 1,150m in the foothills of the Andes in eastern Peru (Schulenberg *et al.* 2007) and to 1,400m on the slopes of the tepuis in southern Venezuela (Hilty 2003), but is principally found below 500m.

MOVEMENTS None recorded.

HABITAT Screaming Piha inhabits the understorey to canopy of intact humid lowland forest, rarely at edges, but including flooded *igapó* and *várzea* forests, at least locally. It is also found in sandy-soil stunted forests known as *campinaranas*, at least in Brazil, and occurs in both primary and secondary forests. The species is primarily found in the midstorey.

DESCRIPTION The sexes are alike. Screaming Piha is a somewhat thrush-like cotinga with a short primary projection producing a rounded wing shape. *Adult.* – The plumage is generally grey with a browner or duskier cast to the remiges, greater coverts and rectrices, whilst the underparts are paler than the upperparts, and palest on the throat and, to a lesser extent, on the belly. Underwing and undertail grey. *Juvenile.* – Described (by J. P. O'Neill *in* Cuervo *et al.* 2001) as differing from the adult in having rusty fringes and tips to the wing- and tail-feathers, to the extent that it may even show a rufous band in the primaries. (However, this description does appear somewhat questionable and demands confirmation: T. M. Donegan *in litt.* 2009.) In immature specimens the tertials, outer webs to the primaries and the tips of the rectrices also appear warmer and paler brown than those of adults (RMNH). Following the first complete moult full adult plumage is acquired (Snow 1982, 2004a). *Moult.* – Males moult 2–3 months earlier than females (Snow 1982), and the latter author discovered little evidence for seasonality in moult (and thus breeding) in the centre of the species' range (as is typical of many cotingas at the most equatorial latitudes). *Bare parts.* – Irides black-brown to greyish-brown, the bill is dark brown to black-brown, often with a paler base to the lower mandible, and the legs are dark brown to dark grey or greenish-grey (Snethlage 1908b, Snow 2004b; FMNH; MNRJ).

MEASUREMENTS (BMNH; MNRJ: Bolivia; Brazil, in Amapá, Amazonas, Bahia, Espírito Santo, Mato Grosso, Pará and Pernambuco; Colombia; Ecuador; French Guiana; Peru and Surinam; see also Hellmayr 1929a, Cuervo *et al.* 2001). Wing of male (*n* = 14) 116.0–129.5mm, wing of female (*n* = 13) 115–124mm; tail of male (*n* = 14) 104–114mm, tail of female (*n* = 13) 101–115mm; bill of male (*n* = 14) 22.53–24.69mm, bill of female (*n* = 13) 22.72–28.03mm; tarsus of male (*n* = 5) 20–23mm, tarsus of female (*n* = 5)

18–23mm. For additional mensural data from across the species' western Amazon range, and the Atlantic Forest (Bahia), see Gyldenstolpe (1945, 1951). Wing-chord and tail-length values are almost identical between the sexes, but males average longer in wing values (Brooks *et al.* 1999). Weight (sexes combined): 60.0–94.5g (Haverschmidt 1952, Fry 1970, Dick *et al.* 1984, Bates *et al.* 1989, Graves and Zusi 1990, Silva *et al.* 1990, Willard *et al.* 1991, Brooks *et al.* 1999, Hilty 2003, Snow 2004a, Dunning 2008; FMNH; INPA; MVZ; RMNH). Brooks *et al.* (1999) found that female mass is very fractionally greater than that of males. Note that there is, to some extent, a cline in increasing overall size (and weight) from the north to the southwest of the range; thus birds in Bolivia and Peru are larger and heavier than those in the Guianas (see Gyldenstolpe 1945, Snow 1982, 2004a). However, Gyldenstolpe (1945) also pointed to significant individual variation in wing- and tail-lengths over much of the species' range.

GEOGRAPHICAL VARIATION Screaming Piha has two widely separated populations: in the lowlands of Amazonia and the Atlantic Forest of eastern Brazil. Although isolated, the birds in eastern Brazil are not subspecifically differentiated from the Amazonian population. This suggests that the separation of the two populations is recent. In the extreme south of the range (Peru and Bolivia), the birds are larger than those occurring further north and east in the lowlands of Amazonia and the Guianas. Todd (1950, following Bangs and Penard 1918 *in* Gyldenstolpe 1945) suggested that Bolivian birds deserve subspecific status (*L. v. dispar*) on the basis of the wing- (136–141mm) and tail-lengths (115–118mm) of three males. He pointed to the fact that Hellmayr (1929b) had noted that birds from the Bolivian Yungas are generally larger than other populations, yet had argued for maintaining the species as monotypic. Todd (1950) further considered that Gyldenstolpe's (1945) findings supported his own, but the latter had also found that birds from Beni, Bolivia, do not differ in size from those in Brazil, thereby belying the proposal that all birds from the former country could be differentiated from other populations (cf. also Pinto 1966, who like Gyldenstolpe 1945, 1951, also rejected the need to recognise any subspecies).

VOICE Published recordings exist on the following compilations: English and Parker (1992), Moore (1993, 1996), Boesman (1999, 2006a, 2006b, 2009), Mayer (2000), Schulenberg *et al.* (2000), Krabbe and Nilsson (2003), Marantz and Zimmer (2006), Naka *et al.* (2008), Renaudier and Deroussen (2008) and Minns *et al.* (2009). There are also a great many recordings archived online at www.xeno-canto.org (including from Bolivia, Brazil, Ecuador, French Guiana, Guyana, Peru, Surinam and Venezuela). One of the most easily recognised animal sounds of the lowland rainforest within the species' range, and Screaming Piha has recently been discovered to be one of the loudest birds in the world (Nemeth 2004). At least locally in Brazilian Amazonia, it is known as the 'mother of thunder' (Novaes 1976). Response to playback can be marked and rapid in lone singing birds, but not when other members of a lek are also vocalising. Males are very vocal, and indeed are often one of the few birds to vocalise throughout the day, with comparatively little temporal (but much individual) variation; the piercing, loud *pee pee POO* once heard is never forgotten. This most audible part of the song has three components: an ascending frequency-modulated

portion, a descending frequency-modulated portion and an unmodulated terminus (Fitzsimmons *et al.* 2008). The head is jerked sharply upwards and backwards during each call. This main call is preceded by 1–4 (usually two in southeast Peru) guttural, quiet *grah* or *groo* calls, which are usually but not always much more difficult to hear. Periodically the birds also give loud, whistled *wee-oo* calls. A recent study, by Fitzsimmons *et al.* (2008), set out to investigate individual variation in Screaming Piha songs, based on an examination of recordings made of 26 males at four leks along the Río Tambopata in southeast Peru. Spectrogram cross-correlation revealed significant consistency within individual males but much variability between different males. The authors' analysis of fine structural characteristics revealed that all measured song features were significantly less variable within individuals than amongst different birds, and a discriminant analysis based on these 13 song features correctly classified 93.2% of songs by individual and 76.4% of songs by lek site. The results of this fascinating study indicate that there is sufficient consistency in song features within males and sufficient variation amongst males to identify individuals by their songs and to a lesser extent that song features vary with the lek site of the singer. Fitzsimmons *et al.* (2008) concluded that this piha's songs are individually distinctive and bear a lek signature. Their results have provided yet further recent evidence of more complex patterns of song development (including the possibility of contextual learning) amongst at least some suboscine birds than is often thought to be the case (see also Three-wattled Bellbird *Procnias tricarunculatus*).

NATURAL HISTORY Sluggish and sedentary; males gather at relatively long-standing, traditional lek sites wherein the birds perch 5–10m up on exposed branches, and generally in loose association, with movements towards tighter leks perhaps signalling the arrival of a female(s) (Brooks *et al.* 1999). Usually each bird maintains a distance of 40–60m from its neighbours, with up to 25 (or more) individuals attending each lek, but more usually 4–10. Each male routinely sings from the same few perches, all located in the same small areas (Fitzsimmons *et al.* 2008). Lek sites can be sited close to good food sources.

FOOD AND FEEDING Occasionally, away from a lek site, individual birds (or small groups) are observed at fruiting trees, where they will perch bolt upright and sally for fruits (e.g. *Virola melinonii* and *V. surinamensis*, Myristicaceae). Joins other fruit-eating birds on such occasions, and also sometimes accompanies mixed-species foraging flocks in the midstorey (Jullien and Thiollay 1998). Screaming Piha appears to focus seasonally on either fruit or insect prey, as evidenced by stomach contents, which are usually either one or the other, but not both. Fruit diet is not well described, but Tello (2003) found the species to be one of the two most regular avian visitors to a fruiting *Ficus pertusa* (Moraceae) tree in southeast Peru. The species has been observed with tanagers, caciques, oropendolas and Spangled *Cotinga cayana* and Pompadour Cotingas *Xipholena punicea* at a fruiting *Goupia* (Celastraceae) tree in Guyana (GMK and W. Prince pers. obs.). Occasionally observed apparently following army ant swarms, but not actually seen to take any potential prey that might have been disturbed by the ants (Willis 1983). A Screaming Piha has been observed to take a small (5–6cm) lizard *Anolis* sp., which was hit repeatedly against a branch until it was dead prior to consuming it (Whittaker 1996b).

BREEDING Nesting behaviour is still remarkably poorly known for such a widespread and common species. Oniki and Willis (1982, and *in* Sick 1997) describe and depict the nest as being a very untidy and relatively small collection (for the size of the bird) of thin twigs or tendrils placed between two dry parallel branches, 7m above the ground in a sapling (i.e. similar to other pihas, although perhaps less bulky and solid-looking than the recently described nest of Dusky Piha *L. fuscocinereus*), based on observations at the Reserva Florestal Adolpho Ducke, Amazonas, Brazil, in September. Buzzetti and Silva (2005) photographed a nest with an egg in the Serra do Cachimbo, Pará, constructed of tendrils placed on an angled branch. Further details are unknown. Sick (1993, 1997) also mentioned discovering a nest 7m above the ground, at the Rio Cururu, in southwest Pará; it was constructed of corkscrew vine and placed in the fork of a dead branch. Sick considered it to be comparatively large for a cotinga, indicating that it might have been comparable with that of the Dusky Piha. Érard (1982) found a similarly positioned nest, 8m above the ground, in French Guiana in December. It too was an untidy assemblage of sticks, recalling a weak pigeon-like nest to the observer, and the single egg was laid on 23 December and was incubated for 24 days. The female spent periods of 30 minutes to two hours away from the nest during the incubation period, and the egg was cream to pale ochre in colour with irregular brown to brown-grey markings; the egg photographed by Buzzetti and Silva (2005) was similar. Moult data suggest that the species might breed practically year-round (and leks are rarely silent!) over much of Amazonia, but in the Atlantic Forest at least breeding is likely to be strongly seasonal, and match that of most bird species in this region, i.e. to be principally during the austral spring, although there are no direct data to support this assumption to date. Other direct evidence of breeding behaviour is as follows. MVZ has a male from eastern Peru that was in breeding condition in late July, and in northernmost Pará, and in Amapá, Brazil, males were collected in breeding condition in September (Novaes 1980a) and May (Novaes 1978), respectively. Robbins *et al.* (2007) considered that the species breeds in August/September along the upper Essequibo River in Guyana. In French Guiana, three males collected in January and February were in breeding condition (Dick *et al.* 1984), and three nests have been found in the same country as follows: two at the incubation stage in early December (12m above the ground; Tostain *et al.* 1992) and at the end of the same month (Érard 1982; see above), and the other being constructed, by the female, at the start of October (Tostain *et al.* 1992). F. Haverschmidt collected juveniles in late June and mid July in Surinam (RMNH).

STATUS Screaming Piha is one of the few common cotingas, the species being widespread and ubiquitous in its range, and it is therefore unsurprisingly treated as of Least Concern (BirdLife International 2004, 2008). In suitable habitat in southeast Peru, Terborgh *et al.* (1990) estimated mean densities for this species to be *c.*20 individuals per 100ha, whilst at a similarly sized plot in French Guiana, Thiollay (1994) estimated the density to be 22 individuals. It is known from numerous protected areas throughout the species' range and from all range states. Screaming Piha also may be better able to persist in relatively small areas of forest in close proximity to urban areas than many cotingids (Tostain *et al.* 1992, Vasconcelos *et al.* 2007) as well as in selectively logged forest (Salaman *et al.* 1999). Nonetheless, at the strictly regional level, the species may be considered under threat and, for instance, Screaming Piha is listed as Endangered in the Red Data book for the Brazilian state of Espírito Santo (Passamani and Mendes 2007). Indeed, it is generally not especially common within the Atlantic Forest region, where some of its strongholds are the Sooretama Biological Reserve and Linhares (Vale) reserve complex in Espírito Santo, as well as Una Biological Reserve and Monte Pascoal National Park in Bahia.

REFERENCES Aguilar *et al.* (2000), Aleixo and Guilherme (2010), Almeida *et al.* (2003), Barnett *et al.* (2002), Bates *et al.* (1989), Bernard (2008), BirdLife International (2004, 2008), Blake (1950), Boesman (1999, 2006a, 2006b, 2009), Borges (2007), Borges *et al.* (2001), Braun *et al.* (2007), Brooks *et al.* (1999, 2009), Buzzetti and Silva (2005), Cadena *et al.* (2000), Claessens (1997), Cohn-Haft *et al.* (1997), Cuervo *et al.* (2001), Dantas *et al.* (2010), Dick *et al.* (1984), Dunning (2008), English and Parker (1992), Érard (1982), Fitzsimmons *et al.* (2008), Freitas *et al.* (2004), Fry (1970), Gilliard (1941), González (1998), Graves and Zusi (1990), Guilherme and Santos (2009), Gyldenstolpe (1945, 1951), Haverschmidt (1952), Hellmayr (1929a, 1929b), Hennessey *et al.* (2003a, 2003b), Hidasi (1998, 2007), Hilty (2003), Hilty and Brown (1986), Hornbuckle (1999), Hosner *et al.* (2009), Jullien and Thiollay (1998), Krabbe and Nilsson (2003), Lane *et al.* (2003), Lees *et al.* (2008), Maillard *et al.* (2007), Marantz and Zimmer (2006), Mayer (2000), Mee *et al.* (2002), Merkord *et al.* (2009), Mestre *et al.* (2005, 2010), Minns *et al.* (2009), Moore (1993, 1996), Naka *et al.* (2006, 2008), Nemeth (2004), Novaes (1960, 1976, 1978, 1980a), Olson (1971), Oniki and Willis (1982), Oren and Parker (1997), Ottema *et al.* (2009), Pacheco and Olmos (2005), Pacheco *et al.* (2007), Parker and Goerck (1997), Parker and Wust (1994), Parker *et al.* (1994a, 1994b, 1994c), Passamani and Mendes (2007), Peres and Whittaker (1991), Pinheiro and Dornas (2009a), Pinto (1944, 1966), Renaudier and Deroussen (2008), Restall *et al.* (2006), Ridgely and Greenfield (2001), Ridgely and Tudor (1994, 2009), Robbins *et al.* (2004, 2007), Robinson and Terborgh (1997), Salaman *et al.* (1999, 2008), Schulenberg *et al.* (2000, 2006, 2007), Sick (1993, 1997), Silva (1996), Silva *et al.* (1990), Silveira *et al.* (2003a, 2005), Simon (2009), Snethlage (1907, 1908a, 1908b, 1914), Snow, B. K. (1961), Snow (1979, 1982, 2004a), Snyder (1966), Souza *et al.* (2008), Stotz *et al.* (1996), Tello (2003), Terborgh *et al.* (1990), Thiollay (1994), Todd (1950), Tostain *et al.* (1992), Trolle and Walther (2004), Vasconcelos *et al.* (2007), Vidoz *et al.* (2010), Whittaker (1996b), Willard *et al.* (1991), Willis (1983), Willis and Oniki (1990), J. T. Zimmer (1930), Zimmer and Hilty (1997), Zimmer *et al.* (1997).

Screaming Piha *Lipaugus vociferans*. **Figs. 1–2**. Anavilhanas Jungle Lodge, Amazonas, central Amazonian Brazil, December (*Hadoram Shirihai / Photographic Handbook to Birds of the World*). **Fig. 3**. ZF2 tower, north of Manaus, Amazonas, northern Amazonian Brazil, September (*Hadoram Shirihai / Photographic Handbook to Birds of the World*). This bird was a surprise in the canopy of tall forest. **Fig. 4**. Kourou, coastal French Guiana, February (*Maxime Dechelle*). One of the morphologically 'blandest' birds in the world has the unusual distinction of being probably the loudest vocally; here at 'full throttle'!

RUFOUS PIHA
Lipaugus unirufus   **Plate 20**

Lipaugus unirufus **P. L. Sclater, 1859**, *Proc. Zool. Soc. Lond.* 27: 385, [Playa Vicente,] Oaxaca, Mexico, and Coban, Vera Paz, Guatemala [= Playa Vicente, Veracruz]

The only truly 'trans-Andean' piha, the nesting habits of the Rufous Piha are relatively well known through Dr Alexander Skutch's studies in Costa Rica. This species was suggested to form a superspecies with the previous taxon (Snow 1979a), but there are no molecular data available as yet to confirm or deny this hypothesis, although several other *Lipaugus* have been sampled genetically.

IDENTIFICATION 22.0–26.5cm. A generally all-cinnamon cotinga that is easily confused with the tyrant flycatcher Rufous Mourner *Rhytipterna holerythra*; the latter, however, is smaller (20cm), with a flatter-shaped head and a slimmer bill (Figs. 3–4), whilst the piha also tends to have a paler throat and a darker crown compared with the mourner. Also smaller, the Speckled Mourner *Laniocera rufescens* (of Guatemala to northwest Ecuador) possesses rufous spotting on the otherwise dusky wings and, although it can be hard to see in the field, also shows fine greyish scaling or barring on the breast. The *Laniocera* also lacks the pale eye-ring of the piha and has yellow or orangey pectoral tufts on the wing-bend (although these are usually concealed). All three species are, however, more easily separated by voice. Angehr and Dean (2010) also discuss the possibility of confusion with the very differently shaped and smaller Russet Antshrike *Thamnistes anabatinus*, but the latter has an obvious contrast between the colour of the upper and underparts, as well as a striking supercilium, and strikingly different behaviour.

DISTRIBUTION Widespread over northern Latin America. Rufous Piha ranges in Middle America from southeastern Mexico (in southern Veracruz, northern Oaxaca and northern Chiapas), thence south along the Caribbean slope of Belize, Honduras, Nicaragua, Costa Rica (where also found on the Pacific slope in the southwest of the country) and Panama (where it occurs from western Chiriquí east

to Darién, except on the Azuero Peninsula, and on the Caribbean slope from Bocas del Toro, where rare, to northern Coclé and, in the Canal Zone, from the lower Chagras Valley to San Blas) (Monroe 1968, Wetmore 1972, Ridgely and Gwynne 1976, Stiles and Skutch 1989, Howell and Webb 1995, Jones 2004, Eisenmann and Avendaño 2007, Angehr and Dean 2010). In South America, Rufous Piha is found in north and west Colombia, through the remaining forests in the humid Caribbean lowlands east to the Río Magdalena Valley in Santander, and through the Pacific lowlands, with an isolated population in the Serranía de Macuira on the Guajira Peninsula, to Ecuador, where it is nowadays restricted to the extreme northwest, in Esmeraldas, but it formerly occurred south to northern Manabí and western Pichincha (where its habitat is now virtually entirely destroyed) (Hilty and Brown 1986, Ridgely and Greenfield 2001, Restall *et al.* 2006, Ridgely and Tudor 2009).

MOVEMENTS None known.

HABITAT The species is primarily found in lower and mid levels of humid upper tropical and lower subtropical forests, from the lowlands to 700m, and more locally to 1,200m (e.g. on the Cerro Pirre, in southwestern Panama, and in southern Costa Rica). Mainly found in the subcanopy and canopy, but the species also visits clearings with scattered trees, and is even found at the edge of mangroves in southwest Costa Rica (GMK pers. obs.).

DESCRIPTION The sexes are alike. The bill has a slightly arched culmen and a hooked tip. *Adult.* – Rather thrush (*Turdus*)-like and saturated cinnamon overall, with the underparts slightly paler than the upperparts, and further relief is provided by the slightly paler throat, belly and undertail-coverts, whilst the darkest cinnamon is on the crown (albeit with pale shaft-streaks). There is a tuft of feathers close to the bill base (Jones 2004). Becomes duller over the mantle and the scapulars to rump, with marginally brighter uppertail-coverts, dusky-brown wing-coverts (although the outer webs to the feathers are more rufous-brown), and a rufous-brown uppertail; the underside of the tail is cinnamon-brown. The underwing-coverts and axillaries are pale rufous, and there is a bushy tuft of pale feathers either side of the abdomen (Wetmore 1972). *Juvenile.* – Unknown, but the nestling was briefly described by Skutch (1969; see also Natural History). *Moult.* – There are few published moult data (Tashian 1952 mentioned that one he collected in Mexico in August was moulting the primaries, rectrices and head-feathers); neither one of two collected in northwest Ecuador in February and July appeared to be replacing any feathers, but Snow (1982) reported that in Costa Rica and Nicaragua feather renewal commences in February–May (males) or in April–August (females), suggesting that moult runs to some extent concurrently with nesting (see Breeding), at least in males. Females, on the other hand, may complete the breeding cycle before commencing their moult (which lasts *c.*150 days: Snow 1976a). Further south, the pattern of well-defined seasonality to moult behaviour is maintained (and thus also in nesting), but becomes progressively earlier, i.e. starting in November–March (males) and February–August (females) in western Colombia and Ecuador (Snow 1982). *Bare parts.* – Irides brown to dark brown, or olive-grey, with a dull greenish-yellow orbital ring; the legs and feet are horn brown, dark grey or dull greenish-grey, with dark grey soles; and the bill is fuscous-brown to grey-brown or blackish,

with a slightly paler (even pinkish or pale flesh) base to the lower mandible, and sometimes with a marginally paler tip to the maxilla.

MEASUREMENTS (from Wetmore 1972; BMNH; MECN: Belize, Colombia, Costa Rica, Ecuador, Guatemala, Honduras, Nicaragua and Panama; see also Hellmayr 1911, Monroe 1968, Cuervo *et al.* 2001) Races combined: wing of male (*n* = 17) 124–139mm, wing of female (*n* = 17) 125–137mm; tail of male (*n* = 17) 95.6–106.0mm, tail of female (*n* = 17) 93.8–117.0mm; bill of male (*n* = 17) 21.4–25.2mm, bill of female (*n* = 16) 22.3–27.0mm; tarsus of male (*n* = 15) 20–23mm, tarsus of female (*n* = 17) 20.4–25.0mm. Weight (sexes combined): 69–96g (once 39.8g) (FMNH; MECN; MNCR; Tashian 1952, Snow 1982, Robbins *et al.* 1985, Binford 1989, Stiles and Skutch 1989, Dunning 2008; J. C. Luna/ProAves unpubl. data).

GEOGRAPHICAL VARIATION Polytypic, with two subspecies generally recognised. *L. u. unirufus* occurs throughout the species' range, except in the Chocó region of extreme southwest Colombia and northwest Ecuador, where it is replaced by *L. u. castaneotinctus* (E. Hartert, 1902). In the latter race the upperparts contrast more with the underparts because the mantle is concolorous with the dark cinnamon crown. Colour variation is apparently clinal along the Pacific coast region and the limits of the two subspecies are somewhat arbitrary. Indeed, size is also seemingly clinal (Monroe 1968), the birds being larger in the extreme north of the species' Middle American range but smaller from central Honduras south. This led Monroe (1968) to claim that *L. u. castaneotinctus* occurs as far north as southeastern Honduras, and to restrict the name *L. u. unirufus* to those populations further north. A third race, *L. u. clarus*, was described by Robert Ridgway, from eastern Panama but this name, which has fallen into synonymy since Hellmayr (1929b), effectively represents the midpoint in a cline (see also Peters 1929). We would suggest that future workers, with a larger series of specimens available than we have examined, might examine the question as to whether any geographical variation in this species merits nomenclatural recognition.

VOICE Commercial recordings are available on the following commercial compilations: Delaney (1992), Moore (1992), Ross and Whitney (1995), Ross (2000), Jahn *et al.* (2002), Krabbe and Nilsson (2003) and Knapp and Will (2008), whilst recordings from Belize, Ecuador, Nicaragua and Panama are archived online at www.xeno-canto.org. Loud, very musical and explosive, but the species is easily overlooked when not singing (song bouts are irregular). Song is a whistled *p-wee-e-loo!* or *whee-oo! p-wee'oo!*, which has been likened to the song of the nocturnal Pauraque *Nyctidromus albicollis* or (by Skutch 1969), when given singly, *peer*, as someone trying to attract the attention of a person some distance away. The song is often given in series. Like several other pihas, the species may suddenly call in a response to extraneous loud noises, such as a falling branch (Tashian 1952), hand-clapping (D. Bradley recording, XC3308) or even a Great Tinamou *Tinamus major* flushing (Skutch 1969). Rufous Piha can be attracted by playback or even whistled imitations. Two calls are known, a heavy metallic, rolling *chrrrg* (Stiles and Skutch 1989) and the species also gives a 'squirrel-like chattering *chuh-uh-uh-uh*' (Howell and Webb 1995) or *bdrup bdrup bdrup* (Jones 2004).

NATURAL HISTORY Two to three birds (but not, apparent-ly, pairs) are often found in close proximity, but Rufous Piha is most often observed singly, and is easily overlooked due to its typical *Lipaugus* habit of remaining quiet and still (hunched slightly forwards) for prolonged periods. At least in Panama and Colombia, the species may form scattered leks (Hilty and Brown 1986), which may remain in the same place for almost 20 years, or more (Willis and Eisenmann 1979). It occasionally joins mobile mixed-species flocks, although the extent of such behaviour and persistence of attendance are unknown (Loiselle 1988, Stiles and Skutch 1989; GMK pers. obs.).

FOOD AND FEEDING The diet consists of fruits, perhaps especially Melastomataceae (e.g. *Miconia*), palm and laurel berries, but also Burseraceae (*Protium* spp.), as well as insects (including large caterpillars) and spiders, which are seized from leaves and branches in a sudden sally and brief hover (the nestling appears to be fed the same range of prey), and at least once (on Barro Colorado Island, Panama) it has been observed attending an *Eciton burchelli* swarm taking insects disturbed by the ants (Willis 1983). Rufous Pihas very occasionally descend to the ground to seize insect prey, including even scorpions (Stiles and Skutch 1989).

BREEDING Skutch (1969) observed apparent courtship feeding in this species, which behaviour is only definitely known for two fruiteaters, Green-and-black *Pipreola riefferii* and Orange-breasted Fruiteaters *P. jucunda*, and perhaps occurs in the berryeaters (*Carpornis*). In Costa Rica, where the breeding season lasts from March to August, Skutch (1969) found five nests in March (*n* = 2), May (*n* = 2) and early August (*n* = 1), all of them placed 5–10m above the ground, on relatively small branches in undergrowth trees within secondary forest adjoining primary growth. All of the nests were the rather flat structures typical of pihas, constructed of tendrils and small twigs (see Dusky *L. fuscocinereus*, Screaming Piha and Cinnamon-vented Pihas *L. lanioides*). Another nest with a very small young was found in Costa Rica, at La Selva OTS Biological Station, in mid April 2010. It was on a *c.*8m-tall Myrtaceae tree beside a trail and *c.*5m up and *c.*30cm from the main trunk, and was constructed of tendrils and some rootlets, placed over a branch *c.*5cm in circumference with two additional, even smaller, 90° supporting branches *c.*20cm from the edge of the tree (GMK pers. obs.). Some tendrils were much longer than the main nest's dimensions. This nest was well shaded, but not closely, by leaves, including several large dead leaves of similar colour to the bird. The nest was roughly circular but very untidily constructed, *c.*10cm wide and <5cm wide, with the bird being much larger. While incubating the female remained very watchful throughout a 2.5-hour observation period, during which it made two sorties for food, one lasting 15 minutes and the second five minutes. Both times on returning it called loudly prior to finally arriving at the nest, flying directly to it from *c.*5m away. The bird perched on the nest's main supporting branch to feed the young, which gave begging calls just audible from *c.*5m away. The first time the female brought an unidentified beetle, which it gave to the young 14 times, grasping the prey afresh and crushing it in the bill between attempts; eventually she gave up and ate the beetle herself. The second time, the prey was an unidentified winged insect, which the chick managed to consume, with assistance, on the 11th attempt.

Nests are solely constructed and attended by the female, and a single egg is laid (dimensions were presented in

Skutch 1969), described as being smoky grey and heavily mottled and blotched deep brown, the markings becoming almost as dark as the ground colour at the thicker end. Incubation occupies 25–26 days and the young on hatching are covered in sparse grey down; they fledge in 28–29 days. Skutch (1969) watched a female destroy an already used nest, and on another occasion he observed a male feed a female, apparently in courtship, which behaviour amongst Cotingidae is known definitely only for *Pipreola* (Skutch 1989). Nest destruction is also apparently a behavioural trait of at least some members of the genus *Cotinga*. Breeding data from elsewhere are sparse, and Russell's (1964) report that he flushed a female from a nest with two pale brown eggs in Belize, 'in a shallow depression beside a sizeable epiphytic bromeliad in a crotch' on a large tree, seems distinctly unlikely to refer to this species (as already intimated by Snow 1982), given that this and other pihas for which breeding data are available all lay one egg. In Oaxaca, Mexico, Binford (1989) observed an adult (presumably a female) feeding a juvenile in November, and reported males with enlarged testes collected in March and May. There is another male from the same state, collected in late February, also in breeding condition (ROM). A female collected in the Central Valley of Costa Rica in the third week of May was in breeding condition (MNCR). A male collected in Ecuador in February had enlarged testes (MECN), as had a male collected in southeast Mexico in August (Tashian 1952).

STATUS Rufous Piha is treated as Least Concern (BirdLife International 2004, 2008) and the species is known from several protected areas throughout its range (see, e.g., Cooper 1997, Vallely and Whitman 1997, Salaman *et al.* 2008, 2009). The race *L. u. castaneotinctus* is endemic to the Chocó Rainforest Centre of endemism (Cracraft 1985). Uncommon to locally fairly common within its extensive range, even within the same country; for example, in Panama, it is generally rather rare on the Caribbean slope,

especially east of the Canal Zone, but west of there Rufous Piha is rather common in the Chagras Valley (Wetmore 1972). Also in Panama, the species has persisted, albeit in much smaller numbers, on Barro Colorado Island, despite isolation for at least 90 years (Robinson 1999) and nearby, in Soberania National Park, Robinson *et al.* (2000a) found a density of 0.5 pairs per 100ha. In Belize the species is commonest in the Maya Mountains (Jones 2004). Rufous Piha is generally fairly common in Costa Rica (Stiles and Skutch 1989), where protected areas known to harbour the species include La Selva OTS Biological Station, Corcovado National Park and Las Cruces Biological Station (Lawson 2010), but it is rare in Honduras (Monroe 1968). In Colombia, the species' range in the Caribbean is largely deforested and although significant suitable habitat remains in the Chocó this is also now threatened with deforestation (T. M. Donegan *in litt.* 2009).

REFERENCES Anderson *et al.* (2004), Angehr and Dean (2010), AOU (1998), Binford (1989), BirdLife International (2004, 2008), Blake and Loiselle (2001), Cooper (1997), Cracraft (1985), Cuervo *et al.* (2001), Delaney (1992), Dunning (2008), Garrigues and Dean (2007), Hartert (1898), Hellmayr (1929b), Hilty and Brown (1986), Howell and Webb (1995), Jahn *et al.* (1992), Jones (2004), Knapp and Will (2008), Krabbe and Nilsson (2003), Lawson (2010), Loiselle (1988), Monroe (1968), Moore (1992), Olson (1971), Peters (1929), Puebla-Olivares *et al.* (2002), Restall *et al.* (2006), Ridgely and Greenfield (2001), Ridgely and Gwynne (1989), Ridgely and Tudor (1994, 2009), Robbins *et al.* (1985), Robinson (1999), Robinson *et al.* (2000a), Ross (2000), Ross and Whitney (1995), Russell (1964), Salaman *et al.* (2008, 2009), Skutch (1969, 1980, 1989), Stiles and Skutch (1989), Snow (1976a, 1979a, 1982, 2004a), Stone (1928), Stotz *et al.* (1996), Tashian (1952), Vallely and Whitman (1997), Wetmore (1972), Willis (1983), Willis and Eisenmann (1979).

1

Rufous Piha *Lipaugus unirufus*. **Fig. 1**. *L. u. unirufus*, Punta Leona Forest Reserve, near Carara National Park, prov. Puntarenas, Costa Rica, April (*Steven Easley / Costa Rica Gateway*). **Fig. 2**. *L. u. unirufus*, Punta Leona Forest Reserve, near Carara National Park, prov. Puntarenas, Costa Rica, February (*Kevin Easley / Costa Rica Gateway*). Given its coloration, Rufous Piha is unlikely to be mistaken for any other piha. **Fig. 3**. Rufous Mourner *Rhytipterna holerythra*, Arenal Observatory Lodge, prov. Alajuela, Costa Rica, January (*Steven Easley / Costa Rica Gateway*). **Fig. 4**. Rufous Mourner *Rhytipterna holerythra*, Arenal Observatory Lodge, prov. Alajuela, Costa Rica, October (*Kevin Easley / Costa Rica Gateway*). Comparison photographs of the ostensibly very similar Rufous Mourner. However, the latter species is smaller, with a flatter-shaped head (less-angled rear crown) and a slimmer bill, whilst the piha also tends to have a paler throat and a darker crown compared to the mourner. Beware also the slimmer possibility of misidentifying Speckled Mourner *Laniocera rufescens*, which possesses rufous spotting on the otherwise dusky wings and also has fine greyish scaling or barring on the breast. The *Laniocera* also lacks the pale eye-ring of the piha.

CINNAMON-VENTED PIHA
Lipaugus lanioides   Plate 19

Turdampelis lanioides **R. P. Lesson, 1844**, *Écho du Monde Savant* 11(7): 156, [Rio de Janeiro,] Brazil

This species generally replaces the on average slightly smaller Screaming Piha *L. vociferans* in southeast Brazil, from Espírito Santo to Santa Catarina. In central Espírito Santo and southern Bahia, where the two species meet, Cinnamon-vented Piha occurs in foothill forests, whereas Screaming Piha inhabits the few remnants of true lowland forest. However, their altitudinal segregation is not complete and the two species have been found in complete sympatry in at least one locality in Bahia (Silveira *et al.* 2005). Thanks to the incredibly detailed observations of Edwin Willis and Yoshika Oniki at two nests of this species in Espírito Santo, our knowledge of this species' breeding biology is surprisingly unparalleled amongst the genus *Lipaugus*. These authors have speculated that the one-parent (female-only) nesting system, which appears to be that adopted by all members of the genus for which nests have been found to date, is presumably an adaptation to nesting in the midstorey and their feeding habits.

IDENTIFICATION 26.5–28.0cm. Although the two species are only very rarely found together (see above) Cinnamon-vented Piha could be confused with the marginally smaller Screaming Piha. The present species is separated from its more widespread congener by the overall more cinnamon-brown, rather than grey, plumage. As the name suggests this colour is at its brightest on the undertail-coverts. The tail is long and usually slightly fanned, displaying its ample proportions, which consequently accentuates the rather short and rounded wings.

DISTRIBUTION Cinnamon-vented Piha is endemic to Brazil in southern Bahia (e.g. at Boa Nova and Monte Pascoal National Park), Espírito Santo, and central and northeast Minas Gerais (e.g. in Rio Doce State Park, and around Teófilo Otoni) south as far as northeast Santa Catarina. Its elevational range reaches 1,400m in Minas Gerais. Cinnamon-vented Piha mainly occurs above 500m and is rarely found in the real lowlands, although it has been

recorded on at least one nearshore island, Ilha Grande, which is less than 2km offshore in Rio de Janeiro state (Alves and Vecchi 2009).

MOVEMENTS None known, but records from extreme lowland forest (down to sea level) in southern São Paulo southwards have been suspected to reflect seasonal movements.

HABITAT Cinnamon-vented Piha occurs from the understorey to the midstorey and in the subcanopy of humid Atlantic Forest, as well as more rarely in drier forest in the interior, e.g. of São Paulo state (Willis and Oniki 1998).

DESCRIPTION The sexes are similar, but females appear on average to be slightly heavier (Snow 1982). The bill is strongly arched with a prominent hook tip. P9 is highly modified, being unusually long, projecting beyond the curved outline of the spread wing, which feature may sometimes even be visible in the field. Some have p9 only marginally longer than the rest. *Adult.* – Crown is dull brown with an almost grey cast, whilst the feathers of the forehead possess pale shafts that produce a scaly effect. Mantle grey-brown becoming rich cinnamon over the rump and uppertail-coverts. Long, broad tail, which is cinnamon-brown with brighter fringes. Wings mainly brown, also with bright cinnamon fringes to the remiges, secondary-coverts and tertials (concolorous with the mantle). Throat paler than the rest of the underparts with cinnamon-white shafts to the feathers, producing a slightly streaked effect. The breast, belly and flanks are pale cinnamon-brown, and slightly paler than the upperparts, whilst the bright cinnamon undertail-coverts contrast with the dull brown undertail, but are not always easy to see or especially striking in the field. *Juvenile.* – Undescribed to date (Snow 2004a). The strange nestling, which appears to mimic a large, buffy-coloured hairy caterpillar, was described in detail by Willis and Oniki (1998); comparison with the arguably even more bizarre nestling of Elegant Mourner *Laniisoma elegans* is inevitable. *Moult.* – Moult data have not been extensively published, but males moult 2–3 months earlier than females, which may even be in wing and tail moult during the nesting period (Willis and Oniki 1998). *Bare parts.* – Legs and bill very dark grey to blackish, the latter often with a slightly paler base to the lower mandible and a pink-yellow inner gape, and the irides are sooty or sometimes grey (once dark chestnut or sepia).

MEASUREMENTS (BMNH; MNRJ: Espírito Santo, Minas Gerais, Rio de Janeiro and São Paulo) Wing of male (*n* = 13) 129–139mm, wing of female (*n* = 8) 129.5–138.0mm; tail of male (*n* = 13) 108–125mm, tail of female (*n* = 8) 115–130mm; bill of male (*n* = 13) 21.74–24.97mm, bill of female (*n* = 8) 21.89–24.35mm; tarsus of male (*n* = 2) 26–27mm, tarsus of female (*n* = 2) 25–28mm. Weight (sexes combined): 70–110g (Willis and Oniki 2002, Snow 2004a, Antunes 2005, Faria and Paula 2008, Dunning 2008; DZUFMG; MNRJ).

GEOGRAPHICAL VARIATION Monotypic.

VOICE Published recordings are available on the following compilations: Gonzaga and Castiglioni (2001), Remold (2002), Boesman (2006a) and Minns *et al.* (2009), and several recordings are also archived online at www.xeno-canto.org. Its voice is characteristic of most *Lipaugus* pihas: a loud and far-carrying four-note whistle, which can be rendered as *skeeo-skeeo, skeeo-sheét* (Snow 2004a), with a strikingly harsh, dull metallic quality and with the second

pair of notes more resonant and emphatic-sounding. As with all or most pihas, calling appears to be highly sporadic, with long periods of silence punctuated by often quite brief periods of pronounced vocal activity. Cinnamon-vented Piha sings equally frequently at almost any time of day, although it is perhaps somewhat less inclined to sing during the absolute hottest hours than *L. vociferans* (GMK pers. obs.). The species is sometimes easily attracted using playback, occasionally from quite long distances, but birds can equally approach very slowly and almost unwillingly. When responding to playback birds may droop their wings and 'shiver' them slightly. As in *L. unirufus* and *L. vociferans*, males may be prompted to sing by apparently extraneous events, such as a mixed flock entering a bird's territory (GMK pers. obs.). The female is described as uttering a series of 'fast-puffing' notes when calling the well-grown young to safety in the presence of perceived danger at the nest-site (Willis and Oniki 1998).

NATURAL HISTORY A sluggish, unprepossessing bird that closely recalls the Screaming Piha in its foraging behaviour. However, unlike the latter species, Cinnamon-vented Piha seems to form much less tightly knit 'exploded' leks of 2–4 birds, one of which at Nova Lombardia, Espírito Santo, in September 1994, was adjacent to a permanent watercourse, with taller trees (gallery forest) than the surrounding woodland. These 'exploded' leks occupy at least *c.*100m, but in our experience the males appear to equally, if not even more, frequently sing alone, as in leks (Medeiros and Alves 2008; GMK pers. obs.). Medeiros and Alves (2008) found that breeding-season territories can occupy up to 8.6km², and that the species possesses comparatively few regularly used song perches.

FOOD AND FEEDING Cinnamon-vented Piha generally feeds at 5–25m above the ground (Willis and Oniki 1998), but individuals are sometimes observed foraging at 3m in a fruiting tree, or even lower, usually perching quietly for long periods, then sidling slowly towards a prey item or performing a short sally and hover-glean for fruit (typical of all *Lipaugus*), following which the bird either returns to the same perch or another nearby, and depending on the species involved, and its size, might bash the fruit against its perch prior to consuming it (Almeida *et al.* 2000). In addition to fruits, the species has also been noted to take large invertebrates, such as cicadas, and their larvae, also usually captured in flight. Nonetheless, Pizo *et al.* (2002) considered the diet of adults to be almost 90% fruit (the other 10% being insects) and identified berries of 38 plant species belonging to 20 families in their study in southern São Paulo state, with *Euterpe edulis* (Arecaceae) being particularly important (*contra* Galetti and Aleixo 1998) and being specialised (compared with other birds) in taking fruits of *Psychotria brasiliensis* (Rubiaceae) (Almeida *et al.* 2000). The young appear to be fed entirely (a wide variety of) insect prey until about halfway through the nestling period, when the female commences also to bring fruit. The species sometimes joins Hooded Berryeaters *Carpornis cucullata* at fruiting melastome trees or at laurels, and may, to a limited extent, associate with mixed-species flocks as they pass through their territories, although such behaviour does not appear to be especially common (GMK pers. obs.).

BREEDING Single-parent nesting and anti-predator behaviour are exceptionally well described for this species (Willis and Oniki 1998), and the same authors also discussed the advantages and disadvantages of this breeding system.

They and their students observed three nests between December and March in the Reserva Biológica Augusto Ruschi (formerly Nova Lombardia), in the state of Espírito Santo (one of which nests was also watched by GMK: pers. obs.), all of them relatively tiny (compared with the adult's size) and placed 7–8m above the ground. The nests were all constructed of small twigs and vines, and lined with small tendrils, and all were tended solely by the presumed female. From the onset of construction to laying the single egg (which is dull brownish with darker spots) occupies at least 11 days. The female's approach to the nest is often very cautious, but movements when they occur are very rapid, whilst during incubation, which lasts 25–26 days, the female usually sits inactive and fairly upright (detailed observations of female construction and incubation behaviour were presented by Willis and Oniki 1998). The single nestling remains in the nest for a similar period to that recorded for incubation, and throughout the nesting period the female would attack male pihas (and some other birds) that came close to the nest, but fled it in the presence of some other large birds or when monkeys passed through the vicinity. Both the female and young were silent throughout such events, to reduce predation risk, except when the female wing-whirred in the presence of a White-throated Woodcreeper *Xiphocolaptes albicollis* or male pihas, and on another occasion when she called the young from the nest. The same authors' incidental observations suggest that, as in the Rufous Piha *Lipaugus unirufus* (and at least some species of the genus *Cotinga*), the female destroys the nest after use. C. S. Balchin (*in* Willis and Oniki 1998) found a bird on a similar nest at the same locality, 7m above the ground, apparently incubating, in late December, with another adult feeding what appeared to be a well-grown fledgling nearby. Birds in breeding condition have been collected in most months between early August and mid January (MNRJ) and, as suggested in Snow (2004a), the season probably lasts until March.

STATUS Listed as Vulnerable in Collar *et al.* (1992), but the species has subsequently been downlisted to Near Threatened (BirdLife International 2004, 2008). Cinnamon-vented Piha is confined to the Serra do Mar Centre of endemism (Cracraft 1985). Rare (especially in the south of the range, where it is known from very few sites in Santa Catarina and Paraná) to locally common, the species is relatively easy to record at some sites, and a population estimate for the Reserva Biológica Augusto Ruschi put the total in the 'low hundreds' (T. A. Parker *in* Collar *et al.* 1992). The species is known from many protected areas (both private and public) throughout its range, as well as from almost 30 Important Bird Areas (Bencke *et al.* 2006). Nonetheless, some local extinctions have undoubtedly occurred, even in comparatively recent decades. For instance, the species was known until at least the 1940s in the Teresópolis region of Rio de Janeiro state, but appears to have been extirpated there sometime since that time (Mallet-Rodrigues *et al.* 2007). Cinnamon-vented Piha also occurred in Itatiaia National Park until the early 1950s (Pinto 1951), and it has also been lost from at least one forest in southern São Paulo during recent decades (Antunes 2005). Recently, the species has been rediscovered elsewhere in the Serra da Mantiqueira, albeit in neighbouring Minas Gerais (Torga *et al.* in press). Human exploitation of *Euterpe* palms (at least locally a key dietary constituent; see above) is undoubtedly an important and still-current threat. However, the species is still easily found at a number of localities in São Paulo (e.g.

Intervales State Park), Rio de Janeiro (e.g. around Trindade, near Parati), Espírito Santo (many sites) and Bahia (e.g. in the Serra da Ouricana near Boa Nova), in particular.

REFERENCES Albano (2010b), Aleixo and Galetti (1997), Almeida *et al.* (2000), Alves and Vecchi (2009), Antunes (2005), Bencke *et al.* (2006), BirdLife International (2000, 2004, 2008), Browne (2005), Collar *et al.* (1992), Cracraft (1985), Dunning (2008), Faria and Paula (2008), Galetti and Aleixo (1998), Gonzaga *et al.* (1995), Guix (1995), Guix *et al.* (1992), Hellmayr (1929b), Luiz *et al.* (2004a, 2004b), Mallet-Rodrigues *et al.* (2007), Medeiros and Alves (2008), Mendonça *et al.* (2004), Minns *et al.* (2009), Müller *et al.* (2003), Parker and Goerck (1997), Pinto (1944, 1951), Pizo *et al.* (2002), Remold (2002), Ribon *et al.* (2004), Ridgely and Tudor (1994, 2009), do Rosário (1996), Schubart *et al.* (1965), Sick (1997), Silveira *et al.* (2005), Simon (2009), Snow (1982, 2004a), Stotz *et al.* (1996), Torga *et al.* (in press), Urben-Filho and Abe (2001), Vasconcelos and Melo Júnior (2001), Vasconcelos and D'Angelo Neto (2009), Whitehouse and Ribon (2010), Willis and Oniki (1998, 2002).

Cinnamon-vented Piha *Lipaugus lanioides*. **Fig. 1**. Bandeira, southeast Minas Gerais, eastern Brazil, October (*Ciro Albano*). **Fig. 2**. Boa Nova, southern Bahia, eastern Brazil, July (*Ciro Albano*). The cinnamon vent can be difficult to see in the field, and is variable in extent and intensity, but is well shown in these two photographs. Note also the pale shaft-streaks over the underparts. **Fig. 3**. Male, Fazenda Santa Teresa, Trindade, near Parati, Rio de Janeiro, southeast Brazil, October (*Hadoram Shirihai / Photographic Handbook to Birds of the World*).

ROSE-COLLARED PIHA
Lipaugus streptophorus   Plate 19

Lathria streptophorus **Salvin & Godman, 1884**, *Ibis* 1884: 448, Roraima, British Guiana (= Venezuela)

Rose-collared Piha is a bird of the tepuis of southeast Venezuela and adjacent Guyana and Brazil, and is considered endemic to the Gran Sabana subcentre of the Pantepui Centre of endemism (Cracraft 1985) as well as the Tepuis Endemic Bird Area (Stattersfield *et al.* 1998). The only sexually dimorphic member of its genus, the magenta on the collar of the male arguably provides a link with the other cotingas that have brilliant red or mauve in their plumage. The Rose-collared Piha is, in many ways, an extremely poorly known bird, and is in need of serious study to elucidate many facets of its behaviour and biology.

IDENTIFICATION 22cm. The male Rose-collared Piha often advertises its presence with a sharp *weest*, which although dissimilar to that of Screaming Piha *L. vociferans* is still readily attributed to a *Lipaugus*. Fleeting glimpses of one of these handsome, treetop dwellers can be frustrating, but their habit of foraging for insects in pairs ensures that the less distinctive female may be safely identified (e.g. from Screaming Piha or Greyish Mourner *Rhytipterna simplex*), even if the chestnut undertail-coverts are not seen.

DISTRIBUTION Rose-collared Piha is endemic to the Pantepui region in northeastern South America. It occurs on the tepuis of extreme southeastern Bolívar in Venezuela (where it is known from the Sierra de Lema, Ptari-tepui, Aprada-tepui, Acopán-tepui, Uei-tepui and the Cerro Roraima), adjacent extreme southwestern Guyana (e.g. on Mts Kowa and Kaieteur) and Mt Roraima and Serra Uei in northernmost Brazil (Phelps and Phelps 1962, Meyer de Schauensee and Phelps 1978, Sick 1997, Barnett *et al.* 2002, Hilty 2003, Snow 2004a, Naka *et al.* 2006, Restall *et al.* 2006).

MOVEMENTS No evidence for any movements, seasonal or altitudinal, or otherwise, has been obtained to date.

HABITAT The species inhabits humid submontane and montane forests, and their borders, within the Pantepui region, from middle levels to the canopy, and from 1,000 to 1,800m (mostly above 1,300m, and is thus altitudinally

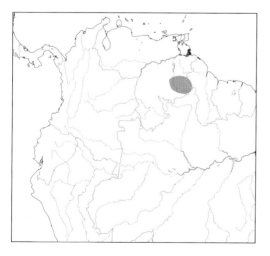

segregated from Screaming Piha in this region), but occurs lower on the Potaro Plateau, Guyana (Barnett *et al.* 2002). It also occurs in dense, older and taller, melastome-dominated second growth (Hilty 2003).

DESCRIPTION The sexes are similar but easily distinguishable given reasonable views. *Adult male.* – Dark slate-grey plumage above including over the scapulars, uppertail-coverts and rump, whilst the tail and primaries are browner. Throat and breast ash-grey, becoming even paler over the belly and flanks. Undertail-coverts pinkish-magenta. Collar pinkish-magenta and broadest below the throat (up to 20mm wide), narrowing on the sides of the neck, but completely encircling the neck. *Adult female.* – Lacks the magenta collar and the undertail-coverts are chestnut to cinnamon-rufous, but in all other respects it resembles the male. *Immature male.* – Separated from adults of the same sex by the mix of rose and buff feathers in the collar (Hilty 2003). *Juvenile.* – Undescribed (Snow 1982, 2004a). *Moult.* – Very few published data on moult, but this appears to possess a well-defined seasonal basis, as all but three of those specimens examined by Snow (1976) had apparently commenced feather renewal in December–May, with no differences being apparent between the sexes. *Bare parts.* – Both sexes have the bill dark brown or blackish-brown, becoming paler at the base of the lower mandible, and the legs grey to blackish, becoming slightly paler on the feet; the irides are dark brown.

MEASUREMENTS (from Snow 1982, except tail and tarsus measurements of female, and bill to skull measurements; BMNH: Guyana) Wing of male (*n* = 8) 121–130mm, wing of female (*n* = 6) 119–126mm; tail of male (*n* = 8) 91–95mm, tail of female (*n* = 2) 93mm; bill of male (*n* = 8) 14.5mm (*n* = 2, to skull, 21–23mm), bill of female (*n* = 2, to skull) 24–25mm; tarsus of male (*n* = 8) 20.5–21.0mm, tarsus of female (*n* = 2) 23mm. Weight (sexes combined): 52–65g (Dunning 2008; FMNH).

GEOGRAPHICAL VARIATION Monotypic.

VOICE Best described by Hilty (2003). To date the Rose-collared Piha's vocalisations have apparently not been published on any commercially-available compilation. Song is always infrequently given, even in the early-morning hours, but vocalisations continue at long intervals throughout the day. Two or three males may sing within a radius of a few hundred metres (Snow 1982), but the species was not speculated to form leks (Hilty 2003), although Barnett *et al.* (2002) observed what they considered to be a lek, similar to those described for Dusky Piha *L. fuscocinereus*, on the Potaro Plateau, Guyana, in late July. The full song is a clear whistle that slides up and down the scale, recalling the primary voice of *L. vociferans* but is more drawn-out, and rendered *sueeet-suEEEeeeeoo* (Hilty 2003). Also, more frequently utters a loud whistled *skreeyr* or *swEEEeeu* (also transliterated as *weee* or *weest*), given at long intervals (Ridgely and Tudor 1994), usually with some 2–5 minutes between calls, more occasionally one minute and, apparently exceptionally, just 30 seconds. Variants include a rising *preeEE!* or longer *SWEEEEEET!* Also gives a lower-pitched *weeoo*, credited by Snow (1982) as perhaps belonging exclusively to the female. Rose-collared Piha also utters soft *wee* notes when foraging (Hilty 2003).

NATURAL HISTORY Canopy-living and far more prone than any other member of the genus to perch out in the open, on exposed high bare stumps, the Rose-collared

Piha is arguably more staid than other pihas. In our experience, and that of Snow (1982), Hilty (2003) and other commentators, this piha is predominantly a pair-living species. Two observed by GG and C. I. Bushell gave very good views perched in the open at the forest edge beside a road, where they appeared to be loosely associated with a mixed-species feeding flock. Their movements were somewhat more akin to those of a larger tanager such as a *Tachyphonus* than most other pihas.

FOOD AND FEEDING The species seems to feed principally on insects in the canopy. However, small groups of 3–5 (perhaps family groups) may assemble to feed at fruiting trees (especially melastomes), mashing the berries prior to swallowing them (Hilty 2003).

BREEDING The nest is still unknown, although Snow (1982) observed a female apparently gathering nesting material, whilst accompanied by a male, in southeastern Venezuela in April 1976.

STATUS The species is currently treated as Least Concern

(BirdLife International 2004, 2008). Rose-collared Piha is uncommon but is not considered threatened because much unmodified habitat remains within the species' comparatively restricted range. Based on specimen records, Hilty (2003) suggested that the species might be commonest on Ptari-tepui and Aprada-tepui, in southeast Venezuela, but it is also relatively easy to see in the topmost section of the Escalera Road in southern Bolívar, Venezuela, although this piha is far from abundant there, perhaps due to the elevation of the Sierra de Lema being slightly low for the species (Hilty 2003). Rose-collared Piha is generally regarded as scarce in Guyana (Braun *et al.* 2007).

REFERENCES Barnett *et al.* (2002), BirdLife International (2004, 2008), Braun *et al.* (2007), Chapman (1931), Cracraft (1985), Dunning (2008), Hellmayr (1929b), Hilty (2003), Meyer de Schauensee and Phelps (1978), Naka *et al.* (2006), Phelps and Phelps (1962), Restall *et al.* (2006), Ridgely and Tudor (1994, 2009), Sick (1997), Snow (1976, 1982, 2004a), Snyder (1966), Stattersfield *et al.* (1998), Stotz *et al.* (1996).

Rose-collared Piha *Lipaugus streptophorus.* **Fig. 1**. Male, Sierra de Lema, Bolívar, southeast Venezuela, May (*Ron Hoff*). Confined to the tepui region of the Guianan Shield and very poorly known, in terms of its plumage this piha is something of an 'oddball', just like the Red-banded Fruiteater *Pipreola whitelyi*, which shares the same range. **Fig. 2**. Female, Sierra de Lema, Bolívar, southeast Venezuela, March (*Nick Athanas / Tropical Birding*). The female lacks the rosy collar and has overall duller plumage, but note the cinnamon-coloured vent, just visible here.

SCIMITAR-WINGED PIHA
Lipaugus uropygialis   **Plate 19**

Lathria uropygialis **P. L. Sclater & Salvin, 1876**, *Proc. Zool. Soc. Lond.* 1876: 355, Tilotilo, La Paz, Bolivia

Placed in its own genus, *Chirocylla*, by Sclater (1888), Scimitar-winged Piha is restricted to the subtropical zone in southeastern Peru and the 'Yungas' (the humid, heavily forested eastern slopes of the Andes) of northwest Bolivia. *Chirocylla* was widely maintained until as recently as the early 1980s (e.g. by Snow 1979b, 1982), when Remsen *et al.* (1982) recommended it be subsumed within *Lipaugus*, which proposition was subsequently independently supported by Ridgely and Tudor (1994), Prum (2001) and Cuervo *et al.* (2001). Nonetheless, some authors continue to recognise *Chirocylla* (e.g. Boyla and Estrada 2005), and the validity of the name at generic level doubtless should be tested genetically. Scimitar-winged Piha is closely related to the Dusky Piha *L. fuscocinereus*, as was recognised by both Sclater and Salvin (1876) and Ridgway (1907). The sole distinguishing feature of the present species seems to be the strangely modified (scimitar-shaped) primaries, which probably should at least justify retention of the name *Chirocylla* as a subgenus, as was in fact the original suggestion of Sclater and Salvin (1876), the species' describers.

IDENTIFICATION 25–30cm. This species closely resembles Dusky Piha in colour, size and general proportions. The combination of heavy build, long tail, rounded wing shape and fact that the nearest Dusky Pihas are in northern Peru should make this species relatively easy to identify, even if the deep chestnut rear underparts cannot be seen.

DISTRIBUTION Virtually endemic to Bolivia, where the species is restricted to the west of the country, in dptos. La Paz (where Scimitar-winged Piha is known from four localities) and Cochabamba (one locality), on the east slope of the Andes (with another Bolivian locality remaining untraced), and extreme southeast Peru, where it is known almost exclusively from Abra Maruncunca, near Sandia, dpto. Puno (Boyla and Estrada 2005, Schulenberg *et al.* 2007). The species has been predicted to occur in additional localities in Bolivia at least (Remsen and Parker

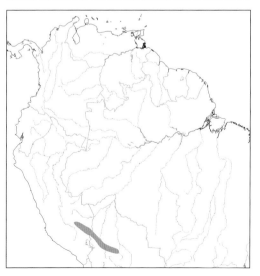

1995). Elevational range is 1,800–2,900m in Bolivia; at 2,100–2,400m in Peru.

MOVEMENTS None known.

HABITAT Scimitar-winged Piha is found in the midstorey and subcanopy (mainly 5–20m above the ground) of the interior or at borders of humid montane forest on steep slopes or ridgetops.

DESCRIPTION The sexes are similar, except that the modification of the remiges is less marked in the female. Most of the primaries are attenuated, pp6–8 strikingly so, with pp9–10 the longest of the series and also recurved; pp5–8 are progressively shorter (see Snow 1982: 123, for diagram). The rictal bristles are well developed. *Adult.* – Very dark slate-grey above, with slightly paler ear-coverts. Deep chestnut over the rump and undertail-coverts, fading on the lower belly and flanks, whilst the rest of the underparts are ash-grey. *Juvenile.* – Undescribed (Snow 2004a). *Moult.* – Data are limited to Snow's (1982) report that a male collected in late July was in advanced wing moult, whilst another male taken in late November was in the early stages of such renewal. *Bare parts.* – Bill blackish-grey with a dark horn lower mandible; the short legs and feet are rather slender and dull grey with yellowish-brown soles (Remsen *et al.* 1982); and the irides are very dark red or red-brown.

MEASUREMENTS (from Snow 1982; BMNH: northwest Bolivia) Wing of male (*n* = 5) 137–145mm, wing of female (*n* = 1) 153mm; tail of male (*n* = 5) 137–143mm, tail of female (*n* = 1) 142mm; bill of male (*n* = 2) 31.0–31.5mm, bill of female (*n* = 1) 31mm; tarsus of male (*n* = 2) 18–19mm, tarsus of female (*n* = 1) 18mm. Weight: 116g (male) and 135g (female) (Remsen *et al.* 1982, Snow 1982, Dunning 2008).

GEOGRAPHICAL VARIATION Monotypic.

VOICE Only recently sound-recorded and described with certainty (Bryce *et al.* 2005), upon which reference the bulk of the following description is based. Display and singing is lek-based and shows similar bursts of activity as in Screaming Piha *Lipaugus vociferans*, with up to four birds present on the display grounds and 2–3 birds sometimes singing simultaneously or nearly so. The species' 'shrieking' vocals are reminiscent of an *Aratinga* parakeet, with bursts of song covering the range 1.5–10.5kHz and comprising 3–4 harmonics, lasting *c.*1 second. Rendered *PEEKsweeA'WEEK!* by Schulenberg *et al.* (2007), who describe the full song as being 'performed in a spiraling, falling display flight, a loud, piercing, high "*tseee'e'e'e tsueee?*" with three mechanically produced "*fff*" sounds at the start, middle, and end of the vocal phrase' (cf. D. F. Lane recording, XC40334). According to the latter recordist's notes the display is repeated several times. Scimitar-winged Piha can respond strongly to playback, calling back and approaching the recording, sometimes perching directly overhead. The previous description of this species' voice, *wheeo, wheeo, whee-whee, whee-whee, whee-whee*, sometimes with an extra *whee* or *whee-whee* notes (Ridgely and Tudor 1994) has since proven to be attributable to Blue-winged Mountain Tanager *Anisognathus flavinucha* (Bryce *et al.* 2005, Ridgely and Tudor 2009). Mechanical wing noises might be expected, given the species' modified primaries, but have yet to be confirmed (Bryce *et al.* 2005). Two recordings from Peru are archived online at www.xeno-canto.org.

NATURAL HISTORY Away from leks, Scimitar-winged Piha

is usually observed singly, or very occasionally in pairs. The species is generally lethargic and lugubrious, as is typical of the genus, but it may also conduct vigorous chases at lek sites (Bryce *et al.* 2005). An individual observed by A. V. Moon (pers. comm.; see also Bryce *et al.* 2005), at 2,900m, was watched for 25–40 minutes. Initially perched fairly high (15–20m off the ground), it remained on one moss-covered perch for about ten minutes, looking around vigorously and twisting its head from side to side. It made several 2–3m upward sallies, returning to the same, or a nearby, perch (probably foraging for small fruits in the subcanopy). It later remained on a lower perch for at least another 15 minutes, where its stance appeared to the observer very cuckoo *Cuculus*-like.

FOOD AND FEEDING Niethammer (1956) reported berries and tree fruits in the stomach of one collected in Bolivia pre-1900. Bryce *et al.* (2005) observed another bird consume a caterpillar. Scimitar-winged Piha joins mixed-species flocks, but the extent of this behaviour and whether it possesses any seasonal bias are unknown.

BREEDING One collected in August in dpto. La Paz had enlarged ovaries, but calling activity had only commenced by October at this site in the same year, at the start of the wet season (Remsen *et al.* 1982), whilst at another La Paz locality vocal activity was pronounced in August–September, but the species was silent at a third locality, also in La Paz, in November (Bryce *et al.* 2005). The nest and eggs are undescribed (Snow 2004a).

STATUS Although not recognised as a threatened species until the start of the 21st century, Scimitar-winged Piha is now treated as Vulnerable and is thought to number fewer than 10,000 individuals (BirdLife International 2000, 2004, 2008), and that small population was considered to be declining by Bryce *et al.* (2005) based on the decreasing number of

observations in recent years and reduced habitat quality in at least one of its best-known localities in dpto. La Paz. The species does appear to be genuinely uncommon and, perhaps like other Andean pihas, of naturally low density (J. V. Remsen *in* BirdLife International 2000) but *L. uropygialis* is doubtless still under-recorded. Scimitar-winged Piha is very poorly known: just 18 specimens and fewer than 20 sight records were available prior to the start of the 21st century (Bryce *et al.* 2005). The latter authors reported that much of the forest habitat where *L. uropygialis* has been recorded has been degraded as a result of selective logging, road construction, agriculture, clearance for plantations, grazing and hunting. Habitat loss and degradation has been particularly dramatic in the environs of the species' Peruvian locality (BirdLife International 2000). Nevertheless, there are still extensive areas of potentially suitable habitat extant within the species' range, estimated at 6,700km² (BirdLife International 2000), and Scimitar-winged Piha is known from at least five protected areas, namely Madidi National Park, Carrasco National Park, Amboró National Park, Altamachi Departmental Park and Pilon-Lajas Biological Reserve, all in Bolivia (cf., for example, Hennessey and Gomez 2003, Boyla and Estrada 2005, MacLeod *et al.* 2005). The species is confined to the South Peruvian Andean subcentre of the Peruvian Andean Centre of endemism (Cracraft 1985).

REFERENCES BirdLife International (2000, 2004, 2008), Bryce *et al.* (2005), Boyla and Estrada (2005), Collar *et al.* (1992), Cracraft (1985), Cuervo *et al.* (2001), Fjeldså and Krabbe (1990), Hellmayr (1929b), Hennessey and Gomez (2003), MacLeod *et al.* (2005), Niethammer (1956), Prum (2001), Remsen and Parker (1995), Remsen and Traylor (1989), Remsen *et al.* (1982), Ridgely and Tudor (1994, 2009), Ridgway (1907), Schulenberg *et al.* (2007), Sclater (1888), Sclater and Salvin (1876), Snow (1979b, 1982, 2004a), Stotz *et al.* (1996), Valqui (2004).

Scimitar-winged Piha *Lipaugus uropygialis*. **Fig. 1**. Coroico, dpto. La Paz, northwest Bolivia, October (*Joe Tobias / Edward Grey Institute, Oxford University*). Formerly placed in its own genus, *Chirocylla*, Scimitar-winged Piha is a rare and local inhabitant of southeast Peruvian and northwest Bolivian humid montane forests.

Genus *Tijuca*: southeast Brazilian cotingas

This genus comprises two closely related but dissimilar montane cotingas, namely the Black-and-gold Cotinga *T. atra*, which is strongly sexually dimorphic, and the Grey-winged Cotinga *T. condita*, which virtually lacks any plumage differences between the sexes. *Tijuca* appears to reflect a close association with the pihas placed in the genus *Lipaugus*, and the Grey-winged Cotinga's vocalisation is also reminiscent in some respects of Screaming Piha *L. vociferans*, whilst both species of *Tijuca* appear to have lek displays (albeit of differing natures), shared with some *Lipaugus*. At least one recent genetic study has recovered evidence of a close relationship between *Lipaugus* (Rufous Piha *L. unirufus* and Dusky Piha *L. fuscocinereus* were sampled) and *T. atra*, but did not establish reciprocal monophyly (Ohlson *et al.* 2007) and thus it is too early to recommend the genera be merged, with *Lipaugus* having priority (Tello *et al.* 2009). The latter authors did not sample *Tijuca*. Both species of *Tijuca* are dependent on the viability of montane forests that are relatively free of development pressures, but not necessarily of incursions from campers, walkers, etc. Both are also confined to very small ranges within the Serra do Mar Centre of endemism (Cracraft 1985). Breeding ecology is presumably similar in both species but far more data are needed (and the nest of neither species has been found to date), with the nesting season almost certainly coinciding with the onset of the austral summer.

BLACK-AND-GOLD COTINGA
Tijuca atra   Plate 21

Tijuca atra **Férussac, 1829,** *Bull. Sci. Nat.* 19: 324, [Serra do Mar, Rio de Janeiro,] interior of Brazil

The male of this cotinga's vocalisation is undoubtedly *the* characteristic sound of the upper elevations of Itatiaia National Park, on the borders of São Paulo, Minas Gerais and Rio de Janeiro states, in southeast Brazil, from where it was evocatively first described by Ernest Holt at the end of the 1920s. The species' haunting, ventriloquial whistle, which gives rise to one of its local names, the Saudade (a Brazilian term referring to 'longing for'), can be heard throughout the often mist- or fog-shrouded slopes of this region.

IDENTIFICATION 26.5–28.0cm. The male is virtually instantly recognisable by virtue of its all-black plumage relieved by the striking yellow wing-panel and bright orange bill. The only species with broadly similar plumage found in the same forests is the Golden-winged Cacique *Cacicus chrysopterus* (the two are quite regularly observed in the same trees). However, the cacique has a longer, conical and differently coloured bill, is also far less plump and thrush-like in overall appearance, with a much longer, narrower tail, and the yellow in the wing is confined largely to the coverts, rather than the flight feathers. Male Black-and-gold Cotinga also recalls the slightly smaller, but similarly shaped Yellow-legged Thrush *Turdus (Platycichla) flavipes*, which however has more contrasting grey and black plumage, lacks any yellow in the wing and, as its name suggests, has bright yellow legs and feet. In their area of overlap, the thrush tends generally to be found at slightly to much lower elevations. Female Black-and-gold Cotinga is also generally unmistakable, a large, rotund mainly green bird of montane forests, with a largely pinkish bill (paler than the male's), but in some areas it overlaps or virtually overlaps with the rather rarer Grey-winged Cotinga *T. condita*. Separation of either sex of the latter species from female Black-and-gold requires reasonable views, but note the usually strikingly greyer wings and tail of *T. condita*, as well as the much greyer face (especially over the throat), much yellower underparts and rump (contrasting with the rest of the upperparts), and the smaller body and slenderer bill.

DISTRIBUTION Endemic to southeast Brazil, where the species is found exclusively in montane areas of Rio de Janeiro, extreme eastern São Paulo (e.g. from the Campos do Jordão, as well as on the Pico dos Marins and south through the Serra da Bocaina, including the Pico da Macela and Pedra Branca in neighbouring southwesternmost Rio de Janeiro) and southernmost Minas Gerais states, with the easternmost documented occurrence apparently in Parque Estadual do Desengano, also in Rio de Janeiro state (Alves *et al.* 2008). The genus name *Tijuca* (= 'muddy water' in Portuguese) is also that of one of the oldest national parks in Brazil, within the city limits of Rio de Janeiro, and it seems possible that this species once occurred there, despite the fact that these mountains are lower than the main elevational range of the species. However, its presence both further north, in Espírito Santo, and further south, in Santa Catarina, discussed by Pacheco and Bauer (2001) and do Rosário (1996), respectively, appears most improbable. The species' elevational range principally lies at 1,200–2,050m, but it is found extremely commonly (and reportedly year-round) above 600m on Pedra Branca in southernmost Rio de Janeiro (Berla 1944); see also next section for seasonal occurrence at lower altitudes.

417

MOVEMENTS Altitudinal movements are poorly documented, but in the austral winter and early spring (July–October) birds are audible in the vicinity of Maromba bridge, Itatiaia National Park (at *c.*1,100m), and the lower portions of Serra dos Órgãos National Park, down to *c.*800m, suggesting at least periodic retreat to lower elevations perhaps in search of certain fruits. Sick (1997) maintained that birds performed elevational movements of up to 500m, which does seem likely based on the available data, but more detailed information would be distinctly welcome.

HABITAT Black-and-gold Cotinga inhabits montane primary forest and its borders; the species generally prefers rather taller forest than its congeneric, Grey-winged Cotinga, and it is only rarely found in areas of more broken terrain.

DESCRIPTION Strongly sexually dimorphic. Both sexes are somewhat thrush-like in size and shape, and the male almost resembles a Eurasian Blackbird *Turdus merula* but with yellow in the wing. The head is rather rounded, the tail of mid length and rather full, and the wings are comparatively short and rounded; the flight feathers lack any modification. Rictal bristles are weakly developed in both sexes and the nostrils are relatively small. The bill is slightly arched along the culmen, with a weakly expressed hooked tip. *Adult male.* – Plumage is entirely sooty-black, relieved only by the striking golden-yellow wing patch, which covers most of the flight feathers apart from the tips (and appears as a yellow-white patch on the underwing). *Adult female.* – Shares the overall shape and, to some extent, bill colour of the male, but is otherwise much more reminiscent of the even more range-restricted Grey-winged Cotinga, with overall dull olive-green body plumage including the head, but most of the wings are somewhat browner, although the flight feather fringes and belly are slightly more yellow in tone; the tertials have slightly paler fringes. There is some variation in the overall depth of the underparts coloration, with some individuals inclining yellower on the belly and ventral region, whilst others are more olive-green as on the breast of all birds. *Juvenile/Immature.* – The plumage initially recalls that of the female, but in the male this is gradually replaced by a subadult plumage in which the contour feathers, especially on the belly, are adult-like. Even in the final stage, when ostensibly fully adult, it may retain a few olive-green feathers on the uppertail-coverts and rump, as well as on the lower back, lower breast, body-sides and flanks. *Moult.* – Moult was documented by Snow (1982) and is probably prolonged as in other cotingids of a similar size (*c.*150 days). Feather renewal appears to last from mid October to March/April, with males generally commencing renewal some weeks prior to females (which perhaps start moulting as late as December). *Bare parts.* – Male has a bright orange bill, but this is slightly duller and browner, especially on the upper mandible, in the female; the irides are red, reddish-brown to brown (no sexual dimorphism has been detected), and the legs are dark brown in both sexes.

MEASUREMENTS (from Snow 1980, 1982; FMNH; MNRJ; Rio de Janeiro) Wing of male (*n* = 24) 141–152mm, wing of female (14) 140–153mm; tail of male (*n* = 24) 110–120mm, tail of female (*n* = 11) 105–119mm; bill of male (*n* = 20) 15.5–17.5mm, bill of female (*n* = 10) 15.5–18.0mm (*n* = 1, to skull, 23.96mm); tarsus of male (*n* = 20) 27–30mm, tarsus of female (*n* = 6) 29–30mm. Weight: 129.4g (MNRJ; male).

GEOGRAPHICAL VARIATION Monotypic.

VOICE Extraordinary and thoroughly distinctive. Once heard, never forgotten. Published recordings have been presented on Gonzaga and Castiglioni (2001), Remold (2002) and Minns *et al.* (2009), and several recordings are also archived online at www.xeno-canto.org. Dominant males sing from an exposed perch (especially in the early morning and late afternoon; at other times the birds continue to sing but usually retreat to a perch within the canopy), several (up to five) in earshot, with subordinate males often singing from the same tree (see Display). The plaintive, far-carrying, ventriloquial and extremely pure whistle lasts 3–4 seconds including a short pause that occurs approximately two-thirds of the way through, and is repeated up to 12–13 times per minute. Because males sing in unison and effectively chorus, this ensures a continual, rather eerie, vocalisation that forms the perfect backdrop to the other sounds of the forest. As the song is given at very high pitch, if only heard at some distance those unfamiliar with the voice might easily overlook it.

NATURAL HISTORY Behaviour was most fully described by Snow and Goodwin (1984). The species is generally encountered solitarily, in the canopy and at mid levels. Black-and-gold Cotinga can be frustratingly difficult to observe, as most males tend to vocalise from within the canopy, although once a favoured songpost (often a dead snag) belonging to a dominant male has been located, birds may be more easily encountered, at least early and late in the day. At some seasons, males may be surprisingly reactive to playback, even approaching the observer from some distance, but such behaviour is not common and generally it is important to find a favoured songpost, which may remain in use for several (even many) years (GMK pers. obs.). Males have more than one favoured perch within a given tree, usually facing in different directions. Thus, the bird sings for several minutes from one and then switches to another perch to sing for a similar period of time but facing up to 180° away (GMK pers. obs.). Another method of observing these birds is to use a telescope to search a distant ridge where birds are vocalising, in order to locate them in the subcanopy.

FOOD AND FEEDING Snow and Goodwin (1984) found the species to feed mainly on lauraceous trees, although one non-lauraceous species, *Oreopanax fulvus* (Araliaceae), which has ivy-like fruits, is also exploited. Pineschi (1990) recorded the species feeding on *Rapanea* (Myrsinaceae) fruits, and Parrini and Pacheco (2011) observed fruits of *Miconia chartacea* and *M. sellowiana* (Melastomataceae) being taken. Insects are also taken, using short aerial sallies, from foliage and in mid-air.

DISPLAY The lek system of this cotinga is remarkably similar to that of certain *Chiroxiphia* manakins, in that 2–3 males cooperate to attract a female, using vocal stimuli in the cotinga, and visual ones in the manakin. Therefore, several males (one of which is always dominant) sing from the same tree, producing a prolonged and almost continuous vocalisation that carries over the hillsides, presumably enhancing the chances of females being responsive. When a female arrives, either on the same high perch as the dominant male or lower down in the tree, two or even all three males may pursue her, calling in chorus around her.

BREEDING The breeding season probably commences in about September, based on moult data, which would accord well with the general season for all birds within this region, but specific data on nests etc. are almost entirely lacking. Goeldi (1900) mentioned finding a nest in November in a patch of cut-over forest, and a male in MNRJ taken in late February had enlarged gonads, but no further information is available.

STATUS Currently considered to be Near Threatened (BirdLife International 2004, 2008). Black-and-gold Cotinga is generally common within areas of intact habitat at suitable elevations, which are generally higher than those subject to the most extensive deforestation in this region. Although Black-and-gold Cotinga is a range-restricted species (as defined by BirdLife International), its habitat is relatively secure from conversion and well protected in at least five areas, all in Rio de Janeiro (Itatiaia and Serra dos Órgãos National Parks, Três Picos and Desengano State Parks, and Macaé de Cima Forest Reserve), although there is a degree of danger from human disturbance and perhaps fires in some of these.

REFERENCES Alves *et al.* (2008, 2009), BirdLife International (2004, 2008), Berla (1944), Browne (2005), Buzzetti (2000), Cracraft (1985), Goeldi (1900), Gonzaga and Castiglioni (2001), Haffer (1974), Hellmayr (1929b), Holt (1928), Mallet-Rodrigues and Noronha (2009), Mallet-Rodrigues *et al.* (2007), Minns *et al.* (2009), Mitchell (1957), Ohlson *et al.* (2007, 2008), Pacheco and Bauer (2001), Parker and Goerck (1997), Parrini and Pacheco (2011), Pimentel and Olmos (2011), Pineschi (1990), Pinto (1944, 1951), Remold (2002), Ridgely and Tudor (1994, 2009), do Rosário (1996), Sick (1997), Snow (1980, 1982, 2004a), Snow and Goodwin (1974), Stattersfield *et al.* (1998), Stotz *et al.* (1996), Tello *et al.* (2009), Willis (1992).

Black-and-gold Cotinga *Tijuca atra.* **Fig. 1**. Male, Parnaso, Rio de Janeiro, southeast Brazil, February (*Rafael Bessa*). **Fig. 2**. Male, Itatiaia National Park, Rio de Janeiro, southeast Brazil, November (*Hadoram Shirihai / Photographic Handbook to Birds of the World*). **Fig. 3**. Male, Reserva Ecológica de Guapiaçu, near Cachoeiras de Macacu, Rio de Janeiro, southeast Brazil, August (*William Price / www.pbase/tereksand-piper*). **Fig. 4**. Female, Macaé da Cima, Rio de Janeiro, southeast Brazil, August (*Andrew Whitehouse*). Note the differences from the next species (the type specimen of Grey-winged Cotinga *T. condita*) went unnoticed among a tray of this species for several decades. In particular, Grey-winged Cotinga has an obviously grey face, wings and tail. Note also the reddish bill in this species.

GREY-WINGED COTINGA
Tijuca condita   **Plate 21**

Tijuca condita **D. W. Snow, 1980**, *Bull. Brit. Orn. Club* 100: 213, near Teresópolis, Rio de Janeiro, Brazil

One of the most recently described cotingas, it was not until the 1970s that the distinguished English ornithologist, David Snow, realised that a unique specimen held in the museum in São Paulo, and long attributed to female Black-and-gold Cotinga *T. atra*, in fact represented a species apart. Within just a couple of years, Grey-winged Cotinga had been found in the field, but despite its highly restricted range within close proximity to Rio de Janeiro, this unassuming cotinga was until comparatively rarely targeted by birdwatchers seeking out the region's endemics, and until very recently has been highly under-studied by ornithologists. Subsequently, H. Sick (*in* Vuilleumeier and Mayr 1987) reported that 'he had known the bird for a number of years, but had thought that it was the young of *T. atra* "that had not yet learned to call correctly", and "consequently had made no attempt to collect a specimen."' Feather protein analysis, which was also used to differentiate the new species, suggested a closer relationship to Screaming Piha *Lipaugus vociferans* than to its sympatric and syntopic congener (Snow 1980).

IDENTIFICATION 24.0–25.5cm. Both sexes of this near-cryptic cotinga require careful separation from the female Black-and-gold Cotinga, which shares the same forests and, to some extent, elevational range (cf. Alves *et al.* 2008 and Carvalho *et al.* 2009 for discussion of the degree of overlap). Compared with the latter species, both sexes of Grey-winged Cotinga are marginally smaller and perhaps less plump of character, with overall brighter green and yellow plumage in the male, which is further distinguished by having a silvery-grey cast to the remiges and rectrices, whilst female Grey-winged Cotinga has a smaller and more delicate bill than Black-and-gold, and is also rather yellower overall with greyer wings. The two species also differ quite markedly in vocalisations.

DISTRIBUTION Grey-winged Cotinga's range was recently extended by Alves *et al.* (2008), who used a modelling

procedure to predict the potential maximum range of the species (*c.*200km²) and then searched for *T. condita* at potential localities (with suitable forest cover above 1,400m) using playback and mist-netting, in 2003–04. The species is endemic to the mountains of central Rio de Janeiro state, southeast Brazil, where it is currently known solely from the Serra dos Órgãos and Serra da Tinguá, at 1,340m (in the latter) or mainly 1,560–2,105m (in the Serra dos Órgãos: Carvalho *et al.* 2009, 2010). Its range extends at least as far east as the Pico da Caledônia, near Nova Friburgo, but apparently not as far as the Parque Estadual do Desengano, where it was searched for without success by Alves *et al.* (2008). The latter authors speculated, perhaps correctly, that this last-named region is perhaps marginally too dry for the cotinga, with apparently fewer bromeliads in its forests.

MOVEMENTS None definitely recorded, although the holotype (and sole specimen) was quite possibly taken below the lowest altitude recorded to date (Snow 2004a), at Fazenda Guinle (at *c.*22°27'S, 43°00'W). Given that Black-and-gold Cotinga also performs altitudinal movements, moving lower in the austral winter (the non-breeding season), it seems possible that Grey-winged Cotinga does so too, but the species is likely to be much more easily overlooked if not vocalising. Carvalho *et al.* (2010) have recently acquired data suggesting the possibility that the species moves marginally lower during September/ October.

HABITAT Grey-winged Cotinga inhabits bromeliad-rich montane elfin forests (with a canopy height of just 5–10m) and forest patches just below the treeline, within otherwise open areas with bamboo and tussock grass. The species has been reported both from exposed ridge-top forests and more sheltered gullies.

DESCRIPTION The sexes are largely similar, but probably separable in the field (and presumably only males sing). A predominantly green and yellow cotinga with grey flight feathers (wings and tail). The culmen is slightly arched with a marginally hooked tip to the bill, at least in some individuals. The following description is based heavily on publications by Snow (1980) and Scott and Brooke (1985), as well as photographs provided by Rafael Bessa Carvalho. *Adult male.* – Upper body is entirely olive-green, but washed much yellower over the rump (contrasting well with the rest of the upperparts) and the crown is duller and more olive than the rest, whilst the scapulars are also slightly darker than the mantle. Chin, throat, supraloral region and ear-coverts mainly dull grey with whitish tips to the feathers closer to the bill (which can be quite obvious and afford the face a slightly mottled appearance). The underparts are mainly olive-yellow, perhaps becoming even brighter and yellower over the belly and undertail-coverts (although on some individuals the breast is occasionally the most pure yellow part); underwing-coverts and tibial feathering also yellowish. Tail grey on both surfaces, with the outer fringes to the feathers distinctively paler (especially on the outermost pair) and some of the central feathers are washed faintly greenish. Uppertail-coverts are also slightly greenish. Wings largely greyish to blackish-brown, contrasting strongly with the body, with paler fringes especially to the flight feathers which are blue-grey (and visible in flight), but the inner secondaries are washed olive-green. The inner margins to the tertials are usually darker, and sometimes the bird has blackish shafts to some of the larger wing-coverts and alula feathers. *Adult female.* – Differs from the male in being overall duller and seemingly smaller, with much less of a silver-grey wing-panel effect, less extensive grey fringes to the tail feathers and rather less grey on the face. Otherwise the sexes are by and large identical. *Juvenile.* – Undescribed to date (Snow 2004a). *Moult.* – There is no detailed information concerning moult, other than that a bird trapped in late November was in extensive moult and that another, also trapped in November, was moulting many of the upper body feathers (Scott and Brooke 1985). *Bare parts.* – Irides brown or grey; the bill has a dark grey upper mandible but at least sometimes has a much paler, yellow-olive or greenish-grey lower mandible, and a bright orange gape; the legs and feet are dark horn to plumbeous grey (usually the latter), with orange or dull yellowish soles (Scott and Brooke 1985, Snow 1980, 2004a). The culmen is less arched and definitely more slender than in Black-and-gold Cotinga.

MEASUREMENTS (from Snow 1980, Scott and Brooke 1985: Rio de Janeiro, Brazil) Wing of female (n = 3) 122–130mm; tail of female (n = 3) 106–109mm; bill of female (n = 3, to feathers) 14.5–21.5mm; tarsus of female (n = 3) 26–29mm. Weight (two females): 80–87g (Scott and Brooke 1985).

GEOGRAPHICAL VARIATION Monotypic.

VOICE Grey-winged Cotinga calls sporadically throughout the day, but principally from dawn to mid morning (07:00–10:30 hours) and again in late afternoon, between 15:00 and 17:00 hours (D. A. Scott and M. L. Brooke *in* Snow 1982). Quite different from Black-and-gold's primary vocalisation, the song comprises a two-note whistle that lasts just 1.25 seconds, and is far less plaintive, *sooee-wheee*. Published recordings are available on the Gonzaga and Castiglioni (2001), Remold (2002) and Minns *et al.* (2009) compilations and several recordings have also been archived online at www.xeno-canto.org. An alternate vocalisation (recordist N. Athanas; XC3811) lasts *c.*2 seconds, is very slightly undulating and could be transcribed *sooooo-ooooo-wheee*. The song can sound quite explosive at short range, with the emphasis on the second *wheeee*, being somewhat similar to the primary vocalisation of many pihas. Vocal activity does not appear weather-dependent, but seems most frequent in calm, overcast conditions and is highly influenced by the use of playback (Carvalho *et al.* 2009; M. A. Raposo and R. Parrini pers. comm.). When vocalising the birds perch noticeably upright, typically with the wings held slightly spread and drooping, the tail pointing vertically down, and the rump puffed out. The call is delivered with the bill wide open, held almost vertically up during the second part, but then brought down to the horizontal. Such postures are also frequently adopted by *Lipaugus* pihas. Birds typically call every 1–3 minutes, but occasionally more frequently (e.g. just 25–40 seconds between calls). This factor, along with the frequent change of song perches, which are often concealed (Grey-winged Cotinga only occasionally ventures to open perches above or in the canopy), makes the species difficult to observe when vocalising.

NATURAL HISTORY Very little known, its habitat being comparatively rarely visited by ornithologists and bird-watchers. Even more difficult to locate than its congener as the species tends to call from the subcanopy and rarely allows protracted views on dead snags in the canopy, unlike the Black-and-gold Cotinga. Individuals of Grey-winged Cotinga will perch motionless for minutes on end, like

many other frugivorous cotingas. Probably forms 'exploded leks', unlike Black-and-gold Cotinga, with calling males well spaced by at least 200m (in some places much further, e.g. in the Serra das Araras, where densities are sufficiently low that some males may occupy territories more than a linear kilometre wide: M. A. Raposo pers. comm.). Carvalho *et al.* (2010) has noted that this species (and Black-and-gold Cotinga) is subordinate to Swallow-tailed Cotinga *Phibalura flavirostris*.

FOOD AND FEEDING Appears to feed principally on small fruits, especially melastomes, but nine different species have been recorded (cf. Carvalho *et al.* 2009, 2010), even hanging virtually upside-down to perch-glean. In addition, Carvalho *et al.* (2010) reported a stick insect (Phasmidae) and a caterpillar (Lepidoptera) also being taken. However, there are so few data that all observations are welcome.

BREEDING Nothing is known of the species' breeding biology, but the Grey-winged Cotinga is seemingly vocal year-round, perhaps especially between November and at least late March, and a female mist-netted in November had a well-developed brood patch (Scott and Brooke 1985). A presumed female has been observed carrying nesting material in mid November (Field Guides tour report).

STATUS Grey-winged Cotinga is categorised as Vulnerable (BirdLife International 2000, 2004, 2008) and is highly range-restricted, being known solely from mountains just north and northeast of the city of Rio de Janeiro. Its conservation status might be upgraded to Endangered should evidence of any significant threat to its habitat become apparent. This appears to be a rather low-density species and field observations are still comparatively few, except at the currently well-visited Pico da Caledônia, near Nova Friburgo. Grey-winged Cotinga currently seems secure within its isolated and remote montane habitat, although the overall area is disturbed by walkers and campers, whilst periodic, accidentally started fires offer some threat to its treeline forests. One site predicted to be occupied by the Alves *et al.* (2008) study, at Fazenda do Amaral, could not be reached by the would-be survey team, and the possibility certainly exists to discover new localities for the species. As noted under Movements, there is a distinct but currently unconfirmed possibility that this species performs seasonal altitudinal movements, and therefore it might be found at lower elevations in the austral winter. However, its detection at this season at lower altitudes will probably require some luck given the species' general similarity to the female Black-and-gold Cotinga. Grey-winged Cotinga is known from four protected areas, especially Serra dos Órgãos National Park and Três Picos State Park, but also Araras and Tinguá Biological Reserves, of which the latter's integrity may be partially threatened by poachers and those exploiting *Euterpe* (Arecaceae) palms (*Cotinga* 24: 7). The extent of available habitat for the species in Tinguá Biological Reserve is <1km².

REFERENCES Alves *et al.* (2008, 2009), BirdLife International (2000, 2004, 2008), Carvalho *et al.* (2009, 2010), Collar *et al.* (1992), Cracraft (1985), Gonzaga and Castiglioni (2001), Mallet-Rodrigues and Noronha (2009), Mallet-Rodrigues *et al.* (2007), Minns *et al.* (2009), Remold (2002), Ridgely and Tudor (1994, 2009), Scott and Brooke (1993), Sick (1997), Snow (1980, 1982, 2004a), Stattersfield *et al.* (1998), Stotz *et al.* (1996), Vuilleumeier and Mayr (1987), Willis (1992).

Grey-winged Cotinga *Tijuca condita*. **Figs. 1–4**. Above Teresópolis, Rio de Janeiro, southeast Brazil, March, May and August (*Rafael Bessa*). Described as recently as 1980, the unique specimen having lain 'passed over' as a female Black-and-gold Cotinga *T. atra*, this cotinga is endemic to a tiny area of the state of Rio de Janeiro, where it is found in partial sympatry with Black-and-gold Cotinga. Grey-winged Cotinga, however, generally occurs at higher elevations than the previous species. With good views it is easily separable from female Black-and-gold Cotinga by the distinctly grey wings, grey tail and face, and duller-coloured bill, among other features.

Genus *Porphyrolaema*: Purple-throated Cotinga

Purple-throated Cotinga occupies a monotypic genus which, in morphology and behaviour, is perhaps closest to members of the genus *Cotinga*. Indeed, *Porphyrolaema* was formerly regarded as conspecific with *Cotinga* and the species was originally described in the latter genus, but even without recent genetic findings (see p. 43) a separate genus appeared warranted on the basis of the much larger and more swollen bill, and square-ended tail. In addition to the bill being stouter than that of any of the blue cotingas, males possess a quite different colour pattern, including the quite uniquely 'scaled' upperparts. Usually found in the tall, dense canopy of lowland tropical forest habitats, Purple-throated Cotinga *P. porphyrolaema* can often be seen in close proximity to two *Cotinga* species, Spangled *C. cayana* and Plum-throated Cotingas *C. maynana*, e.g. from the canopy tower at Sacha Lodge, on the Río Napo, in eastern Ecuador, and also at Manu Wildlife Centre in southeastern Peru.

PURPLE-THROATED COTINGA
Porphyrolaema porphyrolaema　　　Plate 25

Cotinga porphyrolaema **Deville & P. L. Sclater, 1852**, *Rev. Mag. Zool.* (2)4: 226, Sarayacu, Río Ucuyali, Peru

This handsome and generally quite uncommon cotinga is widespread in upper Amazonia but to date very little has been published concerning its behaviour, presumably due to its principally canopy habits and a lack of knowledge of its vocalisations. We present the first nesting data for the species below.

IDENTIFICATION 16.5–18.5cm; males average very marginally smaller than females in total length (Brooks *et al.* 1999). The male should prove unmistakable given good views, as the plumage pattern is completely unique amongst cotingids. The female is also readily recognised given reasonable views, but care will often be needed, especially given a bird at longer range, e.g. if seen in the canopy from the ground, or in the heavy shade of the forest midstory, to distinguish it from the very marginally larger female Spangled *Cotinga cayana* and Plum-throated Cotingas *C. maynana*. The latter two species lack the rufous throat of female Purple-throated Cotinga (although this feature is not always obvious, especially in the shade), as well as the barred underparts and spotted crown, and have a subtly different head shape to the present species. Female Plum-throated also has pale, not dark, irides.

DISTRIBUTION Purple-throated Cotinga is largely endemic to western Amazonia. It occurs from southeastern Colombia (where the species is known from eastern Putumayo, at Leticia, in southern Amazonas, south of Florencia, in western Caquetá, and north as far as Tinigua National Park, in Meta), across the eastern lowlands of Ecuador (from Sucumbíos to Morona-Santiago), and eastern Peru (south as far as Madre de Dios) in which country the species is known from more localities than any other, and thence over western and central Amazonian Brazil (east to the lower Rios Negro, Solimões and Purus, at Cacao Pereira just west of Manaus, Ariquemes, Rondônia, and to northern Mato Grosso, e.g. at Alta Floresta, the species' easternmost known limit). (There is a probable sight record from the Serra dos Carajás, Pará, even further east, which is unconfirmed for now: C. E. Carvalho *per* J. J. Grigolo pers. comm.). Its northernmost locality in Brazil is near São Gabriel da Cachoeira, on the upper Rio Negro, in Amazonas state, relatively close to the southern Venezuelan border. Purple-throated Cotinga was long expected in northern Bolivia, as it is known from as close as the Rio

Mamoré in southern Rondônia, Brazil (Whittaker 1996b), on the country's northeast border, but was only recently confirmed to occur, at Chalalan, near the Río Tuichi, Madidi National Park, La Paz, in the northwest (S. Webb & M. Friggens *per* S. K. Herzog *in litt.* 2007), where it had been predicted to occur by Remsen and Parker (1995), and in the Serranía Sadiri, also in Madidi National Park, La Paz (Hosner *et al.* 2009; P. A. Hosner *in litt.* 2007). The species' elevational range lies mostly below 500m, although it ascends into the eastern Andean foothills of Peru, where it occasionally reaches 900m (Schulenberg *et al.* 2007).

MOVEMENTS None specifically recorded, but the species is absent from the Sacha area in eastern Ecuador at some times of the year (thought to correspond with the fruiting of certain tree species), suggesting some localised movements in response to fruiting events. However, in other areas, e.g. the Cocha Cashu area of Manu National Park, and Tambopata Reserved Zone, both in southeast Peru, Purple-throated Cotinga is apparently a year-round, if sporadically encountered, resident (Robinson 1997; H. Lloyd *in litt.* 2010).

HABITAT *Porphyrolaema* inhabits the canopy and borders of humid lowland tropical forest, including disturbed areas (such as clearings), in *terra firme* forest interior, old floodplain forest interior (southeast Peru), the borders of seasonally flooded swamp forest (southeast Peru) and *várzea* (in Colombia the species is almost entirely recorded in the last named).

DESCRIPTION The sexes differ, including in their feather morphology (females, and young males, have the body feathers looser than adult males, as well as longer and more pointed rectrices). The bill is broad-based with a strongly arched culmen and slightly hooked tip. Rictal bristles are weakly developed in both sexes with small, circular nostrils (these are oval-shaped and larger in *Cotinga*). *Porphyrolaema* further differs from the latter genus in lacking any modification to the primaries. *Male.* – Vaguely recalls an over-sized male Rose-breasted Grosbeak *Pheucticus ludovicianus*, with a black head and neck, and less deep black ground colour to the rest of the upperparts, from the mantle to tail and including the wings, with snowy-white scales to the mantle, back, rump and uppertail-coverts, with in some much narrower, more indistinct and less frequent pale scaling on the lower nape, and an extremely broad, diagonal, cleaner white band across the wing-coverts, with slightly greyer white but very broad fringes to tertials. Very deep rosy-purple chin and throat, merging almost indivisibly into the black ear-coverts, with bright white underparts, becoming marginally duskier over the flanks, especially at rear, bordering the vent, and faintly discoloured purple in the centre of the breast, at least in some individuals. *Female.* – The upperparts are virtually concolorous mid brown, from the crown to the tail, including the wings, with very prominent buffy-white spots on the crown (sometimes with orange admixed), but these are much reduced on the nape and more barred on the forehead, becoming neat, slightly whiter scales over the mantle, back and rump, with some buffier spotting on the small wing-coverts and pale buff or whitish, very narrow fringes to the larger wing-coverts and tertials. It has whitish to pale orange tips and fringes to the innermost six primaries at least, but pale tips to these and many other feathers of the upperparts are lost with wear. The pale buff eye-ring is conspicuous, even more so than shown in Ridgely and Greenfield (2001), as evidenced by video footage (C. F. Collins), although it is often depicted in guides and handbooks as being non-existent or virtually so (e.g. in Snow 1982, 2004a, Schulenberg *et al.* 2007). The chin and throat are cinnamon-rufous (although this can be difficult to see, and it sometimes has purple tips to a handful of feathers on the sides) and the undertail-coverts and vent are almost the same colour, with slightly barred ear-coverts, but the rest of the underparts are slightly paler in ground colour and quite strongly barred blackish. Compared with the male, the tail feathers are longer and more point-tipped with bold buffish (or even pale orange) tips and narrow fringes to both webs, but especially the inner one (the male can have tiny buff tips to a few rectrices), whilst the body plumage is generally looser textured. *Immature.* – The male gradually acquires adult plumage, e.g. it can have both adult and juvenile rectrices, of uneven length (Snow 1982, Hilty and Brown 1986). In one immature male at BMNH (1888.1.13.1650), the purple throat patch is complete, but the rest of the white underparts are extensively barred dark brownish and buffish, whilst the black upperparts possess obvious but narrower whitish (less clean) tips to the feathers, including those of the crown, nape and rectrices, unlike in adult males. Furthermore, the white wing markings are also less obvious and less bright white, and contrast less obviously because the wing feathers are less solidly black (browner) at this age. *Juvenile.* – Much like the female, but apparently paler and buffier overall, with the mantle and back having buff, not whitish, fringes to the feathers, and juvenile rectrices are brown with blackish spots and a subterminal bar (Snow 1982, 2004a). *Moult.* – Pattern not well known, but wing moult has been recorded almost year-round in specimens from Ecuador and Peru. *Bare parts.* – Probably more variable than described here, but few published data or well-labelled specimens examined. Irides brown to dark brown in both sexes, the bill is usually described as being blackish, but in life appears pale grey (clearly contrasting with the head), and the legs and feet (comparatively weak as in *Cotinga*) are also dark grey to blackish.

MEASUREMENTS (FMNH; MNRJ; RMNH; Gyldenstolpe 1945, Snow 1982: Brazil and Peru) Wing of male ($n = 10$) 94–102mm, wing of female ($n = 9$) 92–106mm; tail of male ($n = 10$) 65.5–70.0mm; tail of female ($n = 9$), 67–75mm; bill of male ($n = 4$, to skull, 16.05–17.58mm), bill of female ($n = 7$, to feathers), 11mm ($n = 4$, to skull, 15.32–16.61mm); tarsus of male ($n = 10$) 18–20mm, tarsus of female ($n = 7$) 19.5–21.0mm. Males average shorter in tail-length than females, but possess a marginally longer wing-chord (Brooks *et al.* 1999). Mean weight (sexes combined): 49–60g (Brooks *et al.* 1999, Snow 2004a, Dunning 2008). Brooks *et al.* (1999) found that females average slightly heavier than males.

GEOGRAPHICAL VARIATION Monotypic.

VOICE Generally, Purple-throated Cotinga vocalises rather infrequently. The species' primary song recalls that of Dusky-capped Flycatcher *Myiarchus tuberculifer*, or a raptor (Schulenberg *et al.* 2007), being described by Hilty and Brown (1986) as a high-pitched complaining *preeeeeeer*, which lasts 1–2 seconds and may be repeated over and over from within the crown of a tree. This vocalisation is lightly longer and drops more in pitch than the similar call of the flycatcher (Ridgely and Greenfield 2001). Also gives a tremulous, trisyllabic *werleeyooo*, interspersed with the first call type (Zimmer *et al.* 1997). Recordings of calls are available on the Moore (1996), Krabbe and Nilsson (2003) and Marantz and Zimmer (2006) compilations.

NATURAL HISTORY Noted from the midstorey to canopy of lowland tropical forests and is often difficult to observe unless via a canopy tower or walkway. Purple-throated Cotinga is often recorded in pairs, although birds are also not infrequently observed alone. Pairs can, however, remain well separated whilst feeding.

FOOD AND FEEDING The species regularly joins other frugivorous birds, including other cotingas and toucans, at fruiting events, including at *Cecropia* (Urticaceae) trees, and it also takes *Coussapoa* (Urticaceae) and *Ficus* (Moraceae) fruits, but it often remains relatively inconspicuous even at such melees (GMK pers. obs.). All of Robinson's (1997) observations of this species at Cocha Cashu in southeast Peru were in close proximity to *Coussapoa* trees. *Porphyrolaema* sometimes joins mixed-species feeding flocks (Hosner *et al.* 2009). It has been observed perch-gleaning, bending almost vertically down from a branch in the canopy to reach small fruits (Whittaker 1996a).

BREEDING The few available moult data (see Description) indicate that the species may breed year-round or virtually so, although the only actual breeding data are from the year-end. Very few data exist regarding the species' nesting behaviour. A nest was observed and videotaped from a canopy tower in eastern Ecuador, at Yuturi Lodge, by C. F. Collins (*in litt.* 2007 and 2008), in late December 1997. This nest was placed in a subcanopy tree *c.*20m above the ground, at the junction of at least two more or less horizontal and rather narrow branches, and was reasonably well shaded from direct sunlight. The female alone attended the nest and appeared to be incubating, during which times she remained largely vigilant, but a male (presumed to be the partner) was frequently seen in the general vicinity of the nest, perhaps remaining 'on guard'. Furthermore, there is a male with slightly enlarged testes from southeastern Peru, also collected in December (MVZ). There are no other data available.

STATUS The species is currently treated as of Least Concern (BirdLife International 2004, 2008) although it was formerly listed as Near Threatened (Collar *et al.* 1992). Purple-throated Cotinga is rare to uncommon within its large range, and rather local, especially in Brazil, where despite its very wide range the species is still known from just a couple of handfuls of localities (although at one, Arumã, on the Rio Purus, Samuel M. Klages collected 13 birds in six weeks), and Colombia, where it is also known from very few sites (Hilty and Brown 1986). In southeast Peru, Terborgh *et al.* (1990) found the species to occur at very low densities (just two individuals per 100ha), which is almost certainly also the case elsewhere across

the species' range. *Porphyrolaema* is known from several protected areas, throughout the species' entire range, including the 293,000ha Amacayacu and Tinigua National Parks (Colombia), the 603,000ha Cuyabeno Faunistic Production Reserve and Yasuni National Park (Ecuador), the 1,789,806ha Manu National Park (e.g. at Manu Wildlife Center) and Bahuaja-Sonene National Park (Peru), and the 1,500ha Rio Cristalino Forest Reserve and 258,813ha Guarajá-Mirim State Park (Brazil).

REFERENCES BirdLife International (2004, 2008), Brooks *et al.* (1999, 2009), Cadena *et al.* (2000), Collar *et al.* (1992), Dunning (2008), Gyldenstolpe (1951), Haffer (1974), Hellmayr (1929b), Hilty and Brown (1986), Hosner *et al.* (2009), Krabbe and Nilsson (2003), Lane *et al.* (2003), Marantz and Zimmer (2006), Moore (1996), Ohlson *et al.* (2007), Parker *et al.* (1994c), Pinto (1944), Ridgely and Greenfield (2001), Ridgely and Tudor (1994, 2009), Remsen and Parker (1995), Restall *et al.* (2006), Robinson (1997), Salaman *et al.* (2008), Schulenberg *et al.* (2007), Sibley (1996), Sick (1997), Snethlage (1914), Snow (1982, 2004a), Stotz *et al.* (1996), Tello *et al.* (2009), Terborgh *et al.* (1990), Walker (2009), Walker *et al.* (2006), Whittaker (1996a, 1996b), Zimmer *et al.* (1997).

Purple-throated Cotinga *Porphyrolaema porphyrolaema*. **Fig. 1**. Male, Explornapo Lodge, dpto. Loreto, northeast Peru, July (*Roger Ahlman / www.pbase.com/ahlman*). Generally rare and rather poorly known, males of this cotinga are immediately distinguishable from all other members of the family, being perhaps most reminiscent of an over-sized male Rose-breasted Grosbeak *Pheucticus ludovicianus*. **Fig. 2**. Female, Manu National Park, dpto. Madre de Dios, southeast Peru, November (*Chris Gooddie*). Females are rather less easily identifiable, with particular care being required to separate this species from females of any of the, usually much more frequently encountered, *Cotinga* cotingas in range, especially Spangled *C. cayana* and Plum-throated Cotingas *C. maynana*. This photo, although distant, clearly shows the small orangey chin patch and the barred crown and underparts, which will always identify *Porphyrolaema*.

Genus *Gymnoderus*: Bare-necked Fruitcrow

The Bare-necked Fruitcrow *Gymnoderus foetidus* is now known to form part of the core Cotingidae, namely the subfamily Cotinginae (see Systematics, p. 43), within which it is one for three monospecific genera that comprise the *Gymnoderus* group. Other cotingas or reasonably close allies that share powder-down-covered plumage include the genera *Iodopleura* (purpletufts), *Xipholena* (which too forms part of the so-called *Gymnoderus* group: Tello *et al.* 2009) and *Tityra* (Lowery and O'Neill 1966).

BARE-NECKED FRUITCROW
Gymnoderus foetidus — Plate 27

Gracula foetida **Linnaeus, 1758**, *Syst. Nat.*, edn. 10(1): 108, [Surinam]

This bizarre-looking bird is perhaps less ugly in life than it might appear from illustrations. Bare-necked Fruitcrow is a reasonably common and regular sight across much of the lowlands of Amazonia, being habitually found along rivers, although it also enters wooded *cerrados* on the eastern fringes of the basin in Brazil.

IDENTIFICATION Male 34–39cm, female 30–36cm (Brooks *et al.* 1999 found that males can be significantly larger than females). The male Bare-necked Fruitcrow is unmistakable. At rest the cobalt-blue bare skin of the throat and ocular area permit instant identification of this rather 'vulturine' cotingid. The slighter built female has less extensive bare skin on the long, slender neck; however, the small head with its peak well towards the rear crown, and the slender neck assure its distinctive 'fruitcrow aspect'. The female might recall a female Amazonian Umbrellabird *Cephalopterus ornatus*, and these two species are often found together, but note the fruitcrow's smaller head and longer, slender neck. In flight the male's silvery-grey wing panel is particularly conspicuous at some distance, and the Bare-necked Fruitcrow is perhaps most frequently encountered commuting to and fro across Amazonian tributaries and oxbow lakes. Bare-necked Fruitcrow possesses patches of powder-down (a feature shared with the rather localised Black-faced Cotinga *Conioptilon mcilhennyi*), which gives a pale 'bloom' to the plumage.

DISTRIBUTION Bare-necked Fruitcrow occurs virtually throughout the Amazon basin, although it is, surprisingly, apparently absent from much of the Rio Negro drainage. In southeast Colombia, the species occurs in the Amazon basin and along the eastern base of the Andes, north to southwest dpto. Meta (at the base of the Sierra Macarena) and through Amazonas, as well as in eastern dpto. Vichada, on the border with Venezuela, thence south through eastern Ecuador and eastern Peru to northern Bolivia, as far south as dptos. La Paz, Cochabamba and northern Santa Cruz, thereafter over most of Amazonian Brazil, south to southern and southwest Mato Grosso (including the northern Pantanal), and east to Maranhão and Tocantins (e.g. in Parque Estadual do Cantão); as well as virtually throughout the Guianas, including swampy coastal forests of French Guiana, e.g. around Awala (Tostain *et al.* 1992, Renaudier 2009), and in Surinam (Ottema *et al.* 2009), as well as once in second growth in Guyana (Snyder 1966), and in southern Venezuela across northwest Bolívar and western and central Amazonas. The species has also been listed, without evidence, for Paraguay by Contreras *et al.*

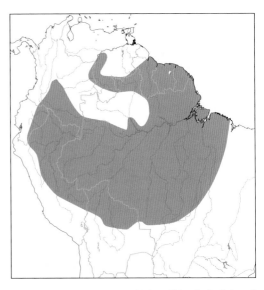

(1990). *Gymnoderus* ranges as high as 650m (in Bolivia and Peru) and 500m (Colombia), but it is mostly found below 300m and not above 200m in Venezuela.

MOVEMENTS The significance of the loose, high-flying flocks (up to 20 strong) that are not infrequently encountered, especially over broad rivers, is unknown, although these are suspected to be performing either short-distance, irregular movements, or perhaps seasonal movements in response to the availability of food supplies, e.g. in northwest Amazonia and coastal Surinam (Haverschmidt and Mees 1994, Lane 2003). The species' occurrence in gallery forests and *cerrados* is perhaps seasonal, mainly in the post-breeding period.

HABITAT Bare-necked Fruitcrow mainly inhabits the forested banks of rivers and oxbow lakes, including seasonally flooded forests, in both *igapó* and *várzea*, and old river islands, but in northeastern Brazil, in Maranhão and Tocantins, it also occurs in better-wooded *cerrados* and gallery forest, albeit usually still in close proximity to rivers. The species also occurs in savanna forests in southern Surinam (Robbins *et al.* 2004) and, as noted above, in waterlogged coastal forests in both French Guiana and Surinam (Tostain *et al.* 1992, Ottema *et al.* 2009). It is also occasionally found well away from water, e.g. in southern Mato Grosso, Brazil (GMK pers. obs.).

DESCRIPTION A large and rather long-necked, but comparatively short-tailed cotingid, with a large patch of bare skin, principally over the neck. Compared with other fruitcrows, to which this species does not appear particularly closely related (see Systematics, p. 43), it has a smaller, less stout and more flattened bill, but the legs and feet are strong, as in other fruitcrows, whilst the head and neck are very densely feathered. *Gymnoderus* lacks rictal bristles. The sexes differ in plumage, and the female is also smaller than the male. *Adult male.* – Rather sleek and long-winged; the small, rather triangular head is covered in short velvety-black feathers on the crown and nape. Neck mostly bare, the skin bluish-white to cobalt-blue, and appearing elaborately folded and wattled, especially over the rear part, with a large knob-like 'boil' immediately below the eye and the rest rather smoother with fewer folds. The few feathers present on the lores and throat are black and also velvety. The body plumage is black with a contrasting silvery-white panel in the wings. Closer inspection reveals that the outer webs to the tertials and secondaries are pale ash-grey (the inner two tertials all grey). The tips and inner webs to these feathers are black, but lie concealed on the folded wing, although in sunlight they can appear as a solid silvery-white area in the wing. Greater coverts ash-grey (median coverts grey, hued blackish). Patches of grey are also present on the outer webs of the greater primary-coverts. Underparts black (although some males have random greyish patches on the flanks). Underwing-coverts black with a greyer underside to the remiges. *Adult female.* – Greyer above than the male, but still very dark and appears basically black in the field. Feathers of the crown are blackest, and are short and velvety as in the male. Lacks the conspicuous silvery-white wing panel of the male; the very narrow tips and fringes to the rectrices and remiges are pale grey, but these are not likely to be apparent in the field. Bare skin of neck cobalt blue, but this largely lacks the ornamental folded effect of the male. There are some whitish-grey feathers on the flanks and belly. Underside of remiges and rectrices grey. *Juvenile/Immature.* – Predominantly white, and likened by Lane (2003) to a miniature Great Potoo *Nyctibius grandis* (!), with a small naked moustachial, narrow dark chevrons on the breast, scaling on the throat and crown, vermiculations on the rump, and dark smudging and subterminal bars on many of the wing feathers, as well as a blackish-grey tail with whitish tips. Some details of the nestling were provided by Béraut (1970). Thereafter plumage progression requires three moults before reaching adulthood, but the species acquires mainly dark body plumage after the first (post-juvenile) moult, albeit with white bands on the belly, chin and scapulars, and a still mainly white crown and face (see Snow 1982, 2004a, Ridgely and Greenfield 2001, Lane 2003). Once the second moult is complete, young females are practically indistinguishable from adults of the same sex, but in subadult males at this stage the wing-coverts are clearly slightly darker than those of adult males (Snow 1982). *Moult.* – There are few published data concerning the annual moult cycle, but Snow (1982) recorded that replacement appears to commence in October–March in southern Peru, Bolivia and Mato Grosso, Brazil, and seems to start roughly at the same time in both sexes. However, further north the onset of feather renewal becomes progressively later, for instance it is principally in December–May in the middle and lower Amazon, and mainly February–May in the Guianas and Venezuela. Snow (1976) suggested that moult occupies *c*.190 days. *Bare parts.* – Bill slate-grey below with a darker tip and the upper mandible is blackish (and mouth lining yellow); the legs are rather short and mid grey to blackish-grey (perhaps more greenish-grey in non-adults and dull olive in juveniles); whilst the large irides are deep brown to golden-brown outwith a broader band of cerulean blue-grey, fading to grey on the outer rim (Lane 2003). There is no geographical variation in iris colour (Lane 2003), as was originally postulated by Snow (1982).

MEASUREMENTS (Gyldenstolpe 1951, Snow 1982, except bill (BMNH); Haverschmidt 1952, Bates *et al.* 1989, Brooks *et al.* 1999, Lane 2003; RMNH for weight) Wing of male (*n* = 15) 205–223mm, wing of female (*n* = 28) 185–202mm; tail of male (*n* = 15) 124–140mm, tail of female (*n* = 28) 118–130mm; bill of male (*n* = 6) 28–33mm, bill of female (*n* = 5) 26–30mm; tarsus of male (*n* = 10) 18.0–20.5mm, tarsus of female (*n* = 13) 18–20mm. Males average slightly larger than females in wing-chord and tail-length (Brooks *et al.* 1999). Weight (only adults): 300–430g (males) and 220–241g (females) (Snow 1982, Lane 2003, Snow 2004a, Dunning 2008; FMNH). Young males may weigh as little as 199g (RMNH), but overall males average slightly heavier than females (Brooks *et al.* 1999).

GEOGRAPHICAL VARIATION Monotypic.

VOICE First described by Penard and Penard (1910). Recalls that of Amazonian Umbrellabird, it being a foghorn-like, bellowing *oooooo*, given whilst simultaneously inflating the bare neck, but which is easily missed above the sound of running water. It was likened by Sick (1997) to a sonorous growl.

NATURAL HISTORY Social, but the species is also frequently encountered alone or in pairs. Sometimes rather wary and Bare-necked Fruitcrows rarely permit very close approach. The species is principally found in the canopy and subcanopy, but Naumburg (1930) related how G. K. Cherrie had collected a male in Mato Grosso, which he flushed from the ground, where he thought it might have been feeding on fallen fruits. Bare-necked Fruitcrow flies with distinctive, deep, rowing wingbeats, not unlike those of Amazonian Umbrellabird (see also Identification). Brooks *et al.* (1999) observed a *Gymnoderus* being 'mobbed' by a female Spangled Cotinga *Cotinga cayana* and a Cinereous Mourner *Laniocera hypopyrrha*.

FOOD AND FEEDING Diet is somewhat more catholic than many cotingas but is still principally frugivorous, with palm *Oenocarpus* and *Euterpe* fruits (Arecaceae), *Cecropia* catkins (Moraceae) and perhaps *Miconia* fruits (Melastomataceae) amongst those genera recorded (Novaes 1980a, Snow 1982, 2004a, Whittaker 1996a, Lane 2003). Comparatively large seeds, of up to 13g, have been found in the species' stomach contents (Schubart *et al.* 1965). Robinson (1997) noted a strong attachment between this species and Lauraceae, the birds often constructing their nests in close proximity to fruiting trees of this family. Groups of up to 25 can congregate at a cluster of fruiting lauraceous trees, including nesting females, sometimes with other 'cotingas' such as White-browed Purpletuft *Iodopleura isabellae* and Spangled Cotinga *Cotinga cayana* (as well as toucans, parrots, oropendolas and tanagers), but lone adults can also defend a tree in fruit. Fruit are plucked whilst perched. Also takes insects, probably opportunistically (or perhaps seasonally), including large mantids and grasshoppers, caught by running across tree branches (toucan-like and highly atypically for a cotinga, but most recalling Amazonian Umbrellabird, or a rail), and flying ants or termites, which are caught during high aerial sallies up to 50m above the treetops (Whittaker 1996a, Robinson 1997, Lane 2003). Groups of up to eight fruitcrows have been noted indulging in such behaviour (Robinson 1997).

427

DISPLAY Displaying males vigorously shake the head and periodically retract the neck whilst simultaneously inflating the neck wattles and calling, the emitting of sound being accompanied by a slight upward dart of the head, with the bill held slightly open (Lane 2003). Males chase each other between trees up to 10m apart in slow flights, sometimes repeatedly; those with the most extensive and bluest folded neck skin appear dominant in such circumstances (Robinson 1997).

BREEDING In the south of its range, the species lays eggs principally in September–February, but the onset of laying probably becomes later further north (based on moult data, as feather renewal presumably occurs post-breeding as in other cotingas). Clutch size is apparently one egg, incubated by the female alone, but only a few nests (from Mato Grosso and the upper Rio Xingu, Brazil, and eastern Ecuador and southeast Peru) have ever been found, and just four have been described in any level of detail. Of the three in Brazil, one was a very small and shallow cup constructed of lichens and/or dry twigs, and fine tendrils, and coated in white fungus. It was placed 6–10m above the ground on a thick horizontal branch. One nest was under construction in late January, another had a chick that hatched on 2 December, and the third, in the crown of a *Caryocar brasiliensis* (Caryocaraceae) tree, was at an unknown stage in October (Sick 1957, Béraut 1970). It seems likely that the female covers the entire nest when incubating. The most recently described nest, in Ecuador, at Sani Lodge, was similar, but was placed 40m above the ground in a *Ceiba* (Bombacaceae) and contained a single small young, just visible above the nest's rim, in late March (Greeney and Gelis 2008). At the same site, a fledged juvenile was observed in early August (GMK pers. obs.). In southeast Peru, Robinson (1997) found six nests in 1980, four in 1982 and two in 1983, 11 of the 12 within 25m of an oxbow lake, eight in *Dipteryx pentandra* (Leguminoseae) trees at 40–50m above the ground, two in *Cedrela odorata* (Meliaceae) at 15 and 17m, one in a *Ficus insipida* (Moraceae) at 20m and the last in an unidentified tree 25m off the ground. The same author noted a group of eight *Gymnoderus*, including two males, drive away three White-throated Toucans *Ramphastos tucanus cuvieri* that were within 100m of two of these nests. There are no other breeding data, and despite the relatively large number of nests that have been found (compared with many of the species covered in this book) this species' breeding ecology certainly still 'begs' serious study.

STATUS Treated as Least Concern by BirdLife International (2004, 2008). Bare-necked Fruitcrow can be regarded as fairly common across much of Amazonia, but is perhaps rarer in the Guianan Shield, where it is considered uncommon in Guyana (Restall *et al.* 2006), uncommon to rare across Surinam (Ottema *et al.* 2009) but locally frequent in French Guiana (principally in the coastal strip) (Tostain *et al.* 1992, Restall *et al.* 2006). At one study site in southeast Peru, Terborgh *et al.* (1990) estimated this species' density to be just two individuals per 100ha. It has only recently been recorded in the Brazilian state of Amapá (Pacheco 2000). The species also seems inexplicably patchily distributed through the Rio Negro drainage, although *Gymnoderus* is known from Jaú National Park (Borges *et al.* 2001), as well as from a great many other protected areas over its wide range.

REFERENCES Aleixo and Guilherme (2010), Ames (1971), Bates *et al.* (1989), Béraut (1970), BirdLife International

(2004, 2008), Blake (1962), Borges (2007), Borges *et al.* (2001), Braun *et al.* (2007), Brooks *et al.* (1999, 2009), Cadena *et al.* (2000), Cherrie (1916), Contreras *et al.* (1990), Dunning (2008), Greeney and Gelis (2007), Gyldenstolpe (1951), Haffer (1974), Haverschmidt (1952), Haverschmidt and Mees (1994), Hellmayr (1910, 1929b), Hennessey *et al.* (2003a, 2003b), Hilty (2003), Hilty and Brown (1986), Lane (2003), Lane *et al.* (2003), Lees *et al.* (2008), Maillard *et al.* (2007), Mestre *et al.* (2010), Naka *et al.* (2006), Naumburg (1930), Novaes (1980a), Ohlson *et al.* (2007), Olson (1971), Oren and Parker (1997), Ottema *et al.* (2009), Pacheco (2000), Pacheco and Olmos (2005), Pacheco *et al.* (2007), Parker *et al.* (1994a, 1994b, 1994c), Penard and Penard (1910), Peres and Whittaker (1991), Pinheiro and Dornas (2009a), Pinto (1944), Remsen *et al.* (1987), Renaudier (2009), Restall *et al.* (2006), Ridgely and Greenfield (2001), Ridgely and Tudor (1994, 2009), Robbins *et al.* (2004), Robinson (1997), Rosenberg (1990), Salaman *et al.* (2008), Salvin and Godman (1891), Schubart *et al.* (1965), Schulenberg *et al.* (2006, 2007), Sick (1957, 1997), Silva (1996), Snethlage (1907, 1908a), Snow (1976, 1982, 2004a), Snyder (1966), Souza *et al.* (2008), Stotz *et al.* (1996, 1997), Terborgh *et al.* (1990), Governo do Estado Tocantins (2004), Tostain *et al.* (1992), Trolle and Walther (2004), Tubelis and Tomas (2003), Vidoz *et al.* (2010), Warter (1965), Whittaker (1996a), Whittaker and Oren (1999), Willis and Oniki (1990), Zimmer and Hilty (1997), Zimmer *et al.* (1997).

1

Bare-necked Fruitcrow *Gymnoderus foetidus*. **Fig. 1**. Male, Explornapo Lodge, dpto. Loreto, northeast Peru, September (*Hadoram Shirihai / Photographic Handbook to Birds of the World*). This fruitcrow is often first seen in 'woodpecker-like' flight over a river. It is unlikely to be confused with any other species. **Fig. 2**. Male, Amazonia Lodge, Manu National Park, dpto. Madre de Dios, southeast Peru, October (*Hadoram Shirihai / Photographic Handbook to Birds of the World*). A close study of the bizarre head adornments. **Fig. 3**. Female, Manu Wildlife Centre, dpto. Madre de Dios, southeast Peru, month unknown (*Joe Tobias / Edward Grey Institute, Oxford University*). In profile views, females are easily separated from males by the overall dark wings, but when head-on note the much-reduced blue facial skin and the duller black underparts with some white feather tips.

Genus *Conioptilon*: Black-faced Cotinga

This monotypic genus was one of two such taxonomic novelties within the Cotingidae to be described from Peru in the space of less than 15 years during the middle third of the 20th century, the other being *Zaratornis*. However, whilst the latter was discovered within close proximity to the capital, Lima, the Black-faced Cotinga *Conioptilon mcilhennyi* hails from the Peruvian Amazon, which at that time, the early 1960s, was still relatively unexplored by ornithologists. Other cotingas or reasonably close allies that share powder-down-covered plumage, to a greater or lesser extent, include *Iodopleura*, *Xipholena* (which too forms part of the so-called *Gymnoderus* group: Tello *et al.* 2009) and *Tityra* (Lowery and O'Neill 1966).

BLACK-FACED COTINGA
Conioptilon mcilhennyi   Plate 27

Conioptilon mcilhennyi **Lowery & O'Neill, 1966**, *Auk* 83: 3, Balta, Río Curanja, Loreto, Peru

Described as recently as 1966, this distinctly vocal though unremarkably (albeit distinctively) plumaged cotinga was formerly considered endemic to southeast Peru, but within the last decade or so has been discovered in extreme southwest Brazil and northern Bolivia. Like a great many cotingas, our knowledge of this species' life history is still in its infancy and would greatly benefit from specially focused studies.

IDENTIFICATION 23cm. Black-faced Cotinga is unlikely to be confused given its all-black face and throat (in all plumages) and the dark grey upperparts. Tityras are similarly sized but, except the male Black-crowned Tityra *Tityra inquisitor*, always show some red on the face and/or bill, whilst none has an entirely black chin and throat, and the cotinga is also proportionately longer tailed. The Sirystes *Sirystes sibilator*, a flycatcher that regularly occurs high in the canopy (and which too was long ago placed in the Cotingidae), also has superficially similar overall plumage, but it too lacks the black face and throat.

DISTRIBUTION Restricted to a comparatively small area of southwest Amazonia, where it is known from about six localities in southeast Peru, in dptos. Ucayali, Cuzco and Madre de Dios (all but one of these north of the Río

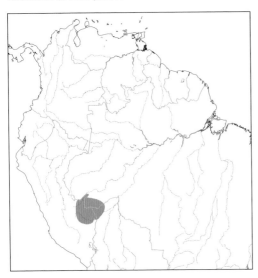

Madre de Dios), and adjacent northwest Bolivia, in Pando (where discovered as recently as July 2001, but speculated to occur in the past due to T. A. Parker's record of Hauxwell's Thrush *Turdus hauxwelli* mimicking the voice *Conioptilon*), and in extreme southwestern Brazil, where known from four localities within the drainage of the upper Rio Juruá, in Acre, all within less than 70km of the Peruvian border (Whittaker and Oren 1999; J. Minns and R. Parrini pers. obs.). More recently the species has been found along the upper Rio Purus, at Estação Ecológica do Rio Acre and in the southeastern part of the Reserva Extrativista Chico Mendes as well as in the municipalities of Bujari and Porto Acre, just north of Rio Branco, all five of which localities are also in Acre, but up to 100km from the Bolivian and Peruvian borders (Aleixo and Guilherme 2008, Guilherme and Dantas 2008, Mestre *et al.* 2009, Aleixo and Guilherme 2010). The Chico Mendes reserve represents the easternmost point of the species' known distribution (Mestre *et al.* 2009). Principally recorded below 300m, Black-faced Cotinga is rarely recorded as high as 450m (e.g. in Manu National Park: Walker *et al.* 2006), but has been seen once at 700m, along the Río Caimisea (G. Angehr *in* Lloyd 2000).

MOVEMENTS None described to date and Black-faced Cotinga certainly does not appear to make seasonal movements in response to changing food resources, at least in southeast Peru (H. Lloyd *in litt.* 2010). However, the species certainly seems capable of some wandering, which might explain the record from the Río Caimisea mentioned above.

HABITAT Black-faced Cotinga is known principally from the canopy of floodplain forest, especially in Peru, both *terra firme* and more especially seasonally flooded forest (*várzea*), at lake and slow-flowing river edges, but as found by Lloyd (2000) the bird is far from being exclusively an edge species. It perhaps shows greatest preference for sites that remain waterlogged year-round (Schulenberg *et al.* 2007), but in southwest Brazil the species has also been recorded around clearings and in treefall gaps within *terra firme* up to 4km distant from any river, and even more surprisingly it seems commoner in burned *terra firme* than unburned forests in this region (Mestre *et al.* 2009).

DESCRIPTION In size and shape Black-faced Cotinga most closely resembles cotingas of the genus *Carpodectes*. Some feathers on the face, crown and throat are slightly elongate with shiny and hardened tips. Abundant patches of powder-down are scattered over the body, and a powdery-white bloom also appears on the remiges and rectrices, as well as over the paler contour feathers. The female is slightly smaller than the male, but their plumage is fundamentally identical (although Lowery and O'Neill 1966 suggested that females incline to be paler and slightly more vermiculated ventrally). Both sexes have well-developed rictal bristles. The bill is broad-based and slightly rounded over the culmen with a slightly hooked tip. *Adult.* – Jet black face, chin, throat and crown, with a partial whitish border at the rear of the ear-coverts, entirely dark grey upperparts, becoming even darker, almost slate, on the wings and tail, whilst the underparts are also grey, but much paler, and grade to whitish on the lower belly and the undertail-coverts. Underwing-coverts grey vermiculated white. *Juvenile/ Immature.* – Juvenile known solely from observations by Tobias (2003b), who observed a well-grown (almost adult-sized) young in the nest which appeared uniformly pale grey (i.e. without any black on the head), with an even paler face and was covered in pale and black-mottled down. The only other information comes from a specimen of a subadult female which has the black feathers of the head and throat, as well as the dark feathers of the wing- and uppertail-coverts tipped whitish, whilst the inner webs of the secondaries are broadly fringed white and the undertail-coverts have noticeable subterminal grey bars (Lowery and O'Neill 1966). *Moult.* – Nothing is known. *Bare parts.* – Irides dark reddish-brown, the bill greyish-brown, and the moderately strong legs and feet are olive-grey (Lowery and O'Neill 1966).

MEASUREMENTS (from Lowery and O'Neill 1966, Whittaker and Oren 1999; culmen from tip to feathers; FMNH: Peru and Brazil) Wing of male ($n = 3$) 146–153mm, wing of female ($n = 9$) 139–143mm; tail of male ($n = 3$) 93–96mm, tail of female ($n = 9$) 90–96mm; bill of male ($n = 3$) 16.5–18.3mm, bill of female ($n = 9$) 16.0–17.6mm; tarsus of male ($n = 3$) 23.4–25.8mm, tarsus of female ($n = 9$) 23.3–24.8mm. Weight: 89–91g (two males) and 81g (a female).

GEOGRAPHICAL VARIATION Monotypic.

VOICE Vocalisations best described by Snow (1982), Whittaker and Oren 1999; Tobias (2003b) and Schulenberg *et al.* (2007), and three examples, from Peru and Brazil, are available online at www.xeno-canto.org. The most frequently heard call (presumably the song) is a squeaky, upwardly inflected *brriiing* or *huuEEE*, which recalls that of Smooth-billed Ani *Crotophaga ani*, but initially sounds like a Screaming Piha *Lipaugus vociferans* warming-up, and is far more ringing and prolonged than that of the cuckoo. Black-faced Cotinga is comparatively noisy for a cotinga and vocalises comparatively frequently. During calling bouts, this voice may be given once every 15–20 seconds or even less. The contact-call is a simple, rather flat *pew* note, given repeatedly interspersing song bouts (J. W. Fitzpatrick *in* Snow 1982; cf. S. M. Dantas recording, XC17649) and is also used between counter-calling pairs (Snow 2004a). Schulenberg *et al.* (2007) also mentioned a quiet descending *coww.*

NATURAL HISTORY Black-faced Cotinga is usually encountered singly or in pairs, occasionally in groups of up to four (Terborgh *et al.* 1984) or six (H. Lloyd *in litt.* 2010). In southwest Brazil, Mestre *et al.* (2009) recorded the species in association with the following other canopy frugivores: Cobalt-winged Parakeet *Brotogeris cyanoptera* (in 31% of their observations), Plumbeous Pigeon *Patagioenas plumbea* (31%), Ruddy Pigeon *P. subvinacea* (23%), Dusky-headed Parakeet *Aratinga weddellii* (23%), Blue-headed Macaw *Primolius couloni* (15%), Mealy Parrot *Amazona farinosa* (15%), Purple-throated Fruitcrow *Querula purpurata*

(15%), Painted Parakeet *Pyrrhura picta* (8%), White-bellied Parrot *Pionites leucogaster* (8%) and Blue-headed Parrot *Pionus menstruus* (8%). Pairs apparently roost together, in the subcanopy, calling frequently on first arriving at the perch, then allopreening (Lloyd 2000).

FOOD AND FEEDING The diet is mainly fruit including *Cecropia, Coussapoa* (Urticaceae) and *Ficus* (Moraceae), taken during a brief hovering flight, like many cotingas, but this is supplemented with an unknown proportion of insects, including winged ants and termites, taken during aerial sallies (Davis *et al.* 1991, Robinson 1997), presumably opportunistically. Perhaps exceptionally, the species is also known to take flower parts. It regularly gathers at fruiting trees with other frugivores, including various tanagers, parakeets and toucanets, as well as Bare-necked Fruitcrow *Gymnoderus foetidus*, Purple-throated Fruitcrow, Plum-throated Cotinga *Cotinga maynana* and Purple-throated Cotinga *Porphyrolaema porphyrolaema*, but Black-faced Cotinga probably does not follow mobile mixed-species flocks.

BREEDING J. W. Fitzpatrick (*in* Snow 1982) suggested that the breeding period was likely to occur between September and December (the main breeding period for most species in the relevant region of Peru), and this has been borne out by subsequent discoveries, with two nests being found in southeast Peru, both in September (Tobias 2003b). The Black-faced Cotinga is distinctly unusual amongst Cotingidae, especially Amazonian species, insomuch as males play some part in provisioning the young, and also remain with the female during the nest construction process. However, much more information is required to accurately quantify the division of parental responsibilities during the breeding period. One pair was observed at a nest 15m above the ground in a *Cecropia* in mid September; after two days the birds abandoned the first nest and commenced to build another in the same tree and at the same height. Only the presumed female was involved in the construction work, bringing scraps of plant fibre which were wound onto a two-way fork, but the male was in constant, close attendance, presumably 'guarding' the female (which behaviour has not been reported in any other Cotingidae, but is known among some other genera covered by this book, e.g. *Iodopleura*). No further data were collected at this nest. A second nesting pair discovered in late September of the same year (2001) also had a tiny, fragile nest sited in a two-way fork, which was virtually invisible from ground level, this one being *c.*35m above the ground in a *Ceiba* (Bombacaceae) tree, and in which there was also a nest of Ornate Hawk-Eagle *Spizaetus ornatus*. Both members of the pair fed the single well-grown nestling. In both instances, the adults vocalised continuously (giving both the 'song' and contact-calls: see Voice). Whittaker and Oren (1999), based on gonadal data, suggested that May marked the end of the reproductive period in southwest Brazil.

STATUS Black-faced Cotinga is a restricted-range species which was formerly treated as Near Threatened (Collar *et al.* 1994), but has since been downlisted to Least Concern with an overall range possibly as large as 150,000km^2 (BirdLife International 2004, 2008). Known solely from the Inambari Centre of endemism (Cracraft 1985), the species' population in suitable forest in southeast Peru and northwest Bolivia was estimated at 1,153–2,178 individuals (Lloyd 2000). It is considered reasonably common at those sites where it has been recently discovered in Brazil (Aleixo and Guilherme 2010) and Black-faced Cotinga is also frequent in parts of Peru, including Manu National Park and Biosphere Reserve (where it can be found in the garden of Romero Rainforest Lodge and at Casa Machiguenga: Walker 2009). *Conioptilon* was frequently observed in the late 1990s in the environs of EcoAmazonia lodge, on the north bank of the Río Madre de Dios (H. Lloyd *et al.* 2010). Terborgh *et al.* (1984) considered it reasonably common at Cocha Cashu, also within the confines of Manu National Park, but even there the same team estimated densities to be just one individual per 100ha (Terborgh *et al.* 1990). However, its range has suffered some disturbance and development, being opened up for oil and gas exploration and extraction, selective logging, and associated road building and human colonisation (see BirdLife International 2004, Mestre *et al.* 2009). The Brazilian state of Acre lies within the so-called 'arc of deforestation' and much suitable habitat for the species there must have been lost prior to this cotinga being

discovered in the country. Black-faced Cotinga appears intolerant of high levels of logging (Lloyd 2000) and recently granted logging concessions within its relatively small range offer significant causes of concern (Lloyd 2004), as do the ongoing surveys for oil and gas throughout Madre de Dios and the recent surge in gold-mining activities in this region (H. Lloyd *in litt.* 2010).

REFERENCES Aleixo and Guilherme (2008, 2010), BirdLife International (2004, 2008), Collar *et al.* (1994), Cracraft (1985), Davis *et al.* (1991), Guilherme and Dantas (2008), Lloyd (2000, 2004), Lowery and O'Neill (1966), Mestre *et al.* (2009, 2010), Ohlson *et al.* (2007), Remsen and Traylor (1989), Ridgely and Tudor (1994, 2009), Robinson (1997), Robinson and Terborgh (1997), Schulenberg *et al.* (2007), Snow (1982, 2004a), Stotz *et al.* (1996), Tello *et al.* (2009), Terborgh *et al.* (1984, 1990), Tobias (2003b), Walker (2009), Walker *et al.* (2006), Whittaker and Oren (1999).

Black-faced Cotinga *Conioptilon mcilhennyi.* **Fig. 1.** Adult, Oceania, Iberia, dpto. Madre de Dios, southeast Peru, October (*Hadoram Shirihai / Photographic Handbook to Birds of the World*). **Fig. 2.** Adult, Oceania, Iberia, dpto. Madre de Dios, southeast Peru, October (*Hadoram Shirihai / Photographic Handbook to Birds of the World*). Unusually, there is no sexual dimorphism in this monospecific genus of cotingas.

Genus *Xipholena*: 'purple or white-winged cotingas'

The three species of *Xipholena* are, in some respects, the epitome of what a cotinga should be. Males are magnificently plumaged, with stiff, lacquer-like feathers, and perform striking displays, whilst females are positively dowdy in comparison, for it is they who are (presumably) entirely responsible for the nesting duties. Recent investigation into the mechanisms determining these remarkable cotingas' coloration focused on the Pompadour Cotinga *Xipholena punicea*, with its immaculate burgundy-coloured feathering. Brush (1968) had already identified two ketocarotenoids in its pigments, but LaFountain *et al.* (2010) identified a total of eight ketocarotenoids therein, six of which contained methoxyl groups, which are produced metabolically. This finding is unique among birds. The genus shares a number of characteristics with the wholly trans-Andean *Carpodectes*, including remarkably similar-plumaged females and largely or all-white wings in males, suggesting that they perhaps derive from the same ancestral stock that diverged into two either side of the uplifting Andean chain (Haffer 1970, Snow 1982). Even Hellmayr (1929b) had placed the two genera together, albeit without specifically drawing attention to their apparent relatedness. These gorgeous, intensely coloured cotingas form a superspecies wholly 'cis-Andean' in distribution, with one species, Pompadour Cotinga, widespread in lower Amazonia, the White-tailed Cotinga *Xipholena lamellipennis* endemic to eastern Amazonia and the third, White-winged Cotinga *Xipholena atropurpurea*, restricted to the Brazilian Atlantic Forest. The last-named species is of conservation concern and the status of White-tailed Cotinga is apparently declining given widespread forest loss in the relevant area of Amazonia. All three species appear to be obligate frugivores, with wide gapes permitting larger fruits such as laurels to be consumed. Males of all three species indulge in showy display flights which make them relatively easy to observe, particularly from vantage points such as the Escalera, in Bolívar, southern Venezuela, where the winding road affords a good view over the forest canopy, and thus the chance to find the beautiful Pompadour Cotinga.

POMPADOUR COTINGA
Xipholena punicea   Plate 22

Turdus puniceus **Pallas, 1764**, in *Vroeg. Cat., Adumbrat.*: 2, South America [= Surinam, *fide* Hellmayr 1929b]

The most widespread and common of the genus, the male Pompadour Cotinga is also, arguably, the most splendid of the group, with a name to match. (The word Pompadour was seemingly first applied to the species by G. Edwards in the *Gleanings of Natural History* 3: 275, whilst Linnaeus named it *Ampelis pompadora* in the 12th edition of his *Systema Naturae*, in 1766. The Marquise de Pompadour, who died in 1764, the same year that Pallas named this cotinga scientifically and Edwards published his work, was the long-standing and influential mistress of Louis XV of France, and also originated an 18th-century female hairstyle in which the hair at the front was piled-up high on a pad.) Nonetheless, it seems surprising that the species is apparently so relatively uncommon and spottily distributed in the lowlands immediately east of the Andes. A watch from dawn at the ZF2 tower just north of Manaus, Brazil, is one place to see this superlative bird at its marvellous best, high up in the treetops.

IDENTIFICATION 18.8–23.0cm. Both sexes should prove unmistakable if seen well, as all three species of *Xipholena* are apparently allopatric, although this species and the next presumably come close and perhaps overlap each other on the west bank of the lower Rio Tapajós, as well as apparently at Borba, on the east bank of the Rio Madeira (see next species). However, male White-tailed Cotinga *Xipholena lamellipennis* is not easily confused with Pompadour, given its overall much darker plumage and longer, white tail, but females of the two are not so easily distinguished. Female Pompadour is overall darker, especially on the underparts, which appear decidedly less mottled (although note that some have almost clean white bellies and undertail-coverts),

with perhaps marginally less white in the wing, and the bill is perhaps marginally paler.

DISTRIBUTION Pompadour Cotinga ranges across the Guianan Shield and central and western Amazonia, including the entire Guianas (where it seems reasonably widespread and common in Guyana, but is generally more restricted to interior sites in Surinam and French Guiana), throughout southern Venezuela (south of the Orinoco), to easternmost Colombia (in eastern Guainía to eastern Vaupés, and once in northern Arauca), with one record in southeast Ecuador (locality untraced, but believed to be in southeast Pastaza; cf. Boyla and Estrada 2005), and is regular at two sites in northeast Peru, in white-sand (*varillal*) forest west of Iquitos, dpto. Loreto (where the species was initially discovered only in 1996; Alvarez Alonso 2002,

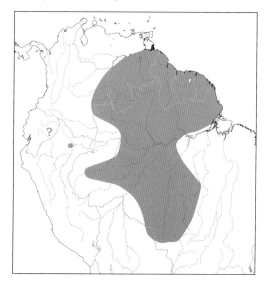

Alvarez Alonso and Whitney 2003, Shany *et al.* 2007). It is found in Brazil, north of the Amazon from the Rio Negro drainage east to Amapá, and south of the river from the Rio Juruá and south of Tefé east to the lower Rios Madeira and Tapajós (in western Pará, in the Serra do Cachimbo), thence south to southern Rondônia, at Guarajá-Mirim (Whittaker 1996b), the northern half of Mato Grosso (e.g. at Alta Floresta, along the Rio Von Den Steinen, and at Barão Melgaço on the Rio Roosevelt) and locally further south in the same state, e.g. at the Serra das Araras Ecological Station (Silva and Oniki 1998), and extreme northeast Bolivia (in northeast Santa Cruz on the Serranía de Huanchaca: Bates *et al.* 1992). Elevational range locally reaches 1,300m in southern Venezuela, on the slopes of tepuis, but Pompadour Cotinga is generally found below 500m.

MOVEMENTS None definitely recorded, although the species probably wanders extensively in search of fruiting trees, and Schomburgk (*in* Chubb 1921) mentioned this species as being recorded in coastal forests of Guyana only in December–February, but specimens from the same country and observations from Surinam do not support this assertion (see Snow 1982, Ottema *et al.* 2009).

HABITAT Pompadour Cotinga was considered to be an obligate white-sand forest specialist by Alvarez Alonso (2002). It inhabits the vine-tangled canopy and borders of humid forest and woodland, principally in *terra firme* forest (many localities, e.g. lower Río Caura, Venezuela), but also *campinarana* (scrubby, low-canopy white-sand forest; e.g. at Junglaven, southern Venezuela), *igapó* (seasonally flooded black-water forest; e.g. at Jaú National Park, Amazonas, northern Brazil) and humid and dry *varillal* (another type of white-sand forest; solely in Peru). At Saint-Eugène, French Guiana, Pompadour Cotinga prefers forest on the slopes and crests of hills (Claessens 1997).

DESCRIPTION The sexes are quite different; the male is resplendently glossy purple and white, and the female predominantly grey with white fringes to the wing-coverts (which are highly modified in the male) and secondaries. Legs and feet are moderately strong. Primaries are un-modified. Lacks rictal bristles. *Adult male.* – Upper body, including the head to back, scapulars and virtually the entire underparts are deep crimson-purple (or wine red), becoming brighter and paler, more crimson to deep pink, and less purple, on the uppertail-coverts to the tail tip, as well as over the tertials and the ventral region. The median and greater wing-coverts are highly modified, being elongated and point-tipped, with whitish shafts, and like much of the rest of the plumage possess a hardened, stiffened texture. The rest of the wings are clean bright white, with dusky-black tips to the primaries (most extensive on the outer webs, and also visible on the underside). There is a strikingly aberrant (apparently leucistic: H. van Grouw pers. comm.) specimen of this species in RMNH, which has some feathers of the underparts (especially the upper breast, chin and flanks) and upperparts (mainly the crown, mantle, scapulars, wing-coverts and rump) golden-yellow. However, the possibility remains that the specimen was at some point exposed to excessive heat or pressure, factors that can affect the carotenoid pigments of male *Xipholena* and *Cotinga* species in such ways, as evidenced by a specimen exposed to fire held in COP (see also Görnitz and Rensch 1924, Völker 1952, Snow 1982: 22). LaFountain *et al.* (2010) mentioned another aberrant (orange-coloured) male specimen held in the American Museum of Natural History

(New York). *Adult female.* – Like all female *Xipholena* this is a short-tailed, thrush-like bird. Plumage is largely ash-grey, with a narrow whitish eye-ring and a slightly paler grey belly to undertail-coverts (sometimes with traces of pinkish), becoming blacker over the remiges and rectrices, with white outer fringes to the greater coverts and secondaries, and slightly narrower and greyer fringes to the lesser and median wing-coverts. *Immature.* – Young males pass through two intermediate stages, acquiring full adult plumage after three annual moults (Snow 2004a), with the adult remiges the last feathers to be acquired, just as in congenerics (Friedmann 1948, Snow 1982). Initially identical to female, except for iris colour, but purple feathers soon emerge on the breast, belly and flanks and, usually to a lesser extent, on the face, nape, scapulars, tertials, mantle, rump and uppertail-coverts, at which point the wings are still basically female-like. However, we have also seen males showing full white feathering but no purple (GMK pers. obs.). *Juvenile.* – Resembles female but the irides are dark (usually brownish-red). *Moult.* – Body moult recorded in January–March specimens from Peru and Venezuela, but there is no published information on annual cycle, although males apparently renew their feathers well in advance of females, as is typical of those cotingas in which males take no part in the nesting cycle or parental care (Snow 1982). *Bare parts.* – Irides are clear yellow to whitish-yellow, sometimes creamy; the bill (broad-based and well arched but becoming flattened towards the tip) is greyish or more usually brownish-black to dark brown, sometimes with a paler base, between yellowish- or pinkish-grey, usually with a slightly darker tip; and the legs are grey, greenish-grey or brownish-black to black, with buff-coloured or yellow soles (Snow 1982, 2004a, Willard *et al.* 1991, Ridgely and Tudor 1994, Alvarez Alonso and Whitney 2003; FMNH; MNRJ).

MEASUREMENTS (from Novaes 1976, Snow 1982, Haverschmidt and Mees 1994; CUMZ; FMNH; MNRJ; ZMA; ZISP: northern Brazil, Guyana, Surinam and Venezuela) Wing of male (*n* = 36) 116–129mm, wing of female (*n* = 20) 112–122mm; tail of male (*n* = 35) 64–78mm, tail of female (*n* = 20) 60–72mm; bill of male (*n* = 8) 12–13mm (*n* = 26, to skull, 17.54–20.53mm), bill of female (*n* = 8) 11.5–12.0mm (*n* = 12, to skull, 18.19–19.57mm); tarsus of male (*n* = 10) 21.55–24.61mm, tarsus of female (*n* = 9) 21–23mm. Weight: 60.0–76.4g (males) and 58–76g (females) (Haverschmidt 1952, Novaes 1976, Snow 1982, Willard *et al.* 1991, Alvarez Alonso and Whitney 2003; FMNH; MNRJ; RMNH).

GEOGRAPHICAL VARIATION Monotypic.

VOICE Long considered, like all other *Xipholena*, to be normally silent. The male gives a loud frog-like rattling croak or gurgling notes in song, which is described as being uttered 'rarely' (Beebe 1924, Haverschmidt 1968), but it is featured on the Naka *et al.* (2008) compilation (cf. also A. Renaudier recording, XC38744). A rustling (mechanical) wing noise is given during the male display-flight. Both sexes give a loud, abrupt barking *purp* with the quality of a gruff squeak, and which is sometimes doubled (with the second note rather lower and quieter). This voice is heard regularly in some areas, e.g. in northeast Peru, even during the midday hours, with females considered to give this call more frequently than males (Shany *et al.* 2007). Other published recordings are available on Krabbe and Nilsson (2003), Marantz and Zimmer (2006) and Boesman (2009), and recordings from Brazil and Peru are also available online at www.xeno-canto.org.

NATURAL HISTORY Usually found alone, except when

displaying (see below), perching quietly in the canopy and subcanopy, being generally rather difficult to observe from the ground, unless from an overlook, although at dawn, late afternoon or during and shortly after rainfall, both sexes tend to select a high, prominent perch.

FOOD AND FEEDING Small groups of up to five gather to feed at fruiting trees (but males especially rarely join mobile mixed-species flocks), sometimes with other cotingas (e.g. Spangled *Cotinga cayana* and Purple-breasted *C. cotinga*), toucans, etc., especially favouring palms, *Ficus* and *Brosimum* (Moraceae) in Guyana (Schomburgk 1848); also *Caraipa* sp. (Clusiaceae) in Peru (Shany *et al.* 2007). Pompadour Cotinga has been observed with tanagers, caciques, oropendolas and Spangled Cotinga at a fruiting *Goupia* (Celastraceae) tree in Guyana (GMK and W. Prince pers. obs.), but *Cotinga cayana* can sometimes actively chase-off the present species (B. W. Davis pers. obs.). Also recorded taking insects, including flying ants and termites, using short aerial sallies. In captivity, a female has been recorded eating anoles *Anolis carolinensis* (Delgado and Brooks 2003).

DISPLAY For detailed descriptions and a discussion of the male's displays (which are similar in all three *Xipholena*) see Snow (1971c, 1977c, 1982), and the supplementary notes by Walther (2004). These basically involve much ritualised group activity (often in the unobtrusive presence of females, which observe but do not engage), involving flying slowly from perch to perch (typically perhaps 10–50m apart), the males (typically 2–4) displacing one another from the different lookouts, in almost 'follow the leader' fashion, with the white wings extremely conspicuous against the dark foliage, being almost opened and closed with each wingbeat. Such 'chases' may persist for 30 minutes or more. Display sites may shift over a relatively large area.

BREEDING Whilst the species' displays are obvious and easily observed (from a tower), very few data on breeding are available. Pompadour Cotinga lays a single egg, and the only published nest was discovered in Guyana in March (Beebe 1924). Attended by the female, which was completely concealed when incubating, it was a tiny, but comparatively deep cup of woody tendrils, sited 18m above the ground. The egg was described as very pale greenish-grey, heavily spotted and blotched in drab colours, especially at the large end. Egg dimensions and weight were presented in Beebe (1924) and were repeated by Snow (1982). Another nest, found by L. Coley and D. J. Fisher (*in litt.* 2009) in the state of Bolívar, southeast Venezuela, also in (mid) March (2007), at the base of the Escalera Road in Canaima National Park, was an untidy, deep, open-cup structure sited high in the four-way fork of a hilltop tree. It was primarily constructed of dead twigs, some of which protruded some distance from the centre of the nest. The nest contained one chick, which appeared well grown, as the head seemed almost the same size as that of the female that attended the nest, visiting it twice during *c.*20 minutes of observation. Other breeding data, indicative of seasonality, are as follows. A female was taken in Venezuela with large gonads in February (FMNH; Willard *et al.* 1991), another female with an egg in the oviduct was collected in northern Mato Grosso, Brazil, in early October (Novaes 1976), a male with enlarged testes in March in Guyana (KUNHM), several males and females

in breeding condition in August in extreme northwest Brazil (MNRJ), and a female was seen carrying hair-like nest material in September in eastern Colombia (Hilty and Brown 1986), but moult data suggest that breeding probably occurs year-round. Indeed, birds of both sexes have been collected in breeding condition in Surinam between August and March (RMNH).

STATUS The species was treated as of Least Concern by BirdLife International (2004, 2008). Pompadour Cotinga is uncommon to locally fairly common, especially in sandy-belt forests over its vast range, which still contains huge areas of undisturbed primary forest, but the species is generally more common north of the Amazon than south of it (Ridgely and Tudor 1994; pers. obs.). In French Guiana, Thiollay (1994) estimated the species' density at 4.5 pairs per 100ha at his study site, which was considerably more numerous than either of the blue cotingas present in the same area. Probably generally uncommon in Colombia, where the species was initially found as recently as 1947 (Dugand and Phelps 1947), although it seems reasonably numerous in northeast Guainía, at the border with Venezuela and Brazil (Hilty and Brown 1986). Pompadour Cotinga is known from a reasonable number of protected areas, including Imataca Forest Reserve and Canaima, Yapacana and Serra de la Neblina National Parks (Venezuela), Jaú National Park, Xixuaú reserve, Parque Nacional Montanhas do Tumucumaque, Lago Piratuba Biological Reserve, and the Rio Cristalino Forest Reserve (Brazil), Noel Kempff Mercado National Park (Bolivia), Iwokrama Forest Reserve (Guyana) and the Allpahuayo-Mishana Reserved Zone (Peru), the last-named lying within an Important Bird Area (Boyla and Estrada 2005). Elsewhere, the species is regularly seen close to the coast at Montagne de Kaw and Angoulême in French Guiana (Renaudier 2009).

REFERENCES Aguiar *et al.* (2010), Alvarez Alonso (2002), Alvarez Alonso and Whitney (2003), Barnett *et al.* (2002), Bates *et al.* (1992), Beebe (1924), Beebe and Beebe (1910), Bernard (2008), Blake (1950), Boesman (2009), Borges (2007), Borges *et al.* (2001), Boyla and Estrada (2005), Braun *et al.* (2007), Chubb (1921), Claessens (1997), Cohn-Haft *et al.* (1997), Delgado and Brooks (2003), Dugand and Phelps (1948), Friedmann (1948), Gilliard (1941), Görnitz and Rensch (1924), Haffer (1974, 1992a, 1992b), Haverschmidt (1952), Haverschmidt and Mees (1994), Hellmayr (1910, 1929b), Hilty (2003), Hilty and Brown (1986), Krabbe and Nilsson (2003), LaFountain *et al.* (2010), Lees *et al.* (2008), Marantz and Zimmer (2006), Mitsch (1975), Naka *et al.* (2006, 2008), Naumburg (1930), Novaes (1976, 1978, 1980a), Olson (1971), Ottema *et al.* (2009), Peres and Whittaker (1991), Pinto (1944), Renaudier (2009), Restall *et al.* (2006), Ridgely and Greenfield (2001), Ridgely and Tudor (1994, 2009), Robbins *et al.* (2004, 2007), Salaman *et al.* (2008, 2009), Schomburgk (1848), Schulenberg *et al.* (2007), Shany *et al.* (2007), Sick (1997), Silva (1996), Silva and Oniki (1988), Snow (1971c, 1977c, 1982, 2004a), Snyder (1966), Stotz *et al.* (1996, 1997), Thiollay (1994), Tostain *et al.* (1992), Trolle and Walther (2004), Tubelis (2007), Völker (1952), Walther (2004), Whittaker (1996a, 1996b), Willard *et al.* (1991), Zimmer and Hilty (1997), Zimmer *et al.* (1997).

Pompadour Cotinga *Xipholena punicea*. **Fig. 1**. Male, Linden, northern Guyana, April (*Andrew Whittaker*). The genus *Xipholena* constitutes a superspecies; consequently, at least over most of their ranges, they are easy to identify, even in female plumage, because only one species occurs in any given area. **Fig. 2**. Male, Petit-Saut, northern French Guiana, July (*Marc Chrétien*). **Fig. 3**. Male, Petit-Saut, northern French Guiana, August (*Maxime Dechelle*). In flight this beautiful bird takes on an even more dramatic appearance. **Fig. 4**. Female, Anavilhanas Jungle Lodge, Amazonas, central Amazonian Brazil, December (*Hadoram Shirihai / Photographic Handbook to Birds of the World*). Best identified from the superficially similar *Cotinga* cotingas that might occur sympatrically by the pale irides and broader white fringes to the wing feathers. **Fig. 5**. Male, Las Claritas, Bolívar, southeast Venezuela, November (*David Southall*). Several males were visiting the same fruiting tree, including the individual in the next photograph. **Fig. 6**. Immature male, Las Claritas, Bolívar, southeast Venezuela, November (*David Southall*). Plumage maturation is similar in all three *Xipholena* cotingas, with males gradually gaining the dark, 'waxy' feathers that make them so uniquely recognisable. Even in such 'patchy' plumage condition, immature males should prove readily identifiable.

WHITE-TAILED COTINGA
Xipholena lamellipennis   **Plate 22**

Ampelis lamellipennis **Lafresnaye, 1839**, *Mag. Zool.* 1, cl. 2, pl. 9, South America [= Belém, Pará, Brazil]

Haffer (1970) considered that the genus *Xipholena* offers a classic example of a superspecies group that has diverged into several different species as a result of isolation within different forest refuges during a more arid epoch. Despite subsequent expansion in their ranges with the onset of more humid conditions, divergence had been sufficient for them to maintain reproductive isolation, so although there is certainly no contact between White-tailed and White-winged Cotingas *X. atropurpurea*, the present species and the more widespread Pompadour Cotinga *X. punicea* appear to come into, perhaps infrequent, contact in southwest Pará and in part of southern Amazonas, plausibly only as a result of seasonal wanderings.

IDENTIFICATION 19.0–21.5cm. Both sexes should prove unmistakable if seen well, as White-tailed Cotinga is virtually entirely allopatric with other *Xipholena*, although White-tailed and Pompadour Cotingas seem to overlap with one another on the west bank of the lower Rio Tapajós (and even as far as the Rio Madeira; see below). Male White-tailed Cotinga is not easily confused with Pompadour, given its overall much darker plumage and longer, white tail, but females of the two are less easily distinguished, and without good views will probably prove inseparable. Female Pompadour (which see for further details) is overall darker, especially on the underparts, with perhaps marginally less white in the wings, and the bill is plausibly on average deeper coloured.

DISTRIBUTION White-tailed Cotinga is one of a handful of well-marked species endemic to east Amazonian Brazil (where it is almost entirely confined to the state of Pará), in the lower Amazon basin south of the river, from the west bank of the Rio Tapajós, e.g. at Parintins, east to northern and western Maranhão (e.g. at Miritiba, Bom Jesus da Mata, the Alto Turiaçu reserve and Açailândia), and south to the Serra das Carajás, the Serra do Cachimbo, as far as

Cachoeiras do Curuá, and the Rio Cururu (Hellmayr 1929a, Haffer 1970, 1992a, Snow 1982, Pacheco and Olmos 2005). There are reports of this species as far west as Borba, on the right (east) bank of the Rio Madeira, in Amazonas, well within the known range of *X. punicea* (which species was collected there by Natterer: cf. Hellmayr 1910). Although no records have been formally published, photographs by multiple observers of *X. lamellipennis* at Borba have been posted online (www.arthurgrosset.com/sabirds/white-tailedcotinga.html; www.surfbirds.com). *X. lamellipennis* is generally found in the lowlands, below 400m, but in the Serra dos Carajás, Pará, the species occurs (commonly) to at least 750m.

MOVEMENTS None recorded, although like Pompadour Cotinga this species probably performs seasonal or more nomadic wanderings in search of fruit supplies.

HABITAT White-tailed Cotinga inhabits the canopy and borders of humid lowland primary forest, principally in tall *terra firme* but also at the ecotone between this type and more open, savanna-like *campinaranas* and *canga* vegetation (see Pacheco and Olmos 2005, Pacheco *et al.* 2007). It has also been recorded recently in *igapó* in northeasternmost Pará (Hohnwald 2009).

DESCRIPTION The sexes are quite different; the male is virtually all dark with white wings and tail, the female predominantly grey with white fringes to the wing-coverts (these feathers being highly modified in the male) and tertials. The legs and feet are moderately strong. The primaries are unmodified. Lacks rictal bristles. *Adult male.* – Upper body, including the head to back, scapulars and virtually the entire underparts are deep purplish-black, becoming clean, bright white on the uppertail-coverts and tail, as well as over the undertail-coverts. The median and greater wing-coverts are highly modified, being elongated and point-tipped, with pale shafts (whitish with purplish edges), especially to the outermost, and like much of the rest of its plumage possess a hardened, stiffened texture, with transverse barring (Brush 1969, Olson 1970). Rest of wings clean bright white. *Adult female.* – Like all female *Xipholena*, this species has the appearance of being a short-tailed, thrush-like bird. Plumage is largely ash-grey, with a narrow whitish eye-ring and slightly paler grey upper breast to undertail-coverts, with a distinctly mottled appearance to the breast. Blacker on the remiges and rectrices, with white outer fringes to the greater coverts and secondaries, and slightly narrower and greyer fringes to the median wing-coverts. *Immature.* – Young males pass through one or two intermediate stages, acquiring the full adult plumage after 2–3 annual moults (Snow 2004a), with the adult remiges the last feathers to be acquired (Snow 1982). Subadult males retain dark grey-black markings on the primary tips (and over much of the shaft on the innermost feathers of this tract) and on the outer fringes of the outermost pair of rectrices (MNRJ). *Juvenile.* – Resembles the female but the head and body are paler and browner, the lower back very pale, and it has extensively white lesser wing-coverts and broader pale fringes to the larger wing-coverts (Snow 1982). *Moult.* – There is no published information concerning the annual moult cycle, although males apparently renew their feathers well in advance of females, as in all cotingas in which the males play no part in raising the young (Snow 1982). *Bare parts.* – Irides pale yellow or greyish-yellow to white; the bill (broad-based and reasonably well arched but becoming flattened towards the tip) is dark brownish-horn to blackish; and the legs are brownish-black to black with buff-coloured soles.

MEASUREMENTS (from Snow 1982; FMNH; MNRJ; RMNH; ROM; ZISP: Pará, east Amazonian Brazil) Wing of male (*n* = 23) 111–121mm, wing of female (*n* = 15) 108–117mm; tail of male (*n* = 23) 74–83mm, tail of female (*n* = 15) 67–78mm; bill of male (*n* = 14) 10.5–12.5mm (*n* = 8, to skull, 18.39–20.64mm), bill of female (*n* = 11) 11.0–12.5mm (*n* = 4, to skull, 17.3–20.27mm); tarsus of male (*n* = 14) 20.0–21.5mm, tarsus of female (*n* = 12) 18.5–22.0mm. Weight: 50.6–57.0g (three males) (MPEG *per* A. C. Lees). Previously unknown (Snow 1982, 2004a, Dunning 2008).

GEOGRAPHICAL VARIATION Best treated as monotypic. Griscom and Greenway (1937) described *X. l. pallidior* from the Santarém region, at the western edge of the species' range, on the basis of the female being paler on the underparts. Recognition, as discussed by Snow (1982), does not appear warranted.

VOICE Both sexes give a loud, rather abrupt *purp* or *whirp* call that is probably indistinguishable from the comparable vocalisation of Pompadour Cotinga, but is distinctly more liquid, less hard and flat than that uttered by White-winged Cotinga, although it is occasionally reduced to a *pup* or *whip* note. In series, may be given every *c.*2–3 seconds. A rustling (mechanical) wing noise is given during the display-flight (Marantz and Zimmer 2006). A recording is archived online at www.xeno-canto.org.

NATURAL HISTORY Similar to its congeners. Usually observed alone, perching quietly in the canopy or subcanopy, and around dawn, in the late afternoon or during and shortly after rainfall, both sexes tend to select a prominent perch.

FOOD AND FEEDING Small groups of up to seven can gather to feed at fruiting trees (but the species probably only very infrequently joins mobile mixed-species flocks), sometimes with other cotingas and close allies (e.g. Spangled *Cotinga cayana* and Purple-breasted Cotingas *C. cotinga*, and even White-browed Purpletuft *Iodopleura isabellae*), as well as other frugivores (e.g. Red-throated Piping Guan *Pipile nattereri* and Gould's Toucanet *Selenidera gouldii*), but there are few, if any, details concerning fruit preferences. No published references to insect-feeding, but one was observed flycatching in the Serra dos Carajás, Pará, in September 2007, flying upwards a couple of metres above the canopy (GMK pers. obs.).

DISPLAY The male's display probably usually lacks the group component that is a feature of Pompadour, involving the bird performing a slow vertical flight of *c.*2m from a high perch, before returning to a nearby perch and repeating the same performance *c.*2 minutes later; between flights the wings are held away from the body to better expose the white feathers (Snow 1977c). Sometimes more 'intermediate' flights are performed, which comprise merely brief fluttering movements. Although no female was observed to 'visit' the male by Snow, GMK and C. F. Collins observed a female perching in close proximity to a displaying male in the canopy at the Tapajós National Forest, Pará, in December 2005. However, several males may display in relatively close proximity to one another, within a radius of *c.*300m, and may occasionally chase each other from their favoured perches, but not in the linear fashion of Pompadour. During these flights, the white wings are

almost opened and closed with each wingbeat, just as in *X. punicea*, but the vertical display also reveals the white tail to full effect.

BREEDING Very few data are available concerning the species' breeding. White-tailed Cotinga lays a single pale bluish egg spotted with ashy-violet, more heavily at one end than the other (Pinto 1953, wherein dimensions were also presented), which was found in the only known nest (undescribed), collected in November 1926, near Belém, and sited in a rubber tree just 5m above the ground.

STATUS Treated as of Least Concern (BirdLife International 2004, 2008), the species is still relatively numerous locally, e.g. around Santarém in the Tapajós National Forest (where it can be observed to particularly good effect from the NASA canopy tower), and the Serra do Cachimbo and Serra dos Carajás, but probably less common in the more deforested Belém region, although it is still easily found at Caxiuanã (Ridgely and Tudor 1994). White-tailed Cotinga is notionally protected within several large protected areas, including the mosaic of protected areas in the Serra dos Carajás, Amazonia (Tapajós) National Park, and the FLONA de Caxiuanã.

REFERENCES BirdLife International (2004, 2008), Brush (1969), Dunning (2008), Griscom and Greenway (1937), Haffer (1970, 1974, 1992a, 1992b), Hellmayr (1929a, 1929b), Henriques *et al.* (2003), Hohnwald (2009), Marantz and Zimmer (2006), Olson (1970), Oren and Parker (1997), Pacheco and Olmos (2005), Pacheco *et al.* (2007), Pinto (1944, 1953), Ridgely and Tudor (1994, 2009), Sick (1997), Snethlage (1907), Snow (1977, 1982, 2004a), Stone (1928), Stotz *et al.* (1996), Willis (1992).

1

White-tailed Cotinga *Xipholena lamellipennis*. **Fig. 1**. Male, Serra dos Carajás, Pará, January (*Nick Athanas / Tropical Birding*). White-tailed Cotinga's plumage is overall the darkest in males of the three *Xipholena* cotingas. The species is confined to a comparatively small area of east Amazonian Brazil. **Figs. 2–3**. Male, Floresta Nacional de Caxiuanã, Pará, east Amazonian Brazil, November (*Arthur Grosset / www. arthurgrosset.com*). White-tailed Cotinga is equally spectacular in flight as Pompadour Cotinga *X. punicea*. **Fig. 4**. Male, Paragominas, Pará, east Amazonian Brazil, October (*Alexander C. Lees*). **Fig. 5**. Female, FLONA de Tapajós, Pará, east Amazonian Brazil, November (*Alexander C. Lees*). Female plumage closely recalls that of the same sex of the partially sympatric Pompadour Cotinga *X. punicea*.

WHITE-WINGED COTINGA
Xipholena atropurpurea   Plate 22

Ampelis atropurpurea Wied, 1820, *Reise Brasilien* 1: 262, Morro d'Arára, Rio Mucuri, Bahia, Brazil

The rarest and most threatened of the three *Xipholena* cotingas, White-winged is endemic to the Atlantic Forest region of eastern Brazil, where numbers have probably declined dramatically and its range has certainly shrunk significantly. Nonetheless, compared with the equally beautiful Banded Cotinga *Cotinga maculata*, another threatened cotinga of the Atlantic Forest region, which at least formerly was found at many of the same sites in Espírito Santo and Bahia, the *Xipholena* seems to be clinging on more successfully, probably because it is capable of withstanding a lot more disturbance to the region's remnant forests.

IDENTIFICATION 19.0–21.6cm. The male is unmistakable, as no other *Xipholena* shares the same eastern seaboard range. However, the female White-winged Cotinga might be confused with the superficially similar female Banded Cotinga, but given good views the two should be readily separated. Banded is overall much browner, has dark eyes, heavily brown-scaled (rather than uniform grey) underparts and lacks the striking white fringes to the wing-coverts and tertials that characterise female White-winged Cotinga. The two species can sometimes be found together at the same fruiting tree.

DISTRIBUTION Endemic to eastern Brazil, where the species is known solely from the Atlantic Forest region, in coastal Paraíba (one 1950s collecting site and several recent records; e.g. at Camaratuba and Uruba: Teixeira and Almeida 1997), eastern Pernambuco (several recent records, and at least ten published localities: Teixeira and Almeida 1997, Roda *et al.* 2003), Alagoas (11 localities mentioned in the literature, but recent records from just three, Murici, Reserva Biológica de Pedra Talhada and Engenho Coimbra: Roda *et al.* 2003) and Sergipe (well known at one site, Crasto: Pacheco and Whitney 1995), eastern Bahia (many sites including 11 Important Bird Areas, from Santo Amaro, near Salvador south, but strongholds include Monte Pascoal National Park, Una Biological Reserve and

Vera Cruz Ecological Station, Porto Seguro), and Espírito Santo (where known from several older localities, but in the present-day only from the contiguous Sooretama Biological Reserve and the privately owned Linhares reserve), as well as in northern Rio de Janeiro state, formerly south as far as the environs of Novo Friburgo (Burmeister 1856), with the only other record (in 1986) from the important, but little visited Desengano State Park (Collar *et al.* 1992, Bencke *et al.* 2006). White-winged Cotinga is mainly found in the lowlands and adjacent foothills to 900m.

MOVEMENTS None known, but White-winged Cotinga presumably wanders to some extent in search of food like other *Xipholena*.

HABITAT The species inhabits primary forest and its borders, tall second growth and *restinga* (sandy-soil) forests on coasts, and adjacent clearings with scattered trees. Mainly a canopy species, but it visits middle and even lower levels, especially within dense forest, albeit at light gaps or along roads.

DESCRIPTION The sexes are quite different; the male is virtually all dark with extensively white wings, the female predominantly grey with white fringes to the wing-coverts (which tract is modified in the male) and secondaries. The legs and feet are moderately strong. Primaries are unmodified. Lacks rictal bristles. *Adult male.* – Upper body, including head to back, scapulars and virtually entire underparts deep blackish-purple, becoming crimson-purple over the uppertail-coverts and tertials. Rectrices slightly more brownish but have extensive pinkish fringes to the outer webs, especially on the outermost tail feathers. The median and some greater wing-coverts are modified, being point-tipped (but not elongated like the other two *Xipholena*), and like much of the rest of the plumage possess a hardened, stiffened texture. Rest of wings clean bright white, although it can show violet-purple outer fringes and tips to the longest tertial, and the primary tips are blackish-brown. *Adult female.* – Like all female *Xipholena*, this is a short-tailed, thrush-like bird. Plumage is largely ash-grey, with a narrow whitish eye-ring and a slightly paler grey upper breast to undertail-coverts, with blacker remiges and rectrices, marked by white outer fringes to the greater coverts and secondaries, and slightly narrower fringes to the lesser and median wing-coverts. The rump and uppertail-coverts are also white-fringed. *Immature.* – Young males pass through four intermediate stages, acquiring full adult plumage after 4–5 annual moults (Snow 2004a), with the adult remiges and rectrices the last feathers to be acquired (Snow 1982; RMNH), appearing initially to acquire adult feathers on the nape, throat and breast, when the entire wings, lower back to rump are still female-like. *Juvenile.* – Presumably resembles the female but has not been specifically described to date (Snow 1982). *Moult.* – There are no published data concerning the annual moult cycle, although males apparently renew their feathers well in advance of females, as would be expected of a species in which the male takes no part in the nesting cycle or care of the young (Snow 1982). *Bare parts.* – Irides pale yellow to white, but recorded as being chestnut in one female that otherwise appeared adult (MNRJ); the bill (broad-based but becoming flattened and slightly hooked towards the tip) is dark grey to brownish-horn, sometimes with darker cutting edges and a paler rose-coloured base to the lower mandible; and the legs are dark grey to brownish-black with buff-coloured soles.

MEASUREMENTS (from Snow 1982; CUMZ; FMNH; MNRJ; RMNH; ZMA; ZISP: Bahia and Espírito Santo, Brazil) Wing of male (n = 28) 108–122mm, wing of female (n = 24) 104–118mm; tail of male (n = 28) 61–73mm, tail of female (n = 24) 57–75mm; bill of male (n = 12) 10.5–12.0mm (n = 16, to skull, 17.82–19.44mm); bill of female (n = 6) 11–12mm (n = 18, to skull, 17.40–19.34mm); tarsus of male (n = 17) 18.89–25.00mm, tarsus of female (n = 11) 19.95–26.00mm. Weight: 58–66g (males) and 56–67g (females) (Snow 2004a, Dunning 2008; FMNH; MNRJ).

GEOGRAPHICAL VARIATION Monotypic.

VOICE Published recordings are available on the recently published Minns *et al.* (2009) compilation and a couple of recordings are available online at www.xeno-canto.org. Both sexes utter a load, flat and abrupt croak, which is much less liquid and more wooden-sounding than either of the other two members of the genus. Males give a croak, apparently similar to that of Pompadour Cotinga *X. punicea*, and probably both sexes give high-pitched *chiu* notes, e.g. whilst foraging; for instance, GMK (pers. obs.) heard female-plumaged birds at Una Biological Reserve, Bahia, giving this call in December, but it is possible, of course, that very young males were involved. In display-flight the males make a quite loud mechanical (hissing) wing noise.

NATURAL HISTORY Apparently largely similar to those of its congeners. May consort in small parties, principally of female-plumaged birds, which occasionally number ten or more (Wege and Long 1995; GMK pers. obs.).

FOOD AND FEEDING White-winged Cotinga feeds principally on fruit, with a quite wide preference documented, but including those of Moraceae, Myrtaceae and Lauraceae, these families also often being favoured by the other *Xipholena* species (Teixeira and Almeida 1996). Sick (1997) mentioned a particular preference for the woody, edge plant *Phytolacca decandra* (Phytolaccaceae). The species regularly joins other frugivorous birds at fruiting events, including other cotingas such as Bare-throated Bellbird *Procnias nudicollis* and Banded Cotinga, but there is probably little propensity to join mobile mixed-species flocks, although like other *Xipholena*, such behaviour is almost certainly more frequently exhibited by females. Not infrequently observed <5m above the ground when feeding, even within tall forest (GMK pers. obs.). Also takes insects using short aerial sallies, and has occasionally been recorded eating flowers.

DISPLAY Males make a short upward flight of several metres (perhaps up to 10m) from an exposed perch, before turning in midair, where the bird acquires the appearance of a gigantic black-and-white butterfly, and descending steeply to the same or a nearby perch (accompanied by a loud wing noise). However, it also appears to perform similar behaviour to White-tailed and Pompadour Cotingas, inasmuch as males also make long, slow flights, revealing their white wings to good effect, in order to displace nearby rivals from their own favoured perches, and sometimes these appear to have a 'knock-on effect'. Specimens in post-breeding moult have been collected in March and April, and gonadal data suggest that the breeding season commences in about October; in Bahia, display is certainly evident from September (GG and GMK pers. obs.). In late September 1977, Sick (1979a) observed a female disappearing into a bromeliad clump *c.*18m above the ground in Sooretama Biological Reserve, where it presumably had a nest. The egg, described by Sick (1970) from one laid by a bird in Rio de Janeiro zoo, is blue-green thickly covered by irregular-sized sepia spots and other marks. More recently, incubation has been reported in October and egg-laying in November, and the nest is apparently similar to that of the Pompadour Cotinga, being a tiny but deep cup, principally constructed of rootlets and placed *c.*20m above the ground in a tree fork (Teixeira and Almeida 1997).

STATUS Treated as Endangered at the global level (BirdLife International 2004, 2008) and considered Critically Endangered in the state of Espírito Santo (Passamani and Mendes 2007). Must also be highly threatened in the state of Rio de Janeiro, where nowadays it is known solely from the extremely important but largely inaccessible and little-visited Desengano State Park (Wege and Long 1995). White-winged Cotinga has surely suffered a huge population decrease since historical times due to the almost complete destruction and fragmentation of lowland forest, especially within the northernmost portion of its range. However, the species can clearly persist in taller second growth and selectively logged areas. Nonetheless, it is more or less confined or dependent upon *c.*13 protected areas throughout its range identified by BirdLife International as being of critical importance for its conservation (several of which are also of keynote importance for the even rarer Banded Cotinga). Compared with the latter species, White-winged Cotinga clearly tolerates some disturbance and, due especially to its distinctive and obvious displays, is easier to observe. Sites of some importance for this fantastic bird most regularly visited by birders include the Porto Seguro region of Bahia, as well as the nearby Una Biological Reserve, the Sooretama Biological Reserve/Linhares Natural Reserve, in Espírito Santo, Crasto in Sergipe, and the recently protected (but still threatened) forests above Murici, in Alagoas. White-winged Cotinga is confined to the Serra do Mar Centre of endemism (Cracraft 1985) and also occurs in two Endemic Bird Areas (Stattersfield *et al.* 1998).

REFERENCES Albano (2010a, 2010b), Bencke *et al.* (2006), BirdLife International (2004, 2008), Burmeister (1856), Collar *et al.* (1992), Cordeiro (2000), Cracraft (1985), Dunning (2008), Freitas *et al.* (2004), Haffer (1974), Hellmayr (1929b), Lamm (1948), Minns *et al.* (2009), Pacheco and Whitney (1995), Parker and Goerck (1997), Passamani and Mendes (2007), Pinto (1944), Ridgely and Tudor (1994, 2009), Roda *et al.* (2003), Sick (1970, 1979a, 1997), Silveira *et al.* (2005), Simon (2009), Snow (1982, 2004a), Stattersfield *et al.* (1998), Stotz *et al.* (1996), Teixeira and Almeida (1997), Wege and Long (1995), Willis (1992).

White-winged Cotinga *Xipholena atropurpurea*. **Figs. 1–2**. Male, Porto Seguro, Bahia, eastern Brazil, February (*Ciro Albano*). The rarest of the *Xipholena* cotingas is no less beautiful than the other two species. These images were taken at one of the species' relatively few remaining strongholds in the Brazilian Atlantic Forest. **Fig. 3**. Female, Porto Seguro, Bahia, eastern Brazil, February (*Ciro Albano*). **Fig. 4**. Female, Porto Seguro, Bahia, eastern Brazil, February (*Pete Morris*). Note the strikingly pale irides, which offers a useful distinguishing mark for any female of the three species of *Xipholena*, all of which otherwise are generally 'unassuming' thrush-like birds.

Genus *Carpodectes*: 'white cotingas'

Wholly 'trans-Andean', the white cotingas are arguably most closely related to the wine-coloured *Xipholena* (cis-Andean) cotingas, mainly based on the relatively close similarities in their female plumages, and the extensive white in the males' wings in all of the species comprising the two genera, although Ames (1971) placed *Carpodectes* close to *Querula* (Purple-throated Fruitcrow) on the basis of syringeal morphology, a relationship since refuted by genetic data. Recent observations of the nest of the Snowy Cotinga *Carpodectes nitidus* further suggest a relatively close relationship with *Xipholena*, although our knowledge of the nesting biology of the latter genus is far from complete. Other aspects of their behaviour also suggest such a linkage, but knowledge of much of the life history of the white cotingas is also still staggeringly poor, and begs attention from dedicated field ornithologists. Although this relationship between *Carpodectes* and *Xipholena* went unconfirmed until recently, Snow (1982) postulated that it indicates that a common ancestor evolved into the two genera, following the isolation of populations west and east of the Andes. Now, however, genetic data confirm the close relationship between the two (see Systematics, p. 44). Hellmayr (1929b) treated the genus *Carpodectes* as constituting a single, polytypic species, and several subsequent commentators have insisted that Snowy and Yellow-billed Cotingas *Carpodectes antoniae* should be considered as the same species (they are very similar), but on current evidence we continue to treat them as valid species, and members of a superspecies (Monroe 1968, Snow 1979a, Sibley and Monroe 1990). All three taxa are mainly birds of lowland and adjacent foothill forests, placing them at risk from the massive habitat destruction that is occurring within their ranges.

BLACK-TIPPED COTINGA
Carpodectes hopkei   Plate 23

Carpodectes hopkei **Berlepsch, 1897**, *Orn. Monatsb.* 5: 174, San José, Río Dagua, Valle, Colombia

The only one of the three white cotingas that is found in South America, Black-tipped Cotinga is wholly allopatric from the other two and was the last to be described, at the close of the 19th century. The species' scientific name celebrates Gustav Hopke, a German field collector who specialised in mammals and who secured the type series of this cotinga in Colombia. Black-tipped Cotinga was sometimes also known as the White Cotinga (e.g. in Wetmore 1972).

IDENTIFICATION 23.5–25.0cm (male) or 19.3–23.5cm (female). The largest of the three white cotingas. The other two species are also entirely restricted to Central America, whereas Black-tipped Cotinga is only just represented in the isthmus, in easternmost Panama, in which country Snowy *Carpodectes nitidus* and Yellow-billed Cotingas *C. antoniae* are found only in the far west. Female Black-tipped Cotinga might be mistaken for a female Blue Cotinga *Cotinga nattereri*, but note the present species' red irides, overall greyer plumage, unmarked underparts and much more striking white fringes to the wing feathers, all of which should be obvious given reasonable views, but might prove difficult to distinguish at long range. Females of all three species of *Carpodectes* are similar, and also resemble those of the genus *Xipholena*, but identification is made straightforward because all three species of *Carpodectes* are allopatric, whilst the genus *Xipholena* is restricted to South America east of the Andes. Becards (*Pachyramphus*) and tityras (*Tityra*), themselves formerly considered to be cotingas, may cause confusion (again principally with females) for the unwary, but their behaviour, habits and the former's sleeker build and bill size, should enable correct diagnosis.

DISTRIBUTION Easternmost Panama in Darién (e.g. on the Cerro Pirre and Cerro de Nique, where at least formerly the species was fairly common), through western Colombia in the Pacific lowlands south to northwest Ecuador, mainly in prov. Esmeraldas, but also in prov. Pichincha, where recorded as far south as Río Palenque Scientific Station, although it is speculated to be only a non-breeding visitor there.

MOVEMENTS None definitely recorded, but may wander upslope in Ecuador and Colombia in the non-breeding season, and in the former it perhaps also moves southwards (see Distribution; AOU 1998, Ridgely and Greenfield 2001).

HABITAT Very much a bird of the ultra-wet Chocó region, where it inhabits the canopy and borders of humid lowland forest, as well as mangrove and occasionally nearby second growth, mainly to *c.*900m (usually at 300–600m in Panama, although it has been recorded to sea level there, and below 500m in Ecuador). Black-tipped Cotinga has been recorded once to 1,450m in Colombia (Hilty and Brown 1986; which perhaps reflects altitudinal migration?), although McMullan *et al.* (2010) only report occurrence to 1,200m in the same country.

DESCRIPTION The largest and bulkiest-bodied of the three white cotingas. No primary modification, but the flight feathers are generally rather broad and rather rounded, and with a sharp break in length between the unmarked pp1–4 and the black-tipped pp5–10. Broad-based bill with a noticeably ridged culmen that is strongly arched and hook-tipped, a character that is perhaps especially marked in males. Female has slightly developed rictal bristles, but the male has none. *Adult male.* – Rather pigeon-like and long-tailed with broad, rounded wings. All-white plumage relieved only by black spots on the tips of the five outermost primaries (which are generally rather inconspicuous in the field). The crown, back and tail have a barely perceptible duller, greyish tinge, which is rarely liable to be discernible in the field. Central tail feathers white with black spots either side of the shaft near the tip. *Immature/Subadult male.* – Former resembles female, albeit being slightly paler grey dorsally with broader white fringes to the wing feathers, whilst the latter is adult male-like, but retains some dark markings on the flight feathers and most, if not all, the rectrices and primaries have dark spots at their tips. Irides described as brown (Hartert 1902). *Adult female.* – Dark greyish-brown above, with dark chocolate-brown wings marked by conspicuous white outer fringes and tips to the coverts, secondaries and tertials. Faint whitish eye-ring. Throat and breast greyer than the upperparts, and becoming paler on the belly, with almost white undertail-coverts. Undertail greyish-brown. Underwing largely pale grey, with darker distal halves and inner webs to the remiges. *Moult.* – Very few published moult data, but a male taken in late May in northwest Ecuador was in body moult. Snow (1982) mentioned that males commence moult in January–April, and also recorded that complete wing and tail moult commences earlier in males than females (as one would expect of species in which the female presumably takes sole or primary responsibility for nestling care) and occupies *c.*140 days in all three *Carpodectes*. *Bare parts.* – Male has the bill black to blackish, whilst the rather short legs and feet are dark grey to black, with brown soles, and the irides are orange to dark red. Female has a slightly larger (sometimes grey) bill, the legs are black, and the irides brown to orange-brown. Both sexes have black bare skin at edge of eyelids (Hellmayr 1911, Kennard and Peters 1928, Wetmore 1972, Stiles and Skutch 1989).

MEASUREMENTS (from Wetmore 1972 [maxima in square brackets from Hellmayr 1929b]; MECN; ROM: Chocó, west Colombia, and Esmeraldas and Pichincha, northwest Ecuador) Wing of male (*n* = 16) 145–170mm [–171mm], wing of female (*n* = 10) 137–150mm; tail of male (*n* = 16) 77–95mm [–102mm], tail of female (*n* = 10) 72–88mm [–90mm]; bill of male (*n* = 15) 19.9–23.4mm, bill of female (*n* = 9) 20.2–22.7mm; tarsus of male (*n* = 10) 24.5–25.5mm, tarsus of female (*n* = 8) 23.0–25.5mm. See also Hartert (1902) and Hellmayr (1911) for additional mensural data for both sexes and immatures from Colombia. Weight: 102–118g (three males; Dunning 2008; MECN).

GEOGRAPHICAL VARIATION Monotypic.

VOICE Frequently stated to be unknown (e.g., Angehr and

Dean 2010). Tape-recorded (Krabbe and Nilsson 2003), although the context of the vocalisation presented therein is unclear. A slightly barking or more squeaky-sounding *quip* lasting *c.*1 second is given, by males at least, sometimes slightly longer but frequently less than this. The sound, especially its softer variant, is not unlike that of any of the *Xipholena* cotingas. No further information.

NATURAL HISTORY Very dove-like in appearance and in flight, which is normally reasonably rapid and direct (Ridgely and Tudor 2009). Females are much less regularly seen than males, except at fruiting trees. Typical of many cotingas; ventures from primary forest into second growth and clearings to fruiting trees, including *Cecropia* (Moraceae) (Hilty and Brown 1986), and will perch high on exposed branches, sometimes in small groups of up to 5–7. Such groups appear to be quite normal, not just temporary aggregations at a rich food source. Capable of crossing quite wide cleared areas between patches of forest. Usually more active than *Cotinga*, but still typically appears sluggish.

FOOD AND FEEDING Diet is apparently exclusively fruit, but there are very few specific data concerning constituent species (or even families).

BREEDING Wholly unknown, other than the availability of five breeding-condition specimens, including a female ready to lay eggs, collected in Colombia during January–March (Hilty and Brown 1986), and two males with enlarged testes have been collected in northwest Ecuador in May and July (MECN). A specimen described as being a juvenile was collected in western Colombia in November (Hellmayr 1911). Males perform an exaggerated slow-flapping display-flight between the treetops (Ridgely and Tudor 2009).

STATUS Treated as Least Concern by BirdLife International (2004, 2008), despite ongoing high rates of deforestation virtually throughout its fortuitously reasonably large range (estimated at >96,000km^2). The species is endemic to the Chocó Rainforest Centre of endemism (Cracraft 1985). Generally uncommon, although relatively easy to see from the railway line at El Placer in Esmeraldas, Ecuador, at Alto Tambo in the same province, and in the partially deforested environs of Buenaventura, southwest Colombia. In addition, newly discovered areas of foothill forest around San Miguel de los Bancos, northwest of Mindo, have also been found to hold this species. Known from several protected areas throughout the species' range, including Darién National Park (Panama), where it is regularly seen around Cana Field Station; Reserva El Pangan and Sanquianga National Park, both in dpto. Nariño (Colombia); and Fundación Jocotoco's Río Canandé Reserve, in Esmeraldas, and the privately owned Río Silanche and Mangaloma reserves, in Pichincha (Ecuador). Seems tolerably common below 600m in the Panamanian Darién.

REFERENCES Angehr and Dean (2010), AOU (1998), BirdLife International (2004, 2008), Cracraft (1985), Dunning (2008), Hartert (1902), Hellmayr (1911, 1929b), Hilty and Brown (1986), Kennard and Peters (1928), Krabbe and Nilsson (2003), McMullan *et al.* (2010), Restall *et al.* (2006), Ridgely and Greenfield (2001), Ridgely and Gwynne (1976, 1989), Ridgely and Tudor (1994, 2009), Robbins *et al.* (1985), Ruiz-Guerra *et al.* (2007), Salaman *et al.* (2008), Snow (1982, 2004a), Stotz *et al.* (1996), Wetmore (1972).

Black-tipped Cotinga *Carpodectes hopkei*. **Fig. 1**. Male, Río Canandé Reserve, prov. Esmeraldas, northwest Ecuador, November (*Ron Hoff*). Like the *Xipholena* cotingas, the three *Carpodectes* 'white' cotingas are by and large easily identified by virtue of their respective (allopatric) geographic ranges. The present species is the only form that occurs in South America, although it ranges also into easternmost Panama. Note the somewhat 'dove-like' head shape (which is common to all three *Carpodectes*) and the small bill.

SNOWY COTINGA
Carpodectes nitidus   **Plate 23**

Carpodectes nitidus **Salvin, 1865**, *Proc. Zool. Soc. Lond.* 1864: 583, pl. 36 [= 35], Tucurriquí, Costa Rica

Certainly the most widespread and probably the commonest of the *Carpodectes*, the Snowy Cotinga is relatively easy to see in the Caribbean lowlands of Costa Rica.

IDENTIFICATION 19.5–22.5cm. Males of this medium-sized, stout-bodied cotinga appear completely white in the field, although the upperparts are in fact pale blue-grey. It is restricted to the Caribbean slope of Honduras, Nicaragua, Costa Rica and Panama, whilst the other entirely Middle American member of this genus, Yellow-billed Cotinga *C. antoniae*, also appears all white but frequents coastal mangroves on the Pacific side. Subadult male Snowy Cotinga resembles the adult male; although the remiges are dark brown, the scapulars and wing-coverts often conceal much of the dark feathering, whilst the tips of the primaries often produce a black-tipped effect. However, this pattern does not resemble that of Black-tipped Cotinga *C. hopkei*, which in any case is never found in sympatry with either of the other species of *Carpodectes*. However, in Central America, observers should be aware which side of the Continental Divide they are on when presented with brief views of a white cotinga!

DISTRIBUTION Endemic to Middle America, from north-western Honduras (e.g. at La Ceiba), through Nicaragua and Costa Rica to westernmost Panama, in western Bocas del Toro, where initially recorded in the 1920s (Kennard and Peters 1928) and westernmost Comarca Ngöbe-Buglé (Angehr and Dean 2010). Entirely restricted to the Caribbean side of the Continental Divide, with a recent (2001) record from eastern Guatemala, on the Manabique Peninsula, which was assumed to represent a bird dispersing from adjacent Honduras (Eisermann 2003).

MOVEMENTS Nothing precise, although clearly does wander nomadically, presumably in search of suitable fruiting trees (probably like many of the true cotingas). The recent record from eastern Guatemala (see above) is perhaps indicative of such movements. Such behaviour, however, appears to vary from locality to locality (Stiles and Skutch 1989).

HABITAT Found in the canopy of rainforest and adjacent clearings, and tall second growth, of the Caribbean lowlands and adjacent foothills, including some forested near-shore islands, from near sea level to *c.*750m (Stiles and Skutch 1989), although it has not been recorded above 450m in western Panama (Angehr and Dean 2010). Snowy Cotinga is often seen in gaps or along streams according to Stiles and Skutch (1989).

DESCRIPTION Mid-sized white cotinga. No primary modification. Broad-based bill with noticeably ridged culmen that is well arched and hook-tipped, especially in males. Female has slightly developed rictal bristles, but the male has none. As noted by Wetmore (1972), the plumage is densely packed like all of the *Carpodectes* species. *Adult male.* – Essentially all white, but at close range a pastel blue-grey hue is evident to the crown (especially), nape, mantle and scapulars. This suffusion is also present over the rump, tail and tertials, but is paler than on the rest of the upperparts. Forehead and lores white, contrasting surprisingly markedly with the crown. Underparts white with a greyish hue to the under surfaces of the remiges and rectrices. Underwing-coverts white. *Immature male.* – Like adult female above, but paler grey, with the head-sides white. The underparts are white with a bluish wash to the breast. *Subadult male.* – Much like the adult male but has largely dark primaries and primary-coverts, and the outer secondaries also are rather extensively dark, with a distinctively smoky-brown rump and uppertail-coverts forming a patch that is obviously darker than the rest of the upperparts. *Adult female.* – Dark grey crown and mantle, with browner scapulars and rump. Remiges blackish-brown, with conspicuous white outer fringes and tips to the secondaries, tertials and coverts. Lores and feathering around eye grey, forming a reasonably conspicuous eye-ring. Throat paler grey than the crown, becoming subtly darker on the breast. Rest of underparts fairly uniform grey, with paler (whiter) feathering around the legs and undertail-coverts. Undertail grey, and axillaries, most of underwing-coverts and inner primary webs white, but the outer coverts are blackish-grey. *Juvenile.* – Female-like, but differs in being more whitish, indistinctly scaled brownish or dusky, above (see Snow 1982, Stiles and Skutch 1989). A specimen of a nestling was described by Wetmore (1972). *Moult.* – Few published data on moult, but Snow (1982) noted that males in Nicaragua and Costa Rica mostly commence feather replacement in April–July, but this occurs during March–April in Panama. None of those, males and females, observed in the third week of April in Costa Rica were in flight feather moult (GMK pers. obs.). Snow (1982) also recorded that complete wing and tail moult commences earlier in males than females (as one would expect of species in which the female presumably takes the sole responsibility for nestling care) and occupies *c.*140 days in all three *Carpodectes*. *Bare parts.* – Male has bill dark grey to bluish-horn, darker on the culmen (or yellowish with a black culmen in subadults), rather short legs and feet that are fuscous or black, with brown soles, and dark brown irides (appearing black at a distance). Female bill is bluish-grey, becoming black on the culmen, and legs and irides are blackish. Both sexes have black bare skin at the edge of the eyelids.

MEASUREMENTS (BMNH; FMNH; MNCR; RMNH; ROM: Costa Rica, Nicaragua and Panama) Wing of male (*n* = 12) 132–150mm, wing of female (*n* = 7) 126–132mm; tail of male (*n* = 10) 58–69mm, tail of female (*n* = 7) 61–67mm;

bill of male (n = 11) 19.25–23.00mm, bill of female (n = 7) 18.78–23.00mm; tarsus of male (n = 10) 22.39–26.35mm, tarsus of female (n = 7) 22.30–27.00mm. Weight (sexes combined): 89–116g (n = 3; Stiles and Skutch 1989, Snow 2004a, Dunning 2008).

GEOGRAPHICAL VARIATION Monotypic.

VOICE Mainly quiet; the only call that has been noted in the literature, which is given solely by the male, is a dry, scratchy *chich* or *chee*, sometimes rapidly repeated 2–8 times, and likened by Slud (1964) to the chatter of an oriole (albeit slower). No published recordings.

NATURAL HISTORY Like all three *Carpodectes*, the Snowy Cotinga is a relatively confident bird, and will perch high up in the canopy in pairs or small groups, exceptionally of up to 15 birds and at least some large groups are all male (Richmond 1893, Slud 1964). May sit completely exposed or screened by foliage. Comes lower in second growth (Stiles and Skutch 1989). Flight is rather dove-like; fast and direct, except presumably when displaying (if like congenerics, and *Xipholena*). R. Gallardo (www.birdsofhonduras.com) observed one male fly over 0.5km to dislodge a second male from its perch at a site in Honduras.

FOOD AND FEEDING Diet entirely frugivorous, with fruit being plucked either whilst perched or following a sally and brief hover. Favours those of various Lauraceae, Loranthaceae (mistletoes) and *Ficus* (Moraceae, figs), but also noted to take fruits of *Casearia corymbosa* (Flacourtiaceae) in Costa Rica (Howe 1977). Joins feeding melees with toucans, flycatchers, tanagers and honeycreepers (GMK pers. obs.).

BREEDING Other than a one-third grown nestling still with some white down feathers, collected in Costa Rica in late March 1891 (AMNH; cf. Wetmore 1972, Snow 1982), all breeding data have been acquired recently. In April 1999, in northern Costa Rica, Klebauskas and Pacheco (2000) found a small cup-shaped nest belonging to this species, sited in a three-pronged fork 10–12m above the ground in a leafless tree (not identified). It contained one nestling, which was being fed by the female. Thereafter, in the same country, Sánchez (2002) described another nest, also constructed in a leafless and rather exposed *Hura crepitans* (Euphorbiaceae) sandbox tree, this time 7.5m above ground, in a four-way fork. It too was a small cup, scarcely large enough to accommodate the adult, loosely constructed of small twigs, woody tendrils and some lichens. The single egg, greyish-white with pale brown blotches at the larger end, hatched on 3 May, following a 27-day incubation period, but the nestling was almost certainly predated the next day. In the same area, at La Selva OTS Biological Station, GMK and E. Carman observed a female frequently chasing other birds from, and returning to, the same tree, in the third week of April 2010, as if the bird had a nest. Based on moult data, Snow (1982) speculated, probably correctly, that the breeding season becomes progressively earlier from north to south through the species' range.

STATUS Rare to locally common, but not considered to be threatened at present by the massive habitat destruction within the species' primarily lowland range, being treated as of Least Concern by BirdLife International (2004, 2008). Seems rather rare and local in Honduras, where it is known from very few localities and has undoubtedly suffered local extirpations (Vallely *et al.* 2010). Sigel *et al.* (2005) considered that the species is probably declining at several

sites in Costa Rica. It is generally uncommon in western Panama, at the other extremity of the species' distribution, but is known from several protected areas through its range, including Río Plátano Biosphere Reserve and Tawahka-Asangni Biosphere Reserve, Honduras, and La Selva OTS Biological Station, Keköldi Indigenous Reserve, and Cahuita and Tortuguero National Parks, all in Costa Rica (see also, e.g., Cooper 1997, Blake and Loiselle 2001, Lawson 2010, Vallely *et al.* 2010). Other good localities to find this species include the environs of Selva Bananito Lodge, in the Caribbean lowlands of Costa Rica (Lawson 2010).

REFERENCES Anderson *et al.* (2004), Angehr and Dean (2010), AOU (1998), BirdLife International (2004, 2008), Blake and Loiselle (2001), Cooper (1997, 1999), Dunning (2008), Eisermann (2003), Eisermann and Avendaño (2007), Garrigues and Dean (2007), Hellmayr (1929b), Howe (1977), Kennard and Peters (1928), Klebauskas and Pacheco (2000), Lawson (2010), Monroe (1968), Richmond (1893), Ridgely and Gwynne (1989), Ridgway (1905), Sánchez (2002), Sigel *et al.* (2005), Slud (1964), Snow (1982, 2004a), Stiles and Skutch (1989), Stotz *et al.* (1996), Vallely *et al.* (2010), Wetmore (1972).

Snowy Cotinga *Carpodectes nitidus*. **Figs. 1–2.** Male, La Selva Biological Station, prov. Heredia, northeast Costa Rica, February (*Steven Easley / Costa Rica Gateway*). All-white birds are always striking, especially when, like these cotingas, they perch atop tall trees. Snowy Cotinga occurs on the opposite side of the Continental Divide to Yellow-billed Cotinga *C. antoniae*, being found exclusively on the Caribbean slope of Central America.

YELLOW-BILLED COTINGA
Carpodectes antoniae **Plate 23**

Carpodectes antoniae **Ridgway, 1884** [based on Zeledón ms.], *Ibis* (5)2: 27, pl. 2, Pozo Azul de Pirris, southwest Costa Rica

This, the third member of the white cotinga group, is endemic to the Pacific slope of Costa Rica and western Panama. It occurs in extensive mangroves and, seasonally, in the nearby forested foothills. The species' unusual specific name commemorates the sister, Antonia Zeledón de Araya, of the person who first collected this species.

IDENTIFICATION 18.8–21.5cm. Yellow-billed Cotinga is marginally the smallest and shortest-tailed of the genus, but the male remains unmistakable (given the lack of sympatry between members of the genus) and cannot be confused with any other species in its small range, although a poorly seen Masked *Tityra semifasciata* or Black-crowned Tityra *T. inquisitor*, both of which occur in the same region, might provide a brief 'trap' for the unwary. This is especially true for subadult male cotingas, which can show some dark on the tail and a dark 'border' to the wing, as well as greyer upperparts, but lacks any red on the face and has a considerably smaller bill. The dark grey female's straw-yellow base to the bill provides a useful clue as to her identity, provided the bird is seen well. For further separation of females from potentially similar becards and tityras, see Black-tipped Cotinga *Carpodectes hopkei*.

DISTRIBUTION Inhabits the Pacific slope of Costa Rica, from the mouth of the Río Tarcoles, in the environs of Carara National Park (Stiles and Skutch 1989) and the southern Golfo de Nicoya (at Pigres), south to the Osa Peninsula (AOU 1998) and at least to Chiriquí and southern Veraguas in western Panama (where until recently very rarely recorded, except close to the Costa Rican border, but see Status). The easternmost limit of the species' distribution appears to be marked by the Gulf of Montijo (Angehr and Dean 2010). In the species' northernmost range, there are recent records from Cerro Lodge (P. O'Donnell). The easternmost record appears to be from Aguadulce, Coclé, *c.*200km beyond its modern-day range, based on a specimen that is now lost (Ridgely and Gwynne

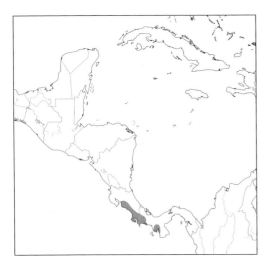

1976, AOU 1998). The species is recorded from sea level to *c.*800m, but only rarely is it found much above the true lowlands, and all records in Panama are from below 500m (Angehr and Dean 2010).

MOVEMENTS Seasonal movements into the foothills are suspected, probably for breeding (the only record of display was well inland, at the upper limit of its altitudinal range: cf. Ridgely and Gwynne 1976, BirdLife International 2008). Records from the Burica Peninsula, in western Panama, are considered to relate to wandering individuals (Angehr 2000, BirdLife International 2008).

HABITAT Humid foothill and mangrove forests, as well as adjacent clearings and scrubby areas, in the subcanopy and canopy. The species does seem to require tall trees, however, whatever the habitat type.

DESCRIPTION The smallest of the three white cotingas. No primary modification. Broad-based bill with a noticeably ridged culmen and the tip of the upper mandible is usually well notched. Female has slightly developed rictal bristles, but the male has none (as in congenerics). Male is generally the larger of the sexes, as in all of the *Carpodectes*. *Adult male.* – A beautiful, all-white, dove-like cotinga, which given closer inspection has a bluish-grey hue to the crown, mantle, scapulars, rump and tail, but this is nearly always most obvious on the head. The tail is short and square-cut, and the wings and underparts are all white. *Subadult male.* – Resembles the adult male, but the primaries are dark grey to brownish-black, usually being darkest on the outer webs. The primary-coverts and alula are white with a brown tip either side of the feather shaft, with brown tips to the proximal web of the innermost secondaries, and the tail is white with a smudgy brown terminal band. The underside of the primary tips is also dark, but the undertail shows an even fainter dark band. It is unknown how many moults are passed before complete adult plumage is reached, but an example of a younger male has been examined (in BMNH). It has the grey tracts of the upperparts washed slightly darker, especially on the lower back and rump, a slightly more distinct terminal tail-band, more extensively dark primary-coverts and alula, almost all-dark primaries (only the bases and shafts are white), with some tertials and secondaries also having brownish on the tips. *Adult female.* – Crown, ear-coverts and mantle dark grey, the scapulars with a browner hue. Wing-coverts dark brown with broad white distal fringes and tips. Remiges brownish-black, the secondaries with white tips to the innermost feathers. Broad white outer fringe to tertials. Tail brown, darker than the greyer-brown rump and uppertail-coverts. Narrow white eye-ring, which can be obvious in the field. The whitish-grey throat merges with the ash-grey breast and flanks. Belly subtly paler, with whiter undertail-coverts and tarsal feathering. Undertail pale greyish-brown. Underwing pale grey with darker distal portions and inner webs to the remiges. *Juvenile.* – Like female, although this plumage might be initially more fluffy feathered than that of an adult female. *Moult.* – Very few published moult data, but Snow (1982) reported that males commence their moult in March–June, but none of those (of both sexes) seen on the Osa Peninsula, in southwest Costa Rica, in mid April appeared to be replacing the flight feathers (GMK pers. obs.). Snow (1982) also recorded that complete wing and tail moult commences earlier in males than females (as one would expect of species in which the female presumably takes sole responsibility for nestling care) and occupies *c.*140 days in all three *Carpodectes*. **Bare parts.** – The male has legs black, irides dark brown (with black eyelids), and bill yellow with an obvious black ridge to the culmen and tip to the upper mandible. Female has base of bill straw yellow to brownish-yellow, a blackish-brown culmen and tip to the lower mandible (covering *c.*50% of the mandibles), whilst the legs are greyish and irides dark brown.

MEASUREMENTS (BMNH; MNCR; ROM: Costa Rica; Wetmore 1972: Panama) Wing of male (*n* = 17) 133.0–144.5mm, wing of female (*n* = 9) 122–132mm; tail of male (*n* = 17) 56–68mm, tail of female (*n* = 9) 56–64mm; bill of male (*n* = 6) 17.5–23.0mm, bill of female (*n* = 7) 17.6–20.0mm; tarsus of male (*n* = 12) 24–28mm, tarsus of female (*n* = 2) 23–24mm. Weight: mean 98g (sample size unknown; Stiles and Skutch 1989, Dunning 2008).

GEOGRAPHICAL VARIATION Monotypic.

VOICE Seldom calls. The only recorded vocalisation, given by the male alone, is a trogon- or dove-like *cah* or *cow*, ending in a throaty scrape (Slud 1964, Stiles and Skutch 1989).

NATURAL HISTORY A social species, like the other members of the genus *Carpodectes*, and flies easily with the manner of a pigeon, or sometimes recalling that of a *Tityra* (Slud 1964). A typical *Carpodectes*; the males in particular are showy and confiding, often perching on bare branches in or above the canopy for long periods, but the females are generally much less frequently seen. Relatively sociable in mangroves and the canopy of adjacent forest, with loose groups of up to at least five recorded fairly regularly, including at fruiting trees. Observed in loose association with both sexes of Turquoise Cotinga *Cotinga ridgwayi*, various flycatchers, Rufous Piha *Lipaugus unirufus* and Rufous Mourner *Rhytipterna holerythra* at fruiting trees on the Osa Peninsula in southwest Costa Rica (GMK pers. obs.).

FOOD AND FEEDING Diet is apparently exclusively frugivorous, including fruits of *Ficus* sp. (Moraceae, figs), Lauraceae, Loranthaceae (mistletoes) and Melastomataceae (Stiles and Skutch 1989; E. Carman pers. comm.). Angehr (2000) and BirdLife International (2008) mention that it has some preference for the fruits of *Schefflera morototoni* (Araliaceae) and GMK (pers. obs.) has witnessed this species taking wild avocado (Lauraceae) fruits. Descends to the midstorey to forage, as well as taking fruits in the canopy and subcanopy. Feeding techniques appear to be unmentioned in the literature, but unsurprisingly consist of upward sally-hovers of up to 2m and extremely clumsy perch gleans, reaching downward to seize fruits (GMK pers. obs.).

BREEDING No data on nesting, although the season is speculated to be March–June, and males may display in much the same way as *C. hopkei* (and, to some extent, *Xipholena*), in slow, flapping flights, of varying length, between treetops. However, Stiles and Skutch (1989) also reported a displaying male, which swooped from one dead branch to another, within the same tree, and also sidled along the same branches, but did not vocalise during this performance. Capper *et al.* (1998) reported observing a female that was carrying dead sticks, presumably for a nest, in May, on a small hill adjacent to mangrove in the environs of Corcovado National Park, in extreme southwest Costa Rica. In the same region, close to the town of Rincón, E. Carman (pers. comm.) observed a female carrying dead sticks in late March. Two weeks later, in the second week of April, females were seen carrying fruits in flight over long distances as if taking them to feed chicks (GMK pers. obs.).

STATUS Formerly classified as Vulnerable (Collar *et al.* 1992), but this was subsequently upgraded to Endangered (BirdLife International 2004, 2008). Considered rare (its overall population is speculated to be <1,000 individuals) and its global range is plainly rather small (estimated at 1,700km²). If dependent on two different biotopes (mangrove and foothill forest), this does not bode well for the species' survival, especially in an area that has been, and continues to be, degraded by human activities. Despite such activities being illegal, at least in Costa Rica, mangrove is being destroyed to make way for shrimp nurseries, salt ponds, rice cultivation and ranching, with the trees being used for construction poles and charcoal production, although rates of destruction have apparently slowed in recent years (BirdLife International 2008). The species is not adequately protected in either Costa Rica or Panama (where principally known, in recent years, from Cerro Batipa Private Reserve, which population is apparently resident), and this must be one of the cotingas most under threat. Until recently it had not been recorded in Panama for almost 15 years, and indeed there were very few records at all prior to the 1980s (see Wetmore 1972, Ridgely and Gwynne 1976), but an important population has now been discovered in mangroves near David, in western Chiriquí (Montañez and Angehr 2007). It might also be present in the nearby Playa de la Barqueta Agrícola Wildlife Refuge (Angehr 2000, BirdLife International 2008). Perhaps easiest to see in Costa Rica, in the environs of Corcovado National Park (where the species is perhaps only seasonally present) and Golfito Wildlife Refuge. Indeed, BirdLife International (2008) considered that its stronghold is probably the Golfo Dulce, in southwest Costa Rica, with the main nesting areas speculated to be the environs of the Sierpe and Coto rivers. Particularly good sites to search for the species include the bridge 3km south of Rincón de Osa, in southwest Costa Rica, at least between December and April, and El Chorogo, on the Burica Peninsula, in Panama (Montañez and Angehr 2007, Lawson 2010). In Costa Rica it has also been found in Carara Biological Reserve, but records are not frequent there.

REFERENCES Angehr (2000), Angehr and Dean (2010), AOU (1998), BirdLife International (2000, 2004, 2008), Capper *et al.* (1998), Collar *et al.* (1992), Dunning (2008), Garrigues and Dean (2007), Hellmayr (1929b), Lawson (2010), Montañez and Angehr (2007), Ridgely and Gwynne (1976, 1989), Slud (1964), Snow (1982, 2004a), Stattersfield *et al.* (1998), Stiles and Skutch (1989), Stotz *et al.* (1996), Wetmore (1972).

Yellow-billed Cotinga *Carpodectes antoniae*. **Fig. 1**. Male, Rincón, Osa Peninsula, prov. Puntarenas, southwest Costa Rica, February (*Kevin Easley / Costa Rica Gateway*). **Fig. 2**. Male and female, Rincón, Osa Peninsula, prov. Puntarenas, southwest Costa Rica, February (*Kevin Easley / Costa Rica Gateway*). **Fig. 3**. Female, Carara National Park, prov. Puntarenas, western Costa Rica, April (*Steven Easley / Costa Rica Gateway*). The rarest of the three 'white' cotingas is endemic to the Pacific coast of southern Central America.

Genus *Procnias*: bellbirds

The bellbirds comprise another easily definable genus of medium to large cotingas. *Procnias* is a widespread grouping, which was speculated by Snow (1973a) to have arisen in the Guianas or eastern Brazil, and found in the modern day from central Middle America in the 'trans-Andean' region (one species), then crosses the Darién gap into South America, ranging north of the Andes into northern Venezuela (including Trinidad) and the Pantepui, thence south into the lowlands of Amazonia (where one species is very local), southeast and east to the Atlantic Forest of Brazil. In common with many cotinga genera, bellbirds face an uncertain future, with the Bare-throated Bellbird *Procnias nudicollis* particularly threatened by habitat destruction. Perhaps best known for their spectacular vocalisations, as well as their incredible plumage and adornments (including various forms of wattles), the genus devolves into two species-pairs (see below).

THREE-WATTLED BELLBIRD
Procnias tricarunculatus   Plate 24

Casmarhynchus tricarunculata J. & E. Verreaux, 1853, *Rev. Mag. Zool.* (2)5: 193, [Bocas del Toro, north side of Isthmus of Panama]

The sole trans-Andean representative of *Procnias*, the amazing anvil-striking *bock* call of this Central American species will be familiar to birdwatchers visiting that region, with the delivery emanating from a huge, inky black, frog-like gape.

IDENTIFICATION 25–30cm (the female is smaller than the male). The bicoloured male should present no challenge in identification, especially if the call is also heard. Immature males resemble females to a certain extent, depending on the stage of maturity, but the white throat is the most obvious characteristic to develop initially, along with wattles of varying length. The female is a rather drab olive cotinga, heavily streaked below; however, the broad gape is always a sure indication of its generic affiliation. Three-wattled Bellbird is most closely related to the allopatric White Bellbird *Procnias albus*, and these two comprise a species-pair. Although the males of the two species possess certain conspicuously different characters, there are nevertheless obvious similarities, especially when compared with the two other members of *Procnias*. In particular, both Three-wattled and White Bellbirds possess an elongated wattle at the base of the upper mandible in the male and the throat is feathered. In females the crown is concolorous with the back and the throat is pale.

DISTRIBUTION Three-wattled Bellbird is endemic to Central America, where it occurs from eastern Honduras (in which country the species breeds solely on the Sierra de Agalta, and seems very common there almost year-round), southwest to Nicaragua (where known solely from the north-west; e.g. at Matagalpa, where it appears tolerably common based on the number of specimens taken there), before reappearing on both slopes of Costa Rica to western Panama, discontinuously east as far as the southern Azuero Peninsula, Los Santos, this population being speculated to be particularly small and threatened (Monroe 1968, Wetmore 1972, Ridgely and Gwynne 1976, Stiles and Skutch 1989, BirdLife International 2000, Snow 2004a, Saranathan *et al.* 2007). In Honduras and northern Nicaragua, it has always wintered mainly on the Caribbean slope and adjacent lowlands, but in Panama, due to forest loss the species now mainly winters on the Caribbean slope, with occasional records in recent years from the Canal Zone

at this season suspected to involve birds displaced from former wintering areas that are no longer suitable (Ridgely and Gwynne 1989, BirdLife International 2004). The species is recorded from the foothills and lowlands, regularly down to sea level in Bocas del Toro (Panama), during the non-breeding season, and to 3,000m immediately post-breeding (see next section).

MOVEMENTS Altitudinal migration is well established for this species (Powell and Bjork 2004, see also *Cotinga* 2: 11). In Costa Rica the Three-wattled Bellbird breeds at 1,200–2,300m, although in the northwest of the country it is found slightly lower, down to *c.*900m (in the Cordillera de Guanacaste: Stiles and Skutch 1989). In Honduras, it occurs year-round at 600–2,100m (Anderson *et al.* 1998), but Anderson *et al.* (2004) and Vallely *et al.* (2010) tentatively concluded that Three-wattled Bellbird is a seasonal visitor to the lowlands of the Río Plátano Biosphere Reserve. On post-breeding dispersal, some individuals initially move upslope as high as 3,000m (e.g. on the Nicoya Peninsula, Costa Rica), before migrating to the lowlands (on both slopes in Costa Rica and Panama, but see above), including to sea level (Slud 1964, Stiles and Skutch 1989, Powell & Bjork 2004). At some foothill localities, e.g. in the Valle del General, Costa Rica, this bellbird is heard year-round and is perhaps resident (Stiles and Skutch 1989), as is probably also the case in Coiba Island National Park, off Veraguas, Panama (BirdLife International 2008), although it has in the past been suspected to be only a non-breeding visitor to the island (Ridgely and Gwynne 1976). The species is present

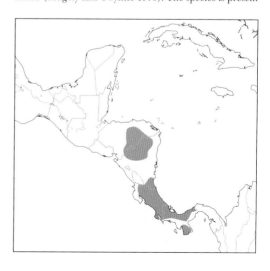

at lowland localities mainly during October–February (early March) in Panama.

HABITAT Three-wattled Bellbird is restricted to primary montane forest in the breeding season, but also tolerates more open, tall second growth at other times. In Panama the species also visits swampy woodland during the non-breeding season (see Wetmore 1972).

DESCRIPTION The sexes differ. The bill is rather weak but broad-based, with rather large, oval-shaped nostrils, but no rictal bristles. The tarsi are comparatively short considering the overall size of the bird. The modified primaries are described below. *Adult male.* – Clean white hood and throat contrasting with the rich rufous-brown body, wings and tail. Breast feathers are white basally. Three grey or black, soft and flexible, worm-like wattles (up to 12.5cm long) hang from the bill, one crossing the upper mandible from left to right, and the other two hanging down either side of the gape. The lores and eye surround are dark grey to black with short bristly feathers. Also has modified outer primaries, with the tips of the inner vanes being slightly hooked and projecting beyond the outer vanes (see Snow 1982: 171, for diagram). Adult plumage is acquired very gradually, over the course of *c.*3 years. *Immature male.* – Variable, but never develops a dark crown. Some at *c.*6–12 months old, which otherwise resemble females, already possess rudimentary wattles (which can reach up to 20mm long by the end of the first year of life), as well as a white chin and throat, with a few rufous feathers on the belly, scapulars and rump. Later-stage males are much as adult males, but the white throat and hood, although first to develop, are often still streaked with olive, and there tends also to be some olive elements retained over the tertials, primaries and some breast and flank feathers. In some, the plumage can appear completely adult, but with some slight darker elements on the ear-coverts and crown (GMK pers. obs.). Fully adult feathering is only acquired after the third complete moult. *Adult female.* – Olive-green above, having the crown concolorous with the rest of the upperparts, an olive-yellow eye-ring, spots and streaks around the eye and ear-coverts, and brownish-grey remiges with brighter olive fringes. Underparts streaked dull olive and yellow, with a few random white feathers, but the streaks are reduced on the throat and absent from the undertail-coverts. Undertail greyish-brown, and the underwing-coverts are blotchy olive and yellow. The underside of the rectrices is greyish-brown. *Immature female.* – Differs from the adult female only in having the streaking below much more blurred (Stiles and Skutch 1989). *Juvenile.* – Seemingly undescribed, insomuch as all descriptions of non-adults in the literature appear to apply to birds that have replaced their juvenile plumage (Snow 2004a). In acquiring adult plumage, this species, like all bellbirds, moults the wing and tail feathers progressively along each row and often the feather bases appear more adult-like than their tips (Snow 1973a, 1982). *Moult.* – Data were summarised by Snow (1982), and Snow (1973a) presented a moult schedule for this species for its four-year acquisition of adult plumage. Complete renewal occupies *c.*160 days (Snow 1976a), and females probably commence replacing their feathers immediately on conclusion of breeding, but males (in common with other cotingas in which this sex is divorced from parental care) moult considerably earlier, on average (starting in the second half of April to early August), than females. Young males commence replacing their feathers prior to adult males,

before the breeding season begins (in March and the first half of April), but feather renewal is still protracted with one taken in northern Costa Rica in early July still replacing the body feathers, outer primaries and secondaries (MNCR). *Bare parts.* – The bill is broad and somewhat flattened, and is black or blackish with a paler gape and greyer cutting edges and basal portion (which are dull greenish-grey in the female); the legs, feet and soles are lead black or dark grey, with olive-grey soles in some younger birds, and the irides are dark brown to dark grey.

MEASUREMENTS (from Wetmore 1972, plus BMNH, RMNH and ZMA, except bill, BMNH and ZMA only: Costa Rica and Panama) Wing of male (*n* = 18) 159–177mm, wing of female (*n* = 24) 136–168mm; tail of male (*n* = 18) 97–115mm, tail of female (*n* = 24) 95–109mm; bill of male (*n* = 8) 27.54–36.00mm, bill of female (*n* = 2) 27.21–29.00mm; tarsus of male (*n* = 18) 25.89–32.00mm, tarsus of female (*n* = 24) 25.20–32.95mm. Snow (1973a) presented additional wing-length data for males, females and immature males. Weight: 194–233g (males) and 145g (one female) (Snow 1982, 2004a, Dunning 2008; FMNH; MNCR; MVZ).

GEOGRAPHICAL VARIATION Monotypic and the different (and to some extent) isolated breeding populations, in southern Honduras/northern Nicaragua, Costa Rica and western Panama, and south-central Panama, are only weakly differentiated genetically (Saranathan *et al.* 2007).

VOICE Varies to some extent with locality (see Stiles and Skutch 1989), i.e. is dialectal, but is typical of the genus in being loud, wooden or metallic and far-carrying. Like all bellbirds, only the male *P. tricarunculatus* vocalises. The typical advertising call is a very loud *bok* (or *brenk* or *bonk!*), with other, quieter squeaks and whistles sometimes interspersed, the whole lasting *c.*6.25 seconds (Snow 1977, 1982). When singing the male extends his wattles to their full length (normally they are only *c.*30% of this), opens the bill to its maximum extent and raises the contour feathers, especially the white feathers (Crandall 1948, Snow 1977). The main call, which is audible up to 0.5km distant, is readily recognised as belonging to a bellbird, even without previous field experience. Kroodsma (2005) documented four main song-types (dialects): that in northern Nicaragua and southern Honduras (mostly comprising slurred whistles with chirpy bonk notes given occasionally), the second in the Tilarán Mts of north-central Costa Rica (a loud ringing *Bonk!* followed by varied swishing notes interspersed by loud pure-toned whistles, some sounding like very brief pulses of electricity), the third in southeast Costa Rica and western Panama (a pair of squawking notes followed by varied swishing notes with an occasional *bock* that lacks the ringing quality associated with the previous vocal type) and the fourth type in the highlands of the Azuero Peninsula of Panama (a loud higher pitched *gbink* and chirp, a pause and then a single pure-toned note). Sonograms of these different song-types were presented by Saranathan *et al.* (2007) and also, to some extent, by Snow (1973a, 1977). However, some males in the Tilarán Mts are bilingual, i.e. they give two song-types, which diversity is not shown by any of the other populations; one bird also sang the northern song-type and another male also gave the southeast Costa Rican and western Panama song-type (Snow 1977, Kroodsma 2005, Saranathan *et al.* 2007). At the height of the breeding season, adult males may spend a very significant percentage of each day singing and displaying. Young males give rasping, more wavering calls, albeit fundamentally similar to those of the adults (learnt, as in all bellbirds, from *c*.15 months old), and Kroodsma (2005) recently showed that young of the present species may take 6–7 years to 'learn' the adult's song, using conspecific males as 'mentors'. Kroodsma (2005) and Saranathan *et al.* (2007) documented changes in the Monteverde population's song-type, both since the Snows' work in the 1970s and during their own research, but also noted that some males appear not to change their songs even over long periods (20 years), despite the general trend. This observation could have significant consequences for our understanding of the importance of vocalisations in taxonomic studies of some suboscines. The dialectal nature of this species' songs was first discussed by Snow (1977) in her study at Monteverde in Costa Rica. Recently, Saranathan *et al.* (2007) revealed not only that the striking geographical variation in the songs of Three-wattled Bellbird has no genetic basis, but that vocal learning is sufficiently pronounced that rapid temporal changes in songs within populations are occurring (cf. also Kroodsma 2005), and that its dialects are therefore subject to constant cultural evolution. From our own unpublished observations, and those made by many others (especially Barbara & David Snow), of the other three species in this genus, it certainly seems to be true that all male *Procnias* take a number of years to 'perfect' their species-specific songs. Several recordings of Three-wattled Bellbird, from Costa Rica, Nicaragua and Panama, are archived online at www.xeno-canto.org, and the species' voice also features on the audio compilations of Ross (2000) and Knapp and Will (2008).

NATURAL HISTORY Three-wattled Bellbird can be very difficult to observe in the tall forests of the region, even when a number of males are calling in an 'exploded lek', but it is perhaps easiest to see in the more open, stunted highland forests of Monteverde, Costa Rica, for example. During the non-breeding season, this bellbird can form small flocks of up to five individuals (Kennard and Peters 1928).

FOOD AND FEEDING As with the other bellbirds, the broad gape enables comparatively large fruits (of up to 23mm) to be taken; *P. tricarunculatus* prefers Lauraceae (e.g. *Ocotea* and *Nectandra* spp.) and, at Monteverde, in the Snows' study, also a species of Rutaceae (*Stauranthus* sp.). Twenty-nine fruit species were known in the Three-wattled Bellbird's diet at the time of Moermond and Denslow's (1985) survey of fruit-eating birds in the Neotropics (other families include Moraceae and Melastomataceae). Of these 29, however, 82% of the diet was considered to comprise fruit of just three families, Flacourtiaceae, Lauraceae and Theaceae (Wheelwright *et al.* 1984). Like other large frugivorous birds, it will visit fruiting trees in the open, where fruit is plucked either from a perch or with a short sally-hover. Because of their wider gape size, males are able to take slightly larger fruits than females (Snow 1973a). Displaying males spend only brief periods feeding, but may pause to visit a particular fruiting tree up to 1km distant from its song-post (Snow 1977).

DISPLAY Like other bellbirds, males call and display (a short, 2–5m, flight occasionally punctuated by brief hovers, before returning to the same branch but in a reversed position), from a perch high in the treetops or above the canopy (a broken-off branch at a shallow angle, termed the 'visiting perch': Snow 1977). However, he usually mates with the female lower down, in the subcanopy (Stiles and Skutch 1989), even apparently sometimes in the understorey (Snow

2004a). Some males with particularly large territories (e.g. up to 450m × 50m, as opposed to 70m × 30m or 80m × 25m) may have up to three visiting perches (Snow 1977). Like other bellbirds, non-adult male males seem to assume less prominent perches from which to call and display (GMK pers. obs.). Male displays were detailed by Snow (1977) and Snow (1982) and have been summarised here. Males can spend up to 93% of their day calling (producing *c*.2,000 calls) and displaying (Snow 1977), but they generally finish well before sunset. In addition to the short flight display described above, which may be given up to three times in a five-minute period (GMK pers. obs.), Snow (1977) described the silent wattle-shaking display, which is only performed when another bellbird visits an adult male. The territorial male assumes a crouched position with the folded wings held slightly away from the body, looking down every few seconds then up at the visitor (in the form of a short bowing movement) whilst shaking its head and wattles. This display continues for several minutes and also incorporates several short quick sideways hops, first one way and then the other. Three-wattled Bellbird's changing-place display (as it was termed by Snow 1977) is apparently unique amongst the genus. Following multiple calls, the male flutters upwards a short distance (usually 30–45cm) from either the visiting perch or another high song-post, before returning to it and assuming a crouched position with the tail spread. Sometimes these flights may be directed slightly downwards and cover over 1m, and they may be repeated at least three times (GMK pers. obs.). Another bellbird, usually a female or immature male, will then arrive on the same branch and the two then swap positions, before the male whose perch it is sidles up to the visiting bird and calls loudly at it (see diagram in Snow 1977, repeated in Snow 1982: 168). This usually causes the visitor to depart, but the bird often returns and the process is repeated. However, in mid April 2010, near San Gerardo Field Station, Monteverde (Costa Rica), GMK *et al.* observed an adult male displaying in this manner at a visiting perch to a female or very young male, during which it uttered no obvious sounds, although the male had been calling regularly prior to the visitor arriving. Snow (1977) occasionally witnessed the original owner of the perch being displaced, and the territory owner being the bird that was called loudly at. Birds of either sex that approach the visiting perch receive the same treatment; the male occupant calls loudly into the ear of the visitor until it departs. Even in the case of females, Snow (1977) never observed copulation ensue at the visiting perch!

BREEDING The nest is known solely from one that was under construction at Monteverde, Costa Rica, a loosely woven structure *c*.20cm in diameter of twigs (like other *Procnias*) sited 6.5m high in an understorey tree at the forest edge (Snow 1977, 1982); it was being constructed by the female alone, but no contents were ever observed and further details of the nest are unavailable. Breeding-condition birds and vocal activity suggest the nesting season is mainly March–June in Costa Rica, but it is suspected that there is much inter-annual and inter-locality variation. MVZ has a male taken with large testes in late June in Costa Rica, and another male in breeding condition taken in Nicaragua in April.

STATUS Considered Vulnerable (BirdLife International 2004, 2008), the species is uncommon, local and declining, principally due to the ongoing destruction of its lowland non-breeding haunts, especially on the Caribbean slope. Its overall range is estimated to be 22,600km² and its population to number between 10,000 and 20,000 individuals (BirdLife International 2008). Local ornithologists in Costa Rica are endeavouring to census and monitor the different subpopulations present in that country (E. Carman pers. comm.). Several conservation units (e.g. La Selva OTS Biological Station, Monteverde National Park and Las Tablas National Park, all in Costa Rica) offer significant protection to the Three-wattled Bellbird's breeding grounds, but perhaps just three, Río Indio-Maíz Biological Reserve (Nicaragua), Corcovado National Park (Costa Rica) and Sansán-Pondsock Wetlands Ramsar site (Panama), offer realistic protection in the non-breeding season. Other nominally protected areas where the species occurs during this period face clearance for agriculture. La Amistad International Park, which spans the border between Costa Rica and Panama, is considered of keynote importance to the species' overall survival prospects (Montañez and Angehr 2007). There are few recent data from Nicaragua or Honduras regarding the species' status in those countries, but it occurs, at least seasonally, in the Río Plátano Biosphere Reserve (Vallely *et al.* 2010); there are records from only Colón and Gracias a Dios departments in the latter country (Anderson *et al.* 1998, Vallely *et al.* 2010).

REFERENCES Anderson *et al.* (1998, 2004), AOU (1998), BirdLife International (2000, 2004, 2008), Blake and Loiselle (2001), Cooper (1997), Crandall (1948), David and Gosselin (2002b), Dunning (2008), Eisenmann and Avendaño (2007), Fulton (2001), Garrigues and Dean (2007), Hellmayr (1929b), Kennard and Peters (1928), Kjeldsen (2004), Knapp and Will (2008), Kroodsma (2005), Lawson (2010), Monroe (1968), Montañez and Angehr (2007), Olson (1971), Powell and Bjork (2004), Ridgely and Gwynne (1989), Ridgway (1905), Ross (2000), Saranathan *et al.* (2007), Skutch (1969), Slud (1964, 1980), Snow, B. K. (1977), Snow (1973a, 1976a, 1982, 2004a), Stiles and Skutch (1989), Stotz *et al.* (1996), Vallely *et al.* (2010), Wenny and Levey (1998), Wetmore (1972), Wheelwright *et al.* (1984).

Three-wattled Bellbird *Procnias tricarunculatus*. **Fig. 1**. Male, San Gerardo Biological Station, near Monteverde, Costa Rica, August (*Steven Easley / Costa Rica Gateway*). A male at 'maximum volume'; note the inky black gape and the scattered immature feathers on the lower breast. The males of this species and Bearded Bellbird *P. averano* are automatically well distinguished from the other two species in not being all white. **Fig. 2**. Male, western Costa Rica, December (*Hadoram Shirihai / Photographic Handbook to Birds of the World*). **Fig. 3**. Singing male, San Gerardo Biological Station, near Monteverde, Costa Rica, April (*Steven Easley / Costa Rica Gateway*). **Fig. 4**. Male, Santa Elena Reserve, Monteverde, Costa Rica, March (*Kevin Easley / Costa Rica Gateway*). Note the second male in the background.

WHITE BELLBIRD
Procnias albus   **Plate 24**

Ampelis alba **Hermann, 1783**, *Tab. Aff. Anim.*: 213, Cayenne [based on Le Guira Panga ou Cotinga Blanc, of Montbeillard *in* Buffon, 1778, *Hist. Nat. Oiseaux* 4: 454]

The resonant double bell-like call of this superb cotingid can be heard throughout the high forests of the Guianan Shield and in a limited area of northern Amazonian Brazil. Males are relatively easily observed at their song-posts, especially if you can access an elevated vantage point, when their snowy white plumage contrasts with the bright green of the lush forests.

IDENTIFICATION 27–29cm (the female is marginally smaller than the male). One of the world's few entirely white non-waterbirds, there should be little difficulty in identifying the male White Bellbird (there is no range overlap with the Bare-throated Bellbird *Procnias nudicollis*). The basically green, streaked yellow females are less obviously assigned to species, especially as they frequent the lower tiers of the forest offering fewer clues to their identity. However, in this bellbird's range, females are only really confusable with the marginally smaller female Bearded Bellbird *Procnias averano*, from which it is largely separated altitudinally for much of the year (e.g. in Venezuela and the Guianas). Although these two species are fundamentally similar in plumage, closer inspection should reveal the darker grey-brown crown and more coarsely and extensively streaked throat and underparts of the Bearded Bellbird, which is also marginally longer tailed and longer billed, although whether such characters would be apparent in the field except in comparative views or without extensive previous experience seems unlikely. Some confusion may also arise with the Red-banded Fruiteater *Pipreola whitelyi* (which see) of the Pantepui region of southeast Venezuela and Guyana, but the bellbird and fruiteater do not normally share the same elevational range, with the latter species being principally found at higher elevations than the bellbird.

DISTRIBUTION Largely restricted to northeast South America, where the White Bellbird is found mainly in eastern and southeastern Venezuela (principally in eastern- and southernmost Bolívar, as far west as the Cerro Urutaní, and the Cerro de la Neblina, in southernmost Amazonas, with an apparently anomalous specimen record from the Cerro Turumiquire, in southern Sucre, in the northeast: Hilty 2003), the Guianas, where it is considered uncommon in Guyana (principally in the montane centre and south, and was recently recorded on the Potaro Plateau in the extreme west: Snyder 1966, Barnett *et al.* 2002), widespread and reasonably common in hill forests of Surinam (known from *c.*15 localities: Ottema *et al.* 2009), and locally frequent in the montane interior and more seasonal on the coastal plain of French Guiana (Tostain *et al.* 1992), and just penetrating northern Amazonian Brazil, in northern Roraima (above 600m) and in northernmost Pará (e.g. at Aramapacú, on the Rio Paru do Leste, and on the Rio Jari, at the border with Amapá), with isolated records as far south as the lower Rio Negro, near Manaus (all nominate *P. a. albus*) (Novaes 1980b, Sick 1997, Naka *et al.* 2006). There is also a breeding population well south of the Amazon in Brazil, in the Serra dos Carajás, southeast Pará (*P. a. wallacei*), with an apparently anomalous record by Alfred Russel Wallace from Belém, Pará, in July 1849, which had

been dismissed by Snow (1982) for want of evidence. The Carajás population is disjunct from any other presumed breeding population by *c.*1,000km. Nominate *P. a. albus* is a vagrant to Trinidad, with six records, all in the Northern Range, in April–September (Kenefick *et al.* 2007). White Bellbird occurs to *c.*1,500m or higher (to 850m in French Guiana); it is principally recorded at 500–750m in the Serra dos Carajás (Roth *et al.* 1984), and generally above 450m in Venezuela, although the species has been sighted as low as 100m in the latter country (Hilty 2003).

MOVEMENTS These are little known, but seasonal altitudinal movements apparently occur in southeast Venezuela, where it moves upslope in December–June/July; in southern Guyana, where they are perhaps driven by changes in food supply (Snow 1973); and in French Guiana, where White Bellbird is recorded in lower-elevation coastal forests in the non-breeding season (Tostain *et al.* 1992). Regular short-range movements have been reported from the southwestern edge of the Iwokrama reserve in south-central Guyana, where the species appears in the early wet season, in October, along the River Burro-Burro and in other areas near Surama village (G. Sway pers. comm.). Records (at Barcelos and *c.*30km upriver from Manaus) in the Rio Negro region, Amazonas, Brazil (Novaes 1980b; specimens MNRJ examined), almost certainly also reflect wandering birds (although Roth *et al.* 1984 suggested that these might also indicate undiscovered breeding populations in montane forest in these regions), as presumably do Trinidad occurrences and the 19th century specimen record from Belém, Pará, mentioned above (see Distribution).

HABITAT A bird of lowland and submontane forests, locally ascending the slopes of the tepuis. The southernmost population in the Serra dos Carajás, Brazil, is restricted to upland tall *terra firme* forests (it seems to be absent from the slopes of the plateau) where it is frequently found at the ecotone with a cerrado-like vegetation locally known as *canga*. In the non-breeding season in French Guiana and Surinam, White Bellbird is found in swampy and white-sand forests, as well as in riverine forests in Guyana (cf. Movements). Snow (1973) noted some movement to higher altitudes in the Kanaku Mts (southern Guyana) in the late dry season, presumably in search of favoured fruits.

DESCRIPTION Sexes differ. The bill is rather weak but broad-based, with rather large, oval-shaped nostrils, but no rictal bristles. The tarsi are comparatively short considering the overall size of the bird. The nominate race is described here. *Adult male.* – Plumage is fittingly all white, with the outer primaries modified (as in Three-wattled Bellbird *P. tricarunculatus*: see Snow 1982: 171, for diagram), and a single (up to 6.2cm) long blackish wattle (which can be extended up to twice its normal length in display), which hangs from the base of the upper mandible (wrapping over it from left to right) and is mainly bare, except for several small, tuft-like and star-shaped white feathers. Adult plumage is acquired gradually. *Immature male.* – Best described as 'peppered' and its plumage is variable depending on the stage of maturity, but the first white feathers appear on the otherwise female-like upperparts, in the remiges, rectrices, and scattered over the mantle and rump. The underparts are largely white with short olive streaks. At this stage, the wattle is almost fully grown, whereas in a male, presumed to be just over one year old, examined by Snow (1982), the wattle was present but still short. A specimen from southeast Pará (*P. a. wallacei*) was considered to be a third-year based on the dark patches on the innermost secondaries (Roth *et al.* 1984). *Adult female.* – Olive above (the crown concolorous with the back), with a browner cast to the remiges, albeit these feathers have olive fringes. Streaked olive and yellow below, and has larger white feathers on the underparts than other female bellbird species. The undertail-coverts are plain yellow, and the undertail grey-brown. Underwing-coverts yellowish-white, the underside of the remiges pale grey, becoming whiter proximally. *Juvenile.* – Seemingly undescribed, insomuch as all descriptions of non-adults in the literature appear to apply to birds that have replaced their juvenile plumage (Snow 2004a). In acquiring adult plumage, this species, like all bellbirds, moults the wing and tail feathers progressively along each row and often the feather bases appear more adult-like than their tips (Snow 1973a, 1982). *Moult.* – The moult cycle is almost certainly prolonged, in males commencing at the onset of egg-laying, but with no clear seasonal pattern, as is often the case with cotingas that occupy a similar geographical range across largely equatorial regions (Snow 1982). *Bare parts.* – Irides blackish or brown; the bill is black or more likely dark grey, with paler cutting edges and a darker tip to the lower mandible (at least in *P. a. wallacei*); and the legs and feet are black or dark grey.

MEASUREMENTS (BMNH; ZMA: French Guiana, Guyana, Surinam and Venezuela) *P. a. albus*: wing of male (*n* = 11) 157–168mm, wing of female (*n* = 4) 136–138mm; tail of male (*n* = 10) 92–106mm, tail of female (*n* = 3) 86–92mm; bill of male (*n* = 7) 26–32mm, bill of female (*n* = 5) 19.78–23.48mm; tarsus of male (*n* = 10) 26–33mm, tarsus of female (*n* = 4) 22–27mm. Snow (1973a) presented additional wing-length data for males, females and immature males. Weight: 210–215g (nominate male) (Snow 1982, 2004a, Dunning 2008). Subspecific data are discussed below, given that the main differences between the two races are mensural in character.

GEOGRAPHICAL VARIATION *P. a. albus* (through most of range), with the recently described *P. a. wallacei* Oren & Novaes, 1985 (in the Serra dos Carajás, southeast Pará, Brazil) differing in having the wings (153–159mm, *n* = 3) and tail (93–97mm, *n* = 3) somewhat shorter than those of the nominate, and the tarsus (29–30mm, *n* = 3), culmen (18.2–19.9mm, *n* = 3) and gape (33–36mm, *n* = 3) significantly larger (the bill and gape are the largest of any

Procnias). All available specimens are males, two of which weighed 219 and 222g (Oren and Novaes 1985). Snow (2004a) opined that *P. a. wallacei* has a slightly grey-tinged throat, but this difference has not proved apparent in the field during our observations (GMK pers. obs.). As noted by J. A. Tobias (*in* Snow 2004a: 55), in at least some birds the wattle hangs from right to left over the bill in *P. a. wallacei* (Sick 1997: 667 stated, based presumably on the same population, that the wattle hangs from the left side of the bill, but may be thrown to the right at the end of a call). However, although this character appears frequent in those birds seen well enough to evaluate it in the field, it is not constant, as evidenced by photographs, in which the wattle may occasionally lie on the right side of the bill when 'at rest' (GMK pers. obs.).

VOICE Ventriloquial: as in other bellbirds, it is only the males that sing, from high in the treetops, where they typically select a bare branch (or preferably several branches) above the canopy (up to 40m or more above the ground), the birds (exceptionally up to ten) forming a very widely spaced lek (perhaps several kilometres wide), and each lek being some distance from the next. This is the bellbird *par excellence*. Its ringing, highly resonant and very loud *klong-klang* (the second syllable higher) is a once-heard, never forgotten sound, and has been compared to a hammer striking an anvil. Like other bellbirds, the male initially cowers on the advertising perch, before pushing the body upwards and almost inwardly exploding as it delivers the call, the head all the while being held still but the bill angle being switched from right to left between notes, and the wattle being temporarily thrown to the left side of the bill at the culmination of the call (see also Geographical Variation). Young males select much less prominent perches, usually in the subcanopy (GMK pers. obs.). Also frequently gives a drawn-out, slightly moaning or droning *boi..i..i.ng...*, this call comprising two parts, with the second part fainter and sounding like an echo of the first. In the north of the continent, vocal activity commences in September (December in southeast Venezuela) and continues until March or April, or even July in Bolívar (Hilty 2003), whilst south of the Amazon (in the Serra dos Carajás) vocalisations start as early as June but are heard only infrequently by February (Roth *et al.* 1984; GMK pers. obs.). The species sings mainly in July–August in the savanna region of Surinam (but October–March over the rest of the country: O. Ottema). *P. albus* is generally silent at other times, and thus easily overlooked, although apparently White Bellbirds even sing occasionally on the non-breeding grounds in French Guiana (Tostain *et al.* 1992). Published recordings are available on the following audio compilations: Boesman (1999, 2006a, 2006b), Marantz and Zimmer (2006) and Renaudier and Deroussen (2008), and recordings from Brazil, French Guiana, Surinam and Venezuela are archived online at www.xeno-canto.org. Sonograms were presented by Snow (1973a).

NATURAL HISTORY White Bellbird is generally solitary, foraging alone in the canopy and subcanopy of tall forest, although females (and perhaps also young males) may occasionally form small congregations at particularly productive food sources.

FOOD AND FEEDING Diet is apparently entirely fruit, especially those belonging to the families Lauraceae and Burseraceae, taken occasionally from a perch but more typically during a brief aerial sally-hover. Because of their wider gape size, males are able to take slightly larger fruits than females (Snow 1973a). The species is sometimes observed to join other cotingas, e.g. Pompadour *Xipholena punicea*, Spangled *Cotinga cayana* and Purple-breasted Cotingas *C. cotinga*, at a fruiting tree.

DISPLAY Male displays (which are similar to those of other *Procnias* spp.) were detailed by Snow (1982) and are summarised here. The male's visiting perch is an open branch or a liana, and the male performs a short silent display flight of 2–5m from either the song-post or the visiting perch, similar to that of the Three-wattled Bellbird. Attendance at the visiting perch and song-post is apparently similar in White Bellbird to that of the previous species (Snow 1973, 1982). If a female arrives at the visiting perch, the male initially crouches to the right and silently shakes his extended wattle, whilst the female silently sidles towards him. When the female gets close, the male calls and swings the wattle over the bill (see Voice) towards the female, which in Snow's (1973) observations in Guyana was always then observed to retreat. Once, Snow witnessed a male perform a flutter-jump in conjunction with the call, suggesting that this is a pre-copulatory display.

BREEDING The mating system is polygamous, but there are very few data concerning breeding and the nest is unknown, although a female was observed to break off fine twigs from a *Eugenia* (Myrtaceae) tree favoured by other cotingids for collecting nesting material, in February, in southern Guyana (Snow 1982) and a male taken in mid March (KUNHM specimen), also in southern Guyana, had enlarged testes. The breeding season is considered to be February–June in Venezuela and the Guianas, but almost certainly differs in southern Amazonian Brazil, where peak calling commences in June and the season was speculated to be centred on August–September by Roth *et al.* (1984); nonetheless, males remain highly vocal as late as the end of December in this region; by mid February they appear to be usually largely silent (GMK pers. obs.).

STATUS White Bellbird is considered Least Concern by BirdLife International (2004, 2008). It is generally uncommon to locally common in the humid forests of northeastern South America, where much pristine habitat fortunately still remains within its largely uninhabited range. White Bellbird is reasonably common, but somewhat locally distributed, in tall tableland *terra firme* forests of the Serra dos Carajás, Brazil, which are protected by a mosaic of conservation units, but the species is perhaps most readily seen on lower and middle sections of the Escalera road, on the Sierra de Lema, in Bolívar, southern Venezuela.

REFERENCES Aleixo *et al.* (2011), Barnett *et al.* (2002), Bernard (2008), BirdLife International (2004, 2008), Boesman (1999, 2006a, 2006b), Braun *et al.* (2007), Burton (1976), David and Gosselin (2002b), Dunning (2008), Gilliard (1941), Hellmayr (1929b), Hilty (2003), Kenefick *et al.* (2007), Marantz and Zimmer (2006), Meyer de Schauensee and Phelps (1978), Naka *et al.* (2006), Novaes (1980a, 1980b), Olson (1971), Oren and Novaes (1985), Ottema *et al.* (2009), Pacheco *et al.* (2007), Pérez-Emán *et al.* (2003), Renaudier (2009), Renaudier and Deroussen (2008), Restall *et al.* (2006), Ridgely and Tudor (1994, 2009), Robbins *et al.* (2004, 2007), Roth *et al.* (1984), Snow, B. K. (1961, 1973), Snow (1973a, 1982, 2004a), Snyder (1966), Stotz *et al.* (1996), Tostain *et al.* (1992), Zyskowski *et al.* (2011).

1

White Bellbird *Procnias albus*. **Figs. 1–3**. Male, *P. a. albus*, Sierra de Lema, Bolívar, southeast Venezuela, January (*Pete Morris*). This series of images shows a displaying a male along the famous 'Escalera' road, where two species of *Procnias* can be found; White and Bearded Bellbirds *P. averano*. The white patches on the wattle are tiny star-shaped 'rosettes' of feathers.

BEARED BELLBIRD
Procnias averano **Plate 24**

Ampelis averano **Hermann, 1783**, *Tab. Aff. Anim.*: 211, [northeastern Brazil] [based on L'Averano, of Buffon, 1778, *Hist. Nat. Oiseaux* 4: 457]

The only bellbird resident on the island of Trinidad, the male is arguably the most exquisite and bizarre of the four species of *Procnias*. Bearded Bellbird forms a species-pair with Bare-throated Bellbird *Procnias nudicollis*; both of them have a throat that is either bare (*P. nudicollis*) or covered with rudimentary black feathers. The nominate subspecies is considered endemic to the Caatinga Centre of endemism (Cracraft 1985).

IDENTIFICATION 25–29cm (the male averages larger than the female). Calling males can be unusually difficult to observe in the subcanopy, from where they utter their distinctive main call (actually rather dissimilar to the sound of a bell), and a sit-and-wait technique may be necessary to observe this handsome bird in the open. Although the 'beard' may be difficult to see at a distance, the male Bearded Bellbird, with its chocolate-brown hood and black wings contrasting with the white or palest of grey bodies, permits straightforward identification. The female could be mistaken for a female White *Procnias albus* (which see) or Bare-throated Bellbird (see Description), or even the much smaller female Red-banded Fruiteater *Pipreola whitelyi*, with which it is sympatric (but largely elevationally parapatric) in the Pantepui region of southern Venezuela and adjacent Guyana. The fruiteater is safely identified by its narrow olive-yellow nuchal collar and supercilia; the underparts are also a paler yellowish-white with bold black streaks. Beware also the possibility, at great distance, of confusion with any of the tityras, but note the pattern of brown (not black) on the head, lack of any red in the bare parts, and the obviously much smaller bill of the bellbird, amongst many other differences.

DISTRIBUTION Bearded Bellbird is found in northeastern South America, where its range is somewhat broader than the generally lower-elevation White Bellbird. It occurs on Trinidad (where this species is locally common in the Northern Range: Kenefick *et al.* 2007), more or less throughout the coastal cordillera of Venezuela (albeit rather locally, from Zulia and Lara east to northern Monagas and the Paria Peninsula; generally at 350–1,600m, occasionally lower: Hilty 2003, Azpiroz and Rodríguez-Ferraro 2006), extreme northeast Colombia (in the northern Sierra de Perijá, at 150–600m, and it perhaps occurred, at least formerly, in the middle Magdalena Valley in Norte de Santander: Hilty and Brown 1986), as well as the Pantepui of southern (on the Cerro de la Neblina, Amazonas) and southeast Venezuela (throughout southern Bolívar, where the species is generally found at 700–1,500m: Hilty 2003), western and southwestern Guyana (at the Adaroo River, Mt Kowa, Mt Twek-Quay and the Kanuku Mts: Snyder 1966, Snow 1973a, Barnett *et al.* 2002), and the Brazilian state of Roraima (on the Cerros Urutaní and Uei-tepui, at 1,070–1,280m, as far south as the Rio Branco: Snow 1973a, Sick 1997). There is also a relatively recently discovered series of disjunct populations in northeast Brazil, from southern Maranhão (where initially discovered in 1924 and the species is reasonably numerous, e.g. at Grajaú, Barra do Corda: Hellmayr 1929a, Camargo 1957, Santos *et al.*

2010), discontinuously south and east through central-east Tocantins (at Guaraí and the Jalapão region), mainly in southern and southwest Piauí (discovered in 1975), Ceará (e.g. in parts of the Chapada do Araripe, at the border with the next state, but also in the extreme northeast on the Serra do Baturité and the Serra da Aratanha, where it seems to be notably abundant: Albano and Girão 2008), Pernambuco (where the species was initially reported by Marcgrave in 1648), northeast Bahia (first reported in 1974) and Alagoas (where it is known from at least four localities between 80 and *c.*500m, and was discovered in 1952) (Sick 1997, Silveira *et al.* 2003a). Bearded Bellbird has been recorded to *c.*1,900m.

MOVEMENTS Bearded Bellbird plausibly undertakes altitudinal movements in some parts of its range; for instance north of the Orinoco in Venezuela (Hilty 2003), although few details are available, the birds appear to move higher at the onset of the breeding season, in April–May, reaching at least 1,600m (Schaefer and Phelps 1954, Snow 1982). However, there is no evidence of vertical movements on Trinidad (Snow 1970).

HABITAT The species inhabits humid wet forest of various types, including *terra firme*, but is also found in drier deciduous forest (in northeast Venezuela), ranging into tall *caatinga* and *cerradão* in northeast Brazil (Silva *et al.* 2004, Santos *et al.* 2010; GMK pers. obs.), as well as mature second growth.

DESCRIPTION Sexes differ. The bill is rather weak but broad-based, with rather large, oval-shaped nostrils, but no rictal bristles. The tarsi are comparatively short considering the overall size of the bird. The following applies to the nominate race. *Adult male.* – 'Beard', formed by rudimentary black throat feathers, often appears uniformly dark in the field (the delicate, stringy moss-like filaments oscillate at the bird's slightest movement, but probably cannot be extended in the manner of the wattles possessed by White and Three-wattled Bellbirds *P. tricarunculatus*). Chocolate-brown hood, bare skin on ocular region and lores possess scattered vestiges of feathers. Wings black, but the underside of the remiges is slightly browner. The rest of the plumage is almost pure white, relieved by a patch of bare pink skin on the outer side of the tibia (as in Bare-throated Bellbird). Outer primaries modified, as are those of other bellbirds, with rounded extensions to the inner vanes (see Snow 1982: 171, for diagram). The male has several distinct phases before attaining basic adult in fourth year (Snow 1982, Restall *et al.* 2006), although the wattles start to develop at *c.*1 year. *Subadult male.* – This plumage is characterised by olive outer webs to the brown rectrices and some of the remiges, a brown crown and grey-brown upperparts, and a few olive-yellow feathers are still visible on the belly. *Immature male.* – Resembles the adult female, as in the closely related Bare-throated Bellbird (with which it forms a species-pair). The crown in *P. averano* passes through an intermediate sooty stage, and the throat is also briefly dark before acquiring the adult colour. The first complete moult towards adult plumage occurs when the bird is one year old, following which the wing and tail are still juvenile, but the back is also sooty-coloured. Then in the second year the subadult plumage is achieved (see above). *Adult female.* – Crown darker olive than rest of upperparts (but is less dark than in *P. nudicollis*), with blacker feather centres making the ground colour of the mantle, rump and uppertail-coverts appear duller than other female bellbirds. From below, it is very similar to the female Bare-throated Bellbird, with which confusion is possible in parts of the Brazilian northeast; the throat appears dark with heavy streaks. Breast and belly streaked olive and yellow; undertail-coverts dull yellow and undertail dull olive. Underwing-coverts yellow. *Juvenile.* – Like the female, but is clearly streaked yellow on olive throat and breast, and streaked above. The grey-white down-covered nestling was briefly described by Snow (1970, 1982) and is also illustrated in Snow (2004a: 66). In acquiring adult plumage, this species, like all bellbirds, moults the wing and tail feathers progressively along each row and often the feather bases appear more adult-like than their tips (Snow 1973a, 1982). *Moult.* – Data were summarised by Snow (1982). Complete renewal occupies *c.*160 days (Snow 1976a) and, at least on Trinidad, females probably commence replacing their feathers during the late breeding season (in the middle of the year), whilst males also conduct most feather renewal between the dual nesting period on this island, i.e. in August/September, although they may commence moulting at any time between late April and September. Furthermore, young males commence replacing their feathers prior to the adult males, between February and June, with the earliest start dates apparently determined by the stage of immaturity (Snow 1982). *Bare parts.* – Irides dark brown, bill black, legs and feet dark grey (female) to black (male), with browner toe pads.

MEASUREMENTS (BMNH; RMNH; ZMA; all *P. a. carnobarba*, except one male *P. a. averano*: Brazil, Trinidad and Venezuela) Wing of male ($n = 8$) 150–164mm, wing of female ($n = 3$) 138–143mm; tail of male ($n = 8$) 72–94mm, tail of female ($n = 3$) 85–89mm; bill of male ($n = 8$) 25–29mm, bill of female ($n = 3$) 22–23mm; tarsus of male ($n = 8$) 26.93–32.00mm, tarsus of female ($n = 3$) 25–28mm. Snow (1973a) presented additional wing-length data for males, females and immature males. Four males from Maranhão (*P. a. averano*: Hellmayr 1929a) had wing 160–166mm and tail 86–93mm. Additional mensural data (from Trinidad) were presented by Junge and Mees (1958). Weight: 111–180g (male averages heavier than the female) (Dickerman and Phelps 1982, Snow 1982, 2004a, Dunning 2008; RMNH).

GEOGRAPHICAL VARIATION *P. a. averano* (of northeast Brazil; described above) and *P. a. carnobarba* (Cuvier, 1816) (rest of range, holotype from Trinidad), which has most

of the body plumage pale grey instead of white. However, at least one specimen of *P. a. averano*, taken probably in the lowlands of Pernambuco, originally in the Salvin and Godman collection, and now held at the BMNH (Tring) has body plumage like that of specimens of *P. a. carnobarba* from Trinidad at the same institution.

VOICE Like other bellbirds, this species is ventriloquial and extremely far-carrying, with the main call audible up to 2km distant. Its vocalisations are similar to those of the partially sympatric Bare-throated Bellbird, perhaps the most familiar and immediately identifiable being the resounding *bok* call (given once every 3–8 seconds with the bill fully open, and sometimes the body thrown slightly backwards), as well as a series of repeated metallic *tink, tink, tink,...* or *tonk, tonk, tonk,...* calls likened to a hammer hitting an anvil, and uttered once every second (sometimes more frequently) in a series of up to 91 notes (Sick 1997). While giving these calls, the bird maintains the bill in an open position, but moves the lower mandible. Bearded Bellbird also has a disyllabic call that more resembles the classic bellbird *klong-king* (up to 18 notes in series), and which is like the common call of the partially sympatric White Bellbird (which see). Bearded Bellbird additionally gives a low *krrro* (Sick 1997). Young males, which may take at least two years to perfect their songs, appear to intersperse the explosive *bock* calls with discordant shrieking and rasping notes, and many 'false starts' punctuating the whole; and this is generally true of most or all bellbirds (GMK pers. obs.). The voice varies to some extent throughout the range, with, for instance, the nominate race apparently giving a slightly more spaced series of *tonk* calls, and birds on Trinidad apparently no longer uttering the more musical *klong-kling* call (unlike those in neighbouring Venezuela). Snow (1973a: 384, 388), however, pointed to evidence that birds on Trinidad formerly did utter this latter or at least a similarly disyllabic call in the 1890s, suggesting that similar cultural mechanisms might be at work in this population as in the Three-wattled Bellbird (which see). Males stop calling in Trinidad between mid August and October (when the birds are apparently moulting), and the species is mainly vocal during March–July in northern Venezuela and December–August in the south (Hilty 2003). In northeast Brazil birds generally commence calling at the onset of the rains in August/September (Snethlage 1928). Published recordings appear on the following audio compilations: Murphy (1991), White (1997), Boesman (1999, 2006a, 2006b), Hammick (2004) and Minns *et al.* (2009). Sonograms were presented by Snow (1973a). Several recordings, from Brazil, Trinidad & Tobago and Venezuela, are archived online at www.xeno-canto.org.

NATURAL HISTORY A relatively inconspicuous bellbird, which like the other species is polygamous in its mating system, with males advertising virtually all day long from a favoured perch, although these tend to be less frequently in the high canopy or above it than in the previous two species, and compared with White Bellbird even males spend considerable periods lower in the canopy or even midstorey.

FOOD AND FEEDING Diet is very similar to that of White Bellbird, exhibiting preferences for the same families of fruits, although it also consumes smaller species. Like other *Procnias* species, the Bearded Bellbird takes most food in flight, using a short sally-hover. Snow (1982) mentioned the presence of 45 species of fruits in this species' diet, of which the most important families were Lauraceae and Burseraceae during the Snows' study on Trinidad, but other principal food sources are fruits of Araliaceae and Melastomataceae (Moermond and Denslow 1985). The seeds are regurgitated. Females may gather at fruiting trees, with up to six individuals sometimes congregating. Because of their wider gape size, males are able to take slightly larger fruits than females (Snow 1973a).

DISPLAY The rather manakin-like display of the male (which is also similar to that of the Bare-throated Bellbird) has been well described and illustrated (see Snow 1970, 1973a, 1982) and comprises rapid jumps of up to 1.2m between two branches with the tail fanned and 'beard' extended and slightly raised to full effect, and is similar both when courting a female or 'jousting' with a rival male. As soon as a female arrives close by, the male ceases calling and performs the silent display jumps, following which if the female moves closer he commences to preen the underwing-coverts, then crouches and displays the bare tibial skin. Usually the female retreats at this point, but she often returns and eventually will permit copulation, initiating this by moving towards the male, which maintains a crouched position facing her, along the visiting perch. Suddenly the male will utter a particularly loud call and jump onto the female's back. Like all bellbirds the male is emancipated from parental care.

BREEDING Data are available only from Trinidad, where ten nests have been found, mainly in April–July, less often in October–November (indicating two breeding seasons per annum). The shallow, deceptively fragile-looking nest (from below the contents are visible) is entirely constructed by the female, a c.18cm platform of small live twigs (of just two different tree species, *Maprounea guianensis*, Euphorbiaceae, and *Terminalia obovata*, Combretaceae, on Trinidad) over a period of 4–5 days and is placed 2.4–15.0m above the ground in the outer branches of small to medium-sized trees (Beebe 1954, Snow 1970). A nest found in Maranhão, northeast Brazil, illustrated in Snow (2004a: 66) appears comparatively more bulky and is perhaps broader in diameter than the Trinidad nests. Unfortunately, further details of this nest seem not to have been published. Nests found by the Snows were on land cultivated with cocoa but close to native forest. The single pale tan egg mottled brown (dimensions were presented in Snow 1970) is laid 3–4 days after the nest is completed, and it is incubated for c.23 days. The Snows (1970, 1982) presented some data on incubation, noting that the female appeared to perform longer on-bouts with time (once incubating for nearly 16 hours without a break on the 21st day). The young, which is fed solely on regurgitated fruit, fledges after c.33 days, although the young bird was still far from adult size at this point. The unsheathed feathers became apparent between days 17 and 21 at one nest. The female alone is responsible for provisioning and brooding the nestling (although the latter ceased after day 6), which is fed at circa hourly intervals during brief, silent visits (for further details see Snow 1970). The female consumed the young bird's faeces and any regurgitated seeds, and roosted beside the nestling during the final four nights prior to its fledging (Snow 1970).

STATUS Beaded Bellbird is treated as Least Concern by BirdLife International (2004, 2008) on account of its wide range, of which significant parts, e.g. in the Pantepui region, are either largely unaffected by human activities or to some extent lie within protected areas, e.g. in the coastal cordillera of Venezuela and on the Paria Peninsula (Sharpe 1997, Hilty 2003, Azpiroz and Rodríguez-Ferraro 2006). However, the nominate race in northeastern Brazil is almost certainly threatened by continuing forest destruction (and is listed as Vulnerable by the Brazilian government), especially in the far east of this region, as well as (at least formerly) trapping for the cagebird trade (e.g. in the Serra do Baturité, Ceará, and parts of Maranhão: Albano and Girão 2008, Santos *et al.* 2010), although ongoing fieldwork is also revealing its range to be somewhat wider than originally considered. Local extinctions seem to have occurred in the far northeast of Brazil, e.g. in the Serra da Ibiapaba, and probably the Serra de Maranguape, both in Ceará (Albano and Girão 2008). Bearded Bellbird is known from a few protected areas in this region of Brazil including the Estação Ecológica de Uruçuí-Una, Piauí (Silveira *et al.* 2001), and Araripe-Apodi National Forest, Ceará (GMK pers. obs.). The species is considered to be fairly common but distinctly local in Guyana (Braun *et al.* 2007).

REFERENCES Albano and Girão (2008), Barnett *et al.* (2002), Beebe (1954), BirdLife International (2004, 2008), Boesman (1999, 2006a, 2006b), Braun *et al.* (2007), Browning and Monroe (1991), Camargo (1957), Chapman (1931), Cracraft (1985), David and Gosselin (2002b), Dickerman and Phelps (1982), Dunning (2008), Hammick (2004), Hellmayr (1929a, 1929b), Hilty (2003), Hilty and Brown (1986), Junge and Mees (1958), Kenefick *et al.* (2007), Minns *et al.* (2009), Moermond and Denslow (1985), Murphy (1991), Naka *et al.* (2006), Olson (1971), Pacheco and Olmos (2010), Phelps and Phelps (1962), Pinto (1944), Restall *et al.* (2006), Ridgely and Tudor (1994, 2009), Schaefer and Phelps (1954), Salaman *et al.* (2008, 2009), Santos (2000), Santos *et al.* (2010), Sharpe (1997), Sick (1993, 1997), Silva *et al.* (2004), Silveira *et al.* (2001, 2003a), Snethlage (1928), Snow, B. K. (1970), Snow (1962, 1973a, 1982, 2004a), Snyder (1966), Soares *et al.* (2009), Sousa e Silva *et al.* (2003), Stotz *et al.* (1996), White (1997), Willis (1992).

Bearded Bellbird *Procnias averano*. **Fig. 1**. Male, *P. a. averano*, Chapada do Araripe, Ceará, northeast Brazil, December (*Ciro Albano*). Highly distinctive due to the spaghetti-like wattles. The nominate race is endemic to northeast Brazil. **Figs. 2–3**. Male, *P. a. carnobarba*, Asa Wright Centre, Trinidad, May (*Steve Garvie / www.pbase.com/rainbirder*). Singing male, showing just how wide the bill is opened when a bellbird is singing. **Fig. 4**. Female, *P. a. carnobarba*, Sierra de Lema, Bolívar, southeast Venezuela, March (*Ron Hoff*). Female (and young male) bellbirds are generally very similar to one another, being primarily green and brown with streaked underparts. Fortunately, the four species are generally well separated geographically, although this species and White Bellbird *P. albus* occur in sympatry in this region of Venezuela. In comparison to the latter species, female Bearded Bellbirds are darker on the throat and marginally shorter billed.

462

BARE-THROATED BELLBIRD
Procnias nudicollis   Plate 24

Ampelis nudicollis **L. J. P. Vieillot, 1817**, *Nouv. Dict. Hist. Nat.*, new edn. 8: 164, [Nova Friburgo, Rio de Janeiro,] Brazil

Currently classified as Vulnerable, this species, the southernmost of the genus, is much sought-after for the commercial cagebird trade (despite being one of the most unmusical singers of all birds), and as a result is generally becoming scarce near large cities. Further evidence of vocal learning in bellbirds was graphically illustrated by Kroodsma (2005) for this species. A young Bare-throated Bellbird that was raised in captivity with a Chopi Blackbird *Gnorimopsar chopi* incorporated into its repertoire trills and whistles whose structure and timing closely matched those of the blackbird.

IDENTIFICATION 25.5–31.0cm (the female is typically slightly smaller than the male). The nearly all-white male sings from high perches above the canopy and, given the lack of any overlap in range with White Bellbird *Procnias albus*, it is unmistakable. The female is a drab olive and yellow bird, heavily streaked below, with a blackish crown and throat. As such it is vaguely reminiscent of a Sharpbill *Oxyruncus cristatus*, a reasonably common (but irregularly seen) inhabitant of many of the same forests, but the latter has a much finer, longer and more conical bill, a much more pale- and bare-faced appearance, is smaller and frequently joins mixed-species mobile flocks, which the bellbird never does. There is some overlap with Bearded Bellbird *Procnias averano* in northeastern Brazil; unlike the female of *P. averano*, however, the female Bare-throated Bellbird has a much more solidly dark crown and, especially, throat. Furthermore, these two species generally replace each other altitudinally in northeast Brazil, with the Bearded Bellbird probably largely confined to remnant lowland forests (Teixeira *et al.* 1986), although GMK has sight records and taped vocalisations of both species from the highland forests of Murici (Alagoas).

DISTRIBUTION Bare-throated Bellbird is endemic to the Atlantic Forest of eastern Brazil, from Pernambuco, Alagoas and perhaps even Paraíba (Berla 1946, Teixeira *et al.* 1986, Pacheco and Whitney 1995, Roda and Carlos 2003), in all of which states it is very local, thence south mainly through coastal Bahia (but only as far north as the environs of Salvador and inland to the Chapada Diamantina) and southern and eastern Minas Gerais to Rio Grande do Sul (south almost as far as the region of Pelotas, and it is even found in the metropolitan region of Porto Alegre), reaching as far inland as the basin of the Rio Paraná in southern Mato Grosso (at the Rio Amambaí) and easternmost Mato Grosso do Sul, as well as locally in northeastern Argentina (principally in Misiones, with a single record from Corrientes) and eastern Paraguay (west as far as Concepción, but perhaps only resident in the extreme east where the species is locally common at a handful of localities: Hayes 1995). Bare-throated Bellbird was previously considered to be perhaps only a transient in Argentina, but the species was found to be quite common at one locality in the extreme north in September 2004 with much vocal activity and males chasing one another (Bodrati and Cockle 2006a,), although Lowen *et al.* (1996) remarked that the species may appear to behave territorially whilst on passage in Paraguay, and Bodrati *et al.* (2010) also

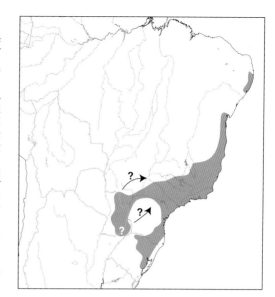

noted such behaviour in Argentina. The species is recorded to *c.*1,810m (Alves *et al.* 2009) but is generally found below 1,150m (Stotz *et al.* 1996), as well as on several Brazilian offshore islands, including Ilha Grande, Rio de Janeiro (Alves and Vecchi 2009). The species has been reported irregularly from various localities within the city limits of Rio de Janeiro, including even the Botanic Gardens (Mitchell 1957, Maciel 2009). Bare-throated Bellbird was treated as restricted to the Serra do Mar Centre of endemism (Cracraft 1985), but its range is actually wider than this.

MOVEMENTS Probably an altitudinal and also a seasonal migrant, purportedly following fruiting events, although details are generally rather scant (Snow 2004a). Snow (1982) found that the species only arrived in cloud forest (at 1,000m) of the Serra do Mar in São Paulo during the first two weeks of November, and, in Rio de Janeiro, it is certainly not obvious (i.e. vocalising frequently) at this altitude until either mid or late October (GMK pers. obs.). Aleixo and Galetti (1997) reported seasonal altitudinal movements in the vicinity of Fazenda Intervales (now a state park), also in São Paulo. Bare-throated Bellbird is probably almost entirely a non-breeding visitor to Misiones, Argentina (Mazar Barnett and Pearman 2001, Bodrati *et al.* 2010), where the species seems to be generally rare, and the single record from Corrientes also hints at migratory movements. *P. nudicollis* is also suspected of making seasonal movements in Paraguay, where birds mainly appear to move northwest through the Oriente in August to early September (late winter), returning in autumn, and the species is seemingly only resident (and vocal all year) in the extreme northeast (Lowen *et al.* 1996). In southernmost Brazil (Rio Grande do Sul), Bare-throated Bellbird is apparently exclusively a summer visitor, being recorded only in early October to mid March (Belton 2003), and further north in Brazil the species might only seasonally occur in dry *restinga* forests in the winter, e.g. in Espírito Santo (Venturini *et al.* 1996, Bauer 1999), presumably as a result of altitudinal movements. The species has been recorded once on Ilha da Queimada Grande, 33km off the southern São Paulo coast, and this record presumably pertains to a wandering individual (Macarrão and Granzinolli 2009).

HABITAT Bare-throated Bellbird is restricted to humid, usually wet (but occasionally dry), forests (including *Araucaria* forest) where it is most frequently observed in the canopy, although females and immature males, in particular, regularly visit the middle to lower strata and even second growth, particularly at forest borders and clearings in primary forest.

DESCRIPTION Sexes differ. The bill is rather weak but broad-based, with rather large, oval-shaped nostrils, but no rictal bristles. The tarsi are comparatively short considering the overall size of the bird. *Adult male.* – White overall, with a short bill, and a patch of greenish bare skin around the lores, eyes and throat, covered in rudimentary black bristly feathering. The bare throat is widest at the gape and narrows distally, the skin often being vivid turquoise, but this is variable and sometimes it inclines to greyish blue or is overall greener. There is also a bare patch of pinkish skin on the outer side of the tibia (as in Bearded Bellbird). The outer three primaries are modified, as in the Bearded Bellbird, with rounded extensions to the inner vanes (see Snow 1982: 171, for diagram). Males acquire adult plumage gradually, over the course of *c*.3 years. Initially female-like, the birds exhibit a sooty-black crown or even the entire head, and a largely white abdomen and vent during the intermediate stage, but the subadult has the facial skin paler blue-green than the adult, becoming grey on the lower throat. Males may develop almost all-white tails whilst the rest of the upperparts are still largely dark. In the final stage, any dark feathers are largely confined to the mantle and scapulars (MNRJ; ZISP), or occasionally the plumage may be entirely clean white with just a few tiny black feathers on the crown (ZMA). The streaking on the underparts is lost only gradually during these changes, and it can persist well into subadulthood. *Adult female.* – Head and throat dark grey to black, whilst the throat, chin and malar are streaked indistinctly white, with a narrow grey-blue eye-ring. The rest of the upperparts and wing-coverts are bright olive, becoming browner or duskier over the remiges which have olive fringes to the outer webs. Underparts from the breast are streaked olive and yellowish-olive, with the dark streaking densest on the breast and sides. The undertail-coverts are yellowish-olive with much less streaking than over the rest of the underparts. Undertail greyish-brown. Underwing-coverts yellowish-white, and the remiges from below appear darker distally. *Juvenile.* – Seemingly undescribed, insomuch as all descriptions of non-adults in the literature appear to apply to birds that have replaced their juvenile plumage (Snow 2004a), but the bare throat of males is acquired during the first year of life (Snow 1973a). In acquiring adult plumage, this species, like all bellbirds, moults the wing and tail feathers progressively along each row and often the feather bases appear more adult-like than their tips (Snow 1973a, 1982). *Moult.* – Data were summarised by Snow (1982) and Snow (1973a) presented a moult schedule for this species for its four-year acquisition of adult plumage. Complete renewal occupies *c*.160 days (Snow 1976a), and females probably commence replacing their feathers immediately on conclusion of breeding, but males (as in many cotingas) moult considerably earlier, on average, than females (also pers. obs. MNRJ). Furthermore, young males commence replacing their feathers prior to adult males. *Bare parts.* – Irides dark brown or chestnut to pale grey, with a blue-grey eye-ring, legs dull flesh-coloured, brownish, dark olive, dark or pale grey, or even blue, and bill blackish or grey, paler at the base and sometimes with paler cutting edges, or occasionally with a bluish lower mandible (Belton 1985, Snow 2004a; MNRJ).

MEASUREMENTS (BMNH; MNRJ; ZMA: Bahia, Rio de Janeiro, Rio Grande do Sul and São Paulo, southeast Brazil) Wing of male (*n* = 9) 152–158mm, wing of female (*n* = 5) 138–142mm; tail of male (*n* = 8) 83–92mm, tail of female (*n* = 5) 82–97; bill of male (*n* = 7) 25.08–30.11mm, bill of female (*n* = 3) 21–26mm; tarsus of male (*n* = 5) 28.5–33.0mm, tarsus of female (*n* = 4) 27–28mm. Snow (1973a) presented additional wing-length data for males, females and immature males. Weight: 126–250g (males, one young male had mass of just 81g) and 122–180g (females) (Snow 1973a, 1982, Teixeira *et al.* 1986, Willis and Oniki 2002, Snow 2004a, Dunning 2008; MNRJ; ROM).

GEOGRAPHICAL VARIATION Monotypic.

VOICE Published recordings are available on the following compilations: Remold (2002), Boesman (2006a) and Minns *et al.* (2009), and several recordings from Brazil and Paraguay have been archived online at www.xeno-canto.org. Sonograms were presented by Snow (1973a). In common with other bellbirds, males have an amazing and very loud 'clanging' ventriloquial voice comprising two main variations. The *bock* call (duller, less metallic-sounding than that of either White or Bearded Bellbirds) is rendered with the gape thrown wide and the head mainly still, and is audible up to 3km distant (Sick 1997, Bodrati *et al.* 2010). Generally this vocalisation is only repeated at intervals of *c*.5 seconds, but on occasion it may be followed directly by an accelerating series of more metallic notes (up to 50, but usually many fewer, e.g. an average of 22 during one study in Paraná: Leuchtenberger and Roper 2003a), *tink, tink, tink,...* which is given with the bill closed. The complete performance lasts 20–60 seconds (Belton 1985). However, either part can be given separately (the *tink* calls often in short series in such circumstances, with intervals of just one second between phrases), and as in other bellbirds the *bock* call is often far less explosive and hammering when uttered by young males, almost as if they are practising. They may take 2–3 years to attain full vocal proficiency (Sick 1997), and this, and the frequency of vocalisations and other similar factors, may serve to alert females to the 'quality' of any prospective mate (Leuchtenberger and Roper 2003a). Males often call in unison, especially at the height of the breeding season, in the form of an 'exploded lek', but with the birds usually in much closer proximity than either White or Bearded Bellbirds. Vocal activity increases notably from July onwards in Rio de Janeiro (Pimentel and Olmos 2011). However, they can be difficult to spot as the males often call from within the canopy (young birds even lower), although older males are perhaps more likely to select a particularly prominent perch and their territories, like those of other bellbirds, seem relatively permanent. Males may call virtually all day at the height of the breeding season (e.g. in October), but will periodically drop from a high perch into the canopy, then return and recommence vocalising. A series of calls may be interrupted by a short flight to another tree where the calling recommences. The warning or alarm-call is *kwa-ok*. Bare-throated Bellbird is vocal virtually year-round in those parts of the range where it is resident, but peak activity seems to be October–March in northeast Brazil, whereas in the southeast calling in earnest probably commences as early as July.

NATURAL HISTORY A very sluggish, large cotinga, which is perhaps easiest to observe when feeding at a fruiting tree (several females may congregate in such circumstances) or when perched in the subcanopy during or just after rain. Alternatively, the more striking adult males may be located by scanning the treetops, especially during the main calling season (see above). A female observed by C. I. Bushell and GG in Sooretama Biological Reserve, Brazil, was in the same tree as a male and female Banded Cotinga *Cotinga maculata* and a male White-winged Cotinga *Xipholena atropurpurea*; all four birds appeared to be drying their plumage following a heavy rainstorm.

FOOD AND FEEDING Entirely frugivorous (see below), Bare-throated Bellbirds appear to favour similar families to other *Procnias*, although the number of species recorded is fewer than some of its congeners (see Snow 2004a), with fruits usually being plucked during a short, rather clumsy aerial sally-hover, but also whilst perched. Because of their wider gape size, males are able to take slightly larger fruits than females (Snow 1973a). Leuchtenberger and Roper (2003b) identified species of the following families in the diet of *P. nudicollis* in Paraná: Araliaceae, Celastraceae, Euphorbiaceae, Lauraceae, Melastomataceae, Meliaceae, Moraceae, Myrsinaceae, Myrtaceae, Malpighiaceae, Rosaceae and Sapindaceae. Elsewhere, Pizo *et al.* (2002) also identified fruits of Arecaceae and Myristicaceae during their study in nearby São Paulo. Diet in southeast Brazil was also studied by Almeida and Teixeira (1996). Pelzeln (1868) and Krabbe (2007) reported that one old specimen apparently had a snail in its stomach contents. This is one of four species of cotingas studied in Paraná, southern Brazil, by Clausi and Baarstch (2009), who found that fruit production and its effect on local movements on bird families such as the Cotingidae could be divided into six periods of the year. Like other bellbirds, this species does not join mixed-species feeding flocks, but may consort with other species at a fruiting tree (see also above).

DISPLAY On Ilha Comprida, in southern São Paulo state, in October, GMK observed an adult male singing just below the crown of a 10m-high tree (there were few trees taller in the vicinity). Several female-plumaged birds visited the same tree within a *c.*30-minute observation period, all of which were vigorously chased by the male, but a subadult male that arrived in the same tree, and had also been calling in the vicinity, was 'tolerated', being subject to no attention. In threat, the adult male would lean forward on a branch towards the 'intruder', raise himself slightly 'up on his haunches', exposing the pink tarsal skin below the white thigh feathering, and cock his tail almost at 90° (Fig. 1). In contrast, at Parque Estadual Intervales, in the same state, in late October, when males were calling day-round and adult males appeared generally territorial, GMK observed one male leave one of its regular song perches and fly to another tree across a small valley, where it was joined by another adult male, and the two remained within 1m of each other for several minutes. At one point, the two even flew together to another tree *c.*10m distant from the first. Like other bellbirds, *P. nudicollis* performs a display-jump, in which the male makes a short flight of *c.*1m from the so-called visiting perch (see Three-wattled Bellbird *P. tricarunculatus*) to an adjacent high treetop perch, whereupon on landing the bird crouches and spreads its tail, and carefully eyes any visitor (Snow 1982).

BREEDING Data are still very few, but males are emancipated from any duties (as in all bellbirds and, indeed, most other cotingas). Egg-laying seems to occur in about

October, although only one nest seems to have been described in any detail. This was a small cup of epiphyte rootlets, lined with fungal fibres, dry palm pinnules and moss, with some green moss on the outside, and placed 23m above the ground in the fork within a tangle of vines on a 41m *Manilkara* (Sapotaceae) tree (Snow 2004a). Clutch size was considered to be one egg (as in Bearded Bellbird) and the egg is described as being dark brown with grey markings at the larger end by de la Peña (1989), who also gave approximate dimensions. Belton (1985) mentioned a nest that had not yet been completed by the female, sited just 6m above the ground, but without further details, and R. Krone in Ihering (1914) that the nest, *c.*16cm in diameter, was a rather pigeon-like, shallow cup structure. Sick (1997: 658) further reported that two other nests of this species in Brazil were both very flimsy pigeon-like structures, with a nest observed distantly by Sick himself in the Serra da Bocaina, São Paulo, being placed at the base of the leaves of a large bromeliad high in a tree. Sick was unable to confirm reports of nests constructed in hollow trees, from Rio de Janeiro, São Paulo and Santa Catarina, but such behaviour would appear distinctly unlikely for a bellbird, and can almost certainly be discounted. Males with enlarged testes were taken in December in Paraguay (KUNHM specimen), and in Rio de Janeiro state, Brazil, in January (MNRJ).

STATUS Bare-throated Bellbird is considered to be Near Threatened (BirdLife International 2000, 2004, 2008, Collar *et al.* 1992, 1994), highly vulnerable to habitat fragmentation, and at risk due to deforestation for urban development, agricultural expansion and road-building, especially in Paraguay and parts of Brazil (e.g. Bahia), with an additional threat coming from the cagebird trade, especially in Bahia, Espírito Santo, São Paulo and Santa Catarina (Brazil) and now also in Paraguay (BirdLife International 2004; GMK pers. obs.), with the result that the ringing tones of a bellbird are perhaps as commonly heard within urban areas as in the wider countryside. This can make the recording of the species difficult, because birds calling in forested areas with any habitation may not necessarily be wild individuals. Nonetheless, it appears adaptable to reforested areas, at least of native species such as *Araucaria angustifolia* (Völpato *et al.* 2010). The species is also considered threatened with extinction at state level in parts of Brazil, e.g. in Minas Gerais. Nonetheless, the Bare-throated Bellbird is known from a great many protected areas, especially in Brazil (the population of uncertain status in Argentina does not appear to be protected in that country, except perhaps within Cruce Cabellero Provincial Park), and is still reasonably common at a significant number of these, e.g. at Monte Pascoal (Bahia), Sooretama Biological Reserve (Espírito Santo), lower elevations of Itatiaia National Park (Rio de Janeiro), the Serra do Mar and Intervales State Parks, and in the Ubatuba region (São Paulo). The species is listed for two Important Bird Areas in Alagoas, eight in Bahia, one in Minas Gerais (Serra do Brigadeiro State Park, where rare), six in Espírito Santo, seven each in Rio de Janeiro and São Paulo, five in Paraná, two in Santa Catarina and one in Rio Grande do Sul (Bencke *et al.* 2006).

REFERENCES Aleixo and Galetti (1997), Almeida and Somenzari (2005), Almeida and Teixeira (1996), Alves and Vecchi (2009), Alves *et al.* (2009), Anjos and Boçon (1999), Bauer (1999), Belton (1985, 2003), Bencke and Kindel (1999), Bencke *et al.* (2006), Berla (1946), BirdLife International (2000, 2004, 2008), Bodrati and Cockle

(2006a), Bodrati *et al.* (2010), Boesman (2006a), Browne (2005), Clausi (2005), Clausi and Baarstch (2009), Clay *et al.* (1998), Collar *et al.* (1992, 1994), Cracraft (1985), Donatelli and Ferreira (2009), Dunning (2008), Favretto and Guester (2008), Fonseca and Antunes (2007), Goerck (1999), Gonzaga *et al.* (1995), Gussoni and Galetti (2007), Hayes (1995), Hayes and Scharf (1995b), Hellmayr (1929b), Herrera (1995), Hinkelmann and Fiebig (2001), Ihering (1914), Krabbe (2007), Kroodsma (2005), Leuchtenberger and Roper (2003a, 2003b), Lowen *et al.* (1995, 1996), Luiz *et al.* (2004a, 2004b), Macarrão (2009), Maciel (2009), Macarrão and Granzinolli (2009), Madroño *et al.* (1997a), Mallet-Rodrigues and Noronha (2003, 2009), Marsden *et al.* (2003), Mazar Barnett and Pearman (2001), Mestre (2004), Minns *et al.* (2009), Mitchell (1957), Mohr and Efe (2003), Olson (1971), Pacheco and Whitney (1995), Parker and Goerck (1997), Parrini and Pacheco (2011), Parrini *et al.* (1999), Patrial *et al.* (2009), Pelzeln (1868), de la Peña (1989), Pinto (1944), Pimentel and Olmos (2011), Pizo *et al.* (2002), Posso *et al.* (2009), Remold (2002), Ridgely and Tudor (1994, 2009), Robbins *et al.* (1999), Roda and Carlos (2003), do Rosário (1996), Santos *et al.* (2004), Schürer and Bock (1995), Sick (1997), Silva *et al.* (2004), Silveira *et al.* (2005), Simon (2009), Snow (1973a, 1976a, 2004a), Stotz *et al.* (1996), Straube (2008a), Straube *et al.* (2002), Teixeira *et al.* (1986), Venturini *et al.* (1996), Volpato *et al.* (2010), Willis and Oniki (2002).

Bare-throated Bellbird *Procnias nudicollis.* **Figs. 1–2**. Male, Ilha Comprida, São Paulo, southeast Brazil, October (*Hadoram Shirihai / Photographic Handbook to Birds of the World*). This male was vigorously defending his territory within an area of *restinga* forest against several other (mainly immature) males (see Display). **Fig. 3**. Subadult male, Ubatuba, São Paulo, southeast Brazil, September (*Pete Morris*). Note the presence of some brownish feathers on the head, tail and upperparts. This, the other species of fundamentally all-white bellbird, is endemic to the Atlantic Forest. It has been heavily trapped for the cagebird trade, as well as being threatened by habitat loss. **Fig. 4**. Female, RPPN Estação Veracel, Porto Seguro, Bahia, eastern Brazil, September (*Nick Athanas / Tropical Birding*).

Genus *Cotinga*: 'blue cotingas'

Perhaps the most celebrated group in the family, indeed regarded by some as the epitome of what constitutes a cotinga, the males' predominantly blue or turquoise-blue plumage is unique within the Cotingidae to this genus. The modification to the primaries of adult males facilitates the mechanical rattling sound produced by a displaying bird. Immature males generally resemble adult females; purple feathers appear on the throat (and belly in some species), turquoise or blue on the mantle, and the inner remiges are black. Three species are entirely trans-Andean, the remaining species occurring east of the Andes. One representative, almost certainly the rarest of the genus, the magnificent Banded Cotinga *C. maculata* is isolated in the Atlantic Forest biome. Several of the Amazonian species are reasonably widespread and relatively easily seen from some of the canopy towers recently constructed at various sites mainly in the west and centre of the basin, where their electric blue plumage contrasts vividly against the green of the surrounding foliage. Such vantage points have also proved extremely useful in elucidating more concerning the natural history of some of the blue (and other) cotingas.

Blue Cotinga *C. nattererii*, Plum-throated Cotinga *C. maynana*, Purple-breasted Cotinga *C. cotinga* and Banded Cotinga, along with the Middle American Lovely Cotinga *C. amabilis* and Turquoise Cotinga *C. ridgwayi*, are considered to form a superspecies (Haffer 1974, AOU 1983, 1998, Sibley and Monroe 1990), but Snow (1979a) only included *C. amabilis*, *C. ridgwayi* and *C. nattererii* within the superspecies, regarding *C. cotinga* and *C. maculata* as forming a separate superspecies. On the other hand, Meyer de Schauensee (1966) had earlier suggested that *C. nattererii*, *C. amabilis* and *C. ridgwayi* might be considered conspecific, whilst *C. maculata* and *C. cotinga* could also be treated as conspecifics, but this recommendation has very rarely been followed.

The *C. amabilis*, *C. ridgwayi* and *C. nattererii* superspecies

This superspecies (*sensu* Snow 1979a; see above) comprises three wholly trans-Andean cotingas of brilliant coloration, which range from southern Mexico to northwestern Ecuador. Hellmayr (1929b) considered that this grouping might be best considered as a single species united with *C. maynana* (Plum-throated Cotinga) of western and central Amazonia, but this proposal never gained much currency, despite being partially repeated by Meyer de Schauensee (1966; see above). These three species are found mainly in the humid lowlands, being difficult to observe in dense forest, but are much easier to locate at the forest edge and in isolated trees within clearings, especially early in the morning or after rain.

LOVELY COTINGA
Cotinga amabilis   Plate 25

Cotinga amabilis Gould, 1857, *Proc. Zool. Soc. Lond.* 25: 64, pl. 123, [northern Alta Verapaz,] Guatemala

A blue cotinga with a rather dove-like head shape, this species occurs on the Caribbean slope of Middle America, from southern Mexico to Costa Rica. Lovely Cotinga is not currently considered threatened given its wide range, but it is unquestionably very uncommon and generally difficult to find at the southern end of the species' distribution.

IDENTIFICATION 18–19cm. Males resemble the two other species of blue cotinga occurring in Middle America, being turquoise-blue with two purple patches on the underparts, which are rather larger when compared with those of its neighbouring congeners, and appear to be separated by a blue breast-band resembling that of Banded Cotinga *C. maculata* of the eastern Brazilian forests. The turquoise-blue upperparts and crown lack the random black markings present in most males of the genus *Cotinga*, including those that might be found together with the present species. Furthermore, male Lovely Cotinga differs from the Turquoise Cotinga *C. ridgwayi* in being slightly larger, with different-structured primaries and longer uppertail-coverts. Compared with same-sex Blue Cotinga *C. nattereri* (no definite overlap, but see relevant account), the present species has a rather brighter and paler throat patch, and also

lacks any black around the eye and lores, although these features will require good views to confirm the identification. Females are arguably the most distinctive of the genus, being very pallid, with a whitish ground colour to the underparts, which are overlain with spots rather than scales, and possess whitish (and buffish) spots and scales over the brown upperparts (for further details see the next species).

DISTRIBUTION Lovely Cotinga is found throughout much of the east slope of Middle America, from eastern Mexico, in southernmost Veracruz, northern Oaxaca and northern Chiapas; the Caribbean slope of northern and eastern Guatemala; the Caribbean slope of southern and western Belize and thence via the east slope of Honduras and Nicaragua to southeastern Costa Rica, almost to the Panama border, with a single sight record from western Panama (in Bocas del Toro) (Monroe 1968, Ridgely and Gwynne 1989, Stiles and Skutch 1989, Winker *et al.* 1992, Howell and Webb 1995, AOU 1998, Jones 2004). It has recently been claimed from the Pacific slope of western Costa Rica, at Los Llanos, near Santa Elena (Garrigues 2001, Mazar Barnett and Kirwan 2002), with even more recent reports from the Pacific slope, also in the Monteverde region (E. Carman pers. comm.). The species is recorded to 1,700m locally, e.g. in Oaxaca (Mexico) and Costa Rica (Binford 1989, Stiles and Skutch 1989), but elsewhere is found lower, e.g. to only 1,200m in Honduras (Monroe 1968). It is generally recorded above 300m, but Lovely Cotinga is found down to sea level in south-east Costa Rica (Stiles and Skutch 1989).

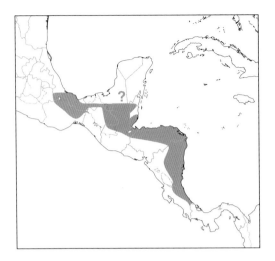

MOVEMENTS None definitely established, although the sight record, in 1978, from western Panama hints at possible seasonal movements (AOU 1998). Howell and Webb (1995) also speculated that the species might perform altitudinal migrations, given that Land (1963) had reported that 'a large flock arrived in the open woodland and cafétal in mid-winter; by March most of the birds had departed', at his study site in eastern Guatemala, and Beavers *et al.* (1991) considered that Lovely Cotinga might only be a seasonal visitor in the Tikal area of Guatemala. At El Copal Biological Reserve, in southern Costa Rica, Lovely Cotinga seems to be most frequently seen in July/August, when its favoured trees are fruiting, although there are records from other times of year as well. Elsewhere in the same country, Lawson (2010) states that the species is best searched for at Silent Mountain in March, again hinting at the possibility of local or seasonal movements.

HABITAT The species inhabits tropical lowland moist forest, including its edges, as well as more open areas with scattered trees and small patches of woodland (see also Breeding).

DESCRIPTION The sexes differ. (See next species for primary modification and Snow 1982: 88 for diagram.) Rictal bristles moderately developed in both sexes; the bill is rather broad-based with a slightly arched culmen and slightly hooked tip, and the nostrils are relatively large and well exposed. *Adult male.* – Rather compact with a gentle, dove-shaped forehead. Beautiful, brilliant turquoise-blue upperparts (including the scapulars), with very few black feather bases exposed and those that are, small and invisible in the field. Upperside of the tail black but almost entirely concealed by the elongated turquoise-blue uppertail-coverts (the longest feathers may even reach *c*.1–2mm beyond the tail tip). The wings are also black, with greenish-blue fringes to the coverts, inner remiges and tertials. The deep purple throat and belly patches are both quite extensive, with the latter extending onto the lower breast and clearly demarcated from the throat patch by a turquoise-blue breast-band. Throat patch is outlined by a darker border, almost black in part. Underwing-coverts black with neat, narrow blue fringes. Flanks and long undertail-coverts turquoise-blue. Undertail black (but only the tip is visible, the rest being hidden by the undertail-coverts). The inner four primaries are modified (note that we number primaries ascendantly,

with p1 being the outermost), being rather narrow and sinuated, with p7 also very short. *Adult female.* – Quite unusually distinctive for this genus. Greyish-brown above with broad whitish-fawn fringes and tips to each feather, thus appearing distinctly scaled. The whitish scaling is especially prominent on the lower back, rump and uppertail-coverts. The wings are darker brown than the rest of the upperparts, with cinnamon, buffy or whitish fringes to the greater coverts and, to a lesser extent, the inner remiges, whilst the outer remiges are very dark brown. The uppertail is blackish-brown with paler greyish-brown fringes. Very pale below and on the head, especially the forehead region, with some individuals being almost whitish, others more inclining to pale buff. The darkest area is the breast, where the feather centres are dark brown, whilst the throat and belly are overall paler with smaller dusky feather centres and larger pale fringes. Pale fawn underwing-coverts. Undertail brown. *Immature.* – Adult male plumage is achieved at age one year, albeit with such birds having a slightly paler purple throat patch. Plumage of male is initially adult female-like, with buff tips to the wing-coverts and flight feathers which soon wear off, with reputedly broader pale fringes to the back feathers (Stiles and Skutch 1989), but in the earliest stage just acquires some blue in the tail, thereafter in the uppertail-coverts and larger wing-coverts, at which point purple feathering begins to appear on the belly (especially), throat and even the flanks. *Moult.* – Very few moult data for adults, but the species presumably replaces its feathers post-breeding, with moult commencing mainly in May in Nicaragua and Costa Rica (Snow 1982), but mentioned for January- and March-taken specimens in Guatemala (Land 1963), which fits the same biogeographical moult pattern noted in several other Cotingidae (Snow 1976a, 1982). Moult has been calculated to occupy *c*.90 days in all *Cotinga* species (Snow 1976a). *Bare parts.* – Resembling those of congeners, the rather broad-based bill and legs are grey to black, the upper mandible usually being darkest, and the irides are dark brown.

MEASUREMENTS (BMNH; FMNH; MNCR; RMNH; ZMA; ZISP: Costa Rica, Guatemala, Honduras, Mexico and Nicaragua) Wing of male (*n* = 19) 112–124mm, wing of female (*n* = 8) 109–120mm; tail of male (*n* = 20) 58–73mm, tail of female (*n* = 8) 63–72mm; bill of male (*n* = 20) 14.12–16.54mm, bill of female (*n* = 8) 15.41–17.02mm; tarsus of male (*n* = 10) 18.25–22.22mm, tarsus of female (*n* = 4) 21–24mm. Weight (sexes combined): 66–75g (Tashian 1952, Snow 2004a, Dunning 2008; FMNH; MVZ).

GEOGRAPHICAL VARIATION Monotypic.

VOICE Dry fluttering rattles are occasionally given in flight, but the male is reported to be otherwise silent (Howell and Webb 1995), although there is evidence to suggest that it utters high-pitched metallic notes, similar to those given by male Turquoise Cotingas (J. Horn pers. comm.). The female apparently utters loud and agonised shrieks in defence of young (against a toucanet), or a repeated low *ic…ic….ic…* also in the presence of young (see Stiles and Skutch 1989, Snow 2004a). We are unaware of any published recordings of this species.

NATURAL HISTORY Lovely Cotinga is usually found alone or in pairs, occasionally small in parties numbering up to six individuals (Howell and Webb 1995), but considerable numbers of birds may visit certain fruiting trees, with, for instance, W. W. Brown collecting an incredible 51 different individuals, at just one tree in Honduras over a three-week period (Peters 1929, Monroe 1968).

FOOD AND FEEDING The study by Kantak (1981) in Campeche, Mexico, found that foraging (for fruit) appeared to be conducted more or less evenly throughout the day, with the exception of notable peaks about one hour after dawn and at midday. The same is perhaps true in Costa Rica (GMK pers. obs.). The diet consists of insects, small lizards (once, see below) and especially fruits (including *Ficus*, Fabaceae, and wild avocados, Lauraceae), with Lauraceae species particularly favoured, at least in Costa Rica (Stiles and Skutch 1989; GMK pers. obs.); berries are usually plucked using short, clumsy aerial sallies into the canopy, sometimes downwards as well as upwards, but sometimes also leaning down to seize fruits while perched (GMK pers. obs.). A female was also watched occasionally catching unknown Hymenoptera present around the edge a fruiting wild avocado, the bird flying downwards *c.*1m to seize prey, before continuing to another branch even lower in the tree (GMK and E. Carman pers. obs.). However, the species can descend lower in shady and even more open clearings presumably also to feed.

BREEDING Nesting is very poorly known, with only two nests having been found to date and one of those was discovered immediately after being partially predated by a toucanet, in Costa Rica, in May. It was sited at *c.*31m in the treetop of a *Sapium* sp. (Euphorbiaceae) and was cup-shaped, but heavily obscured by epiphytes, and contained at least one nestling, which fell to the ground where it continued to be tended by the female for several days (Skutch 1969). Food items brought included *Ocotea pentagona* (Lauraceae) fruits and a small lizard. The female destroyed the nest thereafter (see also Blue Cotinga). The other nest was also discovered in Costa Rica, at Arenal Volcano National Park, in mid April 2010, at the edge of a clearing near a lodge with several fruiting trees in the vicinity and a mean canopy height of *c.*15m (GMK, E. Carman, R. McCann and J. Price pers. obs.). A female was observed carrying a *c.*8cm-long green pine shoot from an introduced *Pinus caribaea* to another tree of the same species, whereupon it added it to a heavily obscured nest, situated *c.*10m above the ground in a *c.*20m-tall pine, on a near-horizontal branch very close to the main trunk and surrounded by many epiphytes. The female briefly tested the nest again before disappearing from view. A male was also in the vicinity, attending the same fruiting tree at which the female fed shortly after first light for *c.*30 minutes, and chasing a pair of Black-cheeked Woodpeckers *Melanerpes pucherani* on several occasions in the general region of the nest. A female taken in July, in Mexico, had enlarged ovaries (FMNH), and Binford (1989) reported a bird with a large

follicle collected in late May in Oaxaca, Mexico. The eggs are undescribed.

STATUS Currently regarded as Least Concern by BirdLife International (2004, 2008), but extensive deforestation throughout its range has probably caused severe declines, and the species is generally considered to be rare and local. Lovely Cotinga is described as being very uncommon to rare in Belize (Jones 2004), very uncommon in Oaxaca (Binford 1989 Winker *et al.* 1992) and uncommon in parts of Veracruz, where it is probably only regularly seen in the Sierra los Tuxtlas (Mexico) (Howell 1999), and the species is rare and local in Costa Rica, where it is probably declining (Sigel *et al.* 2005) with fewer sightings at Rancho Naturalista in recent years (J. Horn pers. comm.). Lawson (2010) states that the best localities for the species in Costa Rica include Silent Mountain, near Rancho Naturalista, as well as Las Heliconias Lodge and Arenal Volcano National Park. It was at least formerly locally common in parts of Guatemala and Honduras (Monroe 1968), but recent work suggests that it is rare at many surveyed localities in both countries (e.g. Vallely *et al.* 2010). Recent sightings are available from six localities in Honduras and it seems tolerably numerous at one of them, Pico Bonito National Park (www.birdsofhonduras.com). Lovely Cotinga is regularly found at the famous Chan Chich lodge in Belize, the Mayan site of Palenque in northern Chiapas, and the nearby San Manuel road (Mexico) (Howell 1999). The species is known from several protected areas throughout its range, e.g. Yaxchilán Natural Monument, Chiapas (Mexico), Tikal National Park, Petén (Guatemala), Pico Bonito National Park and Río Plátano Biosphere Reserve (Honduras), and El Copal Biological Reserve, Cahuita National Park, Tapantí Nature Preserve and Río Negro Jaguar Preserve (Costa Rica) (Beavers *et al.* 1991, Cooper 1997, Wheatley and Brewer 2001, Puebla-Olivares *et al.* 2002, Lawson 2010, Vallely *et al.* 2010).

REFERENCES Andrle (1967), Angehr and Dean (2010), AOU (1998), Beavers *et al.* (1991), Binford (1989), BirdLife International (2004, 2008), Cooper (1997), Dunning (2008), England (2000), Garrigues (2001), Garrigues and Dean (2007), Griscom (1932), Haffer (1974), Hellmayr (1929b), Howell (1999), Howell and Webb (1995), Jones (2004), Kantak (1979), Land (1963), Lawson (2010), Mazar Barnett and Kirwan (2001, 2002), Monroe (1968), Peters (1929), Puebla-Olivares *et al.* (2002), Ridgely and Gwynne (1989), Sigel *et al.* (2005), Skutch (1969), Snow (1976a, 1982, 2004a), Stiles and Skutch (1989), Stotz *et al.* (1996), Tashian (1952), Vallely *et al.* (2010), Wheatley and Brewer (2001), Winker *et al.* (1992).

Lovely Cotinga *Cotinga amabilis*. **Figs. 1–2**. Male, Pico Bonito National Park, near La Ceiba, Honduras, January (*Manfred Kusch*). There is no overlap with the most similar species, Blue Cotinga *C. nattereri*, which is generally darker, deeper blue. Note Lovely Cotinga's 'gentle' head shape and lack of any black spotting on the visible upperparts. **Fig. 3**. Female, Arenal Observatory Lodge, prov. Alajuela, Costa Rica, April (*Steven Easley / Costa Rica Gateway*). This female (note the very pale underparts ground colour) was seen nest building in the nearby vicinity (see main text).

TURQUOISE COTINGA
Cotinga ridgwayi   **Plate 25**

Cotinga ridgwayi **Ridgway, 1887** [based on Zeledón ms.], *Proc. US Natl. Mus.* 10: 1, pl. 6, fig. 3, Pozo Azul, Costa Rica

Confined to a very restricted belt of humid lowland forest on the Pacific slope of Costa Rica and western Panama, the range of this species is 'stifled' by the presence of drier forest to the east and west (Snow 1982).

IDENTIFICATION 17.0–18.5cm. Males of this species most closely resemble the male Blue Cotinga *C. nattererii*. The purple belly patch of Turquoise Cotinga is slightly larger than that of Blue Cotinga, extending lower onto the belly and towards the flanks, but this feature may be hard to judge in a typical field situation. However, the presence of black above the base of the bill, although also difficult to see, is characteristic. Thankfully, these congeners are allopatric! Lovely Cotinga *C. amabilis* is separated from Turquoise Cotinga by the central montane ridge, it being confined to the Caribbean side of southern Central America. Thus, again there is no overlap in range, but the area vacated by both species is probably no more than 30km wide (Snow 1982). The uniform oily turquoise upperparts of Lovely Cotinga (lacking the obvious black spotting of the other two blue cotingas in Middle America) imparts a more pristine appearance to the species. From below, the two purple areas on the underparts of Lovely Cotinga are separated by a rather narrower turquoise breast-band than in the present species. Female Turquoise Cotinga is very different to her two Middle American counterparts. The dark brown upperparts have cinnamon tips to each feather (whiter tips on Lovely, uniform brown on Blue Cotinga), thus the upperparts appear spotted. The throat is cinnamon (whitish on Lovely, dull brown on Blue Cotinga), whilst the feather centres to the breast and belly are dark brown, fringed cinnamon (fringed whitish on Lovely, and again uniform brown on Blue Cotinga).

DISTRIBUTION Turquoise Cotinga inhabits a rather restricted range, on the Pacific slope of southwestern Costa Rica, from westernmost Puntarenas, at Pozo Azul de Pirris, south to western Panama, in western Chiriquí, where in recent years it is known from just two areas, around Santa Clara, west of Volcán, and El Chorogo (Wetmore 1972,

Ridgely and Gwynne 1989, Stiles and Skutch 1989). It has been recorded to 1,850m in the Cordillera de Talamanca, Costa Rica (Stiles and Skutch 1989), but is generally recorded at 1,200–1,600m in Panama, and below 1,400m (especially below 900m) in Costa Rica (Wetmore 1972, Ridgely and Gwynne 1989, AOU 1998).

MOVEMENTS No regular seasonal or altitudinal movements have been described, but the pattern of irregular sightings at known localities (Stiles and Skutch 1989) suggests, as mooted by Snow (2004a), that the species performs erratic wanderings, presumably in search of fruiting trees as might be expected of many congenerics (cf. also Sánchez *et al.* 2007).

HABITAT Turquoise Cotinga typically inhabits tropical moist lowland forest and associated second growth, as well as shade-coffee plantations, other slightly more open forest areas, and even visits the borders of mangrove, at least formerly in Costa Rica.

DESCRIPTION Like the previous species, the male possesses modified primaries, but in Turquoise Cotinga it is only the two innermost that are shorter than the rest, with p9 being especially so, and both p8 and p9 have outer webs sinuated near their bases (see Snow 1982: 88 for diagram). The sexes differ. Rictal bristles are moderately developed in both sexes; the bill is rather broad-based with a slightly arched culmen and slight hook tip, and the nostrils are relatively large and well exposed. *Adult male.* – Superficially resembles male *C. nattererii*. The upperparts are 'oily' turquoise-blue with obvious scattered black spots or chevrons, most prominent and obvious over the wing-coverts, becoming clearer (less turquoise) blue distally. Tail black with neat blue fringes to each feather, but partially obscured by the long uppertail-coverts (albeit shorter than in *C. amabilis*). The wings are also black with greenish-blue fringes to the secondaries, wing-coverts and tertials (broadest on the inner webs). Purple throat patch darker at border (almost blackish) and is almost outlined by black in the region of the chin, which border continues over the base of the upper mandible, making the forehead appear slightly darker. The black surround to the eye is not broad but is distinct, in the field the bird appearing to have a large black eye. Rest of underparts turquoise-blue, with a second purple patch on the belly that extends as an apex ventrally. The undertail is blackish. *Adult female.* – Slightly larger than the male. Dark brown upperparts with a 'spotty' effect, produced by the buff or cinnamon tips to the feathers, with whiter tips to the crown and hindneck. Wings brown with cinnamon fringes and tips to the outer remiges; the rump often has some blue gloss to the feathers. Rectrices brown fringed cinnamon, and the underparts are cinnamon-brown, becoming paler and slightly brighter over the throat, belly and especially the undertail-coverts. The feather centres across the breast, flanks and upper belly are darker, even inclining to blackish, whilst the undertail is pale brown with pale tips and the underwing-coverts are cinnamon. *Immature.* – Plumage maturation much as in the previous species, although we have examined fewer specimens. Adult male plumage is, like other species, achieved at age one year, albeit with a slightly paler purple throat patch. Plumage of the male is initially adult female-like, with brighter, more cinnamon tips to the flight feathers which soon wear off, gradually acquiring the blue feathering of adult plumage and, at first, a dull red spot on the lower throat. A young male observed in southern Costa Rica was essentially female-like, but had a few scattered blue feathers on the ear-coverts and neck-sides, on the mantle and lower back, and blue fringes to some secondaries (GMK pers. obs.). *Moult.* – Presumably, this occurs post-breeding, but pitifully few (if any) published data appear to be available (Snow 1982). Both an adult male and adult female in southern Costa Rica in mid April showed no evidence of renewing the flight feathers (GMK pers. obs.). Moult has been calculated to occupy *c.*90 days in all *Cotinga* species (Snow 1976a). *Bare parts.* – Bill mainly black, greyer at base and becoming almost horn (with a blackish tip) on the lower mandible (perhaps overall slightly paler in females); the irides are dark brown; and the legs and feet are blackish-grey to dark grey.

MEASUREMENTS (BMNH; FMNH; MNCR; ROM: Costa Rica and Panama; Wetmore 1972: Panama) Wing of male (*n* = 17) 101–108mm, wing of female (*n* = 7) 101–106mm; tail of male (*n* = 7) 58–68mm, tail of female (*n* = 3) 59–65mm; bill of male (*n* = 4) 14–18mm, bill of female (*n* = 3) 15.5–17.0mm; tarsus of male (*n* = 13) 18–22mm, tarsus of female (*n* = 5) 18–22mm. Weight: 51.5–57.0g (males) and 63.2–65.7g (females) (Snow 2004b). Dunning (2008) listed 61g as the mean weight of six females.

GEOGRAPHICAL VARIATION Monotypic.

VOICE Until recently this species was considered to be generally silent, like the other blue cotingas, although it was known that the female gives a raucous shriek, presumably in alarm/distress, and the male produces a twittering wing noise in flight, which is presumably the same sound as the 'high-pitched thin and level whistle lasting almost a full second' described by Slud (1964). However, from observations at two sites in southwest Costa Rica, Sánchez *et al.* (2007) described very high-pitched vocalisations being emitted by males perched high in the canopy, much more occasionally lower, down to 4m above the ground (and presented sonograms of these; see also XC13693). The metallic high-pitched call varies very little in frequency, and at least occasionally the bird opens the bill wide in making the sound, which lasts just over half of one second. Most vocalisations did not appear to be stimulated by any obvious event (e.g. an interaction with another or the same species), and vocalisations were sometimes given as frequently as once every 20–30 seconds. Although several young males were observed during the study, none was ever seen to vocalise. A male that was handled by F. G. Stiles (*in* Sánchez *et al.* 2007) gave a raucous, mule-like *caaaoo.*

NATURAL HISTORY Like that of other blue cotingas, Turquoise Cotinga is most frequently encountered perching leisurely on a high exposed perch above or, more typically within, the canopy, including around clearings. J. Horn (pers. comm.) reports that, at least in Costa Rica, males may regularly use the same favoured perch for many years. In the very early morning (i.e. the first hour of daylight) both sexes seem to spend most time preening rather than feeding (GMK pers. obs.). The species is generally noted singly or in loose pairs, although small groups of up to six may congregate, with other birds including tanagers, flycatchers and Yellow-billed Cotinga *Carpodectes antoniae*, at fruiting trees (Stiles and Skutch 1989; GMK pers. obs.).

FOOD AND FEEDING The diet is apparently solely fruit, perhaps favouring those of *Cecropia* (Urticaceae), a *Didimopanax* sp. (Araliaceae), the parasitic mistletoe *Psittacanthus* (Loranthaceae), *Citharexylum* sp. (Verbenaceae),

Erythroxylum sp. (Erythroxylaceae) and various figs (*Ficus* spp., Fabaceae) as well as wild avocados (Lauraceae), but the species may also descend lower, especially at clearings, to take berries of a low-growing pokeweed (*Phytolacca*, Phytolaccaceae) (Skutch 1969, Stiles and Skutch 1989, Sánchez *et al.* 2007; GMK pers. obs.). No published information concerning feeding techniques but has been seen to take fruit during a brief aerial sally, like others of the genus, as well as by perch gleaning (GMK pers. obs.).

BREEDING Nesting is better known than the Lovely Cotinga, although to date only one nest (March) has been described (Skutch 1969). Only the female is apparently responsible for tending the nest and young (as is the case for other *Cotinga* whose nesting has been described to date), and pairs are almost certainly purely transitory for the purposes of mating. Turquoise Cotinga constructs a shallow cup nest of tendrils and fungal strands, supported on a horizontal limb, and in the only known instance this was placed within 1m of the central trunk and 9m above the ground, in an isolated *Cordia* (Boraginaceae) tree near dense forest. According to Skutch (1969) nest building occupied 22 days, and the female laid her eggs within three days of the nest being completed. The species lays two eggs, these being buffy speckled throughout with brown, heaviest at the broader end, and large enough to virtually fill the tiny nest. The female incubated in long stints of 119–156 minutes (once 36 minutes) with off-bouts lasting 35–88 minutes. Unfortunately, the nest was found destroyed after the eggs had been incubated only a week. The only other breeding datum concerns a male with large testes taken in Costa Rica in September (MVZ).

STATUS Currently categorised as Vulnerable (BirdLife International 2000, 2004, 2008), although earlier Collar *et al.* (1992) had considered it to be 'only' Near Threatened. Turquoise Cotinga is generally rare and local, with apparently rather few recent records, all from a handful of sites (e.g. Las Cruces and Las Alturas Biological Stations in southwest Costa Rica: Sánchez *et al.* 2007); and the population (estimated at fewer than 10,000 individuals) is probably under severe pressure from widespread deforestation at lower altitudes in the region. Overall range was estimated at just 8,400km² (BirdLife International 2008). It was formerly considered more numerous in Costa Rica (Slud 1964), especially between the Gulf of Nicoya and the Golfo Dulce. Turquoise Cotinga occurs in a small number of protected areas, among them Carara Biological Reserve (the only modern locality in the northwest of its range) and Corcovado National Park, both in Costa Rica, but much of its small range receives highly inadequate levels of protection (Wege and Long 1995). The species is seen with some regularity at the Wilson Botanic Gardens, near Las Cruces, the privately owned Talari Mountain Lodge, near San Isidro, Las Alturas, and at Bosque del Río Tigre, near Rincón de Osa, all in Costa Rica (Lawson 2010). The species has also been recorded in the El Chorogo-Palo Blanco Important Bird Area in western Panama (Montañez and Angehr 2007).

REFERENCES Angehr and Dean (2010), AOU (1998), BirdLife International (2000, 2004, 2008), Collar *et al.* (1992), Dunning (2008), Garrigues and Dean (2007), Haffer (1974), Hellmayr (1929b), Lawson (2010), Montañez and Angehr (2007), Olson (1971), Ridgely and Gwynne (1989), Sánchez *et al.* (2007), Skutch (1969), Slud (1964), Snow (1976a, 1982, 2004a), Stiles and Skutch (1989), Stotz *et al.* (1996), Wege and Long (1995), Wetmore (1972).

Turquoise Cotinga *Cotinga ridgwayi.* **Fig. 1**. Male, San Isidro de El General, prov. Puntarenas, Costa Rica, April (*Pete Morris*). The purple area on the breast and belly is generally smaller than in the previous species, thus the turquoise-blue breast-band separating it from the purple throat patch appears broader. **Figs. 2–3**. Male, above Buenos Aires, prov. Puntarenas, Costa Rica, September (*Kevin Easley / Costa Rica Gateway*). Note the black spotting on the scapulars, which should serve to discriminate this species from Lovely Cotinga *C. amabilis*; although the two species are not known to be in contact, they apparently are separated by as little as 30 km!

473

BLUE COTINGA
Cotinga nattererii   **Plate 25**

Ampelis nattererii **Boissonneau, 1840**, *Rev. Zool.* (Paris) 3: 2, 'Santa Fé de Bogotá', Colombia

Confined to northwestern South America and eastern Panama, despite being similar to several other blue cotingas, the Blue (or as it was formerly known Natterer's) Cotinga is automatically separable from any other species by range.

IDENTIFICATION 18–20cm. *C. nattererii* is allopatric of its congeners, being found only west of the Andes in South America and to the east of the two solely Middle American blue cotingas (Lovely *C. amabilis* and Turquoise *C. ridgwayi*) in Panama. However, there are a couple of recent brief sightings of 'blue' cotingas on the Caribbean slope in southernmost Costa Rica, which might just as easily pertain to this species as Lovely Cotinga (E. Carman pers. comm.). Which species of 'blue' cotinga inhabits this region, close to the Panama border, is required. The blue of the male Blue Cotinga is rather more turquoise (i.e. paler than in Banded *C. maculata* or Purple-breasted Cotinga *C. cotinga*) but darker than the previous two species, and it appears less immaculately plumaged than the Lovely Cotinga owing to the presence of randomly exposed black bases to the upperparts feathers. Female Blue Cotingas are rather drab brown above, with very indistinct paler fringes to the wing-coverts. They are only slightly paler below, lacking the scaling or spotting usually associated with females of the genus, and they are probably best recognised by their shape, being small and plump, with a dove-like head profile, a 'gentle' expression and upright stance. See Black-tipped Cotinga *Carpodectes hopkei* for discussion of the identification problem associated with females of the latter species.

DISTRIBUTION Wholly 'trans-Andean': Blue Cotinga is recorded from eastern Panama, as far west as the western boundary of the Canal Zone and western Colon, with a recent sighting from Bocas del Toro, then through northwestern South America, in extreme western Venezuela (in the Maracaibo basin, in northwest Táchira and western Mérida), northern and western Colombia, in the humid Caribbean lowlands east to the middle Río Magdalena Valley, in dptos. Bolívar, Antioquia, Santander and western

Boyacá, and south on the Pacific slope to dpto. Nariño, and reaching as far south as extreme northwest Ecuador, in Esmeraldas and northwest prov. Pichincha, in the vicinity of San Miguel de los Bancos (Wetmore 1972, Hilty and Brown 1986, Ridgely and Gwynne 1989, Ridgely and Tudor 1994, Ridgely and Greenfield 2001, Hilty 2003). See previous section for comments concerning the possibility that this species might occur in southeastern Costa Rica. Generally recorded at 0–300m, more occasionally to *c.*1,000m in some parts of the Andes, but in Colombia at least the species is regularly noted to *c.*1,400m (Salaman *et al.* 2002a; T. M. Donegan *in litt.* 2009).

MOVEMENTS None certainly recorded, although Hilty (1997) considered that Blue Cotinga might be a short-distance migrant that only occurred seasonally at his former study site in the Anchicayá Valley, in Colombia. However, most authors have been content to describe the species as being resident, although it is surely unlikely to be sedentary, in common with its congenerics.

HABITAT Blue Cotinga inhabits the canopy of humid lowland forest and secondary woodland.

DESCRIPTION The male has modified primaries, but unlike others of this superspecies, only p10, the innermost, is shorter than the others, and it is only p9 that narrows distally (see Snow 1982: 88 for diagram). Compared with *C. ridgwayi*, the present species has p2 longer (~p3) and apically not attenuated (Hellmayr 1929b). Sexes differ. Rictal bristles are moderately developed in both sexes; the bill is rather broad-based with a slightly arched culmen and slightly hooked tip, and the nostrils are relatively large and well exposed. *Adult male.* – Turquoise above (including the lores and ear-coverts), with scattered black spotting over the crown, mantle, scapulars and, to a lesser extent, the rump and uppertail-coverts, and a black surround to the eye, broadest in front with a very narrow black line at the base of the bill. Tail black with blue fringes to the central rectrices, but extensively obscured by long uppertail-coverts (midway in length between those of the previous two species). Remiges and larger wing-coverts black, fringed blue, but the median and lesser wing-coverts are blue with small black bases. Chin and extensive throat patch are largely black with a faint purple sheen (thus distinctly darker than other members of the superspecies), but becoming bluer on the chin. The second area of purple, on the belly, is rather smaller than in both Turquoise and Lovely Cotingas, and is restricted to the central belly. Hellmayr (1911) described some slight variation in the intensity of the purple on the throat and belly patches. Underwing-coverts and axillaries black with blue fringes. *Adult female.* – Marginally larger than the male, but the size difference is not as great as in the previous species. Dark uniform greyish-brown above, with slightly paler fringes to the greater wing-coverts and tertials, becoming darker over the flight feathers and has an indistinct narrow white line on the lores. Paler brown below but still rather drab and uniform, with subtle paler, buff to whitish fringes to the feathers (although these are probably invisible in the field). Undertail-coverts dull cinnamon-brown, and underwing-coverts pale cinnamon (the latter obvious in flight). *Immature.* – Plumage maturation much as in Lovely Cotinga, although we have examined fewer specimens of the present species. Adult male plumage is, as others of the genus, achieved at age one year, albeit with a slightly paler overall appearance. Plumage of the male is initially adult female-like, with brighter, more cinnamon tips to the flight feathers which soon wear off, gradually and seemingly variably acquiring the blue feathering of adult plumage. *Moult.* – Post-nuptial moult is recorded as commencing in March–April (Snow 1982) and has been calculated to occupy *c.*90 days in all *Cotinga* species (Snow 1976a). *Bare parts.* – Irides dark brown or perhaps even black (Hellmayr 1911); the bill is black, paler greenish-grey at base and neutral grey on the lower mandible; legs and feet neutral grey to blackish.

MEASUREMENTS (BMNH; FMNH; Wetmore 1972 [maxima in square brackets from Hellmayr 1929b]: Panama and Colombia) Wing of male (*n* = 13) 102.5–112.0mm, wing of female (*n* = 13) 106–111mm; tail of male (*n* = 13) 64–70mm, tail of female (*n* = 13) 64.5–69.5mm [–75.0mm]; bill of male (*n* = 12) 14.6–18.0mm, bill of female (*n* = 11) 15.4–20.0mm; tarsus of male (*n* = 12) 20.0–22.5mm, tarsus of female (*n* = 11) 21.6–23.8mm. See also Hellmayr (1911) for additional mensural data. No weight data have been published (Snow 1982, 2004a, Dunning 2008).

GEOGRAPHICAL VARIATION Monotypic, although Hellmayr (1929b) noted that the single Bogotá male specimen (which was not quite adult) appeared paler purple on the underparts than those from western Colombia, and eastern Panama.

VOICE We are unaware of any published recordings of this species. Like others within the superspecies, the vocalisations of the Blue Cotinga are very poorly known. Male apparently makes only mechanical wing sounds, like others of the genus, whilst the female reportedly utters loud shrieks at the nest (also like others of the superspecies, which see).

NATURAL HISTORY Like other *Cotinga*, this species is usually found alone or in pairs, perched high and quietly in the subcanopy and canopy of tall trees, perhaps favouring less exposed situations than some blue cotingas, or in small groups of up to ten birds at fruiting trees (Salaman *et al.* 2002a). Blue Cotinga has at least once been reported to join mobile mixed-species foraging flocks (M. Dennis *in litt.* 2010).

FOOD AND FEEDING Diet is apparently principally frugivorous, but there appear to be few data concerning its preferences, other than to broad references to figs (*Ficus*, Fabaceae), *Cecropia* 'catkins' (Urticaceae), mistletoes and *Euterpe* (Arecaceae) palms, etc., taken following a brief fluttering sally (Bangs and Barbour 1922, Hallinan 1924, Eisenmann 1961, Wetmore 1972, Snow 1982, 2004a, Salaman *et al.* 2002a). At Gamboa, Panama, M. Dennis (*in litt.* 2010) observed a female unsuccessfully pluck a spider from a bark surface following a brief sally-hover.

BREEDING Our knowledge of the breeding biology of this species is, almost characteristically, weak. A female was observed apparently searching for nesting material low above the ground in late February (Wetmore 1972). A tiny shallow-cup nest, used in February and March of successive years, on the island of Barro Colorado, in Panama, was placed 28m above the ground in a *Hura crepitans* (Euphorbiaceae; sandbox) tree, and like many

blue cotingas, was placed within the cover of a patch of epiphytes on a near-horizontal branch, approximately halfway between the trunk and outermost branches of the tree (Chapman 1928, 1929a). The female alone appeared to be responsible for nest building and tending the silvery white down-covered young, which is almost certainly the case with all of the blue cotingas. Clutch size is apparently two. Chapman observed the female bring an unidentified black fruit to feed the nestlings. The first nest was destroyed after use, but then constructed in the same site in the following year, and when that failed (for unknown reasons), the female constructed another nest over a period of *c.*3 weeks in the same tree. Incubation period is unknown, but in the second year of observations, Chapman noted that incubation commenced shortly after 10 February and continued until 12 March. Subsequent observations in the same area of Panama involve single females carrying nest material and incubating, both in March (Willis and Eisenmann 1979). Further south, in northwest Ecuador, R. Ahlman photographed what appeared to be a similar nest in position and structure, also attended by a female, on the Ricaute road, prov. Esmeraldas, on 3 June 2008 (see www.surfbirds.com).

STATUS The species was treated as Least Concern by BirdLife International (2004, 2008), but it is considered a Red Data book species within Ecuador (Granizo *et al.* 2002). Uncommon to fairly common and frequent (e.g. in Panama and Colombia), this cotinga's lowland and foothill habitat is under pressure throughout its range. Considered generally scarce, and probably much reduced in numbers, in Ecuador (Ridgely and Greenfield 2001), where the foothills of Esmeraldas and in Pichincha around San Miguel de los Bancos are among those areas from where this handsome species has been recently reported. Probably extremely rare in Venezuela, where most prime habitat has almost certainly been converted to pasture, and the species is apparently known from just two records (Hilty 2003, Restall *et al.* 2006). The species is seemingly known from rather few protected areas, e.g. Soberania National Park, Panama (Robinson *et al.* 2000), and Río Claro Reserve, Reserva El Paujil, dpto. Boyaca, and Reserva Pauxi pauxi, all in Colombia (Donegan *et al.* 2010). Blue Cotinga is regularly found along the Gamboa Pipeline Road and at Canopy Tower, both of which are close to Panama City, the latter offering a rare opportunity to see this species on its own terms, at treetop level (Wheatley and Brewer 2001).

REFERENCES Angehr and Dean (2010), AOU (1998), Bangs and Barbour (1922), BirdLife International (2004, 2008), Chapman (1928, 1929a), Donegan *et al.* (2010), Dunning (2008), Eisenmann (1961), Granizo *et al.* (2002), Haffer (1974), Hallinan (1924), Hellmayr (1911, 1929b), Hilty (1997, 2003), Hilty and Brown (1983, 1986), Quevedo *et al.* (2006), Restall *et al.* (2006), Ridgely and Greenfield (2001), Ridgely and Gwynne (1989), Ridgely and Tudor (1994, 2009), Robbins *et al.* (1985), Robinson *et al.* (2000), Salaman *et al.* (2002a, 2008), Snow (1976a, 1982, 2004a), Stotz *et al.* (1996), Wetmore (1972), Wheatley and Brewer (2001), Willis and Eisenmann (1979).

Blue Cotinga *Cotinga nattereri*. **Fig. 1**. Male, Pipeline Road, central Panama, November (*Steven Easley / Costa Rica Gateway*). Note the incredibly large-eyed appearance, the darker blue upperparts (compared to the previous two species) and very dark-looking throat patch (although, depending on light conditions, it can look dark in any of the *Cotinga*). **Fig. 2**. Female, Gamboa, central Panama, December (*Mark Dennis*). Note the much more heavily spotted and overall darker underparts compared to female Lovely Cotinga *C. amabilis*.

The remaining blue cotingas are cis-Andean in distribution and comprise a more heterogeneous collection of species than the trans-Andean superspecies. Indeed, two sympatric Amazonian species, Plum-throated and Spangled, are quite different in appearance, whereas the widely separated Banded of the Atlantic Forest, and the smaller but morphologically similar Purple-breasted Cotinga of mainly lower Amazonia, might be considered allospecies. This grouping includes perhaps one of the easiest cotingas to observe, Spangled, as well as one of the most difficult, the globally threatened Banded.

SPANGLED COTINGA
Cotinga cayana   **Plate 26**

Ampelis cayana **Linnaeus, 1766**, *Syst. Nat.*, edn. 12(1): 298, Cayenne [based on Le Cotinga de Cayenne, of Brisson, 1760, *Orn.* 2: 344, pl. 34, fig. 3]

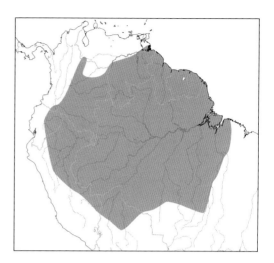

The most widespread of the *Cotinga* cotingas, this species ranges through much of Amazonia to the Guianas. It is also the only blue cotinga to occur sympatrically alongside two other members of the genus in different parts of its range, namely Plum-throated Cotinga *C. maynana* in the west and centre, and Purple-breasted Cotinga *C. cotinga*, principally in the north and east. Some authors have speculated, on the basis of its rather unique plumage pattern, that Spangled Cotinga is less closely related to the other members of the genus than they are to each other.

IDENTIFICATION 20.0–21.5cm; the males average slightly larger than females (Brooks *et al.* 1999). Arguably the commonest and most frequently encountered of the genus *Cotinga* (but see below), it overlaps in range with two others of the group. Plum-throated Cotinga of western Amazonia (where it typically outnumbers Spangled) is unique amongst the blue cotingas by virtue of its yellow irides (admittedly duller in females and some immatures), whilst males lack the black head, wings and upperparts markings of the more widespread and variegated Spangled, as the bases to the blue feathers are whitish bordered by pinkish-purple. Female Spangled Cotinga is rather uniform below, lacking the scaled effect to the underparts prevalent in female Plum-throated. The other sympatric congener, Purple-breasted Cotinga, is marginally but obviously smaller and less bulky (although comparative views will usually be required, especially by less-experienced observers), with much deeper blue upperparts in the male (rather than paler and more turquoise) and extensively purple underparts. The female is rather dark (almost blackish-) brown above, with paler tips to the feathers, whilst from below, female Purple-breasted Cotinga can appear uniform brown at a distance, although closer inspection reveals darker feather centres to the breast than in female Spangled.

DISTRIBUTION The range of Spangled Cotinga basically encompasses the entire Amazonian basin, throughout the Guianas and Venezuela south of the Orinoco (in dptos. Bolívar and Amazonas, and penetrating north of the river in parts of Delta Amacuro and southwestern Táchira), as well as throughout eastern Colombia, eastern Ecuador and eastern Peru north to northernmost Bolivia (reaching south to dptos. La Paz and Cochabamba), and throughout almost all of Amazonian Brazil, south to Rondônia, northern Mato Grosso and northernmost Tocantins, and east as far as western Maranhão (Ridgely and Tudor 1994, Sick 1997, Hidasi 1998, Hilty 2003). Note that reference to Goiás in Ridgely and Tudor (1994) concerns occurrence in Tocantins and that to date the species has not been recorded in the former state (Hidasi 2007). Spangled Cotinga is principally

recorded below 950m, but reaches locally to 1,350m in Peru (Schulenberg *et al.* 2007) and to 1,300m on Mt Kowa, Guyana (Barnett *et al.* 2002), the last speculated as perhaps being a temporary response to widespread drought and fires at lower levels.

MOVEMENTS None definitely recorded, although the species almost certainly performs short-distance local movements or irregular wanderings in search of fruit, e.g. in Venezuela (Hilty 2003) but certainly elsewhere too (see Distribution and Habitat). Schomburgk (1848) reported that Spangled Cotinga was found only seasonally, between November and mid March, in coastal Guyana.

HABITAT Spangled Cotinga inhabits the canopy and subcanopy of lowland tropical forest, including gallery and savanna forests, where it prefers *terra firme* over seasonally flooded forest types (*igapó* and *várzea*, both of which may be used principally seasonally), and is also found around scattered trees in clearings, in both forest and nearby cultivated land.

DESCRIPTION Like the other blue cotingas, the male Spangled Cotinga possesses modified primaries, in this case the two innermost (p9 and p10) are narrow and sinuate, as well as slightly recurved, whilst the barbs to the outer webs of p6 and p7 form a non-interlocking fringe, and the outer secondaries are unusually long (see Snow 1982: 88 for diagram). Sexes differ. Rictal bristles are moderately developed in both sexes; the bill is rather broad-based with a slightly arched culmen and slightly hooked tip, and the nostrils are relatively large and well exposed. *Adult male.* – Crown, mantle, rump and uppertail-coverts bright pale turquoise-blue, with black feather bases exposed on the crown and, to a lesser extent, on the back and rump. Scapulars black with narrow and pale turquoise fringes. Tail black, each feather finely fringed with blue. Wings black, the wing-coverts and inner remiges broadly fringed and tipped with turquoise. Throat purple or wine-red. Rest of underparts as upperparts, but with many fewer black spots. Undertail black. Underwing-coverts black with fine powder-blue fringes. Rest of underwing blackish with white bases to the remiges. *Adult female.* – Essentially somewhat drab, being rather uniform greyish-brown, but slightly paler below due to the paler fringes to the feathers, with an unmarked greyish-buff throat. The undertail-coverts possess a slight cinnamon-brown tone and are also unmarked (no scaled effect). There are paler, buffy fringes to the wing-coverts. *Juvenile/Immature.* – Juvenile appears overall slightly warmer brown than the female, with the entire upperparts, as far as the uppertail-coverts, and ear-coverts and breast covered with neat white fringes, and rather warmer, buffier belly, wing- and tail-feather fringes. Plumage maturation is much as in Lovely Cotinga. Adult male plumage is achieved around age one year. Plumage of the male is initially adult female-like, with brighter, more cinnamon tips to the flight feathers which soon wear off, before gaining very pale blue fringes to the upperparts and then becoming patchy blue below, initially on either the lower flanks, undertail-coverts or mid breast, and sometimes the first purple chin and throat feathers may appear simultaneously (RMNH). Development thereafter is poorly known (Hilty 2003). A nestling in French Guiana was described as being very similar to, but slightly paler than, the attendant adult female, with greyish tips to the primaries, secondaries, larger wing-coverts and rectrices. The outer fringes to the secondaries were also greyish, the dorsal feathers had broader pale greyish fringes and the underparts were paler than the adult female (Ingels 2008). *Moult.* – Light body moult has been recorded in adults collected in southern Venezuela in the first half of March (Willard *et al.* 1991), and Snow (1982) recorded that feather replacement probably commences mainly in the first six months of the year north of the equator, but only slightly further south, e.g. around Belém and Manaus (both in northern Brazil) the onset of moult occurs in the second half of the year. Moult has been calculated to occupy *c.*90 days in all *Cotinga* species (Snow 1976a). *Bare parts.* – Bill blackish with a slightly greyer base to the lower mandible and a black tip (Willard *et al.* 1991); the legs are dark grey to black; and the irides are brown.

MEASUREMENTS (BMNH; FMNH; MNRJ; ZMA; ZISP; Gyldenstolpe 1951: Brazil, Colombia, Guyana, Peru and Surinam) Wing of male (*n* = 35) 96.0–120.5mm, wing of female (*n* = 19) 105–116mm; tail of male (*n* = 34) 63–84mm, tail of female (*n* = 19) 72–86mm; bill of male (*n* = 33) 13.76–20.01mm, bill of female (*n* = 19) 17.12–21.17mm; tarsus of male (*n* = 8) 18.0–21.35mm, tarsus of female (*n* = 6) 19–21mm. Brooks *et al.* (1999) found that males have relatively shorter wing-chord lengths than females, but males average longer in tail-length. Weight (sexes combined): 55–86g (Haverschmidt 1952, Fry 1970, Novaes 1976, Dick *et al.* 1984, Willard *et al.* 1991, Brooks *et al.* 1999, Snow 2004a, Dunning 2008; FMNH; RMNH).

GEOGRAPHICAL VARIATION Monotypic, although *C. c. cayennensis* (d'Orbigny, 1839), originally applied to the Bolivian population, was resurrected for specimens taken at two sites on the Rio Purus, and another in the upper Brazilian Amazon, based on the purportedly deeper, purer blue of the upperparts, compared with those in the lower Amazon and French Guiana (Todd 1950). However, this proposal has not received any support in the subsequent literature, despite the fact that Friedmann (1948) had also identified size differences in these populations. We see no evidence for recognising any geographical variation in this species from our own work on specimens and fieldwork.

VOICE The only published recordings appear to be those on Krabbe and Nilsson (2003) and Naka *et al.* (2008). Males seen to utter a soft, medium-pitched and slightly mournful *hooo*, repeated 2–3 times, presumably in display (Chaves 2001); call also rendered *booo* (A. Whittaker *in* Hilty 2003) or *vooo* (Whittaker 2009). These calls are audible, but easily 'overlooked' by an observer on the forest floor. At the Rio Roosevelt, Amazonas state, Brazil, the latter author observed an adult male *C. cayana* perched on a treetop frequently give its display-call, before being replaced by a rival male. Thereafter, the appearance of a female *C. cayana* nearby caused excited counter-calls between at least two males. One male erected its crown feathers, slightly puffed out its body feathers, held its wings slightly open, whilst leaning forward and occasionally bobbing its head (Whittaker 2009). A faint whistling or whining wing noise has been noted in normal flight, although this is apparently distinctly louder in display, when males fly downwards and outwards up to 40m before braking suddenly and return to the same perch (Hilty 2003, citing Snow 1982, although therein this observation is stated to relate to *C. maynana*!). Chaves (2001) did not record any wing noises during his observations.

NATURAL HISTORY Largely similar to those of congeners. Usually observed alone or, less frequently, in pairs or small groups, but both sexes, perhaps especially females, also appear to quite regularly join mobile mixed-species canopy flocks, at least locally and/or temporally (Whittaker 1996a, Brooks *et al.* 1999; GMK pers. obs.). Like other blue cotingas, this species is most frequently encountered perched in a tall tree, usually within or above the canopy, often on a well-exposed bare branch, and most often in the early morning, late afternoon or following rain. Spangled Cotinga perches inside the canopy at other times, especially during the midday period. Sometimes the species is found in small groups of up to six. One of two males at a fruiting tree, also attended by a Ruddy Pigeon *Patagioenas subvinacea*, twice attempted to land near the pigeon, which wing-stretched and moved its head to dislodge the cotinga; eventually, the latter chased the pigeon over 50m out of sight before returning to the fruiting tree (GMK pers. obs.). In the Peruvian Amazon, Brooks *et al.* (1999) observed a male *C. cayana* and a Cinereous Mourner *Laniocera hypopyrrha* mobbing a female Bare-necked Fruitcrow *Gymnoderus foetidus* in the canopy of primary forest, which they swiftly chased off.

FOOD AND FEEDING Diet includes insects, e.g. winged termites, which are caught in flycatcher fashion from a treetop perch, but the species is principally frugivorous, perhaps specialising in mistletoes (Loranthaceae) and Lauraceae, and gathering at fruiting trees in small groups, often with other fruit-eating birds, including other cotingas (e.g. White-tailed Cotinga *Xipholena lamellipennis*, Purple-breasted Cotinga and White-browed Purpletuft *Iodopleura isabellae*, in the Serra dos Carajás, eastern Brazil: GMK pers. obs.; and in the west of its range with Plum-throated Cotinga or Purple-throated Cotinga *Porphyrolaema porphyrolaema*: Ridgely and Greenfield 2001, Snow 2004a). Spangled Cotinga has been observed with tanagers, caciques, oropendolas and Pompadour Cotinga *Xipholena punicea* at a fruiting *Goupia* (Celastraceae) tree in Guyana (GMK and W. Prince pers. obs.). As in other blue cotingas, fruit is mainly plucked using a brief and short-distance aerial sally, although birds may also lean down and take fruit whilst perched (Whittaker 1996a). A female brought mainly mid-sized fruits to its nestling in French Guiana, but on single occasions a *c.*10cm lizard and *c.*6cm cricket (Ingels 2008).

DISPLAY Chaves (2001) outlined what is presumed to be a type of lekking behaviour, based on observations in eastern Ecuador, during which a group comprising three males and a female Spangled Cotingas interacted as follows. Two males, *c.*40m apart, uttered the above-described *hooo* vocalisation (see Voice), whilst fluffing up their crown- and back feathers, to better expose the black spangling formed by the dark feather bases. Both birds, to some extent, crouched horizontally on their perches, whilst simultaneously moving the wings and spreading the tail, but they did not puff out their throat feathers, unlike in *C. maynana*. Meanwhile the other male and the female fed on mistletoe berries nearby. Hilty (2003) noted that leks may be even more dispersed with males being even several hundred metres apart. A similar grouping of 'excited' Spangled Cotingas was observed by GG at *c.*10m height in a lakeside tree near La Selva, also in eastern Ecuador, the significance of which is explained by Chaves' observations. GMK and A. Whittaker (pers. obs.) observed a male *C. cayana* perched in the early morning within the topmost part of a tall emergent alongside the Rio Maipa, near Borba, Amazonas, Brazil, in mid-September 2009, apparently displaying. Its body, including the tail, assumed a near-horizontal position, although the feathers did not appear to be fluffed out as in Chaves' (2001) observations (however, the observers were perhaps too far away to see this), and the head was held downwards, and moved up and down relatively slowly, forming a 'bowing' motion. After a few seconds, a female Spangled Cotinga flew to the same branch as the male, which then flew downwards and away, out of sight, followed in less than ten seconds by the female. As noted by Snow (1982), display behaviour by this species, and other *Cotinga*, is probably not confined to certain, predetermined sites, but is almost opportunistic, with display grounds effectively following the birds' pattern and requirements. Whittaker (2009) described a different display behaviour as follows:

> At 09h00 on 13 July 2008, on a clear morning at Bem Longe, Pará, I observed an adult male silently chasing a female, rapidly zigzagging through the crowns of *terra firme* trees, but returning regularly to the largest emergent. After *c.*3 minutes, the male perched on one of the topmost branches of the emergent, where I noticed two female-plumaged birds perched below him. The male raised the crown and purple throat feathers, moving the closed wings away from the body in a quivering motion, whilst partially raising the tail. After *c.*15 seconds it launched into a straight-line display-flight, but after a few seconds the course was abruptly changed, using an exaggerated wingbeat, which caused the bird to briefly swerve right then left, before returning to a direct path. The male then disappeared from view into the canopy *c.*100m away. No vocalisation could be heard.'

BREEDING Spangled Cotinga seems to nest in the local dry season, but there is an extreme paucity of relevant data for this species (like other blue cotingas) with the only specific information in the literature as follows. At Villavicencio,

in eastern Colombia, Nicéforo (1947) observed a female apparently brooding a single downy white young on a low branch of an isolated tree, although there was no visible nest (in other species the nests are tiny). The observer concluded that the female might have laid in mid January. Pinto (1953) reported on a nest with a single egg collected near Belém, Brazil; the nest was sited 11m above the ground and was saucer-shaped, constructed of twigs and rootlets and coated with a white fungus, whilst the rather large egg was pale bluish-white with abundant rust-coloured markings, densest at the broad end. Tostain *et al.* (1992) reported a female nest building on 2 October in French Guiana, and in the interior of the same country Ingels (2008) discovered a female attending a nest with a single *c.*15-day-old young in late October 2007. The latter was a tiny cup nest constructed on a *Spondias mombin* (Anacardiaceae) tree, within a village garden, *c.*12m above the ground; the outside was coated in greyish-white fungus to match the bark of the tree. Each feeding visit was made silently and was followed by the female brooding the young; the female always approached the nest gradually and never directly. GMK and J. J. Grigolo (pers. obs.) saw a female Spangled Cotinga attending what appeared to be a nest high (*c.*15m above the ground) in an unidentified tall emergent tree beside a reservoir in the Serra dos Carajás, Pará, Brazil, in the first week of September. To the south, in northern Mato Grosso, a female was observed bringing nesting material to an unidentified canopy-height tree at Cristalino Jungle Lodge, in early September (GMK pers. obs.). A juvenile has been collected in French Guiana in January (Dick *et al.* 1984), but there is no indication of how young the bird (a male) was, and a juvenile was taken in southeast Colombia in late November (ROM). In Surinam a male was collected with large testes towards the end of August, and very young males (scarcely any adult feathers) have been taken in the same country in August, September, December and January (RMNH). Three males collected in Colombia in May–June were in breeding condition (Hilty and Brown 1986), in Venezuela a female taken in March had enlarged gonads (Willard *et al.* 1991) and in Brazil a female with enlarged ovaries was collected in mid January (MNRJ). Some notes concerning the young in captivity were presented by Francis (2006), and other information on the species taken from observations of captive birds was published by Seth-Smith (1930) and Schürer and Bock (1995).

STATUS Treated as Least Concern (BirdLife International 2004, 2008). Locally the species is fairly common and certainly the most frequently recorded blue cotinga in the east of its range, but is rather rarer in the west, e.g. in Colombia, Ecuador and Peru, where it is generally considered uncommon and is often outnumbered by Plum-throated Cotinga, although it gradually replaces the latter completely as one moves north through Amazonian Colombia (Hilty and Brown 1986). However, Spangled Cotinga is overall considered uncommon but widespread in Guyana (Snyder 1966, Braun *et al.* 2007, Robbins *et al.* 2007) and its status seems broadly similar in Surinam (Ottema *et al.* 2009). In French Guiana, Thiollay (1994) estimated the species' density in a 100ha plot at 2.25 pairs. Spangled Cotinga is known from a great many protected areas throughout all range states.

REFERENCES Barnett *et al.* (2002), Beebe (1915), Bernard (2008), BirdLife International (2004, 2008), Blake (1950), Borges (2007), Borges *et al.* (2001), Braun *et al.* (2007),

Brooks *et al.* (1999, 2009), Cadena *et al.* (2000), Chaves (2001), Chubb (1921), Cohn-Haft *et al.* (1997), Crease (2009), Dick *et al.* (1984), Dugand and Phelps (1948), Dunning (2008), Francis (2006), Friedmann (1948), Fry (1970), Gyldenstolpe (1951), Haffer (1974, 1992b), Haverschmidt (1952), Hellmayr (1910, 1929b), Hennessey *et al.* (2003a, 2003b), Henriques *et al.* (2003), Hidasi (1998, 2007), Hilty (2003), Hilty and Brown (1986), Ingels (2008), Krabbe and Nilsson (2003), Lees *et al.* (2008), Mazar Barnett *et al.* (2004b), Mestre *et al.* (2010), Naka *et al.* (2006, 2008), Nicéforo (1947), Novaes (1960, 1976, 1978), Olson (1971), Oren and Parker (1997), Ottema *et al.* (2009), Pacheco and Olmos (2005), Pacheco *et al.* (2007), Parker and Wust (1994), Parker *et al.* (1994a, 1994c), Peres and Whittaker (1991), Pinto (1944, 1953), Restall *et al.* (2006), Ridgely and Tudor (1994, 2009), Robbins *et al.* (2004, 2007), Robinson (1997), Salaman *et al.* (2008), Schomburgk (1848), Schulenberg *et al.* (2006, 2007), Schürer and Bock (1995), Seth-Smith (1930), Sick (1997), Snethlage (1907), Snow (1976a, 1982, 2004a), Snyder (1966), Stone (1928), Stotz *et al.* (1996, 1997), Thiollay (1994), Tostain *et al.* (1992), Vidoz *et al.* (2010), Whittaker (1996a, 2009), Willard *et al.* (1991), Zimmer and Hilty (1997).

Spangled Cotinga *Cotinga cayana*. This species is the most widely distributed of the genus, occurring over all of Amazonia, and is variously in contact with both Plum-throated Cotinga *C. maynana* and Purple-breasted Cotinga *C. cotinga*. **Fig. 1**. Male, Paracou, French Guiana, month unknown (*Pascal Studer*). Depending on the bird's posture, the body shape can appear quite 'lean' as here, but is often slightly dumpier looking. **Fig. 2**. Male, Floresta Nacional de Caxiuanã, Pará, east Amazonian Brazil, July (*Stefan Hohnwald*). Note the comparatively heavily black-spangled upperparts. **Fig. 3**. Female, Explornapo Lodge, dpto. Loreto, northeast Peru, September (*Hadoram Shirihai / Photographic Handbook to Birds of the World*). **Fig. 4**. Female, Surama, Iwokrama, Guyana, October (*Hadoram Shirihai / Photographic Handbook to Birds of the World*). Note the overall very dark plumage (rather warmer in the Guyana bird, which is less in the shade) and dark irides.

PLUM-THROATED COTINGA
Cotinga maynana   Plate 26

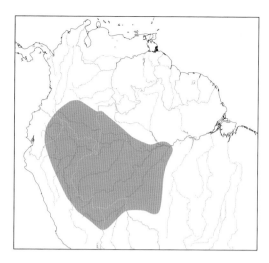

Ampelis maynana **Linnaeus, 1766**, *Syst. Nat.*, edn. 12(1): 298, Maynas, Peru [based on Le Cotinga des Maynas, of Brisson, 1760, *Orn.* 2: 341, pl. 34, fig. 2]

In western Amazonia, this species occurs alongside Spangled Cotinga *C. cayana* in humid tropical forest, but within this range it generally outnumbers the latter.

IDENTIFICATION 19.0–20.5cm; females are on average marginally larger than males (Brooks *et al.* 1999). The slightly larger male Spangled Cotinga has much paler turquoise-blue upperparts and has scattered black markings above and below, as well as largely black wings. Male Plum-throated possesses a much more immaculate appearance, with a yellow iris, smaller purple throat patch and the overall blue plumage broken only by the black outer remiges and scattered patches of pinkish-purple on the underparts which are, in any case, difficult to see in the field. Female Plum-throated Cotinga is more heavily marked than female Spangled, appearing decidedly scaled on the underparts, unlike Spangled which has a rather uniform appearance below. To some extent, where the two species overlap, Plum-throated is more frequently found along rivers and watercourses, whereas Spangled is found more or less exclusively in *terra firme.*

DISTRIBUTION Well distributed in upper Amazonia, Plum-throated Cotinga occurs from southeastern Colombia (north to dptos. Caquetá and Vaupés), through eastern Ecuador and eastern Peru to northern Bolivia (south only to dptos. Beni and northern La Paz), and over western Amazonian Brazil, north of the Amazon east to the western bank of the lower Rio Negro, and south of it east to Rondônia (e.g. along the middle Rio Ji-Paraná), the west bank of the lower Rio Madeira and apparently the Rio Roosevelt (but not found at the latter, e.g. by Whittaker 2009). Even further east, Plum-throated Cotinga has been claimed as far as the Rio Cristalino, in northernmost Mato Grosso (*per* A. C. Lees pers. comm.), but occurrence there, and perhaps anywhere east of the Rio Madeira, seems unlikely. The species is mainly recorded below 700m, but it has exceptionally been noted to 1,200m (a record on the Loreto road near Archidona, eastern Ecuador, in 1992: Ridgely and Greenfield 2001), and *C. maynana* occurs locally to 1,000m in Peru (e.g. in Manu National Park and Biosphere Reserve: Walker *et al.* 2006).

MOVEMENTS None definitely recorded, although the Ecuadorian foothills record mentioned above certainly hints at the possibility of seasonal movements.

HABITAT Plum-throated Cotinga is found in the canopy and borders of lowland tropical forest, both *terra firme* and *várzea*, especially the latter, as well as on older river islands.

DESCRIPTION Like other blue cotingas, the male has modified inner primaries, which in the present species comprise sinuate webs to pp7–10, whilst p8 is extraordinarily slender (see Snow 1982: 88 for diagram). Sexes differ. Rictal bristles are moderately developed in both sexes; the bill is rather broad-based with a slightly arched culmen and a slightly hooked tip, and the nostrils are relatively large and well exposed. *Adult male.* – Upperparts (including the scapulars) are turquoise-blue with an 'oily' quality to the plumage. Unlike males of congenerics, the bases to the feathers are predominately pinkish-purple rather than black, resulting in a more uniform appearance to the overall plumage, as the exposed bases are rather more difficult to see in the field. However, the bases to the scapulars are blackish-brown, producing a 'blotchy' effect to this feather tract. The tail is blackish with quite broad blue fringes: the rectrices appearing blue rather than black when folded. Wing-coverts turquoise-blue. Remiges black, the inner feathers with broad blue fringes distally, thus the folded wing appears essentially blue in the field (unlike Spangled Cotinga, in which the male appears to have largely black wings). The purple throat patch is less extensive than in male Spangled Cotinga. Turquoise-blue below with scattered purple patches (visible feather bases). Undertail blackish. Underwing-coverts mainly blue with blackish feather centres. A large white patch on the underwing contrasts with the dark trailing edge to the wing in flight. *Adult female.* – Dark greyish-brown above, like Spangled Cotinga, but the feathers are fringed fawn, rather than spotted at the tip. Paler below, with a uniform fawn throat and chest and the flanks are scaled perceptibly but softly darker. Belly and undertail-coverts brighter cinnamon-brown, with a mottled appearance, due to the darker feather centres showing through, and contrasting with the dull brown undertail. Underwing-coverts are bright cinnamon-brown (decidedly brighter than in female Spangled Cotinga). *Immature.* – Plumage maturation is much as in the Lovely Cotinga *C. amabilis.* Adult male plumage is achieved around age one year. Plumage of the male is initially adult female-like, with brighter, more cinnamon tips to the flight feathers which soon wear off, but there is no further information concerning development except that young apparently have greyish irides (Ridgely and Greenfield 2001). *Moult.* – Published moult data appear pitifully few (Snow 1982). Moult has been calculated to occupy *c.*90 days in all *Cotinga* species (Snow 1976a). *Bare parts.* – Bill and legs are both recorded as being grey to blackish; the irides are yellow (duller and darker in female, but at least some show pale eyes; see photograph in Walker 2009: 53).

MEASUREMENTS (BMNH; FMNH; MNRJ; RMNH; ZMA: Brazil, Colombia, Ecuador and Peru) Wing of male: (*n* = 16) 107–117mm, wing of female (*n* = 8) 113–117mm; tail of male (*n* = 16) 67–79mm, tail of female (*n* = 8) 71–86mm; bill of male (*n* = 14) 13.98–18.35mm, bill of female (*n* =

8) 16.34–21.0mm; tarsus of male (*n* = 6) 19–21mm, tarsus of female (*n* = 4) 19–23mm. Males average marginally longer in wing-chord than females, but the reverse is true for tail-length (Brooks *et al.* 1999). Weight: mean 69–70g (Brooks *et al.* 1999, Snow 2004a, Dunning 2008). Brooks *et al.* (1999) found that mass is on average slightly greater in females than males.

GEOGRAPHICAL VARIATION Monotypic.

VOICE Very few available data and we have never heard this species in life. Tape-recorded (Moore 1994, Krabbe and Nilsson 2003), a quiet, deep, hollow, descending *pooh*, whilst males, like other male *Cotinga*, are noted to utter a mechanical twittering wing-noise in flight, which becomes louder and more rattling in display (Schulenberg *et al.* 2007; D. F. Lane *in litt.* 2008; P. Donahue recording XC 20924).

NATURAL HISTORY This is surprisingly one of the most poorly known of the *Cotinga* genus. From what we do know, its life-history characteristics appear to be similar to those of the other blue cotingas, the birds being most frequently seen perched quietly and almost immobile for long periods, in a tall tree high in the canopy, often choosing a particularly exposed perch, especially early and late in the day. Seems unusually common along rivers (GMK pers. obs.).

FOOD AND FEEDING Plum-throated Cotinga is usually seen alone, in pairs or in small groups, and is often seen at fruiting trees with Spangled and, less frequently, Purple-throated Cotingas *Porphyrolaema porphyrolaema*, as well as with several parrot species (Brooks *et al.* 1999). Diet is apparently solely fruit, especially *Psittacanthus* (Loranthaceae) mistletoes, *Euterpe* (Arecaceae) palms and *Ficus* (Moraceae) figs, taken either in brief fluttering sally or whilst perched, by leaning downwards. Will at least occasionally visit the forest understorey to feed, even, or perhaps especially, during the middle of the day (GMK pers. obs.). A male in Acre, Brazil, was seen to visit a lone *Cecropia* (Urticaceae) within a small orchard, plucking fruits and then depart carrying them off (Whittaker 1996a).

DISPLAY In display, males fly downwards and outwards from their perch up to 50m, sometimes over water, before braking suddenly with a distinct wing-whirring and then returning to the same perch (Snow 1982, Restall *et al.* 2006). In Ecuador B. K. Snow (*in* Snow 1982) observed an adult male *C. maynana* lean forward on its high perch and inflate the plum-coloured throat feathers in the presence of two female-plumaged birds, as did Brooks *et al.* (1999) in northeast Peru (see also several observations of similar or identical behaviour in Spangled Cotinga detailed in that account).

BREEDING Nothing is known concerning breeding, even its seasonality; although Restall *et al.* (2006) mention that the species builds a tiny cup nest high in the canopy, this is presumably either extrapolation from our knowledge of other species, or in error.

STATUS Treated as Least Concern by BirdLife International (2004, 2008). The species is locally fairly common, usually outnumbering Spangled Cotinga, although at the eastern extremity of its range in southwest Amazonian Brazil, Stotz *et al.* (1997) found *C. maynana* to be rarer than *C. cayana* at two localities in the middle Rio Ji-Paraná basin, Rondônia. Numbers have inexplicably declined in the vicinity of Jatun Sacha, near Tena, eastern Ecuador (B. Bochan *in* Ridgely and Greenfield 2001). Plum-throated Cotinga is known from several protected areas in most, if not all, range states, including Amacayacu National Park, in southeast Colombia, Tiputini National Park, in eastern Ecuador, and Manu National Park and Biosphere Reserve and Tambopata-Candamo Reserved Zone, both in eastern Peru.

REFERENCES BirdLife International (2004, 2008), Brooks *et al.* (1999, 2009), Cadena *et al.* (2000), Dunning (2008), Dyck (1971), Gyldenstolpe (1945), Haffer (1974, 1992b), Hellmayr (1929b), Hilty and Brown (1986), Krabbe and Nilsson (2003), Lane *et al.* (2003), Moore (1994), Parker *et al.* (1994a, 1994b, 1994c), Pinto (1944), Restall *et al.* (2006), Ridgely and Greenfield (2001), Ridgely and Tudor (1994, 2009), Robinson (1997), Rosenberg (1990), Salaman and Donegan (2007), Salaman *et al.* (1999, 2008), Schulenberg *et al.* (2006, 2007), Sick (1997), Snethlage (1908a), Snow (1976a, 1982, 2004a), Stotz *et al.* (1996, 1997), Terborgh *et al.* (1990), Walker (2009), Walker *et al.* (2006), Whittaker (1996a, 2009).

Plum-throated Cotinga *Cotinga maynana.* **Fig. 1**. Male, upper Río Madre de Dios, dpto. Madre de Dios, southeast Peru, May (*Claudia Torres*).
Fig. 2. Female, Sani Lodge, prov. Orellana, eastern Ecuador, November (*Hadoram Shirihai / Photographic Handbook to Birds of the World*).
Note the pale irides, which readily distinguish females of this species from those of Spangled Cotinga *C. cayana*.

PURPLE-BREASTED COTINGA
Cotinga cotinga   **Plate 26**

Ampelis cotinga Linnaeus, **1766**, *Syst. Nat.*, edn. 12(1): 298, [Belém,] Brazil [based on Le Cotinga, of Brisson, 1760, *Orn.* 2: 340, pl. 34, fig. 1]

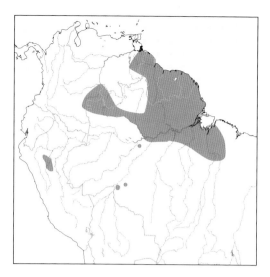

Much remains to be discovered about this beautiful cotingid, as even its range has been subject to substantial clarification during the course of the last two decades, especially with the discovery that, at least very locally, it penetrates western Amazonia. In terms of its life history, this is one of the poorest known of the genus *Cotinga*, with absolutely nothing known of its breeding or many aspects of the species' behaviour.

IDENTIFICATION 18.0–20.5cm. The colour of the upperparts in the male Purple-breasted Cotinga is a deep blue, rather than the pale turquoise-blue of the rather larger male Spangled Cotinga *C. cayana* (the only sympatric congener). Male Banded Cotinga *C. maculata* of eastern Brazil (see below) has a blue band across the chest, rather than the unbroken purple area on the underparts of the present species (and in any case there is no overlap in range). Females are typical of the genus and again most closely resemble the allopatric Banded Cotinga, being distinguished from Spangled Cotinga by their rather more contrasting appearance to the upperparts: dark brown feathers tipped and fringed whitish, from the crown to the uppertail-coverts, and appearing rather spotted above from close range. Female Purple-breasted Cotinga appears much more scaled below than either Spangled or Banded Cotingas. The recent discovery of Purple-breasted Cotinga in northeast Peru and much further south and west in Amazonian Brazil means that the species might potentially come into contact with Plum-throated Cotinga *C. maynana*, but that species too should be easy distinguished from *C. cotinga*, using many of the same features as for *C. cayana* (and note also the pale irides of most Plum-throated).

DISTRIBUTION Largely confined to northeastern South America, and found principally north of the Amazon River, but in recent years Purple-breasted Cotinga has been discovered at a tiny handful of well-scattered localities much further south and west of its traditional range. The species ranges throughout the Guianas (albeit generally locally), southern Venezuela (spottily in eastern Bolívar and southernmost Amazonas), in extreme southeastern Colombia (in eastern Guainía to Vaupés), eastern Amazonian Brazil (mainly north of the Amazon), from the Rio Negro drainage east, south of the Amazon from the Madeira–Purus interfluvium, e.g. at Tapuna, east very discontinuously (known from few specific localities, e.g. Cachoeiras do Curuá and the Serra dos Carajás, Pará: Marantz and Zimmer 2006, Pacheco *et al.* 2007, Lees *et al.* in prep.) to northernmost Tocantins (Hidasi 1998) and western Maranhão, with apparently isolated records, in Rondônia, at Guajará-Mirim (Whittaker 1996b), and southern Amazonas, at the Rio Roosevelt (Whittaker 2009), and northeastern Peru, in the white-sand forests near Iquitos, Jesús del Monte and the Cordillera Azul, San Martín (Alverson *et al.* 2001, Begazo *et al.* 2001, Schulenberg *et al.* 2001). Purple-breasted Cotinga should be looked for in Beni, Bolivia, adjacent to the Rondônia record. Note that reference to Goiás, Brazil, in Ridgely and Tudor (1994) concerns occurrence in Tocantins and that to date the species has not been recorded

in the former state (Hidasi 2007). Recorded to 800m (in Brazil and Venezuela: GG & GMK pers. obs.), and Gilliard (1941) mentioned a specimen taken at 1,100m in southern Venezuela, although Hilty (2003) noted occurrence in the latter country only to 600m.

MOVEMENTS None recorded, although clearly the species presumably might be expected to make short-distance and irregular movements in search of fruit supplies.

HABITAT Purple-breasted Cotinga is, like others of the genus, found in the canopy and borders of humid lowland forest, but appears to particularly favour areas of 'savanna' or 'sandy-belt' forest. It also visits tall trees in clearings, like most of the genus. More exceptionally, the species has been recorded in comparatively dry forest at the transition from Amazonia to the Cerrado of central Brazil in northern Tocantins, presumably outside the breeding period (J. F. Pacheco pers. comm.). In Peru, this cotinga is confined to areas of nutrient-poor white-sand (*varillal*) forest.

DESCRIPTION Compared with other members of the genus, this species is particularly small, slightly shorter-tailed and, especially, smaller-headed, with a somewhat dove-like structure. The bill is also rather short. Male has the inner primaries modified, with a short p7, the outer webs of p8 and p9 sinuate, and p9 and p10 both very narrow and tapered at their tips (see Snow 1982: 88 for diagram). Sexes differ in plumage and the female is marginally smaller than the male. Rictal bristles moderately developed in both sexes; the bill is rather broad-based with a slightly arched culmen and slightly hooked tip, and the nostrils are relatively large and well exposed. *Adult male.* – Upperparts are deep cobalt-blue, from the crown to the long uppertail-coverts. Black feather bases exposed, mainly on the crown and mantle, but only randomly on the scapulars. Uppertail black. Wings, including the coverts, very black, with the finest of blue fringes (invisible in the field, except perhaps on the lesser coverts where they are broadest). Underparts marked by the deep purple throat, breast and mid belly, with the rest of the underparts blue with some black feather bases exposed on the flanks. Undertail-coverts long and blue; undertail black. Underwing black. *Adult female.* – Blackish-brown upperparts, marked with whitish tips and fringes throughout, which are broader and become pale greyish-fawn on the greater coverts and tertials. The fringes and tips to the inner remiges and tips to the rectrices are pale fawn. Underparts dull buff-brown, with darker scaling across the breast and a paler unmarked throat. Undertail-coverts buff-brown and also unmarked; undertail brown. *Immature.* – Plumage maturation is much as in Lovely Cotinga *C. amabilis* (which see for details). Adult male plumage is achieved around age one year. Plumage of the male is initially adult female-like, with brighter, more cinnamon tips to the flight feathers which soon wear off, although perhaps initially paler below, then gains patchy purplish throat and some deep blue feathers on the mantle, back, uppertail-coverts, belly and rear flanks (Restall *et al.* 2006). *Moult.* – Published moult data appear pitifully few, but Snow (1982) suggested that pattern and seasonality might well be as that in Spangled Cotinga. Moult has been calculated to occupy *c.*90 days in all *Cotinga* species (Snow 1976a). *Bare parts.* – Grey bill with blackish tip (culmen slightly curved); grey or dark grey legs; and very dark brown or chestnut irides.

MEASUREMENTS (BMNH; COP; CUMZ; FMNH; MNRJ; RMNH: Brazil, French Guiana, Guyana, Surinam and Venezuela) Wing of male (*n* = 20) 107–112mm (one young had wing 99.5mm), wing of female (*n* = 10) 102–108mm (one young had wing 92mm); tail of male (*n* = 19) 58–71mm, tail of female (*n* = 10) 62–73mm; bill of male (*n* = 18) 14.8–18.0mm, bill of female (*n* = 10) 15–18mm; tarsus of male (*n* = 6) 16–19mm, tarsus of female (*n* = 5) 18–19mm. Weight (from Snow 2004a; MNRJ; RMNH): 50 and 53g (two males), and 55g (single female).

GEOGRAPHICAL VARIATION Monotypic.

VOICE Principally silent, although rarely gives a high-pitched, plaintive and complaining *preeeeeeer*, which may be repeated frequently but is easily overlooked; this vocalisation recalls that of a Dusky-capped Flycatcher *Myiarchus tuberculifer*. Like other blue cotingas, males produce a whistling/rattling sound (with the clicking quality of a child's toy) using the wings in flight (Marantz and Zimmer 2006, Naka *et al.* 2008; D. F. Lane *in litt.* 2008).

NATURAL HISTORY Several individuals may gather at a fruiting tree, but Purple-breasted Cotinga (perhaps on account of its general rarity) is usually seen singly, and the species probably never joins roving mixed-species flocks (but see below). Most frequently observed perched prominently on a dead snag within or above the canopy (especially adult males), or visiting a fruiting tree (EB recorded this species, Spangled Cotinga and Guianan Red Cotinga *Phoenicircus carnifex* at the same fruiting tree in Campamento Río Grande, northern Bolívar, Venezuela). Perches in the open most commonly in the early morning, late afternoon or following rain, like others of the genus, and generally young males and females spend shorter periods of time on open perches (Hilty 2003). Flight is fast and strongly undulating.

FOOD AND FEEDING Whittaker (2009) observed a female feeding on green fruit in stunted sandy-belt forest together with Spangled Cotinga, Pompadour Cotinga *Xipholena punicea*, Black-necked Red Cotinga *Phoenicircus nigricollis* and White-browed Purpletuft *Iodopleura isabellae* in southern Amazonas, Brazil. Walther (2004) mentioned seeing this species, and White-browed Purpletuft, within a foraging canopy flock also containing many tanagers and allies, as well as Gilded Barbet *Capito auratus* and Spot-backed Antwren *Herpsilochmus dorsimaculatus* in Amazonas, Venezuela. It is unclear if his observations pertained to a mobile flock or birds visiting a particular fruiting tree. W. Prince (pers. comm.) observed the species coming low to a strangler fig (*Ficus*, Fabaceae) in fruit beside a dirt road in south-central Guyana, together with Spangled Cotinga, Pompadour Cotinga, and many manakins, Black-spotted Barbet *Capito niger*, tanagers, honeycreepers and dacnises. Diet is apparently exclusively fruit, including those of *Euterpe* (Arecaceae) palms (Snow 1982), taken either during a brief aerial sally or by leaning down, but there are no other data concerning the foraging behaviour and food of this species.

BREEDING Nesting is completely unknown, although a male collected in early October in Surinam had slightly enlarged testes (RMNH).

STATUS Purple-breasted Cotinga is rare to locally un-common in suitable habitat, much of which remains intact, and the species is therefore accorded the status of Least Concern (BirdLife International 2004, 2008), but it appears to be only really numerous in parts of the Guianas (even there, in French Guiana *C. cotinga* is considered much rarer than *C. cayana*, and it is regarded as uncommon in Guyana and rare in Surinam: Tostain *et al.* 1992, Braun *et al.* 2007, Ottema *et al.* 2009). Indeed, at his study site in French Guiana, Thiollay (1994) estimated the density to be just one pair per 100ha, compared with 2.25 pairs in the same area for *C. cayana*. The species is known from a number of protected areas, in all range states, including Peru, where the species is apparently particularly local (Schulenberg *et al.* 2007).

REFERENCES Alverson *et al.* (2001), Begazo *et al.* (2001), Bernard (2008), BirdLife International (2004, 2008), Braun *et al.* (2007), Cohn-Haft *et al.* (1997), Gilliard (1941), Haffer (1974), Hellmayr (1929b), Hidasi (1998, 2007), Hilty (2003), Hilty and Brown (1986), Lees *et al.* (in prep.), Marantz and Zimmer (2006), Naka *et al.* (2006, 2008), Novaes (1978), Oren and Parker (1997), Ottema *et al.* (2009), Pacheco *et al.* (2007), Pinto (1944), Restall *et al.* (2006), Ridgely and Tudor (1994, 2009), Robbins *et al.* (2004), Salaman *et al.* (2008), Schulenberg *et al.* (2001, 2007), Sick (1997), Snow (1976a, 1982, 2004a), Snyder (1966), Stotz *et al.* (1996), Thiollay (1994), Tostain *et al.* (1992), Walther (2004), Whittaker (1996a, 1996b), Willis (1992).

Purple-breasted Cotinga *Cotinga cotinga*. **Fig. 1**. Male, Petit-Saut, northern French Guiana, July (*Marc Chrétien*). One of the most beautiful and unmistakable male cotingas. **Fig. 2**. Female, Surama, Iwokrama, Guyana, October (*Hadoram Shirihai / Photographic Handbook to Birds of the World*). Smaller bodied, smaller billed and considerably paler below than the otherwise superficially similar female Spangled Cotinga *C. cayana*.

BANDED COTINGA
Cotinga maculata   Plate 26

Ampelis maculatus **P. L. S. Müller, 1776,** *Natursyst.,* suppl.: 147, [Rio de Janeiro,] Brazil [based on Daubenton, *Planches Enl.* 188, and Edwards, *Nat. Hist.* 3, pl. 340]

Always the rarest and most range-restricted of the genus *Cotinga*, in recent decades its range has shrunk even further, leaving the species almost entirely dependent on a handful of protected areas, for outside of these forest loss has been near-catastrophic. The Banded Cotinga appears to be most closely related to the similarly plumaged Purple-breasted Cotinga *C. cotinga* of exclusively Amazonian distribution, and these two plausibly form a species-pair; indeed, they were formerly (and clearly erroneously) regarded as being conspecific.

IDENTIFICATION 18.8–22.0cm. This threatened species is the only blue cotinga in its limited range. Another rare cotinga – the White-winged Cotinga *Xipholena atropurpurea* – is often found alongside the Banded Cotinga in the Atlantic Forest of Brazil. Although of a different genus, females of the two may be confused, as their general appearance is of a plump, generally brown cotinga. However, female White-winged is a greyer brown bird with much bolder, white, fringes to the wing-coverts and some remiges. If seen feeding or at rest, the pale irides of the White-winged will also confirm the identification.

DISTRIBUTION Endemic to the Atlantic Forest biome of Brazil, originally from southern Bahia locally south to parts of southern Minas Gerais (no records since the early 1900s, until its recent discovery in the Bandeira/Macarani area on the border with Bahia by Ribon *et al.* 2004) and even northern Rio de Janeiro, as far south as Nova Friburgo and Cantagalo (recorded a few times, all in the 19th century; cf. Hellmayr 1929b, Collar *et al.* 1992), but is otherwise almost certainly confined to southeastern Bahia and northern Espírito Santo (BirdLife International 2000, Bencke *et al.* 2006), and the species appears to be declining even in the latter state within the last decade, during which period virtually all records have come from Bahia. Elevational range is from sea level to *c.*300m, within which altitudinal band habitat loss has been virtually total outside designated protected areas.

HABITAT Inhabits the canopy and subcanopy of humid lowland forest and forest borders, including tall woodland on white sand (*restingas*), partially logged areas and sometimes penetrates into adjacent second growth and isolated tall trees in clearings. Nowadays, Banded Cotinga is virtually confined to the Brazilian littoral.

MOVEMENTS Probably entirely resident, although local movements are reported in the older literature (cf. Collar *et al.* 1992), as the extent of modern-day forest loss has probably put paid to any propensity for wandering in search of fruit supplies.

DESCRIPTION Marginally larger than most of the blue cotingas, being perhaps exceeded in size only by the wholly allopatric Spangled Cotinga *C. cayana*, and with a comparatively large-looking head and bill, although it retains a rather gentle expression, common to most blue cotingas. Male has modified inner primaries, in this case a short p7 whilst p8–10 inclusive possess rather attenuated tips (see Snow 1982: 88 for diagram). Sexes differ in plumage and the female is marginally smaller than the male. Rictal bristles moderately developed in both sexes; the bill is rather broad-based with a slightly arched culmen and slightly hooked tip, and the nostrils are relatively large and well exposed. *Adult male.* – Bright cobalt-blue above (similar to Purple-breasted Cotinga, but marginally paler), with heavy black spotting, particularly over the mantle and scapulars. Wings (including the coverts) and tail black, although latter (like all blue cotingas) is largely cloaked by the long uppertail-coverts which reach almost two-thirds of the way to the tail tip. Outer webs to the central rectrices and fringes to the greater coverts, tertials and secondaries slightly paler cobalt-blue, but these are very narrow. Appears mainly purple below, with a narrow intervening blue band across the breast. Lower belly blue, with a broad central streak of purple reaching towards the blue undertail-coverts, albeit with some black feather bases exposed. The undertail and underwing are entirely black. *Adult female.* – Rather dark brown above, with buff-brown fringes to the feathers (rather than white, as in the slightly smaller female Purple-breasted Cotinga). Warm cinnamon-brown fringes to the wing-coverts and inner remiges. Underparts are contrastingly pale, especially on the throat and belly, with larger dark feather centres to the breast. Undertail-coverts cinnamon-brown and unmarked (like the chin). Underwing-coverts cinnamon, spotted brown, and rest of underwing pale brown. Undertail greyish-brown. *Immature.* – Plumage maturation much as Lovely Cotinga *C. amabilis.* Adult male plumage is achieved around age one year. Plumage of the male is initially adult female-like, with brighter, more cinnamon tips to the flight feathers which soon wear off (Snow 2004a). The first blue elements in the plumage appear on the hindneck, scapulars, mantle, greater coverts and uppertail-coverts, before any purple feathering has appeared on the underparts (RMNH). *Moult.* – Based on specimens, this presumably occurs post-breeding, and commences in November–December (Snow 1982). Moult has been calculated to occupy *c.*90 days in all *Cotinga* species (Snow 1976a). *Bare parts.* – Bill has the upper mandible black with a greyish base and the lower mandible grey with black tip; the legs are dark grey to black; and the irides are dark brown to yellow-brown.

MEASUREMENTS (BMNH; CUMZ; FMNH; MNRJ; RMNH; ROM; ZMA; ZISP: Bahia and Espírito Santo, eastern Brazil) Wing of male (*n* = 16) 112.5–124.0mm (one young had wing 111mm), wing of female (n = 9) 114–120mm; tail of male (n = 16) 66–80mm, tail of female (n = 8) 69–79mm; bill of male (n = 15) 14.61–20.00mm, bill of female (n = 9) 17.68–20.00mm; tarsus of male (n = 8) 20.06–23.91mm, tarsus of female (n = 4) 21.00–23.92mm. Weight: 65g (one male) (MNRJ; Snow 2004b).

GEOGRAPHICAL VARIATION Monotypic.

VOICE No vocalisation has been recorded, although (like all of the blue cotingas) the wings of males make a mechanical whirring in flight, owing to the modified primaries; this sound can be surprisingly loud.

NATURAL HISTORY This gorgeous cotinga is perhaps easiest to observe on dead snags of emergent trees after rain, when individuals perch in the open, presumably to dry and preen their feathers, or similarly in the early morning or late evening, when all of the blue cotingas are more obvious. Banded Cotinga is otherwise most easily and frequently seen at fruiting trees, which may attract both this and White-winged Cotinga, as well as other frugivorous species, although like most of the blue cotingas this species does not appear to regularly join mobile mixed-species flocks (GMK pers. obs.). Loose groups of up to six individuals have been reported (Collar *et al.* 1992).

FOOD AND FEEDING Diet is principally, if not entirely, frugivorous; although there are few specific details, fruits of *Ficus* (Fabaceae), *Ocotea* (Lauraceae) and *Rapanea* (Myrsinaceae) have all been recorded being taken. Old reports in the literature also mention caterpillars and other insects (Descourtilz 1854–56), but these foodstuffs require confirmation (Snow 1982, 2004a); P. F. Develey (pers. comm.) has observed this species consuming a small lizard.

BREEDING Very poorly known. The only nest (attended by a female, which chased another female that appeared in the vicinity) was found on 11 October 1986, at Porto Seguro, Bahia, and was placed in the fork of an almost horizontal branch in the mid-canopy of a tall tree in leaf at a forest border. The nest was a simple, shallow structure, constructed of small twigs, and the female was apparently incubating (Gonzaga and Collar 2010, L. P. Gonzaga *et al.* in Collar *et al.* 1992). Sick's (1985) report, based on an observation by A. Ruschi, of a nest placed in an arboreal termitarium is sufficiently contrary to our knowledge of congenerics to have been questioned by Snow (2004a). Descourtilz (1854–56) mentioned that the species nests high in the treetops, but also that the species remains paired during the breeding season, which latter assertion seems deeply unlikely. Indeed, in general many of Ruschi's published observations are so at variance with other knowledge that many are widely doubted (Willis 2003). Immature males have been collected or observed in the field in January and February (see Collar *et al.* 1992).

STATUS Classified as Endangered (BirdLife International 2004, 2008) and, as noted above (see Distribution), this cotinga's range has almost certainly declined dramatically during the course of the 20th century. Banded Cotinga is considered Critically Endangered in the state of Espírito Santo (Passamani and Mendes 2007). The species was apparently always far less common than the partially sympatric White-winged Cotinga (see Collar *et al.* 1992 for reports going back to the early 19th century concerning its general scarcity) and, furthermore, the latter is seemingly proving more resilient to the ongoing and persistent habitat change and loss. Capture for the cagebird trade, at least formerly, and for its extraordinary plumage, which was used in 'feather-flower' craftwork, may well have hastened its decline (cf. Collar *et al.* 1992: 733). Fewer than 1,000 individuals perhaps remain and the modern-day range was recently estimated at just *c.*780km^2 (BirdLife International 2004) and is plausibly now even less than the latter figure, it having become one of the rarest and most prized by birdwatchers of the Atlantic Forest endemics. Now virtually confined to just six, some only nominally, protected areas, namely Estação Veracruz, near Porto Seguro, Monte Pascoal National Park and APA Itacaré (all in Bahia), the recently acquired Bandeira reserve in Minas Gerais (owned by the American Bird Conservancy/Fundação Biodiversitas), and further south Linhares Natural Reserve and the adjacent Sooretama Biological Reserve (both Espírito Santo). However, the species always appears to have been rare at Monte Pascoal and there have been very few, if any, records at Sooretama since the late 1990s, potentially reducing the core range of the Banded Cotinga to perilously low levels. Snow (2004a) speculated that it might be (still?) present in the Rio Doce State Park, Minas Gerais, but it was not recorded by a recent survey of the area (Faria *et al.* 2006); the most recent (see above) of the three state records comes from near the site of the present-day protected area. The current conservation status of the Barrolândia area, Bahia, where GMK found the species in February 1995 (see Wege and Long 1995), requires investigation.

REFERENCES Albano (2010b), Bencke *et al.* (2006), BirdLife International (2004, 2008), Collar *et al.* (1992), Cordeiro (2000), Descourtilz (1854–56), Faria *et al.* (2006), Fisher (1981), Gonzaga and Collar (2010), Haffer (1974), Hellmayr (1929b), Parker and Goerck (1997), Passamani and Mendes (2007), Patrial *et al.* (2009), Pinto (1944), Ribon *et al.* (2004), Ridgely and Tudor (1994, 2009), Sick (1972, 1985, 1997), Simon (2009), Snow (1976a, 1982, 2004a), Stotz *et al.* (1996), Wege and Long (1995), Whitehouse and Ribon (2010), Willis (1992, 2003).

1

Banded Cotinga *Cotinga maculata*. All images were taken at Estação Veracel, Porto Seguro, Bahia, eastern Brazil, in February. This locality is unquestionably one of the final strongholds of this species, which has the sad distinction of being undoubtedly the rarest of the genus *Cotinga*. **Figs. 1–3**. Male, feeding at a fruiting tree (*Ciro Albano*). Superficially recalls the same sex of Purple-breasted Cotinga *C. cotinga*, although there is of course no geographical overlap, but note the blue breast-band separating the two areas of purple. **Fig. 4**. Female (*Ciro Albano*).

Genus *Haematoderus*: Crimson Fruitcrow

Until recently, the Crimson Fruitcrow's life history was virtually unknown, but its nesting, displays and feeding behaviour have all been documented to some extent within the last two decades. Nonetheless, the species remains a difficult bird to find over much of its range and this strange and extraordinarily striking bird might yet have a few secrets to yield.

CRIMSON FRUITCROW
Haematoderus militaris   Plate 28

Coracina militaris **G. Shaw, 1792**, *Mus. Lever.* 2: 61, Cayenne

This stunning bird is surely one of the most coveted by birdwatching visitors to northern South America. However, over most of its range this is an extremely difficult species to encounter, although with knowledge of its voice, gained only in the last two decades, this fruitcrow is proving rather more numerous, and widespread, than previously supposed. Previously, Cracraft (1985) had considered it to be confined to the Guianan Centre of endemism.

IDENTIFICATION 31.8–36.0cm. Occurring mainly in northeast South America, the Crimson Fruitcrow *Haematoderus militaris* is another cotinga of rather uncertain relationships (cf. Tello *et al.* 2009, and Systematics, p. 44). In terms of its field identification, the overall red plumage is perhaps most likely to promote confusion with the red cotingas, although it only overlaps extensively with one of these, Guianan Red Cotinga *Phoenicircus carnifex*, which is easily distinguished by its midstorey habits (the fruitcrow is principally found in the canopy), much smaller bill and head, and overall much smaller size than the fruitcrow. Recently, *Haematoderus* has been found to also reach as far south and west as the range of the Black-necked Red Cotinga *Phoenicircus nigricollis* (albeit apparently very locally, see below), but the same features elucidated above, as well as the striking contrast in the black neck-band of the male *Phoenicircus*, will serve to distinguish them.

DISTRIBUTION Long thought to be basically restricted to the Guianan Shield, Crimson Fruitcrow has recently been discovered far south of the Amazon River, albeit as yet only extremely locally. Snow (2004a) speculated these new records might indicate a change in the species' 'centre of gravity', but we remain unconvinced of this, and instead consider that increased canopy access, more knowledgeable fieldworkers and relatively long-term studies have all been key to our improved knowledge of this (and other) species' range. Crimson Fruitcrow is known from *c.*5 main areas in Guyana (including the Acari (Acary) Mountains, the Iwokrama Forest and at Parabara, in the Rupununi savannas), at least 36 widespread localities in Surinam (Haverschmidt 1977; http://www1.nhl.nl/~ribot/php4/ov.php4?hami) and it is considered to be rare in French Guiana (although there are records from eight widely scattered localities: Tostain *et al.* 1992). A female was recently observed at one site in extreme southern Venezuela, the base of the Cerro de la Neblina, at the frontier with Brazil (Willard *et al.* 1991). It thereafter occurs south through Brazil, principally north of the Amazon, in Amapá, e.g. in the Serra do Navio (Novaes 1978, Forrester 1993), Cametá on the left bank of the lower Rio Tocantins, Pará, and around Manaus, Amazonas (where discovered only in 1979), with many historical (but no recent) records from the Belém area, at the mouth of the Amazon, in easternmost Pará (Snow 1982, 2004a), although there is a sight record from western Maranhão in the 1980s (Oren 1991). There also seems to have been a distinct decline in records around Manaus in recent years (M. Cohn-Haft and A. Whittaker pers. comm.). It is also found extremely locally at two sites much further south of the Amazon, namely around Pousada Rio Roosevelt, southern Amazonas (Whittaker 2009), and at Cachoeira Nazaré, on the middle Rio Ji-paraná, Rondônia (Stotz *et al.* 1997; at both the species has only recently been discovered).

HABITAT Undoubtedly, Crimson Fruitcrow prefers tall primary *terra firme* forest, e.g. around Manaus, where the canopy is almost uniformly at 35m, with taller emergents reaching up to 55m. However, the species seems also to tolerate some degree of habitat fragmentation (cf. Whittaker 1993, Candia-Gallardo 2006), although Sick (1997) reported that habitat destruction had led to its range contracting in some parts of northern Brazil. At the Rio Roosevelt the species appears to favour sandy-belt *terra firme* along rivers and observations north of Manaus are also from forest on nutrient-poor soils (cf. Bierregaard *et al.* 1987). In Surinam it is also found in the northern savanna forests (Restall *et al.* 2006, Ottema *et al.* 2009). Apparently the species is mainly restricted to areas below 200m.

MOVEMENTS Schomburgk (1848) considered the Crimson Fruitcrow to be solely a migrant in the Kanaku Mts (in southern Guyana), where it appeared only during the wet season in June–July. Furthermore, the fact that specimens have been collected in gardens within the city of Belém, at the mouth of the Amazon, in Brazil, suggests the presence, to an unknown extent, of seasonal movements in this region too. Undoubtedly, the species wanders in

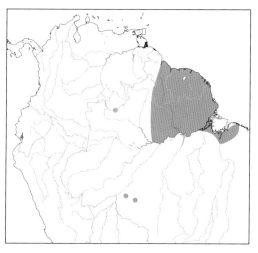

search of fruit, albeit probably mainly locally, and to some extent these movements will possess something of a seasonal component.

DESCRIPTION Sexes differ. A large and highly distinctive cotinga with a heavy, broad-based bill, with a well-arched culmen and a pronounced hook tip, with obvious rictal bristles and oval-shaped nostrils. In contrast, the legs are relatively short and the feet are rather small. Flight feathers are unmodified, but see below for modifications to some of the body feathers. *Male.* – Deep glistening crimson over the head, mantle, underparts and rump; the wings and tail are dusky to dark brown (although the tail is often covered to within 15mm of the tip by the crimson uppertail-coverts). Bushy crest is not always evident. As in many species of Cotingidae, some feathers of the male are modified, including those of the crown, upper back, uppertail-coverts and breast, which are lanceolate, elongated (up to 105mm long) and very glossy. *Immature male.* – Achieved on first moult from juvenile plumage: the back, wings and tail are blackish-brown or dark earth brown, whilst the head and underparts are red; the forehead and cheeks are suffused pinkish-crimson. *Female.* – Closely recalls the immature male. Less intense crimson, more rosy-red, and only so on the head, neck and underparts, the upperparts being dusky to dark brown (or even brown-black), and this colour may extend to the nape (Whittaker 1993). There is a tendency for some of the feathers of the crown and breast to be modified as in the opposite sex, but in general they lack the stiffened texture of the male's (Snow 1982). At least some individuals can show some white bases to the feathers of the rear flanks, even at long range (GMK pers. obs.). *Juvenile.* – Distinctive, being dull brown or grey-brown above, with pink centres to the forehead and crown feathers, brownish and white-vermiculated tips to the tertials, and pale outer fringes to the primaries and secondaries. Also has pale tips to the rectrices, whilst the underparts are pale pink with dark brown fringes to the throat feathers, neck-sides and upper breast (cf. Bierregaard *et al.* 1987). *Moult.* – Very few moult data have been published (but see Whittaker 1993), and Snow (1982) was unable to detect any seasonal pattern (if one exists) from the specimens that he examined. One collected in Rondônia was in body, primary and secondary moult in early March (FMNH). A male observed by GMK in south-central Guyana in the third week of October was moulting the two innermost primaries and probably some rectrices, but two females and another male seen equally well during the immediately following days were clearly not replacing any feathers in the same tracts. *Bare parts.* – Bill of male is dark wine-red or reddish-brown (appears blackish in the field) with a paler red to reddish-brown lower mandible and darker cutting edges; female's bill is blacker. Irides dark brown and legs and feet blackish in both sexes.

MEASUREMENTS (from Snow 1982; FMNH; RMNH; ROM; ZMA: Brazil, French Guiana, Guyana and Surinam) Wing of male (*n* = 8) 213–225mm, wing of female (*n* = 9) 209–216mm; tail of male (*n* = 8) 121–142mm, tail of female (*n* = 9) 105–134mm; bill of male (*n* = 6) 23–28mm (*n* = 2, to skull, 34.19–37.75mm), bill of female (*n* = 4) 23–26mm (*n* = 4, to skull, 34.52–37.83mm); tarsus of male (*n* = 6) 26–30mm, tarsus of female (*n* = 4) 26–29mm. Weight: 227g (one female; FMNH).

GEOGRAPHICAL VARIATION Monotypic.

VOICE Both sexes (principally the male) utter an irregular, low-pitched *bock* or *wock*, which until recently was undescribed (e.g. Snow 1982) and is easily overlooked, especially at distances over 50m. However, once known this sound is also simple to imitate and, at least sometimes, birds are easily attracted by such imitations, as long ago noted by Samuel M. Klages (see Snow 1982) and recently by Whittaker (1993, 2009). Also gives a low-pitched owl-like hooting, which is sometimes doubled or repeated, at irregular intervals (Hilty 2003). This is reported to recall the hooting of Flammulated Owl *Megascops flammeolus* (Bierregaard *et al.* 1987). Females may call at the nest. The first published recording was presented on Naka *et al.* (2008), and recordings have also been archived at several institutions.

NATURAL HISTORY Usually seen singly, but 'groups' of up to five have been reported in Brazil (Bierregaard *et al.* 1987, Whittaker 2009) and even 6–8 in south-central Guyana at the Iwokrama (Atta camp) Canopy Walkway (A. Moses pers. comm.). Wary and, in close proximity to an observer (but sometimes even some distance away), 'peers' slowly around, surveying its environs in the manner of a becard *Pachyramphus*, occasionally bending down, appearing alert, but keeping the tail broadly vertical. Prefers high (and probably specifically chosen) perches in the (usually shaded) canopy or subcanopy, which may be used for display purposes on several consecutive days (cf. Bierregaard *et al.* 1987), or even years (Restall *et al.* 2006). Flight is often slightly undulating and large-woodpecker-like, the bird briefly closing its wings after 2–4 flaps, but equally often the flight path can lack any undulations, being direct but propelled by very shallow flaps of the wings, with the entire movement appearing to be in slow motion. The species sometimes holds the body erect even when not apparently displaying (cf. Whittaker 1993).

FOOD AND FEEDING The species' diet has largely been elucidated recently: Haverschmidt (1977) mentioned Coleoptera in the stomach contents, and Novaes (1978) a Buprestidae, and it is suggested to mainly consume scarab beetles, arthropods and other invertebrates (Coleoptera and Orthoptera), including in flight, making sallies of 10–15m at a 45° angle from the canopy (Novaes 1978, Bierregaard *et al.* 1987, Whittaker 1993). Only recently discovered to consume fruit, although this aspect of the species' behaviour was predicted by Snow (1982) and mentioned without details by Sick (1997). Ottema (2002) observed a male taking fruits of a *Cecropia sciadophylla* (Urticaceae) in Surinam, M. Cohn-Haft has observed birds taking *Cecropia* fruits in central Amazonia and Candia-Gallardo (2006) watched a male feeding on the floral buds of a *Bellucia* sp. (Melastomataceae) north of Manaus, Brazil. Local guides in the Iwokrama reserve, in south-central Guyana, report that they frequently find the species in fruiting *Cecropia* trees (W. Prince *et al.* pers. comm.). Whittaker (2009) described a male performing a 3m diagonally upward sally to hover-glean a fruit. May join other cotingas (and allies) at such food sources; Whittaker (2009) reported the following species feeding in the same fruiting trees: Spangled Cotinga *Cotinga cayana*, Purple-breasted Cotinga *Cotinga cotinga*, Pompadour Cotinga *Xipholena punicea*, Black-necked Red Cotinga *Phoenicircus nigricollis* and White-browed Purpletuft *Iodopleura isabellae*.

DISPLAY Whittaker (1993) provided the first full details concerning display, which he observed north of Manaus, wherein a male erected all of his stiffened feathers, moved the head side to side with the bill, but held the body motionless whilst watching the two females in attendance for *c*.6+ minutes until both females left. This behaviour can be followed by a silent display-flight above the canopy, as a result of which several females may arrive concurrently (Bierregaard *et al.* 1987, Whittaker 1993, 2009). These flights, which may be repeated several times, seem to be especially performed in the mid-morning period; the male flies *c*.30m at 50–60° above the canopy on shallow wingbeats, before 'stalling' and descending slowly, as if parachuting, with the wings held in a V, the tail spread wide (perhaps acting as a brake), and the crown and body feathers puffed out; finally the bird spirals down into a tree when only just above the canopy, or glides horizontally in finale. GMK and H. Shirihai (pers. obs.) witnessed a near-identical display-flight in south-central Guyana in the mid to late afternoon, in the third week of October.

BREEDING Nesting behaviour was long unknown (Snow 1982) and is still very poorly known indeed, but has recently been described from mid-September observations north of Manaus, Brazil; the nest was a small platform constructed of tiny rootlets (and perhaps some mud), 20m high in a horizontal tree fork (Whittaker 1993). In the same region a juvenile was observed in late March (Whittaker 1993), whilst the bird collected in Rondônia had rather large ovaries in March (FMNH) and Robbins *et al.* (2004) considered the species to be breeding in March/April in southern Guyana.

STATUS Treated as of Least Concern (BirdLife International 2004, 2008), despite its apparently being everywhere rather rare or scarce and found at low densities, albeit seemingly widespread throughout much of Surinam and French Guiana. Crimson Fruitcrow was formerly seen with some degree of regularity from the ZF2 tower north of Manaus,

Brazil, but observations there appear to have declined markedly in the last decade (M. Cohn-Haft pers. comm.). It was initially described as being significantly commoner than Spangled or Purple-breasted Cotingas in this region, with one record from the Reserva Adolpho Ducke (Bierregaard *et al.* 1987). There are no recent records from the Belém area of easternmost Pará, Brazil (Snow 1982, 2004a), which might be due to ongoing forest destruction in this region, but this probably does not explain the apparent decline around Manaus. Thus, nowadays, the species is almost certainly best searched for in the Guianas, e.g. at Atta Rainforest Camp Lodge, within the Iwokrama reserve (Collins 2007), or at a nearby site close to Surama Eco-lodge (GMK pers. obs.), as well as in the Central Surinam Nature Reserve (Ottema 2002) and the Kanaku Mountains, Guyana, or around Saül, in French Guiana (Renaudier 2009). However, the species' discovery much further south and west of its previously presumed range north of the Amazon clearly suggests that observers almost anywhere in Amazonia should be on the lookout for this fantastic bird.

REFERENCES Aleixo *et al.* (2011), Bierregaard *et al.* (1987), BirdLife International (2004, 2008), Braun *et al.* (2007), Candia-Gallardo (2007), Cohn-Haft *et al.* (1997), Collins (2007), Cracraft (1985), Forrester (1993), Hellmayr (1929b), Haverschmidt (1977), Haverschmidt and Mees (1994), Hilty (2003), Naka *et al.* (2008), Novaes (1978), Ohlson *et al.* (2007), Oren (1991), Ottema (2002), Ottema *et al.* (2009), Pinto (1944), Renaudier (2009), Restall *et al.* (2006), Ridgely and Tudor (1994, 2009), Robbins *et al.* (2004, 2007), Schomburgk (1848), Sick (1997), Snow (1982, 2004a), Snyder (1966), Stotz *et al.* (1996, 1997), Tello *et al.* (2009), Tostain *et al.* (1992), Whittaker (1993, 2009), Willard *et al.* (1991).

Crimson Fruitcrow *Haematoderus militaris*. All of the following images were taken near Surama, Iwokrama, Guyana, in October (*Hadoram Shirihai / Photographic Handbook to Birds of the World*). **Fig. 1**. Male. **Figs. 2–4**. Female. Note the duller overall coloration and the dark-feathered mantle and nape.

Genus *Querula*: Purple-throated Fruitcrow

Querula is one of the no less than seven monospecific genera that comprise part of the core group of cotingas, as revealed by molecular data. The other six are *Porphyrolaema* (Purple-throated Cotinga), *Gymnoderus* (Bare-necked Fruitcrow), *Conioptilon* (Black-faced Cotinga), *Haematoderus* (Crimson Fruitcrow), *Perissocephalus* (Capuchinbird) and *Pyroderus* (Red-ruffed Fruitcrow). And, of these, only the last-named is not monotypic.

PURPLE-THROATED FRUITROW
Querula purpurata   Plate 27

Muscicapa purpurata **P. L. S. Muller, 1776**, *Natursyst.*, suppl.: 169, [based on the Gobe-Mouche noir à gorge poupre de Cayenne, of Daubenton, *Planches Enl.* 381] Cayenne

Querula is one of the most widespread of the cotinga family and the species is locally common in humid, principally lowland, forests. Indeed the conversational calls of the Purple-throated Fruitcrow *Querula purpurata* can be one of the most familiar sounds anywhere it occurs.

IDENTIFICATION Male 27.5–30.0cm, female 25.5–28.0cm (however, Brooks *et al.* 1999 found that females average slightly larger than males). Despite its name, the 'purple throat' of the male is actually coloured crimson or magenta over most of the species' range, but these sociable birds are nevertheless instantly recognisable by their vocalisations and agile manoeuvres through the forest canopy. (West of the Andes in Colombia the throat does indeed appear purple, at least in the field.) The male's throat colour can be hard to see at a distance or against the light, but even in such circumstances the birds' calls, behaviour and comportment should readily distinguish this fruitcrow from any possible confusion with other large, predominantly all-dark birds (e.g. some caciques or even an umbrellabird). Purple-throated Fruitcrow is easily distinguished even in flight, when its curiously floppy wingbeats and compact shape, with the short block-headed and broad-tailed appearance, render it immediately identifiable, even with relatively minimal previous experience.

DISTRIBUTION Widespread, occurring from southern Central America south to central South America. In Middle America *Querula* occurs almost exclusively in Costa Rica (on

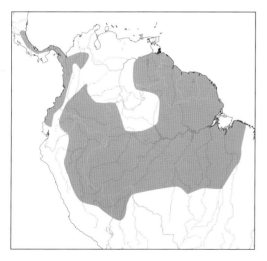

the Caribbean slope) and in Panama (where it is restricted to the Caribbean slope west of the Canal Zone, but is found on both slopes east of there). However, there are also recent records in southeasternmost Nicaragua, albeit very close to the Costa Rican border, where the species seems reasonably frequent (Weidenfeld *et al.* 2001, Múnera-Roldán *et al.* 2007). In South America, Purple-throated Fruitcrow occurs along the Pacific seaboard of Colombia and in the middle Cauca and Magdalena valleys south to northern and eastern dpto. Caldas, and Boyacá (Hilty and Brown 1983, Paiba-Azate *et al.* 2010), thence to northwest Ecuador as far as southern prov. Pichincha in the present day, with old, isolated records from south as far as Bucay in prov. Guayas (Ridgely and Greenfield 2001). It is easily seen from the canopy tower at the Río Silanche Reserve, prov. Pichincha (GMK pers. obs.). The species is even more widespread on the east side of the Andes, where it is found in southeast Colombia (from southern Meta and Vaupés south), in Venezuela south of the Orinoco, throughout the Guianas, and through Amazonian Brazil, where the species seems to be mainly found south of the Amazon (and is largely absent from the Rio Negro/ upper Orinoco drainage, e.g. it is unknown from the well-inventoried Jaú National Park: Borges *et al.* 2001). It also occurs throughout the lowlands of eastern Ecuador and eastern Peru south to northern Bolivia in dptos. Pando, Beni and La Paz. Elsewhere, Purple-throated Fruitcrow reaches to the ecotone with the Cerrado biome, e.g. in central Tocantins, Brazil (Diniz *et al.* 2009; GMK pers. obs.). There are other apparent 'gaps' in the species' range; e.g. *Querula* is apparently rare in Tapajós National Park, Pará, Brazil (Oren and Parker 1997), and has only recently been recorded in the Rio Jurúa basin in the extreme west of the same country (Whittaker and Oren 1999). Altitudinal range is from sea level to 1,200m in Colombia (Hilty and Brown 1986), to 1,000m in Peru (Schulenberg *et al.* 2007) and Bolivia (Tobias and Seddon 2007), but always found below 500m in Ecuador (Ridgely and Greenfield 2001) and probably mostly below 700m throughout the species' range (Snow 2004a).

MOVEMENTS The species is generally considered to be resident more or less throughout its range, but Hilty (1997) uncovered some evidence for altitudinal movements at a study site in western Colombia.

HABITAT In Amazonia, *Querula* probably prefers tall primary and secondary *terra firme* forest on rich alluvial soils, and it seems to be decidedly less common in more stunted forest on white-sand soils. The species is even known from two areas of mangrove forest at the mouth of the Cayenne and Kaw rivers in French Guiana (Tostain *et al.* 1992), and in western Ecuador Purple-throated Fruitcrow appears to favour forest edge, tall secondary forest and a mosaic of patchy woodland, rather than continuous forest (Ridgely and Greenfield 2001). It has been found in dry woodland within the Cerrado in central-southern Tocantins (P. F. Develey pers. comm.). In French Guiana, the species still occurs within close proximity to the capital Cayenne, in the Réserve Naturelle du Mont Grand Matoury (J. Ingels *in litt.* 2010). West of the Andes, in Colombia, it is found in lowland primary and mature secondary forest and at forest borders, and is apparently capable of persisting in rather small patches of suitable habitat (T. M. Donegan *in litt.* 2009). The species is rarely found low above the ground, instead preferring mid levels to the canopy.

DESCRIPTION The sexes differ. *Querula* is a rather chunky cotinga with a blunt bill (separating the all-black female, or a poorly seen male from any cacique), with short legs and broad but relatively long wings for its body size (the secondaries are especially long). Lacks modified flight feathers. *Adult.* – Both sexes appear all sooty black or matt black, the crimson throat patch (extending to the sides of the neck) of the male only being obvious in reasonable light or at close quarters. Males can appear glossier black above than below, and both sexes can show slightly browner fringes to at least some of the wing-coverts and flight feathers. The crimson, magenta or purple throat feathers of the adult male appear gradually (not being closely linked to wing moult) and are modified with flattened and twisted barbs, which present a surface area maximised for reflecting light, but no barbules (Strong 1952). Initially they can appear red with black tips. Females can occasionally show a few crimson feathers in the throat region (Snow 1982). *Juvenile.* – Entirely dull black (the feather fringes being blacker than their sooty-coloured centres), with the wing-coverts brownish-black (barred indistinctly with black) although poorly known, as specimens of this age are rare in collections (see Wetmore 1972). The nestling, which is initially covered in buff-coloured down, and its development were described in Snow (1982). Traces of the buffy down remained evident until the nestling studied by Snow was at least three weeks old. *Moult.* – Moult, which is estimated to occupy fully *c.*200 days largely during the dry season, was also described by Snow (1982). The onset of renewal seems to be concentrated in the period January–April in Panama, or marginally later in Costa Rica (where Foster 1975 found evidence for an overlap in moult and breeding). Further south, in the Guianas, feather replacement seems to be less well defined in its start, and Snow (1982) found that moult records from this region were spread year-round, as is also the case over Amazonian Brazil. However, even further south, in southern Peru and northern Bolivia, moult again appears to possess a strong seasonal bias, with commencement mainly in May–November. This overall pattern of seasonal basis at the northern- and southernmost limits (furthest from truly equatorial regions) is shared by most, if not all, of the very widespread cotinga species. *Bare parts.* – Bill whitish- or blue-grey to grey, sometimes with a blacker tip to the upper mandible, and strong, flattened with a broad base and a hooked tip; rictal bristles well developed. The eyes are dark brown; and the legs and feet are slate-grey or black with yellowish soles, as well as seeming rather unusually short and weak.

MEASUREMENTS (from Wetmore 1972, Snow 1982; wing-lengths of males from across entire range; other mensural data from Guianas and Panama) Wing of male (*n* = 32) 175–195mm, wing of female (*n* = 18) 165–178mm; tail of male (*n* = 18) 106.5–123.0mm; tail of female (*n* = 18) 105–118mm; bill of male (*n* = 18) 20.5–28.5mm, bill of female (*n* = 8) 20.0–27.4mm; tarsus of male (*n* = 8) 23.0–25.6mm, tarsus of female (*n* = 18) 23.1–25.0mm. See also Hellmayr (1911) for additional mensural data from western Colombia, and see Gyldenstolpe (1945, 1951) for data from western Amazonia. Males average larger than females in wing-chord

but the reverse is true for tail-length (Brooks *et al.* 1999). Weight (across entire range): 89–133g (males) and 88–114g (females) (Haverschmidt 1948, 1952, Burton 1975, Strauch 1977, Dickerman and Phelps 1982, Snow 1982, 2004a (which see for regional breakdown of mass data), Dick *et al.* 1984, Robbins *et al.* 1985, Brooks *et al.* 1999, Dunning 2008; MVZ; ROM). Brooks *et al.* (1999) found that on average males are heavier than females by *c.*6%.

GEOGRAPHICAL VARIATION No subspecies have been named, but populations from the Peruvian Andes are larger, and birds from Central America a little larger, than those from Amazonia and the Guianas.

VOICE Calls frequently and the species is likely to be first noticed by its vocalisations, which are audible over some distance. Most frequently heard are low mellow whistles, including a slow, rising *ooouuua* and *weeoooowhuu* (the *ooo* sliding lower and then rising), which may be repeated over and over. Also utters various harsh notes with the bill open, including sharp *wak* notes that may be doubled and which seem to signal low-level alarm (Snow 1982), as well as raspy 'coughs' and a throat-clearing sound (Schulenberg *et al.* 2007). These latter vocalisations were graphically described, by Stiles and Skutch (1989), as recalling a man preparing to spit, or as being like a 'thirsty duck'. Around the nest and in defence of it, Snow (1982) heard 'curious rasping' calls coming from the fruitcrows, which he did not hear the species give at any other time. Easily attracted by either playback or by imitating the sounds, and the birds can approach the observer closely under such circumstances. Published recordings are available on the following audio compilations: English and Parker (1992), Ross and Whitney (1995), Boesman (1999, 2006a, 2006b), Mayer (2000), Ross (2000), Schulenberg *et al.* (2000), Jahn *et al.* (2002), Krabbe and Nilsson (2003), Marantz and Zimmer (2006), Knapp and Will (2008), Renaudier and Deroussen (2008) and Boesman (2009). Recordings from Bolivia, Brazil, Colombia, Ecuador, Nicaragua, Panama, Peru and Venezuela are available online at www.xeno-canto.org.

NATURAL HISTORY *Querula* is a principally group-living species (typically forming bands of 3–8 individuals), but is also more occasionally found in pairs and sometimes joins mixed-species flocks with other larger passerines such as caciques, or non-passerines such as nunbirds or trogons (e.g. Jullien and Thiollay 1998). The number of adult males in a group probably varies with the overall size of the band, but is probably very rarely more than two and usually only one. Different groups appear rarely, if ever, to interact with one another, always maintaining some distance between themselves, although reliable data concerning a group's home range do not seem to be available. Each group roosts together, in close physical contact on the same branch. Capable of wandering over large areas of forest, Purple-throated Fruitcrows appear restless and the flock to be constantly on the move whilst foraging. Flight is swooping and bounding, interspersed by long glides, and the birds shake their tails from side to side (as if removing water), especially when they become excited.

FOOD AND FEEDING Diet is principally frugivorous and especially includes fruits of *Didymopanax morototoni* (Araliaceae), *Hirtella* sp. (Chrysobalanaceae), a Lauraceae and *Guarea trichilioides* (Meliaceae) in Guyana (Snow 1982), *Cecropia* 'catkins' (Urticaceae) in Guyana and Panama (Eisenmann 1961, Snow 1982), as well as Meliaceae and Olacaceae in the latter country (Howe and de Steven 1979,

Howe 1980), and a *Ficus pertusa* (Moraceae) in Peru (Tello 2003). Only eight species of fruits were known in the Purple-throated Fruitcrow's diet at the time of Moermond and Denslow's (1985) study. *Querula* is capable of taking mid-sized fruits and the seeds are defecated whole (Snow 1982). In addition, insects (Orthoptera, Hemiptera, Lepidoptera, ants, beetles) and even occasionally spiders are frequently mentioned in stomach contents (see Schubart *et al.* 1965, Haverschmidt 1968; ROM). Furthermore, the nestling diet appears to be largely insect-based (including larvae; cicadas, mantids and moths being some of those recognised during nest observations), with fruit only introduced from *c.*12 days of age. Fruit is mainly plucked in flight, using an upward sally or a brief stall and flutter; both seemingly surprisingly effortless for such a large species, but at least regionally it regularly perch-gleans (Snow 1982). Fruit-eating is easier to record, but is perhaps naturally more frequent than insect-eating, and Snow (1982) suggested that fruit consumption peaked during the midday hours, perhaps due to the necessity of gaining some liquid.

DISPLAY In display the male slightly erects and puffs out the beautiful throat feathers so that they form a 'fan', which reaches as far as the rear of the ear-coverts, whilst simultaneously 'shivering' the tail, and sidling very close to the female on an exposed branch high in the forest canopy. The male may also gently preen and 'groom' the female at the same time (Fig. 1), but otherwise, as already noted by Snow (1982), there is no special pre-copulatory ritual.

BREEDING Nesting is reasonably well known (compared with many other Cotingidae), due to the observations of Snow (1971a) in Guyana, Ellis (1952) in Panama, and Haverschmidt (1968) in Surinam. (The observations of Olivares 1958, in Colombia, and Abuja 1975, in Ecuador, were regarded as erroneous by Snow 1982, a pronouncement with which we strongly concur.) Much fuller details of the species' breeding can be found in Snow (1971a, 1982) than can be presented here. *Querula* probably mainly nests in the wet season, based on definite records of egg laying (July) and a barely fledged juvenile (October) in Panama (with nest building noted in late March and an active nest in February), egg laying in Guyana (twice in February), a nest (April) in Surinam, and a nest under construction and, separately, young in French Guiana, both in the first week of December (Ellis 1952, Willis and Eisenmann 1979, Tostain *et al.* 1992). In the same country, a male was photographed carrying nesting material in February (M. Dechelle; Fig. 2). A male collected in French Guiana in May was in breeding condition, as was a male taken in dpto. Cauca, Colombia, in September (ROM). Testes and gonad data from Cerro Pirre, eastern Panama (Robbins *et al.* 1985), also suggest that July/August is the breeding season in this region. The nest is a flimsy platform (the egg being visible from below) of twigs and vine panicles, with a lining of finer twigs belonging to several different tree species. Typical of many Cotingidae, the nest is placed high but well supported in the exposed fork of a branch (10–23m above the ground at least). At least in Guyana, the nest trees chosen by the birds were growing clear of other trees which, for instance, would have prevented monkeys from entering them without descending first to ground level (Snow 1982). Far from typical of the family is that additional 'helpers' (two other adults at one nest in Guyana) attend the nest, although the amount of food brought by each bird seems to vary. The group persistently chases other birds, including toucans, jays and raptors (including a Black-faced Hawk

Leucopternis melanops, which steadfastly stood its ground on four occasions), from a zone (mostly 50m but up to 200m) around the nest-site. The harrying of other birds is so persistent that Snow considered that these learn to stay away, as his observations revealed a distinct decline in the number of mobbing events during the construction, incubation and nestling periods. Nest construction was prolonged and intermittent at one of the Guyana nests, lasting 26 days, with material being brought entirely by the female of the pair, but her mate 'tested it for size'. Apparently both pair members were involved in constructing the Panamanian nest, more than one female constructed a second nest in Guyana and the male definitely brought material to that in Surinam, thereby suggesting that male involvement in building is to some extent variable. The pair in Guyana also seemed to check other potential nest-sites during the construction period. The female of the pair incubates the single dark olive egg heavily marked with blackish-brown for 25 days, leaving the nest usually only with other members of the group. (Records of two-egg clutches appear unreliable: see Snow 2004a.) At the Guyana nest studied by the Snows, all four adults in the group visited the nest, apparently to see the egg, within 15 minutes of it being laid (Snow 1982). Young are mainly fed insects (and to a lesser extent larvae), with a small percentage of fruit (see above), and take 32–33 days to fledge. Other breeding data are from Colombia and concern two adults building a nest at Leticia, in the extreme southeast, in June, a female at a nest in the northwest in March, eight breeding-condition birds taken in February–May, and two adults with their still-dependent young at Buenaventura, in the west, in July (Hilty and Brown 1986). More recently, in the same country, a male was observed feeding a nestling in late March at Reserva El Paujil (D. M. Velasco/ProAves unpubl. data) and another nest was active in southeast Venezuela in March (R. Hoff pers. obs.).

STATUS Undoubtedly one of the most widespread and numerous of its family. Categorised as Least Concern (BirdLife International 2004, 2008), Purple-throated Fruitcrow is seemingly common to fairly common through-out its broad Amazonian range as well as elsewhere, e.g. in Central America, and is also seemingly tolerant of moderate habitat modification. In southeast Peru, at their study plot around Cocha Cashu, Terborgh *et al.* (1990) found it to be the second-most numerous cotinga, after Screaming Piha *Lipaugus vociferans*, with ten individuals per 100ha, and in central Panama Robinson *et al.* (2000a) estimated the species' density at 14 individuals per 100ha. In complete contrast, in French Guiana, Thiollay (1994) considered the density of this species to be just one pair per 100ha. The species occurs within a great many protected or semi-protected areas, e.g. Carajás National Forest, Tapajós National Forest, and Cabo Orange, Montanhas do Tumucumaque and Amazonia National Parks (Brazil); Reserva El Paujil, Reserva Reinita Cielo Azul, Reserva Pauxi pauxi, Tinigua National Park and Los Katíos National Park (Colombia); Tortuguero National Park, Hitoy Cerere Biological Reserve, Keköldi Indigenous Reserve and La Selva OTS Biological Station (Costa Rica); Cuyabeno Faunistic Production Reserve, and Yuturi National Park and Biosphere Reserve (Ecuador); Si-a-Paz Reserve (Nicaragua); Soberania National Park (Panama); Manu National Park and Biosphere Reserve, and Tambopata-Candamo Reserved Zone (Peru); Brownsberg National Park (Surinam); and Canaima National Park and Imataca Forest Reserve (Venezuela) (cf. Oren and Parker 1997, Robinson *et al.* 2000a, Snow 2004a, Walker *et al.* 2006,

Múnera-Roldán *et al.* 2007, Pacheco *et al.* 2007, Bernard 2008, Salaman *et al.* 2008, Lawson 2010). The species also may be better able to persist in relatively small areas of forest in close proximity to urban areas than many other cotingids (Vasconcelos *et al.* 2007).

REFERENCES Abuja (1975), Aleixo and Guilherme (2010), Aleixo *et al.* (2011), Almeida *et al.* (2003), Angehr and Dean (2010), AOU (1998), Armacost (2006), Bernard (2008), BirdLife International (2004, 2008), Blake (1950), Blake and Loiselle (2001), Boesman (1999, 2006a, 2006b, 2009), Borges *et al.* (2001), Braun *et al.* (2007), Brooks *et al.* (1999, 2009), Burton (1975), Cadena *et al.* (2000), Chapman (1929a), Cooper (1999), Cuervo *et al.* (2008b), Dick *et al.* (1984), Dickerman and Phelps (1982), Diniz *et al.* (2009), Donegan *et al.* (2010), Dunning (2008), Eisenmann (1952, 1961), Ellis (1952), English and Parker (1992), Foster (1975), Garrigues and Dean (2007), González (1998), Guilherme and Santos (2009), Gyldenstolpe (1945, 1951), Haffer (1974), Haverschmidt (1948, 1952), Hellmayr (1911, 1929b), Hennessey *et al.* (2003b), Henriques *et al.* (2003), Hidasi (1998), Hilty (1997, 2003), Hilty and Brown (1983, 1986), Hosner *et al.* (2009), Howe (1980), Howe and de Steven (1979), Ingels (2001), Jahn *et al.* (2002), Jullien and Thiollay (1998), Kennard and Peters (1928), Knapp and Will (2008), Lane *et al.* (2003), Lawson (2010), Lees *et al.* (2008), Loiselle (1988), Maillard *et al.* (2007), Marantz and Zimmer (2006), Mayer (2000), Mee *et al.* (2002), Merkord *et al.* (2009), Mestre *et al.* (2010), Moermond and Denslow (1985), Múnera-Roldán *et al.* (2007), Naka *et al.* (2006), Novaes (1960, 1978, 1980a), Olivares (1958), Olson (1971), Oren and Parker (1997), Ottema *et al.* (2009), Pacheco and Olmos (2005), Pacheco *et al.* (2007), Paiba-Azate *et al.* (2010), Parker *et al.* (1994a, 1994b, 1994c), Parrado-Rosselli and Amaya-Espinel (2006), Peres and Whittaker (1991), Pinheiro and Dornas (2009a), Pinto (1944, 1966), Quevedo *et al.* (2006), Renaudier and Deroussen (2008), Restall *et al.* (2006), Ridgely and Greenfield (2001), Ridgely and Gwynne (1989), Ridgely and Tudor (1994, 2009), Robbins *et al.* (1985, 2007), Robinson and Terborgh (1997), Robinson *et al.* (2000a), Ross (2000), Ross and Whitney (1995), Salaman *et al.* (1999, 2008), Schubart *et al.* (1965), Schulenberg *et al.* (2000, 2006, 2007), Sick (1997), Silva (1996), Slud (1964), Snethlage (1907, 1908a, 1914), Snow (1971a, 1982, 2004a), Snyder (1966), Souza *et al.* (2008), Stone (1928), Stotz *et al.* (1996, 1997), Strauch (1977), Strong (1952), Tello (2003), Tello *et al.* (2009), Terborgh *et al.* (1990), Thiollay (1994), Tobias and Seddon (2007), Tostain *et al.* (1992), Vasconcelos *et al.* (2007), Wetmore (1972), Whittaker and Oren (1999), Wiedenfeld *et al.* (2000), Willis and Eisenmann (1979).

Purple-throated Fruitcrow *Querula purpurata.* **Fig. 1.** Pair (male behind), Sani Lodge, prov. Orellana, eastern Ecuador, November (*Hadoram Shirihai / Photographic Handbook to Birds of the World*). This photograph shows a male 'grooming' a female (see Display). Purple-throated Fruitcrow is one of the commonest and most easily seen cotingas within Amazonia, and is further remarkable for being group-living. **Fig. 2.** Male, Montagne des Chevaux, French Guiana, February (*Maxime Dechelle*). **Fig. 3.** Female (or young male), Serra dos Carajás, Pará, east Amazonian Brazil, September (*Hadoram Shirihai / Photographic Handbook to Birds of the World*).

Genus *Perissocephalus*: Capuchinbird

Restricted to the Guiana Shield region, Capuchinbird is one of the most spectacular and striking representatives of a most special family. It has long been assigned its own genus, but its closest relatives required fine-scale elucidation until very recently. The molecular work of Ohlson *et al.* (2007) and Tello *et al.* (2009) has proved that Capuchinbird forms a group that also comprises *Querula* (Purple-throated Fruitcrow), *Pyroderus* (Red-ruffed Fruitcrow) and *Cephalopterus* (the umbrellabirds), with *Haematoderus* (Crimson Fruitcrow) as probably sister to these taxa, but relationships within the group are not yet clearly resolved (see also Systematics, p. 44).

CAPUCHINBIRD
Perissocephalus tricolor   Plate 28

Corvus tricolor **P. L. S. Müller, 1776**, *Natursyst.*, suppl.: 85, Cayenne [based on Choucas chauve de Cayenne, of Daubenton, *Planches Enl.* 521]

The remarkable Capuchinbird is unquestionably one of the most immediately recognisable cotingas. In terms of our knowledge of the Capuchinbird's ecology, the pioneering studies of the late Barbara & David Snow, on this and several other cotingas whose distribution is to a large extent centred on the Guianas, made 40 years ago, have in many cases, rather amazingly, yet to be superseded.

IDENTIFICATION 34.5–37.5cm (the male generally averages slightly larger than the female). Undoubtedly one of the most unmistakable cotingas (described, somewhat unfairly, as 'grotesque' by Snow 1982), the Capuchinbird (or Calfbird) also has a reputation for one of the avian world's most incredible vocalisations (see Voice). Away from their well-known leks, this extraordinary bird can be very difficult to find, but once located, usually in the subcanopy, there is no mistaking it given the unfeathered and rather small head, and almost deformed appearance, like a hunchback! Female Guianan Cock-of-the-Rock *Rupicola rupicola* also has a somewhat odd shape and generally brown plumage, but lacks the long heavy bill, any contrast between the wings and tail and the body, and the bald head, but does possess a semblance of the male's forehead 'bump'. Seen very poorly, or only partially, a more serious confusion risk than another cotinga might be a Red Howler Monkey *Alouatta seniculus*, whose fur has a similar colour to the Capuchinbird's body feathers and which primate has a very similar geographical range to the bird.

DISTRIBUTION Capuchinbird is found in northeastern South America and the northern lower Amazon, from easternmost Colombia (where predicted for Vaupés, by Hilty and Brown 1986 and listed without apparent evidence by Snow 2004a, and known from a single sight record in Guainía: Pearman 1994b, Newman 2008) and southern and southeastern Venezuela (in southern Amazonas and eastern Bolívar as far north as the Sierra de Imataca: Hilty 2003), south through the Guianas, where appears generally widespread, being locally common and known from *c.*40 localities virtually throughout Surinam including the Rupununi savanna forests, and is generally frequent in French Guiana where *terra firme* is intact (Tostain *et al.* 1992, Restall *et al.* 2006, Ottema *et al.* 2009), to Brazil north of the Amazon, from the upper Rio Negro and Manaus east to Amapá (Sick 1997). Elevational range lies principally below 600m, but the species ascends to 1,400m in the southern Venezuelan tablelands.

MOVEMENTS None definitely known, but Capuchinbird is apparently occasionally recorded in sand-ridge forests in Surinam during the dry season, suggesting the existence of at least local movements in this region, and the species perhaps wanders indiscriminately searching for good feeding opportunities in other parts of its range too.

HABITAT The species inhabits the canopy and subcanopy of humid, usually relatively low-canopy forest, principally *terra firme*, and including rather disturbed areas in places, with long-standing leks (sometimes centuries-old) apparently capable of persisting in areas which have recently been cut-over. However, in some areas, e.g. in Guyana, its lek sites appear to be more 'fluid' (W. Prince pers. comm.). Elsewhere, leks often appear to be associated with *Cecropia* (Urticaceae) trees (D. Ascanio *in* Restall *et al.* 2006). At least seasonally (in the dry months) the species visits black-water flooded forests to feed (GMK pers. obs.).

DESCRIPTION Sexes similar, although males are somewhat larger. A large, bulky cotingid, which owing to its bare crown and heavy bill appears rather vulturine. Well-developed and robust rictal bristles in both sexes. The legs and feet, and bill, are strong; the latter has a strongly hooked tip and well-arched culmen. The nostrils are oval-shaped, prominent and well exposed. The flight feathers are unmodified, but the undertail-coverts are uniquely 'curled' and used in display (see below). *Adult.* – Upperparts mainly dull cinnamon with blackish remiges (the tertials are brownish-fringed over the outer web), a pale orange wing-bend and a black tail (clearly darker than the remiges), with a prominent cowl formed by the dense, upstanding feathers on the back of the head, which afford the bird a somewhat hunchback-like appearance. Uppertail-coverts blackish with dull cinnamon tips. Underparts deeper cinnamon, especially from the breast rearwards, with females perhaps appearing richer coloured below (Friedmann 1948). Males have long, orange-rufous undertail-coverts (see Natural History), but these are short in females. The underwing-coverts are creamy white, although females are apparently more likely than males to possess a dark patch on this feather tract (Snow 1972). There is a noticeably pale appearance to the underside of the primaries in flight, especially on their shafts. Undertail blackish. The almost bare crown and face are pale bluish-grey to plumbeous blue, or even bright blue (especially in males), becoming more greenish-grey or even orangey (at least in males) below the bill, the whole being covered by sparse hair-like feathers (like an old man's hair brushed over to conceal the scalp). *Juvenile.* – Resembles the adult, but has sparse down over the bare areas of the head. Nestling down is orange (Snow 1972). *Moult.* – Apparently is protracted and is suggested to occupy 220 days (Snow 1976a). Feather replacement apparently commences March–July in Guyana, but is less well defined elsewhere in the species' range, and, perhaps surprisingly, there is little evidence of any difference in start dates between the sexes. One (MNRJ) from northwest Brazil was replacing the secondaries and final primary in July; two males were in moult in March in southern Venezuela (Dickerman and Phelps 1982). *Bare parts.* – Blue-grey or plumbeous legs and feet, with strongly hooked claws and orangey soles; the irides are dark brown or chestnut. The bill is rather long and deep-based, with a hooked tip: the upper mandible is black, and the lower is pale silver blue-grey.

MEASUREMENTS (BMNH, MNRJ and ZMA for bill; other measurements from Snow 1982; figures in square brackets from Friedmann 1948: Brazil, Guianas) Wing of male (*n* = 16) 210–232mm [–236mm], wing of female (*n* = 10) 197–210mm; tail of male (*n* = 16) 100–108mm [–110mm], tail of female (*n* = 10) 87–104mm; bill of male (*n* = 16) 46.43–50.93mm [–53.0mm], bill of female (*n* = 5) 42.51–43.56mm; tarsus of male (*n* = 16) 39–42mm [–45mm], tarsus of female (*n* = 10) 31–37mm. Weight: 320–402g (males) and 258–367g (females) (Snow 1982, 2004a, Dick *et al.* 1984, Dunning 2008; MNRJ; RMNH; ROM).

GEOGRAPHICAL VARIATION Monotypic.

VOICE Remarkable, unforgettable and truly unmistakable. Males sing for *c.*2–3 hours after dawn and at dusk (but occasionally from late afternoon during the peak season) at communal leks with a strictly hierachial system, each attended by at least 2–3 birds (see Natural History). Response to playback can be dramatic, even away from the lek and in the early afternoon, and multiple birds can sometimes approach the recording. The cumulative sound produced by males resembles that of a distant chainsaw, but individually the calls resemble a 'lowing' cow, rendered *oh-wa-a-oo-oow* or *grr-aaa-ooooo*, sometimes interspersed with harsh, grating sounds. Strangely, the different birds' calls do not seem to overlap, at least not when giving the same song-type (see below: Rojas Nossa 2008). Prior to singing, the male leans forward and inhales, creating a low hissing sound (which is audible only at close quarters), following which the bird stands very erect on the perch, the neck feathers (cowl) expanded, the tail raised and the undertail-coverts unfurled to form a 'globular bauble' either side of the body (like Christmas decorations), with the bill held pointing slightly downwards, before sinking back onto the branch as the call is completed (see diagrams in Snow 1982: 157).

Males are not especially faithful to a given calling perch, and indeed continually attempt to displace their neighbours and rivals from a particular branch. Rojas Nossa (2008) studied the species' songs and how they related to posturing behaviour at a site in north-central Amazonian Brazil. She identified five different song-types, as follows. The first of these, rendered *jjj* (the 'half-moo' of Snow 1972), she considered somewhat cat-like, of medium duration (lasting on average just <4.5 seconds) and usually given relatively frequently. Sometimes a second 'syllable' is added (*jjj-oo*), which variation might solely reflect differences in this song-type between adults and younger males, respectively (cf. also Snow 1972). Song-type *jjj-Aaoo* (the 'moo': Snow 1972) is also of mid-length duration (lasting on average 4.08 seconds) and is the most frequently given type during lek displays (50%), at least in this region of Amazonian Brazil. The second 'syllable' sounds particularly nasal, recalling the 'lowing' of a cow. The third type, rendered *auu-jjj-Aaoo* by Rojas Nossa (2008), is the most prolonged on average (lasting 5.99 seconds). Whilst the second and third 'syllables' are identical to those of the second song-type, the first (*auu*) has the quality of a wind instrument. These first three song-types are given most frequently between 05:30 and 06:30 hours, and they are often uttered consecutively, e.g. *jjj*, *jjj-AAoo* and *auu-jjj-AAoo*. Furthermore, stereotypical posturing by the birds is associated with all three, thus. On emitting the *jjj* syllable, the bird maintains the bill open as if inhaling whilst moving the body backwards into an erect position, slightly raising the tail and inflating the undertail-covert 'baubles'. Thereafter, the *AAoo* is given with the bill closed, but with the throat sacs in the throat obviously inflated and the globular 'baubles' still obvious. The fourth song, *rrr* (the 'wark' of Snow 1972), is a low-volume croaking sound of short duration (lasting on average 0.69 seconds). Finally, the fifth song-type, *zzz*, is another low-frequency, low-volume and short-lasting sound (on average 0.52 seconds), which was found to be the most infrequently given song at the Brazilian lek. Both of these two latter song-types were given most frequently between 06:30 and 07:30 hours at the display site north of Manaus, and mainly by males that congregated at the nuclear lek (see Natural History). A short frog-like croak, *rounhh*, is given between songs, especially in the midday hours (D. Ascanio *in* Restall *et al.* 2006), a growling *wark* when foraging (apparently in contact with others) or by males departing the lek to feed (Snow 1982). Females (and perhaps also males) utter a rasping *waaaaaa* or *kack* in alarm. Sonograms of several different vocalisations were published by Rojas Nossa (2008), whilst published recordings are available on the following compilations: Boesman (1999, 2006a, 2006b), Vielliard (2002), Omena Júnior (2007), Naka *et al.* (2008) and Renaudier and Deroussen (2008). Recordings from Brazil and Venezuela are available online (www.xeno-canto.org).

NATURAL HISTORY Best studied by Snow (1972) in the Kanaku Mts of southern Guyana. The species spends most time at lower levels (Snow 1972). It remains placid on its perch for comparatively long periods, contemplating its surroundings, only moving the head very slowly, and regurgitating seeds following a feeding bout.

FOOD AND FEEDING Diet is mainly frugivorous, the birds mostly taking larger fruits, including large palm nuts (swallowed whole, but usually they regurgitate the seeds) in the midstorey or lower canopy, including at forest borders, particularly those of Lauraceae (37% in

Guyana), Burseraceae and Arecaceae (especially *Euterpe* palms), either from a perch or in a short, slow clumsy flight, but also feeds on large insects (grasshoppers, stick insects, cicadas, moths, caterpillars, ants, wasps, etc.) taken in a (usually short, but up to 11m) sally from a midstorey perch (Gilliard 1941, Schubart *et al.* 1965, Snow 1972, 1982). Sally-gleans usually involve the bird selecting a slighter lower perch on which to terminate, whilst to perch-glean the birds occasionally open one wing, apparently to maintain their balance. Harder parts of insects may also be regurgitated. Orthopterans were favoured during the dry season in southern Guyana. Individuals are sometimes seen to almost 'bounce' along larger branches of a fruiting tree between sallies for food, rather in the same manner as a foraging Bare-necked Fruitcrow *Gymnoderus foetidus* (GMK pers. obs.). Capuchinbird has been observed feeding in the same trees as Purple-throated Fruitcrows *Querula querula* in Guyana. The Snows (1972, 1982) listed fruit of 37 species in the Capuchinbird's diet. Once observed to take a bat roosting in the foliage, which was battered against a liana and then carried off, presumably to feed a young at a nest (Whittaker 1996a). Seasonally follows palm fruiting events and very occasionally trails mixed-species feeding flocks, at least in Brazil and French Guiana (Jullien and Thiollay 1998), but the species is apparently only rarely observed to feed at display sites (Rojas Nossa 2008), despite the fact that Snow (1972) found many old *Euterpe* seeds below the display perches in Guyana.

DISPLAY The lekking system, at least in Venezuela and Brazil, is centred around a nuclear lek (where up to 15 different males can be present, although fewer is the norm), with several satellite leks (at which just two or three different males may display) scattered over a 1km radius. The main lek in one Brazilian study had a diameter of 80m, whilst the nuclear of that lek measured 26.5 by 33.0m (Rojas Nossa 2008). Leks are on level ground and males display perches are 9–18m above the ground (often in trees of the genus *Eugenia*; Myrtaceae) and within visual contact of one another (0.5–15.0m apart in the Guyana study). At a lek in central Amazonian Brazil, Rojas Nossa (2008) observed males using the following tree species in which to display: *Lecythis graecieana* (Lecythidaceae), *Chrysophyllum sanguinolentum* (Sapotaceae), *Endopleura uchi* (Humiriaceae), *Scleronema micranthum* (Bombacaceae), *Sclerobium melanocarpum* (Cesalpinioideae), *Virola minutiflora* (Myristicaceae), *Couepia obovata* (Chrysobalanaceae) and *Tapirira retusa* (Anacardiaceae). She also found that display tended to be concentrated at the periphery of the main lek during the first half-hour of daylight, but that thereafter the males tended to assemble at the nuclear lek, before then dispersing to the satellites and with activity generally declining dramatically *c.*1.5 hours after dawn. Adult males can spend up to 65% of daylight hours at the lek, but subadult males probably only visit at dawn and dusk, and intermittently during the rest of the day, and Rojas Nossa (2008), in her Brazilian study, found that most birds left the lek site between 08:20 and 09:15 hours. Subordinate males may form alliances, even displaying in unison close together on the same branch (see photograph in Snow 2004a). However, aggressive interactions are frequent between males, which have two ritualised postures in such situations (described by Snow 1972); the so-called Pouter Pigeon posture sees the upper-breast feathers puffed-out but the posterior body is sleeked back and the tail is held between the legs. Given an increase in the level of aggression, the bird can adopt the fluffed-up

posture, in which all of the body feathers are raised and the wings are held slightly outwards, or sometimes even fully opened, but the tail remains depressed between the legs. Following such displays, males (both adult and immature) often pull off leaves and/or twigs, sometimes even carrying these around the lek site. Several females may attend each main lek and they can also be highly aggressive towards one another, although generally their behaviour is considered to be 'nervous … and [silent]' (B. K. Snow *in* Snow 1982). Snow (1972) also found evidence of social bonds between females, which may nest in relatively close proximity, visit the lek together, and even feed together, at least when foraging for insects. When the main activity at the lek finishes after the first two hours of daylight, birds probably usually remain within hearing if not visual distance. Some of the main posturing behaviours at the lek are listed together with their vocal components under Voice. However, Snow (1972) considered the most important lek-based display posture to be the motionless posture, in which a male whose perch is threatened assumes a horizontal position, flattens all of the body feathers, holds the wings slightly drooped, raises the tail and unfurls the undertail-coverts. This position is typically held for 5–10 minutes, but Snow (1972) observed it being maintained as long as 40–50 minutes, the male all the time keeping an eye on his rival, frequently twisting and turning the head to do so. The rival male will also assume the same posture, and the two birds can face each other off at very close quarters on occasion.

BREEDING Nesting is comparatively well known, with egg laying having been recorded in February–April in Guyana, November–March in Surinam and October in French Guiana, whilst song and display appear to peak in January–March (but continues December–July) in southern Venezuela. Two males from this region had large testes in March (Dickerman and Phelps (1982). A female collected in northwest Brazil in July had active ovaries, and another male collected in Amapá, Brazil, in mid November had large testes. Mating apparently occurs at the lek site, but as with virtually all lekking species of cotingas or manakins actual copulation has only been observed rarely. The nest is a fragile-looking platform construction, usually constructed within 800m of the lek and, typical of many cotingids, is a small, shallow cup of light twigs (four nests examined in southern Guyana were all of *Eugenia* twigs), which is placed 3–6m above the ground in an understorey tree. Snow (1972) found two nests in southern Guyana that were separated by just 5m. One egg (pale khaki with spots and blotches of brown) is laid and incubation lasts 26–27 days (cf. Snow 1972, 1982, for details), but the fledging period is still not certainly known (the one nest followed for the longest period by the Snows in Guyana was empty on the 27th day after hatching, and there had been a full-grown nestling on day 25, but might still have been predated). Only the female broods and feeds the chick (some details of incubation were presented by Snow 1972), and nest visits are made quietly and infrequently (just 1.5 visits per hour prior to day 7, and this rate appeared to decrease with age); chick diet is apparently mainly insectivorous, with few fruits seen. The female removes the faecal sacs from the nest area, but was not seen to consume them. Measurements of eggs and nests were presented by the Snows (1972, 1982), as well as the weight of a newly hatched bird. Data on captive breeding were presented by Lewins *et al.* (1994).

STATUS Treated as Least Concern (BirdLife International

2004, 2008) and the species appears to be tolerably common in southern Venezuela and the Guianas (it is known from many sites in French Guiana, where it is considered very common at Saint-Eugène), but Capuchinbirds are only easily detected at leks and these are often well separated. At his study site in French Guiana, Thiollay (1994) estimated the density of Capuchinbirds at five pairs per 100ha. It seems genuinely rather uncommon in Brazil, e.g. north of Manaus (Cohn-Haft *et al.* 1997) and at some localities in Roraima (Trolle and Walther 2004). Capuchinbird is known from protected areas in Venezuela (e.g. Imataca Forest Reserve), Guyana (Iwokrama Forest Reserve and the privately owned Karanambu Ranch), Surinam (Brownsberg Nature Park and Central Suriname Nature Reserve) and Brazil (Xixuaú Nature Reserve, Jaú, Cabo Orange and Montanhas do Tumucumaque national parks).

REFERENCES Aleixo *et al.* (2011), Barnett *et al.* (2002), Bernard (2008), BirdLife International (2004, 2008), Blake (1950), Boesman (1999, 2006a, 2006b), Borges (2007), Borges *et al.* (2001), Braun *et al.* (2007), Claessens (1997), Cohn-Haft *et al.* (1997), Collins (2007), Dick *et al.* (1984), Dickerman and Phelps (1982), Dunning (2008), Friedmann (1948), Gilliard (1941), Haffer (1974), Hellmayr (1929b), Hilty (2003), Hilty and Brown (1986), Jullien and Thiollay (1998), Lewins *et al.* (1994), Naka *et al.* (2006, 2008), Newman (2008), Novaes (1978, 1980a), Ohlson *et al.* (2007), Olson (1971), Omena Júnior (2007), Ottema (2009), Ottema *et al.* (2009), Pearman (1994b), Pinto (1944, 1966), Renaudier (2009), Renaudier and Deroussen (2008), Restall *et al.* (2006), Ridgely and Tudor (1994, 2009), Robbins *et al.* (2004), Rojas Nossa (2008), Salaman *et al.* (2008), Schubart *et al.* (1965), Sick (1997), Snow, B. K. (1961, 1972), Snow (1976a, 1982, 2004a), Snyder (1966), Souza *et al.* (2008), Stotz *et al.* (1996), Tello *et al.* (2009), Thiollay (1994), Tostain (1988a, 1988b), Tostain *et al.* (1992), Trolle and Walther (2004), Vielliard (2002), Whittaker (1996a), Zyskowski *et al.* (2011).

Capuchinbird *Perissocephalus tricolor*. **Fig. 1**. Near Las Claritas, Bolívar, southeast Venezuela, March (*Pete Morris*). **Figs. 2–3**. Saül, French Guiana, August (*Thierry Nogaro*). **Fig. 4**. Saül, French Guiana, April (*Maxime Dechelle*). **Fig. 5**. Iwokrama River Lodge, Guyana, October (*Hadoram Shirihai / Photographic Handbook to Birds of the World*). The sexes of this species are very similar, although males are larger and possess longer undertail-covert feathers than females. These latter are important in display, as revealed in several of the photographs presented here. **Fig. 6**. Iwokrama River Lodge, Guyana, October (*Hadoram Shirihai / Photographic Handbook to Birds of the World*). All of the images that appear here were taken at one or other of the species' well-known leks.

Genus *Pyroderus*: Red-ruffed Fruitcrow

Red-ruffed Fruitcrow shows some features akin to those of Purple-throated Fruitcrow *Querula purpurata*, but it has been speculated to be most closely related to the umbrellabirds, which also possess 'booming' display-calls, and perhaps most especially to Bare-necked Umbrellabird *Cephalopterus glabricollis* (Snow 1982). Some aspects of the Red-ruffed Fruitcrow's display behaviour also recall that of Capuchinbird *Perissocephalus tricolor*.

RED-RUFFED FRUITCROW
Pyroderus scutatus   Plate 27

Coracias scutata, G. Shaw, 1792, *Mus. Lever.* 4: 199, [Nova Friburgo, Rio de Janeiro, Brazil]

One of the largest cotingas, but despite this not necessarily easy to observe, the Red-ruffed Fruitcrow possesses an interesting and patchy circum-Amazonian distribution, and it is rarely numerous within its wide range. Our knowledge of the species' natural history is cumulatively reasonably substantial, at least compared with some cotingas, but relevant data for several subspecies are still very sparse.

IDENTIFICATION 35.5–46.0cm. This very large (the male is considerably larger than the female) and striking cotinga can only be confused, in poor conditions, with one of the umbrellabirds. Although rather variable across its range, the Red-ruffed Fruitcrow is quite unmistakable if seen well. It is a bulky bird with heavy 'features' (large-billed) and a stocky appearance, and this fruitcrow can be further recognised by the brilliant red patch of 'crinkled' feathers on the throat and upper breast, set off by the otherwise almost all-black plumage (some subspecies have rufous-chestnut lower underparts). Some of the larger icterids appear all black at first but show yellow in the tail, red in the rump or are pale-billed, even if the bird's size cannot be easily judged. Despite its status (locally uncommon at best), Red-ruffed Fruitcrows can be quite unsuspicious (even curious) of observers, once located, and generally should present few identification problems.

DISTRIBUTION Red-ruffed Fruitcrow has a curiously disjunct circum-Amazonian range in South America. In northern South America, it occurs from the Distrito Federal in northern Venezuela west to the Sierra de Perijá and the state of Táchira, on the Colombian border (Hilty 2003), thence south through the East Andes, West Andes and east slope of the Central Andes of Colombia, as far south as northwest Ecuador (the very few records are all from provs. Imbabura, Carchi and Pichincha: Ridgely and Greenfield 2001). There is another population along the east slope of the Andes in northern and central Peru, from dptos. Amazonas to Pasco (Schulenberg *et al.* 2007). The species 'reappears' in the Atlantic Forest and its hinterland in southeast Brazil, from central and coastal Bahia (e.g. in the Chapada Diamantina: Parrini *et al.* 1999) and southeastern Goiás, at Inhumas (Pinto 1944), to southern Rio Grande do Sul (to around just north of Pelotas: Maurício and Dias 1998), penetrating eastern Paraguay (entirely east of the Río Paraguay) and extreme northeast Argentina, in the provinces of Corrientes and Misiones. Red-ruffed Fruitcrow is also present on at least one of the largest, close inshore islands off southeast Brazil, Ilha Grande in Rio de Janeiro state (Alves and Vecchi 2009). Finally, the species also occurs in the Guianan Shield, where it is found very locally in

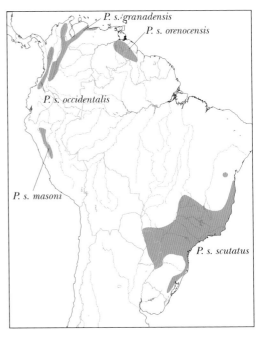

southern Venezuela in northeast Bolívar, from Upata south to around El Dorado (Hilty 2003), and in adjacent Guyana, where its status appears unclear, it being solely known from three specimen localities (Snyder 1966, Braun *et al.* 2007). The overall altitudinal range is from sea level to 2,700m (reaching highest in Colombia), but Red-ruffed Fruitcrow has not been recorded above 900m in southern Venezuela and Guyana, and it principally occurs below 1,300m in the Atlantic Forest (Stotz *et al.* 1996 mentioned occasional records to 2,000m). Elsewhere, it has only been recorded above 650m in the Andes.

MOVEMENTS Red-ruffed Fruitcrow is probably largely resident, but local movements can be expected and indeed in some areas of the Atlantic Forest the species' presence appears to be closely tied to the fruiting of *Euterpe edulis* (Arecaceae) (Galetti *et al.* 1999). See also Natural History.

HABITAT The species prefers humid tropical forest, semi-deciduous forest, cloud forest, and their borders, in the lowlands and to some altitude in the Andes (but mainly in the foothills in southern Brazil), occasionally entering rather drier forests in Venezuela (e.g. west of El Palmar, in northeast Bolívar) and locally (central Colombia) has been recorded in introduced *Fraxinus* (Oleaceae) woodland in near proximity to native forests. Given remnants of suitable habitat, the species can be reasonably tolerant of urbanisation (cf. Macedo and Carrano 2009).

DESCRIPTION The sexes are similar but separable given

reasonable views. Large with a sturdy, corvid-like, bluish-grey (male) or dusky-grey (female) bill. Large-headed, short-tailed and robust-bodied. The most prominent rictal bristles have a wiry quality and are recurved, but most are short and relatively weak. The nostrils are oval-shaped, but almost entirely concealed by the forehead feathers. The following largely applies to the nominate race. *Adult.* – The upperparts are black from the head to tail, being glossed in some subspecies, rather dull in others. Chin black with a large glossy orange-red throat and upper-breast patch, the feathers of which are 'crinkled' (the distal end of the barbs being flattened: Olson 1970) and tipped more intensely red than the orange bases. Rest of underparts vary depending on subspecies from black (nominate *P. s. scutatus*) to pale rufous-chestnut (*P. s. orenocensis* for example, but see below). The ventral region is black. The throat patch of the female tends to be duller than that of the male, but retains the 'crinkled' appearance, whilst the nape feathers tend to be shorter than those of the male. Underwing-coverts rufous-brown. *Juvenile.* – Snow (1982) described this plumage as being generally dull black and variably brown below, with some red feathers swiftly appearing on the throat (even before the wings are fully grown). Juvenile tail feathers are apparently not replaced (along with the rest of the flight feathers) until the first complete moult, and until then are more pointed (and sometimes longer) than the equivalent adult feathers. The nestling of nominate *P. s. scutatus* was briefly described and illustrated by Francisco *et al.* (2008a); see Natural History. *Immature.* – Generally similar to adults of the respective sex, but this plumage has the throat feathers less bright and glossy. *Moult.* – Moult is thought to take *c.*6 months (Snow 1976a), with, as is typical of many cotingas in which males are divorced from nesting responsibilities, males commencing feather renewal 1–2 months earlier than females. In northern Venezuela and Colombia moult commences mainly in March–June, whereas in southeast Brazil it is in September–October (Snow 1982), from where Willis and Oniki (2002) mentioned a female that was ending its wing moult in mid January. *Bare parts.* – Irides blue in some adult males (those described as brown, or grey-brown are perhaps immatures); brown or grey-brown in the female. Bill pale grey or grey-blue in some adult males but black or blackish-grey in others and in females. The upper mandible is darker than the lower. Legs and feet strong; black or blue-black with dull yellow-green soles.

MEASUREMENTS (Taken almost entirely from Snow 1982, except tail and bill of *P. s. masoni* from Hellmayr 1929, who also presented some additional measurements for other subspecies; also ROM for races *P. s. scutatus* and *P. s. occidentalis.*) *P. s. scutatus*: wing of male (*n* = 16) 236–263mm, wing of female (*n* = 17) 213–241mm; tail of male (*n* = 16) 142–179mm, tail of female (*n* = 17) 145–175mm; bill of male (*n* = 15) 29.5–33.0mm, bill of female (*n* = 16) 27.5–31.5mm; tarsus of male (*n* = 15) 41–45mm, tarsus of female (*n* = 16) 38.5–42.0mm. *P. s. orenocensis*: wing of male (*n* = 2) 238–242mm. *P. s. granadensis* (sexes combined): wing (*n* = 15) 207–240mm; tail (*n* = 15) 136–150mm; bill (*n* = 15) 25–28mm; tarsus (*n* = 15) 37–43mm. *P. s. occidentalis*: wing of male (*n* = 10) 230–254mm, wing of female (*n* = 7) 225–235mm; tail of male (*n* = 10) 140–158mm, tail of female (*n* = 7) 144–160mm; bill of male (*n* = 8) 29.0–31.5mm, bill of female (*n* = 7) 27–30mm; tarsus of male (*n* = 8) 42–46mm, tarsus of female (*n* = 7) 38–43mm. *P. s. masoni*: wing of male (*n* = 6) 228–240mm; tail (*n* = 8, sexes combined) 136–148mm; bill (*n* = 8, sexes combined) 36–38mm. Weight:

413–419g (two adult males, nominate *P. s. scutatus*) and 300–390g (five females, three of nominate *P. s. scutatus* and two of *P. s. granadensis*) (Belton 1985, Willis and Oniki 2002, Hilty 2003, Snow 2004a).

GEOGRAPHICAL VARIATION Conspicuous geographical variation exists within the Red-ruffed Fruitcrow, particularly in the extent of chestnut on the underparts, with less obvious differences also evident in size and other plumage characters (e.g. the iridescence on the upperparts). Differences in size also exist *within* subspecies, clouding the issue further, with differences documented in specimens collected at varying altitudes (in *P. s. granadensis* for example, where birds at higher altitudes are larger). Sibley (1996) speculated that *P. s. occidentalis* might be meritorious of species rank, but this recommendation has been neither confirmed nor denied by subsequent work. The following is based heavily on Snow (1982). *P. s. scutatus* of the Atlantic Forest region in southeast Brazil, eastern Paraguay and northeast Argentina has the ruff orange with bright and broad red feather fringes, a few chestnut spots on the centre of the black belly and glossed upperparts. *P. s. orenocensis* (Lafresnaye, 1846) of eastern Venezuela (in northeast Bolívar, from Upata to near El Dorado) and adjacent northwestern Guyana (at the Great Falls and along the Cuyuni and Demerara Rivers) has an orange ruff with narrower red fringes than the nominate race. The belly is dull chestnut-brown, contrasting with the restricted black ventral region, whilst the upperparts are dull lustreless black, with a slight median crest formed by the stiffened feathers. Some commentators have considered *P. s. orenocensis* to be not certainly distinguished from the next subspecies (Zimmer 1936c). *P. s. granadensis* (Lafresnaye, 1846) of north and western Venezuela, and eastern Colombia (including the east slope of the Central Andes) has the ruff as in *P. s. orenocensis*, the rest of the underparts similar to *P. s. scutatus* except that the chestnut spots are paler and more variable in extent (although still largely confined to the central belly), and the black upperparts are glossed. Hellmayr (1929b) considered this subspecies to be rather smaller than nominate *P. s. scutatus*, with a much shorter bill and tarsi. Those in Carabobo to the Distrito Federal of northern Venezuela have the most extensive brown, and thus approach the previous subspecies to some extent, whilst two specimens from the Magdalena Valley in Colombia (precise locality untraced, but speculated to be on the west slope of the East Andes) approach *P. s. occidentalis* in this respect (Snow 1982). *P. s. occidentalis* Chapman, 1914, of western Colombia and northwest Ecuador has the feather fringes of the ruff less bright than in all of the other subspecies. The belly is extensively chestnut (although reaching less far to the rear than in *P. s. orenocensis*), but darker than in *P. s. orenocensis* and the black upperparts are glossed. *P. s. masoni* Ridgway, 1886, which is endemic to the east slope of the Andes in north and central Peru, has the ruff deepest in tone, approaching crimson, whilst the chestnut of the underparts is the dullest of any subspecies, appearing mottled and often revealing a broken black band across the lower breast. The upperparts are dull and lack any iridescence.

VOICE Usually silent. The male advertising-call consists of two short, hollow, booming notes with a slightly electronic quality, likened to blowing across the top of a bottle and, when given in series, has a 'sawing' pattern, as the second of each two notes is slightly louder. Rendered *ooo-m, ooo-m…* (Hilty 2003). Snow (1982, based on P. Schwartz's notes and tape-recordings) also mentioned a 'twangy' call interspersed within bouts of booming calls. These notes were either short and abrupt or more drawn-out, whereupon they might be 'lengthened' into a 'boom'. They were also given both singly and in pairs of notes. Red-ruffed Fruitcrow is generally most vocal in the early morning, but calls can be given at virtually any time of day (Specht *et al.* 2008). Vocalisations are included on the compilations recently published by Remold (2002), Alvarez *et al.* (2007), Boesman (2009) and Minns *et al.* (2009), and sound-recordings from Brazil (nominate) and Colombia (*P. s. occidentalis*) are archived online at www.xeno-canto.org.

NATURAL HISTORY Principally observed solitarily and can approach remarkably closely to observers, including sometimes even in response to playback of the voice of Ferruginous Pygmy Owl *Glaucidium brasilianum* (Francisco *et al.* 2008a, Specht *et al.* 2008; GMK pers. obs.). The flight is laboured and undulating, but the bird never flies above the canopy or over open country, always keeping inside forest. Territories are reported to be large.

FOOD AND FEEDING The diet consists of a wide variety of fruit, both large and small, including palms, nutmegs (Myristicaceae), *Cecropia* (Urticaceae) and *Dendropanax* (Araliaceae), as well as Anacardiaceae, Aquifoliaceae, Arecaceae, Celastraceae, Lauraceae, Loranthaceae, Melastomataceae, Menispermaceae, Monimiaceae, Moraceae, Myrtaceae, Nyctaginaceae, Rubiaceae, Sapindaceae, Sapotaceae and Verbenaceae, as well as the Asian exotic tree *Eriobotrya japonica* (Rosaceae) (Schubart *et al.* 1965, Snow 1982, 2004a, Pizo *et al.* 2002, Ríos 2005, Fonseca and Antunes 2007). Red-ruffed Fruitcrow was one of four species of cotingas studied in Paraná, southern Brazil, by Clausi and Baarstch (2009), who found that fruit production and its effect on local movements of birds such as Cotingidae could be divided into six periods of the year. Fruit is taken either using a short-distance aerial sally or by lunging from a perch. In the Andes, these fruitcrows are sometimes recorded gathering at fruiting trees with Andean Cocks-of-the-Rock *Rupicola peruvianus* and various icterids (Hilty 2003), and loosely associating with Scaled Fruiteater *Ampelioides tschudii* and Olivaceous Piha *Snowornis cryptolophus*, as well as many other fruit-eating passerines (D. Beadle pers. obs.). However, young nestlings are mainly fed insects and their larvae, as well as small lizards, until they are *c.*10 days old (see below). Animal matter has also been recorded in the stomach contents of adults, including various beetles (Snow 1982) and even apparently the bones of a passerine bird (Rheinhardt 1870, Krabbe 2007), whilst there are several recent records of birds following army ant swarms in Colombia (Rios *et al.* 2008).

DISPLAY The rarely seen lek display comprises small groups of (up to 7–10) males perching close together up to *c.*6m above the ground (or in the canopy), from dawn until *c.*1–3 hours after sunrise (Olalla 1943, Snow 1982, Serrano 1994, Maurício and Dias 1998, Hilty 2003), and again in the late afternoon from *c.*2 hours before sunset (Olalla 1943; GMK pers. obs.). Lek behaviour has been observed for nominate *P. s. scutatus* (Olalla 1943, Specht *et al.* 2008), *P. s. orenocensis* (P. Schwartz *in* Snow 1982, Serrano 1994) and *P. s. occidentalis* (GMK pers. obs.). The birds (up to at least six at a lek in eastern Brazil) perch within 3m of one another and call whilst leaning forward, extending the throat feathers, which hang loosely down, before holding the body erect and flaring the bib laterally (by inflating the throat pouch), as

well as sometimes quivering the wings. Calling increases or is prompted by the arrival of other birds (of either sex) at the lek (Hilty 2003), and may continue for several minutes at a time. As soon as one bird calls, others swiftly join in. Males continually look down (perching horizontally, and speculated to be watching for females) as well as occasionally joining chases with one another (sometimes persisting some minutes and during which they perform circular flights), although because birds often chase individuals that are not their direct neighbours, Snow (1982) speculated that this reflected the well-established males' lack of tolerance of subordinate males. Calling can be continuous at such times, only pausing briefly when the birds fly (Specht *et al.* 2008). Wünschmann (1966) described courtship behaviour from observations of a pair of nominate *P. s. scutatus*. The male commenced by quivering the wings and bill-snapping, then sidling towards the female, whereupon he continued to quiver the half-open wings but also ruffled the other feathers, especially the throat feathers, then lowered the head and swung the inflated throat pouch to and fro. Finally, in culminating the ten-second-long display, the male drew himself bolt upright, still with half-open wings, and drew the head back to issue two booming notes through the closed bill, before making a short 'bowing' movement and deflating the throat feathers.

BREEDING Data from the Central Andes of Colombia suggest that laying occurs in March–July, peaking in April–May, and all but one of the described nests are also from northwest South America, all of them found by T. K. Salmon in the 1870s, V. H. Serrano in the final part of the 20th century and, most recently, Muir *et al.* (2008). The nest is a flimsy shallow-cup (and pigeon-sized) structure, the base of which is constructed of twigs and the rest of the outer walls are of a fern (*Nephrolepis*, Lomariopsidaceae), and is sited 5–8m up on a slender tree branch. The clutch is apparently just one egg in *P. s. granadensis* (pale buff with reddish-brown and lilac spots and blotches) (Serrano 1994, Muir *et al.* 2008) and apparently *P. s. orenocensis* (yellowish-grey with brownish markings) (Nehrkorn *in* Ihering 1900). However, Salmon's notes already suggested that more than one egg is laid, and elsewhere, for nominate *P. s. scutatus*, this was recently confirmed from observations at a nest in southeast Brazil (Francisco *et al.* 2008a). It might be mentioned that Euler (1900) recounted that Wied had already mentioned that Red-ruffed Fruitcrow lays two eggs, at least in eastern Brazil, in the first quarter of the 19th century. Muir *et al.* (2008) reported on eight nests discovered between 2003 and 2007 in Yacambú National Park, in the state of Lara, Venezuela. All of them were near streams in steep drainages. The average incubation period at three of these nests was 22.3 days and nest attentiveness during this period averaged 76.3 ± 1.86% and increased only slightly across stages (early, middle, late). On-bout and off-bout durations were relatively similar across incubation stages. A nestling period of 35 days was recorded at one nest and feather pin-break was estimated to occur at day 19. Brooding attentiveness during the early nestling period averaged 62.5 ± 6.41%, and the adult ceased brooding at about feather pin-break. Food was delivered at increasing rates with nestling age and consisted mostly of insects (66.7%) and lizards (25%) with fruit comprising just 8.3% of the nestling diet during the early stages. Provisioning changed to mostly fruit (82.4%) and some insects (17.6%) in the later stages of the nestling's growth. The Brazilian nest was discovered in late November and contained two nestlings of a similar size and both with their primary pin-feathers just visible. The nest was constructed on a horizontal fork of an Euphorbiaceae within tall primary forest, 16.7m above the ground (being well concealed in the tree crown), and was cup-shaped with a substantial base of twigs; the nest dimensions were presented in the paper. The nestlings were thickly covered with brownish down, with a pinkish throat and yellow gape and bill (see photograph in Francisco *et al.* 2008a). Only one adult (not sexed) visited the nest; details of these visits and strategy were presented by Francisco *et al.* (2008a) – the adult brought large insects on more than one-third of feeding visits, but evidence of regurgitated fruits, especially *Euterpe edulis* (Arecaceae), was found at the nest. Regular observations of an adult entering the same forest patch, sometimes with food, in November 2008 at Parque Estadual Intervales, São Paulo, indicated the presence of an undiscovered nest (G. T. Rodrigues pers. comm. to GMK). Potential predators as large as raptors are chased from the vicinity of the nest (Serrano 1994), as well as other Red-ruffed Fruitcrows (Francisco *et al.* 2008a). The incubation period is unknown, but the chick takes 30–35 days to fledge (Snow 2004a). Measurements of two eggs were presented by Snow (1982). Elsewhere, the species is reported to nest at the end of the wet season in the Coastal Cordillera of Venezuela (Schaefer and Phelps 1954) and there was a nest, reported without details, at San Isidro, Barinas, western Venezuela, in February 1995 (Merrill 1995). A female has been taken in breeding condition in mid September in southern Brazil (Belton 1985).

STATUS Red-ruffed Fruitcrow was treated as Least Concern (BirdLife International 2004, 2008), although Stotz *et al.* (1996) considered that both nominate *P. s. scutatus* and *P. s. granadensis* are in decline, as a result of deforestation and hunting, and the former is considered threatened at state level in several parts of southeast Brazil, namely Rio Grande do Sul (where it is considered to be Critically Endangered), São Paulo, Minas Gerais and Rio de Janeiro. For instance, in Rio de Janeiro state, nominate *P. s. scutatus* is now known solely from Itatiaia National Park, Ilha Grande and Reserva Ecológica de Guapiaçu (REGUA), having apparently become extinct elsewhere in the state, e.g. in most of the Serra dos Órgãos (Mallet-Rodrigues *et al.* 2007). Habitat fragmentation elsewhere in southeast Brazil has also led to local extinctions, including almost certainly in the municipality of Rio de Janeiro (cf. Willis 1979, Ribon *et al.* 2003, Maciel 2009). However, in some regions of eastern Brazil, e.g. in parts of Minas Gerais, the species seems to be making a 'comeback' with appropriate reforestation efforts (Cunha and Specht 2009), although it is still considered threatened with extinction in the state. Given the species' at least local dependence on *Euterpe edulis* (Arecaceae) fruiting events (in the Atlantic Forest), the extraction of these trees by the palm heart industry is a significant cause for concern (cf. Galetti *et al.* 1999, Francisco *et al.* 2008a). Other subspecies are at risk too, at least locally. For instance,

the race *P. s. occidentalis* has become regionally extinct in the environs of Santa Elena, Antioquia, Colombia (Castaño-Villa and Patiño-Zabala 2008). The species is considered Data Deficient in Ecuador, from where only two sightings have been published since 1972 (Ridgely and Greenfield 2001), and *Pyroderus* is generally considered to be uncommon to rare, and always local, but is known from quite a number of protected areas across its wide range. These include Sierra Nevada and Yacambú National Parks (Venezuela), Ucumarí Regional Park (Colombia), Araucaria and Cruce Caballero Provincial Parks, and Iguazú National Park (Argentina), and Serra do Mar State Park, Carlos Botelho State Park, Rio Doce State Park, Serra da Canastra National Park, Itatiaia National Park and Sooretama Biological Reserve (Brazil). In Argentina, Red-ruffed Fruitcrow is regularly seen within the private reserve established at Posada Puerto Bemberg, Misiones (Lowen 2010). In Venezuela, it is considered to be declining especially in the Coastal Cordillera and parts of northeast Bolívar, as a result of forest clearance (Hilty 2003). The subspecies *P. s. occidentalis* is endemic to the North Andean Centre of endemism, whilst nominate *P. s. scutatus* is endemic to the expanded Serra do Mar Centre of endemism (Cracraft 1985).

REFERENCES Alves and Vecchi (2009), Andrade (1996), Belton (1985), Bernardi *et al.* (2007), BirdLife International (2004, 2008), Bodrati *et al.* (2010), Boesman (2009), Boesing *et al.* (2007), Braun *et al.* (2007), Castaño-Villa and Patiño-Zabala (2008), Chebez *et al.* (1999), Clausi and Baarstch (2009), Cracraft (1985), Cuervo *et al.* (2008b), Cunha and Specht (2009), Euler (1900), Faetti *et al.* (2009), Faria *et al.* (2006), Fjeldså and Krabbe (1990), Fonseca and Antunes (2007), Francisco *et al.* (2008a), Galetti *et al.* (1999), Gonzaga *et al.* (1995), Hayes (1995), Hellmayr (1929b), Hilty (2003), Hilty and Brown (1986), Ihering (1900), Kaminski and Carrano (2004), Krabbe (2007), Krauczuk and Baldo (2001), Lau (2004), Lowen (2010), Luiz *et al.* (2004a), Macarrão (2009), Macedo and Carrano (2009), Maciel (2009), Mallet-Rodrigues *et al.* (2007), Maurício and Dias (1998), Mazar Barnett and Pearman (2001), Melo Júnior *et al.* (2001), Merrill (1995), Minns *et al.* (2009), Muir *et al.* (2008), Ohlson *et al.* (2007, 2008), Olalla (1943), Olson (1970, 1971), Ohlson *et al.* (2007), Parrini *et al.* (1999), Patrial *et al.* (2009), Pichorim *et al.* (2000), Pimentel and Olmos (2011), Pinto (1944), Pizo *et al.* (2002), Remold (2002), Restall *et al.* (2006), Rheinhardt (1870), Ribon *et al.* (2003), Ridgely and Greenfield (2001), Ridgely and Tudor (1994, 2009), Ríos (2005), Rios *et al.* (2008), Schaefer and Phelps (1954), Schubart *et al.* (1965), Schulenberg *et al.* (2007), Sclater and Salvin (1879), Serrano (1994), Sibley (1996), Sick (1997), Silva (1995), Simon (2009), Snow (1976a, 1982, 2004a), Snyder (1966), Specht *et al.* (2008), Stotz *et al.* (1996), Tello *et al.* (2009), Vasconcelos (1998), Vasconcelos and D'Angelo Neto (2009), Vasconcelos and Roos (2000), Vasconcelos *et al.* (2002), Willis (1979), Willis and Oniki (2002), Wünschmann (1966), J. T. Zimmer (1936c).

Red-ruffed Fruitcrow *Pyroderus scutatus*. **Fig. 1**. Male, *P. s. occidentalis*, La Suiza, Santuario de Fauna y Flora Otún Quimbaya, dpto. Risaralda, western Colombia, February (*Pete Morris*). Note the very extensively red underparts. The sexes are poorly differentiated in this species, but this bird appears to have a bluish-grey rather than dusky-coloured bill. **Fig. 2**. Female, *P. s. occidentalis*, La Suiza, Santuario de Fauna y Flora Otún Quimbaya, dpto. Risaralda, western Colombia, February (*Hadoram Shirihai / Photographic Handbook to Birds of the World*). Based on bill colour, this appears to be a female. **Fig. 3**. Male, *P. s. scutatus*, RPPN Caraça, Minas Gerais, southeast Brazil, November (*Hadoram Shirihai / Photographic Handbook to Birds of the World*). Note the scattered pale red feathers on the breast and belly below the ruff. Bill colour again suggests that this bird is a male. **Fig. 4**. Female, *P. s. masoni*, Afluente, below Abra Patricia, dpto. San Martín, northern Peru, November (*Hadoram Shirihai / Photographic Handbook to Birds of the World*). Note the largely dark underparts, which characterise this subspecies. The bill appears generally dark, suggesting that the bird is a female.

Genus *Cephalopterus*: umbrellabirds

The umbrellabirds comprise a superspecies (Snow 1979a, Haffer 1986, Sibley and Monroe 1990) of spectacular and unique cotingas that are found in primary forests of southern Central and western and central South America. The adjective spectacular is well deserved for their large size (consistently the largest of any of the cotingas), the fancy plumage adornments of the males and the bellowing vocalisations which form an important component of the males' lekking behaviour. The three species (lumped as just one by Hellmayr 1929b, but not by Ridgway 1907) comprise two restricted-range 'trans-Andean' representatives, Bare-necked *C. glabricollis* and Long-wattled Umbrellabirds *C. penduliger* and a single, much more widespread 'cis-Andean' species, Amazonian Umbrellabird *C. ornatus*. They are mainly fruit-eaters, but will also take a range of invertebrates. In common with many other fruit-eating species, males are emancipated from breeding duties and gather in exploded leks where they display in an effort to attract a female. The two restricted-range species are highly threatened due to ongoing habitat loss, hunting and capture for the cagebird trade, but the lowland populations of Amazonian Umbrellabird are presumably relatively secure, at least for now, in the vastness of their Amazon forests.

AMAZONIAN UMBRELLABIRD
Cephalopterus ornatus   Plate 29

Cephalopterus ornatus **Geoffroy Saint-Hilaire, 1809**, *Ann. Mus. Hist. Nat. Paris* 13: 238, pl. 15, [Barcelos, Rio Negro,] Brazil

The most widespread and least threatened of the genus *Cephalopterus*, the handsome Amazonian Umbrellabird is nonetheless usually rather uncommon over much of its wide range, only very locally appearing in reasonable numbers.

IDENTIFICATION 45–51cm (male), 38–43cm (female) (however, Brooks *et al.* 1999 found that males are rarely more than 10% larger than females). This crow-like (*Corvus*) species is amongst the largest of all modern passerines. The male Amazonian Umbrellabird appears glossy black in the field, with white shafts to the bizarre crest feathers and a long pendulous feathered wattle dangling from the lower throat. The irides are silvery white. There is no sympatric umbrellabird: Bare-necked *Cephalopterus glabricollis* frequents the cloud forests of the Caribbean slope of Costa Rica and Panama, whilst the other South American species, Long-wattled *Cephalopterus penduliger*, is a rare inhabitant of the west slope of the Andes in Colombia and Ecuador. Female Amazonian Umbrellabird is less ornate, with only a vestigial crest and wattle. In Amazonia it might therefore be confused with another cotingid, the generally commoner Purple-throated Fruitcrow *Querula purpurata*, the male of which has a deep crimson-purple throat patch, but this can appear much subdued within the dim light of its primary forest haunts; thus, both sexes can appear all black. However, these fruitcrows are considerably more sociable than umbrellabirds, being often found in noisy parties, whereas Amazonian Umbrellabirds usually occur alone (although small groups gather at lek sites). The 'staring' pale iris and large size of either sex of the Amazonian Umbrellabird should seal the identification. Female Bare-necked Fruitcrow *Gymnoderus foetidus*, another widespread Amazonian species, is also an essentially all-black cotingid, but this species' rather vulturine shape should enable swift diagnosis, it having a small head on a long, thin neck, and long wings and a long tail. In northern and central Peru (where a relatively poorly known foothill population of Amazonian Umbrellabird occurs on the lower eastern slope of the Andes), the Red-ruffed Fruitcrow *Pyroderus scutatus* may occur down to about 1,200m. Confusion between the

two could arise, but the flame-red bib of the fruitcrow is usually visible, even in flight.

DISTRIBUTION Amazonian Umbrellabird is found virtually throughout the Amazon Basin, although it is absent from parts of lower Amazonia. The species is found from the upper Amazonian lowlands in southwest Guyana (where known solely from the Rupununi Savanna and from an 1840s specimen obtained in the Kanuku Mts), widely in southern Venezuela (in Amazonas, north to the Orinoco drainage), southeastern Colombia (known north to dpto. Vichada, but principally recorded from western dpto. Boyacá, western dpto. Meta and dpto. Vaupés southwards), eastern Ecuador and eastern Peru (in Peru it is mainly a bird of the eastern foothills, being distinctly uncommon in central and southern Amazonia, but commoner in the northeast), south to northern Bolivia (where recorded south and east as far as western dpto. Santa Cruz), and across much of Amazonian Brazil, as far east as the drainages of the Rio Negro, Rio Xingu and locally the Rio Araguaia in northernmost Tocantins (Hidasi 1998), and south as far as southern Mato Grosso, in the headwaters of the Rio Paraguai and the northernmost Pantanal. However, it was not until the 1950s that its distribution across the Brazilian Amazon started to become known (Pinto and Camargo 1957). Apparently rare in the Rio Negro basin, where only recently recorded in the well-inventoried Jaú National

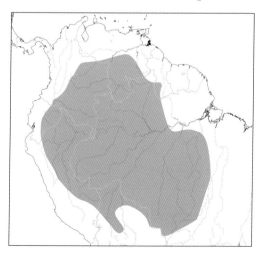

Park, Amazonas, Brazil (Almeida 2008). It occurs locally into the foothills at the western extremities of the Basin, from Colombia south to Cochabamba, Bolivia. Recorded to at least 1,800m in Bolivia (Hennessey 2004b, Macleod *et al.* 2005), but it is mostly found below 300m (below 200m in Venezuela), locally elsewhere at 600–1,650m along the base of the Andes (e.g. Brooks *et al.* 2009).

MOVEMENTS None recorded, although there is an old record from the Ilha Mexiana, the outermost island of those in the mouth of the Amazon (i.e. well outside the modern-day known range), which remains unexplained (Hagmann 1907).

HABITAT Amazonian Umbrellabird favours two distinct habitats through its vast range. In Amazonia, it occurs in *terra firme* forest along rivers, including white-sand and swampy areas, but mainly in *várzea* forests (especially on old river islands) of the Orinoco and Amazon drainages. It is most frequently found at forest borders. Very locally recorded in semi-deciduous dry forest, e.g. in the central Río Tuichi, of La Paz, Bolivia (Perry *et al.* 1997), in an area where a number of other species not usually recorded in such habitat also occur. Secondly, the species inhabits humid foothill and submontane cloud forests, including tall second growth, again often along rivers, in the eastern Andes.

DESCRIPTION The largest passerine found in the Neotropics. The sexes are similar, except in feather adornments. Bill powerful and crow-like in both sexes with well-developed rictal bristles and elongated nostrils. The wing feathers lack any modification. *Adult male.* – Huge *Corvus*-like passerine, with a heavy bill and sturdy legs and feet, as well as extraordinary feather ornamentation consisting of a large umbrella-like crest (the feathers upstanding and curling outwards) and a pendulous, densely feathered and quite broad wattle (up to 14–16cm, but more usually to 10cm), which hangs close to the body (from the lower throat). Plumage appears entirely black (with a slight bluish gloss), apart from the whitish shafts to the feathers of the forehead, at the base of the crest (which are especially conspicuous in display). In bright sunlight, there is a navy-blue sheen produced by the broad dark blue fringes to the black feathers of the nape, mantle, scapulars and wattle, whilst the remiges are brownish-black, becoming browner distally on the wing; the tail is black (and appears rather short in flight) and the underwing brown. *Adult female.* – Less spectacular than the male, being slightly smaller with a less powerful bill, a rather 'bushy' and more pointed crest of loose, erectile feathers (without the white shafts of the male) and a vestigial wattle. The plumage is mainly black; bluish sheen produced by the feather fringes as in male, on the mantle, throat and wattle. Belly browner than the rest of the underparts; the underwing is brown. *Immature/Juvenile.* – Very poorly known, but appears to pass through at least one stage prior to achieving full adult plumage; juvenile plumage appears to be entirely dull black (nestling down is also black) and female-like (Snow 1982, 2004a). *Moult.* – Published moult data are very scarce, but Snow (1976a) considered feather replacement in all *Cephalopterus* to be extremely protracted, lasting *c.*300 days, making it more difficult to detect any seasonal bias to its onset. Furthermore, given that females are responsible for nesting duties, it will surely be the case (as in many other cotingas) that they commence moult later than males. *Bare parts.* – Bill and strong legs and feet black to very dark plumbeous grey (e.g. on the lower mandible). Irides pale blue-grey, appearing almost white in the field.

MEASUREMENTS (from Pinto and Camargo 1957, Snow 1982, 2004, Graves and Zusi 1990) Wing of male ($n = 15$) 268–295mm, wing of female ($n = 9$) 216–250mm; tail of male ($n = 15$) 165–192mm, tail of female ($n = 9$) 144–156mm; bill of male ($n = 15$) 44–52mm, bill of female ($n = 9$) 41–44mm; tarsus of male ($n = 15$) 50–54mm, tarsus of female ($n = 9$) 41.5–47.0mm. Pinto and Camargo (1957) mentioned an apparently adult male from Colombia that seems unusually small in having the wing 243mm, tail 133mm, culmen 36mm and tarsus 55mm. Brooks *et al.* (1999) found that males average larger in wing-chord and tail-length. Weight: 705g (one male) and 370–440g (four females) (Bates *et al.* 1989, Graves and Zusi 1990, Snow 2004a; FMNH), whilst Brooks *et al.* (1999) listed mean mass as 571g and considered that males can be over 60% heavier than females, on average.

GEOGRAPHICAL VARIATION Monotypic.

VOICE The advertising call is typical of the genus: a deep, far-carrying, moaning 'boom', like someone blowing across a bottle top or distant cattle bellowing, which is quite easily imitated, to attract a male into view. Both sexes give a number of deep, but not loud, churring or growling notes, and the female alone utters a succession of disyllabic *goh-ahh, go-uh* calls, wherein the second syllable appears slightly more prolonged. Published recordings are available on the following compilations: Moore (1994), Mayer (2000), Krabbe and Nilsson (2003), Lysinger *et al.* (2005) and Boesman (2009), and there is also a recording from east Amazonian Brazil archived online at www.xeno-canto.org.

NATURAL HISTORY A shy, retiring but sometimes inquisitive bird found in the canopy and subcanopy of tropical forest, where it usually perches in a rather concealed position, more rarely and typically only briefly on an open branch. However, GMK (pers. obs.) found a subadult male using the crown of an almost leafless tree as a songpost over three consecutive mornings in November 2007 at Podocarpus National Park; perhaps surprisingly the same tree was also utilised by the species in January 1992. Once a pair of Plumbeous Kites *Ictinia plumbea* perched in the same tree, and were observed with some 'curiosity' but at a distance of *c.*2m by the umbrellabird, which circled the kites with 'cautious interest'. Locomotion is via springing or jumping (rather toucan-like) movements through the trees, and the flight is somewhat woodpecker-like, with deep wingbeats, and during which the crest is laid back flat and the wings appear very broad. It may fly over quite long distances, occasionally at some distance above the ground. Except at leks, Amazonian Umbrellabird usually occurs alone or, very occasionally, in pairs or small groups (up to 8+).

FOOD AND FEEDING It feeds on fruits and large insects, caterpillars and even *Anolis* lizards (up to 13cm long), all usually taken in brief flight (T. A. Parker *in* Snow 1982). Animal prey is first beaten against a perch before being consumed. Orthopterans and beetles are usually seized from the foliage and branches, whilst fruit diet is known to comprise *Cecropia* (Urticaceae), palms (speculated to be the most important component) and *Byrsonima* (Malpighiaceae).

DISPLAY Males display in loose, well-spread groups of 2–5 (typically three within earshot), situated 10–25m above the ground, leaning forward to sing, with the wattle expanded and the crest fully spread. Calling commences at dawn and may continue throughout the morning, before starting up again shortly before dusk. The males may also engage in ritualised chasing.

BREEDING Females probably largely consort with males only for mating, and they take sole responsibility for all nesting duties. In Colombia, a male and female in breeding condition were taken in March (Hilty and Brown 1986); a juvenile collected in Bolivia in the third week of March indicates January laying (Snow 1982), and Sick (1954) suggested that the species might also breed in December in the upper Rio Xingu region, where he had found a nest in July. GMK observed a female carrying material (sticks) to an unseen nest at Junglaven, southern Venezuela, in late December 2006, and K. J. Zimmer watched a pair carrying nest material south of Puerto Ayacucho, also in Amazonas, Venezuela, at the end of February 1994 (Zimmer and Hilty 1997). M. A. Elwonger *et al.* (unpubl.) also observed a bird carrying sticks just below San Pedro, Manu, southeast Peru, in early August 1995. Just three nests recorded to date (Sick 1951, Snow 1982, Greeney and Sheldon 2008): in Cuzco, southeast Peru (building in October), Mato Grosso, southeast Amazonian Brazil (egg laid in mid July), and Napo, eastern Ecuador (single egg in late October). The nest is a very open structure of twigs in which the egg may be practically visible from below, held together in at least one instance by a film of white fungus, and sited 3.8, 8.0 and 12.0m above the ground in the crown of comparatively low trees. At the nest in Peru, T. A. Parker observed the female collecting nesting material from the ground. The Ecuadorian nest was placed above a dirt road. The clutch is one egg, which is khaki-coloured with blotches of brown, lavender, purple and black, and black squiggles, concentrated at the larger end. To date, it has not been possible to follow a nest to completion of the breeding process, so there is no information on incubation or fledging periods, but Sick (1997) speculated that Amazonian Umbrellabird might breed twice per year. The only other mention of the nest of this species is that by Burmeister (1856 *in* Euler 1900), who stated that Amazonian Umbrellabird constructed a nest of dry sticks high in tall trees. However, his statement that *C. ornatus* lays two eggs is at variance with all subsequent data, and it is unclear from where Burmeister could have gathered any experience with this species.

STATUS Treated as Least Concern (BirdLife International 2004, 2008). Amazonian populations are presumably safe in the vastness of lowland Amazonia, but Andean foothill populations have been reduced by habitat loss, as their altitudinal range corresponds with that most threatened by agricultural colonisation, although locally the species is protected within reserves, such as Podocarpus National Park in Ecuador, at such elevations. Generally scarce to rare over much of its range, e.g. in the upper drainage of the Río Madre de Dios, Peru (Servat and Pearson 1991) but locally the species can be uncommon to locally fairly common, e.g. around Junglaven, southern Venezuela (Zimmer and Hilty 1997) and in the Anavilhanas archipelago, Amazonas, Brazil (Cintra *et al.* 2007). Known from many protected areas, in virtually all range states except Guyana.

REFERENCES Almeida (2008), Balchin and Toyne (1998), Bates *et al.* (1989), BirdLife International (2004, 2008), Boesman (2009), Braun *et al.* (2007), Brooks *et al.* (1999, 2009), Cadena *et al.* (2000), Chapman (1921), Cherrie (1916), Cintra *et al.* (2007), Delacour (1945), Euler (1900), Graves and Zusi (1990), Greeney and Sheldon (2008), Gyldenstolpe (1951), Hagmann (1907), Hellmayr (1910, 1929b), Hennessey (2004b), Hennessey *et al.* (2003a, 2003b), Hidasi (1998), Hilty (2003), Hilty and Brown (1986), Hornbuckle (1998), Krabbe and Nilsson (2003), Lane *et al.* (2003), Lysinger *et al.* (2005), MacLeod *et al.* (2005), Mayer (2000), Merkord *et al.* (2009), Moore (1994), Naka *et al.* (2006), Novaes (1960, 1976), Olson (1971), Pacheco and Olmos (2005), Parker and Parker (1982), Parker and Wust (1994), Peres and Whittaker (1991), Perry *et al.* (1997), Pinto (1944, 1966), Pinto and Camargo (1957), Remsen and Traylor (1989), Remsen *et al.* (1987), Restall *et al.* (2006), Ridgely and Greenfield (2001), Ridgely and Tudor (1994, 2009), Robbins *et al.* (2004, 2011), Rosenberg (1990), Salaman *et al.* (1999, 2008), Schulenberg *et al.* (2007), Servat and Pearson (1991), Sick (1951, 1954, 1955, 1997), Silva (1996), Snow (1976a, 1982, 2004a), Snyder (1966), Solano-Ugalde and Freile (2010), Stotz *et al.* (1996), Tubelis and Tomas (2003), Vidoz *et al.* (2010), Zimmer and Hilty (1997), Zimmer *et al.* (1997).

Amazonian Umbrellabird *Cephalopterus ornatus.* **Fig. 1**. Male, Río Bombuscaro, Podocarpus National Park, prov. Zamora-Chinchipe, southeast Ecuador, November (*Hadoram Shirihai / Photographic Handbook to Birds of the World*). Note the white barbs to the forehead feathers, which identify this bird to sex. This male regularly sang from the same leafless tree each morning. Given the its vernacular name, it is perhaps surprising that the species is generally most abundant in the Andean foothills of the east slope. **Fig. 2**. Female, Yanachaga-Chemillén National Park, dpto. Pasco, Peru, October (*Leif Gabrielsen*). Both sexes possess a large crow-like bill and upstanding crest.

LONG-WATTLED UMBRELLABIRD
Cephalopterus penduliger   Plate 29

Cephalopterus penduliger **P. L. Sclater, 1859**, *Ibis* 1: 114, pl. 3, Pallatanga, Chimborazo, Ecuador

It has been speculated that this species forms a superspecies with the next (Snow 1982), and these two species are certainly the most decidedly ornate of the three umbrellabirds, although Hellmayr (1929b) chose to treat all three umbrellabirds as conspecifics. Long-wattled Umbrellabird was long considered a very poorly known bird, but in recent years a great deal of new information on this globally threatened bird's natural history has been published. The species is perhaps one of the most charismatic endemics of the Chocó Rainforest Centre of endemism (Cracraft 1985).

IDENTIFICATION 41cm (male) or 36cm (female). The male is immediately recognisable as an umbrellabird and is arguably the most bizarre of all the *Cephalopterus*: the crest forms almost a complete 'umbrella' and is full and bushy, virtually entirely covering the bill, whilst the bird's extensible wattle reaches up to 35cm long, and usually hangs well below the perch. Unlike the Amazonian Umbrellabird *Cephalopterus ornatus* (which occurs exclusively east of the Andes), the irides are brown and the underwing-coverts whitish. The female resembles the female Amazonian Umbrellabird, but lacks the white irides of the latter species, whilst the vestigial wattle and uniform blackish throat separate it from Red-ruffed Fruitcrow *Pyroderus scutatus*, of the foothills, and from the Purple-throated Fruitcrow *Querula purpurata* at lower altitudes.

DISTRIBUTION Trans-Andean, being largely confined to the very humid Chocó forests of southwest Colombia (north as far as the Río San Juan) and western Ecuador, although it does occasionally utilise and even nest in tall second growth, and adjacent traditional farmland, provided this lies within a mosaic of forest. In Colombia, it has been recorded from the Pacific slope in the departments of Valle del Cauca, Cauca and Nariño. In Ecuador, *C. penduliger* is known from sites along virtually the entire length of the western slope of the Andes, south to El Oro, but is only frequently recorded in Esmeraldas and Pichincha provinces, and even here the species is apparently very local with many apparently suitable forests at appropriate elevations seemingly unoccupied. The

species is mainly recorded at 500–1,400m, but it is known to occur as low as 80m in Esmeraldas, in extreme northeast Ecuador (with leks recorded at such low altitudes), and Long-wattled Umbrellabird is also locally found to 1,800m in the same country.

MOVEMENTS Previously speculated to undertake nomadic or regular altitudinal migrations, but this theory now seems redundant in light of the discovery of resident populations at low and higher altitudes.

HABITAT Very much a bird of the wet humid forests of the western Andes, including their borders, particularly the moss- and epiphyte-covered 'cloud forests' which typically have a dense understorey (see also Distribution).

DESCRIPTION Sexes similar, except in their feather adornments and the female is smaller than the male. In common with the previous species, Long-wattled Umbrellabird is rather corvid-like. The wattle (of up to 35cm), which dangles from the lower throat, is normally retracted and held close to the body in flight. When perched the bird's wattle can be retracted or extended at will, typically in stages. The bill is powerful and crow-like in both sexes with well-developed rictal bristles and elongated nostrils. Like Amazonian Umbrellabird the wing feathers lack any modification. *Adult male.* – The umbrella-like crest is bluish-black, lacking any white at the base of the frontal feather shafts; the feathers curl outwards and may be lowered to completely obscure the bill or be held straight up, but are usually laid back in flight, as in Amazonian Umbrellabird. The body plumage appears generally black in the field, but a dark blue wash may be apparent at close quarters in particularly favourable conditions, due to the navy-blue fringes to the feathers of the mantle and the densely feathered wattle (but this bluish cast is less obvious than that in Amazonian Umbrellabird). Remiges blackish-brown and outer primaries dark brown. Underwing-coverts whitish and the underside of the remiges is pale brown to pale grey. *Adult female.* – Smaller than the male, with only a vestigial crest and wattle (the latter can be almost entirely lacking). Most of the body plumage is washed glossy navy-blue, as in the male, but, conversely, the belly and remiges are noticeably browner. Underwing-coverts are whitish, contrasting with the rest of the pale brown underwing. *Immature.* – Very poorly known, but appears to pass through at least one stage prior to achieving full adult plumage; however, juvenile plumage is undescribed to date (Snow 2004a). The crest and the wattle both vary in relation to age (being up to four times larger in males than females) and condition, as well as female visitation rate at leks, suggesting that some sexual selection is involved (Karubian and Smith 2007a, Tori *et al.* 2008). See Karubian *et al.* (2003) for a description of the nestling. Hartert (1898) mentioned two (presumably still very) young males with wattles just *c.*25mm long. *Moult.* – Published moult data are very scarce, but Snow (1976a) considered feather replacement in all *Cephalopterus* to be extremely protracted, lasting *c.*300 days, making it more difficult to detect any seasonal bias to its onset. Furthermore, given that females are entirely responsible for nesting duties and parental care of the young, it is surely the case that they commence moult later than males (as in many other cotingas). *Bare parts.* – Relatively massive bill black with a slate-grey or rather bluish or greenish-blue base to lower mandible; blackish or plumbeous-grey legs with dark grey feet, deep brown claws and pale brown soles; irides dark brown (cf. Hartert 1898).

MEASUREMENTS (from Snow 1982) Wing of male (n = 5) 249–259mm; wing of female (n = 3) 226–240mm; tail of male (n = 5) 125–133mm, tail of female (n = 3) 121–127mm, bill of male (n = 5) 47–49mm, bill of female (n = 3) 37.5–44.0mm; tarsus of male (n = 5) 40–43mm, tarsus of female (n = 3) 44–47mm. Males are up to 1.5 times larger than females (Tori *et al.* 2008). Weight: 338g (one male) (Snow 2004b).

GEOGRAPHICAL VARIATION Monotypic.

VOICE The voice and display of this species were intially described by Goodfellow (1901): the male's advertising call is a low but loud, resonant *boooh*, somewhat reminiscent of a distant short foghorn, given at intervals ranging from 19 seconds to over one minute, and is audible over almost half a kilometre (Jahn *et al.* 1999), sometimes preceded by a much higher pitched and very quiet, upslurred scratchy buzzing immediately prior to the boom (A. Spencer recording XC17556). In giving this vocalisation, males assume an almost horizontal position on the perch, with the crest almost fully erect and the wattle pointed downwards, fully inflated and extended (Berg 2000). Both sexes give low grunting calls, rendered *gr, gr, grah* by Berg (2000), which are easily overlooked, but given frequently (every 3–4 minutes) whilst foraging, especially by females. The female is also known to give an *aaugh* call, perhaps in alarm. Females vocalise all year, but in extreme northeast Ecuador males appear to be most vocal in May–October (Berg 2000), although leks are active year-round (Jahn *et al.* 1999). As in Amazonian Umbrellabird, calling at leks commences very soon after dawn and continues until late morning (perhaps peaking in mid morning), and starts again approximately one hour prior to sunset (Jahn *et al.* 1999). Long-wattled Umbrellabird can respond to playback by closely approaching the source of the sound. Recordings have been published on the following compilations: Jahn *et al.* (2002) and Krabbe and Nilsson (2003), and are also available online at www.xeno-canto.org.

NATURAL HISTORY Can be spectacularly difficult to see due to its retiring habits and the (at least former) difficulties of accessing its habitat. The species occurs alone, in pairs or in small groups of 3–5 birds.

FOOD AND FEEDING Like other large cotingids, it is well worth while for observers to carefully scrutinise flocks of large fruit-eating birds such as toucans *Ramphastos* and araçaris *Pteroglossus*, for any umbrellabirds which may be loosely associating with them (Berg 2000), taking large fruits either in a brief swooping, then hovering flight (recalling that of a trogon), or from a perch. Long-wattled Umbrellabird sometimes feeds rather close above the ground (more usually at 10–20m). The diet is heavily biased towards palm fruits, e.g. *Bacteris* (Arecaceae), as well as those of nutmeg (Myristicaceae), laurels (Lauraceae) and Meliaceae, although insects (including butterflies) are occasionally taken, at least; indeed, the nestling found in June in northwest Ecuador was fed chiefly small vertebrates such as lizards, but also a frog and a small snake, as well as large insects and perhaps fruit. A female at a nest in southwest Ecuador was periodically observed to eat leaves that fell on the nest (Greeney *et al.* 2006). The species is probably an important disperser of large-seeded fruits within its restricted range, but it seems to be females that disperse seeds more randomly and over wider areas because males have much smaller core usage areas centred on the leks, although both sexes possess home ranges of *c.*50ha

(Karubian and Smith 2007b). Tori *et al.* (2008) found that males consume more fruit than females, and that male fruit consumption during low lek activity periods was *c.*50% of that during high lek activity periods.

DISPLAY The best chance of seeing a Long-wattled Umbrellabird is at one of its traditional 'exploded' leks, which usually number 5–10 (occasionally up to 15) males that usually maintain up to 50m distance between individuals, but sometimes just 10m (GMK pers. obs.), and which typically perch in the forest midstorey. Well-known lek sites in Ecuador include that at Tinalandia 'moss forest', Buenaventura, near Piñas, and the forest adjacent to the railway line between Ibarra and San Lorenzo, with more recently discovered (post-1994) leks at San Miguel de los Bancos, in subtropical forest near Mindo, and near Jatun Sacha Bilsa Biological Reserve, Esmeraldas. Leks are most active in the dry season, between August and December (Karubian and Smith 2007a), although some males are always present (Tori *et al.* 2008). Many leks contain both strictly territorial and apparently 'floating' males (Tori *et al.* 2008). It has been speculated that the 'floating' males might be younger, competitively inferior males moving in response to spatial and temporal variation in fruit availability, whilst territorial males depart and return to their leks in unison and forage in groups away from their leks (Tori *et al.* 2008). The male's display recalls that of the Amazonian Umbrellabird, as it stretches forward ('bowing'), sometimes maintaining this position for up to one minute, expands the wattle and calls. The display commences with the bird leaning forward, drooping and marginally flexing the wings, spreading and slightly cocking the tail, at the same time as the head is pushed upwards; the sequence is then usually repeated but virtually all of the individual movements are exaggerated in this second part, before the bird dips the body and head forward on the perch and calls. During the second movement, the wattle is also slightly raised, exposing the pale pink throat sacs. The massive, coiffeured-like crest completely covers the bill and almost touches the base of the wattle during the calling phase, and sometimes appears to be slightly split into two at the front. (The crest is extended for display in a single easy movement like closing the cover on a convertible!) The wattle at this point can appear slightly kinked, but is greatly expanded outwards over the lower two-thirds, which part looks somewhat like a feather duster. The bird then either relaxes or vigorously shakes the head and wattle. During more low-intensity calling, the wattle visibly relaxes, very slowly returning to its usual shape, whereas in high-intensity displays the wattle's tip inflates and deflates much more rapidly. Up to three or four complete displays may be given in the course of *c.*1 minute, but usually less. Also performs wing-claps at leks (Jahn *et al.* 2002) and seeks to displace rival males from their perches (Jahn *et al.* 1999, Berg 2000). Display and lek behaviour is described in most detail by Jahn *et al.* (1999). Pairs are regularly seen away from leks, but females were originally reported to rarely visit them (Ridgely and Tudor 1994); however, radio-tracking has revealed that both sexes may visit multiple leks during the course of a single breeding season, and that males frequently depart and arrive at these sites together (see above), suggesting that they also form places for 'information exchange' (Karubian and Smith 2007a). Long-wattled Umbrellabirds appear to be highly faithful to their territories (Berg 2000).

BREEDING Until recently, only one certain nesting record had been detailed in the literature (Snow 1982 noted that old descriptions of nests in tree holes must be considered deeply suspect, whilst none of the three nests thought to be active in February–April, reported by Berg 2000, could be confirmed), but subsequently breeding biology has been well studied in southwest Ecuador (Greeney *et al.* 2006, in press). Karubian *et al.* (2003) described a bulky cup nest of twigs, which contained a single whitish egg speckled brown at both ends in late June. However, Karubian and Smith (2007a) reported that nesting activity is highest in February–April, i.e. when lekking activity is low (Tori *et al.* 2008), and the nest followed by Greeney *et al.* (2006) was initiated in January. The egg reported in the Greeney *et al.* (2006) study was more similar to that of Amazonian Umbrellabird being tan to ochre-coloured with few markings, although it was not examined in detail. Incubation lasts 27–28 days (Greeney *et al.* 2006), while the nestling period was *c.*31 days in the same nest (Greeney *et al.* in press). The latter authors reported in detail on the nestling's diet, and all of the following data are taken from that paper (in press). Of 172 items identified, the majority (*n* = 146) were invertebrates, as follows (in decreasing order of importance): adult cicadas (Heteroptera, Cicadidae), larval Lepidoptera, katydids (Orthoptera, Tettigoniidae), adult Lepidoptera, unidentified Orthoptera, a cockroach (Blaberidae, *Blaberus* sp.), an adult beetle (Coleoptera, Cerambycidae), a dobsonfly (Megaloptera, Corydalidae) and an unidentified arthropod. Vertebrates (*n* = 22) numbered 13 lizards (most of which were apparently Iguanidae), six frogs and three apparently non-venomous snakes. Most vertebrate prey appeared to be brought in dead, but some adult Lepidoptera were alive when fed to the nestling. Four fruits were also fed to the nestling and appeared to be probably of either the family Solanaceae or Araceae. Feeding rates are generally uniform during the course of the day, but increase with the growth of the nestling. Incubation, feeding and brooding of the young, as well as nest building, is by the female alone, who is generally cautious around the nest (flying directly in from *c.*20m distant) and apparently does not vocalise when close by. However, the female's behaviour at the nest followed by Greeney *et al.* (in press) suggests that she called very softly to the young when arriving directly at the nest. The female's visits were generally very brief and she consumed most faecal sacs produced by the young, as well as assisting the nestling to consume larger (vertebrate) prey. The nest followed by Karubian *et al.* (2003) was placed 5m above the ground (4.5m in the Greeney *et al.* 2006 study), in the crotch of a tree-fern, and constructed of dry sticks but lined with thinner twigs, epiphyte roots, tree-fern parts and mosses (i.e. somewhat different from the nest of Amazonian Umbrellabird). Greeney *et al.* (2006) noted no lining of finer materials at the nest in southwest Ecuador, but otherwise the situation and construction of 'their' nest was similar. In common with one of the Amazonian Umbrellabird nests discovered to date, both Long-wattled Umbrellabird nests were some distance from undisturbed forest, and in both cases were also within 1.5km of a known lek of the species. Indeed, the species seems to be comparatively catholic in its choice of habitats for nesting, although failure rates are apparently high (Karubian and Smith 2007a). Dimensions of the nest were presented in Greeney *et al.* (2006), as well as incubation rhythms and many other details.

STATUS Formerly considered Near Threatened (Collar *et al.* 1992), the species has since been upgraded to Vulnerable (BirdLife International 2000, 2004, 2008), and its population is estimated at fewer than 10,000 individuals. Long-wattled Umbrellabird is categorised as Endangered in Ecuador (Jahn and Mena-Valenzuela 2002). Rare and local, this bird is under pressure from habitat destruction and fragmentation, hunting for food by rural dwellers, and trapping for the cagebird trade. However, it does appear to be at least partially tolerant of selectively logged areas and those where a reasonable mosaic of forested lots is maintained; however, leks seem to be usually sited within reasonably pristine areas of forest. There is a lek in close proximity to the Ecuadorian capital, Quito, at Sachatamia Lodge (Cisneros-Heredia 2009). Known from a number of protected areas and several Important Bird Areas, although many face a somewhat uncertain future, throughout the species' range, but those in Ecuador, e.g. Cotacachi-Cayapas Ecological Reserve, Fundación Jocotoco's recently declared Río Canandé and Buenaventura reserves, Awa Ethnic and Forest Reserve, and Mache-Chindul Ecological Reserve (incorporating Jatun Sacha Bilsa Ecological Station), appear particularly important; in Colombia it is known from Munchique National Park (although no recent records therein), Reserva Natural Río Ñambí, Cali National Park, Tambito Natural Reserve, Reserva Natural El Pangán, and Reserva Mirabilis Swarovski (Boyla and Estrada 2005, Salaman *et al.* 2008).

REFERENCES Berg (2000), Best *et al.* (1993), BirdLife International (2000, 2004, 2008), Boyla and Estrada (2005), Cisneros-Heredia (2009), Collar *et al.* (1992), Cracraft (1985), Donegan and Dávalos (1999), Fisher (1981), Goodfellow (1901), Greeney *et al.* (2006, in press), Hartert (1898), Hellmayr (1929b), Hilty (1997), Hilty and Brown (1986), Jahn and Mena-Valenzuela (2002), Jahn *et al.* (1999, 2002), Karubian *et al.* (2003), Karubian and Smith (2007a, 2007b), Krabbe and Nilsson (2003), Lönnberg and Rendahl (1922), Restall *et al.* (2006), Ridgely and Greenfield (2001), Ridgely and Tudor (1994, 2009), Salaman *et al.* (2008), Snow (1976a, 1982, 2004a), Solano-Ugalde and Freile (2010), Stotz *et al.* (1996), Tori *et al.* (2008), Wege and Long (1995).

1

Long-wattled Umbrellabird *Cephalopterus penduliger*. **Figs. 1–5.** Two different males, Buenaventura Reserve, prov. El Oro, southwest Ecuador, July and August (*Hadoram Shirihai / Photographic Handbook to Birds of the World*). The bird in Figs. 2–5 was in full display, but that in Fig. 1 was in a more 'relaxed' state between bouts of display, despite which note the expanded hussar-like crest (covering the bill), although the wattle appears *c.*25% shorter than its total length when displaying. Also note how the neck feathers are also expanded during display in Figs. 3 and 5, which together with the wattle, give the bird the appearance of wearing a scarf.

BARE-NECKED UMBRELLABIRD
Cephalopterus glabricollis   **Plate 29**

Cephalopterus glabricollis **Gould, 1851**, *Proc. Zool. Soc. Lond.* 1850: 92, pl. 20, Cordillera de Chiriquí, Veraguas, Panama

The sole Middle American representative of the genus *Cephalopterus*, Bare-necked Umbrellabird is globally threatened by forest loss. Although its natural history is reasonably well studied, only one nest has ever been found.

IDENTIFICATION 41–45cm (male), 36–38cm (female). Male is unmistakable with a 'Mohican'-style crest that covers the head and bill, and the bare throat and neck are scarlet-coloured. This species, like the Long-wattled Umbrellabird *Cephalopterus penduliger*, is a bird of the subtropical forests, but undertakes an altitudinal migration; in the non-breeding season the species can be found in the lowlands alongside Purple-throated Fruitcrow *Querula purpurata*. The female Bare-necked Umbrellabird has a smaller crest than the male and lacks the bare skin on the throat, and to a certain degree resembles the all-black female Purple-throated Fruitcrow. The umbrellabird is larger, however, with a very short tail (especially obvious in flight, but sometimes incorrectly illustrated in field guides) and its plumage is browner in tone.

DISTRIBUTION Endemic to the Caribbean slope of Costa Rica (from the Cordillera de Guanacaste, e.g. in Rincón de la Vieja National Park, eastwards) and western Panama (east as far as Bocas del Toro and Chiriquí), at sea level to 500m in the non-breeding season (June to mid March), but migrating altitudinally to 750–2,500m to breed (earliest highland record 28 February: Fogden and Fogden 1997). Recently recorded in southernmost Nicaragua, on three occasions since 2003 in the non-breeding season, and Bare-necked Umbrellabird might prove to be a regular visitor there, given the availability of suitable habitat (Múnera-Roldán *et al.* 2007). In Panama, there are also records even further east during the non-breeding season, as far as Veraguas (in 1868) and Coclé (Wetmore 1972, Ridgely and Gwynne 1989, Angehr and Jordán 1998). There are also, to date unexplained, records from the Dota Mts, Costa Rica (Slud 1964), and the Cordillera de Tolé, Panama, in 1866

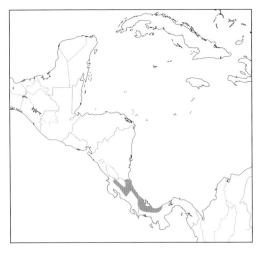

(Wetmore 1972), both of which lie on the Pacific side of the Continental Divide.

MOVEMENTS An altitudinal migrant that follows highest fruit productivity, at least in Costa Rica (many fewer data from Panama, where certainly recorded in the highlands until mid July, but at coastal localities in August): Bare-necked Umbrellabird spends most of the year in foothill and lowland forests (see Distribution). Altitudinal migrations have been best studied in the Tilarán Mts on the Caribbean slope of Costa Rica, in which area the species is found almost exclusively at higher elevations (1,000–1,500m) in the breeding season, with birds present at middle elevations (800m) between January and June and in November, at which altitude fruit productivity is not subject to seasonal peaks (Chaves-Campo *et al.* 2003). However, there are occasional records from La Selva OTS, in the lowlands, during April (i.e. the breeding season). The species might migrate in small groups, including breeding males. During the non-breeding season, females are generally found below 200m, but males at 100–500m (Chaves-Campo *et al.* 2003, Snow 2004a).

HABITAT Dependent on primary forest at all seasons, although second growth can be used for foraging. Found in the upper understorey to subcanopy of primary forest, especially where a range of large fruiting trees is available and usually in areas with a reasonably dense understorey. Populations do not appear to be uniformly spread through suitable habitat, at least in some areas, e.g. Monteverde Biological Reserve, Costa Rica, occupying just 20–30% of available forest (Fogden and Fogden 1997).

DESCRIPTION The sexes are similar, except in their feather adornments, and the female is smaller than the male. Like the two previous species, Bare-necked Umbrellabird is rather corvid-like. The bill is powerful and also crow-like, in both sexes with well-developed rictal bristles and elongated nostrils, but in males is virtually totally concealed by the bird's crest when displaying. The wing feathers lack any modification, and the rectrices are unusually short for the bird's overall body size, with the wings extending well beyond the tail tip at rest. *Adult male.* – A large, bulky cotinga with a heavily compacted, narrow 'bushy' crest (black with a bluish cast) and vivid bare red skin on most of the throat and neck, with a fairly narrow central line of rudimentary black feathers (at the sides the red skin reaches to the level of the bill below the eye). The feathering on the chin directly below the bill is black. Fleshy appendage to pouch terminates in a 'tassel' of narrow black-tipped feathers, which appear as if loose or out of place when the throat pouch is not inflated, but which extend downwards and outwards when the sac is filled with air (GMK pers. obs.). Rest of underparts very dark brown-black. Upperparts appear black; the nape and upper mantle are dark brown with dark blue fringes to the feathers, whilst the lower mantle and rump lack any trace of blue and become browner towards the tail. Scapulars and wings dark brown; underwing-coverts brown, with a paler greyer underside to the remiges and some white near the bend of the wing. *Adult female.* – Resembles a small *Corvus*, being generally browner than the male, especially on the belly, with some blacker feathers in the short crest and a small bare patch of red skin either side of the neck. Underwing-coverts brown dappled white, and rest of underwing pale brown. *Juvenile.* – Males resemble females, with patches of bare skin (less intense than adult males) on the neck. The crest is still rather reduced but shows a hint of blue and the overall dark plumage is slightly greyer. *Immature.* – Very poorly known, but appears to pass through at least one (subadult) stage prior to achieving full adult plumage (Snow 2004a). *Moult.* – Published moult data are very scarce, but Snow (1976a) considered feather replacement in all *Cephalopterus* to be extremely protracted, lasting *c.*300 days, making it more difficult to detect any seasonal bias to its onset. Furthermore, given that females are responsible for nesting duties, it is surely the case that they commence moult later than males (as in many other cotingas and both of the other umbrellabirds). Males observed in Monteverde in mid April were not moulting their flight feathers, but one had very worn rectrices (GMK pers. obs.). *Bare parts.* – Irides brown to dark brown; the bill has the maxilla black and the lower mandible plumbeous, sometimes with a blackish tip; and the legs, feet and soles are blackish to plumbeous.

MEASUREMENTS (BMNH: Costa Rica and Panama; Wetmore 1972: Panama) Wing of male (n = 15) 240–257mm, wing of female (n = 10) 213–240mm; tail of male (n = 15) 109–127mm, tail of female (n = 10) 100–121mm; bill of male (n = 5) 38–45mm, bill of female (n = 2) 30–35mm; tarsus of male (n = 15) 39–47mm, tarsus of female (n = 10) 36–46mm. Weight: 450–463g (two males) and 320g (female) (Snow 2004b, Dunning 2008; MNCR).

GEOGRAPHICAL VARIATION Monotypic.

VOICE A recording of the call from Costa Rica is archived online at www.xeno-canto.org. Various guttural, throaty, coughing or chuckling contact-calls are made, e.g. prior to visiting a fruiting tree, *oooaaahh*, or *hmmmmm* and which were divided into two subtypes, both of low intensity compared with the 'song', by Fogden and Fogden (1997). Rival males utter cat-like screeching notes during 'chases' at the lek site (GMK pers. obs.). In advertisement, males emit a spectacular call at the 'exploded lek' in March–May/June, with calling commencing from *c.*30 minutes prior to dawn (Snow 1982). This consists of a loud *hoom* given whilst the male leans forward with the foreneck sac distended (it being inflated almost in slow motion), followed by a *hik-ratch* emanating from the open bill as the head is thrown back, and completed with a dry *k* as the upright position is regained. The whole sounds like two loud booms in quick succession.

NATURAL HISTORY A spectacular, large cotingid, this species is perhaps surprisingly difficult to locate within its limited range. Like many other primarily fruit-eating cotingas, Bare-necked Umbrellabirds often remain very still for long periods, favouring just 2–3 perches 10–15m above the ground in the subcanopy, on which they spend up to 80% of the daylight hours. Much time is spent preening between bouts of display. They are easiest to see by waiting at a suitable fruiting tree or at the display grounds (for instance, the Peñas Blancas Valley, Monteverde Biological Reserve, Costa Rica, where the population was recently estimated at 60–100 birds but is seemingly declining). Also in Costa Rica, other productive sites for the species include La Selva Biological Station in the Caribbean lowlands, particularly in the tall forest of the Arboretum area, Volcán Tenorio, Arenal National Park, and Braulio Carrillo National Park, near San José (cf. Wege and Long 1995), as well as the Fortuna Forest Reserve in western Panama (Engleman and Engleman 1992).

FOOD AND FEEDING Diet is mainly frugivorous, especially berries of the families Arecaceae, Lauraceae, Cecropiaceae, Piperaceae and Marcgraviaceae, and food is either plucked in a brief swoop and clumsy hovering flight, or gleaned whilst hopping on branches. Fruit of 22 families of trees was identified in the year-round diet of this umbrellabird by Chaves-Campos *et al.* (2003). Bare-necked Umbrellabird is known to join guans, toucanets and motmots at fruiting trees, and a juvenile male was observed following army ant-following birds at an *Eciton burchelli* swarm, taking arthropods that had been flushed 3–4m above the ground; fruit are also sometimes taken at such low levels (Chaves-Campos 2005). Also known to take some lizards, frogs and other large insects, including their larvae, all of these being beaten against a perch prior to swallowing.

DISPLAY Lek displays are not dissimilar to those of other *Cephalopterus*, involving well-separated groups of males (*c.*3–5) that gather in the subcanopy of primary forest to display, each male using several different perches between which it moves rapidly, some of the branches as low as 5m above the ground and sometimes in tall understorey trees. A lek in Monteverde was centred on an old, very overgrown clearing, still with many openings in the canopy, and numerous *Cecropia* (Cecropiaceae) trees in the environs of the arena. The mean canopy height was *c.*25m and the lek was approximately 200m wide. One of the males might sometimes carry several small twigs in the bill, but the significance of this behaviour is unknown (Wetmore 1972). As in other umbrellabirds, the male initially leans forward, emits a low hum, and distends and inflates the bare wattle to its maximum size (10cm), then draws the body upwards whilst making a low *oooo* followed by a hiccup (also likened to the sound of a big cat spitting!) as the head is thrown back, followed by a short bow, and emits the second low *oooo* whilst throwing the head back beyond the vertical (Wetmore 1972, Fogden and Fogden 1997), and seeming to bounce up and down on the branch during the final part of the display (GMK pers. obs.). This performance lasts *c.*4 seconds. Calling commences at dawn or before, but continues for just *c.*60 minutes after first light and thereafter the birds usually do not vocalise throughout the rest of the day, except when preparing to feed, and then usually they utter a lower-intensity call (see Voice). However, at a lek near San Gerardo Field Station, Monteverde, in mid April, the males returned to the lek after an absence of 75 minutes whereupon they commenced a very intense 20-minute period of display, which was more 'vigorous' than that given at dawn. Males attempt to displace each other from perches, the 'victor' briefly spreading the wings in the manner of a cormorant (*Phalacrocorax*), and their behaviour becomes particularly frenetic should a female visit the lek. Chases between perches can be either linear or roughly circular, and vary in their speed and intensity, with the birds appearing to 'crash' into the perches during the most intense periods of display, and regularly uttering screeching and more 'throaty' notes whilst engaged in these pursuits (GMK pers. obs.). During such periods of 'frenetic' activity, the birds sing up to three times (more usually once or twice) between chases from a single perch and also perform side-to-side hops, and about-faces, on the branch. They also perform what appear to be ritualised movements in which the bird jabs its body sideways with the bill pointing slightly downwards several times in the same direction (GMK pers. obs.). Territories appear to be regularly occupied year after year and radio-telemetry has proven that males may even return to the same favoured tree (Chaves-Campo *et al.* 2003). Lekking behaviour diminishes after mid May and the leks are disbanded from June.

BREEDING Bare-necked Umbrellabirds presumably breed in March–June, and the only nest to be recorded in detail was initiated in April (Fogden and Fogden 1997), a comparatively large structure of twigs, leaves and moss *c.*5m above the ground in a relatively isolated tree, which contained two similar nests, suggesting that the site had been occupied in previous years. The species lays a single egg, dirty beige with uniformly spaced reddish-brown markings, incubated by the female alone for at least 24 days. The chick in this nest, which was predated after just over one week, was also tended solely by the female. Wetmore (1972) mentioned three other (oversize thrush-like) nests in Costa Rica that were shown to C. Cordier (so presumably in April or May 1942), which were also comparatively large structures, but placed even lower above the ground.

STATUS This rare, local and restricted-range species is greatly threatened by forest clearance, and has been listed as Vulnerable since the publication of Collar *et al.* (1992). Bare-necked Umbrellabird occurs in the Costa Rica and Panama highlands Endemic Bird Area (Stattersfield *et al.* 1998). The total population is currently estimated at fewer than 10,000 individuals, and the species is considered to be declining in both Panama and the lower Peñas Blancas Valley of northern Costa Rica (Fogden and Fogden 1997, BirdLife International 2000). The threats facing this species mirror those facing other altitudinal migrants in the area: sufficient areas of all biotopes have to be protected from sea level to the uplands if viable populations are to survive. Even in some important areas for this umbrellabird, wherein a mosaic of conservation areas protects a large part of the species' elevational range (e.g. the Tilarán Mts of Costa Rica), destruction of old-growth forest below 400m has been virtually complete, thereby forcing at least some birds to wander beyond the protected zone in the non-breeding season (Chaves-Campo *et al.* 2003). Some 35% of remaining lowland forest in northern Costa Rica was cleared as recently as between 1986 and 1992, mainly for banana plantations and cattle ranching (BirdLife International 2000). One of the species' strongholds is the 207,000ha La Amistad International Park, which spans the Costa Rican/Panamanian border (Wege and Long 1995, Montañez and Angehr 2007).

REFERENCES Angehr and Dean (2010), Angehr and Jordán (1998), AOU (1998), BirdLife International (2000, 2004, 2008), Blake and Loiselle (2001), Chaves-Campos (2005), Chaves-Campos *et al.* (2003), Collar *et al.* (1992), Crenshaw (2002), Dunning (2008), Engleman and Engleman (1992), Fogden and Fogden (1997), Fulton (2001), Garrigues and Dean (2007), Hellmayr (1929b), Mazar Barnett and Kirwan (2001), Montañez and Angehr (2007), Múnera-Roldán *et al.* (2007), Ridgely and Gwynne (1989), Slud (1964), Snow (1976a, 1982, 2004a), Solano-Ugalde and Freile (2010), Stattersfield *et al.* (1998), Stiles and Skutch (1989), Stotz *et al.* (1996), Wetmore (1972), Wege (1993), Wege and Long (1995).

Bare-necked Umbrellabird *Cephalopterus glabricollis*. **Fig. 1**. Male, San Gerardo Field Station, near Monteverde, prov. Alajuela, Costa Rica, May (*Steven Easley / Costa Rica Gateway*). When relaxed the throat sac is relatively unobtrusive. **Figs. 2–3**. Displaying male, San Gerardo Field Station, near Monteverde, prov. Alajuela, Costa Rica, April (*Kevin Easley / Costa Rica Gateway*). Two images of the same singing male; note how the 'tassel' at the base of the throat sac is 'twitched' when the bird is displaying. **Fig. 4**. Male, Las Heliconias Lodge, near Bijagua, prov. Alajuela, Costa Rica, February (*Jason Horn / Costa Rica Gateway*). Given a back view, this umbrellabird is a relatively unremarkable but still somewhat imposing bird.

517

Genus *Carpornis*: berryeaters

The genus *Carpornis* is represented by two closely related species that are confined to the forested belt of eastern and southeastern Brazil. The predominance of black, green and yellow in the plumage points to the berryeaters being the ecological counterparts of the *Pipreola* fruiteaters of the Andes, and these two genera are amongst the very few cotingas known or speculated (Snow 1982) to indulge in courtship feeding.

HOODED BERRYEATER
Carpornis cucullata   Plate 21

Procnias cucullata **Swainson, 1821**, *Zool. Illus.* 1, pl. 37, [Rio de Janeiro,] Brazil

The larger and more robust of the two berryeaters, this species is relatively common and easily seen, at least locally, due to the presence of still relatively large areas of intact forest in the foothills and mountains of its southeast Brazilian haunts. Furthermore, the species is usually easy to locate by virtue of its loud and very distinctive song, which gives rise to its main local name (see Voice). However, another regional name, the cavalo-frouxou, or cowardly horse (J. F. Pacheco *in litt.* 2010), is more difficult to interpret.

IDENTIFICATION 21.5–26.0cm. Unmistakable: much of the range of the Hooded Berryeater lies to the south of its only congeneric, the Black-headed Berryeater *Carpornis melanocephala*. There is, however, an extensive area of overlap in the states of Espírito Santo south to Paraná, in coastal Brazil, although within this region the two are almost entirely altitudinally parapatric, with Hooded almost exclusively occurring above 400m (but see below). Because of their generally inconspicuous behaviour, berryeaters are not often seen well, except in response to playback, thus usually permitting only casual observations and insights into their natural history. Both sexes of the Hooded Berryeater have chestnut mantles (less saturated in the female), yellow underparts and yellowish fringes to the median and greater coverts. Black-headed Berryeater lacks the chestnut-coloured mantle, and has overall much greener (less yellow) and less patterned plumage.

DISTRIBUTION Hooded Berryeater is endemic to the Atlantic Forest of Brazil, from southern and central Espírito

Santo south through Rio de Janeiro, the littoral of São Paulo, eastern Paraná, and Santa Catarina (widespread in the eastern third) to Rio Grande do Sul (where principally restricted to the northeast, but also occurs in the southern hills, e.g. inland of Pelotas). A single undocumented record has been reported from Boa Nova, in southern Bahia (Forrester 1993), but must certainly be in error given that extensive (and intensive) recent fieldwork has subsequently failed to record the species there (e.g. Gonzaga *et al.* 1995). The elevational range of the species is mostly 500–1,600m, but Hooded Berryeater is found down to *c.*100m in southern Rio Grande do Sul (in which region *C. melanocephala* is absent). It principally occurs in more montane areas, typically above 800m, in the north of its range (from the state of Rio de Janeiro to Espírito Santo).

MOVEMENTS None certainly recorded.

HABITAT Confined to humid submontane and montane primary forests of the Serra do Mar, although Snow (2004a) also mentioned occurrence in palm groves.

DESCRIPTION A handsome cotinga of medium proportions, with a rather short, broad-based bill that is hooked and triangular in shape. *Adult male.* – Immaculately patterned. The black hood extends as a bib onto the breast centre, bordered by a yellow collar which separates the hood from the dark brown to chestnut mantle. The colour of the mantle fades somewhat towards the lower back, eventually grading into the dark olive rump. The uppertail-coverts and the tail are olive, whilst the centres of the rectrices are almost maroon in tone, and broaden distally. The wing pattern is somewhat intricate when examined at close quarters. The dark coverts fade distally, with their yellow fringes and tips forming two slight wingbars, whilst the remiges are fringed olive and the dark-centred tertials are fringed yellowish-olive. The underparts are entirely smart sulphur-yellow. *Adult female.* – Plumage mirrors that of the male, but the mantle colour is less intense and the hood and wings have an olive cast, whilst the underparts are marked by pale olive chevrons, especially on the breast-sides and flanks. *Juvenile.* – Pale drab plumage with fluffy feathers (GMK pers. obs.; see below). *Immature.* – Resembles the female but the black on the head is even duller, the wing-coverts are green (lacking any bright fringes) and the yellow on the underparts is duller and more barred/vermiculated (Snow 1982). *Moult.* – There are few published data concerning moult (see Breeding), but a male taken in southern Brazil in mid April was replacing the tertials (MNRJ), and Snow (1982) calculated that moult commences in males in October–December and in females in November–January (the later onset in females suggests that males take no, or little, part in nesting duties, but see Breeding). *Bare parts.* – Irides dark brown, black or even buff and once described as fiery red (MNRJ), whilst the bill is blue-grey or pale grey (once violet-blue), with a dark tip, and the legs are grey- or violet-blue with ochraceous soles.

MEASUREMENTS (BMNH; MNRJ: Espírito Santo, Paraná, Rio de Janeiro and São Paulo, southeast Brazil) Wing of male (*n* = 18) 114–122mm, wing of female (*n* = 13) 110–119mm; tail of male (*n* = 18) 87–100mm, tail of female (*n* = 13) 80.5–98.0mm; bill of male (*n* = 17) 17.96–22.00mm, bill of female (*n* = 13) 18.57–22.00mm; tarsus of male (*n* = 6) 18–24mm, tarsus of female (*n* = 6) 19–28mm. Weight: 71.8–80.0g (males) and 66.5–96.8g (females) (Willis and Oniki 2002, Snow 2004a; MNRJ).

GEOGRAPHICAL VARIATION Monotypic.

VOICE Published recordings exist on the following compilations: Gonzaga and Castiglioni (2001), Remold (2002), Boesman (2006a) and Minns *et al.* (2009), and there are also recordings from across much of the species' range archived online at www.xeno-canto.org. This is one of the most easily identified and characteristic songs of the Atlantic Forest. A whistled, four-syllable *wee-ok wee-kow* is given repeatedly but at irregular intervals (see Snow 1982), which can be difficult to locate, and gives rise to the species' local, onomatopoeic name 'coró-cochó' (see Sick 1997, Bencke 2001). This highly stereotyped territorial song of the male is a characteristic sound of the wetter forests of the Serra do Mar, with individuals frequently vocalising throughout the day, and often slightly throwing the head backwards as they call. Hooded Berryeater is easily attracted, sometimes over long distances (especially if the species' local density is low), using playback, and the birds often approach very closely. Can respond vigorously to playback, usually arriving relatively quietly then calling continuously. However, in areas where the species' density is high, it may sometimes prove more difficult to 'call in'. Also gives a low *graau* in advertisement, a *krrra* in flight and *bibibi* as 'conversational' notes between a pair (Sick 1997). Both sexes give inward grating notes (Snow 1982), which comment probably refers to some of the same vocalisations reported by Sick. Vocalisation activity peaks in late winter and early spring (e.g. July–October), even in the extreme south (where the avian breeding season often commences slightly later than elsewhere in southeast Brazil), but the primary vocalisation remains a highly typical sound of southeast Brazil's montane forests even in February–April, by which months many other species are much less vocal.

NATURAL HISTORY Natural history observations on either of the *Carpornis* are still much lacking, despite the number of birdwatchers who visit southeast Brazil every year and, especially, the relative numbers and experience of home-grown ornithologists. Occurs solitarily, or occasionally in pairs, usually perching quietly and somewhat unobtrusively at mid levels (above 5m) and the canopy. Territories are generally well spaced, with males rarely closer than within distant earshot (pers. obs.; Snow 1982).

FOOD AND FEEDING Diet is principally small to medium-sized soft fruits of a broad range of species (45 species of 15 families were identified by Pizo *et al.* 2002; see also Pineschi 1990, Guix *et al.* 1992, Mendonça-Lima *et al.* 2001, Silva *et al.* 2002, Parrini and Pacheco 2011). Fruits are only occasionally taken in flight and the species has not been noted to join other birds at fruiting trees, although it sometimes appears to associate loosely with mixed-species flocks. (For some details of constituents of these see Venturini *et al.* 2005.) At least one exotic species has been recorded in the species' diet (Pizo *et al.* 2002), which study also found that fruits of epiphytes and vines do not constitute the principal foods, as had been earlier speculated by Snow (1982). Hooded

Berryeater is apparently an important disperser of the fruits of the palm *Euterpe edulis* Arecaceae (Von Matter *et al.* 2010). This was one of four species of cotingas studied in Paraná, southern Brazil, by Clausi and Baarstch (2009), who found that fruit production and its effect on local movements on birds such as Cotingidae could be divided into six periods of the year.

BREEDING The nest of the Hooded Berryeater is apparently unknown, but Belton (1985) mentioned a male with enlarged testes collected in Rio Grande do Sul in July and MNRJ has males and females in breeding condition dated mid June (which seems exceptionally but not impossibly early) to early February, and moult data (presumably post-breeding) suggest that birds lay in September–October. That males moult slightly earlier than females suggests that they take little part in nesting duties (as in most cotingas, with the notable exception of the genera *Phibalura, Pipreola* and apparently *Conioptilon*). However, on 10 March 2006, at the Estrada da Graciosa, Paraná, Kirwan (2009) observed two well-grown but still-dependent young accompanying an apparent pair, which observation requires confirmation and follow-up work (see also Breeding of Black-headed Berryeater). Ihering (1900) described the eggs of this species as being ashy-yellow with numerous grey-brown spots and blotches, and measuring 34 × 23mm.

STATUS Near Threatened (BirdLife International 2004, 2008). Hooded Berryeater is generally uncommon, especially in Rio Grande do Sul, where its overall range has probably contracted, but compared with Black-headed Berryeater this species is still less threatened by habitat destruction (much of it historical, dating to the second major wave of European colonisation), mainly because of its dependence on montane areas, where still relatively large areas of intact forest remain, much of it protected, either privately or publicly. *C. cucullata* is known from at least 23 Important Bird Areas (Bencke *et al.* 2006). It is locally common in some protected areas, for instance: Augusto Ruschi (the former Nova Lombardia) Biological Reserve (Espírito Santo), Serra das Órgãos National Park and Desengano State Park (Rio de Janeiro), Intervales and Serra do Mar State Parks, and Boracéia Biological Station (São Paulo), the Estrada da Graciosa (Paraná) and São Joaquim National Park (Santa Catarina). However, in other areas, the Hooded Berryeater seems inexplicably absent, e.g. Itatiaia National Park (Rio de Janeiro).

REFERENCES Accordi and Barcellos (2006), Alves *et al.* (2009), Antas *et al.* (2007), Belton (1985, 2003), Bencke (2001), Bencke and Kindel (1999), BirdLife International (2004, 2008), Borchardt and Zimmermann (2000), Browne (2005), Burns *et al.* (2001), Carrano *et al.* (2004), Clausi (2005), Clausi and Baarstch (2009), David and Gosselin (2002b), Forrester (1993), Goerck (1999), Gonzaga and Castiglioni (2001), Gonzaga *et al.* (1995), Guix *et al.* (1992), Hellmayr (1929b), Hinkelmann and Fiebig (2001), Ihering (1900), Kaminski and Carrano (2004), Kirwan (2009), Krabbe (2007), Lau (2004), Mendonça *et al.* (2004), Mendonça-Lima *et al.* (2001), Mallet-Rodrigues *et al.* (2007), Maurício and Dias (1998), Minns *et al.* (2009), Oliveira *et al.* (2009), Parker and Goerck (1997), Parrini and Pacheco (2011), Pimentel and Olmos (2011), Pineschi (1990), Pinto (1944), Pizo *et al.* (2002), Remold (2002), Ribon *et al.* (2004), Ridgely and Tudor (1994, 2009), do Rosário (1996), Sick (1997), Silva *et al.* (2002), Simon (2009), Snow (1982, 2004a), Stotz *et al.* (1996), Venturini *et al.* (2005), Von Matter *et al.* (2010), Willis (1992), Willis and Oniki (2002).

Hooded Berryeater *Carpornis cucullata*. **Fig. 1**. Female, Intervales State Park, São Paulo, southeast Brazil, October (*Ron Hoff*). Note the rather paler mantle coloration and duller black plumage compared to the males in the next two photographs. **Fig. 2**. Male, Fazenda Pindobas IV, Espírito Santo, southeast Brazil, August (*Pete Morris*). **Fig. 3**. Male, Intervales State Park, São Paulo, southeast Brazil, October (*Hadoram Shirihai / Photographic Handbook to Birds of the World*). The genus *Carpornis* is endemic to eastern Brazil and the two species are highly sought after by visiting birdwatchers.

BLACK-HEADED BERRYEATER
Carpornis melanocephala   **Plate 21**

Procnias melanocephalus **Wied, 1820**, *Reise Brasilien* 1: 168, Quartel de Barreiras, road from the Rio Itapemirim to the Rio Itabapuana, southern Espírito Santo, Brazil

Due to its dependence on lowland forest in eastern Brazil, this rare cotingid has almost certainly undergone a particularly dramatic decline in numbers and range. The Black-headed Berryeater now occurs mainly in conservation areas and continued protection of these is increasingly essential to its long-term survival.

IDENTIFICATION 20.5–25.0cm. Unobtrusive, this rare species frequents the midstorey of tall primary forest, with often the only indication of its presence being its disyllabic call. The surrounding vegetation (usually dense undergrowth with many lianas) coupled with its retiring habits make this species, unlike its congener, difficult to observe. In addition to its vocalisations, the Black-headed Berryeater is easily distinguished from its more highland counterpart, the Hooded Berryeater *Carpornis cucullata*, by the mainly dull olive-yellow body and wings, and the black hood extending only to the level of the throat (not onto the breast as in Hooded Berryeater).

DISTRIBUTION Endemic to Brazil, its range largely to the north of that of the Hooded Berryeater, perhaps from northeastern Paraná (record in Collar *et al.* 1992 never substantiated, but occurrence seems probable: Scherer-Neto and Straube 1995), through southernmost São Paulo (present in five Important Bird Areas (IBAs)) and Rio de Janeiro (in which state it seems particularly local and uncommon, although it is still known from three IBAs) north to Espírito Santo (five IBAs), Bahia (five IBAs, as well as the recently protected Bandeira/Macarani area just inside Minas Gerais), and with a presumably isolated population in highland Alagoas (where it is known solely from the seemingly ever-declining forests of Murici).

MOVEMENTS None recorded to date.

HABITAT Black-headed Berryeater inhabits humid, wet forests of the Brazilian littoral, mainly from sea level to 300m, but locally to *c.*500–600m (e.g. in Alagoas and central Bahia) and occasionally even to 800 m or higher (in southern Bahia), i.e. in regions where there are no Hooded Berryeaters (cf. Gonzaga *et al.* 1995, Belmonte-Lopes *et al.* in press). Generally, the species favours tall and rather dense vegetation, including tall *restinga* forests, and is probably commonest on dry, sandy soils, e.g. at Linhares, Espírito Santo, and on Ilha Comprida and nearby mainland areas, São Paulo, but Black-headed Berryeater is also occasionally found on wetter ground, e.g. at Una, Bahia.

DESCRIPTION Sexes similar. Smaller and rather less immaculately plumaged than Hooded Berryeater, but it is similar to the latter species (which see) in most structural features, although the tail is comparatively shorter, and the bill is wider distally and more compressed dorso-ventrally (Snow 1982). *Adult.* – The head and throat are black, forming a well-defined and neat hood, with a very narrow yellow hind-collar. Upperparts uniform olive-green, with remiges slightly browner. Underparts: breast olive-yellow with very fine and slightly darker vermiculated barring, becoming paler and slightly plainer on the belly, flanks and undertail-coverts. Female has some olive suffusion to the black of the head, but is otherwise inseparable from the male. *Immature.* – Resembles the female, but the black on the head is even less well developed, whilst the throat and breast are duller yellow and more heavily barred (Snow 1982, 2004a). *Moult.* – Few published data concerning moult, but MNRJ has a female in wing moult dated January, whereas another female taken in early October shows no evidence of any feather replacement. Snow (1982) recorded that males may initiate feather replacement at almost any time between May and December, albeit with most instances in September–October. *Bare parts.* – Irides red, bill blackish or black, with a plumbeous or grey base to the lower mandible, and the legs are grey, plumbeous or blackish with ochre soles.

MEASUREMENTS (BMNH; CUMZ; MNRJ; RMNH; ROM: Bahia and Espírito Santo, eastern Brazil) Wing of male (*n* = 11) 111–118mm, wing of female (*n* = 9) 110–118mm; tail of male (*n* = 12) 75–87mm, tail of female (*n* = 8) 78–88mm; bill of male (*n* = 12) 18.29–19.63mm, bill of female (*n* = 8) 18.11–19.69mm; tarsus of male (*n* = 4) 19–22mm, tarsus of female (*n* = 3) 19–20mm. Weight: 62.7–66.0g (two males) and 64.0–81.5g (two females) (Teixeira *et al.* 1986, Snow 2004a; MNRJ).

GEOGRAPHICAL VARIATION Monotypic.

VOICE Published recordings are available on the following compilations: Remold (2002), Boesman (2006a) and Minns *et al.* (2009), and there are also several recordings available online at www.xeno-canto.org. Easily recognised, although the song is a much less characteristic (and charismatic) sound than the territorial call of its congeneric. A slightly throaty, whistled *wheeow* or monosyllabic *kuawu* that rises in pitch then descends, whose source can be difficult to locate, is frequently given at long and irregular intervals, and whose distance from the observer can be hard to judge. Often responds readily to playback, tending to approach silently, before commencing to call again when at close quarters, but it can still be very hard to spot.

NATURAL HISTORY If anything, even more secretive and generally more solitary than Hooded Berryeater, although one observed in lowland forest near Porto Seguro, southern Bahia, was loosely associated with other species, including Screaming Piha *Lipaugus vociferans*, at a fruiting tree (GG and C. I. Bushell pers. obs.). However, the species does not appear to join mobile mixed-species foraging flocks (Ridgely and Tudor 2009; pers. obs.). Consistently perches upright and alert, at mid levels to the canopy, and often (but not always) in taller forest than that frequented by Hooded Berryeater. Flies comparatively long distances between perches, which are more liable to be concealed than those often used by Hooded Berryeater; thus the species can be difficult to see even if the would-be observer is using playback, especially in tall forest, where the bird tends to remain in the subcanopy.

FOOD AND FEEDING Generally, Black-headed Berryeater appears to take slightly larger fruits than *C. cucullata* (Guix *et al.* 1992, Galetti *et al.* 1999, Pizo *et al.* 2002) and probably takes these more frequently in flight, including at forest borders, with 14 plant species of seven families (Arecaceae, Celastraceae, Monimiaceae, Myrtaceae, Rubiaceae, Sapindaceae and Verbenaceae) recorded in its diet during a study in São Paulo (Pizo *et al.* 2002), whilst Collar *et al.* (1992) reported some additional, incidental and anecdotal reports of feeding behaviour. There is one record of animal prey, a 7cm-long stick insect, being consumed (B. M. Whitney & J. A. Rowlett *in* Collar *et al.* 1992).

BREEDING To date, there are no published data concerning breeding, though vocal activity, which seems strongest in August–February, especially in September–December, and gonad and moult data from specimens all indicate that nesting is likely to be in the early spring and austral summer (as would be expected in this region). In early September 2006, Belmonte-Lopes *et al.* (in press) discovered a nest of this species in southern Bahia. It resembled some aerial leaf litter, placed 4.2m above the ground and was supported from below by a bromeliad leaf and two small tree forks. Materials used to construct the cup-shaped nest were principally dry leaves, with the lining also comprising narrow stems. The nest contained a single egg, believed by the discoverers to be a complete clutch, given the embryo's state (as subsequently found), which was pale horn-coloured becoming greyish-brown over the larger end and marked with small spots and stripes of dark brown over the whole. Dimensions of the nest and egg are presented by Belmonte-Lopes *et al.* (in press). Although only the female was seen incubating, the male remained in close proximity to the nest during two hours of observations, even perching on it once when the female was briefly absent.

The observation of both adults at the nest is interesting in the light of our unconfirmed observations of Hooded Berryeater parental care (see Breeding for *C. cucullata*), and note also the apparent discrepancy in clutch size between the two species, which suggests Kirwan (2009) was incorrect in his claim of two young for *C. cucullata*. Calling birds frequently tend to be much more closely aggregated than in Hooded Berryeater, at least where the species is still reasonably common, e.g. during the austral spring, it is not uncommon to hear several birds calling simultaneously in the vicinity of one spot in Linhares Natural Reserve (Espírito Santo).

STATUS Listed as Vulnerable by the IUCN (Collar *et al.* 1992, BirdLife International 2000, 2004, 2008). The species is rare to uncommon throughout its range, which lies entirely within the Serra do Mar Centre of endemism (Cracraft 1985), and local declines have been suspected (Collar *et al.* 1992). Currently, Black-headed Berryeater is known from at least 16 protected areas throughout its range, but although still at least locally common in the north of its range (e.g. the species is readily encountered in Monte Pascoal National Park, Bahia, and Murici Ecological Station, Alagoas), the overall population in these states must be relatively small. Rather commoner and more continuously distributed further south in the Atlantic Forest, but the species is still conspicuously absent from many areas, in large part due to the extensive destruction of lowland habitats. Remains distinctly common in Linhares Natural Reserve (Espírito Santo), readily though much less easily found in the adjacent Sooretama Biological Reserve, and Black-headed Berryeater is also still common at lower elevations in Intervales State Park (São Paulo).

REFERENCES Albano (2010a, 2010b), Aleixo and Galetti (1997), Belmonte-Lopes *et al.* (in press), Bencke *et al.* (2006), BirdLife International (2000, 2004, 2008), Cordeiro (2000), Cracraft (1985), David and Gosselin (2002b), Forrester (1993), Galetti *et al.* (1999), Gonzaga *et al.* (1995), Guix *et al.* (1992), Gussoni and Galetti (2007), Hellmayr (1929b), Kirwan (2009), Mallet-Rodrigues *et al.* (2007), Marins and Carrano (2007), Marsden *et al.* (2003), Minns *et al.* (2009), Parker and Goerck (1997), Patrial *et al.* (2009), Pinto (1944), Pizo *et al.* (2002), Remold (2002), Ribon *et al.* (2004), Ridgely and Tudor (1994, 2009), Scherer-Neto and Straube (1995), Schunck and Silveira (2010), Sick (1997), Silveira *et al.* (2005), Simon (2009), Snow (1982, 2004a), Stotz *et al.* (1996), Teixeira *et al.* (1986), Wege and Long (1995), Whitehouse and Ribon (2010), Willis (1992).

Black-headed Berryeater *Carpornis melanocephala*. **Fig. 1**. Male, Boa Nova, Bahia, eastern Brazil, November (*Ciro Albano*). **Fig. 2**. Male, Porto Seguro, Bahia, eastern Brazil, February (*Ciro Albano*). Easily separated from Hooded Berryeater *C. cucullata* by virtue of the all-green upperparts, vermiculated underparts and bright red irides, sexing is less easy in this species. These two both appear to be males based on the solidly deep-black hoods.

Genus *Snowornis*: green pihas

This recently described genus comprises just two comparatively rarely observed species confined to the foothills and mid elevations of the Andes. In terms of outward morphology, the overall greenish or yellowish plumage, partially concealed black crown patch, yellow eye-ring and yellow underwing-coverts are the main features differentiating this grouping from the other species traditionally included in *Lipaugus* (Prum 2001).

GREY-TAILED PIHA
Snowornis subalaris   Plate 20

Lipaugus subalaris **P. L. Sclater, 1861**, *Proc. Zool. Soc. Lond.* 1861: 210, Río Napo, Ecuador

Thrush-like in appearance, this montane piha is exclusively restricted to the east slope of the Andes, in humid and wet mossy forests of southern Colombia, south somewhat discontinuously to southern Peru. This and Olivaceous Piha *Snowornis cryptolophus* were formerly placed in the genus *Lathria* by Ridgely and Greenfield (2001), but that name (whose type species is Dusky Piha *Lipaugus fuscocinereus*) is demonstrably unavailable for these two 'oddballs'.

IDENTIFICATION 23–26cm. Grey-tailed Piha is a long- and slender-tailed species. Only likely to be confused with its sibling species, the Olivaceous Piha, whose range extensively overlaps Grey-tailed on the east slope (but is mainly elevationally parapatric). However, Olivaceous Piha is, as its name suggests, a more uniform bird and lacks the contrasting grey belly and tail of Grey-tailed. See also Olivaceous Piha.

DISTRIBUTION Exclusively restricted to the east slope of the Andes of northwestern South America. Grey-tailed Piha is recorded from southern Colombia (in dpto. Huila, Cauca, western dpto. Caquetá and western dpto. Putumayo, where observed in 1962, collected in 1965 and found in the field in August 1993) and the east slope of the Andes throughout Ecuador (except the very south of the country, in most of Loja and Zamora-Chinchipe). There are several, apparently isolated, populations in Peru, in dpto. San Martín (e.g. in the northern Cordillera Azul), at Enenas in dpto. Pasco and in southern dpto. Madre de Dios on the Cerros de Pantiacolla (Willis 1988, Dick 1991, Ridgely and Tudor 1994,

Alverson *et al.* 2001, Ridgely and Greenfield 2001, Salaman *et al.* 2002b, Schulenberg *et al.* 2007, Merkord *et al.* 2009).

MOVEMENTS None known.

HABITAT The species inhabits humid foothill forest, in the understorey and at middle levels, at 570–1,400m in the north of the range (Salaman *et al.* 2002b), and at 790–1,350m in Peru (Schulenberg *et al.* 2007, Brooks *et al.* 2009). At one site in the northern Cordillera Azul, northern Peru, where this species has been observed together with Olivaceous Piha, the latter species replaces Grey-tailed above 1,300m (Alverson *et al.* 2001).

DESCRIPTION The sexes are similar. The bill has an arched culmen (sometimes strongly so) with a hooked tip, and is broader based than that of Olivaceous Piha, whilst the tarsi are somewhat shorter than in *S. cryptolophus*. Primaries unmodified, unlike in *Lipaugus*. *Adult.* – The male has a large black crown patch (always reduced and sometimes wholly lacking in the female), but this is semi-concealed and rarely visible in the field, and the female also has much less yellow and smaller pectoral tufts. The rest of the head is olive with almost black lores and yellow flecks over the ear-coverts. Appears bright olive-green above from the crown to the rump, including the scapulars. The uppertail-coverts and rectrices are ash-grey, contrasting with the rest of the upperparts, whilst the wing-coverts, tertials and fringes to the secondaries are olive, and the rest of the remiges are greyish-brown. There is a pale yellow wash to the throat, becoming bright yellow-olive on the breast (both with highly inconspicuous pale shaft-streaks). Lower belly greyer (which coloration can extend higher, even well onto the breast) and the undertail-coverts are yellowish-white. Undertail pale ash-grey. Underwing-coverts lemon yellow, rest of underwing grey. *Juvenile.* – Undescribed (Snow 2004a). *Moult.* – There are no published data concerning moult, but a male collected in eastern Ecuador in January was moulting the wing, tail and body feathers (MECN). *Bare parts.* – Similar coloration in both sexes: the bill is dark horn to black, but paler (usually bluish-grey) at the base of the lower mandible; the legs and feet are bluish-grey to grey (sometimes slate or lead-coloured); and the irides are dark brown to black, with a narrow grey eye-ring (FMNH; MECN).

MEASUREMENTS (from Snow 1982; MECN; ROM: Putumayo, southeast Colombia, and Morona-Santiago, Sucumbíos and Zamora-Chinchipe, eastern Ecuador) Wing of male ($n = 8$) 124–136mm, wing of female ($n = 6$) 124–133mm; tail of male ($n = 8$) 92–105mm, tail of female ($n = 6$) 96–109mm; bill of male ($n = 5$) 14.0–15.5mm ($n = 2$, to skull, 20.8–21.2mm), bill of female ($n = 4$) 13–15mm ($n = 1$, to skull, 22.8mm); tarsus of male ($n = 5$) 21–22mm, tarsus of female ($n = 4$) 21–22mm. Weight: 70.4–86.3g (12 males) and 74.4–90.0g (six females) (Snow 1982, Salaman and Donegan 2007, Dunning 2008; FMNH; MECN; T. M. Donegan *et al.* unpubl. data).

GEOGRAPHICAL VARIATION Monotypic.

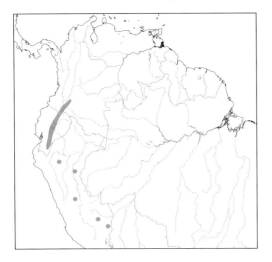

VOICE Seldom heard in many parts of its range (e.g. Peru) and, overall, the species tends to be largely silent. Consequently, the species may be regularly overlooked throughout its range. Its far-carrying and loud vocalisations are often the only giveaway as to the species' presence. It is perhaps less vocal than most *Lipaugus* pihas: a bird in Peru vocalised only every 2–3 minutes (GMK *et al.* pers. obs.), and males can sing at even longer intervals, exceptionally of up to 20 minutes (Schulenberg *et al.* 2007). The male's song is a shrill, drawn-out, two-note whistle *churrrreeeeng*, with the second syllable higher pitched than the first. A softer and shorter *chureeeee?* vocalisation was plausibly attributed to the female (Ridgely and Greenfield 2001, Ridgely and Tudor 2009). This might be the same as the *peeep* reminiscent of a young chicken peeping mentioned by Willis (1988) and Salaman *et al.* (2002b). The species' voice features on the following audio compilations: Schulenberg (2000a), Krabbe and Nilsson (2003) and Lysinger *et al.* (2005), and recordings from Ecuador and Peru are available online at www.xeno-canto.org.

NATURAL HISTORY The species is very inconspicuous, remaining motionless for long periods. These traits doubtless contribute to the fact that so little is known about the species. Limited observations suggest that Grey-tailed Pihas rarely associate with mixed-species flocks, but how typical this is of the species' ecology is unknown (i.e. whether such activity is limited to when the flock passes through the bird's territory, as is probably the case in *Lipaugus*).

FOOD AND FEEDING Like many cotingas the best opportunity for observing the species (unless surveying an area with mist-nets) is when an individual is seen sallying for insects or large spiders, or foraging at a fruiting tree. There is no information on its foraging behaviour, but the species has been observed hover-gleaning insects from foliage.

DISPLAY Birds lek in the upper understorey or the mid-storey, but the number of individuals lekking together may vary between sites. As with most aspects of its ecology, there are few published data on this facet of the bird's life history but Salaman *et al.* (2002b) mentioned the following:

> [This species was] observed at Estación de Bombeo Guamués [dpto. Putumayo], where two individuals were lekking in the central branches of an emergent tree in tall secondary forest on 28 August 1993 (PS). Birds flitted between branches in the open lower canopy, and fanned their tails very wide to reveal the pale outer tail feathers, then irregularly moved the tail from side to side.

BREEDING Our collective data on breeding are limited to a male collected in late September in eastern Ecuador that was in breeding condition (MECN), two females with eggs in the oviduct in early September in southeast Peru (FMNH) and the observation of Greeney and Gelis (2007) of a bird carrying nesting material in Sumaco-Napo Galeras National Park, prov. Napo, Ecuador, on 13 April.

STATUS The species is currently listed as Least Concern (BirdLife International 2004, 2008). Very poorly known in life due to its furtive behaviour and a general lack of familiarity with its vocalisations, the Grey-tailed Piha has been recorded with any degree of regularity at only a few sites; the Loreto road in prov. Napo, Ecuador, and the recently opened Wild Sumaco lodge, west of Coca,

in the same region, are amongst the best areas to search for what is clearly a very uncommon and local bird. It is also considered common at Quebrada Mishquiyacu, near Moyobamba, in dpto. San Martín (GMK pers. obs.), and in the Cordillera Azul, dptos. Loreto/San Martín, both Peru (Valqui 2004). The species occurs in the recently declared Serranía de los Churumbelos National Park (Salaman *et al.* 2008, 2009). Grey-tailed Piha must be threatened by habitat destruction; as is the case with many eastern slope species, the preferred elevational range of this species corresponds with those areas much desired for agricultural development. Nonetheless, it persists around Wild Sumaco lodge in a rather fragmented matrix of cattle pastures and primary and secondary forest patches (GMK pers. obs.).

REFERENCES Alverson *et al.* (2001), Balchin and Toyne (1998), BirdLife International (2004, 2008), Brooks *et al.* (2009), Dick (1991), Dunning (2008), Greeney and Gelis (2007), Hellmayr (1929b), Hilty and Brown (1986), Krabbe and Nilsson (2003), Lysinger *et al.* (2005), Merkord *et al.* (2009), Pearman (1994a), Prum (2001), Restall *et al.* (2006), Ridgely and Greenfield (2001), Ridgely and Tudor (1994, 2009), Salaman and Donegan (2007), Salaman *et al.* (1999, 2002b, 2008, 2009), Schulenberg (2000a), Schulenberg and Awbrey (1997), Schulenberg and Servat (2001), Schulenberg *et al.* (2001, 2007), Snow (1982, 2004a), Stotz *et al.* (1996), Valqui (2004), Willis (1988).

Grey-tailed Piha *Snowornis subalaris*. **Fig. 1**. Male, Wild Sumaco Lodge, prov. Napo, eastern Ecuador, October (*János Oláh*). Comparatively rarely photographed, but the species is regularly seen at this site. Note the grey tail and posterior underparts, which separate this species from the otherwise similar Olivaceous Piha *S. cryptolophus*. The just-visible black feathers on the central crown identify the bird as a male.

OLIVACEOUS PIHA
Snowornis cryptolophus   **Plate 20**

Lathria cryptolopha **P. L. Sclater & Salvin, 1877**, *Proc. Zool. Soc. Lond.* 1877: 522, Monji, eastern Ecuador

This species is more widespread than the Grey-tailed Piha *Snowornis subalaris*. Although there is considerable overlap in their geographical ranges, Olivaceous generally replaces the previous species at higher elevations. To date the two have been found at very few sites in sympatry (and always at different elevations). However, our lack of knowledge of many aspects of this species' ecology, in particular its voice, means that it is considerably harder to observe than its congener.

IDENTIFICATION 23–25cm. Like the previous species, this is a somewhat thrush-like bird, albeit chunkier and with a heavier bill. Compared with Grey-tailed Piha (which is the principal confusion species, at least in eastern Ecuador and northern Peru), the slimmer bill and the longer tarsi might prove attributable to a difference in feeding behaviour. However, there is little known about its habits and this theory remains to be confirmed or disproved. Olivaceous Piha has olive fringes to the rectrices and the underparts are largely olive (both are grey in *S. subalaris*). As in its sister species, the underwing-coverts are bright yellow (*contra* Snow 1982). See comments under Habitat below (and under *S. subalaris*) concerning these two species being apparently elevationally parapatric. Dusky Piha *Lipaugus fuscocinereus*, which might also be confused with the present species under exceptionally unfavourable conditions, is larger and never shows any greenish in the plumage, and usually occurs at rather higher altitudes. Two tanagers, Olive *Chlorothraupis frenata* (west slope) and Ochre-breasted Tanagers *C. stolzmanni* (east slope), might offer confusion risks in parts of the present species' range, but both tanagers have quite different (chunkier) bill shapes, a horizontal and plumper, rather than an upright and sleeker carriage, much more active behaviour, and a variety of small but conclusive plumage differences (e.g. the shorter tails of the tanagers, and lack of pale eye-ring or black crown patch).

DISTRIBUTION Restricted largely to northwestern South America. Olivaceous Piha occurs in the Andes of Colombia (on the west slope of the western Andes, from dpto. Valle

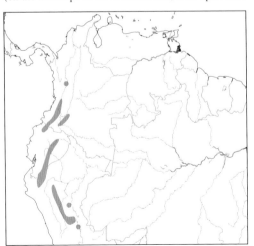

intermittently southwards, and also at the head of the Río Magdalena Valley in dpto. Huila), thence through Ecuador, south to prov. Pichincha on the west slope, and locally throughout on the east slope, to the east slope of the Andes in Peru, where it ranges south as far as northernmost dpto. Junín (Hilty and Brown 1986, Ridgely and Greenfield 2001, BirdLife International 2004, Restall *et al.* 2006, Schulenberg *et al.* 2007).

MOVEMENTS None known.

HABITAT Olivaceous Piha is found in the understorey and midstorey of montane cloud forest, occasionally at its borders, at 1,200–2,300m, but sometimes as low as 900m on the west slope of the Colombian Andes and to 1,050m in eastern Peru (Mee *et al.* 2002). At one site in the northern Cordillera Azul, northern Peru, where this and the previous species have been found in sympatry the two are currently thought to be elevationally parapatric, with Olivaceous Piha replacing Grey-tailed Piha above 1,300m (Alverson *et al.* 2001).

DESCRIPTION The sexes are similar. The bill has an arched culmen with a hooked tip, but is less broad-based than any *Lipaugus* species or even Grey-tailed Piha (Snow 1982). Primaries unmodified, unlike in *Lipaugus*. *Adult.* – Very similar to Grey-tailed Piha. It is usually only the male that has a semi-concealed black crown patch, although it can be heavily reduced and much more brownish (rather than entirely absent) in some females. The lores and ear-coverts are olive, becoming brighter over the latter. Olive-green above, but brightest on the rump, the remiges are brown with olive fringes and olive-green outer webs to the broad tertials. The tail is browner or slightly greyer than the remainder of the upperparts with olive fringes. Mainly olive below with pale shaft-streaks over much of the lower throat, breast and belly, and some lemon-yellow feathers on the undertail-coverts, whilst the underwing-coverts and bend of the wing are lemon-yellow. The rest of the underwing is brown with lemon fringes proximally on the remiges. *Juvenile.* – Undescribed (Snow 2004a). For a brief description of the nestling, based on photographs taken of a nest in northwest Ecuador, see Natural History. *Moult.* – There is no published information on moult, but one taken in northwest Ecuador in November was heavily worn and two collected in eastern Ecuador in June and August were in body moult (MECN). *Bare parts.* – Bill black to dark grey, sometimes with a silvery or grey base, legs and feet bluish-grey, grey or occasionally black, and the irides are dark brown to reddish-brown.

MEASUREMENTS (BMNH; FMNH; MECN; see also Hellmayr 1929b, Zimmer 1936a) *S. c. cryptolophus*: wing of male (*n* = 7) 130–141mm, wing of female (*n* = 5) (120)129–133mm; tail of male (*n* = 7) 98.5–110.0mm, tail of female (*n* = 5) 96–107mm; bill of male (*n* = 4) 22.33–24.12mm, bill of female (*n* = 3) 21.96–24.58mm; tarsus of male (*n* = 1) 25.14mm, tarsus of female (*n* = 3) 22.26–25.52mm (FMNH; MECN). *S. c. mindoensis*: wing of male (*n* = 7) 120–127mm, unsexed (*n* = 1) 122mm; tail of male (*n* = 7) 91–100mm, unsexed (*n* = 1) 94mm; bill of male (*n* = 6) 21.3–24.0mm, unsexed (*n* = 1) 22.21mm; tarsus of male (*n* = 3) 23.95–28.00mm, unsexed (*n* = 1) 23.66mm (BMNH; FMNH; MECN). Weight (both races combined): 72.1–85.0g (males) (MECN; Snow 1982, Dunning 2008).

GEOGRAPHICAL VARIATION Two subspecies are currently recognised. *S. c. cryptolophus* occurs on the east slope of the Andes in Colombia, Ecuador and Peru, and **S. c. mindoensis** (C. E. Hellmayr & Seilern, 1914) occurs on the west slope of the Andes in Colombia (south from dpto. Antioquia) and Ecuador (to prov. Pichincha). The latter subspecies is smaller than the nominate race, notably so in wing length (although our sample size is still small), and the concealed bases of the black crest feathers are extensively creamy white rather than brown (see Snow 1982).

VOICE Virtually nothing is known about the species vocalisations and nothing seems to have been published (Ridgely and Greenfield 2001, Schulenberg *et al.* 2007), and our personal field experience with this bird is very limited. Limited observations suggest that the species is largely silent, rarely vocalising. A recording, of *S. c. mindoensis*, has been archived (XC9860) online by N. Athanas. It is a harsh rattling sound that speeds up slightly and ends quite abruptly, the whole lasting *c.*1 second, and which could be rendered *brrrrrrrhu*. Another recording, of the same taxon, was published on Krabbe and Nilsson (2003), but the sound is barely audible with most of the cut being predominated by a Lineated Foliage-gleaner *Syndactyla subalaris* song. The species' different syringeal morphology from any of the *Lipaugus* species could mean that its vocalisations are unlikely to be as piercing or loud as any species of the latter genus (Prum 2001).

NATURAL HISTORY Typically lethargic and difficult to encounter (principally due to our lack of knowledge of its vocalisations), although Olivaceous Piha may, at least occasionally, join mixed-species foraging flocks (cf. Bohórquez 2003), in Colombia, a 'loose association' with a flock containing Red-headed Barbet *Eubucco bourcierii*, Scaly-throated Foliage-gleaner *Anabacerthia variegaticeps*, White-headed Wren *Campylorhynchus albobrunneus*, Ochre-breasted Tanager *Chlorothraupis stolzmanni* and Yellow-throated Bush Tanager *Chlorospingus flavigularis* (Pearman 1993).

FOOD AND FEEDING Undemonstrative and inconspicuous, as well as often solitary, the best chance of observing Olivaceous Piha is when one or more individuals congregate at a fruiting tree. In northwest Ecuador, P. Noakes (*in litt.* 1996) observed one at a fruiting tree with a pair of Black-chested Fruiteaters *Pipreola lubomirskii*. The diet comprises seeds and fruits taken during a brief flutter and hover movement (sally-hover), or a lunge for larger insects (Hilty and Brown 1986, Ridgely and Tudor 2009). The species has recently taken to occasionally visiting the fruit feeders at Reserva Paz de Aves, near Mindo, in Pichincha province, Ecuador, at least seasonally, where it seems particularly fond of 'grapes' (N. Athanas *et al.*). Like the previous species it appears to occasionally join mixed-species foraging flocks, but the extent and duration of this behaviour are again unknown.

BREEDING Until very recently this facet of the species' life history was fundamentally also unknown, although a specimen collected in southeast Ecuador in June was coming into breeding condition (MECN). In late November 2008, a nest was found at Reserva Paz de Aves on a forested hillside and sited *c.*4.5m above the ground. The relatively shallow, cup-shaped nest was sited in the three-way, partially moss-covered fork of a tree, and appeared to be constructed of small sticks and darker tendrils, much like *Lipaugus* pihas, but the overall construction is distinctly smaller (there does not seem to be any sticks protruding noticeably from the general shape) and more compact, and perhaps more solid-looking than those of *Lipaugus*. Only one bird, presumably

a female, attended the relatively tiny nest, which contained a single down-covered chick (whitish but becoming rather dark grey over the crown and back). The adult completely covered the nest when brooding the chick, its tail and breast protruding well beyond the confines of the nest. Remarkably, another nest of this species was found in the same reserve in early September 2010, a similar structure but sited *c.*9m above the ground in a tree, *c.*2m from the main trunk in the outer foliage, and very close to a small stream. The nest was partially obscured on three sides by dying or live leaves and was heavily shaded from above by live foliage (GMK pers. obs.).

STATUS Olivaceous Piha is currently listed as Least Concern (BirdLife International 2004, 2009). Its status is extremely difficult to ascertain because of the species' retiring nature, but Olivaceous Piha seems to be uncommon to rare (Ridgely and Tudor 1994, 2009, Stotz *et al.* 1996). There is still much habitat remaining within the Olivaceous Piha's known elevational range and it is protected within several reserves and national parks, e.g. in Colombia, Las Orquídeas National Park, dpto. Antioquia, Reserva El Pangan, dpto. Nariño, and Reserva Mirabilis Swarovksi, dpto. Cauca (Boyla and Estrada 2005, Salaman *et al.* 2008), and Reserva Rio Ñambí and Reserva La Planada, both dpto. Nariño (Bohórquez 2003, Snow 2004a). It is considered to be 'regular' in Cueva de los Guácharos National Park, dpto. Huila, Colombia (Hilty and Brown 1986). In Ecuador the species is known from Otonga reserve, prov. Cotopaxi (Freile and Chaves 2004), and Reserva Las Gralarias near Mindo, prov. Pichincha.

REFERENCES Alverson *et al.* (2001), BirdLife International (2004, 2008), Bohórquez (2003), Boyla and Estrada (2005), Dunning (2008), Freile and Chaves (2004), Hellmayr (1929b), Hilty and Brown (1986), Hornbuckle (1999), Kirwan and Marlow (1996), Kirwan *et al.* (2006), Krabbe and Nilsson (2003), Mee *et al.* (2002), Pearman (1993), Prum (2001), Restall *et al.* (2006), Ridgely and Greenfield (2001), Ridgely and Tudor (1994, 2009), Salaman *et al.* (2008, 2009), Schulenberg (2002), Schulenberg *et al.* (2007), Snow (1982, 2004a), Stotz *et al.* (1996), Zimmer (1930, 1936b).

Olivaceous Piha *Snowornis cryptolophus*. **Figs. 1–2**. Sex unknown, *S. c. mindoensis*, Refugio Paz de las Antpittas, prov. Pichincha, northwest Ecuador, July (*Roger Ahlman / www.pbase.com/ahlman*). No black feathers are visible in the crown, which might suggest the bird is a female, but if present these can often be concealed, making sex determination not always possible. **Fig. 3**. Sex unknown, *S. c. mindoensis*, Refugio Paz de las Antpittas, prov. Pichincha, northwest Ecuador, October (*Leif Gabrielsen*). **Figs. 4–5**. Adult and young in the nest, *S. c. mindoensis*, Refugio Paz de las Antpittas, prov. Pichincha, northwest Ecuador, November (*Ron Hoff*). This was the first-ever nest to be discovered by ornithologists; another was found at the same site more recently. Note the relative size of the adult compared to the tiny nest, which is a feature of the nests of many cotingas.

Genus *Rupicola*: cocks-of-the-rock

In outward appearance arguably the closest Neotropical equivalent to the birds of paradise (Paradisaeidae) of Wallacea and the Australo-Papuan regions, the two species of cocks-of-the-rock are frequently considered to be amongst the most spectacular of the great many extravagant Neotropical birds. Both members of the superspecies possess a highly 'colourful' lekking display, and the wispy processes on the secondary feathers of Guianan Cock-of-the Rock *R. rupicola* match closely the plumage of some birds of paradise, further enhancing the similarities.

ANDEAN COCK-OF-THE-ROCK
Rupicola peruvianus   Plate 30

Pipra peruviana Latham, 1790, *Index Orn.* 2: 555, [based on Le Coq-de-Roche du Pérou, of Buffon, *Hist. Nat. Oiseaux* 4: 437, and Daubenton, *Planches Enl.* 745] [Chanchamayo, dpto. Junín,] Peru

Alongside the toucans (Ramphastidae) and macaws (Psittacidae), this denizen of steep Andean ravines will epitomise the Neotropical avifauna for many birdwatchers, and a visit to one of the species' many known lek sites is surely a highlight of any trip to the tropical Andes. Andean Cock-of-the-Rock has been chosen to serve as the National Bird of Peru.

IDENTIFICATION 29.8–34.0cm. Appearance is remarkable and unmistakable within its range, given that the two species of *Rupicola* are allopatric. A large, long-tailed red cotingid with a powerful, broad-based (15mm) bill and strong legs and toes. Both sexes have permanently erected crests; the male's is almost disc-shaped and virtually conceals the bill. Males are orange-red to deep scarlet, depending on race, with contrasting black wings and tail, and the enlarged tertials being ash-grey. The female retains the distinctive *Rupicola* shape, but the crest is more tuft-like and the resplendent oranges and reds of the male are replaced by orange-brown, which becomes more subdued over the wings and tail.

DISTRIBUTION Andean Cock-of-the-Rock is found virtually throughout the tropical section of the Andean chain, from Barinas in Venezuela southwards through all three Andean cordilleras of Colombia (on both their eastern and western slopes); in Ecuador on the west slope as far south as the Cotopaxi area, on the east slope throughout; and in eastern Peru and in northwest Bolivia as far as dptos. La Paz and Cochabamba. The species was long known in Venezuela from just three specimens, two of them of uncertain provenance, until its 'rediscovery' on Cerro El Teteo, Táchira, in March 1969 (Snow 1982). Elevational range: 600–1,550m in Venezuela (Hilty 2003, Weller and Rengifo 2003), but overall Andean Cock-of-the-Rock is recorded from *c*.350m (once in Colombia) to 2,400m (Salaman *et al.* 2002b, Snow 2004a, Schulenberg *et al.* 2007).

MOVEMENTS None known, although Hilty (1997) recorded the species as a vagrant at his study site in the Pacific Andes of Colombia (presumably this was either a wandering individual or reflective of the species' known propensity to cover quite large distances in search of good feeding opportunities. Furthermore, the bird at 350m in Colombia was also presumably a wanderer (Salaman *et al.* 2002b; T. M. Donegan *in litt.* 2009). Generally, however, site fidelity is very strong throughout the year.

HABITAT Very much a bird of the upper tropical and subtropical zones, in montane areas, and is closely associated with ravines, steep-sided river gorges, and rocky outcrops principally in heavily forested areas, at low and mid levels.

DESCRIPTION The sexes differ. Bill, legs and feet are all strong, the bill with an arched culmen and a broad base. Lacks rictal bristles. The casque-like crest is very narrow and comprises separate rows of fluffy feathers that meet along their midline. Primaries are modified only insomuch as p10 has a very long and slender tip that is notched over the inner vane, whilst the secondaries are unusually broad and square-ended. *R. p. peruvianus* is described here (see Geographical Variation below). *Adult male.* – Body feathers (including the crest) as well as the upper and under surfaces of the lesser wing-coverts are bright orange-red. Broad ash-grey tertials contrasting with the jet-black upper surface to the rest of the wing (the tertials also have darker bases, but these are usually concealed). The pale grey shafts to the bases of the primaries show as an indistinct patch at rest. The upper tail feathers are velvety black. Underside of median and greater coverts black, whilst from below the remiges appear grey with almost white bases to the primaries, thus mirroring the pale patch on the upper surface of the wing. Undertail feathers are black. *Adult female.* – Crest is smaller (both laterally and vertically) than that of the male, being almost tuft-like and set further forward on the forehead. The majority of the plumage is orange-brown with a greyer cast to the tail feathers. Wings browner and duskier than the rest of the upperparts, but the fringes of

R. p. sanguinolentus

R. p. aequatorialis

R. p. peruvianus

R. p. saturatus

the coverts and tertials are slightly more ginger-coloured. Underparts rather variable but are generally orange-brown, some individuals being brighter on the belly than others and usually having a darker throat. *Juvenile.* – Apparently undescribed (although presumably broadly recalls that of Guianan Cock-of-the-Rock *Rupicola rupicola*, which see). *Immature.* – Based on observations in captivity, males acquire fully adult plumage at 15 months (although Snow 2004a speculated that this might have been unusually early). Immature males are generally very like adults but have more orange plumage, whilst immature females are probably not separable from same-sex adults. Subadult males may have the body feathers washed olive and the modified secondaries not fully adult (Snow 1982). The crest and upperparts feathers and some of the underparts appear to be the first adult feathers to be acquired. The first primary is initially shaped as in the female, and the wing feathers appear to be among the last to be moulted to adult plumage. *Moult.* – Appears to be initiated between October and January in the south of the species' range. However, in Colombia Snow (1982) noted a distinct lack of synchronisation between breeding and moult, with the latter being initiated any time between January and August and the males almost certainly commence feather renewal prior to egg laying by the females. *Bare parts.* – Bill golden-yellow, legs yellow, and irides yellowish-white to dull orange-pink with a yellow orbital ring in males. Females have the bill blackish with or without a yellow tip, the legs are brownish-black to grey and the irides pale blue to whitish. Bare-parts colorations vary geographically (see below).

MEASUREMENTS (BMNH; ROM; ZMA) *R. p. aequatorialis*: wing of male (*n* = 8) 178–189mm, wing of female (*n* = 7) 170–185mm; tail of male (*n* = 6) 118–132mm, tail of female (*n* = 8) 116–126mm; bill of male (*n* = 8) 25.23–33.0mm, bill of female (*n* = 6) 26–32mm; tarsus of male (*n* = 6) 33–38mm, tarsus of female (*n* = 7) 31–34mm. *R. p. saturatus*: wing of male (*n* = 2) 182–189mm; tail of male (*n* = 2) 120–124mm. Data from live birds (in southern Colombia): wing of male (*n* = 4) 177–194mm, wing of female (*n* = 4) 182–187mm; bill of female (*n* = 2) 28.5–32.0mm; tarsus of female (*n* = 2) 28.0–32.9mm (T. M. Donegan *et al.* unpubl. data). Weight (mainly *R. p. saturatus*): 230–312g (17 males) and 195–239g (13 females) (Snow 2004a, Dunning 2008; FMNH; MVZ; ROM; T. M. Donegan *et al.* unpubl. data; J. C. Luna and J. P. López/ProAves unpubl. data).

GEOGRAPHICAL VARIATION Obvious in males, but distinctly less marked in females. Polytypic, with four subspecies generally recognised (e.g., Dickinson 2003, Snow 2004b). *R. p. sanguinolentus* Gould, 1859, of the West Andes of Colombia and northwest Ecuador has the body plumage of the male scarlet and the irides deep red, whilst the female is rather variable but generally slightly more gingery, with pale red irides and a grey to pinkish-grey orbital ring. *R. p. aequatorialis* Taczanowski, 1889 (synonym *R. p. aureus* Chapman, 1912), occurs in the Andes of northwest Venezuela in dptos. Barinas and southern Táchira (Hilty 2003, Weller and Rengifo 2003); the central and eastern cordilleras of Colombia; eastern Ecuador, and south to dptos. Cajamarca, Amazonas and northern San Martín in Peru. The body plumage of the male is bright orange and the black bases to the tertials are exposed, whereas in the other three subspecies the grey on these feathers extends over the entire area that can be observed in the field. In parallel, females of this subspecies are the reddest

of any of the races. Males have the irides bright yellow to orange-yellow with a yellow orbital ring, and females have whitish to brown irides. Chapman's synonym, *aureus*, was based on two pairs from dpto. Cauca, in the central Andes of Colombia, which he regarded as being more orange, especially on the crest, compared with *peruvianus*, with more restricted grey on the tertials in the male, and the female as being generally more orange, but his diagnosis was based on limited comparative material and has since been shown to be inadequate. Nominate **R. p. peruvianus** occurs in central Peru from southern dpto. San Martín to dpto. Junín. It has the plumage paler orange than *aequatorialis* and is described above. *R. p. saturatus* Cabanis & Heine, 1859, of southeast Peru, in dptos. Cuzco and Puno, to northwest Bolivia has the body plumage deep orange-red, approaching that of *sanguinolentus*, and males have pale blue to whitish irides with a pale orange-yellow orbital ring, whilst females sometimes have brown irides in this race.

VOICE A loud and far-carrying, somewhat pig-like, *uankk* is uttered by both sexes when foraging or in flight, and also when disturbed or surprised. Various squealing and other guttural noises are made by males at the lek site, principally a loud *youii*, which is less raucous than the equivalent vocalisation of *R. rupicola*, and also a *kip-kip-kip* that may be repeated for long periods. Published recordings of the species' voice exist on the following audio compilations: Connop (1996, 2004), Moore and Lysinger (1997), Boesman (1999, 2006b, 2009), Moore *et al.* (1999), Álvarez-Rebolledo (2000), Mayer (2000), Schulenberg (2000a), Krabbe and Nilsson (2003) and Alvarez *et al.* (2007). Recordings from Bolivia, Colombia, Ecuador, Peru and Venezuela are archived online at www.xeno-canto.org.

NATURAL HISTORY Generally, Andean Cock-of-the-Rock is a bird of the tall understorey and midstorey. Perhaps despite their appearance, these birds are powerful and adept in flight, being capable of very rapid changes of direction. Away from lek sites, females are usually met with alone but males forage in 'pairs' (although they roost alone: Snow 1982). Birds disperse widely from the lek site, which is usually sited on sloping ground, throughout the day, often crossing cleared areas, only to reassemble in the mid afternoon (until dusk), where, with patience, a quiet observer can observe one of the most amazing spectacles in the animal world (see below).

FOOD AND FEEDING Andean Cock-of-the-Rock forages for fruit by sallying from a perch into a tree or shrub, plucking a fruit in flight and then landing on a different perch, all attended by much wing noise and disturbance of the foliage. Large insects are taken occasionally, and the species has been twice observed following army ant swarms with other bird species, presumably searching for insect prey disturbed by the ants (Gochfeld and Tudor 1978, Rios *et al.* 2008). Twenty-six species of fruit were known in this cock-of-the-rock's diet at the time of Moermond and Denslow's (1985) survey of fruit eating in Neotropical birds. A few additional species, including *Cecropia telealba* (Urticaceae), have been noted since then (Ríos 2005), but those of three families, Lauraceae, Annonaceae and Rubiaceae, appear to be the most important (Benalcázar and Benalcázar *in* Snow 1982). In captivity Andean Cock-of-the-Rock has been reported taking small mice and anoles (Delgado-V. and Brooks 2003), and small lizards and frogs appear to be significant in nestling diet (like many cotingas, this species seems to select a distinctly more omnivorous diet for its young). Such prey are first beaten against a branch and then presented to the nestlings head-first (Snow 2004a).

DISPLAY The following is summarised from the observations of Benalcázar and Benalcázar (*in* Snow 1982) in southwest Colombia and those of ourselves in northwest and eastern Ecuador and northwest Venezuela. For images of the displays see, for instance, photographs in Snow (2004a: 58–59). In addition to the afternoon display period, the lek is also occupied from first light, again for up to two or three hours, with up to 15 birds, but usually fewer, present at each display ground. However, Olalla and Magalhães (1956) mention discovering a lek site in eastern Ecuador with 'dozens' of males in attendance. Each bird has a series of favoured perches, often lianas (4–15m above the ground), which it uses in rotation and periodically briefly departs the central area of the lek site, only to return again within a few minutes. Each male has his own 'court', but there is a strictly hierachial system and at least at some leks there is a single dominant male whose court is larger than those of the other males in attendance and he is the only one to mate with any females that visit the display area. Benalcázar and Benalcázar (*op cit.*) found that this dominant male usually was the first to arrive and last to leave the display ground, that he would initiate attacks on his male 'partner' (see below), and that it is the dominant male that chases any 'strange' males or juveniles from the lek. Males display in twos (perhaps occasionally in trios), by simultaneously indulging in a 'confrontational display', involving the birds facing each other (thereby displaying the grey tertials), bowing and jumping, flapping their wings (and occasionally snapping their bills), all the while uttering various grunting and squawking calls (see Voice). Males can occasionally appear to overbalance on their perches whilst displaying. The cacophony of sounds (which may be audible several hundred metres away) and the flurry of movement all peak when a female appears (up to five different females, either singly or in small groups, visited the lek studied by Benalcázar and Benalcázar *op. cit.*). Only brief intervals separate each bout of displaying, but copulation only occurred during the morning display period, and then usually very early, at the lek in Colombia. Whenever the dominant male was copulating with a female, his 'partner' male would either remain still or display alone. At the lek studied by Benalcázar and Benalcázar (*op. cit.*) 'pairs' of males were usually separated by 6–9m and the total width of the arena used by the different birds was 20–25m. Away from the lek, even such brightly coloured birds as these can be surprisingly difficult to observe, as they spend long periods perched quietly out of view.

BREEDING This is quite well known (compared with many other cotingas). The nest is a bracket-like structure forming a cone shape and placed 3–12m above the ground, usually on a rock face, and often in relatively close company with other nests. However, this semi-colonial behaviour is, as noted by Snow (1982), presumably a consequence of the relative lack of suitable nesting sites, rather than a predisposition to congregate to breed. The species prefers to nest in wet gorges or at the entrance to caves, in groups of up to at least nine nests, with the birds engaging in some competition for favoured sites both with other female *Rupicola* and other bird species. Nesting sites can be up to 1km distant from the lek (Hilty and Brown 1986). The nest is usually considered to be constructed principally of mud, but the concave cup is lined with coarse vegetable fibres, and may be reused (following some repair) in subsequent nesting seasons (Benalcázar and Benalcázar *op. cit.*, wherein nest and egg dimensions are presented). H. F. Greeney (*in litt.* 2010) has suggested, however, that nests might actually be constructed of compacted vegetable matter with some mud admixed, rather than simply earth. To date, it seems that no one has observed a nest in the process of construction, to either confirm or deny this. The clutch is two and the eggs are pale buffish to buff-brown with lilac-grey and olive-brown spotting concentrated at the larger end. They are incubated for 28 days and laid *c.*24 hours apart. The fledging period is generally 42–44 days (Snow 1982) but occupied 4–6 days more in one instance. Females alone are responsible for tending the nest, eggs and young, and sometimes continue to feed the young once they have fledged. Benalcázar and Benalcázar (*op. cit.*) presented more information on incubation and provisioning of the young. Pérez and Lyons Pérez (1998) described the discovery in September of an *R. peruvianus* nest on the crossbeam below a concrete bridge and *c.*5m above a river; the vegetation in the vicinity was cutover secondary forest. This site was reused in late July the subsequent year (Lyons and Perez 2000) and is still being used periodically more than a decade later (H. F. Greeney *in litt.* 2010). Other breeding data from northwest Ecuador involve 15 nests discovered near Mindo in July 1991 to February 1992 (Pérez and Lyons Pérez 1998), and in the same general area there was a female on a nest in early July and a female brooding a nestling in late August (Greeney and Nunnery 2005). In Colombia the species appears mainly to breed in February–July, just after the main wet season (Snow 1982, Hilty and Brown 1986; MVZ; ROM), there are records of nests of young in Peru in November (Janni *et al.* 2008), and the onset of laying appears to occur in August in Bolivia (Snow 1982, 2004). For further information on the breeding cycle in Bolivia see Maillard and Caballero (2003), and for captive data see Berry *et al.* (1982) and Kendall and Kuehler (1989).

STATUS Andean Cock-of-the-Rock is categorised as Least Concern (BirdLife International 2004, 2008). Individual populations may be threatened anywhere in the species' range by habitat destruction, but *R. peruvianus* as a whole is not threatened at present. Indeed the species can appear to be locally common in some areas, and is protected within many conservation areas, both privately and publicly owned, throughout most of its range. It is perhaps easiest to observe at the San Isidro road in Barinas, western Venezuela; in the Mindo and Tandayapa area (especially at the newly created Refugio Paz de Aves, where there is a specially constructed hide overlooking a lek site), in Pichincha province, northwest Ecuador (the blood red *sanguinolentus*); and below Abra Patricia, in San Martín, and in the Macchu Picchu area and the Manu Road, both in Cuzco, Peru. Another specially constructed hide at Cock-of-the-Rock Lodge along the upper Manu Road provides a comfortable and surefire locality for this beautiful bird (Walker 2009).

REFERENCES Álvarez-Rebolledo (2000), Alvarez *et al.* (2007), Alverson *et al.* (2001), Balchin and Toyne (1998), Benalcázar and Benalcázar (1984), Berry *et al.* (1982), BirdLife International (2004, 2008), Boesman (1998, 1999, 2006b, 2009), Boyla and Estrada (2005), Chapman (1912, 1921), Connop (1996, 2004), David and Gosselin (2002b), Delgado and Brooks (2003), Dickinson (2003), Donegan and Dávalos (1999), Donegan *et al.* (2010), Dunning (2008), Freile and Chaves (2004), Gochfeld and

Tudor (1978), Greeney and Nunnery (2005), Hellmayr (1929b), Hennessey (2004b), Hennessey and Gomez (2003), Hennessey *et al.* (2003a), Hilty (1997, 2003), Hilty and Brown (1986), Hornbuckle (1999), Janni *et al.* (2008), Kendall and Kuehler (1989), Kirwan and Marlow (1996), Krabbe and Nilsson (2003), Lönnberg and Rendahl (1922), Luy and Bigio (1994), Lyons and Perez (2000), MacLeod *et al.* (2005), Maillard and Caballero (2003), Mark *et al.* (2008), Mayer (2000), Mee *et al.* (2002), Meyer de Schauensee (1966, 1970), Mlíkovský (2009), Moermond and Denslow (1985), Moore and Lysinger (1997), Moore *et al.* (1999), Ocampo (2002), Ohlson *et al.* (2007, 2008), Olalla and Magalhães (1956), Olson (1971), Parker and Parker (1982), Parker *et al.* (1982, 1985), Pérez and Lyons Pérez (1998), Perry *et al.* (1997), Restall *et al.* (2006), Ridgely and Greenfield (2001), Ridgely and Tudor (1994, 2009), Ríos (2005), Rios *et al.* (2008), Robbins *et al.* (in press), Robiller (2005), Rodriguez-Ferraro and Azpiroz (2005), Salaman *et al.* (1999, 2008), Schuchmann *et al.* (1989), Schulenberg (2000a), Schulenberg *et al.* (2007), Snow (1962a, 1982, 2004a), Stotz *et al.* (1996), Walker (2009), Walker *et al.* (2006), Weller and Rengifo (2003) , Zimmer (1930).

Andean Cock-of-the-Rock *Rupicola peruvianus*. **Fig. 1**. Male, *R. p. aequatorialis*, Afluente, dpto. San Martin, northern Peru, November (*Hadoram Shirihai / Photographic Handbook to Birds of the World*). Both sexes of this species are unmistakable and males must surely qualify as one of the most spectacular bird species on Earth. **Fig. 2**. Male, *R. p. sanguinolentus*, Refugio Paz de las Antpittas, prov. Pichincha, northwest Ecuador, November (*Hadoram Shirihai / Photographic Handbook to Birds of the World*). Males are blood red in this subspecies, which is found on the west side of the Andes in Colombia and Ecuador. **Fig. 3**. Male, *R. p. saturatus*, Cock-of-the-Rock Lodge, dpto. Cuzco, southeast Peru, July (*Harvey van Diek*). In this subspecies (the southernmost), males are deep orange with pale (white to bluish) irides. **Fig. 4**. Female, *R. p. aequatorialis*, Río Bombuscaro, Podocarpus National Park, dpto. Zamora-Chinchipe, southeast Ecuador, November (*Hadoram Shirihai / Photographic Handbook to Birds of the World*). Variation in overall plumage colour and iris coloration is subtler in females, this bird's irides are whitish, but female *R. p. peruvianus*, at least, can also show very pale irides. **Fig. 5**. Immature male, *R. p. saturatus*, Paradise Lodge, dpto. Cuzco, southeast Peru, September (*Roger Ahlman / www.pbase.com/ahlman*).

GUIANAN COCK-OF-THE-ROCK
Rupicola rupicola   **Plate 30**

Pipra rupicola **Linnaeus, 1766**, *Syst. Nat.*, edn. 12(1): 338, Cayenne

This, the Guianan Shield representative of the genus, is equally (if not even more) spectacular as its Andean congener. In captivity, the species has been reported to live up to 15 years (Blake 1950).

IDENTIFICATION 27–33cm. Like its Andean relative, the male Guianan Cock-of-the-Rock is an exceptionally brightly coloured bird and this species is further adorned with delicate silky plumes on the lower back and scapulars especially, like fine orange peel, provoking comparisons with the birds of paradise. The male is unlikely to be confused with any other species due to the allopatry of its congener, and the female although much less distinctive still bears the combination of heavy shape, broad-based bill and crest that makes this genus so instantly recognisable.

DISTRIBUTION Restricted to the Guianan Shield, *R. rupicola* occurs across all of the Guianas (but mainly in the interior of each country), southern Venezuela (in dptos. Amazonas and Bolívar), easternmost Colombia (in dptos. Vichada south to at least southernmost Vaupés) and northern Brazil north of the Amazon and east of the Rio Negro, in the states of Amazonas, Roraima, Pará and northern Amapá, and reaching its southernmost limit *c.*100km north of the city of Manaus around Presidente Figueiredo. The species' elevational range reaches to at least 1,500m on the Brazilian side of the Cerro de la Neblina (Willard *et al.* 1991) and to 2,000m elsewhere in southern Venezuela (Hilty 2003), but it is usually found at elevations below 1,200m.

MOVEMENTS None definitely recorded, but it is speculated that the extremely long dry season in 1964 might have led to the appearance of an individual at Colakreek, in the northern savannas of Surinam, where the species is not usually found (Ottema *et al.* 2009: 116). On the other hand, Snow (2004a) mentioned that a nesting female that was fitted with a radio transmitter in French Guiana never moved more than 400m from the nest.

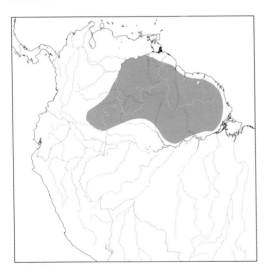

HABITAT The species is found in humid tall rainforest, principally in the lower and middle growth, and especially near the huge boulders and rocky caves required for nesting. Equally at home in tall secondary forest as primary growth, and Guianan Cock-of-the-Rock is also found in lower stature *terra firme* on sandy soil. Leks are generally sited in relatively closed-canopy areas (Omena Júnior 2009).

DESCRIPTION The sexes differ. Bill has a strongly arched culmen and a slightly hooked tip. The tarsal scutes can be pronounced and the tarsi and feet are usually extremely powerful with sharp claws to the feet. There are no rictal bristles. Like the Andean species, *R. rupicola* has a strong bill, and the crest is formed by two rows of compressed feathers that appear almost as if pressed together along the midline. In addition to the plumage modifications noted below, the innermost primary (p10) is modified in an identical manner to the same feather in Andean Cock-of-the-Rock *Rupicola peruvianus. Adult male.* – Unmistakable given the species' bright orange plumage and fan-like crest formed by two rows of feathers pressed together. The tips of the crest feathers are paler orange and bordered by a crimson subterminal line (*c.*1.5mm wide). Feathered eye-ring crimson-orange. The mantle, back and rump are all orange. Feathers of the lower back and rump are modified, with silky filaments that cover most of the tail at rest. Silky orange plumes are also present on the inner secondaries and scapulars. Tertials are rather square-cut, in colour brownish-black with broad orange-buff tips and orange plumes on the outer fringe. Most of the wing is usually obscured by the plumes at rest, but a white patch formed by the paler bases to the primaries is prominent, and the white lengthens on the feathers proximally. Secondaries fringed orange on outer web and tipped whitish. Orange-buff tips to greater primary-coverts. The tail feathers are very warm pale brown with broad pale orange-buff tips, becoming even paler and whiter over the inner webs. Viewed from below (as is often the case, this species sits motionless for lengthy periods and suddenly plucks a fruit in an explosive sally) the male appears totally orange apart from the brown undertail. Underwing-coverts orange, underside of flight feathers brown distally with large white basal areas extending along the inner webs of the inner primaries and secondaries. *Adult female.* – Rather uniformly dark or smoky brown, becoming greyer over the head, apart from the pale orange underwing-coverts and axillaries. Undertail-coverts rather variable, but some females possess a warmer coloration to this tract whilst others are almost pale orange. There are traces of plume-like feathers on the scapulars and outer secondaries. Small tuft-like crest, but this is not fan-shaped as in the male. *Juvenile.* – The only details come from a bird bred in captivity and are taken from Snow (1982). This individual was predominantly dull grey-brown (approaching the colour of the adult female) above, with whitish underparts washed straw yellow, and whitish feathers above and behind the eyes. The secondaries have long whitish to straw-coloured fringes and these are much longer than in the adult female with more white on the inner webs. *Immature.* – The female is like the adult of the same sex, whilst males of the same age are also female-like but are flecked with orange feathers. By two years old they are mainly orange with small brown blotches and they achieve full adult plumage when three years old (Snow 1982), although Omena Júnior and Martins (2007) considered that adult plumage is acquired in as few as 19 months. *Moult.* – There are few published moult data, but Snow (1976a, 1982) summarised the strategy as follows. Feather renewal occupies 5.5 months and, at least in the Guianas, males must commence moulting before females have laid (males starting in February–March versus April–July in females, in Venezuela, with respective data from Amazonas, Brazil, being January–March for males). Snow (1982) suspected that later starting females had probably completed nesting duties prior to the onset of moult, and suggested that those commencing in April were perhaps failed breeders. One specimen collected in southern Venezuela in late February was in light body moult (Willard *et al.* 1991). *Bare parts* – Males have the irides orange-red, the bill orange-red becoming paler at the tip, and the legs and feet orange-red, whereas in females the bill is dark brown with a yellow culmen and tip, the irides are orange and the legs dark to brownish-yellow.

MEASUREMENTS (BMNH; MNRJ; ZMA: northern Brazil/southern Venezuela, Guyana, Surinam: bill-length = exposed culmen) Wing of male (*n* = 20) 173–183mm, wing of female (*n* = 11) 161–178mm; tail of male (*n* = 18) 73–93mm, tail of female (*n* = 7) 70–94mm; bill of male (*n* = 19) 21.16–31.21mm, bill of female (*n* = 10) 25.69–32.01mm; tarsus of male (*n* = 7) 32–33mm, tarsus of female (*n* = 6) 30–36mm. Weight: 186–225g (males) and 140–226g (females) (Dickerman and Phelps 1982, Snow 1982, 2004a, Willard *et al.* 1991, Hilty 2003, Dunning 2008; FMNH; MVZ).

GEOGRAPHICAL VARIATION Monotypic.

VOICE At leks males utter a variety of loud crowing, mono-syllabic, chicken-like notes, whilst both sexes may give a loud *waa-oww* whilst foraging (likened to a rubber duck being strangled). Vocal activity is generally much reduced outside the breeding season, but is augmented considerably by the arrival of a female at the lek (Omena Júnior 2009). Most calls have a frequency around 1kHz and possess a tonal quality similar to the miaowing of a domestic cat (Sick 1997, Omena Júnior 2009). The first males to arrive at the lek site commence vocalising with what Gilliard (1962) termed the 'assembly call', which is a bugle-like *ka-waooh* or *ka-haaow*, and is accompanied by vigorous movements of the head and forebody (Omena Júnior 2009). What effectively is the song, given solely by males, is a *gau* note lasting c.0.5 seconds. The courtship call, given solely in the presence of a female, every four or five seconds, is a vigorous *gáe*. Aggressive interactions can be accompanied by a whinnying whistle that is apparently produced by the modified tenth primary (Gilliard 1962), but also a vocal monosyllabic *an* note given in rapid succession (Omena Júnior 2009). Alarm-calls, which are uttered by both sexes and sometimes by several individuals simultaneously, comprise a bisyllabic *u-ee* given at irregular intervals (Omena Júnior 2009). The males can prove highly responsive to playback of the foraging call, at least during the nesting season, even when away from the lek site (GMK pers. obs.). Omena Júnior (2009) also reported a vigorous and repeatedly uttered *guem* note by a 16-day-old nestling, exchanging similar calls with the female, and presented sonograms of various of the species' vocalisations. Published recordings are available on rather few compilations: Boesman (2006a, 2006b), Omena Júnior (2007) and Renaudier and Deroussen (2008), but recordings from Brazil, Surinam and Venezuela are available online at www.xeno-canto.org.

NATURAL HISTORY Equally as difficult to locate as its congener away from lek sites; equally as spectacular at the display grounds, as with Andean Cock-of-the-Rock, the Guianan species is usually found in the tall understorey and the midstorey. Various large raptors, including species of *Leucopternis, Accipiter, Buteogallus, Micrastur* and *Spizaetus,* have been recorded predating *R. rupicola* (Trail 1987). Omena Júnior (2009) observed a Channel-billed Toucan *Ramphastos vitellinus* attacking two Guianan Cocks-of-the-Rock at a lek, apparently as the former wished to defend a fruiting tree.

FOOD AND FEEDING Diet is principally frugivorous and like Andean Cock-of-the-Rock fruits (and insects) are usually taken in flight, but also, like the latter species, this species is known to predate large insects, small lizards and frogs (Olalla and Magalhães 1956, Snow 2004a, Omena Júnior and Santos 2010), and to occasionally follow *Eciton burchelli* army ant swarms (Willis 1983) and mixed-species flocks (Jullien and Thiollay 1998). Vertebrate prey is probably more important in the diet of nestlings (even including small snakes), but fruit still forms the majority of food offered to the young (Omena Júnior and Santos 2010). Although not specified, it is assumed that this species dispatches vertebrate prey in the same manner as in *R. peruvianus*, and this species seems to prefer to feed mainly in the midstorey and in trees with an abundance of fruits (Omena Júnior and Santos 2010). A wide range of fruits have been recorded in the Guianan Cock-of-the-Rock's diet: for instance, Érard *et al.* (1989) identified 65 plant species belonging to 31 families, of which Annonaceae, Arecaceae, Lauraceae, Burseraceae, Myristicaceae, Meliaceae and Araliaceae were regarded as the most important (Lloyd 1895, Carvalho and Kloss 1950, Olalla and Magalhães 1956, Snow 1971b, Snow 2004b, Omena Júnior and Santos 2010). Many of these families are of particular importance to a great many specialised avian frugivores in the Neotropics (Snow 1982).

DISPLAY The display differs strikingly from *R. peruvianus* in being ground-based, with each court sometimes being just 1–2m apart. First described by Schomburgk (1848), incorrectly, and then by Gilliard (1962), Snow (1971b, 1976b) and Omena Júnior (2009), leks can number up to 50 males (e.g. in Raleigh Falls-Voltzberg National Park, Surinam), although much smaller numbers are more usual. Display arenas are, like those of the previous species, traditionally sited on sloping ground, such as ridges, in forest between 15 and 30m tall, and are used year after year. Lekking is quite strongly seasonal, unlike in some Cotingidae, and for instance in northern Brazil lasts from November to April, although young males may occasionally display outside the breeding season (Omena Júnior 2009). In Guyana (Gilliard 1962) and northern Brazil (Omena Júnior 2009) display is concentrated in the afternoon, although females may also appear at the leks at other times of the day, e.g. the late morning. Each male's court can be up to 1.5 × 2.0m across, but smaller and less-regularly used courts can be as small as 0.5m wide (see Fig. 1 *in* Omena Júnior 2009: 89). The overall size of the arena appears to vary, based on Gilliard, Snow and Trail's separate observations, but are probably similar to the size of those of *R. peruvianus*. Each male uses two or more, basically vertical branches from which to launch the display. The main display consists of the male flying to the ground with a loud squawk, then holding the wings up above the back while beating them. It then crouches motionless and silently, whilst depressing the tail, partially spreading the wing feathers to reveal the white speculum, and fanning the rump feathers. This posture may be held for up to several minutes, but it is unclear as to whether males only visit the ground to display when females are present or not. The legs are also flexed to partially raise the rear part of the body and the male only occasionally makes sudden movements while on the ground. Whilst at the lek, the males spend more time on their display branches just above the cleared ground (the birds remove any vegetation debris) on which they display, defending favoured perches with regular noisy displays (such as head-bobbing with bill-clicking, as well as adopting the same postures used on the ground, but in threat to other males, and expanding the wing filaments and splaying the rectrices). Males may engage in even more violent attacks on one another, at least occasionally (Omena Júnior 2009). Young males regularly visit leks, but are chased away by dominant males. Gilliard (1962), Trail (1987) and Omena Júnior (2009) all thought that it is younger males that possess smaller clearings at the periphery of the lek in contrast to older dominant males, although the last-named author found such hierarchy to be less obvious than other commentators. As mentioned, females also frequently visit the leks, prompting more regular displays and greater intensity of vocalisations, but only seem to mate with those dominant males that occupy the courts at the centre of the lek, or the most preferential sites at its edges, initially landing behind the chosen male and sometimes 'nibbling' at the orange peel-like fringes to the rump and wing feathers prior to copulation, which is rarely observed and is rapid (Omena Júnior 2009). The female descends to the ground in the clearing beside the display-perches and the male swiftly mounts holding the female's head feathers in his bill; the female departs immediately afterwards (Omena Júnior 2009). In addition to the presence of a female, the amount of ambient light reaching the arena is also positively correlated with the intensity of display (Omena Júnior 2009). Snow (1971a, 1982) noted how the Guianan Cock-of-the-Rock's lek displays and their social organisation possess obvious parallels with those of the White-bearded Manakin *Manacus manacus*.

BREEDING Females are entirely responsible for all of the nesting duties, and there is no pair bond (just as in Andean Cock-of-the-Rock). Also like *R. peruvianus*, the nest is a solid bracket of mud lined with plant material such as black rootlets and small dead palm leaves, e.g. *Oenocarpus* spp. (Arecaceae) and *Calophylium brasiliense* (Guttiferae) that weighs up to 900g. It is attached to the near-vertical rock wall of a cave or enormous boulder, crevice or simple overhang, but is always sheltered and heavily shaded, and is normally sited within relatively close proximity to running water. Saliva may be used to cement the nest. Nesting is semi-colonial and the nests can be reused in subsequent years (GMK pers. obs.) and can be as little as 40m from a lekking arena (Omena Júnior 2009), but also up to 200m distant (Trail 1987). At one 'colony' in northern Brazil up to 13 nests were present (Omena Júnior and Martins 2007). Nests can be as low as *c*.2.0m above the ground, i.e. a little above head height, but just out of reach from humans reaching up, and can be sited within <3m of one another (more usually 5m). Other nests are located 9.2m above the ground, but in northern Brazil most were at <4m. Females can permit very close approach when on the nest (GMK pers. obs.). Either one or two eggs are laid (usually the latter in first clutches, but 50:50 in repeat clutches) and these, like those of its sister species, are pale buffish-brown, or white, overlain with lilac-grey and dark brown markings, especially at the larger end. Snow (1982) presented the dimensions and mass of the eggs, as well as some details of incubatory bouts. In Guyana incubation apparently averages 28.5 days and the chicks take 33–44 days to fledge, but in northern Brazil Omena Júnior and Martins

(2007) reported much shorter fledging periods. Clutches are usually initiated in March–April in Guyana (Snow 1982). In French Guiana the species nests from November to April (Tostain *et al.* 1992), and at one site in Surinam nests were active between January and April (Trail 1984, 1985a, 1985b). In northern Brazil, Omena Júnior and Martins (2007) found that the breeding season commenced in late October/early November and continued until late April, but that eggs were laid between 1 January and 7 March (peaking in the second half of February). The first chick fledged on 15 March and the last on 3 May, and of 33 nests followed by these authors 12 were predated by snakes or other birds. The wet season starts in earnest in February in this region, at which time the ground below the nests (even in the normally dry caves it selects for breeding) can be heavily waterlogged. Much earlier, Euler (1900), who perhaps gave the first (very basic) description of this bird's nest, mentioned that nests in northern Brazil had also been found in December and April. A juvenile male was collected near the Rio Mucajaí, Roraima (Brazil), in early April (Pinto 1966), and Olivares (1964) found two nests with nearly grown nestlings in May near Mitú, in eastern Colombia. On the Cerro Tamacuarí, southern Venezuela, both sexes were in breeding condition early in the year (January–March) (Barrowclough *et al.* (1995), the same seemed true in southern Amazonas at the Cerro de la Neblina (Willard *et al.* 1991), as well as elsewhere in the extreme south of the country (Dickerman and Phelps 1982). Hanif (1967) and Duce and Brannian (1990) studied the behaviour of this species in captivity.

STATUS Categorised as Least Concern (BirdLife International 2004, 2008), although the species is included on the Brazilian Red Data list on account of the fact that the young are frequently taken from the nests by animal traffickers, and Hilty and Brown (1986) reported that the species also turns up in the cagebird trade in Colombia. In their study in northern Brazil, Omena Júnior and Martins (2007) monitored 33 young, of which trappers took eight. Locally common to uncommon, with large areas of primary forest remaining within the species' range, but Guianan Cock-of-the-Rock is plainly localised due to the relative scarcity of suitable nest-sites. At a study site in French Guiana, Thiollay (1994) estimated the density of *R. rupicola* at four pairs per 100ha. The species is known from a relatively small number of protected areas, including Canaima National Park, in southern Venezuela, Raleigh Falls-Voltzberg National Park, in Surinam, Iwokrama Forest Reserve, in Guyana, and at least two conservation units in the vicinity of Presidente Figueiredo, Brazil, as well as Parque Nacional Montanhas do Tumucumaque, Amapá, in the same country. Perhaps the most accessible site is that in Venezuela, in southern Bolívar, around km 111 on the Escalera road on the Sierra de Lema, where patient searching should locate a stunning male at almost any time of day. Other accessible lek sites include Kaieteur Falls, Guyana (Collins 2007), and that at Iracema Falls (the 'Palácio do Galo'), near Presidente Figueiredo, Brazil. *R. rupicola* is speculated to occur in Chiribiquete National Park in eastern Colombia (Boyla and Estrada 2005) and it presumably occurs in El Tuparro National Park in easternmost Colombia, as the species is known from the environs of the Maipures rapids at the edge of the park (Dugand and Phelps 1946), but the species is generally local in this country (Hilty and Brown 1986). It is also considered rather local in French Guiana, where there are just three known leks (Tostain *et al.* 1992; J. Ingels *in litt.* 2010), with that at Montagne de Kaw, in the Réserve Naturelle de Kaw-

Roura, the most frequently visited (Renaudier 2009). In 2009, the Groupe d'Étude et de Protection des Oiseaux en Guyane started a scheme to guard this lek and in future hopes to install an observation hide there in order to reduce the impact of visiting birders, especially during the 'high' season of November onwards (J. Ingels *in litt.* 2010). Guianan Cock-of-the Rock is perhaps somewhat widespread in Surinam (being known from *c.*15 sites) although it is never more than locally common (Ottema et al. 2009) and the species is considered fairly common in Guyana (Braun *et al.* 2007).

REFERENCES Barnett *et al.* (2002), Barrowclough *et al.* (1995), Bernard (2008), BirdLife International (2004, 2008), Blake (1950), Boesman (2006a, 2006b), Boyla and Estrada (2005), Carvalho and Kloss (1950), Braun *et al.* (2007), Cherrie (1916), Collins (2007), David and Gosselin (2002b), Dickerman and Phelps (1982), Duce and Brannian (1990), Dugand and Phelps (1946), Dunning (2008), Érard *et al.* (1989), Euler (1900), Frost (1910), Gilliard (1941, 1962), Hanif (1967), Hellmayr (1929b), Hilty and Brown (1986), Jullien and Thiollay (1998), Lemos (1982), Lloyd (1895), Naka *et al.* (2006), Olivares (1964), Olalla and Magalhães (1956), Olson (1971), Omena Júnior (2007, 2009), Omena Júnior and Martins (2007, 2010), Ottema (2009), Ottema *et al.* (2009), Pérez-Emán *et al.* (2003), Pinto (1944, 1966), Renaudier (2009), Renaudier and Deroussen (2008), Restall *et al.* (2006), Ridgely and Tudor (1994, 2009), Robbins *et al.* (2007), Salaman *et al.* (2008), Schomburgk (1848), Schuckmann-Wegert and Schuchmann (1986), Snow (1971b, 1976b, 1982, 2004a), Snyder (1966), Stotz *et al.* (1996), Thiollay (1994), Tostain *et al.* (1992), Trail (1983, 1985a, 1985b), Willard *et al.* (1991), Willis (1983), Zyskowski *et al.* (2011).

Guianan Cock-of-the-Rock *Rupicola rupicola.* **Fig. 1**. Male, Iracema Falls, north of Manaus, Amazonas, northern Brazil, December (*Hadoram Shirihai / Photographic Handbook to Birds of the World*). The bizarre 'orange-peel' extensions to the lower back feathers give males of this species a very special appearance. **Fig. 2**. Male, Montagne de Kaw, northern French Guiana, December (*Maxime Dechelle*). The Guianan Shield representative of the genus is equally as stunning as the Andean species, but exhibits no geographic variation. **Fig. 3**. Female, Iracema Falls, north of Manaus, Amazonas, northern Brazil, December (*Hadoram Shirihai / Photographic Handbook to Birds of the World*). This bird was close to its nest on a large rock face in *terra firme* forest. **Fig. 4**. Female, Montagne de Kaw, northern French Guiana, December (*Maxime Dechelle*).

Genus *Phoenicircus*: 'red cotingas'

The 'red cotingas' are characterised by their intense carotenoid-rich, saturated red coloration, albeit with much black in the male of one species, Black-necked Red Cotinga *Phoenicircus nigricollis*. The species-pair inhabits tall rainforests of the Amazon and its tributaries, mainly in the northern part of the basin. They are usually treated as being most closely related to the cocks-of-the-rock (ever since Sclater 1888 first postulated this relationship), some researchers consider the two *Phoenicircus* as being very close to manakins, based on their similar tarsal scutellation (which is also similar to *Laniisoma*) and lekking system, but Trail and Donahue (1991) also spotlighted the similarity of the advertising call and head-pumping of the Guianan Red Cotinga *Phoenicircus carnifex* to the *Lipaugus* pihas. There is no doubt that their general morphology does resemble that of some of the larger manakins (cf. Trail and Donahue 1991).

Both members of the superspecies (Haffer 1974, Snow 1979, Sibley and Monroe 1990) are noted for their 'exploded leks' which have been extensively studied in one species, *P. nigricollis*, and indeed permit regular observation at sites such as Yuturi Lodge in Napo, Ecuador, and Explornapo Lodge, Loreto, in Peru. Most of our information concerning the Guianan species' lek system comes from Trail and Donahue (1991). Observing *P. carnifex* in the field is generally more problematic, as much of its vast range is still relatively remote, so observations can require luck or the prolonged observation of a fruiting tree.

GUIANAN RED COTINGA
Phoenicircus carnifex   Plate 31

Lanius carnifex **Linnaeus, 1758**, *Syst. Nat.*, edn. 10(1): 94, Surinam [based on The Red Bird from Surinam, of Edwards, *Nat. Hist. Birds* 1: 39, pl. 39]

This beautiful bird, known as the 'ray of sunlight' in parts of northern Brazil (Novaes 1978), is one of the most-desired but least frequently encountered of the cotingas. Much of its known range is very little visited by birdwatchers, and in those parts that are, such as southeastern Venezuela, the species seems particularly uncommon. However, the increasing interest in the Guianas as a birdwatching destination should enable more birders to gain field experience with this fabulous, over-sized manakin-like bird.

IDENTIFICATION 22–24cm (the female is the larger of the two sexes). Given a reasonable view, both sexes of this species will prove unmistakable in the vast majority of its range. However, south of the Amazon, in the region of the lower Rio Tapajós (and perhaps east of there as far as the lower Rio Xingu), both this species and its congener, Black-necked Red Cotinga *Phoenicircus nigricollis*, seem to occur; e.g. both have apparently been collected at Vila Braga, on the left bank and within the modern-day Amazonia (Tapajós) National Park (Pinto 1944, Oren and Parker 1997). However, although both species have been apparently collected from both banks of the Tapajós, problems over inaccurate labelling of specimens mean that our knowledge of the level of purported sympatry is incredibly sparse, and Maués and Aleixo (2008) have suggested that identification errors are the source for any reports of sympatry. The two are the same size and shape and possess similar habits. In males, note that the dark parts of the plumage, including the terminal tail-band, are much darker and blacker in *nigricollis* than in *carnifex*, and the bill of the former is usually deeper based, whilst the irides in Guianan Red Cotinga are reddish-brown, but much darker in Black-necked. Females are much harder to separate, but *P. nigricollis* tends to have a much darker, redder tail (and rump patch), heavier bill, much more red-saturated underparts extending as high as the lower

throat (paler and more washed-out in *P. carnifex*, in which this colour generally extends only to the breast), and again their eye colours differ as in males.

DISTRIBUTION Northeastern South America, mainly in lower Amazonia: the Guianas, where most frequently recorded in the interior of French Guiana and Surinam, and is reasonably numerous, at least locally, in Guyana (M. B. Robbins *in* Hilty 2003) and easternmost Venezuela in eastern Bolívar as far north as Campamento Río Grande and south almost to the base of the Sierra de Lema (Goodwin 2003, Hilty 2003), as well as in northern Brazil, north of the Amazon from Amapá west to the Manaus and Presidente Figueiredo region (Cohn-Haft *et al.* 1997), and south of it from west of the Rio Tapajós east to northwest Maranhão, and south to lower portions of the Serra dos Carajás, in southeastern Pará (Pacheco *et al.* 2007). The species is predicted to occur in Roraima, northernmost Brazil (Naka *et al.* 2007). More data concerning the distribution of this species and the next between the Rios Xingu and Tapajós, and immediately west of the latter, are certainly required,

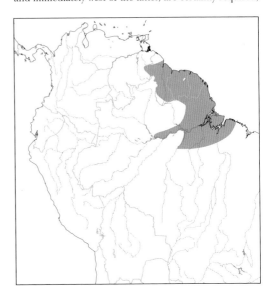

but at Trairão Pacheco and Olmos (2005) found only *P. nigricollis*, and in the Tapajós National Forest Henriques *et al.* (2003) noted only *P. carnifex*, which is also the only *Phoenicircus* species yet found at Santarém at the mouth of the Tapajós. The elevational range of Guianan Red Cotinga reaches to *c.*600m.

MOVEMENTS None recorded to date, although in many parts of the species' range the leks of Guianan Red Cotinga appear to be highly mobile, suggesting that while it is a generally resident species, it is not entirely sedentary.

HABITAT Canopy and subcanopy of lowland humid *terra firme* forest.

DESCRIPTION The sexes are strongly dimorphic (females being larger in all measurements; see below). Males are immediately recognised by their predominantly red and dark brown plumage; females are principally olive-green and pinkish-red. Both sexes have strangely prominent forehead feathers, unique to the genus, which project forwards over the base of the mandible and are bristly in front of the nostrils. The bill is rather short, with large oval-shaped nostrils semi-concealed by the feathers, an arched culmen, but no or only a very slightly hooked tip. The crown feathers are plush and glossy, and the head appears very flat. Rictal bristles are slightly developed. *Adult male.* – Bright red cap reaching to eye level, with the lower back to tail, except the dark brown terminal band, and underparts from the lower breast to undertail-coverts also bright red. There is a very narrow strip of black feathering around the eye, both above and below, like 'eyeliner' which in front of the eye continues as a dark upper border to the lores, and behind it as a slight supercilium. The scapulars have bright buff centres with broad dark chestnut-brown fringes and tips (appearing 'burnt'). Rest of plumage is dark brown, ranging from maroon over most of the wings (the larger coverts with darker browner fringes) to almost blackish on the nape and mantle, and becoming duskier on the highly modified primaries, in which several of the innermost (p7–10) are stiffened, with very narrow and/or twisted tips (see diagram in Snow 1982: 33). Undertail pale pinkish with a marginally darker tip. *Adult female.* – A washed-out version of the male. Crown dull dark reddish, also reaching to eye level, with slightly reddish ear-coverts, but the rest of the head and upperparts, and throat to breast are pale olive-green, becoming browner distally on the tail, with a diffuse darker terminal band. Underparts from lower breast to undertail-coverts pinky-red. *Juvenile.* – Undescribed, but the immature male is female-like, albeit with shorter wings (primary modifications already as adult), rather deeper red coloration on the underparts and crown, and some adult-like feathers have already begun to appear in the scapulars and larger wing-coverts (MNRJ). There is apparently no subadult male plumage, the birds moulting direct to adult feathering. *Moult.* – The pattern and seasonality of moult are unknown (Snow 1982), although the same bird trapped twice, in late January and mid February, showed no evidence of renewal (Trail and Donahue 1991) and singles collected in Amapá and Amazonas, in northern Brazil, in October and April, respectively were not in moult (INPA; MNRJ). *Bare parts.* – The strikingly large irides are red-brown or chestnut (darker, even scarlet, in males); the broad-based bill is horn-coloured (on the upper mandible) to brownish-orange (lower mandible), and the gape is yellow; and the legs and feet are flesh-coloured to pale yellowish-brown (beige).

MEASUREMENTS (from Snow 1982; COP; CUMZ; FMNH; MNRJ; RMNH; ZMA: northern Brazil, Guyana, Surinam and Venezuela) Wing of male (*n* = 34) 88.5–106.5mm, wing of female (*n* = 37) 98–114mm; tail of male (*n* = 33) 67–85mm, tail of female (*n* = 36) 77–94mm; bill of male (*n* = 14) 9.5–11.5mm (*n* = 20, to skull, 12.03–19.30mm), bill of female (*n* = 11) 11.0–12.5mm (*n* = 23, to skull, 14.30–20.64mm); tarsus of male (*n* = 14) 25.0–27.5mm, tarsus of female (*n* = 12) 27.0–28.5mm. Weight (sexes combined): 70–95g (Snow 1982, 2004a, Trail and Donahue 1991, Dunning 2008; INPA; MNRJ; RMNH). Males are smaller in wing-, tail- and bill-length than males of *P. nigricollis*, and females are smaller on average in bill-length than the same sex of its sister species (Maués and Aleixo 2008).

GEOGRAPHICAL VARIATION Monotypic.

VOICE Recordings have been published on Marantz and Zimmer (2006), Naka *et al.* (2008) and Renaudier and Deroussen (2008), and recordings from Guyana and Surinam are available online at www.xeno-canto.org. The male advertising call, which is principally given during the first two hours of daylight, is a trisyllabic *pee-chew-eet*, or *wuuk-peeyeweet…* (which dramatically changes in tone midway through), and a high-pitched whistle immediately preceded by a mechanical, whistling (cricket-like) wing noise, given in aerial, manakin-like display (see below). The wing noise recalls that of the White-bearded Manakin *Manacus manacus*. The whistle is apparently never given without the flight display, but may sometimes be omitted from the latter (Trail and Donahue 1991). Calling and flight displays increase noticeably with the arrival of any females at the lek. Guianan Red Cotinga can be attracted using playback, but might not always prove particularly responsive and, even when they are, may not always be easy to see, as the species tends to select well-concealed perches within the lower midstorey (GMK pers. obs.). Also, both sexes give a monosyllabic *wheep* either singly or in a long series, uttered in alarm or arousal. The species can be quite noisy when foraging. Trail and Donahue (1991) also reported a loud, two-part wing-buzz, given very rarely (once when three males congregated at a fruiting tree).

NATURAL HISTORY A wary, surprisingly inconspicuous (despite its brilliant colours), and very infrequently seen bird. It is occasionally recorded in mixed-species flocks (Jullien and Thiollay 1998). Individuals observed in eastern Bolívar, Venezuela, near the 'infamous' settlement at km 88, have tended to remain faithful to a fruiting tree for several days, but the species is much more difficult to observe there than other cotingas, such as Pompadour *Xipholena punicea*, Spangled *Cotinga cayana* or Purple-breasted Cotingas *C. cotinga*, due in some part to its different habits (i.e. it is extremely unlikely to perch on a dead snag), but probably also reflecting the species' general rarity. Typically perches with the tail slightly twisted to one side to expose the rump to best effect (as in *P. nigricollis*). Restricted to lower and mid levels of tall *terra firme* forest, *P. carnifex* is very rarely seen away from its lek sites, which appear similar in structure, size and hierarchy to those of Black-necked Red Cotinga (see below).

DISPLAY Much of what we know concerning the lek structure comes from the study by Trail and Donahue (1991). Displays last at least from December to May in Surinam (and the same is probably true in eastern Amazonian Brazil), whilst each lek is attended by up to *c.*8 males which perch 8–12m above the ground (not necessarily in sight of their neighbours), holding the body slightly forward and horizontal on the branch, and the wings drooped, in order to display the red rump and tail to best effect. The birds perform display-flights between up to 12 or so different perches, the male uttering a high-pitched whistle and wing noises as it swoops back down onto a branch. Overt aggression seems rare, and at least some leks may be only regularly attended by a much smaller number of birds. In courtship, males apparently continue to sing, but seem to bounce up and down on the branch (D. Ascanio *in* Restall *et al.* 2006). Activity at a lek seems mainly to be confined to the first two hours after dawn, but there may occasionally be a second burst of singing and posturing in late afternoon; furthermore, activity seems greater on sunny rather than cloudy days (Trail and Donahue 1991). One lek in Surinam was in the immediate vicinity of the display ground of the Capuchinbird *Perissocephalus tricolor* (Trail and Donahue 1991). Leks of this species tend to be very mobile in northern Brazil, e.g. north of Manaus (A. Whittaker pers. comm.), but much more stable in most other countries, and even south of the Amazon in Brazil (GMK pers. obs.).

FOOD AND FEEDING Guianan Red Cotinga appears to be entirely frugivorous, with seeds, fruits and berries (especially of Arecaceae, Lauraceae, Moraceae, Passifloraceae, Myrtaceae and Melastomataceae) being taken either in flight, either by stalling and then hovering, or with a snatch in midair, or by perch-gleaning. Palm fruits are a frequent (and often the sole) stomach content in Brazilian specimens (MNRJ). The species apparently never follows mixed-species feeding flocks over most of the species' range, although Willis (1983) noted birds taking an interest in antbirds foraging at antswarms, and GMK (pers. obs.) witnessed a male apparently visiting an active arboreal termitarium to feed. Rarely Guianan Red Cotingas ascend to the canopy when visiting fruiting trees (GMK pers. obs.). Sometimes several may gather at a fruiting tree (Trail and Donahue 1991), and the species has also been observed joining groups of Screaming Pihas *Lipaugus vociferans* at such resources (GMK pers. obs.).

BREEDING Practically unknown, with the only data being that F. Haverschmidt and G. F. Mees (specimens in RMNH)

collected both sexes in breeding condition in September and October in Surinam. In adjacent Amapá, Brazil, a female was collected in breeding condition in late April (Novaes 1978).

STATUS Treated as Least Concern by BirdLife International (2004, 2008). The species is unquestionably rather uncommon to locally frequent throughout its range, being perhaps commonest in the interior of Surinam (although it is still considered uncommon to rare: Ottema *et al.* 2009) and French Guiana (where regularly found around Saint Eugène, Mana and at the Acarouany River: Claessens 1997, Renaudier 2009), but the species seems generally rare in Brazil and Venezuela. Thiollay (1994) estimated this species' density as three pairs per 100ha at his study site in French Guiana. Considered fairly common in Guyana (Braun *et al.* 2007) where this cotinga is regularly encountered close to Atta Rainforest Lodge near the Iwokrama Canopy Walkway (GMK pers. obs.). The species is known from relatively few protected areas, but these include Imataca Forest Reserve (Venezuela), Iwokrama Rainforest Reserve (Guyana), the Adolpho Ducke Reserve, Parque Nacional Montanhas do Tumucumaque, and the Serra dos Carajás mosaic of protected areas (all Brazil).

REFERENCES Aleixo *et al.* (2011), Bernard (2008), BirdLife International (2004, 2008), Braun *et al.* (2007), Claessens (1997), Cohn-Haft *et al.* (1997), Dunning (2008), Goodwin (2003), Haffer (1974, 1992b), Haverschmidt and Mees (1994), Hellmayr (1929b), Henriques *et al.* (2003), Hilty (2003), Jullien and Thiollay (1998), Marantz and Zimmer (2006), Maués and Aleixo (2008), Moermond and Denslow (1985), Naka *et al.* (2007, 2008), Novaes (1978, 1980a), Oren and Parker (1997), Ottema *et al.* (2009), Pacheco *et al.* (2007), Pinto (1944), Renaudier (2009), Renaudier and Deroussen (2008), Restall *et al.* (2006), Reynaud (1998), Ridgely and Tudor (1994, 2009), Robbins *et al.* (2007), Schomburgk (1848), Schubart *et al.* (1965), Sclater (1888), Sick (1997), Snethlage (1907, 1914), Snow (1979, 1982, 2004a), Snyder (1966), Stone (1928), Stotz *et al.* (1996, 1997), Thiollay (1994), Tostain *et al.* (1992), Trail and Donahue (1991), Willis (1983), Zyskowski *et al.* (2011).

Guianan Red Cotinga *Phoenicircus carnifex*. **Fig. 1**. Male, Serra dos Carajás, Pará, east Amazonian Brazil, September (*Hadoram Shirihai / Photographic Handbook to Birds of the World*). **Fig. 2**. Female, Surama, Iwokrama, Guyana, October (*Hadoram Shirihai / Photographic Handbook to Birds of the World*). **Fig. 3**. Female, Dimona (Biological Dynamics of Forest Fragments Project) Reserve, north of Manaus, Amazonas, northern Brazil, October (*Andrew Whittaker*). Note the stiff, brush-like forehead feathers, which extend over the bill base.

BLACK-NECKED RED COTINGA
Phoenicircus nigricollis   Plate 31

Phoenicircus nigricollis **Swainson, 1832**, *in* Swainson & Richardson, *Faun. Bor.-Amer.* 2 (1831): 491, Rio Negro near Barcelos, Brazil [based on *Ampelis carnifex*, of Spix, 1825, *Av. Bras.* 2: 4, pl. 5]

Like the Guianan Red Cotinga *Phoenicircus carnifex*, this species is much coveted by birdwatchers; fortunately, with the opening up of the Ecuadorian and Peruvian Amazon to ecotourism, an encounter with this wonderful bird is infinitely more achievable than it was just 20 years ago. Nonetheless, the species remains a comparatively poorly known bird over much of its range, and its interactions, if any (cf. Maués and Aleixo 2008), with *P. carnifex*, at the eastern limits of the range offer much potential for adventurous but difficult study.

IDENTIFICATION 21.5–26.7cm (the female is, on average, the larger of the two sexes: Brooks *et al.* 1999). Given a reasonable view, both sexes of this species will prove unmistakable over the vast majority of its range. However, south of the Amazon, in the region of the lower Rio Tapajós (and perhaps east of there as far as the lower Rio Xingu), both this species and its congener, Guianan Red Cotinga, seem to occur, although Maués and Aleixo (2008) have disputed the notion that the two are ever sympatric. For further discussion of this issue see the previous species. The two are the same size and shape and possess similar habits. In males, note that the dark parts of the plumage, including the terminal tail-band, are much darker and blacker in *P. nigricollis* than in *P. carnifex*, and the bill of the former is usually deeper based, whilst the irides in Guianan are reddish-brown, but much darker in Black-necked. Females are much harder to separate, but *P. nigricollis* tends to have a much darker tail, heavier bill, much more red-saturated underparts (paler and more washed-out in *P. carnifex*), and again their eye colours differ as in males.

DISTRIBUTION Black-necked Red Cotinga occurs mainly to the west of *P. carnifex* in central and western Amazonia, from extreme southern Venezuela in southern Amazonas (where known from just two localities, both on the border with Brazil: Hilty 2003), southeastern Colombia (where recorded in western Caquetá, western Putumayo, Vaupés and Amazonas: Hilty and Brown 1986), eastern Ecuador (from Sucumbíos south to Morona-Santiago, but seems scarce and local throughout) and eastern Peru (in dptos. Loreto and San Martín), and across Brazil, north of the Amazon east to the west bank of the lower Rio Negro (e.g. in Jaú National Park), and south of it to the lower Rio Tapajós (e.g. at Vila Braga, Amazônia National Park, and Trairão), the Rio Cristalino (at Alta Floresta, northern Mato Grosso), the rio da Dúvida (northwest Mato Grosso), the Rio Curuá (southern Pará) and apparently on the middle Rio Xingu, further east in Pará (Pinto 1944). Like the previous species, it has been predicted to occur in Roraima, northernmost Brazil (Naka *et al.* 2007), and might be expected also in northeast Bolivia, as Black-necked Red Cotinga has been found at two localities on the Bolivian border, on the north bank of the Rio Mamoré, in neighbouring Rondônia (Whittaker 1996b, 2004). Doubtfully recorded east as far as Marabá on the Rio Tocantins, which record was discounted by Snow (1982), but maintained as valid by Sick (1997). Generally recorded to *c.*400m (in Ecuador) and 650m in

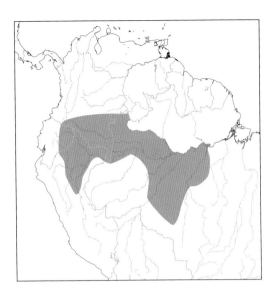

Peru, but its usual elevational range is probably well below this (e.g. to just 200m in Venezuela). However, in the Pongos basin of Amazonian Peru it has been recorded to *c.*1,150m (Brooks *et al.* 2009).

MOVEMENTS None recorded, although see comments under the previous species, which probably also apply to *P. nigricollis*.

HABITAT Inhabits humid lowland *terra firme* forest, including tall forest and at the borders of *campinarana* on white-sand soils, being, for instance, seen occasionally in the Allpahuayo-Mishana Reserved Zone, near Iquitos, dpto. Loreto, Peru (J. Díaz pers. comm.).

DESCRIPTION The sexes are strongly dimorphic (the female averages larger in all measurements; see below). Males can be automatically recognised by their predominantly red and black plumage; females are principally olive-green and pinkish-red. Both sexes have prominent forehead feathers, which are unique to the genus, that project forwards over the base of the mandible and are bristly in front of the nostrils. The crown feathers are plush and glossy. Short bill, with large oval-shaped nostrils semi-concealed by feathers. The rictal bristles are slightly developed. *Adult male.* – Bright red cap reaching to eye level, with lower back to tail, except black terminal band, and underparts from mid breast to undertail-coverts also brilliant scarlet-red. Rest of plumage glossy black including the highly modified primaries, in which several of the innermost are stiffened, with very narrow and or twisted tips. The undertail is pale pinkish to bright red with a brownish-black terminal band. *Adult female.* – A washed-out version of the male. Crown dull dark maroon, reaching to below eye level on the ear-coverts, but the rest of the head and upperparts, as well as the throat to breast are pale olive-green, becoming dull rufous over the tail, with a diffuse darker terminal band. Underparts from the lower breast to undertail-coverts are rose-red, being on average brighter and more saturated than in *P. carnifex. Juvenile.* – Undescribed, but the immature male is female-like, albeit with shorter wings and rather deeper red coloration over the underparts and crown. There is apparently no subadult male plumage, the birds moulting direct to adult feathering. *Moult.* – An adult taken in early

March in southern Venezuela was in wing moult but others from the same period showed no evidence of feather replacement (Willard *et al.* 1991), whilst birds taken in July on the upper Rio Negro and in southernmost Amazonas in the same month were not replacing any feathers (INPA; MNRJ). Pattern and seasonality of moult is basically still unknown (Snow 1982). *Bare parts.* – The irides are dark brown to orange-red or reddish; the broad-based bill is yellow ochre or dark brown with a rosy flesh-coloured base, a slightly hooked tip and the gape is yellow; and the legs and feet are pinkish-red or tan.

MEASUREMENTS (from Snow 1982; FMNH; MNRJ; RMNH; ZMA: Brazil and Peru) Wing of male (*n* = 14) 94–105mm, wing of female (*n* = 7) 110–119mm; tail of male (*n* = 14) 65.5–82.0mm, tail of female (*n* = 7) 82–92mm; bill of male (*n* = 10) 12–15mm (*n* = 2, to skull, 17.58–18.56mm), bill of female (*n* = 7) 12.0–12.5mm (*n* = 1, to skull, 19.75mm); tarsus of male (*n* = 10) 26–27mm, tarsus of female (*n* = 6) 27.5–29.0mm. Females average slightly larger than males in wing-chord and tail-length values (Brooks *et al.* 1999). Weight: 70–112g (male) and 95–107g (female) (Willard *et al.* 1991, Brooks *et al.* 1999, Snow 2004a, Dunning 2008; INPA; MNRJ). Brooks *et al.* (1999) found that, on average, females are very slightly heavier than males.

GEOGRAPHICAL VARIATION Monotypic.

VOICE Male gives an explosive *skreea* or *wuura* in advertisement, which is metallic and crow-like in quality, is sometimes preceded by a much softer *wur* and can be given in a short series, when it tends to possess a slightly laughing quality. Black-necked Red Cotinga tends to perch slightly higher to sing than Guianan Red Cotinga, but like that species it gives a mechanical, whistling (cricket- or bell-like) wing noise, given during the aerial, manakin-like display, which sometimes terminates in a brief *skree* call (which is a mild variant of the main song). Both sexes of *P. nigricollis* utter a monosyllabic *yip* in alarm or threat, and this can also be extended as a short series of 3–4 calls, descending slightly in pitch with the final one higher again. Published recordings are available on the following audio compilations: Moore (1996), Krabbe and Nilsson (2003), Marantz and Zimmer (2006) and Boesman (2009), whilst recordings from Brazil, Colombia, Ecuador and Peru are available online at www.xeno-canto.org.

NATURAL HISTORY Black-necked Red Cotinga is a wary and surprisingly inconspicuous bird of mid levels and the subcanopy of tall forest, which like its closest relative is rarely seen away from its lek sites (which were first described by Olalla 1943). It typically perches with the tail slightly twisted to one side to expose the rump to best effect (much as in *P. carnifex*).

FOOD AND FEEDING The species is apparently almost entirely frugivorous, with fruits and berries being taken either in flight, either by stalling and then hovering, or with a snatch in midair, or by perch-gleaning. There are few data on the species taken but these include *Pagamea plicata* (Rubiaceae: Willard *et al.* 1991) and a *Trichilia* (Meliaceae: Trail and Donahue 1991). Apparently never follows mixed-species feeding flocks, but may ascend into low canopies to feed (as occasionally does Guianan Red Cotinga) and Donahue noted birds joining species such

as Lawrence's Thrush *Turdus lawrencii* and Black-spotted Barbet *Capito niger* at a fruiting tree (Trail and Donahue 1991). Willis (1983) reported birds in both Colombia and Brazil showing interest in antswarms, although they were not observed to feed at them, but Brooks *et al.* (1999) found that arachnids have been occasionally reported in stomach contents.

DISPLAY The majority of what we know concerning the lek structure derives from the study by Trail and Donahue (1991). Seasonality of displays, if any, is unknown, but each lek is attended by up to 6–12 males that perch *c.*10m above the ground (not necessarily in sight of their neighbours), holding the body slightly forward and horizontal on the branch, and the wings drooped, in order to display the red rump and tail to best effect. The display grounds are apparently permanent in some areas, e.g. in eastern Peru and Ecuador (but perhaps more ephemeral at others, e.g. in western Brazil), and always non-resource-based, and are typically 30–60m in diameter. The birds perform display-flights between up to five different perches (typically horizontal lianas), the male uttering a high-pitched whistle and wing noises (see Voice) as they swoop back down onto a branch. Like *Rupicola* and Guianan Red Cotinga, the birds can be surprisingly shy and difficult to observe at the lek.

BREEDING Nothing is known concerning nesting, although Hilty (2003) states (assumes?) that the female is entirely responsible for nesting duties and, concerning seasonality, a male collected in southern Venezuela in March had enlarged gonads (Willard *et al.* 1991) and two taken in July on the Rio Negro, Brazil, also were in breeding condition.

STATUS Categorised as Least Concern (BirdLife International 2004, 2008), but the species is unquestionably rather uncommon over the majority of its range, especially in the north, being very rare and little known in Venezuela and Colombia, and considered to be Near Threatened nationally even in Ecuador, where it is probably most frequently encountered by birdwatchers. Black-necked Red Cotinga is known from several protected areas, including Amacayacu National Park (Colombia), Cerro de la Neblina National Park (Venezuela), Jaú National Park and Sucunduri State Park (both in Amazonas, Brazil), and Cuyabeno Reserve and Yasuni National Park (Ecuador). Local people in some regions covet the bird's feathers and oil exploration and extraction may have caused forest loss in parts of its range in Ecuador.

REFERENCES BirdLife International (2004, 2008), Boesman (2009), Borges (2007), Borges *et al.* (2001), Brooks *et al.* (1999, 2009), Cohn-Haft *et al.* (1997), Dunning (2008), Haffer (1974, 1992b), Hellmayr (1910, 1929b), Hilty (2003), Hilty and Brown (1986), Moore (1996), Krabbe and Nilsson (2003), Marantz and Zimmer (2006), Maués and Aleixo (2008), Mazar Barnett *et al.* (2004b), Naka *et al.* (2007), Novaes (1976), Olalla (1943), Oren and Parker (1997), Pacheco and Olmos (2005), Pinto (1944), Restall *et al.* (2006), Ridgely and Greenfield (2001), Ridgely and Tudor (1994, 2009), Salaman *et al.* (2008), Schulenberg *et al.* (2007), Sclater (1888), Sick (1997), Snethlage (1914), Snow (1979, 1982, 2004a), Stotz *et al.* (1996), Trail and Donahue (1991), Whittaker (1996b, 2004), Willis (1983).

Black-necked Red Cotinga *Phoenicircus nigricollis*. **Fig. 1**. Male, Napo Wildlife Center, prov. Orellana, eastern Ecuador, October (*János Oláh*). The dark parts of the plumage are consistently blacker in this species compared to in Guianan Red Cotinga *P. carnifex*. Fortunately, the two species are apparently only sympatric in a tiny area of east Amazonian Brazil, making their identification generally straightforward over most of their respective ranges.

Genera *Ampelion, Doliornis* and *Zaratornis*:
the high-Andean cotingas

Cotingas of the three genera discussed below are all rather sluggish, thickset birds that share a nuchal crest and a rather solid demeanour. They frequent high-Andean humid cloud forests from elfin treeline forests to forests at subtropical elevations. Those two species treated here as the sole representatives of the genus *Ampelion* were historically placed in the genus *Heliochera* from the late 19th to mid 20th centuries (e.g. Hellmayr 1929b, Phelps and Phelps 1950).

RED-CRESTED COTINGA
Ampelion rubrocristatus   Plate 32

A[*mpelis*] *rubrocristatus* d'Orbigny & Lafresnaye, 1837, *Mag. Zool.* 7: 39, Ayopayo, dpto. Cochabamba, Bolivia

One of the most widespread and most readily identified of the Andean cotingas, the Red-crested Cotinga is a normally conspicuous inhabitant of semi-humid temperate forests, including *Polylepis* (Rosaceae), and other low-stature forests at the treeline.

IDENTIFICATION 18–23cm. Not easily confused with any other species, except perhaps Bay-vented Cotinga *Doliornis sclateri* (both are found at Bosque Unchog in central Peru), the Red-crested Cotinga is often seen atop an emergent tree at the treeline, and is easily located by scanning the flattened tops of elfin forest and by its rather rasping, almost mechanical call. Compared with Bay-vented Cotinga, the present species is separable by virtue of its prominent white tail-band, pale-looking bill and generally slightly paler plumage with no chestnut on the vent. Red-crested Cotinga is more frequently found in humid and semi-humid treeline habitats, whereas the Chestnut-crested Cotinga *Ampelion rufaxilla* is more readily encountered at lower elevations. However, both species are regularly found together at the Serranía de Siberia, in Bolivia (Whitney *et al.* 1994). Juvenile Red-crested Cotinga might be more liable to be confused with its single congener, but even this is unlikely given a reasonable view as it is still far less yellow below, always shows a white tail-band and has no chestnut on the 'shoulders'.

DISTRIBUTION Widespread in the Andes, the Red-crested Cotinga is found from Colombia, where it is present in all three ranges as well as on the Sierra Nevada de Santa Marta and Sierra de Perijá, and in Venezuela (from northeast Trujillo to Táchira, and on the Sierra de Perijá, Zulia). Thereafter, the species occurs south through Ecuador (throughout the central inter-Andean valley and adjacent Andean ridges) and in Peru (widespread on the east slope, but confined to the north and around Lima in the west: Koepcke 1961) to Bolivia, where it appears to reach its southernmost limit on the Serranía de Siberia, dpto. Santa Cruz (Whitney *et al.* 1994). The species is principally found above 2,200m (locally down to 1,900m: Best *et al.* 1993). There is even a sight record close to 1,000m of a subadult bird near Zamora in eastern Ecuador (C. Vits pers. comm.). Occurs to 3,700m in Colombia (where Red-crested Cotinga is mainly found above 2,700m: Hilty and Brown 1986), to 3,250m in Venezuela (Hilty 2003), 3,500m in Ecuador (Ridgely and Greenfield 2001), and to 3,700m further south in Peru and Bolivia (Fjeldså and Krabbe 1990, Schulenberg *et al.* 2007).

MOVEMENTS Presumed to be resident.

HABITAT Inhabits the borders and interior of humid, wet montane forest (including secondary woodland) at the treeline, as well as more fragmented areas with a mosaic of hedgerows, scattered trees, such as groves of *Alnus* (Betulaceae), and bushes. Red-crested Cotinga ranges above the normal treeline in *Polylepis* (Rosaceae), *Escallonia* (Escalloniaceae) and *Oreopanax* (Araliaceae) forests throughout its range, and appears tolerant of some degree of habitat degradation and fragmentation.

DESCRIPTION Despite the lack of any bright pigmentation in its dark plumage, the Red-crested Cotinga is a surprisingly distinctive bird by virtue of its bare-parts coloration and the bright white tail-band, most obvious when the tail is spread or on a flying bird. Feather modification is limited in this species to having the innermost primary unusually pointed. The sexes are alike, although the crest is said to be smaller and shorter in females (Lönnberg and Rendahl 1922). The bill has a strongly arched culmen and, sometimes, a very slightly hooked tip, while the nostrils are relatively prominent. *Adult.* – The general plumage tone is dark plumbeous grey, becoming blacker over the head, throat, wings and tail. The dark red (chestnut-maroon) crest is usually laid flat and is not necessarily obvious unless spread, or if the bird becomes excited, when the crest is raised, slightly flared into a fan, and highly expressive (see Fjeldså and Krabbe 1990: 445). The generally dark, blackish-grey, appearance of this cotinga is relieved only by a paler grey belly, and some greyish streaking on the rump, lower belly and undertail-coverts (where sharp black streaking is also present). A neat white band across the lower part of all but the central pair of tail feathers is visible if seen from below, or on both surfaces in flight. *Immature.* – Paler than the adult, with browner upperparts and at this stage appears streaky on the lower back and rump (the streaks being somewhat yellowish-white). No nuchal crest, although the hindcrown and nape are rufous-brown, whilst the belly and undertail-coverts are yellowish-white, streaked brownish-grey. The scapulars and innermost secondaries possess white subterminal tipping, as can the greater coverts (Zimmer 1930). The tail-band remains the best distinguishing feature even at this age. *Juvenile.* – Generally paler than the adult due to the extensive pale feather fringes (e.g. to the rump, secondaries, tertials and wing-coverts), with cinnamon to pale olive-buff or even yellowish-green underparts (including the throat), streaked dusky, and the upperparts are pale olive to warm brown, appearing streaked due to the sooty feather centres, especially on the mantle and scapulars. The bill is dark and the crown and nape sooty, with rufous webs (which is one of the last juvenile features to be shed). The irides are dark red at this age. Red-brown lateral fringes to the feathers are also obvious on the scapulars and lesser wing-coverts, and these are also retained for quite some time. Nestling described by Vuilleumeier (1969) and Snow (1982). *Moult.* – Snow (1976a, 1982) noted that moult does not appear to show any seasonality in this species, presumably reflecting the equable climate within the regions it inhabits. An apparently breeding female (with a brood patch) showed slight body moult in May in Colombia (F. Guzman/ProAves unpubl. data). *Bare parts.* – Bill ivory or very pale greyish-white, with a dark or black tip, which is sometimes quite extensive covering up to one-third of the bill's length. Irides bright red/scarlet; legs and feet black or dark grey. *Plumage aberration.* – We have seen a leucistic individual of this species, labelled as being from Bogotá, Colombia, and held in the Field Museum of Natural History, Chicago (FMNH 11293). The entire throat to upper breast appears extensively grey-white with darker bases to the feathers, which appear more prominent on the chin, whilst greyish-white feathering is much less obvious (but present) over much of the rest of the underparts. The underwing is extensively white, whilst the upperparts (over the crown and nape) appear to be streaked broadly and quite brightly whitish, and the mantle and back are blotched grey-white. The scapulars are extensively whitish as is the outermost primary, but most of the wings are normally plumaged, and the tail-band is obvious, at least from below. Such plumage aberrations appear to be extremely rare in the Cotingidae (cf. the account for Pompadour Cotinga *Xipholena punicea*).

MEASUREMENTS (BMNH; FMNH: Bolivia, Colombia, Ecuador, Peru and Venezuela) Wing of male ($n = 51$) 107–127mm, wing of female ($n = 22$) 107–123mm; tail of male ($n = 51$) 76–98mm, tail of female ($n = 22$) 77–91mm; bill of male ($n = 44$) 12.31–16.42mm, bill of female ($n = 16$) 12.18–16.91mm; tarsus of male ($n = 6$) 24–26mm, tarsus of female ($n = 6$) 24–25mm. Weight: 46–80g (males) and 45–68g (females) (King 1991, Rahbek *et al.* 1993, Hilty 2003, Snow 2004a, Echeverry-Galvis *et al.* 2006, Dunning 2008; MVZ; ROM; F. Guzman and G. A. Suárez/ProAves unpubl. data).

GEOGRAPHICAL VARIATION Monotypic; despite the species' extensive range through the Andes there is, as long ago noted by Hellmayr (1929b), no evidence of any plumage variation that might warrant the recognition of any races.

VOICE Red-crested Cotinga is generally a quiet species but like most Andean cotingas, one has to be acutely aware of the species' rather subtle primary vocalisations. Ridgely and Greenfield (2001), Hilty (2003) and Ridgely and Tudor (2009) noted that the primary song is a peculiar, stuttering, frog-like chatter, *trrrrrrrr*, described as being like an alarm clock being wound (Fjeldså and Krabbe 1990), given just occasionally, normally when perched but sometimes in flight. Also gives a guttural *gr-grrt*, a deep chucking note, a hoarse *puii* and series of soft *eh-eh-eh-eh-eh* notes (T. A. Parker *in* Snow 1982, Fjeldså and Krabbe 1990, Schulenberg *et al.* 2007). The wings make a soft, mechanical, rattling sound in flight. The species' voice appears on the following audio compilations: Boesman (1999), Mayer (2000), Schulenberg (2000b), Krabbe *et al.* (2001), Krabbe and Nilsson (2003), Alvarez *et al.* (2007) and Boesman (2009), and there are also recordings from Bolivia, Colombia and Peru archived online at www.xeno-canto.org.

NATURAL HISTORY Generally seen alone or in pairs, but occasionally in small groups of up to six, rarely 10–12 individuals (T. A. Parker *in* Snow 1982, Fjeldså and Krabbe 1990, Bloch *et al.* 1991). Red-crested Cotinga does not follow mixed-species foraging flocks. Often perches conspicuously upright on a prominent bare branch, and habitually remains long periods in one place, often motionless (or nearly so), but periodically scanning its surroundings, before appearing to drop down suddenly in rapid flight to its next perch. Like the majority of Andean cotingas, it appears sluggish when feeding.

FOOD AND FEEDING Diet is predominantly fruit, especially mistletoes, e.g. *Phrygilanthus* (Loranthaceae) in Peru (T. A. Parker *in* Snow 1982, Fjeldså and Krabbe 1990, Ridgely and Greenfield 2001). Also takes fruits of the parasitic genus *Tristerix* (Loranthaceae) in Peru, at least (Castañeda Gil 2010). Observations from Bolivia show that the species also feeds on *Berberis* (Berberidaceae) and *Heteromeles* (Rosaceae) using reach manoeuvres when perched or using short upward sally manoeuvres (Remsen *et al.* 1988). This frugivorous diet is supplemented with some insects, captured during short, clumsy flights that begin and end on the same treetop.

DISPLAY Most demonstrative in display (both agonistic and courtship), during which males bow their heads rapidly, flip the tail upwards and spread it, and raise and spread the spiky red crest feathers (like a topknot: cf. Norton 1975 for apparently the first published description of such behaviour). These displays are also given during inter-specific conflicts (e.g. with other frugivores or omnivores) at fruiting trees. The crest feathers may also be simply raised briefly and partially spread, without any of the head-bowing and tail-flipping movements, for unknown reasons (GMK pers. obs.). In central Peru, Bay-vented Cotinga is dominant over this species at fruiting trees (H. Lloyd unpubl. data). Both species employ similar displays and primary vocalisations, while perched in close proximity to each other, before Bay-vented displaces Red-crested.

BREEDING There are few detailed published nesting data, the eggs do not appear to have been described and nothing is known concerning incubation or fledging periods. Peters and Griswold (1943) found a nest in central Peru, in March, *c.*1.3m above the ground in a bush, and another nest was discovered in Bolivia, 1.7m up in a small tree. The latter was a cup-shaped structure of twigs and lichens, stained red (apparently from berries), and held a single full-feathered nestling that weighed 54g (Vuilleumeier 1969). In dpto. Huánuco, Peru, in mid February, T. A. Parker (*in* Snow 1982) found another large cup-shaped nest of this species of mosses, lichens and twigs constructed in a *Polylepis* tree 3m above the ground, and subsequently observed an adult feeding two recently fledged young nearby. A fourth nest, found in Ecuador by R. S. Ridgely (*in* Hilty and Brown 1986), was 5m above the ground, in October. Although not conclusively demonstrated to date, it seems likely that, as in *Zaratornis*, both sexes care for the young.

Other breeding data were summarised by Fjeldså and Krabbe (1990): eggs have been recorded in Bolivia in November, and dptos. Huánuco and Huancavelica (Peru) in January and October, respectively; fledglings in July and February in northern Ecuador, and December in dpto. La Paz (Bolivia); juveniles in June, September, October and December in northern Ecuador, June in dpto. Amazonas (Peru) and August in dpto. Cochabamba (Bolivia); and nest building in February in prov. Loja (southern Ecuador) (Bloch *et al.* 1991). The latter authors also witnessed a fledgling in the company of an adult at the end of May, nest building in early June and display in mid February to early April, all at localities in Loja. On the east slope in prov. Napo, Greeney *et al.* (2011) found nestlings in the fourth week of May. Single juveniles have also been observed in March in Santa Cruz, Bolivia (Whitney *et al.* 1994), and in July in northeast Ecuador (Kirwan *et al.* 2006). Furthermore, records of juveniles/immatures are available from most months across the range, e.g. a juvenile accompanied by an adult in prov. Pichincha, northwest Ecuador, in mid August (GMK pers. obs.). M. A. Carriker (*in* Todd and Carriker 1922) took 11 breeding-condition birds in Colombia's Santa Marta Mountains and northern Andes in February–August, whilst two females in breeding condition have been collected in dpto. Cauca, Colombia, in January and April (ROM), a female with a brood patch

has been trapped in early May (F. Guzman/ProAves unpubl. data) and MVZ has birds of both sexes from the same period also taken in Colombia.

STATUS Currently listed as of Least Concern (BirdLife International 2004, 2008) and is generally fairly common, but rarely numerous, across its range, although Hilty (2003) noted that the species seems slightly less common in Venezuela than further south. Red-crested Cotinga is known from a great many protected areas throughout the species' wide range and although Andean treeline and subtropical forests are highly threatened, it appears tolerant, to a degree, of forest fragmentation and degradation.

REFERENCES Alvarez *et al.* (2007), Best *et al.* (1993), BirdLife International (2004, 2008), Bloch *et al.* (1991), Boesman (1999, 2009), Castañeda Gil (2010), Castaño-Villa and Patiño-Zabala (2008), Chapman (1921), Cisneros-Heredia (2009), Cresswell *et al.* (1999), David and Gosselin (2002b), Dunning (2008), Echeverry-Galvis *et al.* (2006), Fjeldså and Krabbe (1990), Greeney *et al.* (2011), Hartert (1898), Hellmayr (1929b), Hennessey and Gomez (2003), Hilty (2003), Hilty and Brown (1986), Hornbuckle (1999), King (1991), Kirwan *et al.* (2006), Koepcke (1961), Krabbe and Nilsson (2003), Krabbe *et al.* (2001, 2006), Lönnberg and Rendahl (1922), López-Lanús *et al.* (2000), MacLeod *et al.* (2005), Mark *et al.* (2008), Mayer (2000), Norton (1975), Ocampo (2002), Olson (1971), Parker *et al.* (1982, 1985), Peters and Griswold (1943), Phelps and Phelps (1950), Rahbek *et al.* (1993), Remsen and Traylor (1989), Remsen *et al.* (1988), Restall *et al.* (2006), Ridgely and Greenfield (2001), Ridgely and Tudor (1994, 2009), Salaman *et al.* (2008, 2009), Schulenberg (2000b), Schulenberg *et al.* (2007), Snow (1976a, 1982, 2004a), Stotz *et al.* (1996), Strewe and Navarro (2004a), Todd and Carriker (1922), Vellinga *et al.* (2004), Vuilleumeier (1969), Walker *et al.* (2006), Whitney *et al.* (1994), Zimmer (1930).

Red-crested Cotinga *Ampelion rubrocristata.* **Fig. 1**. Adult, Papallacta Pass, prov. Napo, northern Ecuador, October (*Hadoram Shirihai / Photographic Handbook to Birds of the World*). **Fig. 2**. Immature, dpto. Cajamarca, Peru, September (*Claudia Torres*). Note the pale fringes to the mantle and back feathers, and the dull rufous elements on the head and neck, which identify this bird as an immature. **Fig. 3**. Adult, Pululahua, prov. Pichincha, northwest Ecuador, May (*Roger Ahlman / www.pbase.com/ahlman*). This high-altitude cotinga is easily recognised by its white tail-band, otherwise overall charcoal-black plumage and red crest, and pale bill with a dark tip.

CHESTNUT-CRESTED COTINGA
Ampelion rufaxilla **Plate 32**

Ampelis rufaxilla **Tschudi, 1844**, *Archiv. Naturg.* 10(1): 270, [Vitoc Valley, dpto. Junín,] Peru

Whilst Chestnut-crested Cotinga's striking plumage coloration superficially suggests only a distant relationship to the far more 'dowdy' Red-crested Cotinga *Ampelion rubrocristatus*, there are in fact many characters (including morphological) that call for them to be united in a single genus.

IDENTIFICATION 18.5–23.0cm. A highly distinctive cotinga of Andean humid subtropical forests (see the previous species for the relatively remote possibility of confusion with juvenile Red-crested Cotinga). Chestnut-crested Cotinga is unmistakable and is often found perched high on a moss-laden branch in the typical 'sluggish' manner of other Andean cotingas. Though perhaps not as vocal as the Red-crested Cotinga, this species can still be located by its distinctive, rather mechanical and rasping call, although, like other Andean cotingas, this is easily overlooked if one is not familiar with the nature of their vocalisations. When perched, the species appears 'chestnut-headed' rather than just 'chestnut-crested', as the dark facial markings are often obscure on a distant bird.

DISTRIBUTION Widespread but generally patchily distributed throughout most of the Andes, from Colombia (in the Central Andes south to dpto. Quindío and in southwest dpto. Huila; and in the West Andes in dptos. Antioquia, Valle and Cauca), very locally in Ecuador (where known from just three, recently discovered, localities on the east slope, in the extreme north and south of the country, in Sucumbíos and southern Zamora-Chinchipe provinces, respectively) and Peru (again only on the east slope) as far south as dptos. La Paz, Santa Cruz and Cochabamba, in Bolivia, where the species reaches its southernmost limit at Inca Chaca, prov. Chapare, but is most frequently recorded in the country at the Serranía de Siberia, Santa Cruz (Davis *et al.* 1994, Whitney *et al.* 1994). Chestnut-crested Cotinga is principally found above 2,300m, but is observed locally down to 1,700m and has been reported once in Peru as low as 1,430m (S. Hansson *in* Kirwan *et al.* 2006) and in Ecuador exceptionally down at 1,200m, above Copalinga,

near Zamora (C. Vits pers. comm.). The species occurs to 3,150m in Colombia and to 2,700m in Ecuador (Hilty and Brown 1986, Ridgely and Greenfield 2001, Krabbe *et al.* 2006), to 2,800m in Peru (Schulenberg *et al.* 2007) and to 2,900–3,000m in Bolivia (Hennessey *et al.* 2003, MacLeod *et al.* 2005).

MOVEMENTS Presumably resident, but short-distance elevational movements are suspected in southern Peru (H. Lloyd *in litt.* 2010) and, like a great many cotingas, there are arguably too few year-round data from well-studied localities to be too precise on this point.

HABITAT Inhabits tall, well-developed humid forest in the subtropics, often at the forest edge, and occasionally ranges into temperate forest. In southern Peru, this cotinga appears to show some preference for areas dominated by alder (*Alnus* sp.), which it uses for nesting (see Breeding).

DESCRIPTION Sexes alike. Bill has a slightly arched culmen, with a very slightly hooked tip; the nostrils are rather small. *A. r. rufaxilla* is described here. *Adult.* – Easily identified by its rather long and bushy, extensively chestnut-tipped crest, contrasting with the greyish face and black loral region and central crown. The crest is sometimes flared in a fan-like fashion (as in Red-crested Cotinga), e.g. in response to playback (GMK pers. obs.), but is always far more apparent than in the latter species, even when it is laid flat. The rest of the head (throat, head-sides and collar) is bright chestnut or cinnamon-rufous sharply demarcated by a greyish-fawn band across the breast. Mantle olivaceous-grey, streaked dusky, becoming browner on the rump. Wings and tail are blackish-brown. Bright chestnut (sometimes brownish) patch on the 'shoulder' (the lesser and median coverts). The belly is pale yellow, broadly streaked with blackish-brown or blackish (except in the centre). *Juvenile/Immature.* – Undescribed (cf. Snow 1982, Fjeldså and Krabbe 1990). *Moult.* – Moult data are few, but in Colombian specimens feather renewal was apparently initiated in January–July, and in August–December in Peru (FMNH). Observations of a nesting pair in southeast Peru in December (see Breeding) revealed that both birds were moulting to some lesser extent (Snow 1982). *Bare parts.* – Irides are bright red; bill bluish-grey with a darker or black tip; and the legs are dark olive or grey (Snow 1982, 2004a).

MEASUREMENTS (BMNH; FMNH: Colombia and Peru) *A. r. rufaxilla*: wing of male ($n = 2$) 116–122mm, wing of female ($n = 2$) 113–114mm; tail of male ($n = 2$) 78.5–79.0mm, tail of female ($n = 2$) 74–77mm; bill of male ($n = 2$) 16.82–17.46mm, bill of female ($n = 2$) 14.21–16.94mm; tarsus of male ($n = 2$) 21–22mm, tarsus of female ($n = 2$) 20.8–22.0mm. *A. r. antioquiae*: wing of male ($n = 3$) 117.5–124.0mm, wing of female ($n = 2$) 117.5–120.0mm; tail of male ($n = 3$) 82–84mm, tail of female ($n = 2$) 78–81mm; bill of male ($n = 1$) 16.82mm, bill of female ($n = 1$) 16.94mm (also Hellmayr 1929b). Weight: 63.2–78.0g (males) and 69–74g (females) (Snow 2004a, Dunning 2008; FMNH; MVZ).

GEOGRAPHICAL VARIATION Two subspecies are generally recognised (Snow 1982, 2004a, Dickinson 2003). *A. r. antioquiae* (Chapman, 1924) is found in the Andes of western Colombia as far north as the Páramo de Frontino, southern dpto. Antioquia, and it is presumably this race which also occurs in extreme northern Ecuador (in prov. Sucumbíos). It differs from the nominate in its larger size, more saturated chestnut areas and underparts being more heavily streaked with blackish-brown, but was considered to be only doubtfully valid by Fjeldså and Krabbe (1990), and a re-examination of this issue appears warranted. We have seen too few specimens to comment very meaningfully, but we agree that the proposed differences are hard to validate, other than perhaps that of size. *A. r. rufaxilla* inhabits the rest of the species range, from extreme southern Ecuador through Peru and Bolivia.

VOICE The first data were presented by Taczanowski (1884). Gives a series of *reh* notes, sometimes interspersed with slightly softer calls, and a long, stuttering *eh-eh-rrrreh*, which ends in a croak (recalling Red-crested Cotinga), and is considered by some to recall the whirl of a fishing reel and/or the primary song of White-tipped Plantcutter *Phytotoma rutila* (Fjeldså and Krabbe 1990, Hennessey 2004, Schulenberg *et al.* 2007). Published recordings of its voice exist on the following compilations: Mayer (2000), Schulenberg (2000b), Krabbe *et al.* (2001), Krabbe and Nilsson (2003), Alvarez *et al.* (2007) and Boesman (2009), and there are also recordings from Ecuador and Peru archived online at www.xeno-canto-org.

NATURAL HISTORY Many aspects of the species' ecology are generally very similar to that of other high-Andean cotingas. Usually encountered alone or in pairs, and often on an exposed perch high in the canopy (cf. video footage by J. del Hoyo), and rarely consorts with other birds (or follows mixed-species flocks).

FOOD AND FEEDING Diet extremely poorly known, but Chestnut-crested Cotinga regularly sallies to the air for insects (R. S. Ridgely *in* Hilty and Brown 1986), whilst the stomach contents of four birds collected in Bolivia and Peru were either solely of fruits (*n* = 3) or insects (*n* = 1). The species has also been observed to 'snap' flying insects from a perched position (Whitney *et al.* 1994), or to sally to a bromeliad to seize a caterpillar (GMK pers. obs.). At least sometimes defends a fruiting tree, the observed bird being seen chasing tanagers (Thraupidae) and a thrush *Turdus* sp. away (Hennessey 2004a).

DISPLAY This is similar to what is known of Red-crested and White-cheeked Cotingas *Zaratornis stresemanni* (T. A. Parker *in* Snow 1982), and J. del Hoyo's video (mentioned above and viewable at www.ibc.hbw.com/ibc/) shows one bird head-bobbing several times apparently to another bird nearby. GMK (pers. obs.) watched an apparent pair at Abra Patricia, dpto. San Martín, Peru, head-bobbing to each other and calling, in response to playback. H. Lloyd (*in litt.* 2010) reports that birds will head-bob towards other individuals, whether pair members or not. Hennessey (2004a) described an arcing flight-display in which a bird flew up to *c.*15m above a fruiting tree, stalling at the highest point then returning to a point closer to the centre of the tree, and which he speculated was directed at an unseen female. All of the displays observed by Hennessey involved an audible wing noise during the descent, which usually sounded as if the bird was 'braking'.

BREEDING Observations from southeast Peru (dptos. Puno and Cuzco) have revealed that the nest is a shallow open cup, constructed of slender twigs and fruticose lichens, with no lining (T. S. Schulenberg *in* Snow 1982). The nest is placed 12m up, either in the crown of a tree near the edge of cloud forest habitat at *c.*2,000m (T. S. Schulenberg *in* Snow 1982), or halfway up in alder (*Alnus* sp.) trees, in the interior of alder-dominated cloud forest (*c.*2,700m). In the

latter case, the nest was positioned 2m from the main trunk, along a prominent branch with only partially leaf vegetation cover (H. Lloyd *et al.* unpubl. data). The depth of the nest depression and overall size of the nest can vary and may be deeper and larger than described in Snow (H. Lloyd *et al.* unpubl. data). Both members of the pair tend the nest (T. S. Schulenberg *in* Snow 1982) and share incubation duties (H. Lloyd *et al.* unpubl. data). When swapping over during the incubation period, both adults emit a series of short *reh* calls to each other (sometimes head-bobbing too), while one bird remains perched atop the nest tree before flying down to replace its partner, which promptly assumes a similar position (H. Lloyd *et al.* unpubl. data). The presumed female will occasionally leave the nest for very short periods (3–4 minutes), flying to immediately neighbouring alder trees, while the presumed male remains perched atop the nest tree, occasionally vocalising (H. Lloyd *et al.* unpubl. data). Limited observations suggest that incubation occurs during the last week of November in southeast Peru (H. Lloyd *et al.* unpubl. data) but that nest construction can still be underway during early December (T. S. Schulenberg *in* Snow 1982). The eggs (one or more) are greenish-blue, heavily marked and spotted dusky (for dimensions of the nest and egg, see Snow 1982).

Another nest, photographed by S. Bird (archived on the Surfbirds website, www.surfbirds.com), at Jardin, dpto. Antioquia, Colombia, in May 2009, appears to be constructed of similar materials to the Peruvian nest described by T. S. Schulenberg. Greeney *et al.* (2010) observed an active nest at 2,300m and another with two nestlings at 2,350m, in southeast Ecuador, both in the second week of May. M. A. Carriker (in Hilty and Brown 1986) collected two breeding-condition birds in southwest dpto. Huila, Colombia, in March–April, MVZ holds two males in breeding condition in Peru in late August and early October, and Whitney *et al.* (1994) observed an adult and independent juvenile together in Bolivia in mid March (interestingly, also with a juvenile *A. rubrocristatus* in close proximity).

STATUS Listed as of Least Concern (BirdLife International 2004, 2008) and Stotz *et al.* (1996) considered the species to be a low conservation priority, although the Chestnut-crested Cotinga's range is decidedly patchy and the species appears more restricted to large areas of undisturbed interior forest habitat than Red-crested Cotinga. Treated as Vulnerable in Colombia, where fragmentation and outright loss of habitat has had significant effects, and the species has not been recorded recently at several localities from which it was formerly reported, e.g. San Antonio, Santa Elena and Parque Nacional Natural Munchique, although on the positive side it has recently been found in Parque Nacional Natural Tatamá (Cuervo and Renjifo 2002b, Castaño-Villa and Patiño-Zabala 2008) and the Reserva Florestal Río Blanco, Manizales (Ocampo 2002). In Ecuador the species was only discovered recently (in 1984) and is distinctly rare and local (considered inexplicably so by Ridgely and Greenfield 2001), but it occurs in both Tapichalaca Biological Reserve (Greeney et al. 2010) and the adjoining Podocarpus National Park (Fjeldså and Krabbe 1990). Schulenberg *et al.* (2007) considered the species to be 'rare' in Peru too, contrary to previous literature erroneously describing it as 'fairly common' in the same country (Clements and Shany 2001). Nevertheless, the species is regularly observed at Abra Patricia, dpto. San Martín, and along the upper Manu Road, dpto. Cuzco (both Peru), as well as in two ProAves-owned reserves in Colombia, namely Reserva Loro Orejiamarillo and Reserve El Colibrí del Sol, both in dpto. Antioquia (Salaman et al. (2008).

REFERENCES Alvarez *et al.* (2007), Alverson *et al.* (2001), BirdLife International (2004, 2008), Boesman (2009), Boyla and Estrada (2005), Castaño-Villa and Patiño-Zabala (2008), Chapman (1924), Clements and Shany (2001), Cuervo and Renjifo (2002b), David and Gosselin (2002b), Davis *et al.* (1994), Dickinson (2003), Dunning (2008), Fjeldså and Krabbe (1990), Greeney *et al.* (2010), Hellmayr (1929b), Hennessey (2004a), Hennessey *et al.* (2003), Hilty and Brown (1986), Hornbuckle (1999), Kirwan *et al.* (2006), Krabbe and Nilsson (2003), Krabbe *et al.* (2001, 2006), MacLeod *et al.* (2005), Mayer (2000), Ocampo (2002), Remsen and Traylor (1989), Restall *et al.* (2006), Ridgely and Greenfield (2001), Ridgely and Tudor (1994, 2009), Salaman *et al.* (2008), Schulenberg (2000b), Schulenberg *et al.* (2007), Snow (1982, 2004a), Stotz *et al.* (1996), Taczanowski (1884), Walker *et al.* (2006), Whitney *et al.* (1994).

Chestnut-crested Cotinga *Ampelion rufaxilla*. **Fig. 1**. Adult, *A. r. rufaxilla*, Abra Patricia, dpto. Amazonas, northern Peru, October (*Hadoram Shirihai / Photographic Handbook to Birds of the World*). **Fig. 2**. Adult, *A. r. antioquiae*, Ventanas Road, Jardín, dpto. Antioquia, western Colombia, February (*Hadoram Shirihai / Photographic Handbook to Birds of the World*). **Fig. 3**. Adult, *A. r. antioquiae*, Ventanas Road, Jardín, dpto. Antioquia, western Colombia, May (*Diego Calderón-Franco / Colombia Birding*). Note the darker chestnut-coloured areas of the plumage, which is one of the characters that distinguishes this subspecies from nominate *rufaxilla*.

Genus *Doliornis*

Doliornis is a superspecies that comprises two allospecies, one of them only very recently described. Both *Doliornis* species inhabit the Andean treeline ecotone, at the interface between elfin forest and *páramo*, where they can be conspicuous at times, but their general rarity makes them difficult to observe. Many aspects of their ecology remain unknown. Their known ranges, being separated by the Marañón Gap in northern Peru, conform to a pattern shown by other high-Andean genera, e.g. some *Pipreola* fruiteaters. In common with other high-Andean cotingas, it is widely believed that both species are almost certainly obligate frugivores, and possibly mistletoe specialists.

BAY-VENTED COTINGA
Doliornis sclateri   Plate 32

Doliornis sclateri **Taczanowski, 1874**, *Proc. Zool. Soc. Lond.* 1874: 136, pl. 20, Maraynioc, Peru (cf. Warren and Harrison 1971, Mlíkovský 2009)

Both species of *Doliornis* are very poorly known cotingas. Whereas Chestnut-bellied Cotinga *Doliornis remseni* went undescribed until the close of the 20th century, Bay-vented Cotinga was initially encountered in 1874, when a pair was collected in central Peru by Jelski, but thereafter, until the early 1970s, it was known from just three additional specimens, all taken in 1921 by Harry Watkins at the same locality as the types. This was despite three months of fieldwork at the type locality, Maraynioc, specifically to try and find *D. sclateri* by J. A. Griswold in 1923 (Peters and Griswold 1943). To date, we still have much to learn about these two unassuming cotingas that occupy one of the least known (ecologically) and most threatened high-Andean ecotones of Colombia, Ecuador and Peru.

IDENTIFICATION 21.5cm. Throughout its limited Peruvian range, this rather plumbeous-coloured cotinga is only likely to be mistaken for Red-crested Cotinga *Ampelion rubrocristatus*, which is more common in similar treeline woodlots. The latter species can easily be distinguished by its conspicuous white tail-band, especially when swooping upwards onto an exposed perch following a low-level flight. In stark contrast, Bay-vented Cotingas are much more rarely seen, preferring to perch inconspicuously in the canopy near the tops of the tallest trees. The recently (1989) discovered Chestnut-bellied Cotinga occupies similar habitats but is solely found north of the Marañón Gap.

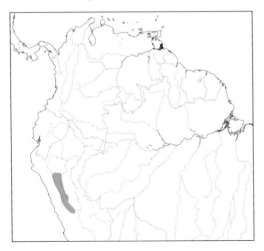

DISTRIBUTION Endemic to Peru, where it is restricted to the east slope of the central east Andes, at Puerto del Monte and three localities around Huicongo in dpto. San Martín, east of Tayabamba and at Buldiboyo in eastern dpto. La Libertad, in the Carpish Mountains in dpto. Huánuco (where known from at least seven localities), at two localities along the Pozuzo–Chaglla trail in dpto. Pasco, and at Maraynioc in dpto. Junín (the type locality) (BirdLife International 2008). Jiguet *et al.* (2010) listed this cotinga from 13 localities, but suggested that its true range might prove to be wider than is currently known. The Bay-vented Cotinga is found at elevations of 2,500–3,800m, but is generally commoner above 3,000m.

MOVEMENTS None known. The species is recorded as being extremely sedentary, with limited observations suggesting that birds remain in the same small patch of elfin forest habitat for long periods of time.

HABITAT Inhabits the flattened, wind-buffeted canopy of elfin forest habitat dominated by *Escallonia* (Escalloniaceae) and *Weinmannia* (Cunoniaceae) (which is largely impenetrable and periodically mist-enshrouded throughout the day), but is most often found at the higher elevation Andean treeline ecotone (the elfin forest–*páramo* interface).

DESCRIPTION *D. sclateri* is a dumpy-proportioned cotinga with a rather small bill and short tail; the female is marginally smaller than the male, although this is unlikely to be noticeable in the field. The bill has a strongly arched culmen with a moderately hooked tip. The sexes differ slightly in plumage. *Adult male.* – Glossy black cap with a semi-concealed reddish-chestnut crest. Upper back dark greyish, becoming browner towards the rump and tail. The wings are greyish-brown. The throat and the sides of the head and neck are paler grey than the rest of the upperparts, and also contrast with the brown underparts. In fresh plumage, the chest and upper breast of both sexes are paler with subterminal pale buff bars and darker terminal bars to the feathers (Zimmer 1936b, Robbins *et al.* 1994). The dark terminal bar is lost rapidly, and in extremely worn individuals the subterminal buff bar can be almost absent. Rufous-chestnut undertail-coverts. *Adult female.* – Resembles the male, but lacks the all-black crown, it having the crown entirely grey with dusky shaft-streaks, a duller red centre, a short blackish stripe through the lores, a paler belly, back and uppertail-coverts than the male, perhaps a slightly browner throat and slightly paler undertail-coverts (from Zimmer 1936b; FMNH). *Juvenile.* – Recently described by Robbins *et al.* (1994). Breast and belly clay-coloured and indistinctly streaked olive-brown, whilst the crown is concolorously grey (no red crest). Nestling undescribed (Snow 1982). *Moult.* – Plumage maturation unknown, but two adults collected in late January were in body moult and another from June was completing its wing and tail renewal, whilst a male taken in July had fresh remiges and rectrices. Like *D. remseni* and *Ampelion rubrocristatus*, this species is almost certainly capable of breeding in non-adult plumage (Robbins *et al.* 1994). *Bare parts.* – Irides grey but dull brown in juveniles; the bill is black with the base of the lower mandible bluish-grey and tip black (the entire bill is apparently black in juveniles); and the legs are dark grey (medium olive in the juvenile).

MEASUREMENTS (all measurements from Robbins *et al.* 1994) Wing of male (*n* = 16) 99.0–104.6mm, wing of female (*n* = 12) 88.4–101.0mm; tail of male (*n* = 16) 81.7–91.2mm, tail of female (*n* = 12) 82.8–90.9mm; bill of male (*n* = 16) 18.2–20.2mm, bill of female (*n* = 12) 17.4–21.0mm; tarsus of male (*n* = 16) 24.4–27.8mm, tarsus of female (*n* = 12) 24.0–27.5mm. Weight: 54–69g (males) and 53–67g (females) (Robbins *et al.* 1994).

GEOGRAPHICAL VARIATION Monotypic.

VOICE Generally a rather quiet species, but the Bay-vented Cotinga's voice has recently been published for the first time (Boesman 2009), whilst several recordings are archived online at www.xeno-canto.org. The most commonly heard vocalisation given by Bay-vented Cotinga is a rather harsh, rising *rhee*, *shhh* or *rhee-ah*, which varies in length and intensity, but despite sometimes sounding rather mewing is louder and scratchier than the equivalent vocalisations of Red-crested Cotinga (cf. recordings archived on www.xeno-canto.org). The inter-note interval appears to be context-dependent, with for instance the rate of calling increasing in response to playback. Whether the *rhee-ah* notes represent calls or the primary song is unknown (Schulenberg *et al.* 2007), although H. Lloyd (*in litt.* 2010) considers it to represent the primary song. What is clear is that the first bird to call is often answered by one member (usually the male) of the neighbouring pair (T. A. Parker *in* Snow 1982; A. Spencer recording XC41676), but females occasionally enter the fray too (H. Lloyd *in litt.* 2010). From the contexts under which the weaker-sounding *shhh* note is given (T. A. Parker *in* Snow 1982), this seems more likely to represent the call.

NATURAL HISTORY Few details of the Bay-vented Cotinga's life history are known. Often difficult to encounter without using playback or familiarity with its primary vocalisation, which (rather surprisingly) can sometimes be heard over considerable distances, due to the acoustic properties of the high-Andean treeline environment. Its behaviour is broadly similar to that of many other Andean cotingas. Birds perch quietly for long periods in the subcanopy, with any activity usually confined to foraging. The Bay-vented Cotinga is usually encountered in pairs and these often perch rather phlegmatically when faced by an observer, but can occasionally head-bob and assume a more upright position in response to playback of their calls.

FOOD AND FEEDING Observed feeding on melastomes, but the species also takes some insects and seeds. The Bay-vented Cotinga is dominant over Red-crested Cotinga at fruiting trees (H. Lloyd *in litt.* 2010).

DISPLAY This aspect of the species' life history merits amplification in the literature but apparently involves two birds facing one another, whereupon one individual flies vertically up before plunging directly back to its perch, then repeating the exercise, but apparently without emitting any vocalisation (Fjeldså and Krabbe 1990).

BREEDING There are no concrete breeding data, although an occupied nest was found in April or May; it was placed 4m above the ground in the fork of a slender tree, but no further details were apparently recorded (T. A. Parker *in* Snow 1982). A juvenile female was collected in dpto. Huánuco, in July (Fjeldså and Krabbe 1990).

STATUS This species is endemic to the East Peruvian Andean subcentre of the Peruvian Andean Centre of endemism (Cracraft 1985) and it occurs in the North-east Peruvian cordilleras Endemic Bird Area (EBA; Stattersfield *et al.* 1998). Bay-vented Cotinga is considered rare to locally uncommon (Ridgely and Tudor 1994, Stotz *et al.* 1996), but was formerly treated as of Least Concern by BirdLife International (2004), despite its known range being rather small (estimated at 13,100km²). The species has subsequently been categorised as Vulnerable (BirdLife International 2008) and even if, as has been recently speculated, its range proves to be larger than presently understood its conservation status is unlikely to be improved (Jiguet *et al.* 2010). The species' population is estimated to be fewer than 10,000 individuals, and is speculated to be declining given that suitable habitat might have declined by *c.*50% within the last 25 years principally due to unsustainable fire management of high-Andean pastureland (G. Engblom *in* BirdLife International 2008). Bay-vented Cotinga is known from the Río Abiseo National Park, dpto. San Martín (Boyla and Estrada 2005), although suitable habitat therein is speculated to be under increasing anthropogenic pressure in recent years (G. Engblom *in* BirdLife International 2008). Quantitative population studies are urgently required to help address any potential problems associated with changes in Andean agricultural land-use patterns within the North-east Peruvian cordilleras EBA, themselves associated with climate change, to which high-Andean forest and *páramo* habitats are already highly susceptible (Vuille and Bradley 2000, Bradley *et al.* 2006). The comparative remoteness of the Bay-vented Cotinga's habitat can no longer be considered rationale for assuming the species faces no immediate conservation concerns.

REFERENCES BirdLife International (2004, 2008), Boesman (2009), Boyla and Estrada (2005), Bradley *et al.* (2006), Cracraft (1985), Fjeldså and Krabbe (1990), Hellmayr (1929b), Jiguet *et al.* (2010), Mlíkovský (2009), Parker *et al.* (1982), Peters and Griswold (1943), Ridgely and Tudor (1994, 2009), Robbins *et al.* (1994), Schulenberg *et al.* (2007), Snow (1982, 2004a), Stattersfield *et al.* (1998), Stotz *et al.* (1996), Vuille and Bradley (2000), Warren and Harrison (1971), Zimmer (1936b).

Bay-vented Cotinga *Doliornis sclateri*. **Fig. 1**. Adult male, Bosque Unchog, dpto. Huánuco, central Peru, November (*Hadoram Shirihai / Photographic Handbook to Birds of the World*). **Fig. 2**. Adult male, Bosque Unchog, Huánuco, central Peru, September (*Leif Gabrielsen*). **Fig. 3**. Adult female, Bosque Unchog, dpto. Huánuco, central Peru, November (*Hadoram Shirihai / Photographic Handbook to Birds of the World*). **Fig. 4**. Habitat of Bay-vented Cotinga, Bosque Unchog, Huánuco, central Peru (*Huw Lloyd*).

CHESTNUT-BELLIED COTINGA
Doliornis remseni   Plate 32

Doliornis remseni **Robbins, Rosenberg & Sornoza, 1994,** *Auk* 111: 2, *c.*3 km southeast of Impueran, west slope of Cerro Mongus, prov. Carchi, Ecuador

Discovered as recently as 1989, the Chestnut-bellied Cotinga was originally found in northeast Ecuador, at the Cerro Mongus; soon it became apparent that other sightings, originally attributed to Bay-vented Cotinga *Doliornis sclateri*, which is endemic to Peru, from southern Ecuador and central Colombia, also in fact involved *remseni*.

IDENTIFICATION 20.0–21.5cm. In all plumages, Chestnut-bellied Cotinga can be distinguished from the entirely allopatric Bay-vented by virtue of the former's rich rufous-chestnut underparts, which extend from the mid breast to the vent. On Bay-vented Cotinga the rufous is restricted to the vent and this part has a more orange hue than the underparts of Chestnut-bellied. The face, throat and breast of Chestnut-bellied are darker grey than its congener, and there is less contrast with the crown than in Bay-vented Cotinga. Compare with Red-crested Cotinga *Ampelion rubrocristatus*, which has a striking white tail-band, a larger and paler bill, no red on the underparts, bright red irides and a much longer and more obvious red crest.

DISTRIBUTION Chestnut-bellied Cotinga is known from just nine localities (BirdLife International 2008) although Jiguet *et al.* (2010) listed only seven. Initially considered endemic to Ecuador, this species was recorded in the Central Andes of Colombia, in Quindío/Tolima (Renjifo 1994), prior to the type description being published, leading the observers of the Colombian birds to understandably (but erroneously) attribute their records to Bay-vented Cotinga. In Ecuador, Chestnut-bellied Cotinga is known from eight disjunct localities in the eastern Andes, from southeastern Carchi (two localities) south to Podocarpus National Park, prov. Loja (at which latter locality the species involved was initially suspected to be Chestnut-bellied: cf. Bloch *et al.* 1991), and southeast of Jimbura, prov. Zamora-Chinchipe, close to the border with Peru (Robbins *et al.* 1994). There is also an unconfirmed record from the well-visited Cotopaxi National Park in north-central Ecuador (BirdLife International 2008). Occurrence in extreme northern Peru,

north of the Marañón Valley, is plausible given that the species has been reported from close to the border with northernmost dpto. Piura and close to dpto. Cajamarca (see Robbins *et al.* 1994, Schulenberg *et al.* 2007, Jiguet *et al.* 2010), but to date its presence in the country has not been confirmed. The elevational range of Chestnut-bellied Cotinga lies at 2,875–3,650m, but the species is principally found above 3,100m.

MOVEMENTS None known, and it seems probable that Chestnut-bellied Cotinga is as sedentary as its congener.

HABITAT Broadly similar to that favoured by *D. sclateri*, i.e. dense, moist montane forest comprising trees 5–10m tall, heavily covered with epiphytes, mosses and lichens, and interspersed with thick bushes (Henry 2008). Like *D. sclateri*, this species will also utilise low-level scrub immediately adjacent to treeline forest.

DESCRIPTION Like the previous species, this is a rather dumpy-proportioned cotinga with a rather small bill and short tail (although *D. remseni* is longer winged and longer tailed than *D. sclateri*: Robbins *et al.* 1994); the female is marginally smaller than the male. *Adult male.* – Crown jet black and this colour extends to just below the eye. Lores also black. Crest in centre of crown semi-concealed (and rarely raised), orange-red. Mantle, scapulars, wing-coverts, rump and uppertail-coverts blackish-grey. Remiges and rectrices are also blackish-grey. Chin, throat, ear-coverts, foreneck and upper chest are dark grey, contrasting with the lower breast, belly, flanks and undertail-coverts, which are rich, deep rufous-chestnut. *Adult female.* – Resembles the male but the black crown feathers are fringed grey, which in the field render the crown almost concolorous with the face and throat. Area in front of the eye pale grey, contrasting with the black lores and imparting an indistinctly spectacled appearance. *Immature.* – Like the respective adult, but juvenile rectrices, at least, are retained, and the species seems almost certainly capable of breeding in such plumage (Robbins *et al.* 1994). *Moult.* – Nothing is known. *Bare parts.* – Irides dark red-brown; the bill and legs and feet are dark grey to black.

MEASUREMENTS (from Robbins *et al.* 1994) Wing of male (n = 6) 97.8–115.9mm, wing of female (n = 1) 101.1mm; tail of male (n = 6) 87.1–98.1mm, tail of female (n = 1) 90.4mm; bill of male (n = 6) 17.3–19.7mm, bill of female (n = 1) 20.7mm; tarsus of male (n = 6) 26.5–28.2mm, tarsus of female (n = 1) 27.4mm. Weight 58.5–72.0g (males) and 64g (one female) (Robbins *et al.* 1994).

GEOGRAPHICAL VARIATION Monotypic.

VOICE Unknown.

NATURAL HISTORY Similar to *D. sclateri*; two male and two female Chestnut-bellied Cotingas observed in the crowns of *Escallonia* (Escalloniaceae) trees spent 'the majority of the time perched motionless ... one male sat in the crown ... for a period of 8 minutes without moving' (Robbins *et al.* 1994). Another lone female, observed during the same study, appeared to be loosely associated with a mixed-species flock dominated by typical high-Andean tanager species. Flight reported to be usually short and rather heavy (Bloch *et al.* 1991), and pairs appear to keep in close (<10m) contact, feeding in the tops of 1–3m-tall trees. Chestnut-bellied Cotinga sometimes feeds in close proximity to Red-crested Cotinga, and probably briefly joins mixed-species feeding flocks (see above).

FOOD AND FEEDING This species' diet appears, thus far, to be entirely frugivorous, with small berries and seeds of *Escallonia* and *Miconia chlorocarpa* (Melastomataceae), and possibly a *Tournefortia* sp. (Boraginaceae), recorded to date.

BREEDING Data are completely lacking, although several specimens are immature, collected in March and July, and a male with enlarged testes was collected in late October (Robbins *et al.* 1994). Mention of a juvenile in late October in Colombia (Renjifo 1994) is almost certainly erroneous (cf. Rasmussen *et al.* 1996).

STATUS Chestnut-bellied Cotinga is currently treated as Vulnerable (BirdLife International 2004, 2008), and the species' disjunct populations are presumably the result of already extensive habitat modification (due to burning, agricultural expansion, firewood extraction, etc.), and render it at considerable risk from such ongoing events. BirdLife International (2008) consider Chestnut-bellied Cotinga to be declining and its overall range and population to be 10,900km² and fewer than 10,000 individuals, respectively. Renjifo *et al.* (2002) estimated that just fewer than 2,000 individuals might occur in the Colombian portion of its range, but also that less than 10% of the original timberline (i.e. suitable) habitat remains in that country and that 78% of this has been lost as recently as within the last decade or so. The species is known from eight protected areas, namely: Cañon del Quindío National Park and Reserva El Mirador y Loro (Colombia), and Guandera Biological Reserve, Cayambe-Coca Ecological Reserve, Llanganates National Park, Sangay National Park, Podocarpus National Park and Bosque Protector Colambo-Yacuri (Ecuador), as well as several Important Bird Areas, e.g. Páramos y Bosques Altoandinos de Génova, dpto. Quindío, Colombia (Boyla and Estrada 2005). The other Ecuadorian localities are currently unprotected, although in general high-Andean, non-*Polylepis* woodlots are perhaps less vulnerable than lower submontane areas. Nonetheless, grazing, firewood-extraction, uncontrolled burning and cultivation are all low-intensity threats. The species does appear to be generally rare and local, even allowing for its unobtrusive nature, and its conservation status perhaps warrants review, although Jiguet *et al.* (2010) suggested that its overall range might prove larger than currently known.

REFERENCES BirdLife International (2004, 2008), Bloch *et al.* (1991), Boyla and Estrada (2005), Cresswell *et al.* (1999), Fjeldså and Krabbe (1990), Henry (2008), Jiguet *et al.* (2010), Rasmussen *et al.* (1996), Renjifo (1994), Renjifo *et al.* (2002), Restall *et al.* (2006), Ridgely and Greenfield (2001), Ridgely and Tudor (2009), Robbins *et al.* (1994), Salaman *et al.* (2008), Snow (2004a), Stotz *et al.* (1996), Williams *et al.* (1997).

Genus *Zaratornis*: White-cheeked Cotinga

Discovered by Maria & Hans-Wilhelm Koepcke in October 1953, remarkably within less than 100km of the capital of Peru, Lima, the genus *Zaratornis* was frequently subsumed within the superficially similar *Ampelion* (initially by Bond 1956; also, e.g. by Snow 1982 and Stotz *et al.* 1996) until comparatively recently, despite the fact that its skull structure has long been known to be unique (Lowery and O'Neill 1966). Until 1966 the male was unknown and the two sexes were not even observed together until the late Ted Parker found the species breeding above Yánac, in Ancash, central Peru, in 1976 (whence a specimen, collected by Melbourne A. Carriker in 1932, had subsequently come to light: Bond 1955). Prior to Parker's survey, it was (bizarrely and incorrectly) widely believed that the two sexes were segregated by habitat and might only come together to breed (Lüthi 1970).

WHITE-CHEEKED COTINGA
Zaratornis stresemanni   Plate 32

Zaratornis stresemanni **M. Koepcke, 1954**, *Publ. Mus. Hist. Nat. Javier Prado* ser. A., zool., 16: 3, Zárate, Río Rimac, Lima, Peru

This highly localised and globally threatened cotinga inhabits high-elevation woodlands dominated by trees of the genus *Polylepis* (Rosaceae) almost at the treeline in the Andes of western Peru. It occurs syntopically with the superficially similar Red-crested Cotinga *Ampelion rubrocristatus* at some sites, a species with which it was once considered congeneric (see Introduction above). A mistletoe specialist, the ecology of this species is inextricably linked to the viability of the high-altitude forests that it inhabits.

IDENTIFICATION 18–21cm. White-cheeked Cotinga shares the streaked underparts with immature Red-crested Cotinga which, however, always has a white tail-band (particularly conspicuous in flight), and lacks the white cheeks of its rarer relative. There is no overlap with either of the similar-sized, but relatively longer-tailed and smaller-billed *Doliornis* species, both of which are easily distinguished given clear views of the head and underparts. White-cheeked Cotinga's sluggish foraging behaviour and habit of perching on partially exposed branches or conspicuously atop trees, woody shrubs or snags within its stunted woodland habitat often permits prolonged observations, thereby greatly facilitating the species' identification.

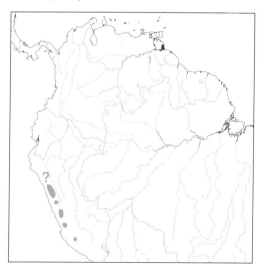

DISTRIBUTION *Z. stresemanni* is endemic to Peru, where it is almost entirely restricted to the west slope of the West Andes, from La Libertad south locally as far as Ayacucho, at Pampa Galeras, and Hortigal, in Lima, with one locality on the west slope of the East Andes, at Tayabamba, La Libertad (although it is not certainly resident at Tayabamba). The species is known from *c.*10 localities in total. Its principal elevational range is 3,250–4,250m, where it is just about the only avian frugivore, but individuals presumed to be (wandering) non-breeders have been recorded at 2,500–2,900m and even, on occasion, as low as 2,000m.

MOVEMENTS White-cheeked Cotinga is suspected of performing localised elevational movements, following the fruiting of mistletoes (see Food and Feeding) in high-altitude woodland and apparently descending in the dry (non-breeding) season to mixed woodland. Parker (1981) noted that mistletoes seemed less abundant during the dry months (August–October) at Tútapac and in the upper Santa Eulalia Valley.

HABITAT Remnant mixed woodlots of *Polylepis*, *Gynoxys* (Compositae), *Baccharis* (Asteraceae), *Symplocos* (Symplo-caceae) and *Mauria* (Anacardiaceae) trees, typically on steep slopes (Ríos 2010), during the breeding season. Other typical woody plants noted by Parker (1981) at his survey sites included species of *Vernonia*, *Chuquiraga* and *Senecio* (Asteraceae), *Lupinus* (Leguminosae) and *Berberis* (Berberidaceae). At other times (August–November), White-cheeked Cotinga visits lower temperate-zone mixed forest dominated by other genera of trees (cf. Ferreyra 1978). Usually inhabits small patches of woodland of less than 1ha in extent with a mean tree height of less than 5m (Parker 1981), largely separated from the nearest adjacent area of similar habitat by grassy or rocky *puna* or *páramo*.

DESCRIPTION Sexes are similar. The bill has a reasonably strongly arched culmen and a very slight hooked tip. The nostrils are relatively small and partially obscured by the feathers of the forehead. *Adult.* – The jet black crown extends to eye level and contrasts quite markedly with the white cheeks, which extend from the lores to the ear-coverts, grading gradually into the grey-brown nape, with buffish tips to the feathers of the neck-sides. The remainder of the upperparts feathers are fuscous, streaked heavily with buff and whitish. Dusky wing feathers are indistinctly fringed paler, being fringed narrowly whitish over both webs of the primaries, secondaries and tertials (which feathers are otherwise rather browner), and some of the larger coverts. However, some of the greater wing-coverts, all of the smaller wing-coverts and the scapulars are rufous-fringed, especially over the proximal part of the web closer to the tip, but generally becoming paler basally. The tail is also mostly dusky. Throat to breast greyish-brown, with a buffish chin, and rest of underparts ochraceous-buff, streaked broadly with fuscous, except over the central belly, which is slightly brighter and unmarked. *Immature.* – Fjeldså and Krabbe (1990) recorded that juveniles have a paler throat, and the lores and cheeks are only slightly paler (thus less contrasting) than the rest of the head. *Moult.* – There are seemingly no published data on moult. *Bare parts.* – The irides are bright red; the bill is dark to paler greyish-blue becoming even paler towards the tip; and the legs are dark brown to blackish (Parker 1981, Snow 1982).

MEASUREMENTS (from Parker 1981, Snow 1982: western Peru) Wing of male (n = 5) 110–115mm, wing of female (n = 6) 111–114mm; tail of male (n = 5) 84–89mm, tail of female (n = 6) 83–90mm; bill of male (n = 5) 11mm, bill of female (n = 6) 9–11mm; tarsus of male (n = 5) 25.5–26.5mm, tarsus of female (n = 6) 26.5–27.5mm. Weight 46–57g (males) and 47–55g (females) (Snow 2004b; MVZ).

GEOGRAPHICAL VARIATION Monotypic.

VOICE The presumed primary song is a loud (but easily overlooked), low-pitched series of nasal *reh-reh-REH-REH-rrrrrrrrrr-re-re* notes, which speed up in the middle, and then terminates with two emphatic notes, with a frequency range of 2–4kHz. The whole sound lasts *c.*4 seconds and is given 3–6 times at intervals of 30–60 seconds, but often with long periods between calling bouts (Parker 1981). Limited observations suggest that this 'song' is usually given from 07:00 to 09:00 hours, when the first sunlight hits the steep wooded slopes that the birds inhabit, with a second peak between 11:00 hrs and 14:00 hrs (Ríos 2010), and to some extent late afternoon, with birds from adjacent woodlots occasionally answering each other. Sounds frog-like and also recalls the vocalisations of *Ampelion*, *Doliornis* and *Phytotoma* (see Parker 1981). Also utters a drawn-out *raaa-aaah* in alarm (Parker 1981) or when disturbed, at which times the species also head-bobs and flicks its tail like *Ampelion* and *Doliornis*, but the 'song' is given whilst perched upright and still (Parker 1981). Short *reh* notes are given in contact between pairs or when feeding (Parker 1981). The species is also known to emit a burry series of emphatic quacks recently described: *djee-djee-DJEE-DJEE-DJEEP* (Parker 1981, Fjeldså and Krabbe 1990, Schulenberg *et al.* 2007). The species' voice has recently featured on the compilation published by Boesman (2009) and several recordings have been archived online at www.xeno-canto.org.

NATURAL HISTORY White-cheeked Cotinga is probably easiest to observe between 07:00 and 10:00 hrs (Ríos 2010; R. Innes pers. comm.). The birds usually perch rather upright albeit less so than *Ampelion* and with the head hunched into the neck, perusing their surroundings rather nervously (Parker 1981). The flight is rather like that of Red-crested Cotinga, being low and level, before swooping up onto a chosen perch almost in the manner of a shrike (*Lanius*) or falcon (*Falco*). Favoured exposed perches can be occupied for long periods, the birds apparently surveying their territories (Koepcke 1958). Territories average *c.*100m × 60m (Parker 1981).

FOOD AND FEEDING T. A. Parker (*in* Snow 1982) suggested that the species probably occasionally hawks insects in flight, as do the *Ampelion* species, although such behaviour has not been observed to date. Indeed, *Zaratornis* is apparently an obligate frugivore of two particular, epiphytic, mistletoe genera (*Tristerix* and *Ligaria*: Loranthaceae), for which the

species is speculated to be probably the main dispersal agent of their seeds (Koepcke 1958, Parker 1981, Castañeda Gil 2010), although *Zaratornis* has recently been also observed feeding on the shrub *Berberis lutea* (Berberidaceae). Like *Doliornis* and *Ampelion*, fruit is plucked whilst the bird is perched, up to five in quick succession, and the seeds are regurgitated onto the branches (Parker 1981). During the non-breeding season (August–September), the species sometimes forms aggregations of 4–10 birds whilst foraging (Parker 1981).

DISPLAY The display has been observed only once (by Parker 1981) and resembles those described for *Doliornis*, including the lack of any vocal component. The two birds (presumably male and female) face each other at very close quarters and bow slightly, then commence head-bobbing and wing-flicking for between 30 seconds and one minute, whereupon they regurgitate seeds onto an exposed branch (Parker 1981).

BREEDING Data on breeding are based on limited observations (mainly by Parker 1981, who found five nests of the species, at Quebrada Tútapac and in the upper Santa Eulalia Valley, all above 3,600m). *Zaratornis* appears to lay three greenish eggs marked with brownish flecks (especially at the larger end: cf. *Bull. Brit. Orn. Club* 101: 261), in April–May, and constructs a deep cup nest of mosses and lichens, supplemented with a few small twigs and the whole is lined with coarse grasses. The nest is usually well concealed within mistletoe on a *Polylepis* tree, within 1–3m of the trunk and sited 4–7m above the ground, always in areas that receive the most sunlight. Dimensions of the eggs and nest were presented by Parker (1981). Both adults feed the young solely on regurgitated fruit although they never visit the nest simultaneously, but one parent appeared to take responsibility for incubating the eggs and one, presumed to be the male, was usually more demonstrative in defending the nest. A juvenile was collected in August, in dpto. Lima, and others have been observed in the Cordillera Blanca in June, birds with large gonads from dptos. Ancash and Lima in March, and nest building has also been recorded in March, also in dpto. Lima (Parker 1981, Fjeldså and Krabbe 1990, Ríos 2010). MVZ holds two females that were in breeding condition in October and November.

STATUS White-cheeked Cotinga is considered to be either rare to uncommon and very local (Ridgely and Tudor 1994, 2009, Stotz *et al.* 1996). It is categorised as Vulnerable (BirdLife International 2004, 2008), with the overall population estimated at perhaps just 1,500–6,000 individuals in recent years, of which the largest subpopulation censused in 1987 (*c.*500 birds: Fjeldså and Kessler 1996) is at Pueblo Quichas, north of Oyón, at 4,000–4,200m (Boyla and Estrada 2005). Additional areas of conservation importance include the upper Santa Eulalia Valley (probably at least 250 birds have been estimated) and the Río Cañete drainage (where *Zaratornis* is fairly commonly encountered), also within dpto. Lima (BirdLife International 2004). White-cheeked Cotinga is known from two protected areas, the 340,000ha Huascarán National Park (dpto. Ancash) and the 6,500ha Pampa Galeras National Reserve (dpto. Ayacucho), but neither is inviolate. Within Huascarán National Park, the Alpamayo and Cedros regions support the greatest numbers of White-cheeked Cotingas (S. Sevillano *in litt.* 2010). Habitat destruction and degradation, through collection of firewood, charcoal production, grazing pressure and uncontrolled fires, are common problems throughout the species' range, even within protected areas (Boyla and Estrada 2005). The type locality, Bosque de Zárate, Lima, was recently listed as an Important Bird Area (IBA), as is the southernmost known locality, Hortigal, which is considered a particularly important locality for the species (Boyla and Estrada 2005). However, IBA designation does not entitle these areas to any degree of protected status nor prevents further habitat loss or degradation. The IBA designation has also been applied to five other localities (Boyla and Estrada 2005).

REFERENCES Ames (1971), Begazo *et al.* (2001), BirdLife International (2004, 2008), Boesman (2009), Bond (1955), Boyla and Estrada (2005), Castañeda Gil (2010), Collar *et al.* (1992), Ferreyra (1978), Fjeldså and Kessler (1996), Fjeldså and Krabbe (1990), Koepcke (1954, 1958), Lowery and O'Neill (1966), Lüthi (1970), Ohlson *et al.* (2008), Parker (1981), Remsen *et al.* (2008), Ridgely and Tudor (1994, 2009), Ríos (2010), Schulenberg *et al.* (2007), Snow (1982, 2004b), Stotz *et al.* (1996), Tello *et al.* (2009).

White-cheeked Cotinga *Zaratornis stresemanni*. **Figs. 1–2.** Adult, Santa Eulalia canyon, dpto. Lima, western Peru, September (*Hadoram Shirihai / Photographic Handbook to Birds of the World*). Another highly distinctive, but only recently discovered cotinga from the Peruvian high Andes. Separate generic status for this species is now widely accepted, although some previous authors placed it within *Ampelion*.

Genus *Phytotoma*: plantcutters

The genus *Phytotoma*, which is applied to a group of just three species (all but one confined to the southernmost parts of the South American continent), was erected comparatively early, in 1782, compared with many of the genera currently placed in the Cotingidae. Of the three species, one, the Peruvian Plantcutter *Phytotoma raimondii*, is rare and seemingly still in decline, but the other two species are rather easily encountered in scrubby country in the southern third of the continent.

PERUVIAN PLANTCUTTER
Phytotoma raimondii   Plate 33

Phytotoma raimondii **Taczanowski, 1884**, *Proc. Zool. Soc. Lond.* 1884: 71, pl. 17, Tumbes, northwest Peru

This species, which forms a superspecies with White-tipped Plantcutter *Phytotoma rutila* (Short 1975, Sibley and Monroe 1990), is entirely restricted to the Peruvian Arid Coastal Centre of endemism (Cracraft 1985).

IDENTIFICATION 18.5–19.0cm. Peruvian Plantcutter is the rarest of the plantcutters, being a highly restricted-range (and threatened) species. Given the lack of overlap with either of its two congeners, there is no identification challenge, although the less distinct, streaked, female might recall a Streaked Saltator *Saltator striatipectus* or other finch, but various features should easily reveal its true identity. The male most closely resembles the White-tipped Plantcutter; however, the appearance of *raimondii* is that of a generally grey bird with white wingbars and rufous patches on the chest and belly. The male White-tipped, on the other hand, has completely rufous underparts.

DISTRIBUTION Peruvian Plantcutter is endemic to Peru, where the species is restricted to the northern littoral, from northern dpto. Piura south to northern dpto. Lima (Schulenberg *et al.* 2007, Flanagan *et al.* 2009), and where it is known from *c.*54 past and present localities on the coastal plain (Flanagan *et al.* 2009, Suárez Pingo 2011). Although frequently listed in the literature from the far northwest,

in dpto. Tumbes (e.g. Collar *et al.* 1992), reasons for not including this department within the species' known range, either past or present, have been put forward by Flanagan *et al.* (2009). The latter authors' comprehensive review of the literature and specimen record, as well as personal fieldwork, also reveals that there have been no records since the early 1980s in dpto. Lima (and just two ever), and just four in dpto. Ancash; thus, the species principally occurs from dpto. La Libertad northwards. Occurs to 550m (Snow 2004a) but the vast majority of known localities lie below 200m, although there is a specimen record, from 1978, apparently as high as 950m (Schulenberg *et al.* 2007, Flanagan *et al.* 2009).

MOVEMENTS None known and is generally considered to be resident.

HABITAT Prefers open, dry forest dominated by *Prosopis*, *Acacia* (Leguminosae), *Cucurbita* (Cucurbitaceae) and other trees, with a dense shrubby understorey including various species of *Capparis* (Capparidaceae), *Cordia* (Boraginaceae) and *Galvezia* (Scrophulariaceae), some of which are highly localised, but the plantcutter will also occupy desert scrub and riparian thickets; again, these are usually dominated by *Prosopis* trees.

DESCRIPTION Peruvian Plantcutter displays the short, shaggy, expressive crest and rounded bill (with serrated edges) typical of the genus. The culmen has a pronounced curve and the tip can be slightly hooked, especially in males. Sexes differ. *Male.* – The head and upperparts are largely ash-grey with a cinnamon-rufous patch on the forehead of somewhat variable extent, though never very large, and sometimes extending around the eyes. The uniform appearance of the upperparts is relieved only by some black streaking on the crown and back, a small reddish patch below the base of the bill (scarcely visible in the field) and by the two white wingbars. The upper wingbar is considerably broader than the lower, being formed by the white lesser and median wing-coverts, with just small white tips and fringes to the greater coverts, forming a narrow bar. The grey tertials are tipped white. The tail is dusky grey, tipped white at the feather tips. The chin to breast is ash-grey, which colour extends to the flanks. The belly and undertail-coverts are cinnamon-rufous, again of variable extent and depth, but always contrasting with the dark grey undertail, which is relieved by white tips. *Female.* – Generally greyish-fawn overall, although the upperparts are slightly darker than this. The upperparts (including the crest and face) are streaked with black, broadest on the back. The wings are a darker brown with two narrow whitish wingbars. The tail is dusky-brown with white tips to each rectrix. Underparts paler with blackish streaks. *Juvenile.* – Undescribed until recently, when Rosina and Romo (2010) observed and photographed recently fledged individuals, which appeared similar to adult males, except in lacking any trace of reddish in the plumage, other than on the extreme ventral region. They also had dark irides and had a brownish frontal crest. Immature males have the upperparts and wings mainly female-like with heavy dark mantle streaking, but with darker tail feathers and some reddish coloration appearing on the ventral region (specimen in BMNH). *Moult.* – Nothing is known. *Bare parts.* – Irides bright yellow or pale orange; bill and legs brown to dark grey or black; and mouth lining dark pinkish-red, at least in males (FMNH; GMK pers. obs.).

MEASUREMENTS (BMNH; FMNH: Peru) Wing of male (*n* = 7) 90–94mm, wing of female (*n* = 3) 86–92mm; tail of male (*n* = 8) 78–84mm, tail of female (*n* = 6) 80–85mm; bill of male (*n* = 8) 16.92–18.41mm, bill of female (*n* = 5) 16.68–18.41mm; tarsus of male (*n* = 7) 21.00–25.37mm, tarsus of female (*n* = 3) 22–24mm. Weight (sexes combined): 36–44g (Snow 2004a, Dunning 2008).

GEOGRAPHICAL VARIATION Monotypic.

VOICE This species' vocalisations were recently published by Boesman (2009) and are also available online at www.xeno-canto.org. Likened to a rusty gate being opened, the song is, as described by Schulenberg *et al.* (2007), an overall descending series of rising and falling nasal *REEEH reeeh reeeh* notes, which sounds as if the bird is 'annoyed'. The song is similar to that of White-tipped Plantcutter, but is overall less mechanical-sounding and squeakier. Call notes consist of various, equally 'annoyed' nasal whining notes. Generally does not respond particularly aggressively to playback, usually being 'content' to respond but not 'visit' the sound source (GMK pers. obs.).

NATURAL HISTORY Not very well known, although the species is usually seen in pairs and perches conspicuously, being not difficult to observe.

FOOD AND FEEDING Exclusively herbivorous and is usually encountered foraging in pairs or in small groups. Peruvian Plantcutter prefers the buds, shoots and leaves of *Prosopis* trees, as well as those of some other shrubs, but will also take fruits (cf. also Rosina and Romo 2010). All are taken whilst perched, either by reaching slightly upwards, or 'lunging' downwards or sideways, then neatly twisting and tearing the piece of foliage selected (GMK pers. obs.).

BREEDING Behaviour and biology practically unknown although Flanagan and Millen (2008) have recently described and illustrated the eggs, based on two clutches held in the Royal Ontario Museum, Toronto, taken in the 1930s near Talara. Based on the collector's notes, both clutches were apparently of three eggs (Snow 2004a speculated that clutch size would be 2–4), and both were taken from nests sited a couple of metres above the ground in *Prosopis* trees, in late March and early April (according well with previous data; see below). The nests were not well described, but both were probably rather shallow cups constructed of twigs, in which the eggs were visible from below. Flanagan and Millen (2008) described the eggs as being drab varying to greyish-olive, the broader end having fine to coarse dark brownish-olive flecks. Earlier, Walters (2006) had mentioned that the eggs of this species closely match those of *P. rutila*. Even more recently, Rosina and Romo (2010) described the discovery of two active nests in dpto. Ancash. Both nests were constructed in *Grabowskia boerhaaviaefolia* (Solanaceae) trees 1.2m above the ground and within 70m of one another. Dimensions of the nests are presented in the paper, and both were principally constructed using dry branches of the same species of tree in which they were built. Both nests were found in the first week of April, one had two eggs and the other two young considered to be 10–15 days old when found on 7 April and which had fledged by 14 April. Thus the period from hatching to fledging appears to be similar to that in other *Phytotoma*, although more data are clearly desirable. At the other nest, the authors of the paper determined that the eggs were laid sometime apart, but were unable to record the interval. The eggs were similar to those described by Flanagan and Millen (2008), but their ground colour was initially whiter (less grey). Approximate dimensions of the eggs were published in Rosina and Romo (2010). Snow (2004a) summarised other breeding data, almost all from specimens: males with active gonads and a laying female taken in March, a male with slightly enlarged testes in April, and a male seen holding a twig with a female nearby in August. Birds that were plainly not in breeding condition have been collected in April, August and September.

STATUS Treated as Endangered (BirdLife International 2004, 2008) and restricted to the Tumbesian Region Endemic Bird Area (Stattersfield *et al.* 1998) including several Important Bird Areas (Boyla and Estrada 2005). The species' overall status was most recently reviewed by Flanagan *et al.* (2009) and an Action Plan for the species has also been published (Flanagan 2009). Peruvian Plantcutter, along with many other species in South America, has recently been added to the Federal Register by the US Fish & Wildlife Service, in an effort to heighten awareness of this species' plight. Over-grazing, burning, cutting for timber and charcoal production, and conversion of forested areas to agriculture, especially sugar cane, are significant and seemingly constant threats to the species' survival, although conservation interest in, and efforts on behalf of, this plantcutter have increased. Despite the relatively large number of traced localities known to have harboured the species (see above; Flanagan *et al.* 2009), perhaps as few as eight seem to have been occupied within the last decade, and many apparently suitable areas are seemingly 'missing' the species. Formerly recorded south as far as dpto. Lima, but current range is very much centred on the Talara area of dpto. Piura, wherein some 50,000ha of suitable habitat is speculated to support 500–1,000 individuals and is currently largely owned (and protected by) the PetroPerú company. Three sites have been identified recently as conservation priorities for this species in dpto. Piura (see *Cotinga* 27: 11), where a population of *c*.200 pairs has been estimated in the environs of Talara (Boyla and Estrada 2005). Peruvian Plantcutter is also readily found in the vicinity of Chiclayo, dpto. Lambayeque, for instance at Mocupe Nuevo and Batan Grande, Santuario Historico Bosque de Pomac (Valqui 2004), but some well-known sites, e.g. Rafán, in dpto. Lambayeque, are now much degraded, and the species is consequently scarcer as a result (D. Beadle pers. comm.) although earlier the population was estimated at 20–30 individuals (Boyla and Estrada 2005). Known from a few other protected areas, such as Chaparrí Private Protection Area, where only recently discovered, there are just two records (and another nearby) and its precise status is still unknown (Boyla and Estrada 2005, Flanagan *et al.* 2009).

REFERENCES Begazo *et al.* (2001), Best and Kessler (1995), BirdLife International (2004, 2008), Boesman (2009), Boyla and Estrada (2005), Collar *et al.* (1992), Cracraft (1985), Dunning (2008), Flanagan (2009), Flanagan and Millen

(2008), Flanagan *et al.* (2009), Hellmayr (1929b), Koepcke (1961), Parker *et al.* (1982), Ridgely and Tudor (1994, 2009), Rosina and Romo (2010), Schulenberg *et al.* (2007), Short (1975), Sibley and Monroe (1990), Snow (2004a), Stattersfield *et al.* (2008), Stotz *et al.* (1996), Suárez Pingo (2011), Valqui (2004), Walters (2006).

Peruvian Plantcutter *Phytotoma raimondii.* **Fig. 1.** Male, Bosque de Pomac, dpto. Lambayeque, northwest Peru, September (*Dušan Brinkhuizen*). **Fig. 2.** Male, Quebrada Pariñas, Talara, dpto. Piura, northwest Peru, August (*Alexander More*). **Fig. 3.** Female, Bosque de Pomac, dpto. Lambayeque, northwest Peru, September (*Dušan Brinkhuizen*). **Fig. 4.** Female, Quebrada Pariñas, Talara, dpto. Piura, northwest Peru, August (*Alexander More*). Males and females are readily separable, and identification to species is also easy, given that this is the only plantcutter in range.

WHITE-TIPPED PLANTCUTTER
Phytotoma rutila   Plate 33

Phytotoma rutila Vieillot, 1818, *Nouv. Dict. Hist. Nat.*, new edn. 26: 64, [based on Azara, no. 91] Paraguay

Within their respective ranges, this and the next species are two of the most easily observed birds covered by this book. Whereas the Rufous-tailed Plantcutter *Phytotoma rara* is basically confined to Patagonia, the present species breeds north into the highlands of Bolivia and some of its southeastern populations move north in winter, at which season it has been recorded irregularly as far afield as eastern Brazil.

IDENTIFICATION 18.0–19.5cm. Whilst not as striking as the male Rufous-tailed Plantcutter, the White-tipped Plantcutter presents few identification problems to field observers. The superficial resemblance of male Peruvian Plantcutter *Phytotoma raimondii* to male White-tipped can be ignored due to their allopatric ranges. Although there is no range overlap, male Rufous-tailed Plantcutter can be discounted anyway by the fact that the latter has more extensive and deeper red on the underparts and crown, and it also has more extensive and more noticeable white in the wings. Female *Phytotoma* are even more similar, although the female Rufous-tailed is generally warmer in plumage tone, with less obvious white tips to the wing-coverts and a more notable pale supercilium behind the eye, but again due to the lack of sympatry any likelihood of confusion is automatically negated.

DISTRIBUTION White-tipped Plantcutter occurs in southern South America east of the Andes, from the highlands of central Bolivia (in dptos. La Paz and Santa Cruz south to Tarija), thence across northern Argentina (south as far as Mendoza, La Pampa, Río Negro and, less frequently, in

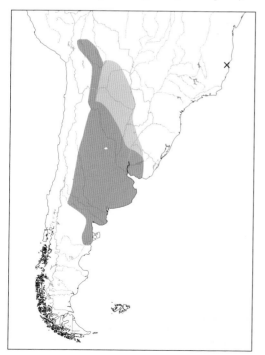

northeast Chubut). In the austral winter its range extends through Paraguay, mainly east of the Río Paraguay (but known from four of seven of the country's geographical regions: Hayes *et al.* 1994, Hayes 1995), as well as southern and western Uruguay, from where there are *c.*10 published records (Cuello and Gerzenstein 1962, Gore and Gepp 1978) and *c.*25 unpublished/specimen records from at least nine departments (Claramunt and Cuello 2004; A. Azpiroz *in litt.* 2008) (see also Movements). The species is probably only a vagrant to Brazil (see Movements for specific details). Elevational range is from sea level to 3,600m, but White-tipped Plantcutter generally occurs below 1,800m, except in the Andes.

MOVEMENTS Seemingly largely resident across the central part of its range, but those at higher altitudes almost certainly wander lower in winter (e.g. at a study site in dpto. Santa Cruz, Bolivia: Schmitt *et al.* 1997) and those populations further south almost certainly move north to an unknown degree at this season. Even in those areas where the species is apparently resident, a percentage of the population might move out in winter. For instance, Sferco and Nores (2003) considered *P. rutila* to be resident in the Reserva Natural Chancaní, in the province of Córdoba, but reported that the species was scarce there, other than in spring and summer, when it was frequently recorded, suggesting some degree of emigration. Elsewhere, in far northwest Argentina, Echevarria and Chani (2006) recorded White-tipped Plantcutter only in summer and autumn at their study site in Tucumán. In Argentina as a whole, *P. rutila* is known solely as a winter visitor to the northeastern provinces of Entre Ríos and Corrientes (and has apparently never been recorded in Misiones), and becomes locally common at some sites, e.g. in Buenos Aires province, where it is unknown in summer. Uruguayan records solely pertain to migrants (Azpiroz 2001), the species arriving in late March/April and returning to the breeding areas in August/September, whilst in Paraguay it is only recorded between 3 June and 20 October, and is generally considered uncommon to rare (Hayes 1995). The nominate race has been recorded as a vagrant three times in Brazil: a flock of five in southwesternmost Rio Grande do Sul in May 1974 (Belton 1978, 1985), two exceptionally far north in northern coastal Espírito Santo in May 2005 (Venturini *et al.* 2007), and another record, for which full details are yet to be published, again in extreme southwest Rio Grande do Sul, post-2007 (Damiani *et al.* 2009).

HABITAT White-tipped Plantcutter prefers *Chaco* woodland, with a particular fondness for areas with *Berberis* (Berberidaceae) and *Prosopis* (Leguminosae) in the Andes. Specific habitats in which the species is found in Bolivia were described by Herzog *et al.* (1997). Found anywhere within its wide range in Argentina characterised by open woodland, scrub (often thorny, both in lowlands and highlands), orchards, agricultural areas, gardens with bushes and cover, groves of *Acacia* (Leguminosae), and other suitable habitat, generally in semi-arid regions and sometimes on sandy soils. The species can be common in areas of suitable habitat as small as 1ha (Dardanelli *et al.* 2006).

DESCRIPTION The species' general characters are typical of the genus (see previous species). The bill is short, stout and conical, with a slightly hooked tip (especially in males) and heavily serrated edges. *Male.* – Characterised by being mostly rufous below and dark grey above, with a short crest and stubby, conical (finch-like) bill and pale irides.

Forehead conspicuously rufous (more so than in Peruvian Plantcutter) contrasting with the grey crown and face, and sometimes with sparse red feathers occurring onto the rear crown. The upperparts are slaty grey with fine black streaking and dusky blackish-grey wings, with a conspicuous white upper wingbar (on the lesser and median coverts) and a more obscure lower white bar formed by the white tips to the greater coverts (which is lost when the plumage is heavily worn). The tertials can show fine white tips. Underparts mainly cinnamon or orange-rufous, with a grey wash to the flanks and body-sides. Tail grey with conspicuous white tips to all but the central rectrices. Cinnamon-rufous undertail-coverts, and a dusky-grey undertail with white tips; underwing-coverts whitish. *Female.* – Greyish-brown above, boldly streaked blackish with some white streaks in the crest. Wings blackish-brown with two narrow white wingbars and fringes to the tertials. Tail dusky greyish-brown with pale whitish outer webs to the outer tail feathers. Underparts pale buff to grey-brown, streaked with blackish-brown (which is heaviest across the chest). *Juvenile.* – Resembles female but has plainer underparts; the upper wingbar is still broadest, but narrower than the adult, whilst the tail is female-like; at this age females have the streaks narrower than males, sometimes with a buffy suffusion to the underparts (Wetmore 1926). *Immature male.* – Obscurely dark brown-streaked upperparts and the rufous of the adult is replaced by buffy grey-brown below, with a whiter belly (some rufous-buff is detectable on the flanks, breast and throat), becoming tawny-olive over the undertail-coverts, streaked less heavily throughout than the female (usually confined to the breast and upper belly). The rufous on the head is sometimes amongst the last feathers of adult plumage to be acquired (after the entire underparts have become adult-like). *Immature female.* – Resembles adults of the same sex, but has the vent more ochraceous. *Moult.* – Nothing published to date. *Bare parts.* – Irides pale yellow, orange to hazel or ochraceous-buff; the bill is dark grey to dark green or brown, often with the culmen and cutting edges darker than the base of the lower mandible, and the legs are dark grey to dark horn-coloured (Wetmore 1926, Belton 1985, Snow 2004a; BMNH).

MEASUREMENTS (BMNH: Argentina) *P. r. rutila*: wing of male (*n* = 6) 86–89mm, wing of female (*n* = 6) 87–88mm; tail of male (*n* = 6) 37–42mm, tail of female (*n* = 6) 35–42mm; bill of male (*n* = 6) 15.55–16.89mm, bill of female (*n* = 6) 14.54–16.29mm; tarsus of male (*n* = 6) 21–22mm, tarsus of female (*n* = 6) 20–21mm. *P. r. angustirostris* (from Hellmayr 1929b, who examined 25 Bolivian specimens, but did not provide totals for each sex): wing of male 94–100mm, wing of female 94–97mm; tail of male 88–94mm, tail of female 85–89mm. Weight (sexes combined): 30–57g (Fiora 1934, Contreras 1979, Belton 1985, Schmitt *et al.* 1997, Snow 2004a, Dunning 2008).

GEOGRAPHICAL VARIATION Two races are generally recognised (Dickinson 2003, Snow 2004a). *P. r. angustirostris* Lafresnaye & d'Orbigny, 1837, occurs in the highlands of southern and central Bolivia, and northern Argentina (where apparently confined to Jujuy and perhaps around Pichanal, in northern Salta; previously listed further south, but this was definitively rejected by Hellmayr 1929b, who also questioned its occurrence in Salta province). It is characterised by its stronger bill (in males, depth at feathers 7.55–7.87mm (*n* = 5) from eastern Argentina, vs. 8.52–9.08mm (*n* = 5) from Bolivia), overall larger size, and

broader white tail tips than in nominate *P. r. rutila*, which occurs across western Paraguay, the rest of northern and much of eastern Argentina, and western Uruguay. However, Fjeldså and Krabbe (1990) considered that the two taxa intergrade in northwest Argentina. This question does not appear to have received subsequent attention.

VOICE Published recordings are available on the following compilations: Minns *et al.* (2009) and Imberti *et al.* (2009), and recordings from Argentina and Bolivia are available online at www.xeno-canto.org. White-tipped Plantcutter's voice is not dissimilar to that of the next species. Within its core Argentine range this species is the source of one of the commonest and almost certainly one of the most swiftly learnt avian sounds. Both sexes utter a mechanical-sounding *errrrrr*, recalling an alarm clock being wound, two trees rubbing against each other in the wind, or the squeaking of leather (Wetmore 1926, Fjeldså and Krabbe 1990). This is often followed by a rather lower and shorter *errrr*, sounding almost like an afterthought due to the pause between them. The species also produces various scratchy sounds while foraging.

NATURAL HISTORY Usually encountered in pairs, but the species is also sometimes seen in family groups or small flocks, and exceptionally in large, loose flocks of up to hundreds of individuals in the non-breeding season. Flight is slightly undulating on rather slow wingbeats, rarely high above the ground, and usually short between perches. The bird frequently spreads the tail on alighting to display its white tip (if not already splayed open in flight). When perched, birds regularly jerk their tails, again to display the white tip, and typically hold the crest erect (just like congeners). Although it usually perches at 3–4m above the ground on a bush, post or fence, White-tipped Plantcutter will readily drop to the ground to feed (more so than the next species). It also readily perches on telephone wires and high posts, but is typically less conspicuous during the comparative heat of the midday hours.

FOOD AND FEEDING Diet is principally foliage (*c*.90%), with some fruits, flowers and seeds also taken, and favouring the following taxa: *Lycium* (Solanaceae), *Celtis tala* (Ulmaceae), *Schinus longifolia* (Annonaceae), *Prosopis* and *Acacia* (Leguminosae). In central Santa Fé province, de la Peña and Pensiero (2003) recorded the species feeding on nine species, of the genera *Celtis* (Ulmaceae), *Geoffroea* (Leguminoseae), *Grabowskia* (Solanaceae), *Holmbergia* (Amaranthaceae), *Morrenia* (Apocynaceae), *Muehlenbeckia* (Polygonaceae), *Prosopis* (Leguminosae), *Sapium* (Euphorbiaceae) and *Schinus* (Annonaceae) (e.g. Fjeldså and Krabbe 1990, Snow 2004a).

BREEDING Like all plantcutters, both sexes take an equal share in nesting responsibilities, except incubation (which situation is generally anomalous amongst cotingas), thus males also help build the nest and tend the young. The breeding season occupies September–February, with fledglings noted in December–January and juveniles in December, February, March and May (cf. Fjeldså and Krabbe 1990). Males had enlarged testes at a site in dpto. Santa Cruz, Bolivia, during January–February (Schmitt *et al.* 1997). Two broods are perhaps attempted in a year, as long ago noted by Wetmore (1926). White-tipped Plantcutter constructs a shallow, basket-shaped nest of thin twigs and lined with softer material, placed 1–4m above the ground in a low tree or bush, but sometimes even closer to the ground in especially dense vegetation, and typically in a horizontal fork. Nest dimensions were presented in Snow (2004a). The clutch is 2–4 eggs (typically three in Argentina), which are intense ochre-green with spots and lines of dark brown and, to a lesser extent, grey concentrated at the larger end, or as described by Walters (2006) 'has a reddish pigment added to the blue, creating a warm olive-buff egg with almost black spotting'. They are incubated for 14–15 days, by the female alone. Dimensions of the eggs were presented by de la Peña (1989). The nestlings remain in the nest for c.17 days.

STATUS Treated as of Least Concern (BirdLife International 2004, 2008), due to its being generally common and widespread, especially in Argentina, the species' core range state, where it may even prove locally abundant on a seasonal basis. Prefers undisturbed mattoral, but 'makes do' with agricultural areas and gardens (e.g. in La Paz, Bolivia, where, at least formerly, considered to be fairly common). White-tipped Plantcutter is known from at least 11 national parks in Argentina (Chebez *et al.* 1998, Alonso and Virgolini 2008). Pugnali (2008) listed localities for the species around Buenos Aires where it can be found, mainly in winter. Generally rare in Paraguay, where White-tipped Plantcutter is only an austral migrant and the species is similarly uncommon

in Uruguay (see Distribution and Movements). Elsewhere it has declined markedly in Bolivia (*P. r. angustirostris*) due to fragmentation and degradation of natural brushlands in highland regions; in this country it is known from a single protected area, Palmarcito (dpto. Chuquisaca).

REFERENCES Alonso and Virgolini (2008), Azpiroz (2001), Babarskas and Flombaum (1998), Babarskas *et al.* (1996), Belton (1978, 1985), BirdLife International (2004, 2008), Chebez *et al.* (1998), Claramunt and Cuello (2004), Contreras (1979), Couve and Vidal (2003), Cuello and Gerzenstein (1962), Damiani *et al.* (2009), Dardanelli *et al.* (2006), Dickinson (2003), Dunning (2008), Echevarria and Chani (2006), Fiora (1934), Fjeldså and Krabbe (1990), Gore and Gepp (1978), Hayes (1995), Hayes *et al.* (1994), Hellmayr (1929b), Herzog *et al.* (1997), Imberti *et al.* (2009), Krabbe *et al.* (1996), Marateo *et al.* (2008), Minns *et al.* (2009), Navas and Bó (2000), de la Peña and Pensiero (2003), Pugnali (2008), Remsen and Traylor (1989), Ridgely and Tudor (1994, 2009), Schmitt *et al.* (1997), Sferco and Nores (2003), Short (1975), Simon (2009), Snow (2004a), Stotz *et al.* (1996), Venturini *et al.* (2007), Walters (2006), Wetmore (1926).

White-tipped Plantcutter *Phytotoma rutila*. **Figs. 1–2**. Male, Capilla del Monte, prov. Cordoba, northwest Argentina, January (*Hadoram Shirihai / Photographic Handbook to Birds of the World*). **Fig. 3**. Female, Tilcara, prov. Jujuy, northwest Argentina, January (*Hadoram Shirihai / Photographic Handbook to Birds of the World*).

RUFOUS-TAILED PLANTCUTTER
Phytotoma rara   **Plate 33**

Phytotoma rara **Molina, 1782**, *Saggio Stor. Nat. Chili*: 254, Chile

Rufous-tailed Plantcutter has the southernmost range of any cotinga, or any other species covered in this book. *P. rara* is generally fairly common and easily observed, much like the previous species, and is also to some extent migratory, although its movements are less marked than White-tipped Plantcutter *Phytotoma rutila*. Rufous-tailed even occurs in gardens in some areas and has acquired the status of 'agricultural pest' due to its habit of raiding orchards.

IDENTIFICATION 18.0–21.4cm. The male Rufous-tailed Plantcutter is the most striking in the genus and quite unmistakable (see the Identification section of the previous species). The rasping call (the species name *rara* derives from its call rather than the status of the bird, as it is far from rare) can be heard in many types of arid, mattoral or other more or less open country in southern South America, even close to habitation. The female, although less distinct, does not occur alongside any other *Phytotoma* species, and in any case will usually be in the close company of a male.

DISTRIBUTION Restricted to the southernmost part of South America on both slopes of the Andes, Rufous-tailed Plantcutter occurs from central Chile (around Vallenar, in southern Atacama) and western Argentina (in northwest Mendoza, Neuquén and Río Negro) south in both countries almost as far as Tierra del Fuego, and including immediately offshore islands such as Chiloé, Quinchao and Lemay, in Chile. The species is a vagrant to the Falkland Islands (for details see Movements). Principally recorded from sea

level to 1,500m, but the species is known locally to 2,300m (Hellmayr 1932, Ridgely and Tudor 1994, Jaramillo 2003) and perhaps even 2,700m (Stotz *et al.* 1996).

MOVEMENTS Largely resident (e.g. in Chile), but those populations in the far south apparently move north in winter, albeit not beyond the species' overall range, whilst those at higher altitudes can wander lower (Hellmayr 1932, Johnson 1967, Fjeldså and Krabbe 1990). For instance, Rufous-tailed Plantcutter is known solely as an austral summer visitor to parts of XI Region and the extreme northwest of XII Region in southernmost Chile (i.e. between October and April). It is exclusively a non-breeding visitor to Las Chinchillas National Reserve, 300km north of Santiago (Jaksic and Lazo 1999), while populations wintering in the lowlands of Aconcagua, Chile, arrive in March/April and depart in early August (Hellmayr 1932: 149). Recorded as a vagrant to the Falkland Islands, where an adult female was collected in March 1937 (BMNH 1940.12.6.79; Hamilton 1939, Woods 1988), and the species is listed without details as an accidental visitor to Isla Grande de Tierra del Fuego (Couve and Vidal 2003), although not by Humphrey *et al.* (1970).

HABITAT Rufous-tailed Plantcutter prefers open or dense thorny scrub, from sea level up to perhaps 2,700m (see above; but generally below 2,150m), with a particular fondness for *Berberis* (Berberidaceae) and *Embothrium coccineum* (Proteaceae) bushes (Fjeldså and Krabbe 1990, Couve and Vidal 2003, Jaramillo 2003). It is frequently found at the edges of woodland, less frequently in clearings within *Nothofagus* (southern beech: Fagaceae) forests (Fjeldså and Krabbe 1990), as well as being reasonably commonly in farmland, orchards, vineyards and gardens. Generally found in slightly wetter habitats than either of the other two *Phytotoma* (Vuilleumeier 1985).

DESCRIPTION Typical plantcutter jizz (see Peruvian Plantcutter *Phytotoma raimondii*). The plumage differs markedly between the sexes, and the male is marginally larger than the female. Bill is short, stout and conical, with a slightly hooked tip and serrated edges. *Male.* – Chestnut-rufous crown contrasting with blackish cheeks bordered by mottled white patches on the lower cheeks and at the base of the malar. The dark face emphasises the bright red irides. Hindneck and upperparts pale grey-brown, heavily and broadly streaked blackish-brown. Wings dusky-brown to blackish with a sharply contrasting broad white bar on the lesser and median coverts and a narrower one (often barely noticeable) formed by the pale tips to the greater coverts and the middle of the outer webs of the outer primaries. Tertials fringed buffish. Uppertail black with rufous-chestnut on the inner webs of the feathers. These rufous fringes to the rectrices are more readily visible from below. Underparts cinnamon-rufous, becoming slightly paler on the belly. Underwing-coverts blackish and undertail dusky with a broad rufous subterminal band on all but the central rectrices, and tiny rufous-grey tips to the same feathers. *Female.* – Pale grey- or olive-brown upperparts (but browner than female White-tipped Plantcutter), heavily streaked blackish-brown from the crown to the rump. The wings are brown with two narrow, pale buff wingbars and fringes to the tertials, thus lacking any obvious wing patch (even compared with the immature male, see below). Tail largely male-like, but lacks pale tips and the outer web of the outermost feathers has a narrow whitish fringe. Underparts buff with dark brown streaks, fading over the belly, and most obvious on the breast and sides. *Juvenile.* – More uniform grey-brown with narrow buffy wingbars. *Immature male.* – Somewhat recalls adult female, but the blackish-brown streaks over the crown are weaker and less obvious, and most of the plumage is still male-like, but the underparts are buff to rufous-buff, with only some red admixed, and streaked blackish-brown. Rufous feathers have buffy tips in fresh plumage. Compared with the adult male, the pale wingbars are rather reduced in extent. *Moult.* – Very few published moult data, but one in March was in very worn plumage. *Bare parts.* – The irides are usually deep red or occasionally orange, the bill is black or blackish, and the legs and feet are deep greyish (Snow 2004a).

MEASUREMENTS (BMNH; FMNH: Argentina and Chile) Wing of male ($n = 20$) 89–101mm, wing of female ($n = 11$) 86–95mm; tail of male ($n = 20$) 73–80mm, tail of female ($n = 11$) 71–81mm; bill of male ($n = 20$) 10.31–13.93mm, bill of female ($n = 11$) 11.36–14.69mm; tarsus of male ($n = 6$) 22–25mm, tarsus of female ($n = 6$) 22–24mm. See also Kuroda (1933) for additional mensural data. Weight (sexes combined): 38–52g (Snow 2004a, Dunning 2008; RMNH).

GEOGRAPHICAL VARIATION Monotypic.

VOICE There are published recordings on the audio compilations of Egli (2002) and Imberti *et al.* (2009), and a small number of recordings from Chile are archived online at www.xeno-canto.org. Its vocalisations recall those of White-tipped Plantcutter. Best known is a mechanical, stuttering, rasping sound, rendered *e-e-e-e-e-e-e-e-e-errrrrrrr*, which initially accelerates and rises in volume but descends in pitch across the first part, whilst the finale has been likened to either the winding mechanism on an old-fashioned alarm clock or the trilling of a fishing line when a large fish has been landed (Egli 2002, Jaramillo 2003, Snow 2004a). In contact or alarm the species gives a mechanical *rara-rara* (the source of the species' scientific modifier).

NATURAL HISTORY Like other plantcutters, the species perches conspicuously and is usually easy to see. Flight is slightly undulating and usually short between perches (Couve and Vidal 2003). Most frequently encountered in pairs in the breeding season, but it is sometimes seen in family groups or small flocks of up to 12 at other times of year; there are no published records of larger flocks (Fjeldså & Krabbe 1990).

FOOD AND FEEDING Although it usually perches on bushes or low trees, Rufous-tailed Plantcutter will occasionally drop to the ground to feed. Principally feeds in bushes, using its specialised bill to cut buds and fruits, shoots, leaves and grasses, especially of legumes. Leaves of wheat and oat, and berries of *Rubus ulmifolius* (Rosaceae), *Aristotelia chilensis* (Elaeocarpaceae), *Cestrum parqui* (Solanaceae) and *Myoporum tenuifolium* (Scrophulariaceae) are clearly favoured according to the literature (cf. Snow 2004a). Insects are also taken, to an unknown extent, by

adults, whilst nestlings are apparently fed an exclusive diet of insect matter.

BREEDING Like all plantcutters, both sexes take an equal share in nesting responsibilities (which situation is generally anomalous amongst cotingas), thus males also help build the nest and tend the young. Data on this species' breeding biology appeared in the literature as early as the 1840s. There are two breeding seasons within the annual cycle, in October–November and December–January, with eggs having been noted in January and October–December and nestlings in November (Hellmayr 1932, de la Peña 1989, Fjeldså and Krabbe 1990, Snow 2004a). Rufous-tailed Plantcutter constructs a shallow, cup-shaped nest of thin dry twigs and lined with root fibres, placed 1–3m above the ground in a dense thorn bush, or sometimes higher in a tree, and typically in a horizontal fork. Nest dimensions were presented in Snow (2004a). The clutch is 2–4 eggs (typically three in Argentina), which are either clear blue or greenish-blue with black marks at the larger end, and they are incubated for *c.*2 weeks. Walters (2006) considered '*Phytotoma rara* [to have] distinctive greenish-blue eggs, sparsely but darkly spotted with brown, the spots tending to cluster at the large end.' Dimensions of the eggs were presented by de la Peña (1989). The nestling period has not been documented to date. As noted by Snow (2004a), former reports of 5–6 eggs in a clutch are presently considered erroneous.

STATUS Treated as Least Concern (BirdLife International 2004, 2008), this plantcutter is generally widespread and reasonably common, being tolerant of more disturbed habitats including second growth and gardens (Fjeldså and Krabbe 1990), and is known from a reasonable number of protected areas. In Chile, in addition to being found in parks and gardens within the capital, Santiago (Schmitt 2010), the species occurs in La Campana Peñuelas Biosphere Reserve, near Valparaíso, and Laguna del Laja and Puyehué National Parks, for example. In Argentina Rufous-tailed Plantcutter is known from the following national parks (*fide* Chebez *et al.* 1998): Los Alerces and Lago Puelo (Chubut), Los Arrayanes, Nahuel Huapi and Lanín (Neuquén), and Los Glaciares and Perito Moreno (Santa Cruz). Indeed, it has acquired the status of an agricultural pest in some areas, due to its consumption of the young leaves of commercial cereal crops, as well by 'raiding' gardens and orchards, a fact noted as early as Hellmayr (1932).

REFERENCES BirdLife International (2004, 2008), Chebez *et al.* (1998), Couve and Vidal (2003), Dunning (2008), Egli (2002), Fjeldså and Krabbe (1990), Hamilton (1939), Hellmayr (1929b, 1932), Humphrey *et al.* (1970), Imberti *et al.* (2009), Jaksic and Lazo (1999), Jaramillo (2003), Johnson (1967), Küchler (1936), Kuroda (1933), Marín (2004), Mazar Barnett and Pearman (2001), Pearman (1995), de la Peña (1989), Ridgely and Tudor (1994, 2009), Schmitt (2010), Snow (2004a), Stotz *et al.* (1996), Vuilleumier (1985), Walters (2006), Woods (1988).

Rufous-tailed Plantcutter *Phytotoma rara*. **Fig. 1**. Male, El Chaltén, prov. Santa Cruz, southern Argentina, November (*James Lowen / www.pbase. com/james_lowen*). **Fig. 2**. Female, El Chaltén, prov. Santa Cruz, southern Argentina, November (*James Lowen / www.pbase.com/james_lowen*). The southernmost representative of the genus is a common inhabitant of thorn scrub, wooded edges and even gardens and farmland. **Fig. 3**. Male, El Chaltén, prov. Santa Cruz, Argentina, November (*James Lowen / www.pbase.com/james_lowen*). **Fig. 4**. Villa Pehuenia, prov. Neuquén, Argentina, December (*James Lowen / www.pbase.com/james_lowen*).

Genus *Piprites*: piprites

No longer considered to be 'true manakins', but placed as *Incertae Sedis* by amongst others Remsen *et al.* (2009), the *Piprites* species, in our view, nonetheless resemble manakins in the field more than they do any other group of birds, although they have been compared closely with becards *Pachyramphus* (Ridgely and Tudor 1994). There is one widespread polytypic species, the Wing-barred (*P. chloris*), and two restricted-range taxa, one of which (Black-capped *P. pileata*) is considered globally threatened. Snow (1975) noted how the plumage of *P. pileata*, and to a lesser extent its bill shape, differed strikingly from the *P. chloris* and *P. griseiceps* (Grey-headed) superspecies, which might suggest they are better ranked in two genera. However, neither he nor any subsequent author has taken the step of resurrecting the genus *Hemipipo*, Cabanis, 1847, for *P. chloris* and *P. griseiceps*. *P. pileata*, one of so many remarkably distinct birds endemic to the Atlantic Forest region, was perhaps an early isolate from the main genus stock (cf. Snow 1975, Willis 1983).

GREY-HEADED PIPRITES
Piprites griseiceps   Plate 34

Piprites griseiceps **Salvin, 1864** [= 1865], *Proc. Zool. Soc. Lond.* 1864: 583, Tucurriquí, Costa Rica

An enigmatic species restricted to lowland Central America, the Grey-headed Piprites is the least studied of the genus and seems to be very infrequently seen throughout much of its range, perhaps most especially in recent years. It is very similar in plumage to the Wing-barred Piprites *Piprites chloris* and these two probably form a species-pair.

IDENTIFICATION 10–12cm. Grey-headed Piprites is quite unlike any other 'manakin' in range. The rather long-tailed appearance (common to all of the *Piprites*), coupled with the chunky shape, may lead to confusion with a female Barred Becard *Pachyramphus versicolor* or even one of the *Tolmomyias* flycatchers, especially if the bird remains high in the subcanopy. However, Grey-headed Piprites lacks the scaled underparts of the becard and the wings lack any rufous fringes, whilst if seen well the pale eye-ring should be prominent. Flycatchers of the genus *Tolmomyias* are large-headed with broad, flattened bills, and share the yellow-olive wing fringes of the *Piprites*. But, Grey-headed Piprites is far more inactive than the 'busy' flycatchers, even when following mixed-species flocks of understorey species. As such, given reasonable views the piprites should be relatively easily identified.

DISTRIBUTION Grey-headed Piprites is restricted to the Caribbean slope of Central America, from northeasternmost

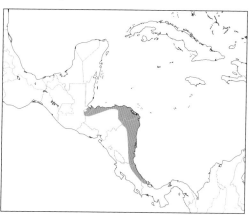

Guatemala (where it is known only from Izabál: Land and Wolf 1961, Land 1963; and the Cerro San Gil: Eisermann and Avendaño 2007), through Honduras (known only from a locality on the Río Guampú, in the northeast; Monroe 1968, Batiltuk, southwest of Las Marías, in the Moskitia, in February 1996 (Anderson *et al.* 2004), and more recent sightings at Pico Bonito Lodge (www.picobonito.com/PB_files/bird.html) near La Ceiba), in eastern Nicaragua to Costa Rica (where the species possibly occurs along the entire base of the Cordillera de Talamanca to Suretka, but sightings seem to be very infrequent: K. Easley *in litt.* 2009; J. Horn pers. comm.) and in westernmost Panama (on the Cerro Guaba, Bocas del Toro: *El Tucan* 22(8): 8, *Cotinga* 7: 76). The species is mainly found at 100–600m, occasionally to 800m locally (AOU 1998; e.g. in Río Negro Jaguar Preserve, Costa Rica) and in southern Costa Rica to 1,000m at El Copal Biological Reserve (GMK pers. obs.).

MOVEMENTS None recorded.

HABITAT Very much a bird of the understorey and middle levels of tall lowland evergreen forest and secondary growth; it descends to shrub level at gaps and edges.

DESCRIPTION Sexes are apparently alike. Grey-headed Piprites shares the large-headed, big-eyed appearance common to its genus, but is especially similar in morphology to Wing-barred Piprites. The culmen is moderately arched with a somewhat hooked tip. *Adult.* – Prominent white eye-ring set within the slate-grey head, admixed olive on the crown and nape, and reaching the ear-coverts and throat-sides. Rest of upperparts olive with olive-yellow fringes to the dark-centred wing-coverts, secondaries and primaries, and paler, whiter fringes to the tertials, especially to the outer webs, and a yellow or creamy wing-bend; flight feathers dark and the tail is dark with greenish webs. Chin whitish and throat yellow, becoming olive at the sides and merging with the grey of the ear-coverts. Olive wash across the breast and flanks, whilst the belly to undertail-coverts are yellow. *Juvenile.* – Lacks the slate-grey colour to the head, which is olive-coloured, but it retains the distinctive white eye-ring (Howell and Webb 1995, Snow 2004b). *Moult.* – Nothing is known. A male collected in March appears to be in rather fresh plumage (FMNH). *Bare parts.* – Irides dark (brown in one male), the bill is black or blackish, becoming greyer on the lower mandible and it has a strongly arched culmen, with plumbeous to lead-grey legs and feet.

MEASUREMENTS (BMNH; FMNH: Costa Rica and Nicaragua) Wing of male (*n* = 3) 61–66mm; tail of male (*n* = 3) 43–46mm; bill of male (*n* = 2) 12mm; tarsus of male (*n* = 3) 14.02–16.38mm. One unsexed (holotype): wing (*n* = 1)

63mm; tail (*n* = 1) 39mm; bill (*n* = 1) 11.37mm; tarsus (*n* = 1) 15.52mm. Weight: 16.0g (Snow 2004b, Dunning 2008).

GEOGRAPHICAL VARIATION Monotypic.

VOICE Various calls have been described in the literature (the following is based very much on Stiles and Skutch 1989 and a recent R. Gallardo recording from Honduras on www. xeno-canto.org). A soft, liquid *purr* or *wurr*, a soft *chip* note (which is accompanied by tail-flicking movements), and an elaborate, structured medley of staccato and rolling notes lasting *c*.2 seconds that forms the song, rendered *pik, pik, prrrity peer* (or variations on this). This latter has a quality similar to the songs of the other species in this genus (GMK pers. obs.). The Grey-headed Piprites' vocalisations were considered to be very flycatcher-like (Slud 1964). In response to playback the species rarely appears to closely approach the source, unlike either of the other *Piprites*, preferring to remain some distance away, and generally staying high in the trees, often on the same perch for some time before moving rapidly over distances of up to some tens of metres (GMK pers. obs.).

NATURAL HISTORY *P. griseiceps* can be very difficult to observe and our cumulative knowledge of its life history is very weak. It is usually seen alone or in pairs (and presumably also in family groups post-breeding like congenerics). However, like other *Piprites* it will join mixed-species feeding flocks, especially those involving small antbirds and greenlets (Slud 1964) but also Golden-hooded Tanagers *Tangara larvata* and migrant parulids (Anderson *et al.* 2004). At El Copal Biological Reserve, in southern Costa Rica, a pair that was apparently territorial in early April moved around within an area of several hundred metres, but regularly joined any passing flocks, including one containing Rufous-browed Tyrannulet *Phylloscartes superciliaris*, Black-and-yellow Tanager *Chrysothylpis chrysomelas*, Ashy-throated Bush Tanager *Chlorospingus canigularis* and various woodcreepers (GMK pers. obs.).

FOOD AND FEEDING In such instances as described above, it perches quietly, searching intently for insects (e.g. beetles, small grasshoppers) or fruit, which are taken using short aerial sally-gleans to the vegetation. In southern Costa Rica, the species has been observed visiting an unidentified fruiting melastome also frequented by White-ruffed Manakins *Corapipo leucorrhoa* (GMK pers. obs.). Grey-headed Piprites visits both the forest canopy and the undergrowth while foraging (Anderson *et al.* 2004), but there seem to be no specific published data concerning the species' diet.

BREEDING Males apparently sing in an 'exploded lek' from dense foliage, again either in the subcanopy or the understorey, with each bird only just within hearing distance of the next. Seemingly nothing further is known concerning the species' breeding biology (Snow 2004b) and elucidating this facet of the Grey-headed Piprites' natural history remains a considerable challenge, and prize, awaiting Central American fieldworkers.

STATUS Grey-headed Piprites was listed as Near Threatened in Collar *et al.* (1992), but the species was subsequently downlisted and it was most recently evaluated as Least Concern (BirdLife International 2004, 2008). Nonetheless, Grey-headed Piprites seems to be unquestionably uncommon and local, undoubtedly being threatened to some extent by the massive deforestation that has occurred over much of the species' range. It seems genuinely rare at the southern and northern extremities of its range (see Distribution), but

in Costa Rica the species is known from several protected areas, amongst them Braulio Carrillo National Park (Stiles and Skutch 1989), the privately owned Finca El Plástico, Heredia province (Rosselli 1994), El Copal Biological Reserve (GMK pers. obs.) and La Selva Biological Reserve (Blake and Loiselle 2001). Nonetheless, recent sightings (in the last decade or so) are apparently decidedly scarce, with for instance apparently just about one per year at Rancho Naturalista, a reserve southeast of Turrialba, despite regular observer activity at this small, privately protected area (K. Easley *in litt.* 2009). Grey-headed Piprites has been recorded in the Río Platano Biosphere Reserve, southeast Honduras (R. Gallardo, XC46016), and in El Quebracho Private Reserve, eastern Nicaragua (L. Sandoval *in litt.* 2010). Recent sightings in northern Honduras at Pico Bonito are also probably from within a protected area.

REFERENCES Anciães and Peterson (2009), Anderson *et al.* (2004), Angehr and Dean (2010), AOU (1998), BirdLife International (2004, 2008), Blake and Loiselle (2001), Collar *et al.* (1992), Cooper (1997), Dunning (2008), Eisermann and Avendaño (2007), Garrigues and Dean (2007), Hellmayr (1929b), Howell and Webb (1995), Land (1963), Land and Wolf (1961), Lawson (2010), Monroe (1968), Rosselli (1994), Slud (1964), Snow (1975, 2004b), Stiles and Skutch (1989), Stotz *et al.* (1996).

Grey-headed Piprites *Piprites griseiceps*. **Figs. 1–2.** Adult, Rancho Naturalista, prov. Cartago, Costa Rica, August (*Jason Horn / Costa Rica Gateway*). Two rare images (involving the same individual) of this poorly known and uncommon bird, which is widespread in Central America. Note the very prominent pale eye-ring set in the grey head.

WING-BARRED PIPRITES
Piprites chloris
Plate 34

Pipra chloris **Temminck, 1822** [ex. Natterer ms.], *Nouv. Rec. Planches Color.* pl. 172, fig. 2, Brazil [= Ipanema, São Paulo state]

Similar to the previous species, although completely allopatric, the Wing-barred Piprites is relatively speaking a much more widespread and commoner bird, although it must be added that in many parts of its wide range *P. chloris* is distinctly local and far from frequently encountered.

IDENTIFICATION 12.5–14.5cm. The large dark eye, emphasised by the yellowish-white eye-ring and loral area, affords the Wing-barred Piprites a spectacled appearance. Although the plumage pattern (wingbars, white tertial fringes, eye-ring, etc.) resembles a tyrannid or a vireo, once seen well Wing-barred Piprites is reasonably straightforward to identify. Its rather rotund, short-tailed and short-billed structure, separating it from any becard, renders this piprites an atypical 'manakin', and it is rather unlikely to be confused with any Pipridae in range.

DISTRIBUTION Widespread across South America, from the Guianas (where it is generally rather local, e.g. being mainly confined to forests of the interior in French Guiana, either uncommon to rare across Surinam and known from relatively few localities in Guyana); Venezuela (extremely discontinuously through the Coastal Cordillera, from the Paria Peninsula west to Carabobo, thence the Sierra de Perijá and extreme southwest, but more widely south of the Orinoco River); northern and eastern Colombia, including the more humid Caribbean lowlands and east of the Andes (except the llanos); eastern Ecuador, eastern Peru and the northern half of Bolivia (south to dptos. La Paz, Cochabamba and Santa Cruz), as well as most of Amazonian Brazil east as far as northern Maranhão and south to south-central Mato Grosso, e.g. around Vila Bela

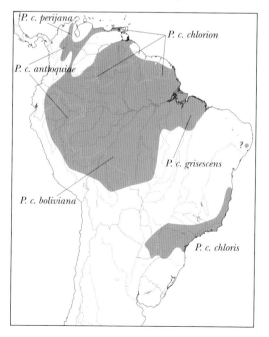

P. c. perijana
P. c. chlorion
P. c. antioquiae
P. c. grisescens
P. c. boliviana
P. c. chloris

da Santíssima Trindade and the Serra das Araras Ecological Station, with an isolated population in southeast Brazil (in southern Bahia, where only recently discovered, thence from Espírito Santo south to northernmost Rio Grande do Sul, but at all frequently only as far south as Paraná and there is just one published record from the state of Rio de Janeiro: Pimentel 2010, Pimentel and Olmos 2011), eastern Paraguay (west to Paraguarí) and in northeast Argentina (Misiones). The species has also recently been recorded in northeast Brazil, at Fazenda Morim in the municipality of São José da Corôa Grande (08°51'38.03"S, 35°12'37.04"W), and at Engenho Cachoeira Linda in the municipality of Barreiros (08°48'08.05"S, 35°18'63.08"W), both of which localities are in Pernambuco (Roda and Dantas 2008; S. M. Dantas and G. Farias recordings, XC6659, 7260 and 33273). Subsequently, it was found at a third site in the same state, Engenho Roncadorzinho (08°47'S, 35°17'W) (Pereira *et al.* in press). Wing-barred Piprites is usually found below 1,100m, but has been recorded to 1,500m (e.g. in Ecuador and Colombia), to 1,900m in Peru (Hornbuckle 1999), 1,800m in Bolivia (Hennessey 2004b), and is found to 2,000m north of the Orinoco in Venezuela, and to 1,700m south of that river.

MOVEMENTS None recorded.

HABITAT Wing-barred Piprites inhabits the canopy and borders of humid primary and older secondary forest, including *Araucaria* forest in the extreme south, foothill to premontane cloud forests (locally in the north), *terra firme* in Amazonia, where it is a typical member of lower storey flocks, as well as sandy-soil and savanna forests. Although rarely seen low down, the species appears to generally favour forests with a well-developed understorey and many vine tangles.

DESCRIPTION The sexes are basically alike, both also having well-developed rictal bristles. Just like the previous species, Wing-barred Piprites typically appears large-headed and big-eyed. Nominate race is described here. *Adult.* – Notwithstanding the geographical variation described below, most individuals have bright olive upperparts with the distinctive spectacled face. The ear-coverts, neck-sides and nape are grey. *P. chloris* has a distinctive wing pattern, produced by the yellowish-white tips to the coverts (although the uppermost are often overlain by the scapulars) and tertials. The remiges are dull olive with brighter fringes to the secondaries. Underparts pale yellow with some olive suffusion on the breast. *Juvenile.* – Apparently undescribed, although Friedmann (1948) considered, in referring to the race *P. c. tschudii*, the immature to be brighter yellow on the throat and more orange on the lores and forehead than adults of the same form. *Moult.* – There seem to be no published data, other than that a male *P. c. chloris* was in wing moult in February (Willis and Oniki 2002), but three from Rondônia (Brazil) taken in March and November (*n* = 2) were replacing the head and body feathers, and two from southeast Peru taken in November were also in moult (FMNH). *Bare parts.* – Bill (well hooked and strongly arched) has a blackish or dark horn maxilla and dark grey mandible (or dark silver throughout, in at least some *P. c. tschudii*); the legs and feet are pale bluish-slate to grey, although perhaps paler and browner in the races *P. c. boliviana*, *P. c. tschudii* and *P. c. chlorion* at least (cf. Gyldenstolpe 1945), with yellow soles; and the irides are dark brown or chestnut to ruby brown, occasionally black (*P. c. tschudii*; FMNH).

MEASUREMENTS *P. c. chloris* (CUMZ; BMNH; FMNH;

MNRJ; Partridge 1954; Argentina, Paraguay and Brazil): wing of male (*n* = 6) 67.5–71.0mm, wing of female (*n* = 7) 67.0–71.5mm; tail of male (*n* = 6) 51–55mm, tail of female (*n* = 7) 50–58mm; bill of male (*n* = 5) 10.31–12.09mm, bill of female (*n* = 7) 10.18–12.37mm; tarsus of male (*n* = 6) 15.00–17.88mm, tarsus of female (*n* = 6) 16.75–18.01mm. *P. c. chlorion* (BMNH, FMNH; MNRJ; Gilliard 1941; Venezuela, Guyana, Surinam and Brazil): wing of male (*n* = 5) 66.5–72.0mm, wing of female (*n* = 4) 65.0–72.5mm; tail of male (*n* = 5) 46–52mm, tail of female (*n* = 4) 47–50mm; bill of male (*n* = 5) 10.16–12.57mm, bill of female (*n* = 3) 11.66–13.19mm; tarsus of male (*n* = 3) 15.69–16.43mm, tarsus of female (*n* = 8) 15.69–17.50mm. *P. c. antioquiae* (FMNH: central Colombia): wing of male (*n* = 4) 68.0–69.5mm; tail of male (*n* = 4) 44–49mm; bill of male (*n* = 4) 10.19–11.19mm; tarsus of male (*n* = 4) 14.49–17.53mm. *P. c. grisescens* (MPEG; east Amazonian Brazil; cf. Novaes 1964; FMNH: female): wing of male (*n* = 5) 64.4–68.6mm, wing of female (*n* = 1) 65.5mm; tail of male (*n* = 5) 40.8–46.8mm, tail of female (*n* = 1) 43.5mm; bill of male (*n* = 5) 9.5–10.9mm, bill of female (*n* = 1) 12.21mm; tarsus of female (*n* = 1) 14.01mm. *P. c. tschudii* (males: FMNH; Peru; female: J. Hornbuckle unpubl. data from live birds; Peru): wing of male (*n* = 4) 69–71mm, wing of female (*n* = 1) 73mm; tail of male (*n* = 4) 45–51mm, tail of female (*n* = 1) 50mm; bill of male (*n* = 4) 10.96–12.41mm, bill of female (*n* = 1) 11.70mm; tarsus of male (*n* = 4) 17.61–20.60mm, tarsus of female (*n* = 1) 16.5mm. *P. c. boliviana* (FMNH; MNRJ; Acre and Rondônia, southeast Brazil; Peru; Gyldenstolpe 1945; Bolivia): wing of male (*n* = 3) 61.5–68.0mm, wing of female (*n* = 1) 67mm; tail of male (*n* = 3) 44–49mm, tail of female (*n* = 1) 45mm; bill of male (*n* = 2) 10.67–11.76mm, bill of female (*n* = 1) 11.43mm; tarsus of male (*n* = 2) 15.00–15.07mm, tarsus of female (*n* = 1) 15.85mm. Weight (sexes and races combined): 14.8–21.1g (Dick *et al.* 1984, Belton 1985, Hilty 2003, Snow 2004a, Antunes 2005, Dunning 2008; FMNH; MVZ; ROM; J. Hornbuckle unpubl. data; T. M. Donegan *et al.* unpubl. data).

GEOGRAPHICAL VARIATION Seven races are currently recognised. A much-needed taxonomic revision of *P. chloris* is underway, being conducted by S. M. Dantas, G. Thomas and E. Portes, following the discovery of a morphologically quite different population (from those in Amazonia and the southern Atlantic Forest) north of the Rio São Francisco in northeast Brazil (see also Distribution). The following draws heavily on the text and illustrations in Restall *et al.* (2006) for populations in northern South America. *P. c. tschudii* (Cabanis, 1874) (in eastern Ecuador, extreme southeast Colombia (e.g. at Macacuní, Guainía) and southernmost Venezuela, south through eastern Peru, and western Amazonian Brazil, e.g. on the upper Rio Negro and north of the Rio Solimões) is duller olive above than the nominate, with a greyer cast to the head, especially on the nape and hindneck; the underparts are yellow-olive with pale grey flanks. This race seems to grade into *P. c. chlorion* in the lower Rio Negro/Rio Purus region of Brazil (Hellmayr 1929b, Gyldenstolpe 1951). *P. c. antioquiae* Chapman, 1924 (of northern and central Colombia), resembles *P. c. tschudii*, but is brighter above as far as the uppertail-coverts, with bright yellow underparts and lores, and a greater coverts wingbar of medium width. Phelps (1944) questioned whether *antioquiae* should not be regarded as representing individual variation within *P. c. tschudii*. Indeed, Restall *et al.* (2006: 459) depicted what they considered to be a 'hybrid' between these two subspecies, based on a specimen

from southern Venezuela (i.e. well within the range of *P. c. tschudii*, making the 'hybrid' label inappropriate). This bird presumably indicates that individual variation within *P. c. tschudii* is still incompletely understood. It is also worth noting that a bird photographed from well within the purported range of *P. c. antioquiae* (Figs. 3–4) clearly shows as many characters associated with *P. c. tschudii* (e.g. the overall coloration of the upper- and underparts, and the greyish cheeks) as with the present subspecies. Further research into the validity of *P. c. antioquiae* is clearly required. *P. c. perijana* Phelps & Phelps, Jr., 1949 (of northeastern Colombia and westernmost Venezuela, in Perijá, Táchira and presumably this race has been recently discovered in eastern Mérida close to the border with Barinas; *Cotinga* 28: 90), is slightly duller than *P. c. antioquiae*, with a very broad wingbar and a pale olive wash to the breast-sides and flanks. *P. c. chlorion* (Cabanis, 1847) (in the Guianas, over the rest of Venezuela, parts of eastern Colombia and lower Amazonian Brazil, as far west as Borba, on the lower Rio Madeira, and around Manaus) is rather distinctive, being very grey on the breast and belly (the grey extending as a band over the hindneck), with a contrasting yellow throat, thighs, vent and undertail-coverts, a very narrow wingbar and rather smaller white tertial tips than other northern South American races, very little yellow on the lores and a greenish forehead. Gyldenstolpe (1945) considered that *P. c. chlorion* reaches as far southeast as northern Maranhão. Restall *et al.* (2006) described and illustrated birds from the Ríos Casiquiare and Guainía, southern Venezuela, which appear to represent intergrades between this race and *P. c. tschudii*, and Blake (1950) in discussing two specimens from the Sierra Macarena, dpto. Meta (Colombia), remarked that they too approach *P. c. tschudii*. Hellmayr's (1910) discussion of variation within the overall range of this subspecies seems to have been compromised by immaturity in some specimens. *P. c. grisescens* Novaes, 1964 (in eastern Pará and northwest Maranhão, Brazil), is overall greyer above and below than any other race, with a paler, brighter bill. Yellow coloration is restricted to the throat and fore face, and the pale wing feather fringes are somewhat reduced, especially on the coverts, and overall more yellowish. *P. c. boliviana* Chapman, 1924 (of northern Bolivia and southwest Amazonian Brazil), generally recalls *P. c. chlorion*, but is yellower on the breast and ventral region, with a grey band across the abdominal region, and these two plausibly intergrade in the Rio Purús–Madeira interfluvium in Brazil south of the Amazon; recent field observations by GMK at Tupana, Amazonas, appear to support the intergrade hypothesis (cf. also Gyldenstolpe 1945, 1951, who also mentioned that *P. c. chlorion* perhaps approaches *P. c. boliviana* along the Rio Tapajós). *P. c. chloris* (virtually endemic to the Atlantic Forest region of eastern Brazil, eastern Paraguay and northeast Argentina, and from southern Mato Grosso do Sul, Brazil) is described above; to date, the subspecies involved in northeast Brazil (Pernambuco), where the species has only recently been discovered, is unknown (Roda and Dantas 2008; S. M. Dantas pers. comm.).

VOICE Well known but infrequently given; a distinctive and far-carrying, hesitant *whip, pip-pip, pididip, whip, whip*, variable, often rather nasal or squeaky, but always with the hesitation (Ridgely and Tudor 1994, 2009). It has been likened to a shorebird, e.g. a curlew *Numenius*, in quality by Hilty (2003), who rendered the song *quee, quee quee queedle-le quee, quee?* In southeast Brazil rendered *wi-wi-JI-dip*, *wi-Di-dip, wi-dip* (E. O. Willis *in* Belton 1985) and in Peru *hoo hoo hoo hoo hooHEE'EE hoo hoo* (Schulenberg *et al.* 2007), suggesting remarkable uniformity across the range, and in our experience (from virtually across the species' entire range) we have yet to come across any significant differences in song, or a population that did not respond well to recordings from elsewhere in the species' range. Pairs duet, with the second bird responding to the first with the same song at a slightly higher pitch (Sick 1997). Wing-barred Piprites generally sings most frequently in the early rainy season (e.g. September–October in southeast Brazil, and May–June in northern Venezuela). Published recordings are available on the following compilations: Straneck (1990), English and Parker (1992), Boesman (1999, 2006a, 2006b), Mayer (2000), Schulenberg *et al.* (2000), Remold (2002), Krabbe and Nilsson (2003), Marantz and Zimmer (2006), Alvarez *et al.* (2007), Naka *et al.* (2008), Renaudier and Deroussen (2008), Boesman (2009) and Minns *et al.* (2009). Online, recordings are available from Bolivia (*P. c. boliviana*), Brazil (*P. c. chloris, P. c. chlorion* and *P. c. grisescens*), Colombia, Ecuador and Peru (*P. c. tschudii*), Paraguay (*P. c. chloris*) and Venezuela (*P. c. chlorion*), archived at www.xeno-canto.org.

NATURAL HISTORY Wing-barred Piprites is found alone or in pairs, often within mixed-species foraging flocks of insectivores, e.g. flycatchers, becards, foliage-gleaners and antwrens, where brief glimpses of an actively foraging bird are the norm. Birds are usually encountered at mid levels to the subcanopy in the Atlantic Forest, but occasionally lower, especially at edges. In contrast, Munn (1985) found it to be restricted to understorey flocks in southeast Peru, and that has also been our almost identical experience in central and eastern Brazil (GMK pers. obs.). (For some details of the other constituent species of these flocks in the Atlantic Forest see Venturini *et al.* 2005.) Wing-barred Piprites responds, slowly and deliberately, to playback, approaching the caller much in the same manner as Black-capped Piprites *Piprites pileata* does (which see), but is less frequently inclined to tarry, especially when in a mixed-species flock. Its movements seem far quicker and more abrupt than Black-capped Piprites, and this species is frequently difficult to follow, despite its distinctive appearance. At other times, i.e. when alone, Wing-barred Piprites is more placid and especially becard-like, and can perch semi-upright, quite unlike any vireo.

FOOD AND FEEDING Principally feeds on insects, including their larvae (e.g. once a 3cm caterpillar; FMNH), which are taken by perch-gleaning, rarely using hover-gleaning sallies, with only a small proportion of fruits and berries in its diet. Beebe (1915) mentioned seeing the species visiting a fruiting Lauraceae tree.

BREEDING Almost nothing is known concerning the breeding biology of this species, but one nest has apparently been found, constructed in a tree cavity (Snow 2004b), quite different from the definitive data for *P. pileata* (see below). However, subsequent correspondence with D. W. Snow (*in litt.* 2007) failed to unearth the original source for this statement concerning *P. chloris*, thus confirmation of the nest type of this species (and Grey-headed Piprites *Piprites griseiceps*) is urgently required. K. Cockle (pers. comm. 2010) reports that F. Avelino Ribeiro found a nest of this species in Parque Estadual Intervales, São Paulo, Brazil, sited below a bank, which offered some protection from the elements; it was an open cup supported on a narrow branch. Other breeding data are as follows. A male collected in May in Colombia was in breeding condition (M. A. Carriker *in* Hilty and Brown 1986), as were females in Amazonian Brazil in July and November, a male in Amapá, Brazil, in late May (Novaes 1978), both sexes taken in southeast Peru in mid July (FMNH) and a male in early September (MVZ), and a male from French Guiana in May (ROM); Robbins *et al.* (2007) considered that the species' breeding season along the upper Essequibo River in southern Guyana is August/September. De la Peña (1989) stated that the eggs are rose-coloured, marked with purple and reddish-brown lines and some dark spots, but his basis for this statement is also unclear.

STATUS Wing-barred Piprites is treated as Least Concern due to its extremely wide South American range (BirdLife International 2004, 2008). Nonetheless, based on modelling techniques Anciães and Peterson (2006) predicted that this species could be very badly impacted by habitat modification in the face of potential climate change. Variously considered uncommon to fairly common across the species' wide range, the Wing-barred Piprites is apparently distinctly uncommon over much of northern South America; only in French Guiana is the species considered locally common to very common, e.g. around Saint-Eugène (Tostain *et al.* 1992, Claessens 1997). In southeast Peru, Terborgh *et al.* (1990) reported densities of 5.5 pairs per 100ha, and mean territory size of 8ha, but in French Guiana Thiollay (1994) estimated a density of just one pair per 100ha. Further south, it is generally rather uncommon and probably much reduced in range throughout the Atlantic Forest region, with very few records from both Rio Grande do Sul and Santa Catarina (Belton 1985, do Rosário 1996, Bencke 2001, Naka *et al.* 2001), and some local extinctions have occurred in recent decades (see, e.g., Antunes 2005). The species is generally uncommon in Paraguay (Hayes 1995) and in Surinam (Ottema *et al.* 2009). Nevertheless, *P. chloris* is known from many protected areas virtually throughout the species' range, although relatively few of these are in the Atlantic Forest region, one for instance being Parque Estadual Intervales, São Paulo (see, e.g., Hayes and Scharf 1995a, Madroño *et al.* 1997a, 1997b, Snow 2004b, Patrial *et al.* 2009, Bodrati *et al.* 2010).

REFERENCES Aleixo and Guilherme (2010), Almeida *et al.* (2003), Alvarez *et al.* (2007), Anciães and Peterson (2006, 2009), Antunes (2005), Balchin and Toyne (1998), Beebe (1915), Belton (1985), Bencke (2001), Bernard (2008), BirdLife International (2004, 2008), Blake (1950), Bodrati *et al.* (2010), Boesman (1999, 2006a, 2006b, 2009), Borges (2007), Borges *et al.* (2001), Brooks *et al.* (2009), Chubb (1921), Claessens (1997), Cohn-Haft *et al.* (1997), Cuervo *et al.* (2008b), David and Gosselin (2002b), Dick *et al.* (1984), Dugand and Phelps (1948), Dunning (2008), English and Parker (1992), Friedmann (1948), Gilliard (1941), Gonzaga *et al.* (1995), Guilherme and Santos (2009), Gyldenstolpe (1945, 1951), Hayes (1995), Hayes and Scharf (1995a), Hellmayr (1910, 1929b), Hennessey (2004b), Hennessey *et al.* (2003a, 2003b), Henriques *et al.* (2003), Hilty (2003), Hilty and Brown (1983, 1986), Hinkelmann and Fiebig (2001), Hornbuckle (1999), Hosner *et al.* (2009), Kohler *et al.* (2009), Krabbe and Nilsson (2003), Lane *et al.* (2003), MacLeod *et al.* (2005), Madroño *et al.* (1997a, 1997b), Maillard *et al.* (2007), Marantz and Zimmer (2006), Mayer (2000), Mazar Barnett and Pearman (2001), Mee *et al.* (2002), Merkord *et al.* (2009), Minns *et al.* (2009), Mlíkovský

(2009), Munn (1985), Naka *et al.* (2001, 2006, 2008), Novaes (1964, 1978), Ohlson *et al.* (2008), Oren and Parker (1997), Ottema *et al.* (2009), Pacheco and Olmos (2005), Pacheco *et al.* (2007), Parker and Goerck (1997), Parker and Parker (1982), Parker and Wust (1994), Parker *et al.* (1994a, 1994b, 1994c), Partridge (1954), Patrial *et al.* (2009), de la Peña (1989), Pereira *et al.* (in press), Peres and Whittaker (1991), Perry *et al.* (1997), Phelps (1944), Pimentel (2010), Pimentel and Olmos (2011), Pinto (1944), Renaudier and Deroussen (2008), Remold (2002), Remsen and Traylor (1989), Remsen *et al.* (1987), Restall *et al.* (2006), Ridgely and Greenfield (2001), Ridgely and Tudor (1994, 2009), Robbins *et al.* (2004, 2007), Robinson and Terborgh (1997), Roda and Dantas (2008), do Rosário (1996), Salaman *et al.* (1999, 2008), Schulenberg *et al.* (2000, 2006, 2007), Silva (1996), Silva and Oniki (1988), Simon (2009), Snethlage (1907, 1908b), Snow (2004b), Snyder (1966), Stotz *et al.* (1996, 1997), Straneck (1990), Straube *et al.* (2002), Terborgh *et al.* (1990), Thiollay (1994), Thom *et al.* (2007), Tostain *et al.* (1992), Tubelis (2007), Venturini *et al.* (2005), Vidoz *et al.* (2010), Willard *et al.* (1991), Willis and Oniki (1990, 2002), Zimmer and Hilty (1997), Zimmer *et al.* (1997).

Wing-barred Piprites *Piprites chloris*. **Fig. 1**. Adult, *P. c. chloris*, Intervales State Park, São Paulo, southeast Brazil, April (*Arthur Grosset / www. arthurgrosset.com*). **Fig. 2**. Adult, *P. c. chloris*, Volta Velha Reserve, Itapoá, Santa Catarina, southern Brazil, August (*Nick Athanas / Tropical Birding*). The commonest and most widespread of the genus, Wing-barred Piprites exhibits rather complex geographical variation in plumage, but apparently little or no such vocal variation. **Figs. 3–4**. Adult, *P. c. antioquiae*, Arrierito Antioqueño Bird Reserve, Anorí, dpto. Antioquia, Central Andes, Colombia, January (*Hadoram Shirihai / Photographic Handbook to Birds of the World*). Subspecies is based on range, but many of the observable plumage features (e.g. overall coloration of the upper- and underparts, and the greyish cheeks) are more suggestive of the subspecies *P. c. tschudii*, which otherwise ranges over most of northern and central South America. Note how the lores contrast with the throat, breast and belly, unlike 'classic' *P. c. antioquiae*, wherein these tracts should be largely concolorous. *P. c. antioquiae* is perhaps best treated as a synonym of *P. c. tschudii* (see main text).

BLACK-CAPPED PIPRITES
Piprites pileata   **Plate 34**

Pipra pileata **C. J. Temminck, 1822** [ex. Natterer ms.], *Nouv. Rec. Planches Color.* pl. 172, fig. 1, Curitiba, Paraná state, southern Brazil

This stunning bird is one of the specialties of the Serra do Mar region of southeastern Brazil, where it is most easily found at upper levels of Itatiaia National Park, Rio de Janeiro, but the species was recently and dramatically rediscovered in Argentina, where it was previously known from just a single specimen. Its nest, which is quite unlike that of any manakin, or apparently even the Wing-barred Piprites *Piprites chloris*, raises new questions concerning the monophyly of the genus *Piprites*. Like so many species endemic to the Atlantic Forest region, the Black-capped Piprites is considered globally threatened.

IDENTIFICATION 12.0–12.5cm. The distinctive black cap, cinnamon-buff underparts, chestnut mantle in males (green in the female), white wing 'speculum' and orange tones to the bill and legs make this beautiful species quite impossible to mistake.

DISTRIBUTION Near endemic to Brazil, where it is known from rather few localities in southern Minas Gerais (as far north as Pico do Papagaio, Aiuruoca municipality, and might conceivably occur in nearby Ibitipoca National Park, where suitable habitat exists, although it has not been recorded to date: Pacheco *et al.* 2008) and in Rio de Janeiro states (principally in Itatiaia National Park, but also at nearby Visconde de Mauá in 2000) southwards, highly discontinuously, to northern Rio Grande do Sul (in which state it was recorded from Aparados da Serra National Park in 1991, at two sites including the nearby FLONA São Francisco de Paula in the mid 1990s, and twice at Fazenda das Amoreiras in the 1970s). Nonetheless, Bencke and Kindel (1999) speculated that *P. pileata* might prove reasonably numerous in the FLONA São Francisco de Paula. The species is mentioned in the literature for Espírito Santo, but without basis (Collar *et al.* 1992, Pacheco and Bauer 2001), and there is an old specimen from Nova Friburgo, Rio de Janeiro (cf. Pinto 1944), some way to the east of modern-day records. In São Paulo, Black-capped Piprites is best known from the Campos do Jordão and the Serra da Bocaina, in the southeast of the state. In Paraná, the species has only been recorded recently at Fazenda Santa Rita, where rare, in the upper Rio Tibagi basin, just northwest of Curitiba (Anjos and Graf 1993, Anjos *et al.* 1997), and at Parque Estadual das Lauráceas, near Adrianópolis (Bencke *et al.* 2006), but there are several old records and Natterer collected ten (the type series) in the environs of Curitiba in 1820. In Santa Catarina, the species is known from just seven localities, six of them recent (São Joaquim National Park, Anitápolis and Parque Estadual da Serra do Tabuleiro in the south, and Fazenda Cachoeira, Timbó Grande municipality, Reserva Biológica Estadual do Sassafrás, Doutor Pedrinho municipality, and Fazenda Corredeiras, Rio Negrinho municipality, in the north: Collar *et al.* 1992, Bencke *et al.* 2006, Rupp *et al.* 2007, Santos *et al.* 2008, Ghizoni-Jr and Azevedo 2010). Black-capped Piprites is also known from extreme northeastern Argentina, in Misiones (a September 1959 specimen from Tobuna, and rediscovered, in April–May 2006, at Caá Yarí Provincial Park and Área Experimental Guaraní, within Yabotí Biosphere Reserve, where a small population that inhabits a single

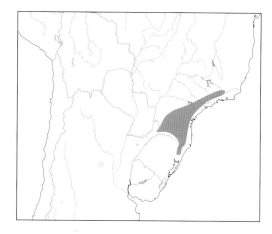

valley (*c.*6 pairs) is now the subject of intensive study: Partridge 1961, Maders *et al.* 2007, Bodrati *et al.* 2009b). A seventh territory, within the Reserva Natural Cultural Papel Misionero, has been discovered even more recently (Bodrati *et al.* 2009a; K. Cockle *in litt.* 2009). The species was listed without evidence for Paraguay by Contreras *et al.* (1990). Altitudinal range in Brazil is 750–2,100m, but the species is unquestionably most frequently recorded above 1,200m with very few reports from below 900m. Recent records in Argentina are from 500m.

MOVEMENTS The species presumably undertakes altitudinal movements in the high parts of the Serra do Mar, as in Itatiaia National Park, Brazil, during the austral spring and summer it is principally recorded above 1,500m (on the Agulhas Negras road and Três Picos trail), but at other seasons Black-capped Piprites is regularly recorded down to 1,100m or even lower. However, it is worth mentioning that GMK has records even from the apparent breeding season (e.g. in November) from as low as *c.*900m, and there does not seem to be any indication that the species might make any kind of elevational movements further south in its range.

HABITAT A bird of the canopy and borders of humid submontane and montane forests of the region, in the south (and also in the north, in the Serra da Mantiqueira of Minas Gerais) of its range associated with *Araucaria* stands intermixed with subtropical forest. However Black-capped Piprites, as long ago noted by Ted Parker, is not an *Araucaria* specialist. In the south of its range in Brazil and in northern Argentina it appears to be closely associated with relatively low-stature forest (Santos *et al.* 2008, and references therein, Bodrati *et al.* 2009b). It seems heavily dependent on and is probably restricted to forest dominated by the laurel *Ocotea pulchella* in Misiones, Argentina (Bodrati *et al.* 2009b). Black-capped Piprites has been observed at least once in the understorey of *Chusquea* bamboo, in Itatiaia National Park (Collar *et al.* 1992), but such behaviour appears curiously atypical.

DESCRIPTION Chunky, with proportionately long wings and tail (for a 'manakin'). Black-capped Piprites has well-developed rictal bristles just like other piprites. *Adult male.* – Crown black (not reaching level with the eye), lores and supercilium cinnamon, ear-coverts and neck-sides becoming paler orange-buff, and rest of upperparts (mantle and back) rich chestnut. The rectrices are blackish with broad chestnut tips and cinnamon outer fringes. Remiges blackish with white bases forming a small 'speculum', and broad yellow-olive fringes to the secondaries (appearing like a panel on the closed wing). Underparts orange-buff from the chin to undertail-coverts, but becoming paler from the lower belly rearwards (the area between the legs can appear very pale greenish in the field), with a dull chestnut undertail and whitish feathers sometimes visible at the wing bend. *Adult female.* – Superficially resembles the male, but the crown is much less black and is heavily mixed with dull olive. Mantle also dark olive, becoming chestnut on the rump. Wing-coverts generally dark with dull greyish wingbars (formed by broad tips to the lesser and greater coverts), whilst the speculum has a yellowish-white hue, the tertials are dark with broad greyish fringes, and the fringes to the secondaries are also much paler and less distinct. Females are also generally paler orange, and more buffish, below, especially on the belly rearwards and on the throat, than males. *Juvenile.* – Much like the female, with dull wingbars, and the young male already shows signs of a blacker cap (GMK pers. obs.). *Moult.* – There are no published data on moult, but one taken in May was rather worn and birds collected in July are in much fresher plumage than those taken in January. *Bare parts.* – Irides dark brown to blackish (pers. obs.) or chestnut (Belton 2003), and the bill is bright yellow (blunt with a strongly arched culmen and hooked tip), with the female having the maxilla dusky and both sexes having dark rictal bristles, and the legs and feet orange-straw.

MEASUREMENTS (BMNH; ZISP; MNRJ: Rio de Janeiro, Brazil) Wing of male (*n* = 6) 73–79mm, wing of female (*n* = 2) 72–73mm; tail of male (*n* = 6) 49–52mm, tail of female (*n* = 2) 49–51mm; bill of male (*n* = 5) 9.67–11.66mm, bill of female (*n* = 2) 8.98–9.48mm; tarsus of male (*n* = 2) 18mm, tarsus of female (*n* = 1) 17mm. Weight (one male): 15g (Belton 2003, Dunning 2008).

GEOGRAPHICAL VARIATION Monotypic.

VOICE Like other *Piprites* this species is relatively vocal and frequently very responsive to tape playback, even birds feeding in flocks (surveys of areas from where the species is unknown but suspected should rely on such techniques). As noted by Bodrati *et al.* (2009b) pairs of birds usually respond, with the male approaching the sound first, followed shortly thereafter by the female. Males give a disjointed but fast and rollicking *chik, chick, cheeut, chee-unh,* variable (e.g. sometimes just gives one or two notes) but always with the same chortling quality, whilst females utter a repeated *cheenh* of similar quality (Ridgely and Tudor 1994, Gonzaga and Castiglioni 2001, Remold 2002, Minns *et al.* 2009). In addition to the published recordings available on the last three-named references, several recordings are available online at www.xeno-canto.org.

NATURAL HISTORY Most frequently observed in the canopy or subcanopy of 10–25m-tall primary forest. Black-capped Piprites is typically found alone or in pairs, once a group of three (two males and a female) and post-breeding in small family parties, and appears to very frequently associate with mixed-species foraging flocks, particularly those with Brassy-breasted Tanagers *Tangara desmaresti* (GG and GMK pers. obs.), but also many other species (see Collar *et al.* 1992, Bodrati *et al.* 2009b), among them White-spotted Woodpecker *Veniliornis spilogaster,* Rufous-backed Antvireo *Dysithamnus xanthopterus,* Scaled Woodcreeper *Lepidocolaptes squamatus,* Pallid Spinetail *Cranioleuca pallida,* Sharp-billed Treehunter *Heliobletus contaminatus,* Mottle-

cheeked Tyrannulet *Phylloscartes ventralis,* Serra do Mar Tyrant-Manakin *Neopelma chrysolophum,* Rufous-crowned Greenlet *Hylophilus poicilotis* and Red-rumped Warbling Finch *Poospiza lateralis* (Torga *et al.* in press). In response to playback in such situations, the birds will approach the observer gradually, peering about constantly, flying back and forth frequently between two or three different trees, and eventually sometimes descending to just above the observer, all the time responding vocally at intermittent intervals. The species seems highly faithful to specific areas, year-round in Argentina (Bodrati *et al.* 2009b) and probably so in Brazil (M. F. Vasconcelos pers. obs.; GMK pers. obs.).

FOOD AND FEEDING Diet is both frugivorous (preferring smaller fruits, including *Rapanea*: Myrsinaceae) and insectivorous (principally small arthropods but also larvae), although in northern Argentina Bodrati *et al.* (2009b) never observed the species take fruits. Black-capped Piprites also appears to join feeding melees at bird tables in Itatiaia National Park in winter (GMK pers. obs.), and a group of three was observed flycatching for winged termites in April (Olson and Alvarenga 2006). When feeding the species perhaps tends to maintain a position on the periphery of the flock, where its foraging style can look very *Tangara*-like as it sidles along branches searching for fruits and insects, although it also hover-plucks invertebrate prey.

BREEDING Until recently, the species' breeding ecology was virtually unknown, although a male was collected with much-enlarged testes, and courtship display (involving wing- and tail-fanning) was observed in September, in Rio Grande do Sul (Belton 2003), and subadult birds have been collected in March and May. GMK observed a family party involving a pair and two juveniles in mid February at Itatiaia National Park. Santos *et al.* (2008) considered that one of three birds observed within a mixed-species flock in northern Santa Catarina in early June was a juvenile. In October 2006, a pair was discovered nest building at Parque Provincial Caá Yarí, Misiones, in northeast Argentina, with construction work being conducted entirely by the female, but the male following and performing distraction flights (as described in the literature for a number of Tyrannidae and *Euphonia,* amongst others) coinciding directly with the female's visits to the nest. The nest was a loosely constructed sphere, placed 8m above the ground, in a fork in the trunk of a laurel, and measured 15cm tall × 14cm wide × 13cm deep, with a side entrance, and was constructed of at least two different species of moss (Cockle *et al.* 2008). Nearby, the same authors observed a second pair engaged in similar behaviour but no nest was found. No further information, but there is an intriguing observation of a minimum of ten involved in display at Itatiaia National Park in late October 1987 (J. F. Pacheco *in* Collar *et al.* 1992).

STATUS Listed as Vulnerable (Collar *et al.* 1992, BirdLife International 2004, 2008), this wonderful bird is still known from very few localities across its comparatively wide range in the southern Atlantic Forest region. Many of the species' currently known haunts are protected (see Distribution) and being a principally highland species it has doubtless suffered much less as a result of deforestation, which has only been extreme at lower elevations. This in turn might suggest that the Black-capped Piprites has been always rather rare and local. It is not quite confined to the Serra do Mar Centre of endemism, as thought by Cracraft (1985).

REFERENCES Anciães and Peterson (2009), Anjos and Graf (1993), Anjos *et al.* (1997), Bauer and Pacheco (2000),

Belton (2003), Bencke and Kindel (1999), Bencke *et al.* (2006), BirdLife International (2004, 2008), Bodrati *et al.* (2009a, 2009b), Cockle *et al.* (2008), Collar *et al.* (1992), Contreras *et al.* (1990), Cracraft (1985), David and Gosselin (2002b), Dekker (2003), Dunning (2008), Ghizoni-Jr and Azevedo (2010), Gonzaga and Castiglioni (2001), Hellmayr (1929b), Maders *et al.* (2007), Minns *et al.* (2009), Ohlson *et al.* (2008), Olson and Alvarenga (2006), Pacheco and Bauer (2001), Pacheco *et al.* (2008), Parker and Goerck (1997), Partridge (1961), Pineschi (1990), Pinto (1944), Remold (2002), Ridgely and Tudor (1994, 2009), do Rosário (1996), Rupp *et al.* (2007), Santos *et al.* (2008), Scherer-Neto and Straube (1995), Sick (1997), Snow (1975, 2004b), Stotz *et al.* (1996), Torga *et al.* (in press), Vasconcelos (1999, 2008), Vasconcelos and D'Angelo Neto (2009), Willis (1983, 1992), Willis and Oniki (1981).

Black-capped Piprites *Piprites pileata*. All of the following images were taken at Itatiaia National Park, Rio de Janeiro, southeast Brazil, which is one of this globally threatened species' strongholds. **Fig. 1**. Male, November (*Hadoram Shirihai / Photographic Handbook to Birds of the World*). Very much the 'oddball' of the genus in terms of its coloration. **Fig. 2**. Male, May (*Nick Athanas / Tropical Birding*). **Fig. 3**. Female, November (*Hadoram Shirihai / Photographic Handbook to Birds of the World*). Compared to the male, note especially the greenish mantle, duller crown, dusky maxilla, and the marginally duller underparts.

Genus *Calyptura*: Kinglet Calyptura

One of the least known of all genera of Neotropical birds, the monospecific genus *Calyptura* continues to capture the imagination of both birdwatchers and systematists, the former as to when it might make its next, long-awaited appearance, and the latter as to its correct position within the Suboscines.

KINGLET CALYPTURA
Calyptura cristata   Plate 14

Pardalotus cristatus Vieillot, 1818, *Nouv. Dict. Hist. Nat.*, new edn., 24: 528, [Rio de Janeiro,] Brazil

The considerable loss of lowland and, to a lesser extent, foothill Atlantic Forest in the hinterland of the city of Rio de Janeiro, Brazil, appeared to have condemned this tiny, enigmatic 'cotinga' to extinction, it being last collected around 1890. The species' remarkable but frustratingly brief rediscovery in late October 1996, by one of the most brilliant of the current generation of Brazilian ornithologists, Ricardo Parrini, was thus one of the most long-awaited events in Neotropical ornithology; Kinglet Calyptura had almost literally risen from the ashes, like a Phoenix (Tobias *et al.* 2006). Unfortunately, since the heady days of October 1996, more than ten years have elapsed without further confirmed sightings (there have been a few unconfirmed sightings), leading ornithologists to wonder just how long the calyptura will continue to baffle us. To some extent the rediscovery mirrored that of the Black-hooded Antwren *Formicivora erythronotus*, in the 1980s, another species from the same general area long considered extinct. The rediscovery of the antwren offered salutary lessons concerning reliance on the labelling of museum skins and correct generic assignment, for it proved that *F. erythronotus* had been entirely misclassified in an inappropriate genus, leading ornithologists to expect the bird to vocalise entirely differently and to occupy a rather different habitat to that in which it was eventually found. From specimen data, the antwren was presumed to inhabit premontane forests of the Serra do Mar northeast of Rio de Janeiro, but was rediscovered in the littoral well to the southwest, where shade and secondary scrub forest in the lowlands rises into the foothills. This understandably gave rise to speculation that, to some extent, the same would hold true for the calyptura, although its rediscovery eventually took place within the species' presumed historical range. Lambert

and Kirwan (2010) have recently presented a résumé of our sparse and sometimes contradictory knowledge of the species, in an effort to ensure that it does not, once again, fall off the ornithological radar.

IDENTIFICATION 7.5–8.0cm. The Kinglet Calyptura should prove unmistakable if seen well, by someone with experience of Atlantic Forest birds. The species' tiny size (it is the smallest species traditionally placed in the Cotingidae) already renders it difficult to confuse. Coupled with the brilliant red crest (at least sometimes held erect like a frontal shield, not flattened, on the basis of the 1996 observations), black stripe on the crown-sides, double white wingbars, green upperparts, yellow underparts and rump band, and the Kinglet Calyptura becomes one of the most distinctive, yet apparently hard-to-see, birds in southeast Brazil.

DISTRIBUTION Endemic to Brazil, where its historical range was probably largely restricted to Rio de Janeiro state, in the foothills of the Serra do Mar (but see below). Evidence for its purported occurrence in Espírito Santo is based solely on the notoriously unreliable Ruschi (see Collar *et al.* 1992). Nonetheless it might be remarked that other species 'lost' either globally (Cherry-throated Tanager *Nemosia rourei*) and at state level (Black-legged Dacnis *Dacnis nigripes*) have recently resurfaced in southern Espírito Santo (Bauer *et al.* 2000, Whittaker *et al.* 2010b). Furthermore, given that quite some of our information about *Calyptura* comes from Descourtilz, who probably made many of his observations in the same state, the possibility certainly exists that the species did, at least formerly, occur there. Despite the presence of over 55 specimens in museums (Collar *et al.* 1992, Lima 2005, McGhie 2005, Krabbe 2007; GMK pers. obs.; M. A. Raposo and R. Stopiglia pers. comm.) specific localities are rather few, but include Cantagalo, Nova Friburgo and the Morro Queimado, near Rosário (*c.*22°06'S, 42°25'W: Krabbe 2007, although as discussed by Lambert and Kirwan 2010 this site might in fact be on the outskirts of Nova Friburgo). All of these localities are in the general environs of Rio de Janeiro city, at altitudes of 150–900m (although specimens could have been collected at anything up to 1,500m in the surrounding mountains). Pinto (1944) mentioned that Delalande had collected *Calyptura* within the immediate environs of the city. A specimen in the Berlin Museum, from Sellow, is labelled as being from 'Sao Paulo' (Stopiglia *et al.* 2009) and the evidence of the historical literature indicates that there is no reason to suggest that the label has been incorrectly modified more recently (M. A. Raposo and R. Stopiglia pers. comm.). The rediscovery site, Buraco da Sunta, on the slopes of the Serra dos Órgãos, below Teresópolis, lies at *c.*550m. Since then, the species has been reported from the Estação Experimental de Agronomia de Ubatuba, São Paulo, on 27 March 1997 (L. Hockey), and at Folha Seca, Praia Douro, near Ubatuba, also in São Paulo, in March 2006, close to sea level (M. Schaefer; cf. Kirwan *et al.* 2006, Lambert and Kirwan 2010), but this latter sighting appears to lack credibility, given that the observer (unfamiliar with Atlantic Forest birds)

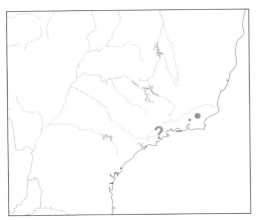

reported at least one other species in the same mixed flock as the calyptura that is unknown from the region (despite extensive ornithological fieldwork there) (cf. Lambert and Kirwan 2010). Furthermore, the bird was searched for the following day without success (R. Raby pers. comm.). In contrast, Hockey, despite being unaware of the details of the species' rediscovery the previous year, mentioned the raised crest (a feature previously unmentioned in the literature at that time). Subsequently, another sighting, involving two Kinglet Calypturas within a mixed-species foraging flock, including tanagers, euphonias and tyrant flycatchers, also from the Ubatuba region came to light, by Sigrist (2006). These birds were seen in July 1990, in riverine forest at Picinguaba (150m above sea level). Most recently, G. Bernardon (*in litt.* 2010) has reported seeing a Kinglet Calyptura at a fruiting tree with many tanagers and other birds, at Fazenda Angelim, also near Ubatuba, São Paulo, on 19 September 2008 (23°23'44.9"S, 45°03'49.9"W).

MOVEMENTS None certainly known although it is strongly suspected that the species performs altitudinal movements, coinciding with the local fruiting of melastomes. That the birds in 1996 were observed in the same place, performing the same routine for several days, before disappearing strongly suggests that the species is either an altitudinal migrant or wanders erratically in search of fruit. However, historical data are more ambiguous and suggest far more sedentary behaviour.

HABITAT Primary and secondary pre-montane Atlantic Forest, but also frequently (most readily seen) venturing into second growth in abandoned clearings, and P. W. Lund mentioned collecting at least one specimen in shrubbery (cf. Krabbe 2007).

DESCRIPTION For observers from temperate regions, comparisons with a *Regulus* species are almost inevitable, but note the much shorter tail (almost entirely obscured by the wings) and thicker bill. Sexes differ, but not strikingly. Rictal bristles moderately developed. For bill structure see below. *Adult male.* – Most of the upperparts are bright olive-green, with a bright yellow rump, becoming olive-green again over the uppertail-coverts and has grey-brown rectrices with olive outer webs. Crown bright orange-red with broad deep black lateral crown-stripes enclosing the crown patch, with some black on the nape; forehead very bright yellow, but restricted to patch immediately above bill. Wings are principally pale brown to dusky, but more olive on some of the coverts, with broad white tips to the median and greater coverts, and fringes and tips to the tertials, with olive-green fringes to the secondaries and some primaries. Throat and face are primarily olive-green, slightly yellower but almost concolorous with the upperparts, becoming distinctly yellower and brighter from the upper breast rearwards, including the undertail-coverts. Underwing-coverts are yellowish-cream to almost whitish. *Adult female.* – Rather similar to the male, but distinguished as follows. Forehead and forecrown largely dark olive-green, with paler orange-red restricted to the rear crown where intermixed with black; although black is chiefly on the crown-sides, it does not form lateral stripes. White tips to wing-coverts and tertials perhaps generally narrower, but still broad and obvious, and rump patch less bright yellow. *Immature/Juvenile.* – The latter plumage is unknown, but immature males apparently have a pale (whitish) throat and greenish cast to the flanks (J. Fjeldså illustration of P. W. Lund specimen *in* Krabbe 2007). *Moult.* – Nothing is known. *Bare parts.* – Not precisely

recorded by contemporary observers, but bill and legs were apparently dark. Bill conical and culmen strongly arched, occasionally with slightly hook tip.

MEASUREMENTS (from Snow 1982; CUMZ; MNRJ; RMNH; ZISP: Brazil) Wing of male (*n* = 11) 46.0–51.5mm, wing of female (*n* = 6) 46.5–49.0mm; tail of male (*n* = 11) 22.0–25.5mm, tail of female (*n* = 5) 21–24mm; bill of male (*n* = 4) 5.0–5.5mm (*n* = 7, to skull, 8.03–9.14mm), bill of female (*n* = 4, to skull) 8.97–9.41mm; tarsus of male (*n* = 7) 13.38–15.50mm, tarsus of female (*n* = 1) 15.43mm. Weight (sexes combined): 19.8–20.2g (Snow 2004b).

GEOGRAPHICAL VARIATION None known.

VOICE Unknown with certainty, as the birds observed in 1996 were not heard to vocalise (Pacheco and Fonseca 2001), but P. W. Lund (*in* Collar *et al.* 1992 and Krabbe 2007) mentions an almost sparrow-like chirp and J. T. Descourtilz (also cited by Collar *et al.* 1992) mentioned that pairs called frequently with a rather loud voice, described by him as 'brief, raucous and disagreeable' (cf. Snow 1982).

NATURAL HISTORY Very few data, but historical accounts (recounted in Collar *et al.* 1992) suggest that the species generally occurred in pairs, being generally found at mid levels, rather than in the canopy, exploring vines and clumps of *Tillandsia* (Bromeliaceae) bromeliads, searching for small berries, seeds and insects (this also based on stomach contents), particularly either *Acnistus cauliflora* (Solanaceae) and/or *Solanum* (*Bassovia*) *lucida*, both of which grow to only *c.*3m in height (see Snow 1982). Descourtilz mentioned that it fed on the fruits of the marianeira *Acnistus arborescens* (Solanaceae), at least seasonally. In contrast to the early reports, the two individuals observed in 1996 were generally extremely difficult to see in the canopy of the mistletoe-laden trees in which they appeared on three mornings out of four between 27 and 30 October (Pacheco and Fonseca 2001). However, R. Parrini initially observed these two birds in relatively low trees in a second-growth situation (cf. Lambert and Kirwan 2010).

BREEDING Effectively unknown. Of the *c.*55 known specimens, two are immature males, collected in January and May. (Collar *et al.* 1992 mentioned a total of 'at least' 45 specimens, but we are aware of others in at least four or five institutions not mentioned by those authors, details of some of which have subsequently been published.) P. W. Lund mentioned collecting specimens in January and June, both of which had small testes, suggesting that they were not breeding at the time (cf. Krabbe 2007).

STATUS Critically Endangered (BirdLife International 2004, 2008) and confined to the Serra do Mar Centre of endemism (Cracraft 1985). Any attempt to speculate on the bird's population is impossible at present, although there are still relatively extensive tracts of well-preserved pre-montane and montane forest in the region, including of course that in the Serra dos Órgãos National Park, although much forest below 800–900m has been destroyed. Even by the early part of the 19th century, considerable destruction had been wrought, principally for coffee production, and some early travellers describe forests in this region that seem quite unlike those found in the general area in the present day (cf. Lambert and Kirwan 2010, which see for a speculative discussion concerning the Kinglet Calyptura's survival prospects and reasons for its apparent extraordinary rarity and ability to evade detection by birdwatchers). But, equally, in many areas this destruction occurred in the late

19th and early 20th centuries, implying that if the species has survived for another 100 years then a viable breeding population must persist. Following the enterprising attempt by Frank Lambert (cf. Lambert and Kirwan 2010) to rediscover *Calyptura cristata*, the next challenge is to organise a complete survey of all remaining forest in Rio de Janeiro, and adjacent areas in Minas Gerais, São Paulo and Espírito Santo, to find new 'sites' for the species, in order to produce an Action Plan to ensure the Kinglet Calyptura's survival.

REFERENCES Bauer *et al.* (2000), BirdLife International (2000, 2004, 2008), Butchart and Bird (2010), Collar *et al.* (1992), Cracraft (1985), Dickinson (2003), Fisher (1981), Gonzaga (1997), Gill and Wright (2006), Haffer (1974), Hellmayr (1929b), Kirwan *et al.* (2006), Krabbe (2007), Lambert and Kirwan (2010), Lima (2005), Maciel (2009), Mallet-Rodrigues *et al.* (2007), McGhie (2005), Ohlson *et al.* (2010), Olalla (1943), Pacheco and Fonseca (2001), Pinto (1944), Remsen *et al.* (2008), Ridgely and Tudor (1994, 2009), Ruschi (1953), Sigrist (2006), Snow (1982, 2004a), Stopiglia *et al.* (2009), Stotz *et al.* (1996), Tello *et al.* (2009), Tobias *et al.* (2006), Whittaker *et al.* (2010b), Willis (1992).

Figs. 1–2. Male, locality unknown beyond Brazil (*Guy M. Kirwan* / © *The Natural History Museum, Tring*).

Genus *Phibalura*: Swallow-tailed Cotinga

Morphologically a very distinct genus, *Phibalura* shares its black, or mainly black, crown and erectile red nuchal crest with the Andean cotingas of the genera *Ampelion* and *Phytotoma*. This feature, shared by genera from the Andes and the Atlantic Forests of Brazil, has given rise to speculation as to the origin of these related cotingas; Atlantic Forest cotingas which have colonised the Andes, or vice versa? The population of Swallow-tailed Cotinga in Bolivia might suggest convergent evolution by separate Andean and southeast South American species with similar features, although the origin of a common ancestor requires further research. Although primarily a specialist feeder on mistletoes (Loranthaceae), the Swallow-tailed Cotinga also frequently 'hawks' insects by aerial pursuit, perhaps further suggesting a close relationship with *Ampelion* (or, of course, convergent evolution in this character trait). Concerning the issue of whether to treat *Phibalura* as monospecific or not, for now we, like Snow (2004a), BirdLife International (2008) and Remsen *et al.* (2009) but *contra* Gill and Wright (2006) and Ridgely and Tudor (2009), prefer to regard the genus as containing a single polytypic species (see Geographical Variation). Our view echoes a biogeographical pattern shown to a greater or lesser extent by a number of other species whose taxonomy is not questioned.

SWALLOW-TAILED COTINGA
Phibalura flavirostris   Plate 32

Phibalura flavirostris L. J. P. Vieillot, 1816, *Analyse Nouv. Orn.*: 68, [Rio de Janeiro, Brazil, by designation of Pinto 1944]

Surely one of the most distinctive birds covered in this book and also one of the most coveted by birdwatchers, especially first-time visitors to the Atlantic Forest region. Fortunately for would-be observers, it is not uncommon at certain well-known localities on the southeast Brazil birdwatching circuit, despite its listing as Near Threatened by BirdLife International.

IDENTIFICATION 21.0–23.5cm. One of those species that is practically impossible to mistake. The short triangular bill, long wings and 'swallow tail' make the Swallow-tailed Cotinga unique amongst the cotingas in appearance, and easily identifiable even in flight or by the inexperienced observer. Hooded *Carpornis cucullata* and Black-headed Berryeaters *C. melanocephala* (in southeast Brazil; the latter rarely found, if ever, in the same areas), or a *Pipreola* fruiteater (Bolivia), are the only species that might be potentially confused with *Phibalura*. However, the yellow and white underparts, heavily barred and scaled with black (browner in females), should not fail to attract the attention, even if you fail to immediately notice the dramatic, forked tail. This species is easily overlooked, despite its preference for more open country, as it resorts to the shady foliage of trees, although it can also be seen at canopy height at the forest edge.

DISTRIBUTION Swallow-tailed Cotinga exhibits a curiously disjunct range, separated by *c.*2,500km. *P. f. boliviana* is restricted to western Bolivia, in the foothills of La Paz (where it is known from fewer than a handful of old specimens, as well as modern-day records from the Apolo area, in Madidi National Park, where the species was rediscovered in the country as recently as 2000). In this area, the species is mainly restricted to areas south and east of Apolo (Rosario Avalos 2011). Elsewhere, nominate *P. f. flavirostris* occurs in eastern Paraguay, west only to Guairá, and in which country it is known from very few records, none of them more recent than 1977 (Hayes 1995), as well as in extreme northeast Argentina, solely in the province of Misiones, where it is generally rare (Mazar Barnett and Pearman 2001), although there were apparent influxes in February–March 1952 (Partridge 1954) and August 1977,

from whence the only records in the well-watched Iguazú National Park date (Saibene *et al.* 1996), but the species was also recently recorded at several sites and on six occasions in June, July and September 2004, and in May and August 2005 (Bodrati and Cockle 2006b, Bodrati *et al.* 2010). The main range is in southeastern Brazil, where it is known principally from southern Espírito Santo and central Minas Gerais south to São Paulo and thence, increasingly sparsely, to Rio Grande do Sul, with, e.g. very few records from the state of Santa Catarina (do Rosário 1996, Piacentini *et al.* 2006, Rupp *et al.* 2007). There are also recent records even further north, in southern and central Bahia, north as far as the Chapada Diamantina (Gonzaga *et al.* 1995, Parrini *et al.* 1999), and single Swallow-tailed Cotingas were collected in south-central Goiás, at the Rio Claro in mid-May 1941 and at Goiânia in mid-January 1965 (Pinto 1944; FMNH 344709; see also below). There is also a recent record, documented photographically, from the state in winter by R. Parrini (*per* J. F. Pacheco *in litt.* 2010). Elevational range is 1,300–1,900m in Bolivia (Rosario Avalos 2011); in Brazil it was thought to be restricted to below 1,200m in the Atlantic Forest region by Ridgely and Tudor (1994), but as noted by Stotz *et al.* (1996), Vasconcelos and Melo Júnior (2001) and Snow (2004a) *Phibalura* occurs to at least 2,000m, e.g. in Itatiaia National Park, Rio de Janeiro (GMK pers. obs.), and the Serra do Caraça, Minas Gerais, at least during the breeding season.

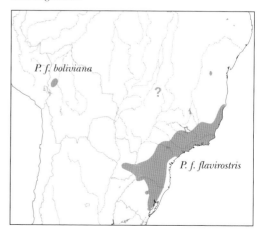

MOVEMENTS Swallow-tailed Cotinga is partially migratory in the Atlantic Forest, but apparently resident in Bolivia. For example, the species principally appears in Rio Grande do Sul (in southern Brazil) during the austral summer (Belton 1985, 1994), and in Misiones (Argentina) in the winter and early spring (Bodrati and Cockle 2006b). However, there are summer records from the latter country, where overall the species has been recorded between February and September (cf. Bodrati *et al.* 2010). All of the very few Paraguayan records are dated June–October, suggesting that it is principally a (very rare) winter visitor to that country (Hayes 1995). In Rio Grande do Sul all records are from between late September and late March (Belton 1985, 1994). The species may, to some extent, retreat north in winter, with the only published record from Goiás being from this season (although there is also a specimen record from January), and it being also occasionally recorded in the early 1980s in the cerrados of central São Paulo during the winter (Willis 2006), at which season there is also a record from southern Minas Gerais in 1981 (J. F. Pacheco *in litt.* 2010). The species is also an altitudinal migrant, it often moving lower during the austral winter, although such movements appear locally complex; e.g. it is generally found at higher altitudes, above 1,100m, in Rio de Janeiro during the breeding season, and the same appears true in central Minas Gerais, but some birds at least seem to remain at relatively high altitudes in the austral winter, suggesting that fruit supplies and relative temperatures may determine their precise behaviour. *Phibalura* has occurred within the city limits of Rio de Janeiro in June, July and August, although there is only one modern (2007) record from the municipality, in Tijuca National Park (Pelzeln 1870, Sick 1997, Serpa and Gagliardi 2007, Maciel 2009).

HABITAT In southeastern South America, Swallow-tailed Cotinga is often found in relatively open areas (e.g. in wooded meadows, roadsides and gardens), but it is generally found at forest borders and in partially wooded areas, both in tall forest and much lower second growth, with no obvious preferences apparent. It has been recorded in *cerradão* at least occasionally in winter (Willis 2006). In Bolivia, *P. f. boliviana* occurs in semi-humid forest fragments and their edges, and is capable of crossing quite large open spaces between such woodlots (Bromfield *et al.* 2002).

DESCRIPTION There is slight sexual dimorphism. Delicate and sleek, with the 'swallow tail' formed by the long outer rectrices which curve outwards at their tips; the male's tail is longer than that of the female. Wings rather long and pointed, and the species has a very short, broad-based bill with oval-shaped and semi-concealed nostrils, and somewhat bristly feathers at its base, especially on the forehead. No rictal bristles and the flight feathers are unmodified. The nominate race is described here. *Adult male.* – Crown very dark, glossy navy-blue, with dark crimson-red crest feathers (which are usually partially concealed), and fawn-brown or greyish-brown lateral crown feathers, which continue onto the nape to form a rear collar. Blackish-blue lores and ear-coverts. Mantle (with some white shaft-streaks), scapulars and rump/uppertail-coverts are bright yellowish-olive or even canary-yellow, heavily scaled with bluish-black subterminal markings to each feather, becoming narrower and less noticeable posteriorly. The wings are intense bluish-black (including the coverts) and contrast with the rest of the upperparts, although the central tertial may be slightly browner with a black tip (wear-related?) and the primaries

have brownish inner webs. Throat, belly and undertail-coverts are bright yellow and unmarked, with a white breast (extending just onto the sides of the throat), heavily scaled across its entirety, and these markings continue randomly onto the flanks and the nape. Uppertail largely black, undertail greyish. *Adult female.* – The crown of the female is paler, composed mainly of greyish-brown feathering, and the red is usually much duller with darker feather centres. The ear-coverts are much duller black than in males. The mantle, scapulars and rump are generally duller olive, with much narrower and less obvious subterminal markings (which again become less noticeable posteriorly), affording less obvious contrast with the wings, which have conspicuous olive fringes to the remiges, and dark olive-green coverts with dark brown bases to these feathers. Compared with the male, the throat is slightly duller yellow with dull grey-brown spotting of variable intensity, and the barring on the upper breast is slightly more extensive, but more brownish (less blackish), as well as being more evenly spaced and does not extend to the nape. On the lower breast, belly and flanks, females have the ground colour slightly less lemon-yellow, with irregular black-brown barring, often with much white at the base of each feather and a white shaft-streak, this pattern extending to the undertail-coverts in most. The tail fork is probably on average shallower, although some have it equally as deep, and the upper tail is largely much browner than that of the male, especially on the webs. *Juvenile.* – Plumage resembles that of the respective adults, but this plumage has an olive-green (with darker centres) and white-tipped tail that is only slightly notched, brownish-olive upperparts (including the scapulars), with dark but very narrow subterminal barring to these feathers and rather bold white terminal spotting, and a similar pattern to the crown. The wings are largely olive-green with darker shafts and flight feathers, almost white outer webs to the tertials and some whitish spotting at the bases of the greater coverts. The underparts are principally whitish with some, irregular and coarse, brownish barring, and become slightly more yellow on the centre of the breast and the undertail-coverts. Plumage progression is undescribed, although the immature seems very adult-like, albeit with heavier barring on the underparts, browner-coloured black areas of the plumage, black-spotted throat feathers and broader green fringes to the wing feathers. A description of the nestling was presented by Snow (1982) and this plumage is also illustrated in Snow (2004a: 67) and on the back cover of *Cotinga* 6 (1996). *Moult.* – Data are rather sparse, but there is some suggestion that females might renew their feathers earlier than males, a strategy unique amongst the Cotingidae (if confirmed). Complete renewal occupies *c.*120 days (Snow 1976a) and most birds commence their moult in November–January, with late individuals starting in February–April (Snow 1982). Single males and females collected at the same locality in eastern Brazil in March were both in wing moult (Willis and Oniki 2002). *Bare parts.* – Irides red to chestnut-brown; the bill is pinkish-white to white (in young it is variously described as black or yellow: Sick 1997, Rochido and Andrade 2000, respectively); and the slender legs and feet are yellowish, straw-coloured or bluish-white (described as pinkish-orange in *P. f. boliviana*).

MEASUREMENTS (mensural data from Snow 1982, Krabbe 1984; culmen measured to nares; weights from Belton 1985, Snow 2004a, Dunning 2008; MNRJ; (other specimens examined but not measured by us in BMNH, MNRJ, MZUSP, ZISP)) *P. f. flavirostris* (with *P. f. boliviana* in square brackets, represented by two males and one female). Wing of male

(n = 14) 96–108mm [101mm], wing of female (n = 10) 94–105mm [100mm]; tail of male (n = 14) 106–125mm [114–131mm], tail of female (n = 10) 96–104mm [110mm]; bill of male (n = 14) 8.5–9.5mm [8.0mm], bill of female (n = 10) 8.5–9.5mm; tarsus of male (n = 14) 18–20mm [18mm], tarsus of female (n = 10) 18–19mm. For other mensural data see also Partridge (1954). Weight: 43.5–59.1g (three males), and 44 and 52g (two females).

GEOGRAPHICAL VARIATION Two races recognised which, it has been postulated, might represent separate species: *P. f. flavirostris* (main range); and *P. f. boliviana* Chapman, 1930 (northwest Bolivia). The latter, on the basis of the three specimens available, is potentially longer tailed, with a clean white postocular area, less yellow on the throat, fewer bars below, more orange-toned feet and reportedly weaker sexual dimorphism (Bromfield *et al.* 2002, Snow 1982, 2004a). Krabbe (1984) noted apparent differences in wing formula and that the tips of the outer rectrices are apparently narrower in *P. f. boliviana*. We cannot comment on the former character, but suggest that any such difference in the tail feathers must be extremely marginal. Snow (2004a) noted that *P. f. boliviana* might represent a separate species, whilst Bromfield *et al.* (2002) promised a future manuscript arguing such status, and Gill and Wright (2006) already took this view, naming the species Palkachupa Cotinga, in reference to the bird's name ('forked tail') amongst the indigeneous community. We are less impressed as to the claims for species status for *P. f. boliviana*, notwithstanding its unquestionable (albeit untested) genetic isolation from the Atlantic Forest population, for the following reasons. Too few mensural data are, as yet, available to draw reasonable conclusions concerning any such differences between the taxa; we have noted greater variation in tail-length, amongst over 60 specimens examined by us, than was indicated by Snow's measurements. The field observations of Bromfield *et al.* (2002) hint at not dissimilar levels of variation between males and females of *P. f. boliviana*, compared with our reasonably extensive museum studies of *P. f. flavirostris*, which have elucidated some sex-related differences that would be extremely difficult to detect in a field situation. From the published photographs (Bromfield *et al.* 2002), we are unconvinced that *P. f. boliviana* does indeed show consistently less yellow on the throat or a cleaner white postocular area, especially given that the describer (Chapman 1930) of *P. f. boliviana* also had much less comparative material of *P. f. flavirostris* to hand than we have seen. Nonetheless, it does seem to be the case that *P. f. boliviana* shows considerably less barring on the posterior underparts, perhaps in both sexes, than *P. f. flavirostris*. For now, *contra* several other recent treatments (see introduction), we maintain *P. flavirostris* as a single species awaiting evidence of significant differences between the two populations. In our opinion, although it is likely that genetic studies, when they become available, will suggest some level of differentiation between the Bolivian and Brazilian populations, the morphological differences separating them represent insufficient support for the two-species theory.

VOICE There seems to be no published recordings of this species, other than that by Remold (2002). Swallow-tailed Cotinga is generally silent, but Sick (1997) and Snow (2004a) reported that a 'tremolo' and a high guttural whistle, *gut, gut*, have been noted for nominate *P. f. flavirostris*, whilst GMK has only once, during many observations, heard this species call; a pair in Minas Gerais, busily feeding low above the ground,

several times gave a very low, slightly metallic *pik* note, which was sometimes doubled. Rochido *et al.* (2003) noted, however, that the birds vocalise during nest construction, but did not provide further details. An almost-fledged young, in a nest at Parque Estadual Intervales, São Paulo, in late November, gave a repeated *chep* note whilst raised up 'on its haunches' begging for food (GMK pers. obs.). For *P. f. boliviana*, Bromfield *et al.* (2002) recorded a rather harsh but weak contact note, given frequently at the rate of slightly more than one per second, repeated up to 18 times.

NATURAL HISTORY Unobtrusive, except when breeding, and the species is very social, forming flocks of up to 15–20 birds, especially in the austral winter (e.g. in June–September), but it is also frequently found in small, rather loosely associated bands that sometimes all perch up in the canopy of trees, particularly when feeding, at any season of the year. Swallow-tailed Cotinga also appears to loosely follow mixed-species feeding flocks, including with Green-backed Becard *Pachyramphus viridis* in Argentina (Bodrati and Cockle 2006b), but the state or duration of such associations are unknown. It is also sometimes seen with other 'cotingas', including Elegant Mourner *Laniisoma elegans* (especially in winter), Red-ruffed Fruitcrow *Pyroderus scutatus* and Cinnamon-vented Piha *Lipaugus lanioides*, or Sharpbills *Oxyruncus cristatus*. They are excellent fliers, resembling *Pyrrhura* parakeets (or even Budgerigars *Melopsittacus undulatus*) as they bound forward, opening and closing their wings as they travel, although, *contra* Ridgely and Tudor (1994), three observed at Caraça Natural Park in Minas Gerais, Brazil, flew with the longest tail feathers in a forked shape. In our experience, the tail fork is usually reasonably obvious in flight.

FOOD AND FEEDING The species feeds quietly, in either high or low trees, sometimes just 1–2m above the ground, occasionally in planted *Eucalyptus* (Myrtaceae) in gardens within close proximity of native forest. Swallow-tailed Cotinga is a mistletoe (Loranthaceae) specialist, picking ('reaching' and 'gleaning') fruits by leaning forwards or down, never up, but also hawks aerially (sally-strikes of up to 20m) for insects (*Phibalura* is almost certainly the most consistent exponent of this habit within the entire family). Insects (e.g. Hymenoptera) are usually taken in flight, but sometimes on substrates (Avalos 2009), and the latter author's systematic observations also revealed that there seems to be sex-specific differences in foraging behaviour. Other fruits that are taken include species of Moraceae, Myrsinaceae, Rubiaceae and (in *P. f. boliviana*) Araliaceae (especially *Schefflera morototoni*). In Brazil, *Myrsine* spp. (Myrsinaceae) might be preferred (Rochido 2000) while *Phibalura* also takes *Miconia pusilliflora* (Melastomataceae) (Parrini and Pacheco 2011) and *Rapanea* fruits (Myrsinaceae: Pineschi 1990). (However, it should be noted that one such species, *Myrsine gujanensis*, was formerly placed in the genus *Rapanea*: cf. Torga *et al.* in press.) This is one of four species of cotingas studied in Paraná, southern Brazil, by Clausi and Baarstch (2009), who found that fruit production and its effect on local movements on birds such as Cotingidae could be divided into six periods of the year. Avalos (2009) studied the foraging behaviour of the subspecies *P. f. boliviana*, and found that the birds seem to prefer fruit in the early morning and mid afternoon, but switched to foraging largely on insects at other times of day. In Bolivia, Swallow-tailed Cotingas have been observed foraging in close company with species such as White-crested Elaenia

Elaenia albiceps, Pale-breasted Thrush *Turdus leucomelas*, Swallow Tanager *Tersina viridis* and apparently even Paradise Tanager *Tangara chilensis* (Avalos 2009).

BREEDING Behaviour is reasonably well known, presumably due to the species being regular at many sites frequented by birdwatchers and its habit of regularly nesting in the same area, sometimes even perhaps the same trees, year after year. However, in Bolivia, the species will also nest in well-sheltered areas on rocks in montane savanna, although tree nests are commoner, by a factor of three (Rosario Avalos 2011). The nest of this species is also relatively conspicuous, both in its structure and positioning, compared with many cotingas, which fact is speculated to be due to the relatively limited number of predators within its elevational range (Snow 1982). Lays eggs in October–January (Snow 1982, 2004a), but recently fledged young have been observed at Parque Estadual Intervales, São Paulo, as 'early' as late September and October (GMK pers. obs.), indicating that at least some pairs commence breeding earlier. Nonetheless, the main nesting season seems to commence in October in Brazil, based on observations in Rio de Janeiro, Minas Gerais and Espírito Santo, October in Paraguay, and September–October in Bolivia (where the most detailed study of the species' breeding biology is that by Rosario Avalos 2007, 2011). She found that nests on trees tended to be characterised by the selected trees being thicker trunked and more lichen-covered, although the nests were usually relatively far from the main trunk and well-supported by branches (Rosario Avalos 2010). Both sexes appear to take responsibility for provisioning and caring for the young (see Snow 1982, 2004a: 67), and the evidence for male involvement in nest building and incubation duties has been quantified recently (Avalos 2011). The male is also reported to feed the female on the nest, which is typically sited 2–18m above the ground in Brazil (but at less than 2m in the highland forests of Bolivia), and is a slight, shallow cup structure (dimensions reported in Rochido 2000), almost or entirely constructed of lichens (especially *Usnea longissima*, Parmeliaceae), usually in the fork or on a prominent bough of a tall, often somewhat isolated, tree in Brazil (e.g. *Lafoensia pacari*, Lythraceae, or a *Sapium* sp., Euphorbiaceae), sometimes with a slight (<10cm) tail of *Tillandsia* (Bromeliaceae) moss. The nest is far from visible when the adults are not tending it. Swallow-tailed Cotinga sometimes reuses the same nest in subsequent seasons, or even in the same season (with a gap of 15 days between the successful nesting attempts: Rochido 2000). To date, there has been no confirmation of the theory posited by Snow (1982), based on somewhat ambiguous data, that once a first breeding effort is well advanced, the pair may initiate a second clutch in a different nest, with the male remaining to feed the young at the first nest, and recent observations in Bolivia appear to refute this notion (Avalos 2011). A near-fledged young at Parque Estadual Intervales, São Paulo, was fed by both adults in fairly rapid succession (GMK pers. obs.). The clutch comprises 2–3 eggs, pale pastel green or greenish-blue with dark brownish-red spots and lines in both Bolivian and Brazilian clutches (dimensions of the eggs were presented by Goeldi 1894). Pairs may build nests within 300m of one another (Rochido and Andrade 2000), but the birds do not tolerate others of the same species in very close proximity to the nest (GMK pers. obs.). Seemingly no published data on incubation period from Brazil, but in Bolivia it is 17–19 days (Avalos 2011), and only the female spends the night on the nest from the initiation of incubation until three days before the nestlings fledge (Rochido and Andrade 2000; GMK pers.

obs.), and the young are fed large food balls, so large that the adults are unable to close the mandibles when carrying them (Snow 1982). Fledging period was reported as 29 days at one nest in Minas Gerais (Rochido and Andrade 2000) and 25–30 days at nests in Bolivia (Avalos 2011). The species is often very tame and easily approached when nesting, and will even construct its nests close to busy roads, although in Bolivia nesting attempts closer to trails were more prone to failure (Rosario Avalos 2011), and overall nesting success was less than 20% (Avalos 2011). At least within protected areas it seems that breeding success is relatively high (Rochido and Andrade 2000).

STATUS Treated as Near Threatened by BirdLife International (2004, 2008) and is considered Vulnerable in the states of Espírito Santo (Passamani and Mendes 2007) and São Paulo, and at national level in Argentina (Fraga 1997). Although this superb and highly distinctive bird has a rather extensive range, the species appears to have undergone a population decline recently, and being a migrant must be threatened by further habitat loss throughout its range. The Bolivian population, not recorded until recently for almost 100 years, is nominally protected within Madidi National Park, but the population is probably very small (a total of 192 individuals was recorded during surveys in 2007 and 2008) and therefore to some extent threatened, especially through ongoing habitat loss (Rosario Avalos 2011). In Brazil, Swallow-tailed Cotinga is known from a reasonable number of privately and publicly protected areas, but it is perhaps easiest to see in Itatiaia and Serra dos Órgãos National Parks, Rio de Janeiro, or in Caraça Natural Park and at nearby Caeté, in Minas Gerais. However, appearances in Itatiaia can be sporadic, presumably linked to the availability of mistletoe at the time, and *the* sites to find this magnificent cotinga are probably Caraça, and Parque Estadual Intervales, both of which also support many other avian specialities of the Atlantic Forest. *Phibalura* is known from the following Important Bird Areas in Brazil by state (listed north to south): Bahia (three), Minas Gerais (three), Espírito Santo (three), Rio de Janeiro (four), São Paulo (four), Paraná (four) and Rio Grande do Sul (one) (Bencke *et al.* 2006).

REFERENCES Aleixo and Galetti (1997), Avalos (2007, 2009, 2011), Belton (1985, 1994), Bencke *et al.* (2006), BirdLife International (2000, 2004, 2008), Bodrati and Cockle (2006b), Bodrati *et al.* (2010), Boyla and Estrada (2005), Bromfield *et al.* (2004), Bushell (1996), Chapman (1926b, 1930), Clausi and Baarstch (2009), Dunning (2008), Fjeldså and Krabbe (1990), Fraga (1997), Gill and Wright (2006), Goeldi (1894), Gonzaga *et al.* (1995), Hayes (1995), Hellmayr (1929b), Hempel (1949), Hennessey (2002), Hidasi (2007), Hinkelmann and Fiebig (2001), Krabbe (1984, 2007), Krauczuk and Baldo (2004), Macarrão (2009), Maciel (2009), Magalhães (1999), Mallet-Rodrigues and Noronha (2009), Mallet-Rodrigues *et al.* (2007), Mazar Barnett and Pearman (2001), Parker and Goerck (1997), Parrini and Pacheco (2011), Parrini *et al.* (1999), Partridge (1954), Passamani and Mendes (2007), Pelzeln (1870), Piacenteni *et al.* (2006), Pimentel and Olmos (2011), Pineschi (1990), Pinto (1944, 1951), Pizo *et al.* (2002), Remsen *et al.* (2009), Ridgely and Tudor (1994, 2009), Rochido (2000), Rochido and Andrade (2000), Rochido *et al.* (2003), do Rosário (1996), Rosario Avalos (2010, 2011), Rupp *et al.* (2007), Saibene *et al.* (1996), Serpa and Gagliardi (2007), Sick (1997), Simon (2009), Snow (1976a, 1982, 2004a), Stotz *et al.* (1996), Straube *et al.* (2002), Torga *et al.* (in press), Vasconcelos and Melo Júnior (2001), Vasconcelos *et al.* (2002), Willis (2006), Willis and Oniki (2002).

Swallow-tailed Cotinga *Phibalura flavirostris*. **Fig. 1**. Male, *P. f. flavirostris*, RPPN Caraça, Minas Gerais, southeast Brazil, November (*Hadoram Shirihai / Photographic Handbook to Birds of the World*). The differences between the sexes are well illustrated in this photograph and the next. Males possess much blacker crowns, heavier and blacker throat and breast markings, forming a deep-gorgeted effect, blacker wing feathers and a deeper yellow throat patch, among other features (see text). **Fig. 2**. Female, *P. f. flavirostris*, RPPN Caraça, Minas Gerais, southeast Brazil, November (*Hadoram Shirihai / Photographic Handbook to Birds of the World*). The nominate subspecies is endemic to the Atlantic Forest. Few birds are perhaps so immediately identifiable. **Fig. 3**. Male, *P. f. flavirostris*, Teresópolis, Rio de Janeiro, southeast Brazil, November (*Arthur Grosset / www.arthurgrosset.com*). This bird is either a young male or less likely an adult in very fresh plumage such that the blacker markings of the head and breast appear duller and more reduced. **Fig. 4**. Flock, *P. f. flavirostris*, RPPN Caraça, Minas Gerais, southeast Brazil, August (*Pete Morris*). Along with the plantcutters, Swallow-tailed Cotinga is one of the few cotingas that form true flocks usually in the non-breeding season. This flock of nine birds certainly contains both adult males (the birds third and sixth from right) and adult females, but perhaps also juveniles.

BIBLIOGRAPHY

Abreu, C. R. M. & Mattos, G. T. 2004. Avifauna da Unidade Ambiental Volta Grande, Triângulo Mineiro, Minas Gerais. In: Congr. Bras. Orn. XII, Blumenau, *Resumos*: 128.

Abuja, C. M. 1975. Reproducción en cinco especies de aves del Occidente del Ecuador. *Rev. Univ. Católica Ecuador* 3: 167–183.

Accordi, I. A. & Barcellos, A. 2006. Composição da avifauna em oito áreas úmidas da bacia hidrográfica do Lago Guaíba, Rio Grande do Sul. *Rev. Bras. Orn.* 14: 101–115.

Acheson, N. & Davis, S. 2001. Birding in Parque Nacional Noel Kempff Mercado, Bolivia. *Cotinga* 16: 94–100.

Agro, D. J. & Ridgely, R. S. 1998. First record of the Striped Manakin *Machaeropterus regulus* in Guyana. *Bull. Brit. Orn. Club* 118: 122–123.

Aguiar, K. M. O., Naiff, R. H., Araújo, A. S., Campos, C. E. C. & Coltro, L. A. 2005. Dados biométricos de *Pipra aureola* (Pipridae) na Área de Proteção Ambiental do rio Curiaú, Macapá, Amapá, Brasil. In: Congr. Bras. Orn. XIII, Belém, *Resumos*: 188.

Aguiar, K. M. O., Naiff, R. H. & Xavier, B. 2010. Aves da Reserva Biológica do Lago Piratuba, Amapá, Brasil. *Ornitologia* 4: 1–14.

Aires, R. P., Ferreira, G. N., Silva, A. L. & Valle, N. C. 2008. Dieta do *Antilophia galeata* (Aves, Passeriformes: Pipridae) em quatro regiões de cerrado. In: Congr. Bras. Orn. XVI, Palmas, *Resumos*: 216.

Albano, C. 2010a. Birding in north-east Brazil, part 1: Ceará, Pernambuco, Alagoas and northern Bahia. *Neotrop. Birding* 6: 56–63.

Albano, C. 2010b. Birding in north-east Brazil, part 2: the vast state of Bahia. *Neotrop. Birding* 7: 49–61.

Albano, C. & Girão, W. 2008. Aves das matas úmidas das serras de Aratanha, Baturité e Maranguape, Ceará. *Rev. Bras. Orn.* 16: 142–154.

Albano, C. & Girão, W. 2009. Araripe Manakin *Antilophia bokermanni*. *Neotrop. Birding* 5: 71–74.

Aldrich, J. W. & Bole, B. P. 1937. The birds and mammals of the western Azuero Peninsula (Republic of Panama). *Sci. Publ. Cleveland Mus. Nat. Hist.* 7: 1–198.

Aleixo, A. 1997. Composition of mixed-species bird flocks and abundance of flocking species in a semideciduous forest of southeastern Brazil. *Ararajuba* 5: 11–18.

Aleixo, A. & Galetti, M. A. 1997. The conservation of the avifauna in a lowland Atlantic Forest in south-east Brazil. *Bird Conserv. Int.* 7: 235–261.

Aleixo, A. & Guilherme, E. 2008. Birds of Estação Ecológica do Rio Acre, on the Brazil/Peru border. In: Congr. Bras. Orn. XVI, Palmas, *Resumos*: 305.

Aleixo, A. & Guilherme, E. 2010. Avifauna da Estação Ecológica do Rio Acre, estado do Acre, na fronteira Brasil/Peru: composição, distribuição ecológica e registros relevantes. *Bol. Mus. Para. E. Goeldi Cienc. Nat.* 5: 279–309.

Aleixo, A., Poletto, F., Lima, M. F. C., Castro, M., Portes, E. & Sousa Miranda, L. 2011. Notes on the Vertebrates of northern Para, Brazil: a forgotten part of the Guianan Region, II. *Avifauna. Bol. Mus. Para. E. Goeldi Cienc. Nat.*, Belém 6: 11–65.

Alker, D., Prestel, D. & Schuchmann, K.-L. 1982. Biologie und Haltung der Schnurrvogel (Pipridae). *Trochilus* 3: 112–121.

Allen, J. A. 1893. On a collection of birds from Chapada, Matto Grosso, Brazil, by Mr. H. H. Smith. Part III. Pipridae to Rheidae. *Bull. Amer. Mus. Nat. Hist.* 5: 107–158.

Allen, J. A. 1905. Supplementary notes on birds collected in the Santa Marta District, Colombia, by Herbert H. Smith, with descriptions of nests and eggs. *Bull. Amer. Mus. Nat. Hist.* 21: 275–295.

Almeida, A. F. & Somenzari, M. 2005. Caracterização da avifauna do Parque Ibirapuera. In: Congr. Bras. Orn. XIII, Belém, *Resumos*: 117.

Almeida, A. C. C. & Teixeira, D. M. 1996. Sobre a biologia de *Procnias nudicollis* (Vieillot, 1817) (Aves, Cotingidae). In: Congr. Bras. Orn. V, Campinas, *Resumos*: 2.

Almeida, A., Couto, H. T. Z. & Almeida, A. F. 2003. Diversidade beta de aves em hábitats secundários da Pré-Amazônia maranhense e interação com modelos nulos. *Ararajuba* 11: 157–171.

Almeida, E. M., Von Matter, S. M. & Alves, M. A. S. 2000. Consumo de frutos por espécies de aves em *Psychotria brasiliensis* (Rubiaceae), em área de Mata Atlântica, Ilha Grande, Rio de Janeiro. In: Straube, F. C., Argel-de-Oliverira, M. M. & Cândido, J. F. (eds) *Ornitologia brasiliera no século XX*. Pp 360–361. Universidade do Sul de Santa Catarina & Sociedade Brasileira de Ornitologia, Curitiba.

Almeida, E. M., Costa, P. F., Buckeridge, M. S. & Alves, M. A. S. 2006. Potential bird dispersers of *Psychotria* in a [*sic*] area of Atlantic forest on Ilha Grande, RJ, southeastern Brazil: a biochemical analysis of the fruits. *Braz. J. Biol.* 66: 1–8.

Almeida, R. A. M. 2008. Novos registros de aves para o Parque Nacional do Jaú, Amazonas – Brasil. In: Congr. Bras. Orn. XVI, Palmas, *Resumos*: 368.

Alonso, J. M. & Virgolini, A. L. R. 2008. Avifauna del Parque Nacional Pre-Delta, Entre Ríos, Argentina. *Cotinga* 29: 126–134.

Alström, P. & Ranft, R. 2003. The use of sounds in avian systematics and the importance of bird sound archives. In: Collar, N. J., Fisher, C. T. & Feare, C. J. (eds) *Why Museums Matter: Avian Archives in an Age of Extinction. Bull. Brit. Orn. Club* Suppl. 123A.

Alteff, E., Damiani, R., Fonseca, P., Bernadon, B., Bessegatto, A., Amorim, S., Rezende, C., Jackson, B., Machado, E., Costacurta, M., Aparecida, G., Ferreira, L., Beuno, F., Valadão, R., Pascotto, M. M., Oliveira, D., Pinheiro, R., Lacerda, R., Fraxe, F. & Roos, A. 2009. Avifauna da Estação Ecológica Serra das Araras, Porto Estrela/Cáceres – MT: registros obtidos durante o curso regional de anilhamento de aves UFMT/CEMAVE, 2008. In: Simon, J. E., Raposo, M. A., Stopiglia, R. & Peres, J. (eds) *XVII Congresso Brasileiro de Ornitologia Resumos, Aracruz, ES: Biogeografia das aves da Mata Atlântica*: 94.

Alvarez, M., Caro, V., Laverde, O. & Cuervo, A. M. 2007. *Guía Sonora de las Aves de los Andes colombianos*. CDs. Banco de Sonidos, Instituto Alexander von Humboldt, Villa de Levya.

Alvarez Alonso, J. 2000. The breeding system of the Orange-crowned Manakin. *Condor* 102: 181–186.

Alvarez Alonso, J. 2001. The cryptic nest of the Orange-crowned Manakin *Heterocercus aurantiivertex*. *Cotinga* 16: 87–89.

Alvarez Alonso, J. 2002. Characteristic avifauna of white-sand forests in northern Peruvian Amazonia. MSc thesis, Louisiana State University, Baton Rouge.

Alvarez Alonso, J. & Whitney, B. M. 2003. New distributional records of birds from white-sand forests of the northern Peruvian Amazon, with implications for biogeography of northern South America. *Condor* 105: 552–566.

Alvarez del Toro, M. 1952. Contribución al conocimiento de la oología y nidología de las aves Chiapanecas. *Ateneo* 4: 11–21.

Álvarez-Rebolledo, M. 2000. *Cantos de Aves de la Cordillera Oriental de Colombia*. CD. Banco de Sonidos, Instituto Alexander von Humboldt, Villa de Levya.

Álvarez-Rebolledo, M. & Córdoba-Córdoba, S. 2002. *Guia Sonora de las Aves del Departamento de Caldas, Colombia*. CD. Instituto Alexander von Humboldt, Villa de Levya.

Alverson, W. S., Rodríguez, L. O. & Moskovits, D. K. (eds) 2001. *Perú: Biabo Cordillera Azul*. Rapid Biological Inventories Report 2. The Field Museum, Chicago.

Alves, M. A. S. & Vecchi, M. B. 2009. Birds, Ilha Grande, state of Rio de Janeiro, southeastern Brazil. *Check List* 5: 300–313.

Alves, M. A. S., Pimm, S. L., Stornia, A., Raposo, M. A., Brooke, M. de L., Harris, G., Foster, A. & Jenkins, C. N. 2008. Mapping and exploring the distribution of the Vulnerable grey-winged cotinga *Tijuca condita*. *Oryx* 42: 562–566.

Alves, M. A. S., Jenkins, C. N., Pimm, S. L., Stornia, A., Raposo, M. A., Brooke, M. de L., Harris, G. & Foster, A. 2009. Birds, montane forest, state of Rio de Janeiro, southeastern Brazil. *Check List* 5: 289–299.

Amaral, F. Q., Fernandes, A. M. & Rodrigues, M. 2003. Aves de um fragmento florestal do vale do Rio Doce. In: Machado, C. G. (ed.) *XI Congresso Brasileiro de Ornitologia Resumos, Feira de Santana, BA:* 161.

American Ornithologists' Union (AOU) 1983. *Check-list of North American Birds*, 6th edn. AOU, Washington, DC.

American Ornithologists' Union (AOU) 1998. *Check-list of North American Birds*, 7th edn. AOU, Washington, DC.

Ames, P. L. 1971. The morphology of the syrinx in passerine birds. *Bull. Peabody Mus. Nat. Hist.* 37: 1–194.

Anciães, M. 2007. Evolution of visual signals and ecological niches among manakins from the tribe Ilicurinii (Aves: Pipridae). *Abstracts VIII Neotrop. Orn. Congr., Maturín, Venezuela, mayo 13–19 2007:* 46.

Anciães, M. & Del Lama, S. N. 2002. Sex identification of Pin-tailed Manakins (*Ilicura militaris*: Pipridae) using the polymerase chain reaction and its application to behavioral studies. *Orn. Neotrop.* 13: 159–165.

Anciães, M. & Prum, R. O. 2008. Manakin display and visiting behaviour: a comparative test of sensory drive. *Anim. Behav.* 75: 783–790.

Anciães, M. & Straube, F. C. 1997. A relação entre altitude e latitude na distribuição de *Ilicura militaris* (Pipridae, Passeriformes). In: Congr. Bras. Orn. VI, Belo Horizonte, *Resumos:* 155.

Anciães, M. & Peterson, A. T. 2006. Climate change effects on Neotropical manakin diversity based on ecological niche modelling. *Condor* 108: 778–791.

Anciães, M. & Peterson, A. T. 2009. Ecological niches and their evolution among Neotropical manakins (Aves: Pipridae). *J. Avian Biol.* 40: 591–604.

Anciães, M., Sebaio, F. & Marini, M. Â. 2000. Um caso de variação na plumagem de *Ilicura militaris* (Pipridae, Passeriformes). In: Straube, F. C., Argel-de-Oliverira, M. M. & Cândido, J. F. (eds) *Ornitologia brasileira no século XX*. Pp. 277–279. Universidade do Sul de Santa Catarina & Sociedade Brasileira de Ornitologia, Curitiba.

Anciães, M., Coelho, M. M. & Chaves-Cordeiro, P. H. 2001. Records for the Elegant Mourner (*Laniisoma elegans*) in forest fragments of Minas Gerais state, Brazil. *Melopsittacus* 4: 44–46.

Anciães, M., Nemésio, A. & Sebaio, F. 2005. A case of plumage aberration in the Pin-tailed Manakin *Ilicura militaris*. *Cotinga* 23: 39–43.

Anciães, M., Fernandes, M. H. & Peterson, A. T. 2010. Distribution and diversity of Neotropical manakins under paleoclimates predicted by ecological niche modeling: the interplay among interglacial and glacial periods. In: Miyaki, C. M., Höfling, E. & Donatelli, R. J. (eds) *Abstracts 25th Int. Orn. Congr., Campos do Jordão, Brazil, 22–28 August 2010:* 426.

Anderson, D. L., Bonta, M. & Thorn, P. 1998. New and noteworthy bird records from Honduras. *Bull. Brit. Orn. Club* 118: 178–183.

Anderson, D. L., Wiedenfeld, D. A., Bechard, M. J. & Novak, S. J. 2004. Avian diversity in the Moskitia region of Honduras. *Orn. Neotrop.* 15: 447–482.

Andrade, M. A. 1996. Observaciones sobre el pajaro torero (*Pyroderus s. scutatus*) en el Brasil. *Bol. Soc. Antioqueña Orn.* 7: 8–12.

Andrle, R. F. 1967. The birds of the Sierra de Tuxtla in Veracruz, Mexico. *Wilson Bull.* 79: 163–187.

Angehr, G. 2000. Red Data bird: Yellow-billed Cotinga. *World Birdwatch* 22(2): 24–25.

Angehr, G. R. & Christian, D. G. 2000. Distributional records from the highlands of the Serranía de Majé, an isolated mountain range in eastern Panama. *Bull. Brit. Orn. Club* 120: 173–178.

Angehr, G. R. & Dean, R. 2010. *The Birds of Panama: A Field Guide*. Cornell University Press, Ithaca, NY.

Angehr, G. R. & Jordán, O. 1998. *Report on the Panama Important Bird Areas Program*. Panama Audubon Society/BirdLife International, Ancon.

Angehr, G. R., Christian, D. G. & Aparicio, K. M. 2004. A survey of the Serranía de Jungurudó, an isolated mountain range in eastern Panama. *Bull. Brit. Orn. Club* 124: 51–62.

Anjos, L. & Boçon, R. 1999. Bird communities in natural forest patches in southern Brazil. *Wilson Bull.* 111: 397–414.

Anjos, L. & Graf, V. 1993. Riqueza de aves da Fazenda Santa Rita, região dos Campos Gerais, Palmeira, Paraná, Brasil. *Rev. Bras. Zool.* 10: 673–693.

Anjos, L., Schuchmann, K.-L. & Berndt, R. 1997. Avifaunal composition, species richness, and status in the Tibagi river basin, Paraná state, southern Brazil. *Orn. Neotrop.* 8: 145–173.

Anon. 1982. Balz der Fadenpipra (*Pipra filicauda*). *Trochilus* 3: 21.

Antas, P. T. Z. 2004. *Pantanal: Guia de Aves*. SESC, Rio de Janeiro.

Antas, P. T. Z., Sartório, R. C., Joenck, C. M., Mendonça-Lima, A., Silveira, A. B., Accordi, I. A., Scopel, E. T., Pereira, M. A. & Alves, M. K. L. 2007. Monitoramento da avifauna nos plantios e áreas de conservação da Aracruz Celulose. In: Fontana, C. S. (ed.) *XV Congresso Brasileiro de Ornitologia Resumos, Porto Alegre, RS:* 70.

Antas, P. T. Z., Sartório, R. C., Scopel, E. T., Pereira, M. A., Pissinati, J. F. & Lima, S. 2009. Areas de preservação permanente como vias de conexão para aves na Mata Atlântica de baixada, municípios de Aracruz e Serra, ES. In: Simon, J. E., Raposo, M. A., Stopiglia, R. & Peres, J. (eds) *XVII Congresso Brasileiro de Ornitologia Resumos, Aracruz, ES: Biogeografia das aves da Mata Atlântica:* 25.

Antonini, R. D. & Piratelli, A. 2005. Frugivoria por aves em *Miconia cinnamifolia* em área de floresta Atlântica na Ilha da Marambaia (RJ). In: Congr. Bras. Orn. XIII, Belém, *Resumos:* 174.

Antonini, R. D., Ritter, P. D., Almeida, E. & Alves, M. A. S. 2000. Observações de aves em *Miconia prasina* (Melastomataceae) em uma área de Mata Atlântica, Ilha Grande, Rio de Janeiro. In: Straube, F. C., Argel-de-Oliverira, M. M. & Cândido, J. F. (eds) *Ornitologia brasileira no século XX*. Pp. 357–358. Universidade do Sul de Santa Catarina & Sociedade Brasileira de Ornitologia, Curitiba.

Antunes, A. Z. 2005. Alterações na composição da comunidade de aves ao longo do tempo em um fragmento florestal do sudeste do Brasil. *Ararajuba* 13: 47–61.

Arango, C. S. 1990. Aspectos morfológicos y de comportamiento de las aves frugivoras y su efectividad como dispersoras de semillas en la Reserva Biológica de Carpanta (Cundinamarca, Colombia). Unpubl. thesis, Pontificia Universidad Javeriana, Bogotá.

Araujo, H. F. P., Rodrigues, R. C. & Nishida, A. K. 2006. Composição da avifauna em complexos estuarinos no Estado do Paraíba, Brasil. *Rev. Bras. Orn.* 14: 249–259.

Araujo Gussoni, C. O., Camargo Guaraldo, G. L. A., Cesar Costa, J., Guedes, J., Rodrigues Alves, J., Pedrassoli, S., Andrade Figueiredo, L. F. & Essington Brown, T. 2005. Nova ocorrência do "rei-dos-tangaras", em Corumbatai, Estado de São Paulo, Brasil. *Atualidades Orn.* 128: 8–9.

Arévalo, J. E. & Heeb, P. 2005. Ontogeny of sexual dimorphism in the Long-tailed Manakin *Chiroxiphia linearis*: long maturation of display trait morphology. *Ibis* 147: 697–705.

Armacost, J. W. 2006. Birds of a palm-dominated *terra firme* forest: the contribution of habitat heterogeneity to regional avian diversity. *Cotinga* 25: 33–37.

Assumpção, A. 1985. Observações sobre a reprodução do tangará dançarino em cativeiro. *SO Bol.* 6: 13–16.

Avalos, V. del R. 2007. Biología reproductiva de la Palkachupa (*Phibalura flavirostris boliviana*, Cotingidae), ave amenazada del norte de La Paz, Bolivia. Thesis, Universidad Mayor de San Andrés, La Paz.

Avalos, V. del R. 2009. Aspectos del comportamiento de forrajeo de *Phibalura flavirostris boliviana* (Cotingidae, Passeriformes). *Ecol. Bolivia* 44: 62–66.

Avalos, V. del R. 2011. Biparental care and nesting success of the Swallow-tailed Cotinga in northwestern Bolivia. *Wilson J. Orn.* 123: 251–258.

Aversa, T. & Vallely, A. C. 1999. A nest of the Scarlet-breasted Fruiteater *Pipreola frontalis* in eastern Ecuador. *Cotinga* 12: 70.

Awade, M., Boscolo, D., Develey, P. F. & Metzger, J. P. 2003. O efeito de estradas na movimentação do Tangará (*Chiroxiphia caudata*). In: Machado, C. G. (ed.) *XI Congresso Brasileiro de Ornitologia Resumos*, Feira de Santana, BA: 37.

Azevedo Júnior, S. M., Nascimento, J. L. X. & Nascimento, I. L. S. 2000. Novos registros de ocorrência de *Antilophia bokermanni* Coelho & Silva, 1999 na Chapada do Araripe, Ceará, Brasil. *Ararajuba* 8: 133–134.

Azpiroz, A. & Rodríguez-Ferraro, A. 2006. Noteworthy observations of the birds of Falcón state, northwestern Venezuela. *Orn. Neotrop.* 17: 445–451.

Babarskas, M. & Flombaum, P. 1998. Nuevos registros de aves para la provincia de Chubut, Argentina. *Nuestras Aves* 38: 13–14.

Babarskas, M., Viega, J. & Filiberto, F. 1996. Nuevos registros de aves para la provincia de Neuquén. *Nuestras Aves* 34: 44–46.

Balchin, C. S. & Toyne, E. P. 1998. The avifauna and conservation status of the Río Nangaritza valley, southern Ecuador. *Bird Conserv. Int.* 8: 237–253.

Bandeira, R. S., Rego, P. S., Aleixo, A., Schneider, H., Sampaio, I. & Vallinoto, M. 2008. *Lepidothrix vilasboasi* (Sick, 1959): espécie válida? Uso de marcadores moleculares no estudo de uma ave amazônica, endêmica e ameaçada. In: Congr. Bras. Genética 54, Salvador, *Resumos*: 148.

Bangs, O. & Barbour, T. 1922. Birds from Darien. *Bull. Mus. Comp. Zool. Harvard* 65: 191–229.

Bangs, O. & Peters, J. L. 1928. A collection of birds from Oaxaca. *Bull. Mus. Comp. Zool. Harvard* 68: 385–404.

Barber, B. R. & Rice, N. H. 2007. Systematics and evolution in the Tityrinae (Passeriformes: Tyrannoidea). *Auk* 124: 1317–1329.

Barnes, R., Butchart, S. H. M., Davies, C. W. N., Fernández, M. & Seddon, N. 1997. New distributional information on eight bird species from northern Peru. *Bull. Brit. Orn. Club* 117: 69–74.

Barnés, V. 1955. A new form of *Corapipo* from Cerro Marahuaca, Amazonas, Venezuela. *Auk* 72: 412–413.

Barnett, A., Shapley, R., Benjamin, P., Henry, E. & McGarrell, M. 2002. Birds of the Potaro Plateau, with eight new species for Guyana. *Cotinga* 18: 19–36.

Barnett, J. R., Stenzler, L. M., Ruiz-Gutierrez, V., Bogdanowicz, S. M. & Lovette, I. J. 2008. Isolation and characterization of microsatellite markers from the white-ruffed manakin *Corapipo altera* (Aves, Pipridae). *Mol. Ecol. Res.* 8: 215–218.

Barrowclough, G. F. 1982. Geographic variation, predictiveness, and subspecies. *Auk* 99: 601–603.

Barrowclough, G. F., Escalante-Pliego, P., Aveledo-Hostos, R. & Perez-Chinchilla, L. A. 1995. An annotated list of the birds of the Cerro Tamacuarí region, Serranía de Tapirapecó, Federal Territory of Amazonas, Venezuela. *Bull. Brit. Orn. Club* 115: 211–219.

Barrowclough, G. F., Lentino R., M. & Sweet, P. R. 1997. New records of birds from Auyán-tepui, Estado Bolívar, Venezuela. *Bull. Brit. Orn. Club* 117: 194–198.

Bartholomew, G. A., Vleck, C. M. & Bucher, T. L. 1983. Energy metabolism and nocturnal hypothermia in two tropical passerine frugivores, *Manacus vitellinus* and *Pipra mentalis*. *Physiol. Zool.* 56: 370–379.

Bates, J. M., Garvin, M. C., Schmitt, D. C. & Schmitt, C. G. 1989. Notes on bird distribution in northeastern Dpto. Santa Cruz, Bolivia, with 15 species new to Bolivia. *Bull. Brit. Orn. Club* 109: 236–244.

Bates, J. M., Parker, T. A., Capparella, A. P. & Davis, T. J. 1992. Observations on the *campo, cerrado* and forest avifaunas of eastern Dpto. Santa Cruz, Bolivia, including 21 species new to the country. *Bull. Brit. Orn. Club* 112: 86–98.

Bates, J. M., Stotz, D. F. & Schulenberg, T. S. 1998. Avifauna of Parque Nacional Noel Kempff Mercado. In: Killeen, T. J. & Schulenberg, T. S. (eds) *A Biological Assessment of Parque Nacional Noel Kempff Mercado, Bolivia.* RAP Working Papers 10. Conservation International, Washington, DC.

Bauer, C. 1999. Padrões atuais de distribuição de aves florestais na região sul do Estado do Espírito Santo, Brasil. *Atualidades Orn.* 88: 2.

Bauer, C. & Pacheco, J. F. 2000. Lista das aves da região de Visconde de Mauá, Serra da Mantiqueira, no limite dos Estados do Rio de Janeiro e Minas Gerais. *Atualidades Orn.* 97: 7.

Bauer, C., Pacheco, J. F., Venturini, A. C. & Whitney, B. M. 2000. Rediscovery of the Cherry-throated Tanager *Nemosia rourei* in southern Espírito Santo, Brazil. *Bird Conserv. Int.* 10: 97–108.

Beavers, R. A., Delaney, D. A., Leahy, C. W. & Oatman, G. F. 1991. New and noteworthy bird records from Petén, Guatemala, including Tikal National Park. *Bull. Brit. Orn. Club* 111: 77–90.

Becker, C. D. & Agreda, A. 2005. Bird community differences in mature and second growth garúa forest in Machalilla National Park, Ecuador. *Orn. Neotrop.* 16: 297–319.

Becker, C. D. & López Lanús, B. 1997. A bird survey in Reserva Ecológica de Loma Alta, Ecuador. *Cotinga* 8: 66–74.

Beebe, C. W. 1909. An ornithological reconnaissance of northeastern Venezuela. *Zoologica* 3: 69–114.

Beebe, C. W. 1915. Birds of Para, Brazil. *Zoologica* 2(3): 55–106.

Beebe, W. 1924. The rarest of nests on the tallest of grass stems. *Bull. NY Zool. Soc.* 27: 114–117.

Beebe, W. 1954. Discovered.—The nest and egg of the Black-winged Bell-bird. *Anim. Kingd.* 57: 115–118.

Beebe, M. & Beebe, W. 1910. *Our Search for a Wilderness.* Henry Holt & Co., New York.

Beebe, W., Hartley, G. I. & Howes, P. G. 1917. *Tropical Wild Life in British Guiana.* New York Zoological Society, New York.

Begazo, A. J., Valqui, T., Sokol, M. & Langlois, E. 2001. Notes on some birds from central and northern Peru. *Cotinga* 15: 81–87.

Belcher, C. & Smooker, G. D. 1937. Birds of the colony of Trinidad and Tobago. Part V. Pipridae–Tyrannidae. *Ibis* (14)1: 225–249.

Belmonte-Lopes, R., Maurício, G. N. & Bornschein, M. R. in press. Description of the nest and egg of an Atlantic Forest endemic, the Black-headed Berryeater, *Carpornis melanocephala* (Cotingidae). *Wilson J. Orn.*

Belton, W. 1978. Supplementary list of new birds for Rio Grande do Sul, Brazil. *Auk* 95: 413–415.

Belton, W. 1985. Birds of Rio Grande do Sul, Brazil part 2: Formicariidae through Corvidae. *Bull. Amer. Mus. Nat. Hist.* 180.

Belton, W. 1994. *Aves do Rio Grande do Sul: Distribuição e Biologia.* Ed. UNISINOS, São Leopoldo.

Benalcázar, C. E. & Benalcázar, F. 1984. Historia natural del gallo de roca andino (*Rupicola peruviana sanguinolenta*). *Cespedesia* 13: 59–92.

Bencke, G. A. 2001. *Lista de Referência das Aves do Rio Grande do Sul.* Fundação Zoobotânica do Rio Grande do Sul, Porto Alegre.

Bencke, G. A. & Kindel, A. 1999. Bird counts along an altitudinal gradient of Atlantic Forest in northeastern Rio Grande do Sul. *Ararajuba* 7: 91–107.

Bencke, G. A., Kindel, A. & Mahler, J. K. 2000. Adições a avifauna de Mata Atlântica do Rio Grande do Sul. In: Alves, M. A. S., Silva, J. M. C., Sluys, M. van, Bergallo, H. G. & Rocha, C. F. D. (eds) *A Ornitologia no Brasil: Pesquisa Atual e Perspectivas.* Pp. 317–323. Ed. Universidade Estadual Rio de Janeiro, Rio de Janeiro.

Bencke, G. A., Maurício, G. N., Develey, P. F. & Goerck, J. M. 2006. *Áreas Importantes para a Conservação das Aves no Brasil Parte I — Estados do Domínio da Mata Atlântica.* SAVE Brasil, São Paulo.

Béraut, E. 1970. The nesting of *Gymnoderus foetidus. Ibis* 112: 256.

van den Berg, A. B. & Bosman, C. A. W. 1984. Range extensions and rare records of birds in Ecuador. *Bull. Brit. Orn. Club* 104: 152–154.

Berg, K. S. 2000. Field notes on the biology of the Long-wattled Umbrellabird *Cephalopterus penduliger* in west Ecuador. *Cotinga* 14: 26–29.

Berg, S. B. & Abreu, T. L. S. 2004. Monitoramento da avifauna da APA do Gama e Cabeça de Veado, Brasília. In: Congr. Bras. Orn. XII, Blumenau, *Resumos*: 162.

Berla, H. F. 1944. Lista das aves colecionadas em Pedra Branca,

Município de Parati, Estado do Rio de Janeiro, com algumas notas sobre sua biologia. *Bol. Mus. Nac., Rio de Janeiro* 18: 1–21.

Berla, H. F. 1946. Lista das aves colecionadas em Pernambuco, com descrição de uma subespécie n., de um alótipo e notas de campo. *Bol. Mus. Nac., Rio de Janeiro* 65: 1–35.

Berlepsch, H. G. 1908. On the birds of Cayenne. Part 1. *Novit. Zool.* 15: 103–164.

Berlepsch, H. & Hartert, E. 1902. On the birds of the Orinoco region. *Novit. Zool.* 9: 1–134.

Bernard, E. (ed.) 2008. Inventários biológicos rápidos no Parque Nacional Montanhas do Tumucumaque, Amapá, Brasil. *RAP Bull. Biol. Assessment* 48. Conservation International, Arlington, VA.

Bernardi, I. P., Teixeira, E. M. & Jacomassa, F. A. F. 2007. Registros relevantes para a avifauna do médio alto Uruguai, Rio Grande do Sul. In: Fontana, C. S. (ed.) *XV Congresso Brasileiro de Ornitologia Resumos, Porto Alegre, RS*: 70.

Berres, M. E. 2002. Long-term persistence of White-bearded Manakin (*Manacus manacus*) leks in the Arima Valley of Trinidad, West Indies. *Occ. Pap. Dept. Life Sci., Univ. West Indies* 11: 131–137.

Berry, R. J., Todd, W. & Plasse, R. 1982. Breeding the scarlet cock-of-the-rock *Rupicola peruviana* at the Houston Zoological Gardens. *Int. Zoo Yearbook* 22: 171–175.

Berv, J. S. & Zyskowski, K. 2010. Mitochondrial DNA sequence data help to elucidate the ancestry and genetic differentiation of South American savanna birds. In: Miyaki, C. M., Höfling, E. & Donatelli, R. J. (eds) *Abstracts 25th Int. Orn. Congr., Campos do Jordão, Brazil, 22–28 August 2010*: 831.

Best, B. J. & Kessler, M. 1995. *Biodiversity and Conservation in Tumbesian Ecuador and Peru.* BirdLife International, Cambridge, UK.

Best, B. J., Clarke, C. T., Checker, M., Broom, A. L., Thewlis, R. M., Duckworth, W. & McNab, A. 1993. Distributional records, natural history notes, and conservation of some poorly known birds from southwestern Ecuador and northwestern Peru. *Bull. Brit. Orn. Club* 113: 234–255.

Bierregaard, R. O., Stotz, D. F., Harper, L. H. & Powell, G. V. N. 1987. Observations on the occurrence and behaviour of the Crimson Fruitcrow *Haematoderus militaris* in Central Amazonia. *Bull. Brit. Orn. Club* 107: 134–137.

Binford, L. C. 1989. *A Distributional Survey of the Birds of the Mexican State of Chiapas. Orn. Monogr.* 43: 1–418.

BirdLife International 2000. *Threatened Birds of the World.* Lynx Edicions, Barcelona & BirdLife International, Cambridge, UK.

BirdLife International 2004. *Threatened Birds of the World 2004.* CD-ROM. BirdLife International, Cambridge, UK.

BirdLife International 2008. *Threatened Birds of the World 2008.* CD-ROM. BirdLife International, Cambridge, UK.

Blake, E. R. 1950. Birds of the Acary Mountains southern British Guiana. *Fieldiana Zool.* 32: 419–474.

Blake, E. R. 1958. Birds of Volcán de Chiriquí, Panama. *Fieldiana Zool.* 36: 499–577.

Blake, E. R. 1961. Notes on a collection of birds from northeastern Colombia. *Fieldiana Zool.* 44: 25–44.

Blake, E. R. 1962. Birds of the Sierra Macarena, eastern Colombia. *Fieldiana Zool.* 44: 69–112.

Blake, J. G. 2007. Neotropical forest bird communities: a comparison of species richness and composition at local and regional scales. *Condor* 109: 237–255.

Blake, J. G. & Loiselle, B. A. 2001. Bird assemblages in second-growth and old-growth forests, Costa Rica: perspectives from mist nets and point counts. *Auk* 118: 304–326.

Blake, J. G. & Loiselle, B. A. 2002. Manakins (Pipridae) in second-growth and old-growth forests: patterns of habitat use, movement, and survival. *Auk* 119: 132–148.

Blake, J. G. & Loiselle, B. A. 2008. Estimates of apparent survival rates for forest birds in eastern Ecuador. *Biotropica* 40: 485–493.

Blake, J. G. & Loiselle, B. A. 2009. Species composition of Neotropical understory bird communities: local versus regional perspectives based on capture data. *Biotropica* 41: 85–94.

Blamires, D., Diniz-Filho, J. A. F., Sant'ana, C. E. R. & Valgas, A. B. 2002. Relação entre abundância e tamanho do corpo em uma comunidade de aves no Brasil Central. *Ararajuba* 10: 1–14.

Blendinger, B. G., Loiselle, B. A. & Blake, J. G. 2008. Crop size, plant aggregation, and microhabitat type affect fruit removal by birds from individual melastome plants in the Upper Amazon. *Oecologia* 158: 273–283.

Bloch, H., Poulsen, M. K., Rahbek, C. & Rasmussen, J. F. 1991. *A Survey of the Montane Forest Avifauna of the Loja Province, Southern Ecuador.* ICBP Study Report 49. International Council for Bird Preservation, Cambridge, UK.

Bock, W. J. 1994. History and nomenclature of avian family-group names. *Bull. Amer. Mus. Nat. Hist.* 222: 1–281.

Bodrati, A. & Cockle, K. 2006a. New records of rare and threatened birds from the Atlantic Forest of Misiones, Argentina. *Cotinga* 26: 20–24.

Bodrati, A. & Cockle, K. 2006b. Habitat, distribution, and conservation of Atlantic Forest birds in Argentina: notes on nine rare or threatened species. *Orn. Neotrop.* 17: 243–258.

Bodrati, A., Lammertick, M. & Segovia, J. M. 2009a. El Bailarín Castaño (*Piprites pileata*) está en la Reserva Natural Cultural Papel Misionero, provincia de Misiones, Argentina. *Nuestras Aves* 54: 76–78.

Bodrati, A., Maders, C., Di Santo, G., Cockle, K., Areta, J. I. & Segovia, J. M. 2009b. Distribución, hábitat, y historia natural del Bailarín Castaño *Piprites pileata*, una especie Críticamente Amenazada en Argentina. *Cotinga* 31: 95–100.

Bodrati, A., Cockle, K., Segovia, J. M., Roesler, I., Areta, J. I. & Jordan, E. 2010. La avifauna del Parque Provincial Cruce Caballero, Provincia de Misiones, Argentina. *Cotinga* 32: 41–64.

Boesing, A. L., Corrêa, L., Woldan, D. R. H. & Bazílio, S. 2007. Registros de aves raras na região sudoeste do Paraná, Brasil. In: Fontana, C. S. (ed.) *XV Congresso Brasileiro de Ornitologia Resumos, Porto Alegre, RS*: 205–206.

Boesman, P. 1995. Caño Colorado: a lowland tropical forest in north-east Venezuela. *Cotinga* 3: 31–34.

Boesman, P. 1998. Some new information on the distribution of Venezuelan birds. *Cotinga* 9: 27–37.

Boesman, P. 1999. *Birds of Venezuela.* DVD-ROM. Westernieland, Bird Sounds International.

Boesman, P. 2006a. *Birds of Brazil.* MP3 CD. Winsum, Birdsounds. nl.

Boesman, P. 2006b. *Birds of Venezuela.* MP3 CD. Winsum, Birdsounds.nl.

Boesman, P. 2006c. *Birds of Mexico.* MP3 CD. Winsum, Birdsounds. nl.

Boesman, P. 2009. *Birds of Peru.* MP3 CD. Winsum, Birdsounds. nl.

Bohórquez, C. I. 2003. Mixed-species bird flocks in a montane cloud forest of Colombia. *Orn. Neotrop.* 14: 67–78.

Bond, J. 1956. Additional notes on Peruvian birds II. *Proc. Acad. Nat. Sci. Philadelphia* 108: 227–247.

Bond, J. & Meyer de Schauensee, R. 1942. The birds of Bolivia. Part I. *Proc. Acad. Nat. Sci. Philadelphia* 94: 307–391.

Borchardt-Júnior, C. A. & Zimmermann, C. E. 2000. Levantamento preliminar da avifauna do Morro Azul, Timbó, Santa Catarina. In: Straube, F. C., Argel-de-Oliverira, M. M. & Cândido, J. F. (eds) *Ornitologia brasileira no século XX*. Pp. 207–208. Universidade do Sul de Santa Catarina & Sociedade Brasileira de Ornitologia, Curitiba.

Borchardt-Junior, C. A., Veber, L. M. & Zimmermann, C. E. 2004. Primeiros registros de *Laniisoma elegans* (Thunberg, 1823) e *Catharus ustulatus* (Nuttall, 1840) em Santa Catarina. In: Congr. Bras. Orn. XII, Blumenau, *Resumos*: 173.

Borges, S. H. 1994. Listagem e novos registros de aves para a região de Boa Vista, Roraima, Brasil. *Bol. Mus. Para. E. Goeldi, Sér. Zool.* 10: 191–202.

Borges, S. H. 2007. Análise biogeográfica da avifauna da região oeste do baixo Rio Negro, amazônia brasileira. *Rev. Bras. Zool.* 24: 919–940.

Borges, S. H., Cohn-Haft, M., Carvalhaes, A. M. P., Henriques, L. M., Pacheco, J. F. & Whittaker, A. 2001. Birds of Jaú National

Park, Brazilian Amazon: species check-list, biogeography and conservation. *Orn. Neotrop.* 12: 109–140.

Boss, R. L. & Aguiar, K. M. O. 2008. Levantamento da avifauna na área de influência direta da Pequena Central Hidrelétrica (PCH) Capivara – Rio Amaparí – AP. In: Congr. Bras. Orn. XVI, Palmas, *Resumos*: 363.

Bostwick, K. S. 2000. Display behaviors, mechanical sounds, and evolutionary relationships of the Club-winged Manakin (*Machaeropterus deliciosus*). *Auk* 117: 465–478.

Bostwick, K. S. 2010. Feathers are pre-adapted for sound production. In: Miyaki, C. M., Höfling, E. & Donatelli, R. J. (eds) *Abstracts 25th Int. Orn. Congr., Campos do Jordão, Brazil, 22–28 August 2010*: 357.

Bostwick, K. S. & Prum, R. O. 2003. High-speed video analysis of wing-snapping in two manakin clades (Pipridae: Aves). *J. Experiment. Biol.* 206: 3693–3706.

Bostwick, K. S., Elias, D. O., Mason, A. & Montealegre-Z., F. 2010. Resonating feathers produce courtship song. *Proc. Roy. Soc. Lond. B* 277: 835–841.

Botêlho, M. C. N., Rodrigues, R. C. & Amaral, A. C. A. 2003. Ectoparasitos em *Pipra fasciicauda* Hellmayr, 1906 (Pipridae) na Área de Proteção Ambiental do Maciço do Baturité, CE. In: Machado, C. G. (ed.) *XI Congresso Brasileiro de Ornitologia Resumos, Feira de Santana, BA*: 137.

Boyla, K. A. & Estrada, A. (eds) 2005. *Áreas importantes para la conservación de las aves en los Andes tropicales: sitios prioritarios para la conservación de la biodiversidad.* BirdLife International & Conservation International, Quito.

Boyle, W. A., Norris, D. R. & Guglielmo, C. G. 2010. Storms drive altitudinal migration in a tropical bird. *Proc. Roy. Soc. Lond. B*: doi: 10.1098/rspb.2010.0344.

Brace, R. C. & Hornbuckle, J. 1998. Distributional records of and identification notes on birds of the Beni Biological Station, Beni, Bolivia. *Bull. Brit. Orn. Club* 118: 36–47.

Brace, R. C., Hornbuckle, J. & Pearce-Higgins, J. W. 1997. The avifauna of the Beni Biological Station, Bolivia. *Bird Conserv. Int.* 7: 117–159.

Bradley, R. S., Vuille, M., Diaz, H. F. & Vergara, W. 2006. Threats to water supplies in the tropical Andes. *Science* 312: 1755–1756.

Bradshaw, C. G. & Kirwan, G. M. 1995. A description of the nest of Fiery-capped Manakin *Machaeropterus pyrocephalus* from northern Bolívar, Venezuela. *Cotinga* 4: 30–31.

Brandt, C. S., Zimmermann, C. E., Laps, R. R., Testoni, C., Grüener, C. G., Dallacorte, F., Vegini, G. A. M., Cordeiro, L. & Saviato, M. J. 2005. Endemismos de Mata Atlântica na composição da avifauna de uma área particular de floresta ombrófila densa de encosta em Gaspar (SC). In: Congr. Bras. Orn. XIII, Belém, *Resumos*: 143.

Braun, M. J., Finch, D. W., Robbins, M. B. & Schmidt, B. K. 2007. *A Field Checklist of the Birds of Guyana*, 2nd edn. National Museum of Natural History, Washington, DC.

Brawn, J. D., Karr, J. R. & Nichols, J. D. 1995. Demography of birds in a Neotropical forest: effects of allometry, taxonomy, and ecology. *Ecology* 76: 41–51.

Braz, V. S. & Cavalcanti, R. B. 2001. A representatividade de áreas protegidas do Distrito Federal na conservação da avifauna do Cerrado. *Ararajuba* 9: 61–69.

Breitwisch, R. & Pliske, M. 1974. Anthurium fruit as a food of the White-bearded Manakins. *Ibis* 116: 365.

Bromfield, G., Ritchie, W. N., Bromfield, V., Ritchie, J. & Hennessey, A. B. 2004. New information on plumage, nesting, behaviour and vocalisations of the Bolivian Swallow-tailed Cotinga *Phibalura flavirostris boliviana* from the Apolo area of Madidi National Park. *Cotinga* 21: 63–67.

Brooke, M., Scott, D. A. & Teixeira, D. M. 1983. Some observations made at the first recorded nest of the Sharpbill *Oxyruncus cristatus*. *Ibis* 125: 259–261.

Brooks, D. M., Pando-Vasquez, L. & Ocmin-Petit, A. 1999. Comparative life history of cotingas in the northern Peruvian Amazon. *Orn. Neotrop.* 10: 193–206.

Brooks, D. M., O'Neill, J. P., Foster, M. S., Mark, T., Dauphiné, N. & Franke, I. J. 2009. Avifauna of the Pongos Basin, Amazonas Department, Peru. *Wilson J. Orn.* 121: 54–74.

Browne, P. W. P. 2005. The birds of Parati, south-east Brazil. *Cotinga* 24: 85–98.

Brumfield, R. T. 1999. Evolution of brilliant male plumage traits in *Manacus*. PhD dissertation, University of Maryland, College Park, MD.

Brumfield, R. T. & Braun, M. J. 2001. Phylogenetic relationships in bearded manakins (Pipridae: *Manacus*) indicate that male plumage color is a misleading taxonomic marker. *Condor* 103: 248–258.

Brumfield, R. T., Jernigan, R. W., McDonald, D. B. & Braun, M. J. 2001. Evolutionary implications of divergent clines in an avian (*Manacus*: Aves) hybrid zone. *Evolution* 55: 2070–2087.

Brumfield, R. T., Liu, L., Lum, D. E. & Edwards, S. V. 2008. Comparison of species tree methods for reconstructing the phylogeny of bearded manakins (Aves: Pipridae: *Manacus*) from multilocus sequence data. *Syst. Biol.* 57: 719–731.

Brush, A. H. 1969. On the nature of "cotingin". *Condor* 71: 431–433.

Bryce, R., Hennessey, A. B., MacLeod, R., Evans, K., Ewing, S. R., Herzog, S. K., Maccormick, A. & Gomez, M. I. 2005. First sound recordings, new behavioural and distributional records, and a review of the status of Scimitar-winged Piha *Lipaugus uropygialis*. *Cotinga* 24: 102–106.

Bucher, T. L. & Worthington, A. 1982. Nocturnal hypothermia and oxygen consumption in manakins. *Condor* 84: 327–331.

Bueno, B., Castro, S. L. R., Oliveira, M. T. & Bomediano, L. 2008. Levantamento de aves em fragmentos florestais na região de Dourados – MS. In: Congr. Bras. Orn. XVI, Palmas, *Resumos*: 248.

Bugoni, L., Mohr, L. V., Scherer, A., Efe, M. A. & Scherer, S. B. 2002. Biometry, molt and brood patch parameters of birds in southern Brazil. *Ararajuba* 10: 85–94.

Burmeister, H. 1856. *Systematische Uebersicht der Thiere Brasiliens welche während einer Reise durch die Provinzen von Rio de Janeiro und Minas Geraes gesammelt oder beobachtet wurden von Dr. Hermann Burmeister.* Bd. 2. Georg Reimer, Berlin.

Burton, P. J. K. 1975. Passerine bird weights from Panama and Colombia, with some notes on 'soft-part' colours. *Bull. Brit. Orn. Club* 95: 82–86.

Burton, P. J. K. 1976. Structure and histology of the wattle in the White Bellbird (*Procnias alba*). *J. Zool. Lond.* 178: 285–293.

Bushell, C. 1996. Photo spot: Swallow-tailed Cotinga *Phibalura flavirostris*. *Cotinga* 6: 75–76.

Butchart, S. H. M. & Bird, J. P. 2010. Data Deficient birds on the IUCN Red List: what we don't know and why does it matter? *Biol. Conserv.* 143: 239–247.

Buzzetti, D. R. C. 2000. Distribuição altitudinal de aves em Angra dos Reis e Parati, sul do Estado do Rio de Janeiro, Brasil. In: Alves, M. A. S., Silva, J. M. C., Sluys, M. van, Bergallo, H. G. & Rocha, C. F. D. (eds) *A Ornitologia no Brasil: Pesquisa Atual e Perspectivas*. Pp. 131–148. Ed. Universidade Estadual Rio de Janeiro, Rio de Janeiro.

Buzzetti, D. & Silva, S. 2005. *Berços da Vida*. Ed. Terceiro Nome, São Paulo.

Cadena, C. D., Alvarez, M., Parra, J. L., Jiménez, I., Mejía, C. A., Santamaría, M., Franco, A. M., Botero, C. A., Mejía, G. D., Umaña, A. M., Calixto, A., Aldana, J. & Londoño, G. A. 2000. The birds of CIEM, Tinigua National Park, Colombia: an overview of 13 years of ornithological research. *Cotinga* 13: 46–54.

Camacho, A., Biamonte, E., Sandoval, L. & Sánchez, C. 2010. Sharpbill *Oxyruncus cristatus frater* nesting ecology in Costa Rica. *Cotinga* 32: 118–120.

Camargo, E. A. 1957. Resultados ornitológicos de uma excursão ao Estado do Maranhão. *Pap. Dep. Zool. São Paulo* 13: 75–84.

Camargo, H. F. A. & Camargo, E. A. 1964. Ocorrência de *Iodopleura p. pipra* no Estado de São Paulo, Brasil, e algumas notas sobre *Iodopleura isabellae*. *Pap. Dep. Zool. São Paulo* 16: 45–55.

Campos, C. E. C., Naiff, R. H., Silva, É. C. P. & Aguiar, K. M. O. 2009. Diversidade de Piprídeos (Aves: Pipridae) da Amazônia oriental. In: Simon, J. E., Raposo, M. A., Stopiglia, R. & Peres, J. (eds) *XVII Congresso Brasileiro de Ornitologia Resumos, Aracruz, ES: Biogeografia das aves da Mata Atlântica*: 26.

Campos, J. V., Conceição, B. S. & Anciães, M. 2010. Use of secondary forests by understory birds in a fragmented landscape in Central Amazonia. In: Miyaki, C. M., Höfling, E. & Donatelli, R. J. (eds) *Abstracts 25th Int. Orn. Congr., Campos do Jordão, Brazil, 22–28 August 2010*: 835.

Campos, R. C. & Varassin, I. G. 2009. Potencial de aves dispersoras de *Miconia dodecandra* em Floresta Atlântica, Guaraqueçaba, PR. In: Simon, J. E., Raposo, M. A., Stopiglia, R. & Peres, J. (eds) *XVII Congresso Brasileiro de Ornitologia Resumos, Aracruz, ES: Biogeografia das aves da Mata Atlântica*: 47.

Candia-Gallardo, C. E. 2007. Observations on feeding and habitat use by Crimson Fruitcrow *Haematoderus militaris* in Amazonian Brazil. *Cotinga* 28: 82–83.

Cândido, J. F. 2000. The edge effect in a forest bird community in Rio Claro, São Paulo state, Brazil. *Ararajuba* 8: 9–16.

Canevari, P. 1992. *Oxyruncus cristatus*, una reconfirmación. *Nuestras Aves* 27: 35.

Capobianco, J. P. R., Veríssimo, A., Moreira, A., Sawyer, D., Santos, I. & Pinto, L. P. (eds) 2001. *Biodiversidade na Amazônia brasileira: avaliação e ações prioritárias para a conservação, uso sustentável e repartição de benefícios*. Instituto Socioambiental, São Paulo.

Capper, D. R., Clay, R. P. & Lowen, J. C. 1998. Recent sightings of threatened birds around Corcovado National Park, Costa Rica. *Cotinga* 10: 102.

Carrara, L., Antas, P. T. Z., Faria, L. C. P., Matos, J. R. & Sartório, R. C. 2009. Deslocamento de aves entre remanescentes de Mata Atlântica e plantios comerciais de eucalipto na região serrana do Espírito Santo. In: Simon, J. E., Raposo, M. A., Stopiglia, R. & Peres, J. (eds) *XVII Congresso Brasileiro de Ornitologia Resumos, Aracruz, ES: Biogeografia das aves da Mata Atlântica*: 27.

Carrano, E. & Marins, M. 2008. Frugivoria por aves em *Symplocos uniflora* (Symplocaceae) em floresta de baixada no Município de Paranaguá, Paraná. In: Congr. Bras. Orn. XVI, Palmas, *Resumos*: 242.

Carrano, E., Santos, R. E. F., Patrial, E. W., Ribas, C. F. & Klemann Júnior, L. 2004. Composição e conservação de aves na Floresta Estadual do Palmito, município de Paranaguá, Paraná. In: Congr. Bras. Orn. XII, Blumenau, *Resumos*: 189.

Carriker, M. A. 1932. Descriptions of new birds from Peru and Bolivia. *Proc. Acad. Nat. Sci. Philadelphia* 83: 455–467.

Carriker, M. A. 1934. Description of new birds from Peru, with notes on the nomenclature and status of other little-known species. *Proc. Acad. Nat. Sci. Philadelphia* 86: 317–334.

Carriker, M. A. 1935. Descriptions of new birds from Bolivia, with notes on other little-known species. *Proc. Acad. Nat. Sci. Philadelphia* 87: 313–359.

Carvalho, J. C. M. & Kloss, G. R. 1950. Sobre a distribuição do galo-da-serra, *Rupicola rupicola* (Linnaeus 1766), com observações de sua vida no habital natural e em cativeiro. *Rev. Bras. Biol.* 10: 65–72.

Carvalho, R. B. A., Mendonça, E. C., Rajão, H. B. R. & Gonzaga, L. P. 2009. Biologia e conservação de *Tijuca condita* no Parque Nacional da Serra dos Órgãos, RJ. In: Simon, J. E., Raposo, M. A., Stopiglia, R. & Peres, J. (eds) *XVII Congresso Brasileiro de Ornitologia Resumos, Aracruz, ES: Biogeografia das aves da Mata Atlântica*: 36.

Carvalho, R. B. A., Rajão, H., Mendonça, E. & Gonzaga, L. 2010. Abundance, elevational distribution and diet of the gray-winged cotinga (*Tijuca condita*) at Serra dos Órgãos National Park, Rio de Janeiro, Brazil. In: Miyaki, C. M., Höfling, E. & Donatelli, R. J. (eds) *Abstracts 25th Int. Orn. Congr., Campos do Jordão, Brazil, 22–28 August 2010*: 837.

Castañeda Gil, K. 2010. Propagación de Tristerix sp. por cotingas en el Parque Nacional Huascarán. *Bol. Inf. UNOP* 5(3): 21–22.

Castaño-Villa, G. J. & Patiño-Zabala, J. C. 2008. Extinciones locales de aves en fragmentos del bosque en la región de Santa Elena, Andes centrales, Colombia. *Hornero* 23: 23–34.

Castelino, M. & Saibene, C. 1989. Nidificación de aves en Misiones. *Nuestras Aves* 20: 7–9.

Castro Astor, I. N., Correia, J. M. S. & Alves, M. A. S. 1997. Predação de *Manacus manacus* (Pipridae) por ofídio *Corallus hortulanus* (= *C. enydris*) (Boidae), no sudeste do Brasil. In: Congr. Bras. Orn. VI, Belo Horizonte, *Resumos*: 130.

Castro-Astor, I. N., Alves, M. A. S. & Cavalcanti, R. B. 2004. Display behavior and spatial distribution of the Red-headed Manakin in the Atlantic Forest of Brazil. *Condor* 106: 320–335.

Castro-Astor, I. N., Alves, M. A. S. & Cavalcanti, R. B. 2007. Display behavior and spatial distribution of the White-crowned Manakin in the Atlantic Forest of Brazil. *Condor* 109: 155–166.

Cavalcanti, R. B. & Marini, M. Â. 1993. Body masses of birds of the *cerrado* region, Brazil. *Bull. Brit. Orn. Club* 113: 209–212.

Cerqueira, M. C., Sohn, N. & Anciães, M. 2008. Comportamento de corte e repertório vocal em leques do uirapuru-de-chapéu-azul (*Lepidothrix coronata*, Pipridae) na Amazônia brasileira. In: Congr. Bras. Orn. XVI, Palmas, *Resumos*: 82.

Cestari, C., Ferreira, M. A. P. & Lopes, I. T. 2010. The use of auxiliary arenas by the lek-forming white-bearded manakin (*Manacus manacus*). In: Miyaki, C. M., Höfling, E. & Donatelli, R. J. (eds) *Abstracts 25th Int. Orn. Congr., Campos do Jordão, Brazil, 22–28 August 2010*: 474.

Chapman, F. M. 1912. Diagnoses of apparently new Colombian birds. *Amer. Mus. Novit.* 31: 139–167.

Chapman, F. M. 1915. Diagnoses of apparently new Colombian birds. 4. *Bull. Amer. Mus. Nat. Hist.* 34: 635–662.

Chapman, F. M. 1917. The distribution of bird-life in Colombia. *Bull. Amer. Mus. Nat. Hist.* 36: 1–729.

Chapman, F. M. 1921. The distribution of bird life in the Urubamba Valley of Peru. *Bull. US Natl. Mus.* 117: 1–138.

Chapman, F. M. 1924. Descriptions of new genera and species of Tracheophonae from Panama, Ecuador, Peru, and Bolivia. *Amer. Mus. Novit.* 123: 1–9.

Chapman, F. M. 1925. Remarks on the life zones of northeastern Venezuela with descriptions of new species of birds. *Amer. Mus. Novit.* 191: 1–15.

Chapman, F. M. 1926a. The distribution of bird-life in Ecuador. *Bull. Amer. Mus. Nat. Hist.* 60: 1–784.

Chapman, F. M. 1926b. *Phibalura flavirostris* Vieill. in Bolivia. *Auk* 43: 99–100.

Chapman, F. M. 1928. The nesting habits of Wagler's Oropendola (*Zarhynchus wagleri*) on Barro Colorado Island. *Bull. Amer. Mus. Nat. Hist.* 58: 123–166.

Chapman, F. M. 1929a. *My Tropical Air Castle*. Appleton, New York.

Chapman, F. M. 1929b. Descriptions of new birds from Mt. Duida, Venezuela. *Amer. Mus. Novit.* 380: 1–27.

Chapman, F. M. 1930. A new race of *Phibalura flavirostris* from Bolivia. *Auk* 47: 87–88.

Chapman, F. M. 1931. The upper zonal bird-life of Mts. Roraima and Duida. *Bull. Amer. Mus. Nat. Hist.* 63: 1–135.

Chapman, F. M. 1935. The courtship of Gould's Manakin (*Manacus vitellinus vitellinus*) on Barro Colorado Island, Canal Zone. *Bull. Amer. Mus. Nat. Hist.* 68: 471–525.

Chapman, F. M. 1939. The riddle of *Oxyruncus*. *Amer. Mus. Novit.* 1047: 1–4.

Chaves, L. 2001. Observations on diet, foraging behaviour, vocalisations and displays of Spangled Cotinga *Cotinga cayana*. *Cotinga* 16: 103–104.

Chaves-Campos, J. 2005. Bare-necked Umbrellabird (*Cephalopterus glabricollis*) foraging at an unusually large assemblage of army ant-following birds. *Wilson Bull.* 117: 418–420.

Chaves-Campos, J., Arévalo, J. E. & Araya, M. 2003. Altitudinal movements and conservation of the Bare-necked Umbrellabird (*Cephalopterus glabricollis*) of the Tilarán Mountains, Costa Rica. *Bird Conserv. Int.* 13: 45–58.

Chebez, J. C., Rey, N. R., Barbaskas, M. & Di Giacomo, A. G. 1999. *Las Aves de los Parques Nacionales de la Argentina*. Literature of Latin America, Buenos Aires.

Cherrie, G. K. 1916. A contribution to the ornithology of the Orinoco region. *Mus. Brooklyn Inst. Arts & Sci. Bull.* 2(6).

Chesser, R. T. 2004. Molecular systematics of New World suboscine birds. *Mol. Phylogenet. Evol.* 32: 11–24.

Chesser, R. T., Banks, R. C., Barker, F. K., Cicero, C., Dunn, J. L., Kratter, A. W., Lovette, I. J., Rasmussen, P. C., Remsen, J. V., Rising, J. D., Stotz, D. F. & Winker, K. 2011. Fifty-second supplement to the American Ornithologists' Union *Check-list of North American Birds*. *Auk* 128: 600–613.

Cheviron, Z. A., Hackett, S. J. & Capparella, A. P. 2005. Complex evolutionary history of a Neotropical lowland forest bird (*Lepidothrix coronata*) and its implications for historical hypotheses of the origin of Neotropical avian diversity. *Mol. Phylogenet. Evol.* 36: 338–357.

Cheviron, Z. A., Hackett, S. J. & Brumfield, R. T. 2006. Sequence variation in the coding region of the melanocortin-1 receptor gene (MC1R) is not associated with plumage variation in the blue-crowned manakin (*Lepidothrix coronata*). *Proc. Roy. Soc. Biol. Sci. Ser.* B 273: 1613–1618.

Christian, D. G. 2001. Nests and nesting behavior of some little known Panamanian birds. *Orn. Neotrop.* 12: 327–336.

Chubb, C. 1910. On the birds of Paraguay. Part IV. *Ibis* 4: 571–647.

Chubb, C. 1921. *The Birds of British Guiana*. Bernard Quaritch, London.

Cintra, R., Sanaiotti, T. M. & Cohn-Haft, M. 2007. Spatial distribution and habitat of the Anavilhanas archipelago bird community in the Brazilian Amazon. *Biodivers. Conserv.* 16: 313–336.

Cisneros-Heredia, D. F. 2009. Capital birding: Quito. *Neotrop. Birding* 4: 40–47.

Claessens, O. 1997. Effects de la fragmentation de l'habitat sur les peuplements d'oiseaux forestiers tropicaux : le cas de la mise en eau du barrage de Petit Saut (Guyane française). PhD thesis, Muséum National d'Histoire Naturelle, Paris.

Clausi, B. 2005. Aves mais freqüentemente observadas se alimentando de frutas em duas áreas da região leste do Estado do Paraná, Brasil. In: Congr. Bras. Orn. XIII, Belém, *Resumos*: 184.

Clausi, B. & Baarstch, C. 2009. Padrões de sazonalidade na produção de frutos em quatro florestas subtropicais em diferentes altitudes no leste do Estado do Paraná e impactos na avifauna frugívora. In: Simon, J. E., Raposo, M. A., Stopiglia, R. & Peres, J. (eds) *XVII Congresso Brasileiro de Ornitologia Resumos, Aracruz, ES: Biogeografia das aves da Mata Atlântica*: 50.

Clay, R. P. 1995. Photo spot: Blue Manakin *Chiroxiphia caudata*. *Cotinga* 4: 80–81.

Clay, R. P. 2009. Musing on manakins: homage to David Snow. *Neotrop. Birding* 5: 12–15.

Clay, R. P., Capper, D. R., Mazar Barnett, J., Burfield, I. J., Esquivel, E. Z., Kennedy, C. P., Perrens, M. & Pople, R. G. 1998. White-winged Nightjars *Caprimulgus candicans* and cerrado conservation: the key findings of Project Aguará Ñu 1997. *Cotinga* 9: 52–56.

Clay, R., Jack, S. & Vincent, J. 1995. A stronghold for Long-wattled Umbrellabird discovered in Ecuador. *Cotinga* 4: 6–7.

Cleary, D. 1991. *The Brazilian Rainforest: Politics, Finance, Mining and the Environment*. Economist Intelligence Unit (Spec. Rep. 2100), London.

Clements, J. F. & Shany, N. 2001. *A Field Guide to the Birds of Peru*. Ibis Publishing, Temecula, CA.

Cockle, K., Maders, C., Di Santo, G. & Bodrati, A. 2008. The Black-capped Piprites *Piprites pileata* builds a spherical moss nest. *Cotinga* 29: 166–168.

Coelho, G. & Silva, W. 1998. A new species of *Antilophia* (Passeriformes: Pipridae) from Chapada do Araripe, Ceará, Brazil. *Ararajuba* 6: 81–84.

Cohn-Haft, M., Whittaker, A. & Stouffer, P. C. 1997. A new look at the "species-poor" central Amazon: the avifauna north of Manaus, Brazil. In: Remsen, J. V. (ed.) *Studies in Neotropical Ornithology Honoring Ted Parker. Orn. Monogr.* 48: 205–235.

Cohn-Haft, M., By, R. de, Bechtoldt, C. L., Serique, K. J. A. & Santos, J. L. C. 2009. O "Ornitólogo Automático": um *website* novo para a previsão da composição de espécies por localidade na Amazônia. In: Simon, J. E., Raposo, M. A., Stopiglia, R. & Peres, J. (eds) *XVII Congresso Brasileiro de Ornitologia Resumos, Aracruz, ES: Biogeografia das aves da Mata Atlântica*: 51.

Collar, N. J. & Andrew, P. 1988. *Birds to Watch: the ICBP World Checklist of Threatened Birds*. International Council for Bird Preservation, Cambridge, UK.

Collar, N. J., Gonzaga, L. P., Krabbe, N., Madroño Nieto, A., Naranjo, L. G., Parker, T. A. & Wege, D. C. 1992. *Threatened Birds of the Americas: the ICBP/IUCN Red Data Book*. International Council for Bird Preservation, Cambridge, UK.

Collar, N. J., Crosby, M. J. & Stattersfield, A. J. 1994. *Birds to Watch 2: the World List of Threatened Birds*. BirdLife International, Cambridge, UK.

Collins, C. 2007. Guyana: South America's overlooked birding destination. *Neotrop. Birding* 2: 69–75.

Collins, C. T. 1972. Weights of some birds of north-central Venezuela. *Bull. Brit. Orn. Club* 92: 151–153.

Collins, C. T. 1982. The natal pterylosis of *Manacus manacus. Bull. Brit. Orn. Club* 102: 37–39.

Collins, C. T. 2010. A review of natal pterylosis of passerines: useful information or avian marginalia? *Bull. Brit. Orn. Club* 130: 96–101.

Connop, S. 1996. *Birdsongs of Ecuador*. Cassette. Turaco Nature Inc., Toronto.

Connop, S. 2004. *Birdsongs of Ecuador*, 2nd edn. Cassette. Turaco Nature Inc., Toronto.

Contreras, J. R. 1979. Bird weights from northeastern Argentina. *Bull. Brit. Orn. Club* 99: 21–24.

Contreras, A. O., Vitale, C., Davies, Y. E. & Ramírez, J. L. 1990. La avifauna del Departamento de Misiones, República del Paraguay. In: Acevedo Gómez, C. (ed.) *Resúmenes y programa, II Encuentro Paraguayo-Argentino de Ornitología*, Asunción.

Cooper, D. S. 1997. Birds of the Río Negro Jaguar Preserve, Colonia Libertad, Costa Rica. *Cotinga* 8: 17–22.

Cooper, D. S. 1999. Notes on the birds of Isla Popa, western Bocas del Toro, Panama. *Cotinga* 11: 23–26.

Cordeiro, P. H. C. 2000. Levantamento em oito fragmentos de Mata Atlântica no sul da Bahia. In: Straube, F. C., Argel-de-Oliveira, M. M. & Cândido, J. F. (eds) *Ornitologia brasileira no século XX*. Pp. 187–188. Universidade do Sul de Santa Catarina & Sociedade Brasileira de Ornitologia, Curitiba.

Cordier, C. 1971. Über Lebensraum und Lebensweise der Felsenhahne. *Gefiederte Welt* 95: 133–136.

Corrêa, L., Bazílio, S., Woldan, D. & Boesing, A. L. 2008. Avifauna da Floresta Nacional de Três Barras (Santa Catarina, Brasil). *Atualidades Orn.* 143: 38–41 [www.ao.com.br].

Couve, E. & Vidal, C. 2003. *Birds of Patagonia, Tierra del Fuego and [sic] Antarctic Peninsula*. Fantastico Sur, Punta Arenas.

Cracraft, J. 1985. Historical biogeography and patterns of differentiation within the South American avifauna: areas of endemism. In: Buckley, P. A., Foster, M. S., Morton, E. S., Ridgely, R. S. & Buckley, F. G. (eds) *Neotropical Ornithology. Orn. Monogr.* 36: 49–84.

Crandall, L. S. 1948. Notes on the display of the Three-wattled Bellbird (*Procnias tricarunculata*). *Zoologica (NY)* 33: 113–114.

Crease, A. 2009. Avian range extensions from the southern headwaters of the río Caroní, Gran Sabana, Bolívar, Venezuela. *Cotinga* 31: 5–19.

Crenshaw, M. C. 2002. Seeds in droppings of Bare-necked Umbrellabird *Cephalopterus glabricollis* in Monteverde, Costa Rica: analysis of overlap in fruit diet. *Cotinga* 18: 74–76.

Cresswell, W., Mellanby, R., Bright, S., Catry, P., Chaves, J., Freile, J., Gabela, A., Hughes, M., Martineau, H., MacLeod, R., McPhee, F., Anderson, N., Holt, S., Barabas, S., Chapel, C. & Sanchez, T. 1999. Birds of the Guandera Biological Reserve, Carchi province, north-east Ecuador. *Cotinga* 11: 55–63.

Cuervo, A. M. & Renjifo, L. M. 2002a. *Ampelion rufaxilla*. In: Renjifo, L. M., Franco-Maya, A. M., Amaya-Espinel, J. D., Kattan, B. H. & López-Lanús, B. (eds) *Libro Rojo de Aves de Colombia*. Instituto de Investigación de Recursos Biológicos Alexander von Humboldt & Ministerio del Medio Ambiente, Bogotá.

Cuervo, A. M. & Renjifo, L. M. 2002b. *Lipaugus weberi*. In: Renjifo, L. M., Franco-Maya, A. M., Amaya-Espinel, J. D., Kattan, B. H. & López-Lanús, B. (eds) *Libro Rojo de Aves de Colombia*. Instituto de Investigación de Recursos Biológicos Alexander von Humboldt & Ministerio del Medio Ambiente, Bogotá.

Cuervo, A. M., Salaman, P. G. W., Donegan, T. M. & Ochoa, J. M. 2001. A new species of piha (Cotingidae: *Lipaugus*) from the Cordillera Central of Colombia. *Ibis* 143: 353–368.

Cuervo, A. M., Stiles, F. G., Cadena, C. D., Toro, J. L. & Londoño, G. A. 2003. New and noteworthy bird records from the northern sector of the Western Andes of Colombia. *Bull. Brit. Orn. Club* 123: 7–24.

Cuervo, A. M., Pulgarin, P. & Calderon, D. 2008a. New distributional bird data from the Cordillera Central of the Colombian Andes, with implications for the biogeography of northwestern South America. *Condor* 110: 526–537.

Cuervo, A. M., Pulgarín, P. C., Calderón-F., D., Ochoa-Quintero, J. M., Delgado-V., C. A., Palacio, A., Botero, J. M. & Múnera, W. A. 2008b. Avifauna of the northern Cordillera Central of the Andes, Colombia. *Orn. Neotrop.* 19: 495–515.

Cunha, F. C. R. & Specht, G. V. A. 2009. Avifauna associada a um área de reflorestamento de eucalipto, no município de Antônio Dias, MG – um estudo comparativo em um intervalo de 17 anos. In: Simon, J. E., Raposo, M. A., Stopiglia, R. & Peres, J. (eds) *XVII Congresso Brasileiro de Ornitologia Resumos, Aracruz, ES: Biogeografia das aves da Mata Atlântica*: 81.

DaCosta, J. M., Spellman, G. M. & Klicka, J. 2007. Bilateral gynandromorphy in a White-ruffed Manakin (*Corapipo altera*). *Wilson J. Orn.* 119: 289–291.

Damiani, R. V., Ribeiro, A. C. & Martins-Ferreira, C. 2009. Avifauna do Parque Estadual do Espinilho – RS, registros obtidos durante atividades de campo do projeto cardeal-amarelo. In: Simon, J. E., Raposo, M. A., Stopiglia, R. & Peres, J. (eds) *XVII Congresso Brasileiro de Ornitologia Resumos, Aracruz, ES: Biogeografia das aves da Mata Atlântica*: 82.

Dantas, S. M., Faccio, M. & Lima, M. F. C. 2010. Avifaunal inventory of the Floresta Nacional do Pau-Rosa, Maués, state of Amazonas, Brazil. In: Miyaki, C. M., Höfling, E. & Donatelli, R. J. (eds) *Abstracts 25th Int. Orn. Congr., Campos do Jordão, Brazil, 22–28 August 2010*: 950.

Dardanelli, S., Serra, D. A. & Nores, M. 2006. Composición y abundancia de la avifauna de fragmentos de bosque de Córdoba, Argentina. *Acta Zool. Lilloana* 50: 71–83.

Darnton, I. 1958. The display of the manakin *M. manacus*. *Ibis* 100: 52–58.

Darrieu, C. A. & Camperi, A. R. 1991. Estudio de una colección de aves de Corrientes. 2. (Formicariidae, Cotingidae, Pipridae). *Neotropica (La Plata)* 37(97): 75–80.

David, N. & Gosselin, M. 2002a. Gender agreement of avian species names. *Bull. Brit. Orn. Club* 122: 14–49.

David, N. & Gosselin, M. 2002b. The grammatical gender of avian genera. *Bull. Brit. Orn. Club* 122: 257–282.

David, N. & Gosselin, M. 2011. Gender agreement of avian species-group names under Article 31.2.2 of the ICZN Code. *Bull. Brit. Orn. Club* 131: 103–115.

Davies, C. W. N., Barnes, R., Butchart, S. H. M., Fernandez, M. & Seddon, N. 1994. The conservation status of the Cordillera de Colan. A report based on bird and mammal surveys in 1994. Unpubl. report.

Davis, D. E. 1945. The occurrence of the incubation-patch in some Brazilian birds. *Wilson Bull.* 57: 188–190.

Davis, S. E., Rocha O. O., Sarmiento, J. & Hanagarth, W. 1994. New departmental records and notes for some Bolivian birds. *Bull. Brit. Orn. Club* 114: 73–85.

Davis, T. A. W. 1949a. Display of White-throated Manakins *Corapipo gutturalis*. *Ibis* 91: 146–147.

Davis, T. A. W. 1949b. Field notes on the Orange-crested Manakin *Neopelma chrysocephalum* (Pelz.). *Ibis* 91: 349–350.

Davis, T. H. 1979. Additions to *The birds of Surinam*. *Continental Birdlife* 1: 136–146.

Davis, T. H. 1982. A flight-song display of White-throated Manakin. *Wilson Bull.* 94: 594–595.

Davis, T. J. 1986. Distribution and natural history of some birds from the departments of San Martín and Amazonas, northern Peru. *Condor* 88: 50–56.

Davis, T. J., Fox, C., Salinas, L., Ballon, G. & Arana, C. 1991. Annotated checklist of the birds of Cuzco Amazonico, Peru. *Occas. Pap. Mus. Nat. Hist. Univ. Kansas* 144: 1–19.

Day, L. B., McBroom, J. T. & Schlinger, B. A. 2006. Testosterone increases display behaviors but does not stimulate growth of adult plumage in male Golden-collared Manakins (*Manacus vitellinus*). *Horm. Behav.* 49: 223–232.

Day, L. B., Fusani, L., Hernandez, E., Billo, T. J., Sheldon, K. S., Wise, P. M. & Schlinger, B. A. 2007. Testosterone and its effects on courtship in Golden-collared Manakins (*Manacus vitellinus*): seasonal, sex, and age differences. *Horm. Behav.* 51: 69–76.

Dekker, R. W. R. J. 2003. Type specimens of birds in the National Museum of Natural History, Leiden. Part 2. Passerines: Eurylaimidae – Eopsaltriidae (Peters's sequence). *Natl. Natuur. Mus. Tech. Bull.* 6.

Delacour, J. 1945. L'Oiseau-Parasol (*Cephalopterus ornatus*). *Oiseau* 15: 130–140.

Delaney, D. 1992. *Bird Songs of Belize, Guatemala, and Mexico*. Cassette. Library of Natural Sounds, Cornell Laboratory of Ornithology, Ithaca, NY.

Delgado-V., C. A. 2000. Ampliación distribucional del Saltarín Mayor (*Schiffornis major*) en Colombia. *Bol. Soc. Antioqueña Orn.* 11: 38–42.

Delgado-V., C. A. & Brooks, D. M. 2003. Unusual vertebrate prey taken by Neotropical birds. *Orn. Colombiana* 1: 63–65.

Della-Flora, F., Brodt, M. S. C., Bastos, G. D. & Cáceres, N. C. 2010. Foraging tactics of the blue manakin *Chiroxiphia caudata* on understorey fruiting plants in a southern deciduous Atlantic Forest area. In: Miyaki, C. M., Höfling, E. & Donatelli, R. J. (eds) *Abstracts 25th Int. Orn. Congr., Campos do Jordão, Brazil, 22–28 August 2010*: 487.

Descourtilz, J. T. 1854–56. *Ornithologie brésilienne ou histoire des oiseaux du Brésil remarquables par leur plumages, leur chant ou leurs habitudes*. Thomas Reeves, Rio de Janeiro.

Devenish, C., Díaz Fernández, D. F., Clay, R. P., Davidson, I. & Yépez Zabala, I. (eds) 2009. *Important Bird Areas Americas – Priority Sites for Biodiversity Conservation*. BirdLife International, Quito.

Dick, J. A. 1991. Grey-tailed Piha in Colombia. *Bull. Brit. Orn. Club* 111: 172.

Dick, J. A., McGillivray, W. B. & Brooks, D. J. 1984. A list of birds and their weights from Saül, French Guiana. *Wilson Bull.* 96: 347–365.

Dickerman, R. W. & Phelps, W. H. Jr. 1982. An annotated list of the birds of Cerro Urutaní on the border of estado Bolívar, Venezuela and Territorio Roraima, Brasil. *Amer. Mus. Novit.* 2732: 1–20.

Dickey, D. R. & van Rossem, A. J. 1938. The birds of El Salvador. *Field Mus. Nat. Hist. Zool. Ser.* 23: 1–609.

Dickinson, E. C. (ed.) 2003. *The Howard and Moore Complete Checklist of the Birds of the World*, 3rd edn. Christopher Helm, London.

Dickinson, E. C., Bruce, M. D. & Dowsett, R. J. 2006. *Vivarium naturae* or *The Naturalist's Miscellany* (1789–1813) by George Shaw: an assessment of the dating of the parts and volumes. *Archiv. Nat. Hist.* 33: 322–343.

Dickinson, E. C., Overstreet, L. K., Bruce, M. D. & Dowsett, R. J. 2011. Jardine's Contributions to Ornithology 1848–1853: II. Contents and dates of issue. *Zool. Biblio.* 1: 44–66.

Diniz, F. C., Nogueira Campos Lobato, D., Enoult, A. M. J. & Antonini, Y. 2009. Tocantins central: as aves e o ecótono Cerrado-Amazônia. In: Simon, J. E., Raposo, M. A., Stopiglia, R. & Peres, J. (eds) *XVII Congresso Brasileiro de Ornitologia Resumos, Aracruz, ES: Biogeografia das aves da Mata Atlântica*: 53.

Donald, P. F., Collar, N. J., Marsden, S. J. & Pain, D. J. 2010. *Facing Extinction: The World's Rarest Birds and the Race to Save Them*. T. & A. D. Poyser, London.

Donatelli, R. J. & Ferreira, C. D. 2009. Aves da Estação Ecológica de Caetetus, Gália, SP. *Atualidas Orn.* 148: 55–57 [www. ao.com.br].

Donegan, T. M. & Dávalos, L. M. 1999. Ornithological observations from Reserva Natural Tambito, Cauca, south-west Colombia. *Cotinga* 12: 48–55.

Donegan, T. M., Avendaño C., J. E., Briceño L., E. R. & Huertas, B. 2007. Range extensions, taxonomic and ecological notes from Serranía de los Yariguíes, Colombia's new national park. *Bull. Brit. Orn. Club* 127: 172–213.

Donegan, T., Salaman, P. & Caro, D. 2009. Revision of the status of various bird species occurring or reported in Colombia. *Conserv. Colombiana* 8: 80–86.

Donegan, T. M., Avendaño-C., J. E., Briceño-L., E. R., Luna, J. C., Roa, C., Parra, R., Turner, C., Sharp, M. & Huertas, B. 2010. Aves de la Serranía de los Yariguíes y tierras bajas circundantes, Santander, Colombia. *Cotinga* 32: 23–40.

Dornas, T., Ribeiro, E. L. & Faleiro, M. A. 2005. Levantamento preliminar da avifauna da Estação Ecológica Mata do Cedro, Carmópolis de Minas-MG. In: Congr. Bras. Orn. XIII, Belém, *Resumos*: 139.

Doucet, S. M. & Hill, G. E. 2009. Do museum specimens accurately represent wild birds? A case study of carotenoid, melanin, and structural colours in long-tailed manakins *Chiroxiphia linearis*. *J. Avian Biol.* 40: 146–156.

Doucet, S. M. & Mennill, D. J. 2005. First description of the nest of the Round-tailed Manakin (*Pipra chloromeros*). *Orn. Neotrop.* 16: 433–434.

Doucet, S. M., McDonald, D. B., Foster, M. S. & Clay, R. P. 2007a. Plumage development and molt in Long-tailed Manakins (*Chiroxiphia linearis*): variation according to sex and age. *Auk* 124: 29–43.

Doucet, S. M., Mennill, D. J. & Hill, G. E. 2007b. The evolution of signal design in manakin plumage ornaments. *Amer. Naturalist* (Suppl.) 169: 62–80.

Duce, S. & Brannian, J. 1990. Social behavior of the Guianan cock-of-the-rock (*Rupicola rupicola*) in captivity. *Zoo Biol.* 9: 223–232.

Dugand, A. & Phelps, W. H. 1946. El status geografico de las aves de Maipures (Colombia). *Caldasia* 4: 243–276.

Dugand, A. & Phelps, W. H. 1948. Aves de la ribera colombiana del rio Negro (frontera de Colombia y Venezuela). *Caldasia* 5: 225–245.

Dujardin, J.-L. 1987. Découverte du nid et de la ponte du Manakin à front blanc (*Pipra serena*). *Oiseau & RFO* 57: 57–58.

Dunning, J. B. (ed.) 2008. *CRC Handbook of Avian Body Masses*, 2nd edn. CRC Press, Boca Baton, FL.

Durães, R. 2007. Costs, benefits, and the dynamics of lekking in the Blue-crowned Manakin *Lepidothrix coronata* (Pipridae). *Abstracts VIII Neotrop. Orn. Congr., Maturín, Venezuela, mayo 13–19 2007*: 104.

Durães, R. 2009. Lek structure and male display repertoire of Blue-crowned Manakins in eastern Ecuador. *Condor* 111: 453–461.

Durães, R. & Marini, M. Â. 2005. A quantitative assessment of bird diets in the Brazilian Atlantic Forest, with recommendations for future diet studies. *Orn. Neotrop.* 16: 65–83.

Durães, R., Loiselle, B. A. & Blake, J. G. 2007. Intersexual spatial relationships in a lekking species: blue-crowned manakins and female hot spots. *Behav. Ecol.* 18: 1029–1039.

Durães, R., Greeney, H. F. & Hidalgo, J. R. 2008a. First description of the nest and eggs of the Western Striped Manakin (*Machaeropterus regulus striolatus*), with observations on nesting behavior. *Orn. Neotrop.* 19: 287–292.

Durães, R., Loiselle, B. A. & Blake, J. G. 2008b. Spatial and temporal dynamics at manakin leks: reconciling lek traditionality with male turnover. *Behav. Ecol. Sociobiol.* 62: 1947–1957.

Durães, R., Loiselle, B. A., Parker, P. G. & Blake, J. G. 2009. Female mate choice across spatial scales: influence of lek and male attributes on mating success of blue-crowned manakins. *Proc. Roy. Soc. Lond. B* 276: 1875–1881.

DuVal, E. H. 2005. Age-based plumage changes in the Lance-tailed Manakin: a two-year delay in plumage maturation. *Condor* 107: 915–920.

DuVal, E. H. 2007a. Adaptive advantages of cooperative courtship for subordinate male lance-tailed manakins. *Amer. Natur.* 169: 423–432.

DuVal, E. H. 2007b. Social organization and variation in cooperative alliances among male lance-tailed manakins. *Anim. Behav.* 73: 391–401.

DuVal, E. H. 2007c. Cooperative display and lekking behaviour of the Lance-tailed Manakin (*Chiroxiphia lanceolata*). *Auk* 124: 1168–1185.

DuVal, E. H. & Kempenaers, B. 2008. Sexual selection in a lekking bird: the relative opportunity for selection by female choice and male competition. *Proc. Roy. Soc. Lond. Ser. B* 275: 1995–2003.

DuVal, E. H. & Nutt, K. J. 2005. Isolation and characterization of polymorphic microsatellite loci in the Lance-tailed Manakin (*Chiroxiphia lanceolata*). *Mol. Ecol. Notes* 5: 112–114.

DuVal, E. H., Carter, K. L. & Kempenaers, B. 2007. Isolation and characterization of novel microsatellite loci for parentage assessment in the lance-tailed manakin (*Chiroxiphia lanceolata*). *Mol. Ecol. Notes* 7: 1111–1113.

Dyck, J. 1971. Structure and colour-production of the blue barbs of *Agapornis roseicollis* and *Cotinga maynana*. *Z. Zellforsch. Mikrosk. Anat.* 115: 17–29.

Echeverri, E. H. 1986. *Avifauna parcial, Parque "Las Orquídeas"*. INDERENA, Medellín.

Echevarria, A. & Chani, J. M. 2006. Aves migratorias, la importancia del Embalse El Cadillal (Tucumán, Argentina) como sitio de tránsito e invernada. *Acta Zool. Lilloana* 50: 97–108.

Echeverry-Galvis, M. Á. & Córdoba-Córdoba, S. 2007. New distributional and other bird records from Tatamá Massif, West Andes, Colombia. *Bull. Brit. Orn. Club* 127: 213–224.

Echeverry-Galvis, M. Á., Córdoba-Córdoba, S., Peraza, C. A., Baptiste, M. P. & Ahumada, J. A. 2006. Body weights of 98 species of Andean cloud-forest birds. *Bull. Brit. Orn. Club* 126: 291–298.

Efe, M. A., Mohr, L. V., Bugoni, L., Scherer, A. & Barbosa Scherer, S. 2001. Inventário e distribuição da avifauna do Parque Saint Hilaire, Viamão, Rio Grande do Sul, Brasil. *Tangara* 1: 12–25.

Egli, G. 2002. *Voces de Aves Chilenas*. UNORCH, Santiago.

Eisenmann, E. 1952. Annotated list of birds of Barro Colorado Island, Panama Canal Zone. *Smiths. Misc. Coll.* 117(5): 1–62.

Eisenmann, E. 1961. Favorite foods of Neotropical birds: flying termites and *Cecropia* catkins. *Auk* 78: 636–638.

Eisermann, K. 2003. First records of the White-crowned Pigeon (*Columba leucocephala*), the Rufous-necked Wood-Rail (*Aramides axillaris*), and the Snowy Cotinga (*Carpodectes nitidus*) for Guatemala. *Orn. Neotrop.* 14: 127–128.

Eisermann, K. & Avendaño, C. 2007. *Lista Comentada de las Aves de Guatemala*. Lynx Edicions, Barcelona.

Eisermann, K. & Avendaño, C. 2009. Important Bird Areas of the Neotropics: Guatemala. *Neotrop. Birding* 5: 4–11.

Ellis, H. R. 1952. Nesting behavior of a Purple-throated Fruit-crow. *Wilson Bull.* 64: 98–100.

Endler, J. A. & Théry, M. 1996. Interacting effects of lek placement, display behavior, ambient light, and color patterns in three Neotropical forest-dwelling birds. *Amer. Natur.* 148: 421–452.

England, M. C. 2000. The Landbird Monitoring Programme at Lamanai, Belize: a preliminary assessment. *Cotinga* 13: 32–43.

Engleman, D. & Engleman, L. 1992. Birding spots in Panama: the Fortuna reserve. *Tucan* 18(7): 5–7.

English, P. H. & Parker, T. A. 1992. *Birds of Eastern Ecuador*. Cassette. Cornell Laboratory of Ornithology, Ithaca, NY.

Érard, C. 1982. Le nid et la ponte de *Lipaugus vociferans*, Cotingidé, et de *Grallaria varia*, Formicariidé. *Alauda* 50: 311–313.

Érard, C., Théry, M. & Sabatier, D. 1989. Régime alimentaire de *Rupicola rupicola* (Cotingidae) en Guyane française: relations avec la frugivorie et la zoochorie. *Rev. Ecol. (Terre Vie)* 44: 47–74.

Ericson, P. G. P., Zuccon, D., Ohlson, J. I., Johansson, U. S., Alvarenga, H. & Prum, R. O. 2006. Higher-level phylogeny and morphological evolution of tyrant flycatchers, cotingas, manakins, and their allies (Aves: Tyrannida). *Mol. Phylogenet. Evol.* 40: 471–483.

Euler, C. 1900. Descripção de ninhos e ovos das aves do Brasil. *Rev. Mus. Paulista* 3: 9–148.

Everitt, C. 1963. Breeding the Black-throated Cotinga (*Pipreola riefferii*). *Avicult. Mag.* 69: 141–144.

Fadini, R. F. & Marco, P. 2004. Interações entre aves frugívoras e plantas em um fragmento de Mata Atlântica de Minas Gerais. *Ararajuba* 12: 97–103.

Faetti, R. G., Lombardi, V. T. & D'Angelo Neto, S. 2009. Levantamento preliminar da avifauna do Parque Ecológico Quedas do Rio Bonito – Lavras – MG. In: Simon, J. E., Raposo, M. A., Stopiglia, R. & Peres, J. (eds) *XVII Congresso Brasileiro de Ornitologia Resumos, Aracruz, ES: Biogeografia das aves da Mata Atlântica*: 84.

Fagan, J. 2009. Birding El Salvador. *Neotrop. Birding* 5: 61–70.

Faria, C. M. A. & Rodrigues, M. 2009. Birds and army ants in a fragment of the Atlantic Forest of Brazil. *J. Field Orn.* 80: 328–335.

Faria, C. M. A., Rodrigues, M., Amaral, F. Q., Módena, É. & Fernandes, A. M. 2006. Aves de um fragmento de Mata Atlântica no alto Rio Doce, Minas Gerais: colonização e extinção. *Rev. Bras. Zool.* 23: 1217–1230.

Faria, I. P. & Paula, W. S. 2008. Body masses of birds from the Atlantic Forest region, southeastern Brazil. *Orn. Neotrop.* 19: 599–606.

Favretto, M. A. & Geuster, C. J. 2008. Observações ornitológicas no oeste de Santa Catarina, Brasil – parte I. *Atualidades Orn.* 143: 49–52 [www.ao.com.br].

Fearnside, P. M. 2005. Deforestation in Brazilian Amazonia: history, rates, and consequences. *Conserv. Biol.* 19: 680–688.

Fearnside, P. M. 2009. Comment: Brazil's evolving proposal to control deforestation: Amazon still at risk. *Environm. Conserv.* 36: 177–179.

Ferreira, A. A. & Cavalcanti, R. B. 1997. Uso diferencial de nicho espacial entre machos e fêmeas de *Antilophia galeata*. In: Congr. Bras. Orn. VI, Belo Horizonte, *Resumos*: 152.

Ferreira, A. A. & Cavalcanti, R. B. 2000. Efeitos da fragmentação de matas de galeria sobre *Antilophia galeata* (Pipridae). In: Straube, F. C., Argel-de-Oliveira, M. M. & Cândido, J. F. (eds) *Ornitologia brasileira no século XX.* Pp. 378–379. Universidade do Sul de Santa Catarina & Sociedade Brasileira de Ornitologia, Curitiba.

Ferreira, A. A. & Cavalcanti, R. B. 2001. Efeitos da alteração da matriz ambiental sobre *Antilophia galeata* (Pipridae). In: Congr. Bras. Orn. IX, Curitiba, *Resumos*: 70.

Ferreira, A. A., Anunciação, C. E. & Cavalcanti, R. B. 2001a. Análise populacional de *Antilophia galeata* em matas de galeria do Distrito Federal. In: Congr. Bras. Orn. IX, Curitiba, *Resumos*: 68.

Ferreira, A. A., Anunciação, C. E. & Cavalcanti, R. B. 2001b. Diversidade genetica de *Antilophia galeata* em três matas de galeria do Distrito Federal. In: Congr. Bras. Orn. IX, Curitiba, *Resumos*: 69.

Ferreira, A. A., Figueiredo-Neto, A., Paula, J. P., Machado, N., Azevedo, P. L. & Laranjeiras, T. O. 2010. Ocorrência de *Laniisoma elegans* (Aves: Tityridae) no Estado de Goiás. *Atualidades Orn.* 156: 9.

Ferreira, G. N., Aires, R. P., Silva, G. G. & Valle, N. C. 2008. Dieta do *Pipra fasciicauda* (Aves, Passeriformes: Pipridae) em seis regiões de cerrado. In: Congr. Bras. Orn. XVI, Palmas, *Resumos*: 91.

Ferreira, N., Guimarães, T. V. C. & Peña, A. P. 2009. Estudo da avifauna em seis municípios do Estado de Goiás. In: Simon, J. E., Raposo, M. A., Stopiglia, R. & Peres, J. (eds) *XVII Congresso Brasileiro de Ornitologia Resumos, Aracruz, ES: Biogeografia das aves da Mata Atlântica*: 85.

Ferreyra, R. 1978. Flora y vegetacion del monte de Zárate. *Bol. Colonia Suiza en el Perú* 13: 51–58.

ffrench, R. 1991. *A Guide to the Birds of Trinidad and Tobago*, 2nd edn. Cornell University Press, Ithaca, NY.

ffrench, R. & Kenefick, M. 2003. Verification of rare bird records from Trinidad and Tobago. *Cotinga* 19: 75–79.

Fierro-Calderón, K., Estela, F. & Chacón-Ulloa, P. 2006. Observaciones sobre las dietas de algunas aves de la Cordillera Oriental de Colombia a partir del análisis de contenidos estomacales. *Orn. Colombiana* 4: 6–15.

Finch, D. W. 1991. Novedades ornitologicas argentinas. *Nuestras Aves* 24: 25.

Fischer, E., Munin, R. L., Longo, J. M., Fischer, W. & Souza, P. R. 2010. Using interpubic distance for sexing manakins in the field. *J. Field Orn.* 81: 49–63.

Fisher, C. T. 1981. Specimens of extinct, endangered or rare birds in the Merseyside County Museums, Liverpool. *Bull. Brit. Orn. Club* 101: 276–285.

Fitzsimmons, L. P., Barker, N. K. & Mennill, D. J. 2008. Individual variation and lek-based vocal distinctiveness in songs of the Screaming Piha (*Lipaugus vociferans*), a suboscine songbird. *Auk* 125: 908–914.

Fjeldså, J. & Krabbe, N. 1990. *The Birds of the High Andes.* Zoological Museum, University of Copenhagen, Copenhagen & Apollo Books, Svendborg.

Fjeldså, J. & Mayer, S. 1996. *Recent Ornithological Surveys in the Valles Region, Southern Bolivia.* DIVA Tech. Rep. 1. Centre for Research on the Cultural and Biological Diversity of Andean Rainforests, Rønde.

Fjeldså, J., Zuccon, D., Irestedt, M., Johansson, U. S. & Ericson, P. G. P. 2003. *Sapayoa aenigma*: a New World representative of 'Old World suboscines'. *Proc. Roy. Soc. Biol. Sci. Ser.* B 270 (Suppl. 2): S238–S241.

Flanagan, J. N. M. 2009. *Plan de Acción: Cortarrama Peruana, Peruvian Plantcutter, Phytotoma raimondii.* PROFONANPE, Lima.

Flanagan, J. N. M. & Millen, B. M. 2008. First nest and eggs records of Peruvian Plantcutter *Phytotoma raimondii*, by O. D. Boggs. *Bull. Brit. Orn. Club* 128: 271.

Flanagan, J. N. M., Engblom, G., Franke, I., Valqui, T. & Angulo, F. 2009. Distribution of the Peruvian Plantcutter *Phytotoma raimondii* (Passeriformes: Cotingidae). *Rev. Peru. Biol.* 16: 175–182.

Flores, B., Rumiz, D. I. & Cox, G. 2001. Avifauna del bosque semidecíduo Chiquitano (Santa Cruz, Bolivia) antes y después de un aprovechamiento forestal selectivo. *Ararajuba* 9: 21–31.

Fogden, M. P. L. & Fogden, P. M. 1997. Notes on the behaviour of Bare-necked Umbrellabird *Cephalopterus glabricollis* in the Monteverde Cloud Forest Preserve, Costa Rica. *Cotinga* 8: 23–26.

Forrester, B. C. 1993. *Birding Brazil: A Check-List and Site Guide.* Privately published, Irvine.

Fonseca, F. Y. & Antunes, A. Z. 2007. Frugivoria e predação de sementes por aves no Parque Estadual Alberto Löfgren, São Paulo, SP. *Rev. Inst. Flor., São Paulo* 19: 81–91.

Foster, M. S. 1975. The overlap of molting and breeding in some tropical birds. *Condor* 77: 304–314.

Foster, M. S. 1976. Nesting biology of the Long-tailed Manakin. *Wilson Bull.* 88: 400–420.

Foster, M. S. 1977a. Ecological and nutritional effects of food scarcity on a tropical frugivorous bird and its fruit source. *Ecology* 58: 73–85.

Foster, M. S. 1977b. Odd couples in manakins: a study of social organization and cooperative breeding in *Chiroxiphia linearis. Amer. Natur.* 11: 845–853.

Foster, M. S. 1981. Cooperative behavior and social organization of the Swallow-tailed Manakin (*Chiroxiphia caudata*). *Behav. Ecol. Sociobiol.* 9: 167–177.

Foster, M. S. 1987. Delayed maturation, neoteny, and social system differences in two manakins of the genus *Chiroxiphia. Evolution* 41: 547–558.

Foster, M. S. 1996. Evolution of lek social systems in manakins: alternative models and proofs. *Anais V Congr. Bras. Orn.*: 39–42.

Fraga, R. M. 1997. Aves. In: García Fernández, J.J. (ed.) *Mamíferos y Aves Amenazados de la Argentina.* Pp. 155–219. FUCEMA y Administración de Parques Nacionales, Buenos Aires.

Franchin, A. G. & Marçal Júnior, O. 2003. A riqueza da avifauna no Parque do Sabiá, zona urbana de Uberlândia (MG). In: Machado, C. G. (ed.) *XI Congresso Brasileiro de Ornitologia Resumos, Feira de Santana, BA*: 84.

Franchin, A. G., Araújo, F. P., Jardim, M. H., Gomide, F., Silva, G. B. M., Silva, M. R. & Pioli, D. 2001. Levantamento da avifauna do Parque do Sabiá, Uberlândia (Minas Gerais): dados preliminares. In: Congr. Bras. Orn. IX, Curitiba, *Resumos*: 76.

Franchin, A. G., Melo, C., Silva Júnior, E. L. & Marçal Júnior, O. 2007. Levantamento preliminar da avifauna na RPPN Reserva Ecológica do Panga, Uberlândia (MG). In: Fontana, C. S. (ed.) *XV Congresso Brasileiro de Ornitologia Resumos, Porto Alegre, RS*: 87–88.

Franchin, A.G., Silva, L. J. & Marçal Júnior, O. 2009. Levantamento da avifauna no Parque Municipal Bosque John Kennedy, Araguari, MG. In: Simon, J. E., Raposo, M. A., Stopiglia, R. & Peres, J. (eds) *XVII Congresso Brasileiro de Ornitologia Resumos, Aracruz, ES: Biogeografia das aves da Mata Atlântica*: 85.

Francis, J. E. R. 2006. Hand-rearing a spangled cotinga *Cotinga cayana*. *Avicult. Mag.* 112: 19–23.

Francisco, M. R. & Galetti, M. 2001. Frugivoria e disperção de sementes de *Rapanea lancifolia* (Myrsinaceae) por aves numa área de cerrado do Estado de São Paulo, sudeste do Brasil. *Ararajuba* 9: 13–19.

Francisco, M. R. & Galetti, M. 2002. Consumo dos frutos de *Davilla rugosa* (Dilleniaceae) por aves numa área de cerrado em São Carlos, Estado de São Paulo. *Ararajuba* 10: 193–198.

Francisco, M. R., Galetti, P. M. & Gibbs, H. L. 2004. Isolation and characterization of microsatellite loci in the Blue Manakin, *Chiroxiphia caudata* (Aves, Pipridae). *Mol. Ecol. Notes* 4: 758–760.

Francisco, M. R., Galetti, M. & Galetti, P. M. 2006. Atlantic forest fragmentation and genetic diversity of an isolated population of the Blue-manakin [*sic*], *Chiroxiphia caudata* (Pipridae), assessed by microsatellite analysis. *Rev. Bras. Orn.* 14: 21–28.

Francisco, M. R., Gibbs, H. L., Galetti, M., Lunardi, V. O. & Galetti, P. M. 2007. Genetic structure in a tropical lek-breeding bird, the blue manakin (*Chiroxiphia caudata*) in the Brazilian Atlantic Forest. *Mol. Ecol.* 16: 4908–4918.

Francisco, M. R., Oliveira, P. R. R. & Lunardi, V. O. 2008a. Nest and fledglings of the Red-ruffed Fruitcrow (*Pyroderus scutatus*). *Wilson J. Orn.* 120: 413–416.

Francisco, M. R., Gibbs, H. L. & Galetti, P. M. 2008b. Estruturação populacional em *Chiroxiphia caudata* (Pipridae) em áreas contínuas de Mata Atlântica e suas implicações para a conservação. In: Congr. Bras. Orn. XVI, Palmas, *Resumos*: 415.

Francisco, M. R., Gibbs, H. L. & Galetti, P. M. 2009. Patterns of individual relatedness at Blue Manakin (*Chiroxiphia caudata*) leks. *Auk* 126: 47–53.

Freiberg, M. D. 2005. A range extension for Elegant Mourner *Laniisoma elegans* in Brazil. *Cotinga* 24: 114–115.

Freile, J. F. 2004. Range extensions and other noteworthy and new bird records from mainland Ecuador. *Bull. Brit. Orn. Club* 124: 188–202.

Freile, J. F. & Chaves, J. A. 2004. Interesting distributional records and notes on the biology of bird species from a cloud forest reserve in north-west Ecuador. *Bull. Brit. Orn. Club* 124: 6–16.

Freitas, A. B., Galvão do Nascimento, E. P., Silva, M. & Neto, M. R. 2005. Composição da avifauna da Reserva Particular do Patrimonio Natural Senador Antonio Farias, Mata Estrela, Baia Formosa, Rio Grande do Norte, Brasil. In: Congr. Bras. Orn. XIII, Belém, *Resumos*: 134.

Freitas, M. A. 2008. Todos os Santos: Ilha de Itaparica de duas ilhas da Baía de e Ilha Bimbarras/Bahia/Brasil. *Atualidades Orn.* 145: 33–35 [www.ao.com.br].

Freitas, M. A., Figueiredo Moraes, E. P., Brasileiro, Â. G. R., Moysés, L. E. & Silva, T. F. S. 2004. Ornitofauna da Fazenda Timbó, São Sebastião do Passé, Bahia. In: Congr. Bras. Orn. XII, Blumenau, *Resumos*: 224.

Friedmann, H. 1944. A new manakin from Cerro Yapacana, upper Orinoco Valley, southern Venezuela. *Proc. Biol. Soc. Wash.* 57: 99–100.

Friedmann, H. 1948. Birds collected by the National Geographic Society's expeditions to northern Brazil and southern Venezuela. *Proc. US Natl. Mus.* 97: 373–570.

Friedmann, H. & Smith, F. D. 1950. A contribution to the ornithology of northeastern Venezuela. *Proc. US Natl. Mus.* 100: 411–538.

Friedmann, H. & Smith, F. D. 1955. A further contribution to the ornithology of northeastern Venezuela. *Proc. US Natl. Mus.* 104: 463–524.

Frost, W. 1910. The cock-of-the-rock. *Avicult. Mag.* 3: 319–324.

Fry, C. H. 1970. Ecological distribution of birds in north-eastern Mato Grosso state, Brazil. *An. Acad. Bras. Ciênc.* 42: 275–318.

Fulton, G. R. 2001. Threatened and extinct bird specimens held in the Macleay Museum, University of Sydney, Australia. *Bull. Brit. Orn. Club* 121: 39–49.

Fusani, L. 2010. The proximate and ultimate causes of courtship behavior in golden-collared manakins. In: Miyaki, C. M., Höfling, E. & Donatelli, R. J. (eds) *Abstracts 25th Int. Orn. Congr., Campos do Jordão, Brazil, 22–28 August 2010*: 37.

Fusani, L., Giordano, M., Day, L. B. & Schlinger, B. A. 2007. High-speed video analysis reveals individual variability in the courtship displays of male Golden-collared Manakins. *Ethology* 113: 964–972.

Galetti, M. & Aleixo, A. 1998. Effects of palm heart harvesting on frugivores in the Atlantic forest of Brazil. *J. Appl. Ecol.* 35: 286–293.

Galetti, M. & Pizo, M. A. 1996. Fruit eating by birds in a forest fragment in southeastern Brazil. *Ararajuba* 4: 71–79.

Galetti, M., Zipparro, V. B. & Morellato, P. C. 1999. Fruiting phenology and frugivory on the palm *Euterpe edulis* in a lowland Atlantic Forest of Brazil. *Ecotropica* 5: 115–122.

Garrigues, R. 2001. *The Gone Birding Newsletter* 2(4).

Garrigues, R. & Dean, R. 2007. *Birds of Costa Rica*. Christopher Helm, London.

Garske, C. E. S. & Anjos, L. 2005. Avaliação preliminar da diversidade de aves em remanescentes de Mata Atlântica da bacia hidrográfica do rio Timbuí, Espírito Santo. In: Congr. Bras. Orn. XIII, Belém, *Resumos*: 98.

Gatto, C. A. F. R. 2005. Novo híbrido intergenérico em Pipridae: *Antilophia galeata* × *Chiroxiphia pareola* do sul da Chapada Diamantina, Bahia. In: Congr. Bras. Orn. XIII, Belém, *Resumos*: 29.

Gatto, C. A. F. R. & Roper, J. J. 2004. Corte e sucesso reprodutivo entre leks cooperativos do Tangará, *Chiroxiphia caudata* (Shaw & Nodder, 1793) (Aves: Pipridae). In: Congr. Bras. Orn. XII, Blumenau, *Resumos*: 229.

Gelis, R. A., Greeney, H. F., Cooper, M. & Dingle, C. 2006. The nest, eggs, nestlings and fledglings of Fiery-throated Fruiteater *Pipreola chlorolepidota* in north-east Ecuador. *Cotinga* 26: 10–12.

Gerritz, H. A. 1955. Care and feeding of the cock-of-the-rock. *Avicult. Mag.* 61: 146–148.

Ghizoni-Jr, I. R. & Azevedo, M. A. G. 2010. Registros de algumas aves raras ou com distribuição pouco conhecida em Santa Catarina, sul do Brasil, e relatos de três novas espécies para o Estado. *Atualidades Orn.* 154: 33–46.

Gill, F. & Wright, M. 2006. *Birds of the World: Recommended English Names*. Christopher Helm, London.

Gilliard, E. T. 1941. The birds of Mt. Auyan-tepui, Venezuela. *Bull. Amer. Mus. Nat. Hist.* 77: 439–508.

Gilliard, E. T. 1959a. Notes on some birds of northern Venezuela. *Amer. Mus. Novit.* 1927: 1–33.

Gilliard, E. T. 1959b. Notes on the courtship behavior of the Blue-backed Manakin (*Chiroxiphia pareola*). *Amer. Mus. Novit.* 1942: 1–19.

Gilliard, E. T. 1962. On the breeding behavior of the Cock-of-the-Rock (Aves, *Rupicola rupicola*). *Bull. Amer. Mus. Nat. Hist.* 124: 31–68.

Girão, W. & Souto, A. 2005. Breeding period of Araripe Manakin *Antilophia bokermanni* inferred from vocalisation activity. *Cotinga* 24: 35–37.

Gochfeld, M. & Tudor, G. 1978. Ant-following birds in South American subtropical forests. *Wilson Bull.* 90: 139–141.

Goeldi, E. A. 1894. On the nesting of *Phibalura flavirostris* and *Lochmias nematura*. *Ibis* (6)6: 484–494.

Goeldi, E. A. 1900. *As Aves do Brasil*, Vol. 2. Livraria Clássica de Alves & Co., Rio de Janeiro e São Paulo.

Goerck, J. M. 1999. Distribution of birds along an elevational gradient in the Atlantic forest of Brazil: implications for the conservation of endemic and endangered species. *Bird Conserv. Int.* 9: 235–253.

Gomes, A. L. S. & Marceliano, M. L. V. 2009. Morfometria de *Dixiphia pipra* (Pipridae) procedentes do Parque Ecológico de Gunma, município de Santa Bárbara, Estado do Pará. In: Simon, J. E., Raposo, M. A., Stopiglia, R. & Peres, J. (eds) *XVII Congresso Brasileiro de Ornitologia Resumos, Aracruz, ES: Biogeografia das aves da Mata Atlântica*: 54.

Gomes, A. L. S., Marceliano, M. L. V. & Jardim, M. A. G. 2008. Consumo dos frutos de *Miconia ciliatta* (Rich.) DC (Melastomataceae) por aves na Amazônia Oriental. *Rev. Bras. Orn.* 16: 383–386.

Gomes, V. S. M. & Silva, W. R. 2002. Spatial variation in understory frugivorous birds in an Atlantic Forest fragment of southeastern Brazil. *Ararajuba* 10: 219–225.

Gondim, M. J. C. 2001. Disperção de sementes de *Trichilia* spp. (Meliaceae) por aves em um fragmento de mata mesófila semidecídua, Rio Claro, SP, Brasil. *Ararajuba* 9: 101–112.

Gonzaga, L. P. 1986. Composição da avifauna em uma parcela de mata perturbada na baixada, em Majé, estado do Rio de Janeiro, Brasil. MSc dissertation, Universidade Federal do Rio de Janeiro.

Gonzaga, L. A. P. 1989. Catálogo dos tipos na coleção ornitológica do Museu Nacional. II. Passeriformes. *Bol. Mus. E. Goeldi, ser. Zool.* 5: 41–69.

Gonzaga, L. P. 1997. Kinglet Calyptura survives in south-east Brazil! *Cotinga* 7: 9.

Gonzaga, L. P. & Collar, N. J. 2010. A nest of Banded Cotinga *Cotinga maculata*. *Cotinga* 32: 165–166.

Gonzaga, L. P. & Castiglioni, G. D. A. 2001. *As Aves das Montanhas do Sudeste do Brasil*. CD. Arq. Sonoro Elias Coelho, Rio de Janeiro.

Gonzaga, L. P., Pacheco, J. F., Bauer, C. & Castiglioni, G. D. A. 1995. An avifaunal survey of the vanishing montane Atlantic forest of southern Bahia, Brazil. *Bird Conserv. Int.* 5: 279–290.

González-García, F. 1993. Avifauna de la Reserva de la Biosfera "Montes Azules", Selva Lacandona, Chiapas, Mexico. *Acta Zool. Mexicana* (N. Ser.) 55: 1–86.

González M., O. E. 1998. Birds of the lowland forest of Cerros del Sira, central Peru. *Cotinga* 9: 57–60.

Goodfellow, W. 1901. Results of an ornithological journey through Colombia and Ecuador. *Ibis* 8(1): 300–319, 458–480, 699–715.

Goodwin, M. L. 2003. *Birding in Venezuela*, 5th edn. Lynx Edicions, Barcelona.

Görnitz, K. & Rensch, B. 1924. Ueber die violette Färbung der Vogelfedern. *J. Orn.* 72: 113–118.

Gorton, R. 2010. Remembering Paul A. Schwartz (1917–1979): pioneer Neotropical bird recordist and taxonomist. *Birding* 42(5): 40–50.

Graham, D. 1996. Diet and foraging behaviors of two abundant frugivorous understory birds, *Pipra mentalis* (Pipridae) and *Mionectes oleaginous* (Tyranidae) in a humid lowland Neotropical forest. PhD thesis, University of Miami, FL.

Graham, G. L., Graves, G. R., Schulenberg, T. S. & O'Neill, J. P. 1980. Seventeen bird species new to Peru from the Pampas de Heath. *Auk* 97: 366–370.

Granizo, T., Pacheco, C., Ribadeneira, M. B., Guerrero, M. & Suárez, L. (eds) 2002. *Libro Rojo de las Aves de Ecuador*. SIMBIOE, Conservation International, EcoCiencia, Ministerio del Ambiente & IUCN, Quito.

Graves, G. R. 1981. Brightly coloured plumage in female manakins (*Pipra*). *Bull. Brit. Orn. Club* 101: 270–271.

Graves, G. R. 1993. A new hybrid manakin (*Dixiphia pipra* × *Pipra filicauda*) (Aves: Pipridae) from the Andean foothills of eastern Ecuador. *Proc. Biol. Soc. Wash.* 106: 436–441.

Graves, G. R. & Zusi, R. L. 1990. Avian body weights from the lower Rio Xingu, Brazil. *Bull. Brit. Orn. Club* 110: 20–25.

Graves, G. R., Robbins, M. B. & Remsen, J. V. 1983. Age and sexual difference in spatial distribution and mobility in manakins (Pipridae): inferences from mist-netting. *J. Field Orn.* 54: 407–412.

Greeney, H. F. 2006. A Blue-crowned Manakin *Lepidothrix coronata* successfully defends its nest from *Labidus* army ants. *Cotinga* 25: 85–86.

Greeney, H. F. & Gelis, R. A. 2007. Breeding records from the north-east Andean foothills of Ecuador. *Bull. Brit. Orn. Club* 127: 236–241.

Greeney, H. F. & Gelis, R. A. 2008. Further breeding records from the Ecuadorian Amazon lowlands. *Cotinga* 29: 62–68.

Greeney, H. F. & Nunnery, T. 2006. Notes on the breeding of north-west Ecuadorian birds. *Bull. Brit. Orn. Club* 126: 38–45.

Greeney, H. F. & Sheldon, K. S. 2008. The nest and egg of Amazonian Umbrellabird *Cephalopterus ornatus* in the foothills of eastern Ecuador. *Cotinga* 29: 171–172.

Greeney, H. F., Gelis, R. A. & White, R. 2004. Notes on breeding birds from an Ecuadorian lowland forest. *Bull. Brit. Orn. Club* 124: 28–37.

Greeney, H. F., McLean, A., Bücker, A. D. L., Gelis, R. A., Cabrera,

D. & Sornoza, F. 2006. Nesting biology of the Long-wattled Umbrellabird (*Cephalopterus penduliger*). Part 1. Incubation. *Orn. Neotrop.* 17: 395–401.

Greeney, H. F., Simbaña, J., Gelis, R. A. & Manzaba-B., O. G. 2009. The nest and egg of Dusky Piha *Lipaugus fuscocinereus* in eastern Ecuador. *Cotinga* 31: 129–130.

Greeney, H. F., Juiña J., M. E., Harris, J. C. B., Wickens, M. T., Winger, B., Gelis, R. A., Miller, E. T. & Solano-Ugalde, A. 2010. Observations on the breeding biology of birds in south-east Ecuador. *Bull. Brit. Orn. Club* 130: 61–68.

Greeney, H. F., Martin, P. R., Gelis, R. A., Solano-Ugalde, A., Bonier, F., Freeman, B. & Miller, E. T. 2011. Notes on the breeding of high-Andean birds in northern Ecuador. *Bull. Brit. Orn. Club* 131: 24–31.

Greeney, H. F., Kirwan, G. M. & Miller, E. T. in press. Nesting biology of the Long-wattled Umbrellabird *Cephalopterus penduliger*, part 2: nestling provisioning. *Cotinga* 33.

Greenway, J. C. 1987. Type specimens of birds in the American Museum of Natural History. Part 4. Passeriformes: Tyrannidae, Pipridae, Cotingidae, Oxyruncidae, Phytotomidae, Pittidae, Philepittidae, Acanthisittidae, Menuridae, Atrichornithidae. *Amer. Mus. Novit.* 2879: 1–63.

Griscom, L. 1932. The distribution of bird-life in Guatemala. *Bull. Amer. Mus. Nat. Hist.* 64: 1–439.

Griscom, L. 1933. Notes on the Havemeyer collection of Central American birds. *Auk* 50: 297–308.

Griscom, L. & Greenway, J. C. 1937. Birds of Lower Amazonia. *Bull. Mus. Comp. Zool. Harvard* 88: 83–344.

Guaraldo, A. C., Staggemeier, V. G., Brown, T. E. & Gussoni, C. O. A. 2008. Novas observações sobre o 'rei-dos-tangarás' no município de Corumbataí, São Paulo, Brasil. *Cotinga* 30: 59–60.

Guerra, T. J. & Marini, M. Â. 2002. Bird frugivory on *Struthanthus concinnus* (Loranthaceae) in southeastern Brazil. *Ararajuba* 10: 187–192.

Guevara, E. A., Solano, A. & Buitrón, G. 2008. Noteworthy records from the eastern Andean slopes of northern Ecuador. *Orn. Colombiana* 7: 78–82.

Guilherme, E. 2004. Levantamento ornitológico em Assis Brasil, Estado do Acre, na fronteira tri-nacional, Brasil, Peru e Bolívia. In: Congr. Bras. Orn. XII, Blumenau, *Resumos*: 240.

Guilherme, E. & Borges, S. H. 2008. Resultados ornitológicos de uma expedição a uma mancha de campinarana no alto Juruá, Estado do Acre, Brasil. In: Congr. Bras. Orn. XVI, Palmas, *Resumos*: 400.

Guilherme, E. & Dantas, S. M. 2008. Resultados ornitológicos de uma pesquisa no alto rio Purus, Estado do Acre, Brasil. In: Congr. Bras. Orn. XVI, Palmas, *Resumos*: 401.

Guilherme, E. & Santos, M. P. D. 2009. Birds associated with bamboo forests in eastern Acre, Brazil. *Bull. Brit. Orn. Club* 129: 229–240.

Guimarães, T. C. V., Ferreira, N. & Peña, A. P. 2009. Levantamento parcial da avifauna do Parque Estadual Serra de Caldas Novas (PESCAN-GO). In: Simon, J. E., Raposo, M. A., Stopiglia, R. & Peres, J. (eds) *XVII Congresso Brasileiro de Ornitologia Resumos*, *Aracruz, ES: Biogeografia das aves da Mata Atlântica*: 86.

Guix, J. C. 1995. Aspectos da frugivoria, disseminação e predação de sementes por vertebrados nas florestas nativas do Estado de São Paulo, sudeste do Brasil. PhD thesis, University of Barcelona.

Guix, J. C., Tabánez, A. A. J., Silva, A. N., López, C., Martínez, C., Matheu, E., Souza, F. L., Pisciotta, K. R., Bradbury, N. & Portilho, W. G. 1992. Viagem de reconhecimento científico a algumas áreas desconhecidas da Fazenda Intervales, Estado de São Paulo, durante a período de 04 a 16 de outubro de 1991. Grupo de Estudos Ecologicos Sér. 4, São Paulo.

Gussoni, C. O. A. & Galetti, M. 2007. Avifauna do Parque Estadual Turístico do Alto Ribeira, SP. In: Fontana, C. S. (ed.) *XV Congresso Brasileiro de Ornitologia Resumos*, Porto Alegre, RS: 126.

Gyldenstolpe, N. 1945. The bird fauna of the rio Juruá in western Brazil. *K. Svenska Vetensk. Akad. Zool.*, ser. 3(22): 1–338.

Gyldenstolpe, N. 1951. The ornithology of the rio Purus region in western Brazil. *Ark. Zool.*, ser. 2(2): 1–320.

Haffer, J. 1959. Notas sobre las aves de la region de Uraba (1). *Lozania* 12: 1–56.

Haffer, J. 1967a. Speciation in Colombian forest birds west of the Andes. *Amer. Mus. Novit.* 2294: 1–57.

Haffer, J. 1967b. Some allopatric species pairs of birds in north-western Colombia. *Auk* 84: 343–365.

Haffer, J. 1970. Art-Entstehung bei einigen Waldvögeln Amazoniens. *J. Orn.* 111: 285–331.

Haffer, J. 1971. Nachtrag zur Verbreitung von *Pipra fasciicauda* and *Pipra iris* in Brasilien. *J. Orn.* 112: 460–461.

Haffer, J. 1974. *Avian speciation in tropical South America.* Publ. Nuttall Orn. Club 14. Cambridge, MA.

Haffer, J. 1975. The avifauna of northwestern Colombia, South America. *Bonn. Zool. Monogr.* 7. Zoologisches Forschungsinstitut und Museum Alexander Koenig, Bonn.

Haffer, J. 1985. Avian zoogeography of the Neotropical lowlands. In: Buckley, P. A., Foster, M. S., Morton, E. S., Ridgely, R. S. & Buckley, F. G. (eds) *Neotropical Ornithology. Orn. Monogr.* 36: 113–146.

Haffer, J. 1986. Superspecies and species limits in vertebrates. *Z. Zool. Syst. Evol. Forsch.* 24: 169–190.

Haffer, J. 1992a. On the "river effect" in some forest birds of southern Amazonia. *Bol. Mus. Para. E. Goeldi Ser. Zool.* 8: 217–245.

Haffer, J. 1992b. Parapatric species of birds. *Bull. Brit. Orn. Club* 112: 250–264.

Haffer, J. 1997a. Foreword: Species concepts and species limits in ornithology. In: del Hoyo, J., Elliott, A. & Sargatal, J. (eds) *Handbook of the Birds of the World.* Vol. 4. Pp. 11–24. Lynx Edicions, Barcelona.

Haffer, J. 1997b. Contact zones between birds of southern Amazonia. In: Remsen, J. V. (ed.) *Studies in Neotropical Ornithology Honoring Ted Parker. Orn. Monogr.* 48: 281–305.

Haffer, J. 2002. A rare hybrid manakin (Aves, Pipridae) and the origin of vertebrate species in Amazonia. *Rudolstaedter Naturhistor. Schrift.* Suppl. 4: 47–73.

Haffer, J. 2003. Avian zoogeography, speciation and the museum tradition. *Bull Brit. Orn Club* Suppl. 123A: 7–25.

Hagmann, G. 1907. Die Vogelwelt der Insel Mexiana, Amazon-enstrom. *Zool. Jb. (Syst.)* 26: 11–62.

Hallinan, T. 1924. Notes on some Panama Canal Zone birds with special reference to their food. *Auk* 41: 304–326.

Hamilton, J. E. 1939. Additions to the Falkland Islands list. *Ibis* (14)3: 139–140.

Hammick, J. 2004. *Birds of Trinidad & Tobago.* CDs. Mandarin Productions, Wimborne.

Hanif, M. 1967. Observations of the nesting behaviour of the cock of the rock, *Rupicola rupicola*, in captivity. *Timehri* 43: 28–33.

Hansbauer, M. M., Storch, I., Leu, S., Nieto-Holguin, J.-P., Pimentel, R. G., Knauer, F. & Metzger, J. P. W. 2008. Movements of neotropical understory passerines affected by anthropogenic forest edges in the Brazilian Atlantic rainforest. *Biol. Conserv.* 141: 782–791.

Hansbauer, M. M., Storch, I., Végvári, Z., Borntraeger, R., Hettich, U., Pimentel, R. G. & Metzger, J. P. W. 2010. Microhabitat selection of three forest understory birds in the Brazilian Atlantic rainforest. *Biotropica* 42: 355–362.

Hartert, E. 1898. On a collection of birds from north-western Ecuador collected by Mr. W. F. H. Rosenberg. *Novit. Zool.* 5: 477–505.

Hartert, E. 1902. Some further notes on the birds of north-west Ecuador. *Novit. Zool.* 9: 599–617.

Hartert, E. 1903. On a remarkable new oligomyodian genus and species from Ecuador. *Novit. Zool.* 10: 117–118.

Harvey, M. G., Winger, B. M., Seeholzer, G. F. & Cáceres A., D. 2011. Avifauna of the Gran Pajonal and southern Cerros del Sira, Peru. *Wilson J. Orn.* 123: 289–315.

Hasui, É., Mota Gomes, V. S., Kiefer, M. C., Tamashiro, J. & Silva, W. R. 2009. Spatial and seasonal variation in niche partitioning between Blue Manakin (*Chiroxiphia caudata*) and Greenish Schiffornis (*Schiffornis virescens*) in southeastern Brazil. *Stud. Neotrop. Fauna Environ.* 44: 149–159.

Haugaasen, T. & Peres, C. A. 2008. Population abundance and biomass of large-bodied birds in Amazonian flooded and unflooded forests. *Bird Conserv. Int.* 18: 87–101.

Haverschmidt, F. 1948. Bird weights from Surinam. *Wilson Bull.* 60: 230–239.

Haverschmidt, F. 1952. More bird weights from Surinam. *Wilson Bull.* 64: 234–241.

Haverschmidt, F. 1958. Display of *Manacus manacus. Ibis* 100: 626.

Haverschmidt, F. 1965. Variations in plumage of male and female *Pipra aureola. Auk* 82: 502.

Haverschmidt, F. 1968. *Birds of Surinam.* Oliver & Boyd, Edinburgh & London.

Haverschmidt, F. 1971. Variations in plumage of male and female White-crowned Manakins (*Pipra pipra*). *Bull. Brit. Orn. Club* 91: 18.

Haverschmidt, F. 1977. The occurrence of the Crimson Fruitcrow *Haematoderus militaris* in Surinam. *Bull. Brit. Orn. Club* 97: 76.

Haverschmidt, F. & Mees, G. F. 1994. *Birds of Suriname.* VACO, Paramaribo.

Hayes, F. E. 1995. *Status, Distribution and Biogeography of the Birds of Paraguay.* Monogr. Field. Orn. 1. Colorado Springs, American Birding Association.

Hayes, F. E. & Samad, I. 2002. Avifauna of the "Dragon's Teeth": the Bocas Islands, northern Gulf of Paria, between Venezuela and Trinidad. *Occ. Pap. Dept. Life Sci., Univ. West Indies* 11: 62–85.

Hayes, F. E. & Scharf, P. A. 1995a. The birds of Parque Nacional Ybycuí, Paraguay. *Cotinga* 4: 14–19.

Hayes, F. E. & Scharf, P. A. 1995b. The birds of Parque Nacional Cerro Corá, Paraguay. *Cotinga* 4: 20–24.

Hayes, F. E., McNair, D. B., Lucas, F. B., Ramjohn, C. L., Johnson, N. C., Ballah, S. T., Doodnath, L. W. & Garcia, K. M. 2003. Noteworthy observations of birds, including two globally threatened species, in the eastern Paria Peninsula, Venezuela. *Cotinga* 20: 101–102.

Heindl, M. 2002. Social organization on leks of the Wire-tailed Manakin in southern Venezuela. *Condor* 104: 772–779.

Heindl, M. & Winkler, H. 2003a. Vertical lek placement of forest-dwelling manakin species (Aves, Pipridae) is associated with vertical gradients of ambient light. *Biol. J. Linn. Soc.* 80: 647–658.

Heindl, M. & Winkler, H. 2003b. Interacting effects of ambient light and plumage color patterns in displaying Wire-tailed Manakins (Aves, Pipridae). *Behav. Ecol. Sociobiol.* 53: 153–162.

Hellebrekers, W. P. J. 1942. Revision of the Penard oölogical collection from Surinam. *Zool. Med. Leiden* 24: 240–275.

Hellebrekers, W. P. J. 1945. Further notes on the Penard oölogical collection from Surinam. *Zool. Med. Leiden* 25: 93–100.

Hellmayr, C. E. 1903. Über neue und wenig bekannte südamerikanische Vögel. *Verh. Ges. Wien* 53: 199–223.

Hellmayr, C. E. 1906a. Critical notes on the types of little-known species of Neotropical birds. Part 1. *Novit. Zool.* 13: 305–352.

Hellmayr, C. E. 1906b. Notes on a second collection of birds from the district of Pará, Brazil. *Novit. Zool.* 13: 353–385.

Hellmayr, C. E. 1906c. [Exhibition of seven new subspecies of neotropical birds]. *Bull. Brit. Orn. Club* 16: 82–86.

Hellmayr, C. E. 1906d. A revision of the species of the genus *Pipra. Ibis* (8)6: 1–46.

Hellmayr, C. E. 1908. An account of the birds collected by Mons. G. A. Baer in the State of Goyaz, Brazil. *Novit. Zool.* 15: 13–102.

Hellmayr, C. E. 1910. The birds of the Rio Madeira. *Novit. Zool.* 17: 257–428.

Hellmayr, C. E. 1911. A contribution to the ornithology of western Colombia. *Proc. Zool. Soc. Lond.* 1911: 1084–1213.

Hellmayr, C. E. 1929a. A contribution to the ornithology of northeastern Brazil. *Field Mus. Nat. Hist., Zool. Ser.* 12: 235–501.

Hellmayr, C. E. 1929b. Catalogue of birds of the Americas. Part VI. *Field Mus. Nat. Hist., Zool. Ser.* 13: 1–258.

Hellmayr, C. E. 1932. The birds of Chile. *Field Mus. Nat. Hist., Zool. Ser.* 19: 1–472.

Hellmayr, C. E. & Gyldenstolpe, N. 1937. Two new birds from the Brazilian Amazon. *Ark. Zool.* 29: 1–5.

Hempel, A. 1949. Estudo da alimentação natural de aves silvestres do Brasil. *Arq. Inst. Biol.* 19: 237–267.

Hennessey, A. B. 2002. First Bolivian observation of Swallow-tailed Cotinga *Phibalura flavirostris* in 98 years. *Cotinga* 17: 54–55.

Hennessey, A. B. 2004a. Flight display and interspecific aggressive behaviour in Chestnut-crested Cotinga *Ampelion rufaxilla*. *Cotinga* 21: 81–82.

Hennessey, A. B. 2004b. A bird survey of Torcillo-Sarayoj, the lower Yungas of Madidi National Park, Bolivia. *Cotinga* 22: 73–78.

Hennessey, A. B. & Gomez, M. I. 2003. Four bird species new to Bolivia: an ornithological survey of the Yungas site Tokoaque, Madidi National Park. *Cotinga* 19: 25–33.

Hennessey, A. B., Herzog, S. K., Kessler, M. & Robson, D. 2003a. Avifauna of the Pilon Lajas Biosphere Reserve and communal lands, Bolivia. *Bird Conserv. Int.* 13: 319–349.

Hennessey, A. B., Herzog, S. K. & Sagot, F. 2003b. *Lista Anotada de las Aves de Bolivia*, 2nd edn. Asociación Armonía, Santa Cruz de la Sierra.

Henriques, L. M. P. & Wunderle, J. 2001. A avifauna de sub-bosque da Floresta Nacional do Tapajós. In: Congr. Bras. Orn. IX, Curitiba, *Resumos*: 103.

Henriques, L. M. P., Wunderle, J. M. & Willig, M. R. 2003. Birds of the Tapajós National Forest, Brazilian Amazon: a preliminary assessment. *Orn. Neotrop.* 14: 307–338.

Henry, P.-Y. 2008. Aves, Cotingidae, *Doliornis remseni*: filling distribution gap, [*sic*] habitat, and conservation, Ecuador. *Cheetal* 4: 1–4.

Herrera, G. A. 1995. Nueva observación del Pájaro Campana en Misiones. *Nuestras Aves* 31: 19–20.

Herzog, S. K., Kessler, M., Maijer, S. & Hohnwald, S. 1997. Distributional notes on birds of Andean dry forests in Bolivia. *Bull. Brit. Orn. Club* 117: 223–235.

Herzog, S. K., Fjeldså, J., Kessler, M. & Balderrama, J. A. 1999. Ornithological surveys in the Cordillera Cocapata, depto. Cochabamba, Bolivia, a transition zone between humid and dry intermontane Andean habitats. *Bull. Brit. Orn. Club* 119: 162–177.

Hidalgo, J., Ryder, T. B., Tori, W. P., Durães, R., Blake, J. G. & Loiselle, B. A. 2008. Nest architecture and placement of three manakin species in lowland Ecuador. *Cotinga* 29: 57–61.

Hidasi, J. 1998. *Lista Preliminar das Aves do Tocantins*. Ed. UNITINS, Palmas.

Hidasi, J. 2007. *Aves de Goiás*. Ed. UCG & Ed. Kelps, Goiânia.

Hilty, S. L. 1977. *Chlorospingus flavovirens* rediscovered, with notes on other Pacific Colombian and Cauca Valley birds. *Auk* 94: 44–49.

Hilty, S. L. 1997. Seasonal distribution of birds at a cloud-forest locality, the Anchicayá Valley, in western Colombia. In: Remsen, J. V. (ed.) *Studies in Neotropical Ornithology Honoring Ted Parker. Orn. Monogr.* 48: 321–343.

Hilty, S. L. 2003. *Birds of Venezuela*. Princeton University Press, Princeton, NJ.

Hilty, S. L. & Brown, W. L. 1983. Range extensions of Colombian birds as indicated by the M. A. Carriker Jr. collection at the National Museum of Natural History, Smithsonian Institution. *Bull. Brit. Orn. Club* 103: 5–17.

Hilty, S. L. & Brown, W. L. 1986. *A Guide to the Birds of Colombia*. Princeton University Press, Princeton, NJ.

Hinkelmann, C. & Fiebig, J. 2001. An early contribution to the avifauna of Paraná, Brazil. The Arkady Fiedler expedition of 1928/29. *Bull. Brit. Orn. Club* 121: 116–127.

Hinojosa, M., Martinez, O. & Guerra, J. F. 1998. Acerca de la avifauna del trayecto Pelechuco-Mojos-Apolo, Prov. Franz Tamayo, Dpto. La Paz. In: Sagot, F. & Guerrero, J. (eds) *Actas del IV Encuentro Boliviano para la Conservación de las Aves, 25 a 27 de octubre de 1997, Tarija, Bolivia*. Santa Cruz.

Höglund, J. & Shorey, L. 2003. Local genetic structure in a White-bearded Manakin population. *Mol. Ecol.* 12: 2457–2463.

Höglund, J. & Shorey, L. 2004. Genetic divergence in the superspecies *Manacus*. *Biol. J. Linn. Soc.* 81: 439–447.

Hohnwald, S. 2009. Bird records from the rural landscape of Igarapé-Açu municipality, northeastern Pará. *Bol. Mus. Para. E. Goeldi Cienc. Nat.* 4: 119–131.

Holt, E. G. 1925. The dance of the Tangara (*Chiroxiphia caudata* (Shaw)). *Auk* 42: 588–590.

Holt, E. G. 1928. An ornithological survey of the Serra do Itatiaia, Brazil. *Bull. Amer. Mus. Nat. Hist.* 57: 251–326.

Hornbuckle, J. 1999. The birds of Abra Patricia and the upper río Mayo, San Martín, north Peru. *Cotinga* 12: 11–28.

d'Horta, F. M., Kirwan, G. M. & Buzzetti, D. in prep. The juvenal plumages of Cinereous Mourner (*Laniocera hypopyrra*) and Elegant Mourner (*Laniisoma elegans*).

Hosner, P. A. 2010. Birding off the beaten path: visiting and documenting the birdlife of poorly surveyed areas. *Neotrop. Birding* 7: 42–47.

Hosner, P. A., Behrens, K. D. & Hennessey, A. B. 2009. Birds (Aves), Serrania Sadiri, Parque Nacional Madidi, Depto. La Paz, Bolivia. *Check List* 5: 222–237.

Howe, H. F. 1977. Bird activity and seed dispersal of a tropical wet forest tree. *Ecology* 58: 539–550.

Howe, H. F. 1980. Monkey dispersal and waste of a Neotropical fruit. *Ecology* 61: 944–959.

Howe, H. F. & de Steven, D. 1979. Fruit production, migrant bird visitation, and seed dispersal of *Guarea glabra* in Panama. *Oecologia* 39: 185–196.

Howell, S. N. G. 1999. *Where to Watch Birds in Mexico*. Christopher Helm, London.

Howell, S. N. G. & Webb, S. 1992. New and noteworthy bird records from Guatemala and Honduras. *Bull. Brit. Orn. Club* 112: 42–49.

Howell, S. N. G. & Webb, S. 1995. *A Guide to the Birds of Mexico and Northern South America*. Oxford University Press, Oxford.

Howell, T. R. 1957. Birds of a second-growth rain forest area of Nicaragua. *Condor* 59: 73–111.

Hudon, J., Capparella, A. P. & Brush, A. H. 1989. Plumage pigment differences in manakins of the *Pipra erythrocephala* superspecies. *Auk* 106: 34–41.

Humphrey, P. S., Bridge, D., Reynolds, P. W. & Peterson, R. T. 1970. *Birds of Isla Grande (Tierra del Fuego)*. Smithsonian Institution, Washington, DC.

Iartelli, R. 2004. Anilhamento da avifauna em ambientes alterados de Mata Atlântica, na Serra do Itapety, Mogi das Cruzes, SP. In: Congr. Bras. Orn. XII, Blumenau, *Resumos*: 247.

Ihering, H. von. 1898. As aves do Estado de S. Paulo. *Rev. Mus. Paulista* 3: 113–476.

Ihering, H. von. 1900. Catalogo critico-comparativo dos ninhos e ovos das aves do Brasil. *Rev. Mus. Paulista* 4: 191–300.

Ihering, H. von. 1902. Contribuições para o conhecimento da ornitologia de São Paulo. *Rev. Mus. Paulista* 5: 261–329.

Ihering, H. von. 1914. Novas observações sobre ninhos e ovos de aves do Brasil. *Rev. Mus. Paulista* 9: 420–448.

Imberti, S., Areta, J. I., Pearman, M., Mazar Barnett, J., Pugnali, G., Roesler, I., Monteleone, D., Casañas, H. & Rodríguez Goñi, H. 2009. *Bird Sounds of Argentina and Adjacent Areas*, Vol. 1. DVD-ROM. WildSounds, Salthouse.

Ingels, J. 1981. Notes on some Surinam birds. *Bull. Brit. Orn. Club* 101: 363–370.

Ingels, J. 2001. Notes on some French Guianan birds. *Tangara* 1: 139–145.

Ingels, J. 2008. Nest, nestling care, and breeding season of the Spangled Cotinga (*Cotinga cayana*) in French Guiana. *Wilson J. Orn.* 120: 871–874.

Ingels, J. & Vinot, A. 2010. First nest of Dusky Purpletuft *Iodopleura fusca*, from French Guiana. *Bull. Brit. Orn. Club* 130: 71–72.

Ingui, D. L. & Parruco, C. H. 2009. Diferenciação e uso de habitat pela aves: estudo de caso na Estação Ecológica do Jataí, Luiz Antônio (SP). In: Simon, J. E., Raposo, M. A., Stopiglia, R. & Peres, J. (eds) *XVII Congresso Brasileiro de Ornitologia Resumos, Aracruz, ES: Biogeografia das aves da Mata Atlântica*: 55.

Irestedt, M., Ohlson, J. I., Zuccon, D., Kallersjo, M. & Ericson, P. G. P. 2006. Nuclear DNA from old collections of avian study skins reveals the evolutionary history of the Old World suboscines (Aves, Passeriformes). *Zool. Scripta* 35: 567–580.

Isler, M. L. 1997. A sector-based ornithological Geographic Information System for the Neotropics. In: Remsen, J. V. (ed.) *Studies in Neotropical Ornithology Honoring Ted Parker. Orn. Monogr.* 48: 345–358.

Jacobs, M. & Walker, J. S. 1999. Density estimates of birds inhabiting fragments of cloud forest in southern Ecuador. *Bird Conserv. Int.* 9: 73–79.

Jahn, O. & Mena-Valenzuela, P. 2002. *Cephalopterus penduliger*. In: Granizo, T., Pacheco, C., Ribadeneira, M. B., Guerrero, M. & Suárez, L. (eds) *Libro Rojo de las Aves del Ecuador*. SIMBIOE, Conservation International, EcoCiencia, Ministerio del Ambiente & UICN, Quito.

Jahn, O., Vargas Grefa, E. E. & Schuchmann, K.-L. 1999. The life history of the Long-wattled Umbrellabird *Cephalopterus penduliger* in the Andean foothills of north-west Ecuador: leks, behaviour, ecology and conservation. *Bird Conserv. Int.* 9: 81–94.

Jahn, O., Moore, J. V., Valenzuela, P. M., Krabbe, N., Coopmans, P., Lysinger, M. & Ridgely, R. S. 2002. *The Birds of Northwest Ecuador. Vol. 2: The Lowlands and Lower Foothills*. CDs. John V. Moore Nature Recordings, San Jose, CA.

Jaksic, F. M. & Lazo, I. 1999. Response of a bird assemblage in semiarid Chile to the 1997–1998 El Niño. *Wilson Bull.* 111: 527–535.

Janni, O., Boano, G., Pavia, M. & Gertosio, G. 2008. Notes on the breeding of birds in Yanchaga-Chemillén National Park, Peru. *Cotinga* 30: 42–46.

Jaramillo, A. 2003. *Birds of Chile including the Antarctic Peninsula, the Falkland Islands and South Georgia*. Christopher Helm, London.

Jenkins, P. G. (ed.) 1982. *Report on the Royal Air Force Ornithological Society Expedition to Belize 1981*. RAFOS, Surbiton.

Jiguet, F., Barbet-Massin, M. & Henry, P.-Y. 2010. Predicting potential distributions of two rare allopatric sister species, the globally threatened *Doliornis* cotingas in the Andes. *J. Field Orn.* 81: 325–339.

Jobling, J. A. 1995. *A Dictionary of Scientific Bird Names*. Oxford University Press, Oxford.

Johansson, U. S., Irestedt, M., Parsons, T. J. & Ericson, P. G. P. 2002. Basal phylogeny of the Tyrannoidea based on comparisons of cytochrome b and exons of nuclear c-myc and RAG-1 genes. *Auk* 119: 984–995.

Jones, H. L. 2004. *Birds of Belize*. Christopher Helm, London.

Jones, J., Ramoni-Perazzi, P., Carruthers, E. H. & Robertson, R. 2002. Species composition of bird communities in shade coffee plantations in the Venezuelan Andes. *Orn. Neotrop.* 13: 397–412.

Jullien, M. & Thiollay, J.-M. 1998. Multi-species territoriality and dynamic of Neotropical forest understorey bird flocks. *J. Anim. Ecol.* 67: 227–252.

Junge, G. C. A. & Mees, G. F. 1958. The avifauna of Trinidad and Tobago. *Zool. Verhandelingen* 37.

Juniper, T. 2004. *Spix's Macaw: the Race to Save the World's Rarest Bird*. Atria Books, London.

Kaiser, M. 1999. Erfolgreiche Zucht der Rotbauchpipra (*Pipra aureola*) im Tierpark Berlin-Friedrichsfelde. *Milu* 9: 637–645.

Kaminski, N. & Carrano, E. 2004. Comunidade de aves em um ecótone (floresta ombrófila densa e f.o. mista) na Serra do Cabral, município de Tijucas do Sul, Paraná. In: Congr. Bras. Orn. XII, Blumenau, *Resumos*: 252.

Kantak, G. E. 1979. Observations on some fruit-eating birds in Mexico. *Auk* 96: 183–186.

Karubian, J. & Smith, T. B. 2007a. Lek dynamics and sexual selection in the Long-wattled Umbrellabird (*Cephalopterus penduliger*, Cotingidae). *Abstracts VIII Neotrop. Orn. Congr., Maturín, Venezuela, mayo 13–19 2007*: 46.

Karubian, J. & Smith, T. B. 2007b. Causes and consequences of non-random seed dispersal by the Long-wattled Umbrellabird (*Cephalopterus penduliger*, Cotingidae). *Abstracts VIII Neotrop. Orn. Congr., Maturín, Venezuela, mayo 13–19 2007*: 46.

Karubian, J., Castañeda, G., Freile, J. F., Salazar, R. T., Santander, T. & Smith, T. B. 2003. Nesting biology of a female Long-wattled Umbrellabird *Cephalopterus penduliger* in north-western Ecuador. *Bird Conserv. Int.* 13: 351–360.

Kendall, A. & Kuehler, C. 1989. Artificial incubation and hand-rearing of an Andean cock of the rock (*Rupicola peruviana*). *Avicult. Mag.* 95: 153–158.

Kenefick, M., Restall, R. & Hayes, F. 2007. *Birds of Trinidad & Tobago*. Christopher Helm, London.

Kennard, F. H. & Peters, J. L. 1928. A collection of birds from the Almirante Bay region of Panama. *Proc. Boston Soc. Nat. Hist.* 38: 443–465.

King, J. R. 1991. Body weights of some Ecuadorean birds. *Bull. Brit. Orn. Club* 111: 46–49.

King, W. B. 1978–1979. *Red Data Book, 2. Aves*, 2nd edn. International Union for the Conservation of Nature & Natural Resources, Morges.

Kirwan, G. M. 2008. The range of the Pin-tailed Manakin *Ilicura militaris* extends to central Brazil. *Rev. Bras. Orn.* 16: 260–261.

Kirwan, G. M. 2009. Notes on the breeding ecology and seasonality of some Brazilian birds. *Rev. Bras. Orn.* 17: 121–136.

Kirwan, G. M. 2011. External characters suggest that Long-tailed Manakin *Chiroxiphia linearis* is monotypic. *Bull. Brit. Orn. Club.* 131: 76–80.

Kirwan, G. M. & Marlow, T. 1996. A review of avifaunal records from Mindo, Pichincha province, north-western Ecuador. *Cotinga* 6: 47–57.

Kirwan, G. M. & Pacheco, J. F. in press. *Ararajuba* (now the *Revista Brasiliera de Ornitologia*). In: Dickinson, E. C., Overstreet, L. K., Dowsett, R. J. & Bruce, M. D. (eds) *The Dating of Scientific Names in Ornithology; A Directory*. The Ray Society, London.

Kirwan, G. M., Wallace, G. & Minns, J. (compilers) 2006. Neotropical notebook: Brazil, Ecuador and Peru. *Cotinga* 26: 78–96.

Kirwan, G. M., Calderón, D., Minns, J. & Roesler, I. (compilers) 2008. Neotropical notebook: Argentina. *Cotinga* 29: 187.

Kirwan, G. M., Calderón, D., Minns, J. & Roesler, I. (compilers) 2009. Neotropical notebook: Venezuela. *Cotinga* 31: 167.

Kirwan, G. M., Durand, A., Beadle, D. & Shirihai, H. submitted. First nesting data for the Cerulean-capped Manakin (*Lepidothrix coeruleocapilla*), from southeast Peru. *Orn. Neotrop.*

Kjeldsen, J. P. 2004. Aves del municipio de Prinzapolka. *Wani* 38: 56–74.

Klebauskas, G. & Pacheco, A. 2000. The nest of the Snowy Cotinga *Carpodectes nitidus* in Costa Rica. *Cotinga* 14: 102.

Knapp, D. & Will, T. 2008. *Birdsounds of Nicaragua*. MP3 CD. Winsum, Birdsounds.nl.

Koepcke, M. 1954. *Zaratornis stresemanni* nov. gen. nov. spec., un cotingido nuevo del Peru. *Publ. Mus. Hist. Nat. Javier Prado Ser. A (Zool.)* 16: 1–8.

Koepcke, M. 1958. Die Vögel des Waldes von Zárate. *Bonn. Zool. Beitr.* 9: 167–168.

Koepcke, M. 1961. Birds of the western slope of the Andes of Peru. *Amer. Mus. Novit.* 2028: 1–31.

Koepcke, M. 1970. *The Birds of the Department of Lima, Peru*. Livingston Publishing, Wynnewood, PA.

Knox, A. G. & Walters, M. P. 1994. *Extinct and Endangered Birds in the Collections of The Natural History Museum*. British Ornithologists' Club Occ. Publ. 1, Tring.

Kohler, G., Legal, E. & Testoni, C. 2009. Registros de aves raras ou ameaçadas em novas localidades no Estado de Santa Catarina, sul do Brasil. *Cotinga* 31: 104–107.

Komar, O. 1998. Avian diversity in El Salvador. *Wilson Bull.* 110: 511–533.

Krabbe, N. 1984. An additional specimen of the Swallow-tailed Cotinga *Phibalura flavirostris boliviana*. *Bull. Brit. Orn. Club* 104: 68–69.

Krabbe, N. 2007. Birds collected by P. W. Lund and J. T. Reinhardt in south-eastern Brazil between 1825 and 1855, with notes on P. W. Lund's travels in Rio de Janeiro. *Rev. Bras. Orn.* 15: 331–357.

Krabbe, N. 2008. *Birds of the Sierra Nevada de Santa Marta, Colombia*. CDs. John V. Moore Nature Recordings, San Jose, CA.

Krabbe, N. & Nilsson, J. 2003. *Birds of Ecuador*. DVD-ROM. Bird Songs International, Westernieland.

Krabbe, N. & Sornoza, M. F. 1994. Avifaunistic results of a subtropical camp in the Cordillera del Condor, southeastern Ecuador. *Bull. Brit. Orn. Club* 114: 55–61.

Krabbe, N., Poulsen, B. O., Frølander, A., Hinojosa, B. M. & Quiroga, O. C. 1996. Birds of montane forest fragments in

Chuquisaca Department, Bolivia. *Bull. Brit. Orn. Club* 116: 230–243.

Krabbe, N., Poulsen, B. O., Frølander, A., Hinojosa, B. M. & Quiroga, O. C. 1997. Range extensions of cloud forest birds from the high Andes of Ecuador: new sites for rare or little-recorded species. *Bull. Brit. Orn. Club* 117: 248–256.

Krabbe, N., Flórez, P., Suárez, G., Castaño, J., Arango, J. D. & Duque, A. 2006. The birds of Páramo de Frontino, Western Andes of Colombia. *Orn. Colombiana* 4: 39–50.

Krauczuk, E. R. & Baldo, J. D. 2001. Las aves del Parque Provincial de la Araucaria (San Pedro, Misiones, Argentina) y su importancia en la conservación del área protegida. In: Congr. Bras. Orn. IX, Curitiba, *Resumos*: 105.

Krauczuk, E. R. & Baldo, J. D. 2004. Contribuição para o conhecimento da avifauna de um fragmento de floresta com araucária em Misiones, Argentina. *Atualidades. Orn.* 119: 6.

Kricher, J. C. & Davis, W. E. 1992. Patterns of avian species richness in disturbed and undisturbed habitats in Belize. In: Hagan, J. M. & Johnston, D. W. (eds) *Ecology and Conservation of Neotropical Migrant Landbirds.* Pp. 240–256. Smithsonian Institution Press, Washington, DC.

Krijger, C. L., Opdam, M., Théry, M. & Bongers, F. 1997. Courtship behaviour of manakins and seed bank composition in a French Guianan rain forest. *J. Trop. Ecol.* 13: 631–636.

Kroodsma, D. 2005. *The Singing Life of Birds: The Art and Science of Listening to Birdsong.* Houghton Mifflin, New York.

Küchler, W. 1936. Anatomische Untersuchungen an *Phytotoma rara* Mol. *J. Orn.* 84: 352–362.

Kuroda, N. 1933. On a collection of birds from Chile. *Tori* 8: 128–147.

Lack, D. 1966. *Population Studies of Birds.* Clarendon Press, Oxford.

Lack, D. 1968. *Ecological Adaptations for Breeding in Birds.* Methuen, London.

LaFountain, A. M., Kaligotla, S., Cawley, S., Riedl, K. M., Schwartz, S. J., Frank, H. A. & Prum, R. O. 2010. Novel methoxy-carotenoids from the burgundy-colored plumage of the Pompadour Cotinga *Xipholena punicea. Archiv. Biochem. Biophysics* 504: 142–153.

Lambert, F. & Kirwan, G. M. 2010. The twice-vanishing 'pardalote': what future for the Kinglet Calyptura? *Neotrop. Birding* 6: 4–17.

Lamm, D. W. 1948. Notes on the birds of the states of Pernambuco and Paraíba, Brazil. *Auk* 65: 261–283.

Land, H. C. 1963. A collection of birds from the Caribbean lowlands of Guatemala. *Condor* 65: 49–65.

Land, H. C. & Wolf, L. L. 1961. Additions to the Guatemalan bird list. *Auk* 78: 94–95.

Lane, D. F. 2003. First description of song display and other notes on the Bare-necked Fruitcrow (*Gymnoderus foetidus*, Cotingidae). *Orn. Neotrop.* 14: 491–497.

Lane, D. F., Pequeño, T. & Villar, J. F. 2003. Birds. In: Pitman, N., Vriesendorp, C. & Moskovits, D. (eds) *Perú: Yavarí.* Rapid Biological Inventories Report 11. The Field Museum, Chicago.

Langley, N. 2010. Species action updates. *World Birdwatch* 32(3): 22–23.

Lanyon, S. M. & Lanyon, W. E. 1989. The systematic position of the plantcutters, *Phytotoma. Auk* 106: 422–432.

Lanyon, W. E. 1985. A phylogeny of the myiarchine flycatchers. In: Buckley, P. A., Foster, M. S., Morton, E. S., Ridgely, R. S. & Buckley, F. G. (eds) *Neotropical Ornithology. Orn. Monogr.* 36: 383–389.

Laranjeiras, T. O., Moura, N. G., Carvalho, A. R. & Sant'Ana, C. R. 2004. Avifauna do *campus* da Universidade Estadual de Goiás (UEG), Anápolis, Brasil. In: Congr. Bras. Orn. XII, Blumenau, *Resumos*: 259.

Lau, R. 2004. Listagem preliminar da avifauna do Morro Gaúcho e arredores do vale do Taquari, Rio Grande do Sul. In: Congr. Bras. Orn. XII, Blumenau, *Resumos*: 261.

Laucht, S., DuVal, E. H. & Kempenaers, B. 2008. Maternal correlates of brood sex ratio variation in the lekking lance-tailed manakin *Chiroxiphia lanceolata. J. Avian Biol.* 39: 198–205.

Lawson, B. 2009. *Where to Watch Birds in Costa Rica.* Christopher Helm, London.

Le Maitre, C. & Reynaud, P. A. 1994. Crimson-hooded Manakin display in a dense population: cooperation versus competition. In: Dittami, J., Bock, W., Taborsky, M., van den Elzen, R. & Vogel-Millesi, E. (eds) *Research Notes on Avian Biology 1994: Selected Contributions from the XXI International Ornithological Congress. J. Orn.* 135 (Suppl.).

Lebbin, D. J., Hosner, P. A., Andersen, M. J., Valdez, U. & Tori, W. P. 2007. First description of nest and eggs of the White-lined Antbird (*Percnostola lophotes*), and breeding observations of poorly known birds inhabiting *Guadua* bamboo in southeastern Peru. *Bol. Soc. Antioqueña Orn.* 17: 119–132.

Leck, C. F. 1972. Seasonal changes in feeding pressure of fruit- and nectar-eating birds in Panama. *Condor* 74: 54–60.

Lees, A. C., Davis, B. J. W., Oliveira, A. V. G. & Peres, C. A. 2008. Avifauna of a structurally heterogeneous forest landscape in the Serra dos Caiabis, Mato Grosso, Brazil: a preliminary assessment. *Cotinga* 29: 149–159.

Lees, A. C., Zimmer, K. J., Whittaker, A., Marantz, C. A. & Whitney, B. M. (in prep.) Alta Floresta revisited: a new avifaunal survey for the most heavily inventoried site in the southern Brazilian Amazon.

Lemos, M. 1982. Notas sobre a criação do galo-das-rochas em cativeiro (Rupicolidae, Aves). *Fund. Bras. Conserv. Nat. Bol. Inform.* 17: 96–100.

Lentino, M., Pérez, L., Barrowclough, G. & Sweet, P. 1998. Notas sobre las aves de la cima del Auyantepuy, Parque Nacional Canaima, Estado Bolívar, Venezuela. *Acta Terramaris* 11: 1–12.

Lentino, M., Bonaccorso, E., García, M. A., Fernández, E. A., Rivero, R. & Portas, C. 2003. Longevity records of wild birds in the Henri Pittier National Park, Venezuela. *Orn. Neotrop.* 14: 545–548.

Leuchtenberger, R. & Roper, J. 2003a. O canto de *Procnias nudicollis* informa à fêmea sobre a qualidade do cantor? In: Machado, C. G. (ed.) *XI Congresso Brasileiro de Ornitologia Resumos*, Feira de Santana, BA: 50.

Leuchtenberger, R. & Roper, J. 2003b. A composição da dieta de *Procnias nudicollis* pode influir na qualidade do canto? In: Machado, C. G. (ed.) *XI Congresso Brasileiro de Ornitologia Resumos*, Feira de Santana, BA: 51.

Levey, D. J. 1987. Sugar-tasting ability and fruit selection in tropical fruit-eating birds. *Auk* 104: 173–179.

Levey, D. J. 1988. Spatial and temporal variation in Costa Rican fruit and fruit-eating abundance. *Ecol. Monogr.* 58: 251–269.

Lewins, E., Ordonez, L. & Schulenburg, W. 1994. Breeding the Capuchinbird. *Avicult. Mag.* 100: 3–7.

Lill, A. 1974a. Sexual behaviour in the lek-forming White-bearded Manakin (*Manacus manacus trinitatis* Hartert). *Z. Tierpsychol.* 36: 1–36.

Lill, A. 1974b. Social organization and space utilization in the lek-forming White-bearded Manakin, *Manacus manacus trinitatis* Hartert. *Z. Tierpsychol.* 36: 513–530.

Lill, A. 1975. The evolution of clutch-size and male "chauvinism" in the White-bearded Manakin. *Living Bird* 13: 211–231.

Lill, A. 1976. Lek behaviour in the Golden-headed Manakin, *Pipra erythrocephala*, in Trinidad (West Indies). *Advances in Ethology* 18.

Lima, C. A., Siqueira, P. R., Gonçalves, R. M. M., Vasconcelos, M. F. & Leite, L. P. 2010. Dieta de aves da Mata Atlântica: uma abordagem baseada em conteúdos estomacais. *Orn. Neotrop.* 21: 425–438.

Lima, L. C. 2005. O acervo ornitológico brasileiro do Finnish Museum of Natural History, Helsinki, Finlândia. In: Congr. Bras. Orn. XIII, Belém, *Resumos*: 160.

Lima, P. C., Santos, S. S., Magalhães, Z. S. & Rocha Lima, R. C. F. 2001. Avifauna da Mata Atlântica no Baixo Sul, Bahia. In: Congr. Bras. Orn. IX, Curitiba, *Resumos*: 114.

Linhares, K. V., Soares, F. A. & Machado, I. C. S. 2010. Nest support plants of the Araripe Manakin *Antilophia bokermanni*, a Critically Endangered endemic bird from Ceará, Brazil. *Cotinga* 32: 121–125.

Lint, K. C. & Dolan, J. M. 1966. Successful breeding of the Orange-breasted Cotinga (*Pipreola jucunda*) in the San Diego Zoological Gardens. *Avicult. Mag.* 72: 18–20.

Lloyd, C. A. 1895. Stray notes from Pirara. *Timehri* 9: 220–232.

Lloyd, H. 2000. Population densities of the Black-faced Cotinga *Conioptilon mcilhennyi* in south-east Peru. *Bird Conserv. Int.* 10: 277–285.

Lloyd, H. 2004. Habitat and population estimates of some threatened lowland forest bird species in Tambopata, south-east Peru. *Bird Conserv. Int.* 14: 261–277.

Lo, V. K. 1994. Ocorrência de *Laniisoma elegans* (Thunberg, 1823) (Cotingidae) e *Fluvicola nengeta* (Linnaeus, 1766) (Tyrannidae) no município de São Paulo, SP. *Bol. CEO* 10: 35–41.

Loiselle, B. A. 1988. Bird abundance and seasonality in a Costa Rican lowland forest canopy. *Condor* 90: 961–972.

Loiselle, B. A. & Blake, J. G. 1999. Dispersal of melastome seeds by fruit-eating birds of tropical forest understory. *Ecology* 80: 330–336.

Loiselle, B. A., Blake, J. G., Durães, R., Ryder, T. B. & Tori, W. 2007a. Environmental and spatial segregation of leks among six co-occurring species of manakins (Pipridae) in eastern Ecuador. *Auk* 124: 420–431.

Loiselle, B. A., Blendinger, P. G., Blake, J. G. & Ryder, T. B. 2007b. Ecological redundancy in seed dispersal systems: a comparison between manakins (Aves: Pipridae) in two tropical forests. In: Dennis, A. J., Schupp, E. W., Green, R. & Westcott, D. W. (eds) *Seed Dispersal: Theory and its Application in a Changing World.* Pp. 178–195. CAB International Publishing, Wallingford.

Loiselle, B. A., Ryder, T. B., Durães, R., Tori, W., Blake, J. G. & Parker, P. G. 2007c. Kin selection does not explain male aggregation at leks of 4 manakin species. *Behav. Ecol.* 18: 287–291.

Londoño, G. A. & Cadena, C. D. 2003. The nest and eggs of the Cinereous Mourner (*Laniocera hypopyrra*). *Wilson Bull.* 115: 115–118.

Lönnberg, E. & Rendahl, H. 1922. A contribution to the ornithology of Ecuador. *Arkiv. Zool.* 14: 1–87.

Lopes, L. E. & Braz, V. S. 2007. Aves da região de Pedro Afonso, Tocantins, Brasil. *Rev. Bras. Orn.* 15: 530–537.

Lopes, L. E., Fernandes, A. M. & Marini, M. Â. 2005. Diet of some Atlantic Forest birds. *Ararajuba* 13: 95–103.

Lopes, L. E., Malacco, G. B., Vasconcelos, M. F., Carvalho, C. E. A., Duca, C., Fernandes, A. M., D'Angelo Neto, S. & Marini, M. Â. 2008. Aves da região de Unaí e Cabeceira Grande, noroeste de Minas Gerais, Brasil. *Rev. Bras. Orn.* 16: 193–206.

Lopes, L. E., Batista de Pinho, J., Bernardon, B., Ficagna de Oliveira, F., Bernardon, G., Ferreira, L. P., Vasconcelos, M. F., Maldonado-Coelho, M., Albonette de Nóbrega, P. F. & Rubio, T. C. 2009. Aves do Chapada dos Guimarães, Mato Grosso, Brasil: uma síntese histórica do conhecimento. *Pap. Avuls. Zool., Mus. Zool., Univ. São Paulo* 49: 9–47.

López-Lanús, B. 2000. Display and mechanical sound in Dusky Piha *Lipaugus fuscocinereus. Cotinga* 13: 44–45.

López-Lanús, B., Salaman, P. G. W., Cowley, T. P., Arango, S. & Renjifo, L. M. 2000. The threatened birds of the río Toche, Cordillera Central, Colombia. *Cotinga* 14: 17–23.

Losada-Prado, S., Gonzalez-Prieto, A. M., Carvajal-Lozano, A. M. & Molina-Martínez, Y. G. 2003. Especies endémicas y amenazadas registradas en la cuenca del río Coello (Tolima) durante estudios rápidos en 2003. *Orn. Colombiana* 3: 76–80.

Low, R. 2009. *Go West for Parrots!* Insignis Publications, Mansfield.

Lowe, P. R. 1942. The anatomy of Gould's Manakin (*Manacus vitellinus*) in relation to its display. *Ibis* 6: 50–83.

Lowe, P. W. 1979. The introduction, management, care and behaviour of the bare-throated bellbird (*Procnias nudicollis*) at the West Country Wild Life Park, Cricket St Thomas, Chard, Somerset. *Int. Zoo News* 26: 18–20.

Lowen, J. 2010. New birding 'lodges' in Argentina. *Neotrop. Birding* 6: 49–55.

Lowen, J. & Bernardon, G. 2010. Seeing Pantanal specialities along the Transpantaneira. *Neotrop. Birding* 6: 40–47.

Lowen, J. C., Clay, R. P., Brooks, T. M., Esquivel, E. Z., Bartrina, L., Barnes, R., Butchart, S. H. M. & Etcheverry, N. I. 1995.

Bird conservation in the Paraguayan Atlantic Forest. *Cotinga* 4: 58–64.

Lowen, J. C., Bartrina, L., Clay, R. P. & Tobias, J. A. 1996. *Biological Surveys and Conservation Priorities in Eastern Paraguay.* CSB Conservation Publications, Cambridge, UK.

Lowery, G. H. & O'Neill, J. P. 1966. A new genus and species of cotinga from eastern Peru. *Auk* 83: 1–9.

Luiz, E. R., Mattos, G. T., Morais, F. C., Paula, G. A. & Ribon, R. 2004a. Avifauna do alto rio Mucuri, região de Teófilo Otoni, Minas Gerais. In: Congr. Bras. Orn. XII, Blumenau, *Resumos*: 281.

Luiz, E. R., Morais, F. C., Mattos, G. T. & Ribon, R. 2004b. Avifauna das Fazendas Limoeiro e Bela Vista, município de Almenara, Minas Gerais. In: Congr. Bras. Orn. XII, Blumenau, *Resumos*: 282.

Lüthi, H. 1970. Blick in die Natur: der geheimnisvelle Zárate. *Bol. Colonia Suiza en el Perú* 5: 15–17.

Luy G., A. & Bigio E., D. 1994. Notes on the feeding habits of the Andean Cock-of-the-rock (*Rupicola peruviana*). *Orn. Neotrop.* 5: 115–116.

Lyons, J. & Perez, V. 2000. New records and updates for Mindo, Ecuador. *Cotinga* 13: 67–68.

Lysinger, M., Moore, J. V., Krabbe, N., Coopmans, P., Lane, D. F., Navarrete, L., Nilsson, J. & Ridgely, R. S. 2005. *The Birds of Eastern Ecuador. Vol. 1: The Foothills and Lower Subtropics.* CDs. John V. Moore Nature Recordings, San Jose, CA.

Macarrão, A. 2009. Levantamento preliminar da avifauna de Paranapiacaba – Santo André, SP. In: Simon, J. E., Raposo, M. A., Stopiglia, R. & Peres, J. (eds) *XVII Congresso Brasileiro de Ornitologia Resumos, Aracruz, ES: Biogeografia das aves da Mata Atlântica*: 89.

Macarrão, A. & Granzinolli, M. A. M. 2009. Os visitantes da ilha da Queimada Grande, SP. In: Simon, J. E., Raposo, M. A., Stopiglia, R. & Peres, J. (eds) *XVII Congresso Brasileiro de Ornitologia Resumos, Aracruz, ES: Biogeografia das aves da Mata Atlântica*: 59.

Macedo, R. C. & Carrano, E. 2009. Riqueza e estrutura da comunidade de aves no campus I – PUCPR, Curitiba, Paraná. In: Simon, J. E., Raposo, M. A., Stopiglia, R. & Peres, J. (eds) *XVII Congresso Brasileiro de Ornitologia Resumos, Aracruz, ES: Biogeografia das aves da Mata Atlântica*: 59.

Maciel, E. 2009. *Aves do Município do Rio de Janeiro*, 2nd edn. Ed. Technical Books, Rio de Janeiro.

Maciel, F. G., Dalbeto, A. C., Ferreira, C. D. & Donatelli, R. J. 2009. Aves de sub-bosque em um fragmento de mata estacional no Estado de São Paulo, Brasil. In: Simon, J. E., Raposo, M. A., Stopiglia, R. & Peres, J. (eds) *XVII Congresso Brasileiro de Ornitologia Resumos, Aracruz, ES: Biogeografia das aves da Mata Atlântica*: 59.

MacLeod, R., Ewing, S. K., Herzog, S. K., Bryce, R., Evans, K. L. & Maccormick, A. 2005. First ornithological inventory for the yungas forests of the Cordilleras Cocapata and Mosetenes, Cochabamba, Bolivia. *Bird Conserv. Int.* 15: 361–382.

Maders, C., Farina, N. & Bodrati, A. 2007. Redescubrimiento del Bailarín Castaño (*Piprites pileata*) en Argentina. *Orn. Neotrop.* 18: 127–131.

Madroño N., A., Clay, R. P., Robbins, M. B., Rice, N. H., Faucett, R. C. & Lowen, J. C. 1997a. An avifaunal survey of the vanishing interior Atlantic forest of San Rafael National Park, departments Itapúa/Caazapá, Paraguay. *Cotinga* 7: 45–53.

Madroño N., A., Robbins, M. B. & Zyskowski, K. 1997b. Contribución al conocimiento ornitológico del Bosque Atlántico interior del Paraguay: Parque Nacional Caaguazú, Caazapá. *Cotinga* 7: 54–60.

Magalhães, V. S., Azevedo Júnior, S. M. & Souza, D. P. 2004. Estrutura da comunidade de aves silvestres através de análises ecológicas em um fragmento de Mata Atlântica, Igarassu, PE, Brasil. In: Congr. Bras. Orn. XII, Blumenau, *Resumos*: 290.

Magalhães, V. S., Azevedo Júnior, S. M., Lyra-Neves, R. M., Telino-Júnior, W. R. & Souza, D. P. 2007. Biologia de aves capturadas em um fragmento de Mata Atlântica, Igarassu, Pernambuco, Brasil. *Rev. Bras. Biol.* 24: 950–964.

Mähler Junior, J. K. F., Repenning, M., Rovedder, C. E. & Fontana, C. S. 2007. Avifauna do Município de Osório, nordeste do Rio

Grande do Sul, Brasil. In: Fontana, C. S. (ed.) *XV Congresso Brasileiro de Ornitologia Resumos, Porto Alegre, RS*: 72–73.

Maillard Z., O. & Caballero, E. 2003. Nidificación del Gallito de la Roca (*Rupicola peruviana*) en el valle de San Onofre, Cochabamba, Bolivia. *Orn. Neotrop.* 14: 263–265.

Maillard Z., O., Bates, J. M., Tello, J. G. & Aponte, M. A. 2007. Avifauna del Río Manupare y cráter Iturralde, un bosque amazonico en el departamento de La Paz, Bolivia. *Orn. Neotrop.* 18: 519–534.

Mallet-Rodrigues, F. 2005. Molt-breeding cycle in passerines from a foothill forest in southeastern Brazil. *Rev. Bras. Orn.* 13: 155–160.

Mallet-Rodrigues, F. 2008. Táxons de aves de validade questionável com ocorrência no Brasil. XI – Suboscines Tyrannoidea. *Atualidades Orn.* 147: 8–9.

Mallet-Rodrigues, F. & Noronha, M. L. M. 2003. The avifauna of low elevations in the Serra dos Órgãos, Rio de Janeiro state, Brazil. *Cotinga* 20: 51–56.

Mallet-Rodrigues, F. & Noronha, M. L. M. 2009. Birds in the Parque Estadual dos Três Picos, Rio de Janeiro state, south-east Brazil. *Cotinga* 31: 61–71.

Mallet-Rodrigues, F., Parrini, R. & Pacheco, J. F. 2007. Birds of the Serra dos Órgãos, state of Rio de Janeiro, southeastern Brazil: a review. *Rev. Bras. Orn.* 15: 5–35.

Mallet-Rodrigues, F., Alves, V. S., Noronha, M. L. M., Serpa, G. A., Soares, A. B. A., Couto, G. S., Maciel, E., Madeira, S. & Draghi, J. 2008. Aves da Baixada de Jacarepaguá, Município do Rio de Janeiro, Estado do Rio de Janeiro. *Rev. Bras. Orn.* 16: 221–231.

Mallorquin, A. & Quevedo, A. 2002. Variaciones en la intensidad de exhibición y selección de perchas en un lek de *Manacus manacus*. *Bol. Soc. Antioqueña Orn.* 13: 5–11.

Manhães, M. A. & Dias, M. M. 2009. Variação temporal e espacial de aves frugívoras e frutos de sub-bosque em um fragmento de Mata Atlântica, sudeste do Brasil. In: Simon, J. E., Raposo, M. A., Stopiglia, R. & Peres, J. (eds) *XVII Congresso Brasileiro de Ornitologia Resumos, Aracruz, ES: Biogeografia das aves da Mata Atlântica*: 60.

Marantz, C. A. & Zimmer, K. J. 2006. *Bird Voices of Alta Floresta and Southeastern Amazonian Brazil*. CDs. Library of Natural Sounds, Cornell Laboratory of Ornithology, Ithaca, NY.

Marateo, G., Povedano, H. & Alonso, J. 2008. Inventario de las aves del Parque Nacional El Palmar, Argentina. *Cotinga* 31: 47–60.

Marçal Júnior, O., Franchin, A. G. & Valadão, R. M. 2004. Levantamento preliminar da avifauna na Usina Hidrelétrica de Jaguara – CEMIG (Sacramento, MG). In: Congr. Bras. Orn. XII, Blumenau, *Resumos*: 295.

Marceliano, M. L. V., Rodrigues Cardoso, L. G. & Gomes, A. L. S. 2009. Dieta de aves de sub-bosque no Parque Ecológico de Gunma, Município de Santa Barbara do Pará. In: Simon, J. E., Raposo, M. A., Stopiglia, R. & Peres, J. (eds) *XVII Congresso Brasileiro de Ornitologia Resumos, Aracruz, ES: Biogeografia das aves da Mata Atlântica*: 72.

Marín, M. 2004. *Lista Comentada de las Aves de Chile*. Lynx Edicions, Barcelona.

Marini, M. A. 1992a. Foraging behavior and diet of the Helmeted Manakin. *Condor* 94: 151–158.

Marini, M. Â. 1992b. Notes on the breeding and reproductive biology of the Helmeted Manakin. *Wilson Bull.* 104: 168–173.

Marini, M. Â. 2001. Effects of forest fragmentation on birds of the cerrado region, Brazil. *Bird Conserv. Int.* 11: 13–25.

Marini, M. Â. & Cavalcanti, R. B. 1992. Mating system of the Helmeted Manakin (*Antilophia galeata*) in central Brazil. *Auk* 109: 911–913.

Marini, M. Â. & Hackett, S. J. 2002. A multifaceted approach to the characterization of an intergeneric hybrid manakin (Pipridae) from Brazil. *Auk* 119: 1114–1120.

Marini, M. Â., Pereira, M. de F., de Oliveira, G. M. & de Melo, C. 1997a. Novos registros de ninhos e ovos de três espécies de aves do Brasil Central. *Ararajuba* 5: 244–245.

Marini, M. Â., Motta-Junior, J. C., Vasconcellos, L. A. S. & Cavalcanti, R. B. 1997b. Avian body masses from the Cerrado region of central Brazil. *Orn. Neotrop.* 8: 93–99.

Marini, M. Â., Aguilar, T. M., Andrade, R. D., Leite, L. O., Anciães, M., Carvalho, C. E. A., Duca, C., Maldonado-Coelho, M., Sebaio, F. & Gonçalves, J. 2007. Biologia da nidificação de aves do sudeste de Minas Gerais, Brasil. *Rev. Bras. Orn.* 15: 367–376.

Marins, M. & Carrano, E. 2007. Ocorrência de aves ameaçadas de extinção no Parque Estadual do Acaraí, Santa Catarina. In: Fontana, C. S. (ed.) *XV Congresso Brasileiro de Ornitologia Resumos, Porto Alegre, RS*: 83–84.

Mark, T., Augustine, L., Barrio, J., Flanagan, J. & Vellinga, W.-P. 2008. New records of birds from the northern Cordillera Central of Peru in a historical perspective. *Cotinga* 29: 108–125.

Marsden, S., Whiffin, M., Sadgrove, L. & Guimaraes, P. R. 2003. Bird community composition and species abundance on two inshore islands in the Atlantic forest region of Brazil. *Ararajuba* 11: 181–187.

Maués, A. M. R. & Aleixo, A. 2008. Limites inter-específicos no gênero *Phoenicircus* (Aves: Cotingidae) a partir de caracteres morfométricos e de plumagem. In: Congr. Bras. Orn. XVI, Palmas, *Resumos*: 423.

Maurício, G. N. & Dias, R. A. 1998. Range extensions and new records for forest birds in southern Rio Grande do Sul, Brazil. *Bull. Brit. Orn. Club* 118: 14–25.

Mayer, S. 2000. *Birds of Bolivia 2.0*. DVD-ROM. Bird Songs International, Westernieland.

Mayr, E. 1971. New species of birds described from 1956 to 1965. *J. Orn.* 112: 302–316.

Mayr, E. & Amadon, D. 1951. A classification of recent birds. *Amer. Mus. Novit.* 1496: 1–42.

Mayr, E. & Phelps, W. H. 1967. The origin of the bird fauna of the south Venezuelan highlands. *Bull. Amer. Mus. Nat. Hist.* 136: 273–327.

Mazar Barnett, J. & Kirwan, G. M. (compilers) 1999. Neotropical notebook: Brazil. *Cotinga* 12: 87.

Mazar Barnett, J. & Kirwan, G. M. (compilers) 2000a. Neotropical notebook: Bolivia. *Cotinga* 13: 75.

Mazar Barnett, J. & Kirwan, G. M. (compilers) 2000b. Neotropical notebook: Ecuador. *Cotinga* 14: 107.

Mazar Barnett, J. & Kirwan, G. M. (compilers) 2001. Neotropical notebook: Panama and Guatemala. *Cotinga* 16: 63–75.

Mazar Barnett, J. & Kirwan, G. M. (compilers) 2002. Neotropical notebook: Costa Rica. *Cotinga* 18: 108.

Mazar Barnett, J. & Pearman, M. 2001. *Lista Comentada de las Aves de Argentina*. Lynx Edicions, Barcelona.

Mazar Barnett, J., Kirwan, G. M. & Tobias, J. (compilers) 1998. Neotropical notebook: Bolivia and Colombia. *Cotinga* 9: 91.

Mazar Barnett, J., Minns, J., Kirwan, G. M. & Remold, H. 2004a. Informações adicionais sobre as aves dos estados do Paraná, Santa Catarina e Rio Grande do Sul. *Ararajuba* 12: 55–58.

Mazar Barnett, J., Kirwan, G. M. & Minns, J. 2004b. Neotropical notebook: Bolivia and Ecuador. *Cotinga* 21: 76–87.

McDonald, D. B. 1989a. Correlates of male mating success in a lekking bird with male–male cooperation. *Anim. Behav.* 37: 1007–1032.

McDonald, D. B. 1989b. Cooperation under sexual selection: age-graded changes in a lekking bird. *Amer. Natur.* 134: 709–730.

McDonald, D. B. 1993a. Demographic consequences of sexual selection in the long-tailed manakin. *Behav. Ecol.* 4: 297–309.

McDonald, D. B. 1993b. Delayed plumage maturation and orderly queues for status: a manakin mannequin experiment. *Ethology* 94: 31–45.

McDonald, D. B. 2003. Microsatellite DNA evidence for gene flow in Neotropical lek-mating Long-tailed Manakins. *Condor* 105: 580–586.

McDonald, D. B. 2007. Predicting fate from early connectivity in a social network. *Proc. Natl. Acad. Sci. USA* 104: 10910–10914.

McDonald, D. B., Clay, R. P., Brumfield, R. T. & Braun, M. J. 2001. Sexual selection on plumage and behavior in an avian hybrid zone: experimental tests of male-male interactions. *Evolution* 55: 1443–1451.

McGhie, H. 2005. Specimens of extinct and endangered birds in the collections of The Manchester Museum, The University of Manchester, UK. *Bull. Brit. Orn. Club* 125: 247–252.

McKay, B. D., Barker, F. K., Mays, H. L., Doucet, S. M. & Hill, G. E. 2010. A molecular phylogenetic hypothesis for the manakins (Aves: Pipridae). *Mol. Phylogenet. Evol.* 55: 733–737.

McMullan, M., Donegan, T. M. & Quevedo, A. 2010. *Field Guide to the Birds of Colombia.* ProAves, Bogotá.

Medeiros, C. & Alves, M. A. S. 2008. Comportamento territorial de *Lipaugus lanioides* (Cotingidae) em Mata Atlântica da Ilha Grande, RJ. In: Congr. Bras. Orn. XVI, Palmas, *Resumos:* 40.

Mee, A., Ohlson, J., Stewart, I., Wilson, M., Örn, P. & Diaz Ferreyra, J. 2002. The Cerros del Sira revisited: birds of submontane and montane forest. *Cotinga* 18: 46–57.

Mees, G. F. 1974. Additions to the avifauna of Suriname. *Zool. Meded. Leiden* 48: 55–67.

Mello, J. R. S., Candia-Gallardo, C., Signoretti, R. P. & Kuniy, A. A. 2008. Avifauna do ecótono entre os biomas Amazônico e Cerrado na região de Tangará da Serra, MT. In: Congr. Bras. Orn. XVI, Palmas, *Resumos:* 313.

Melo, C. & Oliveira, P. E. 2009. Frugivory in *Lacistema hasslerianum* Chodat (Lacistemaceae), a gallery forest understory treelet in Central Brazil. *Braz. J. Biol.* 69: 201–207.

Melo Júnior, T. A., Vasconcelos, M. F., Fernandes, G. W. & Marini, M. Â. 2001. Bird species distribution and conservation in Serra do Cipó, Minas Gerais, Brazil. *Bird Conserv. Int.* 11: 189–204.

Mendonça, E. C. & Gonzaga, L. P. 2000. Nidificação de *Iodopleura pipra* (Cotingidae) em Angra dos Reis, Rio de Janeiro. In: Straube, F. C., Argel-de-Oliverira, M. M. & Cândido, J. F. (eds) *Ornitologia brasileira no século XX.* Pp. 172–173. Universidade do Sul de Santa Catarina & Sociedade Brasileira de Ornitologia, Curitiba.

Mendonça, L. B., Serafini, P. P., Anjos, L. dos, Volpato, G. H., Boçon, R., Lopes, E. V., Fávaro, F. L. & Bisheimer, M. V. 2004. Aves frugívoras de médio e grande porte em diferentes regiões fitoecológicas da Mata Atlântica no sul do Brasil. In: Congr. Bras. Orn. XII, Blumenau, *Resumos:* 299.

Mendonça, L. B., Lopes, E. V. & Anjos, L. 2009. On the possible extinction of bird species in the Upper Paraná River floodplain, Brazil. *Braz. J. Biol.* 69 (Suppl.): 747–755.

Mendonça-Lima, A. & Fontana, C. S. 2000. Composição, freqüência e aspectos biológicos da avifauna no Porto Alegre Country Clube, Rio Grande do Sul. *Ararajuba* 8: 1–8.

Mendonça-Lima, A., Fontana, C. S. & Mähler, J. K. F. 2001. Itens alimentares consumidos por aves no nordeste do Rio Grande do Sul, Brasil. *Tangara* 1: 115–124.

Merkord, C. L., Mark, T., Susanibar, D., Johnson, A. & Witt, C. C. 2009. Avifaunal survey of the Río Chipaota Valley in the Cordillera Azul region, San Martín, Peru. *Orn. Neotrop.* 20: 535–552.

Merrill, I. 1995. Andean Cock-of-the-rock in Venezuela. *Birding World* 8: 349–350.

Mestre, L. A. M. 2004. Avifauna da Fazenda Arapongas – Floresta com Araucária – Lapa – Paraná. In: Congr. Bras. Orn. XII, Blumenau, *Resumos:* 301.

Mestre, L., Andretti, C., Vargas, C., Costa, T. & Cohn-Haft, M. 2005. Comunidade de aves em seis parcelas de floresta de terra firme na Amazônia central. In: Congr. Bras. Orn. XIII, Belém, *Resumos:* 141.

Mestre, L. A. M., Barlow, J., Thom, G. & Cochrane, M. A. 2009. Burned forests as a novel habitat for the Black-faced Cotinga (*Conioptilon mcilhennyi*) in the western Brazilian Amazon. *Orn. Neotrop.* 20: 467–470.

Mestre, L. A. M., Thom, G., Cochrane, M. A. & Barlow, J. 2010. The birds of Reserva Extrativista Chico Mendes, south Acre, Brazil. *Bol. Mus. Para. E. Goeldi Cienc. Nat.* 5: 311–333.

Meyer de Schauensee, R. 1966. *The Species of Birds of South America.* Livingston Publishing, Narberth, PA.

Meyer de Schauensee, R. 1970. *A Guide to the Birds of South America.* Livingston Publishing, Wynnewood, PA.

Meyer de Schauensee, R. & Phelps, W. H., Jr. 1978. *A Guide to the Birds of Venezuela.* Princeton University Press, Princeton, NJ.

Miller, A. H. 1963. Seasonal activity and ecology of the avifauna of an American equatorial cloud forest. *Univ. Calif. Publ. Zool.* 66: 1–78.

Miller, W. de W. 1908. A review of the manakins of the genus *Chiroxiphia. Bull. Amer. Mus. Nat. Hist.* 24: 331–343.

Minns, J. C., Buzzetti, D. R. C., Albano, C. G., Whittaker, A.,

Grosset, A. E. & Parrini, R. 2009. *Birds of Eastern Brazil: Atlantic Forest, Caatinga, Cerrado and Pantanal.* DVD-ROM. Ed. Avis Brasilis, Vinhedo.

Mitchell, M. H. 1957. *Observations on Birds of Southeastern Brazil.* University of Toronto Press, Toronto.

Mitsch, H. 1975. Beobachtungen am Pompadour-Schmuckvogel. *Gefiederte Welt* 99: 106–109.

Mittermeier, J. C., Zyskowski, K., Stowe, E. S. & Lai, J. E. 2010. New additions to the avifauna of the Sipaliwini Savanna (Suriname) confirm its affinity to the Brazilian cerrado. *Bull. Yale Univ. Peabody Mus.* 51: 97–122.

Mlíkovský, J. 2009. Types of birds in the collections of the Museum and Institute of Zoology, Polish Academy of Sciences, Warszawa, Poland. Part 3: South American birds. *J. Natl. Mus. (Prague), Nat. Hist. Ser.* 178: 17–180.

Mobley, J. A. & Prum, R. O. 1995. Phylogenetic relationships of the Cinnamon Tyrant, *Neopipo cinnamomea*, to the tyrant flycatchers (Tyrannidae). *Condor* 97: 650–662.

Moermond, T. C. & Denslow, J. S. 1985. Neotropical avian frugivores: patterns of behavior, morphology, and nutrition, with consequences for fruit selection. In: Buckley, P. A., Foster, M. S., Morton, E. S., Ridgely, R. S. & Buckley, F. G. (eds) *Neotropical Ornithology. Orn. Monogr.* 36: 865–897.

Mohr, L. V. & Efe, M. A. 2003. Lista comentada da avifauna do município de Porto Alegre, Rio Grande do Sul. In: Machado, C. G. (ed.) *XI Congresso Brasileiro de Ornitologia Resumos, Feira de Santana, BA:* 103.

Monroe, B. L. 1968. *A Distributional Survey of the Birds of Honduras. Orn. Monogr.* 7.

Montañez, D. & Angehr, G. R. 2007. Important Bird Areas of the Neotropics: Panama. *Neotrop. Birding* 2: 12–19.

Moore, J. V. 1992. *A Bird Walk at Chan Chich, Belize.* Cassette. John V. Moore Nature Recordings, San Jose, CA.

Moore, J. V. 1993. *Sounds of La Selva.* Cassette. John V. Moore Nature Recordings, San Jose, CA.

Moore, J. V. 1994. *More Bird Vocalizations from the Lowland Rainforest.* Vol. 1. Cassette. John V. Moore Nature Recordings, San Jose, CA.

Moore, J. V. 1996. *More Bird Vocalizations from the Lowland Rainforest.* Vol. 2. Cassette. John V. Moore Nature Recordings, San Jose, CA.

Moore, J. V. 2008. Ecuador's avifauna: the state of knowledge and availability of sound-recordings (1987–2007). *Cotinga* 29: 19–21.

Moore, J. V. & Lysinger, M. 1997. *Birds of Cabañas San Isidro, Ecuador.* Cassettes. John V. Moore Nature Recordings, San Jose, CA.

Moore, J. V., Coopmans, P., Ridgely, R. S. & Lysinger, M. 1999. *The Birds of Northwest Ecuador. Vol. 1: The Upper Foothills and Subtropics.* CDs. John V. Moore Nature Recordings, San Jose, CA.

Moskovits, D., Fitzpatrick, J. W. & Stotz, D. F. 1985. Lista preliminar das aves da Estação Ecológica de Maracá, Território de Roraima, Brasil, e áreas adjacentes. *Pap. Avuls. Zool., São Paulo* 36(6): 51–68.

Moyle, R. G., Chesser, R. T., Prum, R. O., Schikler, P. & Cracraft, J. 2006. Phylogeny and evolutionary history of Old World suboscine birds (Aves: Eurylaimides). *Amer. Mus. Novit.* 3544: 1–22.

Muir, J. A., Licata, D. & Martin, T. E. 2008. Reproductive biology of the Red-ruffed Fruitcrow (*Pyroderus scutatus granadensis*). *Wilson J. Orn.* 120: 862–867.

Müller, J. A., Scherer Neto, P., Carrano, E., Andreiv, J. & Zimmermann, A. F. 2003. A diversidade de aves de uma reserva florestal particular no Município de Blumenau, Santa Catarina. In: Machado, C. G. (ed.) *XI Congresso Brasileiro de Ornitologia Resumos, Feira de Santana, BA:* 105.

Muller-Bierl, M. & Cordier, C. 1991. Vom Klippenvogel oder Felsenhahn *Rupicola. Gefiederte Welt* 115: 234–237.

Múnera-Roldán, C., Cody, M. L., Schiele-Zavala, R. H., Sigel, B. J., Woltmann, S. & Kjeldsen, P. 2007. New and noteworthy records of birds from south-eastern Nicaragua. *Bull. Brit. Orn. Club* 127: 152–161.

Munn, C. A. 1985. Permanent canopy and understory flocks in

Amazonia: species composition and population density. In: Buckley, P. A., Foster, M. S., Morton, E. S., Ridgely, R. S. & Buckley, F. G. (eds) *Neotropical Ornithology*. Orn. Monogr. 36: 683–712.

Murphy, W. L. 1991. *Birds of Trinidad & Tobago*. Cassette. Privately published.

Musser, J. M., Prum, R. O. & Barker, F. K. 2010. Detecting patterns and intensity of sexual selection in lekking manakins (Pipridae) with population genetics. In: Miyaki, C. M., Höfling, E. & Donatelli, R. J. (eds) *Abstracts 25th Int. Orn. Congr., Campos do Jordão, Brazil, 22–28 August 2010*: 805.

Naka, L. N., Mazar Barnett, J., Kirwan, G. M., Tobias, J. A. & Buzzetti, D. 2001. Records of bird species previously considered uncommon in Santa Catarina state, Brazil. *Cotinga* 16: 68–70.

Naka, L. N., Rodrigues, M., Roos, A. L. & Azevedo, M. A. G. 2002. Bird conservation on Santa Catarina Island, southern Brazil. *Bird Conserv. Int.* 12: 123–150.

Naka, L. N., Cohn-Haft, M., Mallet-Rodrigues, F., Santos, M. P. D. & Torres, M. F. 2006. The avifauna of the Brazilian state of Roraima: bird distribution and biogeography in the Rio Branco basin. *Rev. Bras. Orn.* 14: 197–238.

Naka, L. N., Cohn-Haft, M., Whittaker, A., Mazar Barnett, J. & Torres, M. F. 2007. Avian biogeography of Amazonian flooded forests in the Rio Branco basin, Brazil. *Wilson J. Orn.* 119: 439–449.

Naka, L. N., Stouffer, P. C., Cohn-Haft, M., Marantz, C. A., Whittaker, A. & Bierregaard, R. O. 2008. *Voices of the Brazilian Amazon. Vol. 1: Birds of the Terra Firme Forests North of Manaus: Guianan Area of Endemism*. CDs. Ed. INPA, Manaus.

Nascimento, J. L. X., Nascimento, I. L. S. & Azevedo Júnior, S. M. 2000. Aves da Chapada do Araripe (Brasil): biologia e conservação. *Ararajuba* 8: 115–125.

Navas, J. R. & Bó, N. A. 2000. Aportes al conocimiento de la distribución, la cría y el peso de aves de las provincias de Mendoza y San Juan, República Argentina. Primera parte. (Aves: Phytotomidae, Mimidae, Troglodytidae, Motacillidae, Emberizidae y Fringillidae). *Hornero* 15: 123–127.

Naumburg, E. C. 1930. The birds of Matto Grosso, Brazil. *Bull. Amer. Mus. Nat. Hist.* 60: 1–432.

Nemeth, E. 2004. Measuring the sound pressure level of the song of the screaming piha *Lipaugus vociferans*: one of the loudest birds in the world? *Bioacoustics* 14: 225–228.

Newman, J. 2008. Sight records of five bird species new to Colombia from Serranía de Naquen, dpto. Guainía. *Cotinga* 29: 160–161.

Nicéforo, M. H. 1947. Notas sobre aves de Colombia II. *Caldasia* 4: 317–377.

Niethammer, G. 1956. Zur Vogelwelt Boliviens (Tiel II: Passeres). *Bonn. Zool. Beitr.* 7: 84–150.

Norton, D. W., Orcés, G. & Sutter, E. 1972. Notes on rare and previously unreported birds in Ecuador. *Auk* 89: 889–894.

Norton, W. J. E. 1975. Notes on the birds of the Sierra Nevada de Santa Marta, Colombia. *Bull. Brit. Orn. Club* 95: 109–115.

Novaes, F. C. 1957. Contribuição à ornitologia do noroeste do Acre. *Bol. Mus. Para. E. Goeldi*, N. Sér. 9: 1–30.

Novaes, F. C. 1960. Sobre uma coleção de aves do sudeste do Estado do Pará. *Arq. Zool., São Paulo* 11: 133–146.

Novaes, F. C. 1964. Una nova raça geográfica de *Piprites chloris* (Temminck) do Estado do Pará (Pipridae, Aves). *Bol. Mus. Para. E. Goeldi (Zool.)* 47: 1–5.

Novaes, F. C. 1970. Distribuição ecológica e abundância das aves em um trecho da mata do baixo rio Guamá (Estado do Pará). *Bol. Mus. Para. E. Goeldi*, N. Sér. 71: 1–54.

Novaes, F. C. 1976. As aves do Rio Aripuanã, Estados de Mato Grosso e Amazonas. *Acta Amazônica* 6(4): 61–85.

Novaes, F. C. 1978. Ornitologia do território do Amapá. II. *Publ. Avuls. Mus. Para. E. Goeldi* 29: 1–75.

Novaes, F. C. 1980a. Observações sobre a avifauna do alto curso do Rio Paru de Leste, Estado do Pará. *Bol. Mus. Para. E. Goeldi*, N. Sér. 100: 1–58.

Novaes, F. C. 1980b. Observações sobre *Procnias alba* (Hermann): araponga branca. *An. Soc. Sul-Riograndense Orn.* 1: 5–7.

Nunes, M. F. C., Buzzetti, D. R. C. & Roos, A. L. 2010. Population status of birds in the Murici Ecological Station, Alagoas, Brazil. In: Miyaki, C. M., Höfling, E. & Donatelli, R. J. (eds) *Abstracts 25th Int. Orn. Congr., Campos do Jordão, Brazil, 22–28 August 2010*: 872.

Nutting, C. C. 1884. On a collection of birds from Nicaragua. *Proc. US Natl. Mus.* 6: 372–410.

Nyári, Á. 2007. Phylogeographic patterns, molecular and vocal differentiation, and species limits in *Schiffornis turdina* (Aves). *Mol. Phylogenet. Evol.* 44: 154–164.

Ocampo T., S. 2002. Río Blanco: reserva hidrografica, florestal, parque ecológico, paraíso de las aves. *Bol. Soc. Antioqueña Orn.* 13: 48–61.

Ohlson, J., Prum, R. O. & Ericson, P. G. P. 2007. A molecular phylogeny of the cotingas (Aves: Cotingidae). *Mol. Phylogenet. Evol.* 42: 25–37.

Ohlson, J., Fjeldså, J. & Ericson, P. G. P. 2008. Tyrant flycatchers coming out in the open: phylogeny and ecological radiation of Tyrannidae (Aves: Passeriformes). *Zool. Scripta* 37: 315–335.

Ohlson, J., Irestedt, M., Ericson, P. G. P. & Fjeldså, J. 2010. The systematic position of *Calyptura cristata* revealed by sequence data from multiple genes. In: Miyaki, C. M., Höfling, E. & Donatelli, R. J. (eds) *Abstracts 25th Int. Orn. Congr., Campos do Jordão, Brazil, 22–28 August 2010*: 924.

Olalla, A. M. 1943. Algumas observações sobre a biologia das aves e mamíferos sul-americanos. *Pap. Avuls. Dep. Zool. São Paulo* 3: 229–236.

Olalla, A. M. & Magalhães, A. C. 1956. Pássaros. Fam. Rupicolidae, galos da serra, da rochas o do Pará. *Bibl. Zool. São Paulo* 2: 26–40.

Olivares, A. 1955. Algunas aves de la Comisaría del Vaupés (Colombia). *Caldasia* 7: 259–275.

Olivares, A. 1964. Adiciónes a las aves de la Comisaría del Vaupés (Colombia), II. *Caldasia* 9: 150–184.

Olivares, O. M. 1958. Aves de la costa del Pacifico, Municipio de Guapi, Cauca, Colombia. III. *Caldasia* 8: 217–251.

Oliveira Junior, T. M., França, B. R. A., Nascimento, É. P. G., Neto, M. R., Silva, M. & Pichorim, M. 2008. Aves de quatro fragmentos florestais no sul do Rio Grande do Norte, Brasil. In: Congr. Bras. Orn. XVI, Palmas, *Resumos*: 301.

Oliveira, D. M. M., Rubio, T. C., Oliveira, F. F., Freitas, B. A., Campos, S. F. & Albues, F. 2009. Avifauna da Parque Estadual Igarapes-Juruena, Mato Grosso. In: Simon, J. E., Raposo, M. A., Stopiglia, R. & Peres, J. (eds) *XVII Congresso Brasileiro de Ornitologia Resumos, Aracruz, ES: Biogeografia das aves da Mata Atlântica*: 82.

Oliveira, S. L., Köhler, A. & Accordi, I. A. 2009. Avifauna da sub-bacia do rio Pardinho: riqueza e conservação. In: Simon, J. E., Raposo, M. A., Stopiglia, R. & Peres, J. (eds) *XVII Congresso Brasileiro de Ornitologia Resumos, Aracruz, ES: Biogeografia das aves da Mata Atlântica*: 37.

Oliveira Rodrigues, P., Silva Junior, E. L., Amâncio, S., Gonçalves, V. F. & Melo, C. 2009. Biometria da *Antilophia galeata* (Pipridae), na Fazenda Experimental do Glória, Uberlândia, Minas Gerais. In: Simon, J. E., Raposo, M. A., Stopiglia, R. & Peres, J. (eds) *XVII Congresso Brasileiro de Ornitologia Resumos, Aracruz, ES: Biogeografia das aves da Mata Atlântica*: 64.

Olmos, F. 2003. Birds of Mata Estrela private reserve, Rio Grande do Norte, Brazil. *Cotinga* 20: 26–30.

Olmos, F. & Brito, G. R. R. 2007. Aves da região da Barragem de Boa Esperança, médio rio Parnaíba, Brasil. *Rev. Bras. Orn.* 15: 37–52.

Olmos, F. & Pacheco, J. F. 2002. Redescoberta de *Pipra vilasboasi*, espécie desaparecida há 45 anos. *Atualidades Orn.* 107: 3.

Olmos, F. & Pacheco, J. F. 2003. Rediscovery of Golden-crowned Manakin *Lepidothrix* [*sic*] *vilasboasi*. *Cotinga* 20: 48–50.

Olney, P. J. 1973. Breeding the Blue-backed Manakin *Chiroxiphia pareola* at London Zoo. *Avicult. Mag.* 79: 1–3.

Olney, P. J. 1974. First breeding of the Blue-backed Manakin *Chiroxiphia pareola* in captivity. *Int. Zoo Yearbook* 14: 105–106.

Olson, D. H. & McDowell, M. K. 1983. A comparison of white-bearded manakin (*Manacus manacus*) populations and lek systems in Suriname and Trinidad. *Auk* 100: 739–742.

Olson, S. L. 1970. Specializations of some carotenoid-bearing feathers. *Condor* 72: 424–430.

Olson, S. L. 1971. Taxonomic comments on the Eurylaimidae. *Ibis* 113: 507–516.

Olson, S. L. 1993. Contributions to avian biogeography from the archipelago and lowlands of Bocas del Toro, Panama. *Auk* 110: 100–108.

Olson, S. L. 1996. Review: W. J. Bock. History and nomenclature of avian family-group names. *Auk* 112: 539–546.

Olson, S. L. 2007. Review: A Carriker trilogy: chapters in a saga of Neotropical ornithology. *Auk* 124: 357–361.

Olson, S. L. & Alvarenga, H. M. F. 2006. An extraordinary feeding assemblage of birds at a termite swarm in the Serra da Mantiqueira, São Paulo, Brazil. *Rev. Bras. Orn.* 14: 297–299.

Omena Júnior, R. 2007. *Vozes e Sons das Florestas do Amazonas.* Fundação Villa-Lobos, Manaus.

Omena Júnior, R. S. 2009. Comportamento do galo-da-serra *Rupicola rupicola* (Cotingidae) no município de Presidente Figueiredo, Amazonas, Brasil. *Rev. Bras. Orn.* 17: 87–95.

Omena Júnior, R. & Martins, C. S. 2007. Comportamento reprodutivo e caracterização de sítios de reprodução de galos-da-serra (*Rupicola rupicola*) no Amazonas. *Rev. Bras. Orn.* 15: 81–84.

Omena Júnior, R. & Santos, J. L. 2010. Dieta de galos-da-serra *Rupicola rupicola* Linaeus [*sic*] 1766 durante o período reprodutivo ao Norte de Manaus, Amazonas. *Ornithologia* 4: 66–73.

O'Neill, J. P. & Parker, T. A. 1981. New subspecies of *Pipreola riefferii* and *Chlorospingus ophthalmicus* from Peru. *Bull. Brit. Orn. Club* 101: 294–299.

Oniki, Y. 1990. Overnight changes in body weight and cloacal temperature of birds from Mato Grosso state, Brazil. *Rev. Bras. Biol.* 50: 681–684.

Oniki, Y. & Willis, E. O. 1982. Breeding records of birds from Manaus, Brazil: III. Formicariidae to Pipridae. *Rev. Brasil. Biol.* 42: 563–569.

Oniki, Y. & Willis, E. O. 1983. A study of breeding birds of the Belém area, Brazil: IV. Formicariidae to Pipridae. *Ciência e Cultura* 35: 1325–1328.

Oniki, Y. & Willis, E. O. 1999. Body mass, cloacal temperature, morphometrics, breeding and molt of birds of the Serra das Araras region, Mato Grosso, Brazil. *Ararajuba* 7: 17–21.

Orejuela, J. E., Cantillo F., G. & Alberico, M. 1982. Observaciones del comportamiento reproductivo del saltarín *Allocotopterus deliciosus* (familia Pipridae, Aves) en Nariño, Colombia. *Cespedesia*, Suplemento 3: 69–79.

Oren, D. C. 1991. Aves do Estado do Maranhão, Brasil. *Goeldiana Zool.* 9: 1–55.

Oren, D. C. & Albuquerque, H. G. 1991. Priority areas for new avian collections in Brazilian Amazonia. *Goeldiana Zool.* 6: 1–11.

Oren, D. C. & Novaes, F. C. 1985. A new subspecies of White Bellbird *Procnias alba* (Hermann) from southeastern Amazonia. *Bull. Brit. Orn. Club* 105: 23–25.

Oren, D. C. & Parker, T. A. 1997. Avifauna of the Tapajós National Park and vicinity, Amazonian Brazil. In: Remsen, J. V. (ed.) *Studies in Neotropical Ornithology Honoring Ted Parker. Orn. Monogr.* 48: 493–525.

Ortega, R. 2008. Primer registro del nido de *Oxyruncus cristatus* (Picoagudo/Sharpbill) en Costa Rica y en América Central. *Zeledonia* 12(2): 1–7.

Ortiz M., L. J. 2004. The hand-rearing of an umbrellabird. *Avicult. Mag.* 110: 108–115.

Ottema, O. 2002. Crimson Fruitcrow *Haematoderus militaris* feeding on *Cecropia sciadophylla*. *Cotinga* 18: 103–104.

Ottema, O. 2009. Birding Suriname. *Neotrop. Birding* 4: 61–68.

Ottema, O. H., Ribot, J. H. J. M. & Spaans, A. L. 2009. *Annotated Checklist of the Birds of Suriname.* WWF Guianas, Paramaribo.

Ouellet, H. 1990. Notes on the iris colour in females of two manakins (Pipridae). *Bull. Brit. Orn. Club* 110: 140–141.

Pacheco, A. M. F. & Cohn-Haft, M. 2010. New evidence for lack of song learning in Neotropical suboscine passerines. In: Miyaki, C. M., Höfling, E. & Donatelli, R. J. (eds) *Abstracts 25th Int. Orn. Congr., Campos do Jordão, Brazil, 22–28 August 2010*: 520.

Pacheco, A. & Laverde, O. 2002. Comportamiento reproductivo del Saltarín Coludo (*Chiroxiphia lanceolata*) en un bosque secundario de Ibague. *Bol. Soc. Antioqueña Orn.* 13: 62–72.

Pacheco, A. & Laverde, O. 2004. Comportamiento reproductivo de *Chiroxiphia lanceolata* (Pipridae: Aves) en un bosque intervenido del Tolima, Colombia. *Acta Biol. Colombiana* 9: 47–54.

Pacheco, J. F. 2000. Alguns registros históricos para a ornitologia do Amapá. *Atualidades Orn.* 96: 5.

Pacheco, J. F. 2001. *Tangara* – gênero de uns, ainda que nome vulgar de outros! *Tangara* 1: 5–11.

Pacheco, J. F. & Bauer, C. 2001. As aves do Espírito Santo do Príncipe Maximiliano de Wied. *Atualidades Orn.* 99: 6.

Pacheco, J. F. & Fonseca, P. S. M. 2001. The remarkable rediscovery of the Kinglet Calyptura *Calyptura cristata*. *Cotinga* 16: 48–51.

Pacheco, J. F. & Olmos, F. 2005. Birds of a latitudinal transect in the Tapajós-Xingu interfluvium, eastern Brazilian Amazonia. *Ararajuba* 13: 29–46.

Pacheco, J. F. & Olmos, F. 2006. As aves do Tocantins 1: região sudeste. *Rev. Bras. Orn.* 14: 85–100.

Pacheco, J. F. & Olmos, F. 2010. As aves do Tocantins, Brasil – 2: Jalapão. *Rev. Bras. Orn.* 18: 1–18.

Pacheco, J. F. & Parrini, R. 1995. O "Rei-dos-tangarás" (*Chiroxiphia caudata* × *Antilophia galeata*) no sul de Minas Gerais. *Atualidades Orn.* 66: 14.

Pacheco, J. F. & Parrini, R. 1996. Ainda sobre o "Rei-dos-tangarás", híbrido entre *Chiroxiphia caudata* e *Antilophia galeata*, notas adicionais. *Atualidades Orn.* 70: 7.

Pacheco, J. F. & Whitney, B. M. 1995. Range extensions for some birds in northeastern Brazil. *Bull. Brit. Orn. Club* 115: 157–163.

Pacheco, J. F., Kirwan, G. M., Aleixo, A., Whitney, B. M., Whittaker, A., Minns, J., Zimmer, K. J., Fonseca, P. S. M., Lima, M. F. C. & Oren, D. C. 2007. An avifaunal inventory of the CVRD Serra dos Carajás project, Pará, Brazil. *Cotinga* 27: 15–30.

Pacheco, J. F., Parrini, R., Lopes, L. E. & Vasconcelos, M. F. 2008. A avifauna do Parque Estadual do Ibitipoca e áreas adjacentes, Minas Gerais, Brasil, com uma revisão crítica dos registros prévios e comentários sobre biogeografia e conservação. *Cotinga* 30: 16–32.

Paclt, J. 2009. *Neolepidothrix*, a replacement name for *Lepidothrix* Bonaparte (Aves, Pipridae), nec Menge (Insecta, Lepidotrichidae). *Zoolsyst. Evol.* 85: 161.

Paiba-Alzate, J. E., López-Orozco, N. & Betancourt, A. F. 2010. Nuevos registros de aves para el Parque Nacional Natural Selva de Florencia, Caldas. *Bol. Cient. Mus. Hist. Nat. Caldas* 14: 114–120.

Parker, T. A. 1981. Distribution and biology of the White-cheeked Cotinga *Zaratornis stresemanni*, a high Andean frugivore. *Bull. Brit. Orn. Club* 101: 256–265.

Parker, T. A. 1991. On the use of tape recorders in avifaunal surveys. *Auk* 108: 443–444.

Parker, T. A. & Goerck, J. M. 1997. The importance of national parks and biological reserves to bird conservation in the Atlantic forest region of Brazil. In: Remsen, J. V. (ed.) *Studies in Neotropical Ornithology Honoring Ted Parker. Orn. Monogr.* 48: 527–541.

Parker, T. A. & Parker, S. A. 1982. Behavioural and distributional notes on some unusual birds of a lower montane cloud forest in Peru. *Bull. Brit. Orn. Club* 102: 63–70.

Parker, T. A. & Remsen, J. V. 1987. Fifty-two Amazonian bird species new to Bolivia. *Bull. Brit. Orn. Club* 107: 94–107.

Parker, T. A. & Wust, W. 1994. Birds of the Cerros del Távara (300-900 m). In: Foster, R. B., Carr, J. L & Forsyth, A. B. (eds) *The Tambopata-Candamo Reserved Zone of Southeastern Perú: A Biological Assessment. RAP Working Papers* 6. Conservation International, Washington, DC.

Parker, T. A., Remsen, J. V. & Heindel, J. A. 1980. Seven bird species new to Bolivia. *Bull. Brit. Orn. Club* 100: 160–162.

Parker, T. A., Parker, S. A. & Plenge, M. A. 1982. *An Annotated Checklist of Peruvian Birds.* Buteo Books, Vermillion, SD.

Parker, T. A., Schulenberg, T. S., Graves, G. R. & Braun, M. J. 1985. The avifauna of the Huancabamba region, northern Peru. In: Buckley, P. A., Foster, M. S., Morton, E. S., Ridgely,

R. S. & Buckley, F. G. (eds) *Neotropical Ornithology. Orn. Monogr.* 36: 169–197.

Parker, T. A., Castillo U., A., Gell-Mann, M. & Rocha O., O. 1991. Records of new and unusual birds from northern Bolivia. *Bull. Brit. Orn. Club* 111: 120–138.

Parker, T. A., Holst, B. K., Emmons, L. H. & Meyer, J. R. 1993. *A Biological Assessment of the Columbia River Forest Reserve, Toledo District, Belize.* RAP Working Papers 3. Conservation International, Washington, DC.

Parker, T. A., Kratter, A. W. & Wust, W. 1994a. Birds of the Ccolpa del Guacamayos, Madre de Dios. In: Foster, R. B., Carr, J. L & Forsyth, A. B. (eds) *The Tambopata-Candamo Reserved Zone of Southeastern Perú: A Biological Assessment.* RAP Working Papers 6. Conservation International, Washington, DC.

Parker, T. A., Schulenberg, T. S. & Wust, W. 1994b. Birds of the lower Río Heath, including Pampas del Heath, Bolivia/Perú. In: Foster, R. B., Carr, J. L & Forsyth, A. B. (eds) *The Tambopata-Candamo Reserved Zone of Southeastern Perú: A Biological Assessment.* RAP Working Papers 6. Conservation International, Washington, DC.

Parker, T. A., Donahue, P. K. & Schulenberg, T. S. 1994c. Birds of the Tambopata Reserve (Explorer's Inn Reserve). In: Foster, R. B., Carr, J. L & Forsyth, A. B. (eds) *The Tambopata-Candamo Reserved Zone of Southeastern Perú: A Biological Assessment.* RAP Working Papers 6. Conservation International, Washington, DC.

Parkes, K. C. 1961. Intergeneric hybrids in the family Pipridae. *Condor* 63: 145–150.

Parrado-Rosselli, A. & Amaya-Espinel, J. D. 2006. Feeding behavior of purple-throated fruitcrow (*Querula purpurata*: Cotingidae) in the Colombian Amazon and its implications for seed dispersal. *Biotropica* 38: 561–565.

Parrini, R. & Pacheco, J. F. 2010. Frugivoria por aves em *Coussapoa microcarpa* (Cecropiaceae) na Mata Atlântica montana do Estado do Rio de Janeiro, sudeste do Brasil. *Atualidades Orn.* 157: 18–21.

Parrini, R. & Pacheco, J. F. 2011. Frugivoria por aves em seis espécies arbóreas do gênero *Miconia* (Melastomataceae) na Mata Atlântica do Parque Nacional da Serra dos Órgãos, Região Sudeste do Brasil. *Atualidades Orn.* 159: 51–58 (www.ao.com.br).

Parrini, R., Raposo, M. A., Pacheco, J. F., Carvalhães, A. M. P., Melo Júnior, T. A., Fonseca, P. S. M. & Minns, J. C. 1999. Birds of the Chapada Diamantina, Bahia, Brazil. *Cotinga* 11: 86–95.

Parry, L., Barlow, J. & Peres, C. A. 2009. Hunting for sustainability in tropical secondary forests. *Conserv. Biol.* 23: 1270–1280.

Parsons, T. J., Olson, S. L. & Braun, M. J. 1993. Unidirectional spread of secondary sexual plumage traits across an avian hybrid zone. *Science* 260: 1643–1646.

Parsons, T. J., Olson, S. L. & Braun, M. J. 1994. Hybrid zones and sexual selection: response. *Science* 265: 122–123.

Partridge, W. H. 1954. Estudio preliminar sobre una colección de aves de Misiones. *Rev. Mus. Argent. Cienc. Nat. "Bernardino Rivadavia" Zool.* 3: 87–153.

Partridge, W. H. 1961. Aves de Misiones nuevas para Argentina. *Neotropica* 7: 25–28.

Passamani, M. & Mendes, S. L. 2007. *Espécies da Fauna Ameaçadas de Extinção no Estado do Espírito Santo.* IPEMA, Vitória.

Passamani, J. A., Simon, J. E., Novaes, T. D., Braga, A. A., Mendes, R. A. & Lima, S. R. 2009. Espécies da avifauna ameaçadas de extinção encontradas recentemente na Reserva Biológica de Sooretama. In: Simon, J. E., Raposo, M. A., Stopiglia, R. & Peres, J. (eds) *XVII Congresso Brasileiro de Ornitologia Resumos, Aracruz, ES: Biogeografia das aves da Mata Atlântica*: 93.

Patrial, L. W., Patrial, E. W. & Copolla, F. 2009. Dados preliminares sobre a avifauna da Área de Proteção Ambiental Itacaré-Serra Grande, sul do Bahia, Brasil. In: Simon, J. E., Raposo, M. A., Stopiglia, R. & Peres, J. (eds) *XVII Congresso Brasileiro de Ornitologia Resumos, Aracruz, ES: Biogeografia das aves da Mata Atlântica*: 93.

Paynter, R. A. 1992. *Ornithological Gazetteer of Bolivia*, 2nd edn. Museum of Comparative Zoology, Harvard University, Cambridge, MA.

Pearce-Higgins, J. W., Brace, R. C. & Hornbuckle, J. 2007. Survival of Band-tailed Manakins. *Condor* 109: 167–172.

Pearman, M. 1993. Some range extensions and five species new to Colombia, with notes on some scarce or little known species. *Bull. Brit. Orn. Club* 113: 66–75.

Pearman, M. (compiler) 1994a. Neotropical notebook: Colombia. *Cotinga* 1: 26.

Pearman, M. (compiler) 1994b. Neotropical notebook: Brazil and Colombia. *Cotinga* 2: 26–31.

Pearman, M. 1995. *The Essential Guide to Birding in Chile.* Worldwide Publications, Belper.

Pelzeln, A. von. 1870–71. *Zur Ornithologie Brasiliens: Resultate von Johann Natterers Reisen in den Jahren 1817 bis 1835.* Vols 2–3. A. Pichler's Witwe & Sohn, Vienna.

de la Peña, M. R. 1989. *Guia de Aves Argentinas.* Tomo VI. Literature of Latin America, Buenos Aires.

de la Peña, M. R. & Pensiero, J. F. 2003. Contribución de la flora en los hábitos alimentarios de las aves en un bosque del centro de la provincia de Santa Fe, Argentina. *Orn. Neotrop.* 14: 499–513.

Pena, M. & Weber, W. H. 2000. Reencuentro del Saltarín Cabecidorado (*Chloropipo flavicapilla*) en Antioquia. *Bol. Soc. Antioqueña Orn.* 11: 46–48.

Penard, F. P. & Penard, A. P. 1910. *De vogels van Guyana (Suriname, Cayenne en Demerara).* Part 2. F. P. Penard, Paramaribo.

Peres, C. A. & Whittaker, A. 1991. Annotated checklist of the bird species of the upper Rio Urucu, Amazonas, Brazil. *Bull. Brit. Orn. Club* 111: 156–171.

Pérez, V. & Lyons Pérez, J. A. 1998. Andean Cock-of-the-rock *Rupicola peruviana* nest under a bridge. *Cotinga* 9: 81–82.

Pérez-Emán, J., Sharpe, C. J., Lentino R., M., Prum, R. O. & Carreño F., I. J. 2003. New records of birds from the summit of Cerro Guaiquinima, Estado Bolívar, Venezuela. *Bull. Brit. Orn. Club* 123: 79–90.

Pereira, A. S., Muniz, M. C. A., Pavão da Silva, D. W. & Rodrigues, A. A. F. 2005. Levantamento preliminar da avifauna de um fragmento florestal da ALUMAR, São Luís-MA, Brasil. In: Congr. Bras. Orn. XIII, Belém, *Resumos*: 113.

Pereira, G. A., Whittaker, A., Whitney, B. M., Zimmer, K. J., Dantas, S. M., Roda, S. A., Bevier, L. R., Coelho, G., Hoyer, R. C. & Albano, C. 2008. Novos registros de aves para Pernambuco, Brasil, com notas sobre algumas espécies pouco conhecidas no Estado. *Rev. Bras. Orn.* 16: 47–53.

Pereira, G. A., Araújo, L. W. L., Leal, S., Medcraft, J., Whittaker, A., Marantz, C. A., Toledo, M. T., Araujo, H. F. P., Albano, C., Pinto, T., Santos, C. H. A. & Serapião, L. C. H. in press. Important records of birds in the states of Alagoas, Pernambuco and Paraíba, north-east Brazil. *Cotinga* 34.

Pereira, R. S., Azambuja, R. & Alves-Costa, C. P. 2008. Avifauna, sua dieta e papel na dispersão de sementes em um fragmento de Mata Atlântica nordestina. In: Congr. Bras. Orn. XVI, Palmas, *Resumos*: 191.

Peres, C. A. & Palacios, E. 2007. Basin-wide effects of game harvest on vertebrate population densities in Amazonian forests: implications for animal-mediated seed dispersal. *Biotropica* 39: 304–315.

Perry, A., Kessler, M. & Helme, N. 1997. Birds of the central Río Tuichi Valley, with emphasis on dry forest, Parque Nacional Madidi, depto. La Paz, Bolivia. In: Remsen, J. V. (ed.) *Studies in Neotropical Ornithology Honoring Ted Parker. Orn. Monogr.* 48: 557–576.

Peters, J. L. 1927. A new manakin from Panama. *Proc. New England Zoöl. Club* 10: 9–10.

Peters, J. L. 1929. An ornithological survey in the Caribbean lowlands of Honduras. *Bull. Mus. Comp. Zool.* 69: 397–478.

Peters, J. L. & Griswold, J. A. 1943. Birds of the Harvard Peruvian expedition. *Bull. Mus. Comp. Zool. Harvard* 92: 281–327.

Peterson, A. T. & Nyári, Á. S. 2008. Ecological niche conservatism and Pleistocene refugia in the Thrush-like Mourner, *Schiffornis* sp., in the Neotropics. *Evolution* 62: 173–183.

Phelps, W. H. 1944. Las aves de Perijá. *Bol. Soc. Venez. Cienc. Nat.* 56: 265–338.

Phelps, W. H. Jr. 1973. Adiciones a las lista de aves de Sur America, Brasil y Venezuela y notas sobre aves venezolanas. *Bol. Soc. Venez. Cienc. Nat.* 30: 23–40.

Phelps, W. H. & Gilliard, E. T. 1941. Seventeen new birds from Venezuela. *Amer. Mus. Novit.* 1153: 1–18.

Phelps, W. H. & Phelps, W. H. Jr. 1946. Descripcion de cinco aves nuevas de Venezuela y comentarios sobre *Columbigallina passerina tortugensis* Fernández y *Machaeropterus regulus aureopectus* Phelps y Gilliard. *Bol. Soc. Venez. Cienc. Nat.* 65/66: 149–161.

Phelps, W. H. & Phelps, W. H. Jr. 1948. Notas sobre aves venezolanas. *Bol. Soc. Venez. Cienc. Nat.* 11: 189–210.

Phelps, W. H. & Phelps, W. H. Jr. 1949. Eight new birds from the subtropical zone of the Paria Peninsula, Venezuela. *Proc. Biol. Soc. Wash.* 62: 33–44.

Phelps, W. H. & Phelps, W. H. Jr. 1950. Lista de las aves de Venezuela con su distribución, parte 2, Passeriformes. *Bol. Soc. Venez. Cienc. Nat.* 12: 1–427.

Phelps, W. H. & Phelps, W. H. Jr. 1962. Cuarentinueve aves nuevas para la avifauna brasileña del Cerro Uei-tepui (Cerro del Sol). *Bol. Soc. Venez. Cienc. Nat.* 23: 32–39.

Phelps, W. H. & Phelps, W. H. Jr. 1965. Lista de las aves del Cerro de la Neblina, Venezuela y notas sobre su descubrimiento y ascenso. *Bol. Soc. Venez. Cienc. Nat.* 26: 11–35.

Piacenteni, V. Q., Ghizoni, I. R., Azevedo, M. A. G. & Kirwan, G. M. 2006. Sobre a distribução de aves em Santa Catarina, Brasil, parte I: registros relevantes para o estado ou inéditos para a Ilha de Santa Catarina. *Cotinga* 26: 25–31.

Piaskowski, V. D., Teul, M., Williams, K. M. & Cal, R. N. 2006. Birds of the Sibun riverine forest, Belize. *Orn. Neotrop.* 17: 333–352.

Pichorim, M., Uejima, A. M. K. & Gatto, C. A. F. R. 2000. Avifauna de um remanescente do sudoeste do Estado do Paraná. In: Straube, F. C., Argel-de-Oliveira, M. M. & Cândido, J. F. (eds) *Ornitologia brasileira no século XX*. Pp. 212–213. Universidade do Sul de Santa Catarina & Sociedade Brasileira de Ornitologia, Curitiba.

Piertney, S. B., Shorey, L. & Höglund, J. 2002. Characterization of microsatellite DNA markers in the White-bearded Manakin (*Manacus manacus*). *Mol. Ecol. Notes* 2: 504–505.

Pimentel, L. M. S. 2010. Primeiro registro documentado de *Piprites chloris* (Temmink, 1822) no Estado do Rio de Janeiro. *Atualidades Orn.* 152: 4.

Pimentel, L. & Olmos, F. 2011. The birds of Reserva Ecológica Guapiaçu (REGUA), Rio de Janeiro, Brazil. *Cotinga* 33 OL: 8–24.

Pina, P. I., Silva, M. B., Zucca, C. F., Souza, C. R., Mamede, S., Reis, I. O., Pereira, E. & Darbello, D. 2005. Dados biomorfométricos de aves de sub-bosque do cerrado na região do complexo do Jauru, nordeste de Mato Grosso do Sul, Brasil. In: Congr. Bras. Orn. XIII, Belém, *Resumos*: 240.

Pineschi, R. B. 1990. Aves como dispersores de sete espécies de *Rapanea* (Myrsinaceae) no maciço de Itatiaia, estados do Rio de Janeiro e Minas Gerais. *Ararajuba* 1: 73–78.

Pinheiro, R. T. & Dornas, T. 2009a. Distribuição e conservação das aves na região do Cantão, Tocantins: ecótono Amazônia/Cerrado. *Biota Neotrop.* 9: 187–205.

Pinheiro, R. T. & Dornas, T. 2009b. Novos registros ornitológicos para o Parque Estadual do Cantão: distribuição e conservação da avifauna do ecótono Amazônia-Cerrado. *Rev. Bras. Orn.* 17: 73–76.

Pinho, J. B. & Marini, M. Â. 2005. Avifauna da região de Pirizal, município de Nossa Senhora do Livramento, Pantanal de Poconé – MT. In: Congr. Bras. Orn. XIII, Belém, *Resumos*: 101.

Pinto, O. M. O. 1938. Nova contribuição a ornitologia amazonica. Estudo crítico de uma collecção de aves do baixo Solimões e do alto Rio Negro. *Rev. Mus. Paulista* 23: 493–604.

Pinto, O. M. O. 1940. Aves de Pernambuco. *Arq. Zool., São Paulo* 1(5): 219–282.

Pinto, O. M. O. 1944. *Catálogo das Aves do Brasil.* Parte 2. Dept. Zool., Secr. Agricult., São Paulo.

Pinto, O. M. O. 1947. Contribuição à ornitologia do baixo Amazonas. Estudo crítico de uma coleção de aves do Estado do Pará. *Arq. Zool., São Paulo* 5(6): 311–482.

Pinto, O. M. O. 1951. Aves do Itatiaia – lista remissiva e novas achegas a avifauna da região. *Pap. Avuls. Dept. Zool., São Paulo* 10: 155–208.

Pinto, O. M. O. 1953. Sobre a coleção Carlos Estevão de peles, ninhos e ovos das aves de Belém (Pará). *Pap. Avuls. Dept. Zool. São Paulo* 11: 113–224.

Pinto, O. M. O. 1966. *Estudo crítico e catálogo remissivo das aves do Território Federal de Roraima.* Instituto Nacional de Pesquisas da Amazônia, Manaus.

Pinto, O. M. O. & Camargo, E. A. 1957. Sobre uma coleção de aves da região de Cachimbo (sul do Estado do Pará). *Pap. Avuls. Dept. Zool., São Paulo* 13: 51–69.

Pinto, O. M. O. & Camargo, E. A. 1961. Resultados ornitológicos de quatro recentes expedições do Departamento de Zoologia ao Nordeste do Brasil, com a descrição de seis novas subespécies. *Arq. Zool. São Paulo* 11: 193–284.

Piratelli, A. & Blake, J. G. 2006. Bird communities of the southeastern Cerrado region, Brazil. *Orn. Neotrop.* 17: 213–225.

Piratelli, A. & Mello, M. C. 2001. Biologia do uirapuru-laranja (*Pipra fasciicauda*) no Estado de Mato Grosso do Sul, Brasil. *Tangara* 1: 157–167.

Piratelli, A. J. & Pereira, M. R. 2002. Dieta de aves na região leste de Mato Grosso do Sul, Brasil. *Ararajuba* 10: 131–139.

Piratelli, A. J., Siqueira, M. A. C. & Marcondes-Machado, L. O. 2000. Reprodução e muda de penas em aves de sub-bosque na região leste de Mato Grosso do Sul. *Ararajuba* 8: 99–107.

Piratelli, A. J., Alves, V. A. & Lima-Filho, M. 2001. Avifauna de fragmentos florestais em área de cultivo de cana-de-açúcar na região norte fluminense. In: Congr. Bras. Orn. IX, Curitiba, *Resumos*: 162.

Piratelli, A. J., Alves, V. A. & Corrêa, J. S. 2003. Avifauna em uma mata de baixada litorânea no Município do Rio de Janeiro (RJ). In: Machado, C. G. (ed.) *XI Congresso Brasileiro de Ornitologia Resumos*, Feira de Santana, BA: 113.

Piratelli, A. J., Gouvêa, E. M. & Gouvêa, J. 2010. Vertical zonation and community structure in an altitudinal gradient in the region of Itatiaia National Park, southeastern Brazil. In: Miyaki, C. M., Höfling, E. & Donatelli, R. J. (eds) *Abstracts 25th Int. Orn. Congr., Campos do Jordão, Brazil, 22–28 August 2010*: 537.

Pires, C. A., Flávia, C. & Cunha, A. C. 1991. Estudo comparativo dos dados de anilhamento registrados durante os anos de 1984 a 1990, das famílias Turdidae e Pipridae na região do Parque Nacional do Itatiaia. In: Congr. Bras. Orn. I, Belém, *Resumos*: 19.

Pizo, M. A., Silva, W. R., Galetti, M. & Laps, R. 2002. Frugivory in cotingas of the Atlantic Forest of southeast Brazil. *Ararajuba* 10: 177–185.

Poletto, F. & Aleixo, A. 2005. Biogeographic implications of new avian records from a patch of white-sand forest in southwestern Brazilian Amazonia. *Rev. Bras. Zool.* 22: 1196–1200.

Posso, S. R., Bueno, F. A., Mizobe, R. S., Pinheiro, L. C. C., Previatto, D. M., Dias, V. B., Filgueiras, V., Lima, B. M., Cancian, D., Miyaji, E. E. & Filho, J. C. M. 2009. Levantamento preliminar da avifauna da Reserva Cisalpina – Brasilândia, Mato Grosso do Sul. In: Simon, J. E., Raposo, M. A., Stopiglia, R. & Peres, J. (eds) *XVII Congresso Brasileiro de Ornitologia Resumos, Aracruz, ES: Biogeografia das aves da Mata Atlântica*: 84.

Poulin, B., Wright, S. J., Lefebvre, G. & Calderón, O. 1999. Interspecifc synchrony and asynchrony in the fruiting phenologies of congeneric bird-dispersed plants in Panama. *J. Trop. Ecol.* 15: 213–227.

Poulsen, B. O. 1992. Range extensions of Orange-cheeked Parrot and White-browed Purpletuft in Amazonian Venezuela. *Bull. Brit. Orn. Club* 112: 276–277.

Poulsen, B. O. 1996. Species composition, function and home-range of mixed-species bird flocks in a primary cloud forest in Ecuador. *Bull. Brit. Orn. Club* 113: 67–74.

Powell, G. V. N. & Bjork, R. D. 2004. Habitat linkages and the conservation of tropical biodiversity as indicated by seasonal migrations of three-wattled bellbirds. *Conserv. Biol.* 18: 500–509.

Pozza, D. D. 2002. Registros de avifauna ameaçada de extinção no nordeste do Estado de Sao Paulo. *Ararajuba* 10: 241–243.

Prado, A. D., Ribeiro, P. H. E., Wilke, S., Barros de Oliveira, J., Rodrigues, M. C. C., Miranda, E. A., Batista, K. S., Pimentel,

L. B. & Martinovski, V. M. 2005. Levantamento da avifauna do Parque Estadual do Lajeado/Palmas/Tocantins. In: Congr. Bras. Orn. XIII, Belém, *Resumos*: 142.

Prestel, D. 1984. Teilerfolg bei der Zucht von Gelbkopfpipras (*Pipra erythrocephala*). *Trochilus* 5: 89–90.

Prum, R. O. 1985. Observations on the White-fronted Manakin (*Pipra serena*) in Suriname. *Auk* 102: 384–387.

Prum, R. O. 1986. The displays of the White-throated Manakin *Corapipo gutturalis* in Suriname. *Ibis* 128: 91–102.

Prum, R. O. 1988. Historical relationships among avian forest areas of endemism in the Neotropics. In: Ouellet, H. (ed.) *Acta XIX Congr. Int. Orn.* National Museum of Natural Sciences, Ottawa.

Prum, R. O. 1990a. Phylogenetic analysis of the evolution of display behavior of the neotropical manakins (Aves: Pipridae). *Ethology* 84: 202–231.

Prum, R. O. 1990b. A test of the monophyly of the manakins (Pipridae) and of the cotingas (Cotingidae) based on morphology. *Occas. Pap. Mus. Zool. Univ. Michigan* 723.

Prum, R. O. 1992. Syringeal morphology, phylogeny, and evolution of the neotropical manakins (Aves: Pipridae). *Amer. Mus. Novit.* 3043: 1–65.

Prum, R. O. 1994a. Phylogenetic analysis of the evolution of alternative social behavior in the manakins (Aves: Pipridae). *Evolution* 48: 1657–1675.

Prum, R. O. 1994b. Species status of the White-fronted Manakin, *Lepidothrix serena* (Pipridae), with comments on conservation biology. *Condor* 96: 692–702.

Prum, R. O. 1997. Phylogenetic tests of alternative intersexual selection mechanisms: trait macroevolution in a polygynous clade (Aves: Pipridae). *Amer. Natur.* 149: 668–692.

Prum, R. O. 1998. Sexual selection and the evolution of mechanical sound production in manakins (Aves: Pipridae). *Anim. Behav.* 55: 977–994.

Prum, R. O. 2001. A new genus for the Andean green pihas (Cotingidae). *Ibis* 143: 307–309.

Prum, R. O. & Johnson, A. E. 1987. Display behavior, foraging ecology, and systematics of the Golden-winged Manakin (*Masius chrysopterus*). *Wilson Bull.* 99: 521–539.

Prum, R. O. & Lanyon, W. E. 1989. Monophyly and phylogeny of the *Schiffornis* group (Tyrannoidea). *Condor* 91: 444–461.

Prum, R. O., Kaplan, J. D. & Pierson, J. E. 1996. Display behavior and natural history of the Yellow-crowned Manakin (*Heterocercus flavivertex*: Pipridae). *Condor* 98: 722–735.

Prum, R. O., Rice, N. H., Mobley, J. A. & Dimmick, W. W. 2000. A preliminary phylogenetic hypothesis for the cotingas (Cotingidae) based on mitochondrial DNA. *Auk* 117: 236–241.

Puebla-Olivares, F., Rodríguez-Ayala, E., Hernández-Baños, B. E. & Navarro S., A. G. 2002. Status and conservation of the avifauna of the Yaxchilán Natural Monument, Chiapas, Mexico. *Orn. Neotrop.* 13: 381–396.

Pugnali, G. 2008. Capital birding: Buenos Aires. *Neotrop. Birding* 3: 44–52.

Quelch, J. J. 1892. Position of the caruncle and method of song of the Bell-Bird. *Timehri, n.s.* 6: 164–166.

Quevedo, A., Salaman, P. & Donegan, T. 2006. Serranía de las Quinchas: establishment of a first protected area in the Magdalena Valley of Colombia. *Cotinga* 25: 24–32.

Rahbek, C., Bloch, H., Poulsen, M. K. & Rasmussen, J. F. 1993. Avian body weights from southern Ecuador. *Bull. Brit. Orn. Club* 113: 103–108.

Raine, A. F. 2006. Breeding bird records from the Tambopata-Candamo Reserve Zone, Madre de Dios, south-east Peru. *Cotinga* 28: 53–58.

Ramirez, G. C. 2010. Biogeographic history of the family Cotingidae. In: Miyaki, C. M., Höfling, E. & Donatelli, R. J. (eds) *Abstracts 25th Int. Orn. Congr., Campos do Jordão, Brazil, 22–28 August 2010*: 435.

Ramírez González, M. G. & Arias García, J. C. 1995. Características reproductivas del saltarín *Allocotopterus deliciosus* en la Reserva Natural La Planada. *Bol. Soc. Antioqueña Orn.* 6: 18–21.

Rasmussen, J. F., Rahbek, C., Poulsen, B. O., Poulsen, M. K. & Bloch, H. 1996. Distributional records and natural history

notes on threatened and little known birds of southern Ecuador. *Bull. Brit. Orn. Club* 116: 26–46.

Rêgo, P. S., Araripe, J., Sampaio, M. I. R., Girão e Silva, W. A., Albano, C., Brito, P. T. P. & Campos, A. A. 2005. Análise da estrutura populacional do soldadinho-do-Araripe *Antilophia bokermanni* (Aves: Pipridae) através marcadores moleculares. In: Congr. Bras. Orn. XIII, Belém, *Resumos*: 209.

Rêgo, P. S., Araripe, J., Marceliano, M. L. V., Sampaio, I. R. & Schneider, H. 2007. Phylogenetic analyses of the genera *Pipra*, *Lepidothrix* and *Dixiphia* (Pipridae, Passeriformes) using partial Cytochrome b and 16S mtDNA genes. *Zool. Scripta* 36: 565–575.

Rêgo, P. S., Araripe, J., Silva, W. A. G., Albano, C., Pinto, T., Campos, A., Vallinoto, M., Sampaio, I. & Schneider, H. 2010. Population genetic studies of mitochondrial pseudo-control region in the endangered Araripe Manakin (*Antilophia bokermanni*). *Auk* 127: 364–371.

Reidy, J. L. 2009. Nest predators of Lance-tailed Manakins on Isla Boca Brava, Panamá. *J. Field Orn.* 80: 115–118.

Reis, G. C., Corteletti, J. M., Bressari, D. A. & Marchiori, J. N. C. 1997. Registro das aves observadas no "Morro do Elefante" em Santa Maria e primeiro registro de *Antilophia galeata* no RS. In: Congr. Bras. Orn. VI, Belo Horizonte, *Resumos*: 38.

Remold, H. 2002. *The Land Birds of Southeast Brazil*. Disc 2. CD. Privately published.

Remsen, J. V. 1984. Natural history notes on some poorly-known Bolivian birds. *Gerfaut* 74: 163–179.

Remsen, J. V. 2010. Subspecies as a meaningful taxonomic rank in avian classification. *Orn. Monogr.* 67: 62–78.

Remsen, J. V. & Parker, T. A. 1995. Bolivia has the opportunity to create the planet's richest park for terrestrial biota. *Bird Conserv. Int.* 5: 181–199.

Remsen, J. V. & Schulenberg, T. S. 1997. The pervasive influence of Ted Parker on Neotropical field ornithology. In: Remsen, J. V. (ed.) *Studies in Neotropical Ornithology Honoring Ted Parker*. *Orn. Monogr.* 48: 7–19.

Remsen, J. V. & Traylor, M. A. 1989. *An Annotated List of the Birds of Bolivia*. Buteo Books, Vermillion, SD.

Remsen, J. V., Parker, T. A. & Ridgely, R. S. 1982. Natural history notes on some poorly known Bolivian birds. *Gerfaut* 72: 77–87.

Remsen, J. V., Traylor, M. A. & Parkes, K. C. 1987. Range extensions for some Bolivian birds, 3 (Tyrannidae to Passeridae). *Bull. Brit. Orn. Club* 107: 6–16.

Remsen, J. V., Schmitt, C. G. & Schmitt, D. C. 1988. Natural history notes on some poorly known Bolivian birds Part 3. *Gerfaut* 78: 363–381.

Remsen, J. V., Cadena, C. D., Jaramillo, A., Nores, M., Pacheco, J. F., Robbins, M. B., Schulenberg, T. S., Stiles F. G., Stotz, D. F. & Zimmer, K. J. 2009. A classification of the bird species of South America (version 15 July 2009). www.museum.lsu.edu/~Remsen/SACCBaseline.html.

Renaudier, A. 2009. Birding French Guiana. *Neotrop. Birding* 5: 39–47.

Renaudier, A. & Deroussen, F. 2008. *Chants d'Oiseaux de Guyane/ Bird Songs from French Guiana*. CDs. Naturophonia/GEPOG/ Muséum National d'Histoire Natural, Paris.

Renjifo, L. M. 1991. Abundancias de aves frugívoras grandes y depredadoras de semillas en un bosque alto andino, implicaciones para su conservación. In: Anon. (ed.) *Resúmenes del IV Congresso de Ornitología Neotropical*. CECIA, Quito.

Renjifo M., L. M. 1994. First records of the Bay-vented Cotinga *Doliornis sclateri* in Colombia. *Bull. Brit. Orn. Club* 114: 101–103.

Renjifo, L. M., Franco-Maya, A. M., Amaya-Espinel, J. D., Kattan, G. H. & López-Lanús, B. 2002. *Libro Rojo de Aves de Colombia*. Instituto de Investigación de Recursos Biológicos Alexander von Humboldt y Ministerio del Medio Ambiente, Bogotá.

Restall, R., Rodner, C. & Lentino, M. 2006. *Birds of Northern South America*. Christopher Helm, London.

Restrepo, C., Salaman, P. & Cuervo, A. M. 2002. *Pipreola chlorolepidota*. In: Renjifo, L. M., Franco-Maya, A. M., Amaya-Espinel, J. D., Kattan, B. H. & López-Lanús, B. (eds) *Libro Rojo de Aves de Colombia*. Instituto de Investigación de Recursos Biológicos Alexander von Humboldt & Ministerio del Medio Ambiente, Bogotá.

Reynaud, P. A. 1998. Changes in understory avifauna along the Sinnamary River (French Guyana, South America). *Orn. Neotrop.* 9: 51–70.

Rheinhardt, J. 1870. Bidrag til kundskab om fugelfaunaen i Brasiliens campos. *Vidensk. Meddr. Dansk Naturh. Foren.* 124.

Ribeiro, M. 2009. Um sentinela à espera de aliados. *Terra da Gente* 6(63): 18–27.

Ribon, R., Simon, J. E. & Mattos, G. T. 2003. Bird extinctions in Atlantic Forest fragments of the Viçosa region, southeastern Brazil. *Conserv. Biol.* 17: 1827–1839.

Ribon, R., Mattos, G. T., Luiz, E. R., Morais, F. C., Andrade, R. N., Resende, F. C., Melo, F. R., Chiarello, A. G. & Abreu, C. R. M. 2004. Avifauna da floresta ombrófila densa do vale do Jequitinhonha, nordeste de Minas Gerais. In: Congr. Bras. Orn. XII, Blumenau, *Resumos*: 345.

Richmond, C. W. 1893. Notes on a collection of birds from eastern Nicaragua and the Río Frío, Costa Rica, with a description of a supposed new trogon. *Proc. US Natl. Mus.* 16: 479–532.

Ricklefs, R. L. 1977. Reactions of some Panamanian birds to human intrusion at the nest. *Condor* 79: 376–379.

Ridgely, R. S. 1980. Notes on some rare or previously unrecorded birds in Ecuador. *Amer. Birds* 34: 242–248.

Ridgely, R. S. & Gaulin, S. J. C. 1980. The birds of Finca Merenberg, Huila Department, Colombia. *Condor* 82: 379–391.

Ridgely, R. S. & Greenfield, P. J. 2001. *The Birds of Ecuador*. Christopher Helm, London.

Ridgely, R. S. & Gwynne, J. A. 1976. *A Guide to the Birds of Panama*. Princeton University Press, Princeton, NJ.

Ridgely, R. S. & Gwynne, J. A. 1989. *A Guide to the Birds of Panama with Costa Rica, Nicaragua, and Honduras*. Princeton University Press, Princeton, NJ.

Ridgely, R. S. & Tudor, G. 1994. *The Birds of South America*. Vol. 2. University of Texas Press, Austin.

Ridgely, R. S. & Tudor, G. 2009. *Birds of South America: Passerines*. Christopher Helm, London.

Ridgely, R. S., Allnutt, T. F., Brooks, T., McNicol, D. K., Mehlman, D. W., Young, B. E. & Zook, J. R. 2003. *Digital Distribution Maps of the Birds of the Western Hemisphere*, version 1.0. NatureServe, Arlington, VA.

Ridgway, R. 1905. A winter with the birds in Costa Rica. *Condor* 7: 151–160.

Ridgway, R. 1907. The birds of North and Middle America. Part IV. *Bull. US Natl. Mus.* 50: 1–973.

Ríos, M. M. 2005. ¿Quién come Yarumo? .. O mejor, ¿quién no come Yarumo en los bosques de montaña? *Bol. Soc. Antioqueña Orn.* 15(2): 5–15.

Rios, M., Londoño, G. & Biancucci, L. 2008. Notes on birds that follow army ants in the northern Andes. *Orn. Neotrop.* 19: 137–142.

Ríos, C. S. S. 2010. Efectos de la fragmentación y degradación de hábitat de *Polylepis* spp. con respecto a la avifauna asociada en la Biosfera del Parque Nacional Huascarán. BSc thesis, Facultad de Ciencias y Filosofía, Universidad Peruana Cayetano Heredia.

Robbins, M. B. 1983. The display repertoire of the Band-tailed Manakin (*Pipra fasciicauda*). *Wilson Bull.* 95: 321–342.

Robbins, M. B. 1985. Social organization of the Band-tailed Manakin (*Pipra fasciicauda*). *Condor* 87: 449–456.

Robbins, M. B., Parker, T. A. & Allen, S. E. 1985. The avifauna of Cerro Pirre, Darién, eastern Panama. In: Buckley, P. A., Foster, M. S., Morton, E. S., Ridgely, R. S. & Buckley, F. G. (eds) *Neotropical Ornithology. Orn. Monogr.* 36: 198–232.

Robbins, M. B., Ridgely, R. S., Schulenberg, T. S. & Gill, F. B. 1987. The avifauna of the Cordillera de Cutucú, Ecuador, with comparisons to other Andean localities. *Acad. Nat. Sci. Philadelphia* 139: 243–259.

Robbins, M. B., Rosenberg, G. H. & Sornoza M., F. 1994. A new species of cotinga (Cotingidae: *Doliornis*) from the Ecuadorian Andes, with comments on plumage sequences in *Doliornis* and *Ampelion*. *Auk* 111: 1–7.

Robbins, M. B., Faucett, R. B. & Rice, N. H. 1999. Avifauna of a

Paraguayan cerrado locality: Parque Nacional Serranía San Lucas, depto. Concepción. *Wilson Bull.* 111: 216–228.

Robbins, M. B., Braun, M. J. & Finch, D. W. 2004. Avifauna of the Guyana southern Rupununi, with comparisons to other savannas of northern South America. *Orn. Neotrop.* 15: 173–200.

Robbins, M. B., Braun, M. J., Milensky, C. M., Schmidt, C. G., Prince, W., Rice, N. H., Finch, D. W. & O'Shea, B. J. 2007. Avifauna of the upper Essequibo River and Acary Mountains, southern Guyana. *Orn. Neotrop.* 18: 339–368.

Robbins, M. B., Geale, D., Walker, B., Davis, T. J., Combe, M., Eaton, M. & Kennedy, K. P. 2011. Foothill avifauna of the upper Urubamba Valley, dpto. Cusco, Peru. *Cotinga* 33 OL: 34–45.

Robiller, F. 2005. Die Balz der Felsenhaehne im tropischen Regenwald Perus. [The mating of the Andean Cock-of-the-Rock in the tropical rainforest of Peru.] *Gefiederte Welt* 129: 378–379.

Robinson, S. K. 1997. Birds of a Peruvian oxbow lake: populations, resources, predation, and social behavior. In: Remsen, J. V. (ed.) *Studies in Neotropical Ornithology Honoring Ted Parker. Orn. Monogr.* 48: 613–639.

Robinson, S. K. & Terborgh, J. 1997. Bird community dynamics along primary successional gradients of an Amazonian whitewater river. In: Remsen, J. V. (ed.) *Studies in Neotropical Ornithology Honoring Ted Parker. Orn. Monogr.* 48: 641–672.

Robinson, W. D. 1999. Long-term changes in the avifauna of Barro Colorado Island, Panama, a tropical forest isolate. *Conserv. Biol.* 13: 85–97.

Robinson, W. D., Brawn, J. D. & Robinson, S. K. 2000a. Forest bird community structure in central Panama: influence of spatial scale and biogeography. *Ecol. Monogr.* 70: 209–235.

Robinson, W. D., Rodden Robinson, T., Robinson, S. K. & Brawn, J. D. 2000b. Nesting success of understory birds in central Panama. *J. Avian Biol.* 31: 151–164.

Rochido, V. B. 2000. Reutilização de ninho por *Phibalura flavirostris* (Tyrannidae [*sic*]: Passeriformes) no Parque do Caraça, Minas Gerais. In: Straube, F. C., Argel-de-Oliveira, M. M. & Cândido, J. F. (eds) *Ornitologia brasileira no século XX*. Pp. 305–306. Universidade do Sul de Santa Catarina & Sociedade Brasileira de Ornitologia, Curitiba.

Rochido, V. B. & Andrade, M. C. M. 2000. Nidificação de *Phibalura flavirostris* (Tyrannidae [*sic*]: Passeriformes) no Parque do Caraça, Minas Gerais. In: Straube, F. C., Argel-de-Oliveira, M. M. & Cândido, J. F. (eds) *Ornitologia brasileira no século XX*. Pp. 332–333. Universidade do Sul de Santa Catarina & Sociedade Brasileira de Ornitologia, Curitiba.

Rochido, V. B., Schetini de Azevedo, C. & Young, R. J. 2003. Etograma de construcao de ninho de *Phibalura flavirostris* (Aves: Cotingidae). In: Machado, C. G. (ed.) *XI Congresso Brasileiro de Ornitologia Resumos, Feira de Santana, BA*: 39.

Roda, S. A. & Carlos, C. J. 2003. New records for some poorly known birds of the Atlantic Forest in north-east Brazil. *Cotinga* 20: 17–20.

Roda, S. A. & Dantas, S. M. 2008. The first two records of Wing-barred Piprites, *Piprites chloris*, in the Pernambuco center of endemism. *Rev. Bras. Orn.* 16: 271–273.

Roda, S. A., Carlos, C. J. & Rodrigues, R. C. 2003. New and noteworthy records for some endemic and threatened birds of the Atlantic forest of north-eastern Brazil. *Bull. Brit. Orn. Club* 123: 227–236.

Rodner, C., Lentino, M. & Restall, R. 2000. *Checklist of the Birds of Northern South America*. Pica Press, Robertsbridge.

Rodrigues, E. B., Carvalho, S. T., Sousa e Silva, M., Sousa, D. D. S. & Santos, M. P. D. 2005. Massa corporal de aves na área do Eco Resort Nazareth e Parque Nacional de Sete Cidades, norte do Estado do Piauí. In: Congr. Bras. Orn. XIII, Belém, *Resumos*: 242.

Rodrigues, R. C., Amaral, A. C. A. & Gonzaga Sales, L. 2003. Inventário da avifauna na Área de Proteção Ambiental do Maciço do Baturité, CE. In: Machado, C. G. (ed.) *XI Congresso Brasileiro de Ornitologia Resumos, Feira de Santana, BA*: 119.

Rodrigues Lima, G. & Anciães, M. 2009a. Caracterização do repertório comportamental da ave *Neopelma chrysocephalum* em uma campina da Amazônia central. In: Simon, J. E., Raposo, M. A., Stopiglia, R. & Peres, J. (eds) *XVII Congresso Brasileiro de Ornitologia Resumos, Aracruz, ES: Biogeografia das aves da Mata Atlântica*: 12.

Rodrigues Lima, G. & Anciães, M. 2009b. Caracterização do repertório vocal da ave *Neopelma chrysocephalum* em uma campina da Amazônia central. In: Simon, J. E., Raposo, M. A., Stopiglia, R. & Peres, J. (eds) *XVII Congresso Brasileiro de Ornitologia Resumos, Aracruz, ES: Biogeografia das aves da Mata Atlântica*: 12.

Rodriguez-Ferraro, A. & Azpiroz, A. B. 2005. Notes on the natural history of the Andean Cock-of-the-Rock (*Rupicola peruviana*) in western Venezuela. *Orn. Neotrop.* 16: 105–108.

Rojas Nossa, S. V. 2008. Organización espacial y patrón temporal de canto en un lek de *Perissocephalus tricolor* (Cotingidae). *Rev. Bras. Orn.* 16: 214–220.

Romero-Zambrano, H. 1978. Primer registro de doce aves para Colombia. *Lozania (Acta Zool. Colombiana)* 26: 1–8.

do Rosário, L. A. 1996. *As Aves em Santa Catarina: Distribuição Geográfica e Meio Ambiente*. Fundação do Meio Ambiente, Florianópolis.

Rosario Avalos, V. 2010. Selección de sitios de anidación por la Palkachupa (*Phibalura flavirostris boliviana*, Cotingidae) en Bolivia. *Orn. Neotrop.* 21: 195–202.

Rosario Avalos, V. 2011. Distribución, población y conservación de la Palkachupa (*Phibalura flavirostris boliviana*, Cotingidae) en la área de Apolo, Bolivia. *Orn. Neotrop.* 22: 1–13.

Rosenberg, G. H. 1990. Habitat specialization and foraging behavior by birds of Amazonian river islands in northeastern Peru. *Condor* 92: 427–443.

Rosina, M. & Romo, M. 2010. Hallazgo de dos nidos activos de *Phytotoma raimondii*, Tackzanowski, [*sic*] 1883, cortarrama peruana. *Rev. Peru. Biol.* 17: 257–259.

Ross, D. L. 2000. *Costa Rican Bird Song Sampler*. CD. Cornell Laboratory of Ornithology, Ithaca, NY.

Ross, D. L. & Whitney, B. M. 1995. *Voices of Costa Rican Birds Caribbean Slope*. CDs. Cornell Laboratory of Ornithology, Ithaca, NY.

Rosselli, L. 1994. The annual cycle of the White-ruffed Manakin *Corapipo leucorrhoa*, a tropical frugivorous altitudinal migrant, and its food plants. *Bird Conserv. Int.* 4: 143–160.

Rosselli, L., Vasquez, P. & Ayub, I. 2002. The courtship displays and social system of the White-ruffed Manakin in Costa Rica. *Wilson Bull.* 114: 165–178.

Roth, P., Oren, D. C. & Novaes, F. C. 1984. The White Bellbird (*Procnias alba*) in the Serra dos Carajás, southeastern Pará, Brazil. *Condor* 86: 343–344.

Rubio, T. C., Ferreira, L. P., Pinheiro, T. G. & Pinho, J. B. 2003. Análise dos hábitos alimentares de aves da região de Chapada dos Guimarães, Mato Grosso. In: Machado, C. G. (ed.) *XI Congresso Brasileiro de Ornitologia Resumos, Feira de Santana, BA*: 155.

Ruiz-Guerra, C., Johnston-González, R., Cifuentes-Sarmiento, Y., Estela, F. A., Castillo, L. F., Hernández, C. E. & Naranjo, L. G. 2007. Noteworthy bird records from the southern Chocó of Colombia. *Bull. Brit. Orn. Club* 127: 283–293.

Ruiz-Gutiérrez, V., Gavin, T. A. & Dhondt, A. A. 2008. Habitat fragmentation lowers survival of a tropical forest bird. *Ecol. Appl.* 18: 838–846.

Rupp, A. E., Thom, G. & Zimmermann, C. E. 2007. Registros documentados de aves raras em Santa Catarina, Brasil. In: Fontana, C. S. (ed.) *XV Congresso Brasileiro de Ornitologia Resumos, Porto Alegre, RS*: 94–95.

Ruschi, A. 1953. Lista das aves do Estado do Espírito Santo. *Bol. Mus. Biol. Prof. Mello Leitão*, Sér. Zool. 11.

Russell, S. M. 1964. *A Distributional Survey of the Birds of the British Honduras*. Orn. Monogr. 1. American Ornithologists' Union, New York.

Ryder, T. B. & Durães, R. B. 2005. It's not easy being green: using molt and morphological criteria to age and sex green-plumage manakins (Aves: Pipridae). *Orn. Neotrop.* 16: 481–491.

Ryder, T. B., Blake, J. G. & Loiselle, B. A. 2006. A test of the environmental hotspot hypothesis for lek placement in three species of manakins (Pipridae) in Ecuador. *Auk* 123: 247–258.

Ryder, T. B., Durães, R., Tori, W. P., Hidalgo, J. R., Loiselle, B. A. & Blake, J. G. 2008a. Nest survival for two species of manakins (Pipridae) in lowland Ecuador. *J. Avian Biol.* 39: 355–358.

Ryder, T. B., McDonald, D. B., Blake, J. G., Parker, P. G. & Loiselle, B. A. 2008b. Social networks in the lek-mating wire-tailed manakin (*Pipra filicauda*). *Proc. Roy. Soc. Lond. B* 275: 1367–1374.

Ryder, T. B., Parker, P. G., Blake, J. G. & Loiselle, B. A. 2009. It takes two to tango: reproductive skew and social correlates of male mating success in a lek-breeding bird. *Proc. Roy. Soc. Lond. B* 276: 2377–2384.

Ryder, T. B., Tori, W. P., Blake, J. G., Loiselle, B. A. & Parker, P. G. 2010. Mate choice for genetic quality: a test of the heterozygosity and compatibility hypotheses in a lek-breeding bird. *Behav. Ecol.* 21: 203–210.

Ryder, T. B., Blake, J. G., Parker, P. G. & Loiselle, B. A. 2011. The composition, stability, and kinship of reproductive coalitions in a lekking bird. *Behav. Ecol.* 22: 282–290.

Saibene, C. A., Castelino, M. A., Rey, N. R., Herrera, J. & Calo, J. 1996. *Inventario de las Aves del Parque Nacional "Iguazu", Misiones, Argentina*. Literature of Latin America, Buenos Aires.

Salaman, P. & Donegan, T. M. 2007. Estudios y conservación en la Serranía de los Churumbelos - Expediciones Colombia '98 y Proyecto EBA. *Conserv. Colombiana* 3: 1–93.

Salaman, P. G. W., Donegan, T. M. & Cuervo, A. M. 1999. Ornithological surveys in Serranía de los Churumbelos, southern Colombia. *Cotinga* 12: 29–39.

Salaman, P. G. W., Donegan, T. M. & Cuervo, A. M. 2002a. New distributional bird records from Serranía de San Lucas and adjacent Central Cordillera of Colombia. *Bull. Brit. Orn. Club* 122: 285–303.

Salaman, P. G. W., Stiles, F. G., Bohórquez, C. I., Álvarez-R., M., Umaña, A. M., Donegan, T. M. & Cuervo, A. M. 2002b. New and noteworthy bird records from the east slope of the Andes of Colombia. *Caldasia* 24: 157–189.

Salaman, P., Donegan, T. & Caro, D. 2008. Checklist to the birds of Colombia 2009. *Conserv. Colombiana* 5: 1–79.

Salaman, P., Donegan, T. & Caro, D. 2009. Checklist to the birds of Colombia 2009. *Conserv. Colombiana* 8: 1–79.

Saldanha, C. J., Colin, J., Schultz, J. D., London, S. E. & Schlinger, B. A. 2000. Telencephalic aromatase but not a song circuit in a sub-oscine passerine, the Golden-collared Manakin (*Manacus vitellinus*). *Brain Behav. Evol.* 56: 29–37.

Salinas, L., Samame, M., Franke, I. & Fjeldså, J. 2003. Primer registro del frutero pechinegro *Pipreola lubomirskii* (Aves, Cotingidae) en la vertiente occidental de los Andes. *Rev. Peru. Biol.* 10: 93–97.

Salvin, O. & Godman, F. D. 1891. *Biologia Centrali-Americana. Aves*. Vol. 2. Taylor & Francis, London.

Samper, K. C. 1992. Courtship feeding in the Orange-breasted Fruit-eater *Pipreola jucunda*. *Bull. Brit. Orn. Club* 112: 133–134.

Sánchez M., C. 2002. Nest, egg, and nesting biology of the Snowy Cotinga (*Carpodectes nitidus*). *Wilson Bull.* 114: 517–519.

Sánchez, C., Ruiz-Gutiérrez, V. & Martínez-A., D. 2007. Description of male vocalizations of the Turquoise Cotinga (*Cotinga ridgwayi*). *Wilson J. Orn.* 119: 455–458.

Santana C., E. & Milligan, B. G. 1984. Behavior of toucanets, bellbirds, and quetzals feeding on lauraceous fruits. *Biotropica* 16: 152–154.

Santos, M. P. D. 2000. Avifauna da Serra do Uruçuí, Piauí. In: Straube, F. C., Argel-de-Oliverira, M. M. & Cândido, J. F. (eds) *Ornitologia brasileira no século XX*. Pp. 237–238. Universidade do Sul de Santa Catarina & Sociedade Brasileira de Ornitologia, Curitiba.

Santos, M. P. D. & Silva, G. C. 2005. Inventário da avifauna da Terra Indígena Nove de Janeiro, Humaitá, Amazonas, Brasil. In: Congr. Bras. Orn. XIII, Belém, *Resumos*. 94.

Santos, M. P. D. & Silva, J. M. C. 2007. As aves das savanas de Roraima. *Rev. Bras. Orn.* 15: 189–207.

Santos, M. P. D., Cerqueira, P. V. & Santos Soares, L. M. 2010. Avifauna em seis localidades no Centro-Sul do Estado do Maranhão, Brasil. *Ornithologia* 4: 49–65.

Santos, R. E. F., Patrial, E. W. & Carrano, E. 2004. Composição, estrutura e conservação da avifauna do Distrito do Bugre, Balsa Nova, Paraná, Brasil. In: Congr. Bras. Orn. XII, Blumenau, *Resumos*: 361.

Santos, R. E. F., Ribas, C. F. & Patrial, E. W. 2008. Observações recentes do caneleirinho-de-chapéu-preto *Piprites pileata* (Temminck, 1822) no Estado de Santa Catarina. *Atualidades Orn.* 146: 11–13.

Saranathan, V., Hamilton, D., Powell, G. V. N., Kroodsma, D. & Prum, R. O. 2007. Genetic evidence supports song learning in the three-wattled bellbird *Procnias tricarunculata* [*sic*] (Cotingidae). *Mol. Ecol.* 16: 3689–3702.

Sari, E. H. R., Vasconcelos, M. F. & Santos, F. R. 2006. *Antilophia galeata* é a mãe! Análise genética de dois híbridos de *Chiroxiphia caudata* × *Antilophia galeata* de Minas Gerais, Brasil. *An. XIV Congr. Bras. Orn., Ouro Preto*: 29.

Schaefer, E. & Phelps, W. H. 1954. Aves de Rancho Grande. *Bol. Soc. Venez. Cienc. Nat.* 6: 3–167.

Scheibler, D. R. & Melo-Júnior, T. A. 2003. Frugivory by birds on two exotic *Ligustrum* species (Oleaceae) in Brazil. *Ararajuba* 11: 89–91.

Scherer Neto, P. & Kajiwara, D. 1997. *Pipra fasciicauda* (Pipridae, Aves) no Parque Estadual de Vila Rica do Espírito Santo, Fenix, Paraná. *Atualidades Orn.* 75: 7.

Scherer-Neto, P. & Straube, F. C. 1995. *Aves do Paraná: História, Lista Anotada e Bibliografia*. Privately published, Curitiba.

Scherer Neto, P., Carrano, E. & Ribas, C. F. 2001. Avifauna da Estação Ecológica do Caiuá (Diamante do Norte, Paraná) e regiões adjacentes. In: Congr. Bras. Orn. IX, Curitiba, *Resumos*: 192.

Schlichting, M. A. & Bispo, A. Á. 2009. Distribuição da avifauna em um remanescente de floresta com Araucária no sul do Brasil. In: Simon, J. E., Raposo, M. A., Stopiglia, R. & Peres, J. (eds) *XVII Congresso Brasileiro de Ornitologia Resumos, Aracruz, ES: Biogeografia das aves da Mata Atlântica*: 69.

Schlinger, B. A. 2010. Hormonal and non-hormonal control of a tropical phenotype: a case study of a Neotropical manakin. In: Miyaki, C. M., Höfling, E. & Donatelli, R. J. (eds) *Abstracts 25th Int. Orn. Congr., Campos do Jordão, Brazil, 22–28 August 2010*: 249.

Schlinger, B. A., Schultz, J. D. & Hertel, F. 2001. Nueromuscular and endocrine control of an avian courtship behaviour. *Horm. Behav.* 40: 276–280.

Schlinger, B., Fusani, L., Wikelski, M. & Barske, J. 2010. Heart rate reflects metabolic output in a bird with a complex courtship display. In: Miyaki, C. M., Höfling, E. & Donatelli, R. J. (eds) *Abstracts 25th Int. Orn. Congr., Campos do Jordão, Brazil, 22–28 August 2010*: 537.

Schmitt, C. G. & Schmitt, D. C. 1987. Extensions of range of some Bolivian birds. *Bull. Brit. Orn. Club* 107: 129–134.

Schmitt, C. G., Schmitt, D. C. & Remsen, J. V. 1997. Birds of the Tambo area, an arid valley in the Bolivian Andes. In: Remsen, J. V. (ed.) *Studies in Neotropical Ornithology Honoring Ted Parker. Orn. Monogr.* 48: 701–716.

Schmitt, F. 2010. Capital birding: Santiago de Chile. *Neotrop. Birding* 6: 28–35.

Schomburgk, R. 1848. *Reisen in Britisch-Guiana in dem Jahren 1840–1844. Part 3*. J. J. Weber, Leipzig.

Schönwetter, M. 1969. *Handbuch der Oologie*. Akademie Verlag, Berlin.

Schubart, O., Aguirre, A. C. & Sick, H. 1965. Contribuição para o conhecimento da alimentação das aves brasileiras. *Arq. Zool.* 12: 95–249.

Schuchmann, K.-L. 1984. Zur Ernährung des Cayenne-Felsenhahnes (*Rupicola rupicola*, Cotingidae). *J. Orn.* 125: 239–241.

Schuchmann, K.-L., Corredor, G., Torres, A. M. & Acevedo, C. 1989. Beobachtungen am Andenfelsenhahn (*Rupicola peruviana*). *Trochilus* 10: 24–29.

Schuckmann-Wegert, G. & Schuchmann, K.-L. 1986. Balzverhalten des Guayana-Felsenhahnes (*Rupicola rupicola*). *Trochilus* 7: 114–118.

Schulenberg, T. S. 2000a. *Voices of Andean Birds: Birds of the Hill Forest of Southern Peru and Bolivia*. CD. Library of Natural Sounds, Cornell Laboratory of Ornithology, Ithaca, NY.

Schulenberg, T. S. 2000b. *Voices of Andean Birds: Birds of the Cloud Forest of Southern Peru and Bolivia*. CD. Library of Natural Sounds, Cornell Laboratory of Ornithology, Ithaca, NY.

Schulenberg, T. S. 2002. Birds. In: Pitman, N., Alverson, W. S. & Moskovits, D. K. (eds) *Ecuador: Serranías Cofán-Bermejo, Sinangoe*. Rapid Biological Inventories Report 3. Field Museum of Natural History, Chicago.

Schulenberg, T. S. & Awbrey, K. (eds) 1997. *The Cordillera del Condor Region of Ecuador and Peru: A Biological Assessment*. RAP Working Papers 7. Conservation International, Washington, DC.

Schulenberg, T. S. & Parker, T. A. 1997. A new species of tyrant-flycatcher (Tyrannidae: *Tolmomyias*) from the western Amazon Basin. In: Remsen, J. V. (ed.) *Studies in Neotropical Ornithology Honoring Ted Parker. Orn. Monogr.* 48: 723–731.

Schulenberg, T. S. & Servat, G. 2001. Avifauna of the northern Cordillera of Vilcabamba, Peru. In: Alonso, L. E., Alonso, A., Schulenberg, T. S. & Dallmeier, F. (eds) *Biological and Social Assessments of the Cordillera de Vilcabamba, Peru*. RAP Working Papers 12. Conservation International, Washington, DC.

Schulenberg, T. S., Marantz, C. A. & English, P. H. 2000. *Voices of Amazonian Birds: Birds of the Rainforest of Southern Peru and Northern Bolivia*. Vol. 3. CD. Library of Natural Sounds, Cornell Lab. of Ornithology, Ithaca, NY.

Schulenberg, T. S., Albujar, C. & Rojas, J. I. 2006. Birds. In: Vriesendorp, C., Schulenberg, T. S., Alverson, W. S., Moskovits, D. K. & Rojas Moscoso, J.-I. (eds) *Perú: Sierra del Divisor*. Rapid Biological Inventories Report 17. The Field Museum, Chicago.

Schulenberg, T. S., Stotz, D. F., Lane, D. F., O'Neill, J. P. & Parker, T. A. 2007. *Birds of Peru*. Christopher Helm, London.

Schultz, J. D. & Schlinger, B. A. 1999. Widespread accumulation of 3H-testosterone in the spinal cord of a sub-oscine bird with an elaborate courtship display. *Proc. Natl. Acad. Sci. USA* 96: 10428–10432.

Schultz, J. D., Hertel, F., Bauch, M. & Schlinger, B. A. 2001. Adaptations for rapid and forceful contraction in wing muscles of the male Golden-collared Manakin: sex and species comparisons. *J. Comp. Physiol.* 187: 677–684.

Schunck, F. & Silveira, L. F. 2010. Altitudinal distribution of birds in Serra do Mar State Park, São Paulo, Brazil. In: Miyaki, C. M., Höfling, E. & Donatelli, R. J. (eds) *Abstracts 25th Int. Orn. Congr., Campos do Jordão, Brazil, 22–28 August 2010*: 621.

Schürer, U. & Bock, J. 1995. Die Zucht der Purpurkehlkotinga (*Cotinga cayana*) und des Nacktkehlglockenvogels (*Procnias nudicollis*) im Zoologischen Garten Wuppertal. *Zool. Garten* 65: 345–356.

Schwartz, P. A. 1972. *Micrastur gilvicollis*, a valid species sympatric with *M. ruficollis* in Amazonia. *Condor* 74: 399–415.

Schwartz, P. & Snow, D. W. 1979. Display and related behavior of the Wire-tailed Manakin. *Living Bird* 17: 51–78.

Sclater, P. L. 1888. *Catalogue of the Birds in the British Museum*. Vol. 14. Trustees of the British Museum, London.

Sclater, P. L. & Salvin, O. 1876. On new species of Bolivian birds. *Proc. Zool. Soc. Lond.* 1876: 352–358.

Sclater, P. L. & Salvin, O. 1879. On the birds collected by the late Mr T. K. Salmon in the State of Antioquia, United States of Colombia. *Proc. Zool. Soc. Lond.* 1879: 352–358.

Sclater, P. L. & Salvin, O. 1880. On new birds collected by Mr C. Buckley in eastern Ecuador. *Proc. Zool. Soc. Lond.* 1880: 155–161.

Scopel, E. T., Scardua, C. E., Pereira, M. A., Almeida, A. C. & Antas, P. T. Z. 2005. O uso de base de dados de biodiversidade como ferramenta para análise e tomada de decisões. In: Congr. Bras. Orn. XIII, Belém, *Resumos*: 59.

Scott, D. A. & Brooke, M. de L. 1985. The endangered avifauna of southeastern Brazil: a report on the BOU/WWF expeditions of 1980/81 and 1981/82. In: Diamond, A. W. & Lovejoy, T. E. (eds) *Conservation of Tropical Forest Birds*. Pp. 115–139. International Council for Bird Preservation, Cambridge, UK.

Scott, D. A. & Brooke, M. de L. 1993. Rediscovery of the Grey-winged Cotinga *Tijuca condita* in south-eastern Brazil. *Bird Conserv. Int.* 3: 1–12.

Seavy, N. E., Whitacre, D. F. & Córdova A., M. 1997. First record of the Speckled Mourner (*Laniocera rufescens*) for the Peten Department of Guatemala. *Orn. Neotrop.* 8: 245–246.

Seitz, A. 1972. Über Felsenhähne (*Rupicola*). *Gefiederte Welt* 96: 14–19.

Seitz, A. 1975. Erste Bruten beim Felsenhahn (*Rupicola*). *Gefiederte Welt* 99: 81–82.

Sekercioglu, C. H., Ehrlich, P. R., Daily, G. C., Aygen, D., Goehring, D. & Sandi, R. F. 2002. Disappearance of insectivorous birds from tropical forest fragments. *Proc. Natl. Acad. Sci. USA* 99: 263–267.

Selvin, E. & Castillo, M. L. 2000. Bird species found in Laguna del Tigre National Park, Petén, Guatemala during the RAP survey. In: Bestelmeyer, B. & Alonso, L. E. (eds) *A Biological Assessment of Laguna del Tigre National Park, Petén, Guatemala*. RAP Bulletin 16. Conservation International, Washington, DC.

Serpa, G. & Gagliardi, R. 2007. Martim-pescador-anão, *Chloroceryle aenea* (Alcedinidae) e tesourinha-da-mata, *Phibalura flavirostris* (Cotingidae): duas celebradas redescobertas no contexto da avifauna carioca. *Atualidades Orn.* 139: 4–5.

Serrano C., V. H. 1994. Selección de habitat, ciclo reproductivo y sistema lek de apareamiento de *Pyroderus scutatus*. Unpubl. thesis, Universidad de Valle, Colombia.

Servat, G. & Pearson, D. L. 1991. Natural history notes and records for seven poorly known bird species from Amazonian Peru. *Bull. Brit. Orn. Club* 111: 92–95.

Seth-Smith, D. 1930. The Purple-throated Cotinga (*Cotinga cayana*). *Avicult. Mag.* 8: 113–114.

Sferco, G. D. & Nores, M. 2003. Lista comentada de las aves de la Reserva Natural Chancaní, Córdoba, Argentina. *Hornero* 18: 21–29.

Shany, N., Diaz Alván, J. & Álvarez Alonso, J. 2007. Finding white-sand forest specialists in Allpahuayo-Mishana Reserve, Peru. *Neotrop. Birding* 2: 60–68.

Sharpe, C. 1997. *Lista de las Aves del Parque Nacional Paria, Estado Sucre, Venezuela*. Sociedad Conservacionista Audubon de Venezuela, Caracas.

Shorey, L. 2002. Mating success on White-bearded Manakin (*Manacus manacus*) leks: male characteristics and relatedness. *Behav. Ecol. Sociobiol.* 52: 451–457.

Shorey, L., Piertney, S., Stone, J. & Höglund, J. 2000. Fine-scale genetic structuring on *Manacus manacus* leks. *Nature* 408: 352–353.

Short, L. L. 1971. Aves nuevas o poco comunes de Corrientes, Republica Argentina. *Rev. Mus. Arg. Cienc. Nat. Bernardino Rivadavia* 9: 284–309.

Short, L. L. 1975. A zoogeographic analysis of the South American Chaco avifauna. *Bull. Amer. Mus. Nat. Hist.* 154: 163–352.

Sibley, C. G. 1957. The evolutionary and taxonomic significance of sexual dimorphism and hybridization in birds. *Condor* 59: 166–191.

Sibley, C. G. 1996. *Birds of the World*, Version 2.0. Thayer Birding Software, Cincinnati, OH.

Sibley, C. G. & Ahlquist, J. E. 1985. Phylogeny and classification of New World suboscine passerine birds (Passeriformes: Oligomyodi: Tyrannides). In: Buckley, P. A., Foster, M. S., Morton, E. S., Ridgely, R. S. & Buckley, F. G. (eds) *Neotropical Ornithology*. *Orn. Monogr.* 36: 396–430.

Sibley, C. G. & Ahlquist, J. E. 1990. *Phylogeny and Classification of Birds*. Yale University Press, New Haven & London.

Sibley, C. G. & Monroe, B. L. 1990. *Distribution and Taxonomy of Birds of the World*. Yale University Press, New Haven & London.

Sibley, C. G. & Monroe, B. L. 1993. *A Supplement to Distribution and Taxonomy of Birds of the World*. Yale University Press, New Haven & London.

Sibley, C. G., Lanyon, S. M. & Ahlquist, J. E. 1984. The relationships of the Sharpbill (*Oxyruncus cristatus*). *Condor* 86: 48–52.

Sick, H. 1942. Die Balz von *Chiroxiphia caudata*. *Orn. Monatsb.* 50: 18.

Sick, H. 1951. An egg of the umbrella bird. *Wilson Bull.* 63: 338.

Sick, H. 1954. Zur Biologie des amazonischen Schirmvogels, *Cephalopterus ornatus*. *J. Orn.* 95: 233–244.

Sick, H. 1955. O anambé prêto, "*Cephalopterus ornatus*" Geoffroy Saint-Hilaire (Cotingidas, Aves). *Rev. Brasil. Biol.* 15: 361–376.

Sick, H. 1957. Roßhaarpilze als Nestbau-Material brasilianischer Vögel. *J. Orn.* 98: 421–431.

Sick, H. 1958. Resultados de uma excursão ornitológica do Museu Nacional a Brasília, novo Distrito Federal, Goiás, com a descrição de um novo representante de *Scytalopus* (Rhinocryptidae, Aves). *Bol. Mus. Nac., Rio de Janeiro* 185: 1–41.

Sick, H. 1959a. Zwei neue Pipriden aus Brasilien. *J. Orn.* 100: 111–112.

Sick, H. 1959b. Um novo piprídeo do Brasil central: *Pipra vilasboasi* sp. n. (Pipridae, Aves). *Rev. Bras. Biol.* 19: 13–16.

Sick, H. 1959c. Zur Entdeckung von *Pipra vilasboasi*. *J. Orn.* 100: 404–412.

Sick, H. 1959d. Estudo comparativo das ceremônias pré-nupcias de piprídeos brasileiros (Pipridae, Aves). *Bol. Mus. Nac., Rio de Janeiro* 213: 1–17.

Sick, H. 1959e. Die Balz der Schmuckvögel (Pipridae). *J. Orn.* 100: 269–302.

Sick, H. 1967. Courtship behavior in the manakins (Pipridae): a review. *Living Bird* 6: 5–22.

Sick, H. 1970. Ueber Eier und Lebensweise der Weissflügel-Kotinga, *Xipholena atropurpurea*. *J. Orn.* 111: 107–108.

Sick, H. 1971. Beobachtungen am Flammenkopf, *Oxyruncus*. *Bonn. Zool. Beitr.* 22: 255–260.

Sick, H. 1979a. Zur Nistweise der Cotingiden *Iodopleura* and *Xipholena*. *J. Orn.* 120: 73–77.

Sick, H. 1979b. Notes on some Brazilian birds. *Bull. Brit. Orn. Club* 99: 115–120.

Sick, H. 1993. *Birds in Brazil*. Princeton University Press, Princeton, NJ.

Sick, H. 1997. *Ornitologia brasileira*. Ed. Nova Fronteira, Rio de Janeiro.

Sigel, B. J., Sherry, T. W. & Young, B. E. 2005. Avian community response to lowland tropical rainforest isolation: 40 years of change at La Selva Biological Station, Costa Rica. *Conserv. Biol.* 20: 111–121.

Sigrist, T. 2006. *Aves do Brasil: Uma Visão Artística*. Ed. Leitura Dinâmica, São Paulo.

Silva, A. M. & Melo, C. 2011. Frugivory and seed dispersal by the Helmeted Manakin (*Antilophia galeata*) in forests of [*sic*] Brazilian Cerrado. *Orn. Neotrop.* 22: 69–77.

Silva, A. S., Soares, L. M. S., Cerqueira, P. V., Sousa, S. A., Lima, C. M. B., Carvalho, D. L., Portes, C. E. B. & Santos, M. P. D. 2009. Avifauna em quatro áreas no centro de endemismo Guiana nos Estados do Pará e Amazonas. In: Simon, J. E., Raposo, M. A., Stopiglia, R. & Peres, J. (eds) *XVII Congresso Brasileiro de Ornitologia Resumos, Aracruz, ES: Biogeografia das aves da Mata Atlântica*: 81.

Silva, C. 1995. Registro de *Laniisoma elegans* (Thunberg, 1823) e *Pyroderus scutatus* (Shaw, 1792) (Cotingidae) no municipio de Sorocaba, S.P. *Bol. CEO* 12: 32–35.

Silva, J. M. C. 1993. The Sharpbill in the Serra dos Carajás, Pará, Brazil, with comments on altitudinal migration in the Amazon region. *J. Field Orn.* 64: 310–315.

Silva, J. M. C. 1995. Avian inventory of the cerrado region, South America: implications for biological conservation. *Bird Conserv. Int.* 5: 291–304.

Silva, J. M. C. 1996. Distribution of Amazonian and Atlantic birds in gallery forests of the Cerrado region, South America. *Orn. Neotrop.* 7: 1–18.

Silva, J. M. C. & Oniki, Y. 1988. Lista preliminar da avifauna da Estação Ecológica Serra das Araras, Mato Grosso, Brasil. *Bol. Mus. Para. E. Goeldi Ser. Zool.* 4: 123–143.

Silva, J. M. C., Lima, M. F. C. & Marceliano, M. L. V. 1990. Pesos de aves de duas localidades na Amazônia Oriental. *Ararajuba* 1: 99–104.

Silva, J. M. C., Oren, D. C., Roma, J. C. & Henriques, L. M. P. 1997. Composition and distribution patterns of the avifauna of an Amazonian upland savanna, Amapá, Brazil. In: Remsen, J. V. (ed.) *Studies in Neotropical Ornithology Honoring Ted Parker*. *Orn. Monogr.* 48: 743–762.

Silva, M. A., Carvalho, B. H. G., Anciães, M. & Henriques, L. M. P. 2010. Effects of insularization on the occurrence of understory frugivorous, omnivorous and insectivorous trunk' and soil' birds in the Central Amazon. In: Miyaki, C. M., Höfling, E. &

Donatelli, R. J. (eds) *Abstracts 25th Int. Orn. Congr., Campos do Jordão, Brazil, 22–28 August 2010*: 623.

Silva, M. L., Baudet, G., Sigrist, T. & Vielliard, J. 2000. Descrição do comportamento de corte do dançarino-de-coroa-vermelha, *Machaeropterus regulus* (Aves, Pipridae). *Bol. Mus. Biol. Mello Leitão* (*N. Ser.*) 11/12: 171–188.

Silva, M. T. B., Anciães, M., Rubim, P., Bruna, E. M. & Uriarte, M. 2010. Do pollination and seed dispersal by birds influence the abundance of *Heliconia acuminata* in a fragmented landscape? In: Miyaki, C. M., Höfling, E. & Donatelli, R. J. (eds) *Abstracts 25th Int. Orn. Congr., Campos do Jordão, Brazil, 22–28 August 2010*: 540.

Silva, W. R., Marco, P., Hasui, É. & Gomes, V. S. M. 2002. Patterns of fruit-frugivore interactions in two Atlantic Forest bird communities of south-eastern Brazil: implications for conservation. In: Levey, D. J., Silva, W. R. & Galetti, M. (eds) *Seed Dispersal and Frugivory: Ecology, Evolution And Conservation*. Pp. 423–436. CAB International, Wallingford.

Silva e Silva, R. & Olmos, F. 2007. Adendas e registros significativos para a avifauna dos manguezais de Santos e Cubatão, SP. *Rev. Bras. Orn.* 15: 551–560.

Silva-Ribeiro, T., Batalha-Filho, H. & Miyaki, C. Y. 2010. Demographic history and phylogeography of *Chiroxiphia caudata* (Pipridae: Aves). In: Miyaki, C. M., Höfling, E. & Donatelli, R. J. (eds) *Abstracts 25th Int. Orn. Congr., Campos do Jordão, Brazil, 22–28 August 2010*: 808.

Silveira, L. F. 1998. The birds of Serra da Canastra National Park and adjacent areas, Minas Gerais, Brazil. *Cotinga* 10: 55–63.

Silveira, L. F., Calonge-Méndez, A. & Brito, G. R. R. 2001. Range extensions and new records for birds in Piauí state, Brazil. *Int. J. Orn.* 4: 219–224.

Silveira, L. F., Olmos, F. & Long, A. J. 2003a. Birds in Atlantic Forest fragments in north-east Brazil. *Cotinga* 20: 32–46.

Silveira, L. F., Olmos, F., Roda, S. A. & Long, A. J. 2003b. Notes on the Seven-coloured Tanager *Tangara fastuosa* in north-east Brazil. *Cotinga* 20: 82–88.

Silveira, L. F., Develey, P. F., Pacheco, J. F. & Whitney, B. M. 2005. Avifauna of the Serra das Lontras–Javi montane complex, Bahia, Brazil. *Cotinga* 24: 45–54.

Simon, J. E. 2009. A lista das aves do Estado do Espírito Santo. In: Simon, J. E., Raposo, M. A., Stopiglia, R. & Peres, J. (eds) *XVII Congresso Brasileiro de Ornitologia Resumos, Aracruz, ES: Biogeografia das aves da Mata Atlântica*: LV–LXXXVIII.

Skutch, A. F. 1949. Life history of the Yellow-thighed Manakin. *Auk* 66: 1–24.

Skutch, A. F. 1968. The cotingas. A study in contrasts. *Anim. Kingd.* 71: 4–9.

Skutch, A. F. 1969. Life histories of Central American birds, III. *Pacific Coast Avifauna* 35: 1–580.

Skutch, A. F. 1970. The display of the Yellow-billed Cotinga *Carpodectes antoniae*. *Ibis* 112: 115–116.

Skutch, A. F. 1980. Arils as food of tropical American birds. *Condor* 82: 31–42.

Skutch, A. F. 1981. *New Studies of Tropical American Birds*. Publ. Nuttall Orn. Club 10. Cambridge, MA.

Skutch, A. F. 1985. Nesting success, and predation on nests of Neotropical birds. In: Buckley, P. A., Foster, M. S., Morton, E. S., Ridgely, R. S. & Buckley, F. G. (eds) *Neotropical Ornithology*. *Orn. Monogr.* 36: 575–594.

Skutch, A. F. 1989. Courtship of the Rufous Piha *Lipaugus unirufus*. *Ibis* 131: 303–304.

Skutch, A. F. 1999. *Trogons, Laughing Falcons, and Other Neotropical Birds*. Texas A. & M. University Press, College Station, TX.

Slud, P. 1957. The song and dance of the Long-tailed Manakin, *Chiroxiphia linearis*. *Auk* 74: 333–339.

Slud, P. 1964. The birds of Costa Rica. *Bull. Amer. Mus. Nat. Hist.* 128: 1–430.

Slud, P. 1980. The birds of Hacienda Palo Verde, Guanacaste, Costa Rica. *Smiths. Contrib. Zool.* 292: 1–92.

Smithe, E. B. 1966. *The Birds of Tikal*. Natural History Press, New York.

Snethlage, E. 1907. Über unteramazonische Vögel (Forts.). *J. Orn.* 55: 283–299.

Snethlage, E. 1908a. Eine Vogelsammlung vom Rio Purús, Brasilien. *J. Orn.* 56: 7–24.

Snethlage, E. 1908b. Ornitologisches vom Tapajoz und Tocantins. *J. Orn.* 56: 493–539.

Snethlage, E. 1914. Catálogo das aves amazonicas. *Bol. Mus. Goeldi* 8: 1–530.

Snethlage, E. 1935. Beiträge zur Brutbiologie brasilianischer Vögel. *J. Orn.* 83: 532–562.

Snethlage, H. 1928. Meine Reise durch Nordbrasilien. II. Biologische Beobachtungen. *J. Orn.* 76: 503–581.

Snow, B. K. 1961. Notes on the courtship behavior of three Cotingidae. *Auk* 78: 150–161.

Snow, B. K. 1970. A field study of the Bearded Bellbird in Trinidad. *Ibis* 112: 299–329.

Snow, B. K. 1972. A field study of the Calfbird *Perissocephalus tricolor*. *Ibis* 114: 139–162.

Snow, B. K. 1973. Notes on the behavior of the White Bellbird. *Auk* 90: 743–751.

Snow, B. K. 1977. Territorial behavior and courtship of the male Three-wattled Bellbird. *Auk* 94: 623–645.

Snow, B. K. 1978. Calls and display of the male Bare-throated Bellbird. *Avicult. Mag.* 84: 157–161.

Snow, B. K. & Snow, D. W. 1985. Display and related behavior of male Pin-tailed Manakins. *Wilson Bull.* 97: 273–282.

Snow, D. W. 1956. The dance of the manakins. *Anim. Kingd.* 59: 86–91.

Snow, D. W. 1961. The displays of the manakins *Pipra pipra* and *Tyranneutes virescens*. *Ibis* 103a: 110–113.

Snow, D. W. 1962a. A field study of the Black and White Manakin, *Manacus manacus*, in Trinidad. *Zoologica* 47: 65–104.

Snow, D. W. 1962b. A field study of the Golden-headed Manakin, *Pipra erythrocephala*, in Trinidad, W.I. *Zoologica* 47: 183–198.

Snow, D. W. 1963a. The display of the Orange-headed Manakin. *Condor* 65: 44–48.

Snow, D. W. 1963b. The display of the Blue-backed Manakin, *Chiroxiphia pareola*, in Tobago, W.I. *Zoologica* 48: 167–175.

Snow, D. W. 1963c. The evolution of manakin displays. *Proc. Int. Orn. Congr.* 13: 553–561.

Snow, D. W. 1971a. Observations on the Purple-throated Fruit-crow in Guyana. *Living Bird* 10: 5–17.

Snow, D. W. 1971b. Social organization of the Blue-backed Manakin. *Wilson Bull.* 83: 35–38.

Snow, D. W. 1971c. Display of the Pompadour Cotinga *Xipholena punicea*. *Ibis* 113: 102–104.

Snow, D. W. 1973a. Distribution, ecology and evolution of the bellbirds (*Procnias*, Cotingidae). *Bull. Brit. Mus. (Nat. Hist.) Zool.* 25: 369–391.

Snow, D. W. 1973b. The classification of the cotingas. *Breviora* 409.

Snow, D. W. 1973c. Notes on the White-collared Manakin and Long-tailed Manakin (*Manacus candei* and *Chiroxiphia linearis*). *Avicult. Mag.* 79: 145–146.

Snow, D. W. 1975. The classification of the manakins. *Bull. Brit. Orn. Club* 95: 20–27.

Snow, D. W. 1976a. The relationship between climate and annual cycles in the Cotingidae. *Ibis* 118: 366–401.

Snow, D. W. 1976b. *The Web of Adaptation: Bird Studies in the American Tropics*. Quadrangle, New York & Collins, London.

Snow, D. W. 1977a. The display of the Scarlet-horned Manakin *Pipra cornuta*. *Bull. Brit. Orn. Club* 97: 23–27.

Snow, D. W. 1977b. Duetting and other synchronised displays of the blue-backed manakins, *Chiroxiphia* spp. In: Stonehouse, B. & Perrins, C. (eds) *Evolutionary Ecology*. Pp. 239–251. Macmillan, London.

Snow, D. W. 1977c. Waltzing cotingas. *Anim. Kingd.* 80: 13–18.

Snow, D. W. 1978. The nest as a factor determining clutch-size in tropical birds. *J. Orn.* 120: 73–77.

Snow, D. W. 1979a. Family Cotingidae. In: Traylor, M. A. (ed.) *Check-list of Birds of the World*. Vol. 8. Pp. 245–280. Museum of Comparative Zoology, Cambridge, MA.

Snow, D. W. 1979b. Family Pipridae. In: Traylor, M. A. (ed.) *Check-list of Birds of the World*. Vol. 8. Pp. 245–280. Museum of Comparative Zoology, Cambridge, MA.

Snow, D. W. 1980. A new species of cotinga from southeastern Brazil. *Bull. Brit. Orn. Club* 100: 213–215.

Snow, D. W. 1982. *The Cotingas.* British Museum (Natural History) & Oxford University Press, London.

Snow, D. W. 2004a. Family Cotingidae (cotingas). In: del Hoyo, J., Elliott, A. & Christie, D. A. (eds) *Handbook of the Birds of the World*, Vol. 9. Pp. 32–108. Lynx Edicions, Barcelona.

Snow, D. W. 2004b. Family Pipridae (manakins). In: del Hoyo, J., Elliott, A. & Christie, D. A. (eds) *Handbook of the Birds of the World*, Vol. 9. Pp. 110–168. Lynx Edicions, Barcelona.

Snow, D. W. & Goodwin, D. 1974. The Black-and-gold Cotinga. *Auk* 91: 360–369.

Snow, D. W. & Lill, A. 1974. Longevity records for some Neotropical land birds. *Condor* 76: 262–267.

Snow, D. W. & Snow, B. K. 1992. Display of the Golden-winged Manakin *Masius chrysopterus*. *Bull. Brit. Orn. Club* 112: 264–270.

Snyder, D. E. 1966. *The Birds of Guyana*. Peabody Museum, Salem, MA.

Soares, L. M. S., Silva, A. S., Sousa, S. A., Farias, E. A. B. & Santos, M. P. D. 2009. Levantamento da avifauna da Serra Vermelha no sul do Estado do Piauí. In: Simon, J. E., Raposo, M. A., Stopiglia, R. & Peres, J. (eds) *XVII Congresso Brasileiro de Ornitologia Resumos, Aracruz, ES: Biogeografia das aves da Mata Atlântica*. 96.

Soares-Filho, B. S., Nepstad, D. C., Curran, L. M., Cerqueira, G. C., Garcia, R. A., Ramos, C. A., Voll, E., McDonald, A., Lefebvre, P. & Schlesinger, P. 2006. Modeling conservation in the Amazon basin. *Nature* 440: 520–523.

Solano-Ugalde, A. in press. Notes on the distribution and natural history of bird species in the Chocó bioregion of Ecuador. *Bull. Brit. Orn. Club*.

Solano-Ugalde, A. & Freile, J. F. 2010. Finding the right umbrella(bird) to foster Neotropical forest conservation. *Neotrop. Birding* 7: 14–23.

Solano-Ugalde, A., Arcos-Torres, A. & Greeney, H. F. 2007. Additional breeding records for selected avian species in northwest Ecuador. *Bol. Soc. Antioqueña Orn.* 17: 17–25.

Sorrie, B. (unpubl.) Avian weights and wing chords from a western Amazonian rainforest. MS.

Souza, D. G. S. 1999. Novos registros de espécies de aves no Estado da Bahia e sua correlação com os ecossistemas. *Atualidades Orn.* 88: 6–7.

Souza, E. A., Nunes, M. F. C., Roos, A. L. & Araujo, A. F. P. 2008. *Aves do Parque Nacional do Cabo Orange: Guia do Campo*. ICMBio/CEMAVE, Amapá.

Specht, G. V. A., Cunha, F. C. R. & Akaki, G. H. S. 2008. Observações sobre o comportamento reprodutivo do pavó, *Pyroderus scutatus* (Shaw, 1792) (Aves: Cotingidae), em Antônio Dias, Minas Gerais. *Atualidades Orn.* 142: 14–15.

Spee, J. 2001. Nachwuchs bei den Prachtpipras. *Gefiederte Welt* 125: 266–267.

Stattersfield, A. J., Crosby, M. J., Long, A. J. & Wege, D. C. 1998. *Endemic Bird Areas of the World: Priorities for Biodiversity Conservation*. BirdLife International, Cambridge, UK.

Stein, A. C. & Uy, J. A. C. 2006. Plumage brightness predicts male mating success in the lekking golden-collared manakin, *Manacus vitellinus*. *Behav. Ecol.* 17: 41–47.

Stiles, F. G. & Skutch, A. F. 1989. *A Guide to the Birds of Costa Rica*. Christopher Helm, London.

Stiles, F. G., Rosselli, L. & Bohórquez, C. I. 1999. New and noteworthy records of birds from the middle Magdalena Valley of Colombia. *Bull. Brit. Orn. Club* 119: 113–129.

Stone, W. 1918. Birds of the Panama Canal Zone, with special reference to a collection made by Mr. Lindsey L. Jewel. *Proc. Acad. Nat. Sci. Philadelphia* 70: 239–280.

Stone, W. 1928. On a collection of birds from the Pará region, eastern Brazil. *Proc. Acad. Nat. Sci. Philadelphia* 90: 149–176.

Stopiglia, R., Straker, L. C. & Raposo, M. A. 2009. Kinglet Calyptura *Calyptura cristata* (Vieillot, 1818): documented record for the state of São Paulo and taxonomic status of the name *Pipra tyrannulus* Wagler, 1830. *Bull. Brit. Orn. Club* 129: 185–188.

Stotz, D. F. 1993. A hybrid manakin (*Pipra*) from Roraima, Brazil, and a phylogenetic perspective on hybridization in the Pipridae. *Wilson Bull.* 105: 348–351.

Stotz, D. F. & Bierregaard, R. O. 1989. The birds of the fazendas

Porto Alegre, Esteio and Dimona north of Manaus, Amazonas, Brazil. *Rev. Bras. Biol.* 49: 861–872.

Stotz, D. F., Fitzpatrick, J. W., Parker, T. A. & Moskovits, D. K. 1996. *Neotropical Birds: Ecology and Conservation*. University of Chicago Press, Chicago.

Stotz, D. F., Lanyon, S. M., Schulenberg, T. S., Willard, D. E., Peterson, A. T. & Fitzpatrick, J. W. 1997. An avifaunal survey of two tropical forest localities in the middle Rio Jiparaná, Rondônia, Brazil. In: Remsen, J. V. (ed.) *Studies in Neotropical Ornithology Honoring Ted Parker*. *Orn. Monogr.* 48: 763–781.

Stotz, D. F., O'Shea, B., Miserendino, R., Condori, J. & Moskovits, D. 2003. Aves/Birds. In: Alverson, W. S., Moskovits, D. K. & Halm, I. C. (eds) *Bolivia: Pando, Federico Román*. Pp. 125–135. Rapid Biological Inventories 6. The Field Museum, Chicago.

Straneck, R. 1990. *Songs of the Birds of Argentina*. Cassettes. Literature of Latin America, Buenos Aires.

Straube, F. C. 2008a. Avifauna da Fazenda Barra Mansa (Arapoti, Paraná), com anotações sobre a ocupação de monoculturas de essências arbóreas. *Atualidades Orn.* 142: 46–50 [www.ao.com.br].

Straube, F. C. 2008b. De onde vem o nome *Ilicura*? *Atualidades Orn.* 144: 42–43 [www.ao.com.br].

Straube, F. C. & Bornschein, M. R. 1995. New or noteworthy records of birds from northwestern Paraná and adjacent areas (Brazil). *Bull. Brit. Orn. Club* 115: 219–225.

Straube, F. C. & Urben-Filho, A. 2008. Notas sobre a avifauna de nove localidades na Bacia do Rio Piquiri (Região Oeste do Paraná, Brasil). *Atualidades Orn.* 141: 33–37 [www.ao.com.br].

Straube, F. C., Willis, E. O. & Oniki, Y. 2002. Aves colecionadas na localidade de Fazenda Caiuá (Paraná, Brasil) por Adolph Hempel, com discussão sobre a sua localização exata. *Ararajuba* 10: 167–172.

Strauch, J. G. 1977. Further bird weights from Panama. *Bull. Brit. Orn. Club* 97: 61–65.

Strewe, R. & Navarro, C. 2004a. The threatened birds of the río Frío Valley, Sierra Nevada de Santa Marta, Colombia. *Cotinga* 22: 47–55.

Strewe, R. & Navarro, C. 2004b. New and noteworthy records of birds from the Sierra Nevada de Santa Marta region, north-eastern Colombia. *Bull. Brit. Orn. Club* 124: 38–51.

Strong, R. M. 1952. A peculiar pigmentation. *Auk* 69: 199–200.

Suárez Pingo, F. É. 2011. Primer registro de la Cortarrama Peruana (*Phytotoma raimondii*) en la Laguna Ñapique, Sechura, Piura. *Bol. UNOP* 6(1): 12–13.

Taczanowski, L. 1884. *Ornithologie du Pérou*. Vol. 1. Oberthur, Paris.

Tashian, R. E. 1952. Some birds from the Palenque region of northeastern Chiapas. *Auk* 69: 60–66.

Tavares, E. & Guilherme, E. 2000. Anilhamento de aves no Parque Zoobotânico da Universidade Federal do Acre para auxiliar estudos de monitoramento e conservação. In: Straube, F. C., Argel-de-Oliveira, M. M. & Cândido, J. F. (eds) *Ornitologia brasileira no século XX*. Pp. 270–271. Universidade do Sul de Santa Catarina & Sociedade Brasileira de Ornitologia, Curitiba.

Teixeira, D. M. & Almeida, A. C. C. de. 1997. A Biologia da "Escarradeira", *Xipholena atropurpurea* (Wied, 1820) (Aves, Cotingidae). Veracruz Florestal, Eunápolis, Brazil.

Teixeira, D. M., Nacinovic, J. B. & Tavares, M. S. 1986. Notes on some birds of northeastern Brazil. *Bull. Brit. Orn. Club* 106: 70–74.

Teixeira, D. M., Nacinovic, J. B. & Pontual, F. B. 1987. Notes on some birds of northeastern Brazil (2). *Bull. Brit. Orn. Club* 107: 151–157.

Teixeira, D. M., Otoch, R., Luigi, G., Raposo, M. A. & Almeida, A. C. C. 1993. Notes on some birds of northeastern Brazil. *Bull. Brit. Orn. Club* 113: 48–52.

Tello, J. G. 2001. Lekking behavior of the Round-tailed Manakin. *Condor* 103: 298–321.

Tello, J. G. 2003. Frugivores at a fruiting *Ficus* in south-eastern Peru. *J. Trop. Ecol.* 19: 717–721.

Tello, J. G., Moyle, R. G., Marchese, D. J. & Cracraft, J. 2009. Phylogeny and phylogenetic classification of the tyrant flycatchers, cotingas, manakins, and their allies (Aves: Tyrannides). *Cladistics* 25: 429–467.

Terborgh, J. W. & Weske, J. S. 1975. The role of competition in the distribution of Andean birds. *Ecology* 56: 562–576.

Terborgh, J. W., Fitzpatrick, J. W. & Emmons, L. 1984. Annotated checklist of bird and mammal species of Cocha Cashu Biological Station, Manu National Park, Peru. *Fieldiana Zool.* 1352: 1–29.

Terborgh, J. W., Robinson, S. K., Parker, T. A., Munn, C. A. & Pierpont, N. 1990. Structure and organization of an Amazonian forest bird community. *Ecol. Monogr.* 60: 213–238.

Théry, M. 1990a. Display repertoire and social organization of the White-fronted and White-throated Manakins. *Wilson Bull.* 102: 123–130.

Théry, M. 1990b. Influence de la lumière sur le choix de l'habitat et le comportement sexuel des Pipridae (Aves: Passeriformes) en Guyane française. *Rev. Ecol.* 45: 215–236.

Théry, M. 1990c. Ecologie et comportement des oiseaux Pipridae en Guyane: leks, frugivorie et dissémination des graines. PhD dissertation, University of Paris.

Théry, M. 1992. The evolution of leks through female choice: differential clustering and space utilization in six sympatric manakins. *Behav. Ecol. Sociobiol.* 30: 227–237.

Théry, M. 1997. Wing-shape variation in relation to ecology and sexual selection in five sympatric lekking manakins (Passeriformes: Pipridae). *Ecotropica* 3: 9–19.

Théry, M. & Larpin, D. 1993. Seed dispersal and vegetation dynamics at a cock-of-the-rock lek in the tropical forest of French Guiana. *J. Trop. Ecol.* 9: 109–116.

Théry, M. & Vehrencamp, S. L. 1995. Light patterns as cues for mate choice in the lekking White-throated Manakin (*Corapipo gutturalis*). *Auk* 112: 133–145.

Thiollay, J.-M. 1994. Stucture, density and rarity in an Amazonian rainforest bird community. *J. Trop. Ecol.* 10: 449–481.

Thom, G. & Mestre, L. A. M. 2009. Avifauna da Reserva Extravista Chico Mendes, sul do Acre, Brasil. In: Simon, J. E., Raposo, M. A., Stopiglia, R. & Peres, J. (eds) *XVII Congresso Brasileiro de Ornitologia Resumos, Aracruz, ES: Biogeografia das aves da Mata Atlântica*: 97.

Thom, G., Rupp, A. E. & Zimmermann, C. E. 2007. Registros notáveis para a avifauna do vale do Itajaí, Santa Catarina, Brasil. In: Fontana, C. S. (ed.) *XV Congresso Brasileiro de Ornitologia Resumos, Porto Alegre, RS*: 148–149.

Thomas, B. T. 1982. Weights of some Venezuelan birds. *Bull. Brit. Orn. Club* 102: 48–52.

Thomas, B. T. 1990. Additional weights of some Venezuelan birds. *Bull. Brit. Orn. Club* 110: 48–51.

Thomas, B. T. 1993. Birds of a northern Venezuelan secondary-scrub habitat. *Bull. Brit. Orn. Club* 113: 9–17.

Thoresen, A. C. 1974. First Shrike-like Cotinga record for Peru. *Auk* 91: 840.

Tobias, J. A. 2003. Notes on breeding behaviour in Black-faced Cotinga *Conioptilon mcilhennyi*. *Cotinga* 19: 80–81.

Tobias, J. A. & Seddon, N. 2007. Nine bird species new to Bolivia and notes on other significant records. *Bull. Brit. Orn. Club* 127: 49–84.

Tobias, J. A., Butchart, S. H. M. & Collar, N. J. 2006. Lost and found: a gap analysis for the Neotropical avifauna. *Neotrop. Birding* 1: 4–22.

Tobias, J. A., Seddon, N., Spottiswoode, C. N., Pilgrim, J. D., Fishpool, L. D. C. & Collar, N. J. 2010. Quantitative criteria for species delimitation. *Ibis* 152: 724–746.

Todd, W. E. C. 1925. Four new birds from Brazil. *Proc. Biol. Soc. Wash.* 38: 111–114.

Todd, W. E. C. 1950. Critical notes on the cotingas. *Proc. Biol. Soc. Wash.* 63: 5–7.

Todd, W. E. C. & Carriker, M. A. 1922. The birds of the Santa Marta region of Colombia: a study in altitudinal distribution. *Ann. Carnegie Mus.* 14.

Torga Lombardi, V., Vasconcelos, M. F. & D'Angelo Neto, S. 2007. Novos registros ornitológicos para o centro-sul de Minas Gerais (alto rio Grande): municípios de Lavras, São João Del Rei e adjacências da região. *Atualidades Orn.* 139: 33–42 (www.ao.com.br).

Torga Lombardi, V., Santos, K. K., D'Angelo Neto, S., Mazzoni, L. G., Rennó, B., Faetti, R. G., Epifânio, A. D. & Miguel, M. in press. Registros notáveis de aves para o sul do Estado de Minas Gerais, Brasil. *Cotinga* 34.

Tori, W., Ryder, B., Durães, R., Barker, P., Blake, J. & Loiselle, B. 2007. Spatial structure and social organization of manakins (Pipridae): potential implications for male reproductive skew. *Abstracts VIII Neotrop. Orn. Congr., Maturín, Venezuela, mayo 13–19 2007*: 46–47.

Tori, W. P., Durães, R., Ryder, T. B., Anciães, M., Karubian, J., Macedo, R. H., Uy, J. A. C., Parker, P. G., Smith, T. B., Stein, A. C., Webster, M. S., Blake, J. G. & Loiselle, B. A. 2008. Advances in sexual selection theory: insights from tropical avifauna. *Orn. Neotrop.* 19 (suppl.): 151–163.

Tostain, O. 1988a. Le nid et la ponte de *Perissocephalus tricolor*, Cotingidae, en Guyane française: *Pipra pipra, P. serena, P. aureola* et *P. erythrocephala*. *Alauda* 56: 153–158.

Tostain, O. 1988b. Nouvelles données sur la nidification de quatre manakins (Pipridae) de Guyane française. *Alauda* 56: 159–170.

Tostain, O. 1988c. Description du nid et de la ponte du Manakin à gorge blanche, *Corapipo gutturalis*, Pipridae. *Alauda* 56: 176–177.

Tostain, O., Dujardin, J.-L., Érard, C. & Thiollay, J.-M. 1992. *Oiseaux de Guyane*. Soc. d'Études Orn., Brunoy.

Trail, P. W. 1984. The lek mating system of the Guianan Cock-of-the-rock: a field study of sexual selection. PhD dissertation, Cornell University, Ithaca, NY.

Trail, P. W. 1985a. A lek's icon: the courtship display of the Guianan Cock-of-the-rock. *Amer. Birds* 39: 235–240.

Trail, P. W. 1985b. Territoriality and dominance in the lek-breeding Guianan Cock-of-the-rock. *Nat. Geogr. Res.* 1: 112–123.

Trail, P. W. 1985c. Courtship disruption modifies mate choice in a lek-breeding bird. *Science* 227: 778–780.

Trail, P. W. 1987. Predation and antipredation behavior at Guianan Cock-of-the-rock leks. *Auk* 104: 496–507.

Trail, P. W. 1990. Why should lek-breeders be monomorphic? *Evolution* 44: 1837–1852.

Trail, P. W. & Adams, E. S. 1989. Active mate choice at cock-of-the-rock leks: tactics of sampling and comparison. *Behav. Ecol. Sociobiol.* 25: 283–292.

Trail, P. W. & Donahue, P. 1991. Notes on the behavior and ecology of the red-cotingas (Cotingidae: *Phoenicircus*). *Wilson Bull.* 103: 539–551.

Trail, P. W. & Koutnik, D. L. 1986. Courtship disruption at the lek in the Guianan cock-of-the-rock. *Ethology* 73: 197–218.

Trainer, J. M. & McDonald, D. B. 1993. Vocal repertoire of the Long-tailed Manakin and its relation to male–male cooperation. *Condor* 95: 769–781.

Trainer, J. M. & McDonald, D. B. 1995. Singing performance, frequency matching and courtship success of Long-tailed Manakins (*Chiroxiphia linearis*). *Behav. Ecol. Sociobiol.* 37: 249–259.

Trainer, J. M. & Parsons, R. J. 2001. Uniformity of Long-tailed Manakin songs from three localities in Costa Rica. *Wilson Bull.* 113: 431–434.

Trainer, J. M., McDonald, D. B. & Learn, W. A. 2002. The development of coordinated singing in cooperatively displaying Long-tailed Manakins. *Behav. Ecol.* 13: 65–69.

Traylor, M. A. 1950. Altitudinal variation in Bolivian birds. *Condor* 52: 123–126.

Trolle, M. & Walther, B. A. 2004. Preliminary bird observations in the rio Jauaperí region, rio Negro basin, Amazonia, Brazil. *Cotinga* 22: 81–85.

Tubelis, D. P. 2004. Species composition and seasonal occurrence of mixed-species flocks of forest birds in savannas in central *Cerrado*, Brazil. *Ararajuba* 12: 105–111.

Tubelis, D. P. 2007. Mixed-species flocks of birds in the *Cerrado*, South America: a review. *Orn. Neotrop.* 18: 75–97.

Tubelis, D. P. & Tomas, W. M. 2003. Bird species of the Pantanal wetland, Brazil. *Ararajuba* 11: 5–37.

Ubaid, F. K., Dias, D. V. & Pires, L. A. S. 2005. Avifauna do Parque Zoológico Municipal do Bauru (SP). In: Congr. Bras. Orn. XIII, Belém, *Resumos*: 149.

Urben-Filho, A. & Abe, L. M. 2001. Inventário preliminar da

avifauna da Fazenda Primavera (Adrianópolis, Paraná). In: Congr. Bras. Orn. IX, Curitiba, *Resumos*: 216.

Uy, J. A. C. & Endler, J. A. 2004. Modification of the visual background increases the conspicuousness of Golden-collared Manakin displays. *Behav. Ecol.* 15: 1003–1010.

Uy, J. A. C. & Stein, A. C. 2007. Sexual selection and the dynamics of display trait introgression across hybrid zones. *Abstracts VIII Neotrop. Orn. Congr., Maturin, Venezuela, mayo 13–19 2007*: 45.

Valqui, T. 2004. *Where to Watch Birds in Peru*. Ed. Gráfica, Lima.

Vallely, A. C. 2001. Foraging at army ant swarms by fifty bird species in the highlands of Costa Rica. *Orn. Neotrop.* 12: 271–275.

Vallely, A. C. & Whitman, A. W. 1997. The birds of Hill Bank, northern Belize. *Cotinga* 8: 39–49.

Vallely, A. C., Gallardo, R. J. & Ascher, J. S. 2010. Notes on the birds of the Río Plátano Biosphere Reserve, including four new species for Honduras. *Bull. Brit. Orn. Club* 130: 52–60.

Valsko, J. & Anciães, M. 2008. Descrição da construção e estrutura de um ninho de *Pipra erythrocephala* (Passeriformes: Pipridae). In: Congr. Bras. Orn. XVI, Palmas, *Resumos*: 42.

Vasconcelos, M. F. 1998. Registros de duas especies de aves ameaçadas de extinção em Unidades de Conservação do Estado de Minas Gerais: *Amazona vinacea* and *Pyroderus scutatus*. *Atualidades Orn.* 86: 6.

Vasconcelos, M. F. 1999. Contribuição ao conhecimento ornitológico do Pico do Papagaio, município de Aiuruoca, Minas Gerais. *Atualidades Orn.* 90: 10–11.

Vasconcelos, M. F. 2007. Comentários sobre a avifauna da Estação de Pesquisa e Desenvolvimento Ambiental de Peti, Minas Gerais, com a lista dos exemplares coletados na região. *Atualidades Orn.* 137: 7–9.

Vasconcelos, M. F. 2008. Aves registradas na Serra do Papagaio, município de Aiuruoca, Minas Gerais. *Atualidades Orn.* 142: 6–7.

Vasconcelos, M. F. & D'Angelo Neto, S. 2007. Padrões de distribuição e conservação da avifauna na região central da Cadeia do Espinhaço e áreas adjacentes, Minas Gerais, Brasil. *Cotinga* 28: 27–44.

Vasconcelos, M. F. & D'Angelo Neto, S. 2009. First assessment of the avifauna of *Araucaria* forests and other habitats from extreme southern Minas Gerais, Serra da Mantiqueira, Brazil, with notes on biogeography and conservation. *Pap. Avuls. Zool., Mus. Zool., Univ. São Paulo* 49: 49–71.

Vasconcelos, M. F. & Melo Júnior, T. A. 2000. An ornithological survey of Serra do Caraça, Minas Gerais, Brazil. *Cotinga* 15: 21–31.

Vasconcelos, M. F. & Roos, A. L. 2000. Novos registros de aves para o Parque Estadual do Morro do Diabo, São Paulo. *Melopsittacus* 3: 81–84.

Vasconcelos, M. F., D'Angelo Neto, S., Brandt, L. F. S., Venturin, N., Oliveira-Filho, A. T. & Costa, F. A. F. 2002. Avifauna de Lavras e municípios adjacentes, sul de Minas Gerais, e comentários sobre sua conservaço. *Unimontes Científica* 4: 153–164.

Vasconcelos, M. F., Vasconcelos, P. N., Maurício, G. N., Matrangolo, G. A. R., Dell'Amore, C. M., Nemésio, A., Ferreira, J. C. & Endrigo, E. 2003. Novos registros ornitológicos para a Serra do Caraça, Brasil, com comentários sobre distribuição geográfica de algumas espécies. *Lundiana* 4: 135–139.

Vasconcelos, M. F., D'Angelo Neto, S. & Maldonado-Coelho, M. 2004. New noteworthy occurrences of the Wied's Tyrant-manakin (*Neopelma aurifrons*) in Brazil. *Orn. Neotrop.* 15: 547–548.

Vasconcelos, M. F., D'Angelo Neto, S. & Nemésio, A. 2005. Observações sobre o Rei-dos-tangarás *Chiroxiphia caudata* × *Antilophia galeata* em Minas Gerais, Brasil. *Cotinga* 23: 65–69.

Vasconcelos, M. F., Pacheco, J. F. & Parrini, R. 2007. Levantamento e conservação da avifauna na zona urbana de Marabá, Pará, Brasil. *Cotinga* 28: 45–52.

Vasconcelos, M. F., Lopes, L. E., Hoffmann, D., Silveira, L. F. & Schunck, F. 2008. Noteworthy records of birds from the Pantanal, Chiquitano dry forest and *Cerrado* of south-western Brazil. *Bull. Brit. Orn. Club* 128: 57–67.

Velho, P. P. P. 1932. Descrição de alguns ovos de aves do Brasil existentes nas coleções do Museu. *Bol. Mus. Nac.* 8: 49–60.

Vellinga, W.-P., Flanagan, J. N. M. & Mark, T. R. 2004. New and interesting records of birds from Ayabaca province, Piura, north-west Peru. *Bull. Brit. Orn. Club* 124: 124–142.

Venturini, A. C., Silva Ofranti, A. M., Varejão, J. B. M. & Paz, P. R. 1996. *Aves e Mamíferos na Restinga: Parque Estadual Paulo Cesar Vinha – Setiba – Guarapari/ES*. Vol. 1. Governo do Estado do Espírito Santo, Vitória.

Venturini, A. C., Rehen, M. P., Paz, P. R. & Carmo, L. P. 2001. Contribuição ao conhecimento das aves da região centro serrana do Espírito Santo: municípios de Santa Maria do Jetibá e Itarana (parte 2). *Atualidades Orn.* 99: 12.

Venturini, A. C., Paz, P. R. & Kirwan, G. M. 2005. A new locality and records of Cherry-throated Tanager *Nemosia rourei* in Espírito Santo, south-east Brazil, with fresh natural history data for the species. *Cotinga* 24: 60–70.

Venturini, A. C., Paz, P. R. & Jacomelli Jr., J. J. 2007. Registro do corta-ramos-de-rabo-branco *Phytotoma rutila* para o sudeste do Brasil: Linhares, Espírito Santo. *Atualidades Orn.* 136: 28.

Verea, C. 2001. Nuevo registro altitudinal del Saltarín Cola de Lanza *Chiroxiphia lanceolata* en Venezuela. *Cotinga* 21: 77.

Verea, C. & Solórzano, A. 1998. La avifauna del sotobosque de una selva decidua tropical en Venezuela. *Orn. Neotrop.* 9: 161–176.

Verea, C. & Solórzano, A. 2001. La comunidad de aves del sotobosque de un bosque deciduo tropical en Venezuela. *Orn. Neotrop.* 12: 235–253.

Verea, C. & Solórzano, A. 2005. Avifauna asociada al sotobosque de una plantación de cacao del norte de Venezuela. *Orn. Neotrop.* 16: 1–14.

Verea, C., Solórzano, A. & Badillo, F. 1999. Pesos y distribución de aves del sotobosque del Parque Nacional Henri Pittier al norte de Venezuela. *Orn. Neotrop.* 10: 217–231.

Vidoz, J. Q. & Alarcón, D. 2010. Birding Santa Cruz, Bolivia's largest department. *Neotrop. Birding* 7: 62–70.

Vidoz, J. Q., Jahn, A. E. & Mamani, A. M. 2010. The avifauna of Estación Biológica Caparú, Bolivia: natural history and range extensions of some poorly known species. *Cotinga* 32: 5–22.

Vielliard, J. 1995. *Guia Sonora das Aves do Brasil*. CD 1. Privately published, Campinas, São Paulo.

Vielliard, J. 1999. *Aves do Pantanal*. CD. Amazilia Ecoturismo, Campinas.

Vielliard, J. 2002. *Vozes das Aves do Brasil*. CD. Amazilia Ecoturismo, Campinas.

Vleck, C. M. & Vleck, D. 1979. Metabolic rate in five tropical bird species. *Condor* 81: 89–91.

Völker, O. 1952. Die Lipochrome in den Federn der Cotingiden. *J. Orn.* 93: 122–129.

Volpato, G. H., Prado, V. M. & Anjos, L. 2010. Bird communities in natural and planted forests from southern Brazil. In: Miyaki, C. M., Höfling, E. & Donatelli, R. J. (eds) *Abstracts 25th Int. Orn. Congr., Campos do Jordão, Brazil, 22–28 August 2010*: 629.

Von Matter, S., Piratelli, A. & Piña-Rodrigues, F. 2010. Seed dispersal effectiveness by birds on the palm *Euterpe edulis* in a highland Atlantic Forest of Brazil. In: Miyaki, C. M., Höfling, E. & Donatelli, R. J. (eds) *Abstracts 25th Int. Orn. Congr., Campos do Jordão, Brazil, 22–28 August 2010*: 896.

Voss, W. A. & Sander, M. 1981. Frutos e sementes vários na alimentação das aves livres. *Trigo e Soja* 58: 28–31.

Vuille, M. & Bradley, R. S. 2000. Mean annual temperature trends and their vertical structure in the tropical Andes. *Geophysical Res. Lett.* 27: 3885–3888.

Vuilleumier, F. 1969. Field notes on some birds from the Bolivian Andes. *Ibis* 111: 599–608.

Vuilleumier, F. 1985. Forest birds of Patagonia: ecological geography, speciation, endemism, and faunal history. In: Buckley, P. A., Foster, M. S., Morton, E. S., Ridgely, R. S. & Buckley, F. G. (eds) *Neotropical Ornithology. Orn. Monogr.* 36: 255–304.

Vuilleumier, F. 1999. The weights of Neotropical birds. *Orn. Neotrop.* 10: 207–209.

Vuilleumier, F. & Mayr, E. 1987. New species of birds described from 1976 to 1980. *J. Orn.* 128: 137–150.

Wagner, H. 1945. Observaciones sobre el comportamiento de

Chinoxiphia linearis durante su propagación. *An. Inst. Biol. Univ. Nac. Auton. Mexico* 16: 539–546.

Walker, B. 2002. Observations from the Tumbes Reserved Zone, dpto. Tumbes, with notes on some new taxa for Peru and a checklist of the area. *Cotinga* 18: 37–43.

Walker, B. 2009. Birding the Manu Biosphere Reserve, Peru. *Neotrop. Birding* 5: 49–58.

Walker, B. & Fjeldså, J. 2002. *Field Guide to the Birds of Machu Picchu, Peru*, 2nd edn. PROFONANPE & The Machu Picchu Program, Lima & Cusco.

Walker, B., Stotz, D. F., Pequeño, T. & Fitzpatrick, J. W. 2006. Birds of the Manu Biosphere Reserve. In: Patterson, B. D., Stotz, D. F. & Solari, S. (eds) Mammals and birds of the Manu Biosphere Reserve, Peru. *Fieldiana Zool. N. Ser.* 110: 23–49.

Walters, M. P. 2006. Colour in birds' eggs: the collections of the Natural History Museum, Tring. *Historical Biol.* 18: 145–208.

Walther, B. A. 2003. Why canopy access is essential to understand canopy birds: four examples from the Surumoni Crane Project. *Orn. Neotrop.* 15: 41–52.

Walther, B. A. 2004. Genus *Laniocera* species accounts. In: del Hoyo, J., Elliott, A. & Christie, D. A. (eds) *The Handbook of the Birds of the World*, Vol. 9. P. 446. Lynx Edicions, Barcelona.

Warren, R. L. M. & Harrison, C. J. O. 1971. *Type specimens of Birds in the British Museum (Natural History)*. Vol. 2. Trustees of the British Museum, London.

Warter, S. L. 1965. The cranial osteology of the New World Tyrannoidea and its taxonomic implications. PhD thesis, Louisiana State University, Baton Rouge.

Wege, D. C. 1993. Red Data bird: Bare-necked Umbrellabird. *World Birdwatch* 15(2): 18–19.

Wege, D. C. & Long, A. J. 1995. *Key Areas for Threatened Birds in the Neotropics*. BirdLife International, Cambridge, UK.

Weller, A.-A. & Rengifo G., C. 2003. Notes on the avifauna of the Cordillera de Mérida, Venezuela. *Bull. Brit. Orn. Club* 123: 261–270.

Wenny, D. G. & Levey, D. J. 1998. Directed seed dispersal by bellbirds in a tropical cloud forest. *Proc. Natl. Acad. Sci. USA* 95: 6204–6207.

Wetmore, A. 1926. Observations on the birds of Argentina, Paraguay, Uruguay, and Chile. *Bull. US Natl. Mus.* 133: 1–448.

Wetmore, A. 1939. Observations on the birds of northern Venezuela. *Proc. US Natl. Mus.* 87: 173–260.

Wetmore, A. 1941. Notes on birds of the Guatemalan highlands. *Proc. US Natl. Mus.* 89: 523–581.

Wetmore, A. 1960. A classification for the birds of the world. *Smiths. Misc. Coll.* 139.

Wetmore, A. 1972. The birds of the Republic of Panama, part 3. *Smiths. Misc. Coll.* 150(3).

Wheatley, N. 1994. *Where to Watch Birds in South America*. Christopher Helm, London.

Wheatley, N. & Brewer, D. 2001. *Where to Watch Birds in Central America and the Caribbean*. Christopher Helm, London.

Wheelwright, N. T., Haber, W. A., Murray, K. G. & Guindon, C. 1984. Tropical fruit-eating birds and their food plants: a survey of a Costa Rican lower montane forest. *Biotropica* 16: 173–192.

White, T. 1977. *Birds of Trinidad & Tobago*. Cassette. Privately published.

Whitehouse, A. J. & Ribon, R. 2010. Seeing Stresemann's Bristlefront in Minas Gerais, Brazil. *Neotrop. Birding* 6: 36–39.

Whitney, B. M. 1997. Birding the Alta Floresta region, northern Mato Grosso, Brazil. *Cotinga* 7: 64–68.

Whitney, B. M., Rowlett, J. L. & Rowlett, R. A. 1994. Distributional and other noteworthy records for some Bolivian birds. *Bull. Brit. Orn. Club* 114: 149–162.

Whitney, B. M., Pacheco, J. F. & Parrini, R. 1995. Two species of *Neopelma* in southeastern Brazil and diversification within the *Neopelma/Tyranneutes* complex: implications of the subspecies concept for conservation (Passeriformes: Tyrannidae). *Ararajuba* 3: 43–53.

Whittaker, A. 1993. Notes on the behaviour of the Crimson Fruitcrow *Haematoderus militaris* near Manaus, Brazil, with

the first nesting record for this species. *Bull. Brit. Orn. Club* 113: 93–96.

Whittaker, A. 1996a. Notes on feeding behaviour, diet and anting of some cotingas. *Bull. Brit. Orn. Club* 116: 58–62.

Whittaker, A. 1996b. Range extensions of some cotingas from Rondônia, Brazil. *Bull. Brit. Orn. Club* 116: 198–199.

Whittaker, A. 2004. Noteworthy ornithological records from Rondônia, Brazil, including a first country record, comments on austral migration, life history, taxonomy and distribution, with relevant data from neighbouring states, and a first record for Bolivia. *Bull. Brit. Orn. Club* 124: 239–271.

Whittaker, A. 2009. Pousada Rio Roosevelt: a provisional avifaunal inventory in south-western Amazonian Brazil, with information on life history, new distributional data, and comments on taxonomy. *Cotinga* 31: 23–46.

Whittaker, A. & Kirwan, G. M. 2008. Natural history of the canopy-dwelling purpletufts *Iodopleura* (Cotingidae), and first documentation of Dusky Purpletuft *I. fusca* for Brazil. *Bull. Brit. Orn. Club* 128: 28–35.

Whittaker, A. & Oren, D. C. 1999. Important ornithological records from the Rio Juruá, western Amazonia, including twelve additions to the Brazilian avifauna. *Bull. Brit. Orn. Club* 119: 235–260.

Whittaker, A., Kirwan, G. M. & Thompson, J. C. 2010a. First nest descriptions for Hoffmanns's Woodcreeper *Dendrocolaptes hoffmannsi* and Snow-capped Manakin *Lepidothrix nattereri*. *Cotinga* 32: 162–164.

Whittaker, A., Parrini, R. & Zimmer, K. J. 2010b. First nesting records of the Black-legged Dacnis *Dacnis nigripes*, with notes on field identification, ecology, conservation, and recent records from Espírito Santo. *Cotinga* 32: 65–74.

Wiedenfeld, D. A., Schulenberg, T. S. & Robbins, M. B. 1985. Birds of a tropical deciduous forest in extreme northwestern Peru. In: Buckley, P. A., Foster, M. S., Morton, E. S., Ridgely, R. S. & Buckley, F. G. (eds) *Neotropical Ornithology. Orn. Monogr.* 36: 305–315.

Wiedenfeld, D. A., Morales M., J. & Lezama L., M. 2000. Sight records of new species for Nicaragua and noteworthy records on range and occurrence. *Cotinga* 15: 53–57.

Wiley, R. H. 2010. Afonso Ollala and his family: the ornithological exploration of Amazonian Peru. *Bull. Amer. Mus. Nat. Hist.* 343: 1–68.

Willard, D. E., Foster, M. S., Barrowclough, G. F., Dickerman, R. W., Cannell, P. F., Coats, S. L., Cracraft, J. L. & O'Neill, J. P. 1991. The birds of Cerro de la Neblina, Territorio Federal Amazonas, Venezuela. *Fieldiana, Zool.* 1429: 1–80.

Williams, R. (compiler) 1995. Neotropical notebook: Bolivia. *Cotinga* 4: 66.

Williams, R. S. R. 2002. Consumption of arboreal snails by Scaled Fruiteater *Ampelioides tschudii*. *Cotinga* 18: 100.

Williams, R. S. R., Best, B. J. & Heijnen, T. 1997. *A Guide to Bird-watching in Ecuador and the Galapagos Islands*. Biosphere Publications, Leeds.

Willis, E. O. 1966. Notes on a display and nest of the Club-winged Manakin. *Auk* 83: 475–476.

Willis, E. O. 1977. Lista preliminar das aves da parte noroeste e áreas vizinhas da Reserva Ducke, Amazonas, Brazil. *Rev. Brasil. Biol.* 37: 585–601.

Willis, E. O. 1979. The composition of avian communities in remanescent woodlots in southern Brazil. *Pap. Avuls. Zool., São Paulo* 33: 1–25.

Willis, E. O. 1983. Flycatchers, cotingas and drongos (Tyrannidae, Muscicapidae, Cotingidae and Dicruridae) as ant followers. *Gerfaut* 73: 265–280.

Willis, E. O. 1984. Manakins (Aves, Pipridae) as army ant followers. *Ciência e Cultura* 36: 817–823.

Willis, E. O. 1988. Behavioral notes, breeding records, and range extensions for Colombian birds. *Rev. Acad. Colombiana Cienc. Exactas, Fis. Nat.* 16: 137–150.

Willis, E. O. 1992. Zoogeographical origins of eastern Brazilian birds. *Orn. Neotrop.* 3: 1–15.

Willis, E. O. 2002. Birds at *Eucalyptus* and other flowers in southern Brazil: a review. *Ararajuba* 10: 43–66.

Willis, E. O. 2003. Bird records in the southern Neotropics: on the need to critically check specimens, literature citations and field observations. *Orn. Neotrop.* 14: 549–552.

Willis, E. O. 2006. Protected *Cerrado* fragments grow up and lose even metapopulational birds in central São Paulo, Brazil. *Braz. J. Biol.* 66: 829–837.

Willis, E. O. & Eisenmann, E. 1979. A revised list of birds of Barro Colorado Island, Panama. *Smiths. Contrib. Zool.* 291: 1–31.

Willis, E. O. & Oniki, Y. 1985. Bird specimens new for the state of São Paulo, Brazil. *Rev. Bras. Biol.* 45: 105–108.

Willis, E. O. & Oniki, Y. 1988a. Winter nesting of *Iodopleura pipra* (Lesson, 1831) (Aves, Cotingidae) in southeastern Brazil. *Rev. Bras. Biol.* 48: 161–167.

Willis, E. O. & Oniki, Y. 1988b. Bright crowns of female and young males [*sic*] Swallow-tailed Manakins, *Chiroxiphia caudata* (Shaw and Nodder 1793) (Aves, Pipridae). *Rev. Brasil. Biol.* 48: 439–441.

Willis, E. O. & Oniki, Y. 1988c. Aves observadas em Balbina, Amazonas e os prováveis efeitos da barragem. *Ciência e Cultura* 40: 280–284.

Willis, E. O. & Oniki, Y. 1990. Levantamento preliminar das aves de inverno em dez áreas do sudoeste de Mato Grosso, Brasil. *Ararajuba* 1: 19–38.

Willis, E. O. & Oniki, Y. 1992. As aves e as formigas de correição. *Bol. Mus. Para. E. Goeldi* 8: 123–150.

Willis, E. O. & Oniki, Y. 1998. One-parent nesting in Cinnamon-vented Pihas (*Lipaugus lanioides*, Cotinginae, Tyrannidae). *Orn. Neotrop.* 9: 129–159.

Willis, E. O. & Oniki, Y. 2002. Birds of Santa Teresa, Espírito Santo, Brazil: do humans add or subtract species? *Pap. Avuls. Zool., São Paulo* 42: 193–264.

Winker, K., Warner, D. W. & Dickerman, R. W. 1992. Additional bird records from Oaxaca, Mexico. *Orn. Neotrop.* 3: 69–70.

Wolfe, J. D., Pyle, P. & Ralph, C. J. 2009. Breeding seasons, molt patterns, and gender and age criteria for selected northeastern Costa Rica resident landbirds. *Wilson J. Orn.* 121: 556–567.

Woods, R. W. 1988. *Guide to Birds of the Falkland Islands.* Anthony Nelson, Oswestry.

Worthington, A. H. 1982. Population sizes and breeding rhythms of two species of manakins in relation to food supply. In: Leigh, E. M., Rand, A. S. & Windsor, D. M. (eds) *The Ecology of a Tropical Forest.* Pp. 213–225. Smithsonian Institution Press, Washington, DC.

Worthington, A. H. 1989. Adaptations for avian frugivory: assimilation efficiency and gut transit time of *Manacus vitellinus* and *Pipra mentalis. Oecologia* 80: 381–389.

Wright, S. J., Stoner, K. E., Beckman, N., Corlett, R. T., Dirzo, R., Muller-Landau, H. C., Nuñez-Iturri, G., Peres, C. A. & Wang, B. C. 2007. The plight of large animals in tropical forests and the consequences for plant regeneration. *Biotropica* 39: 289–291.

Wunderle, J. M., Henriques, L. M. P. & Willig, M. R. 2006. Short-term responses of birds to forest gaps and understory: an assessment of reduced-impact logging in a lowland Amazon forest. *Biotropica* 38: 235–255.

Wünschmann, A. 1966. Die Balz der Rotkropf-Kotinga *Pyroderus scutatus* (Shaw). *Gefiederte Welt* 90: 46–48.

Xavier, B. F. & Silva, J. M. C. 2008. Distribuição espacial e organização social de arenas de *Pipra rubrocapilla* (Pipridae) em um remanescente de floresta Atlântica no Estado de Alagoas, Brasil. In: *Congr. Bras. Orn.* XVI, Palmas, *Resumos*: 91.

Yuri, T., Jernigan, R. W., Brumfield, R. T., Bhagabati, N. K. & Braun, M. J. 2009. The effect of marker choice on estimated levels of introgression across an avian (Pipridae: *Manacus*) hybrid zone. *Mol. Ecol.* 18: 4888–4903.

Zimmer, J. T. 1930. Birds of the Marshall Field Peruvian expedition, 1922–1923. *Publ. Field Mus. (Zool. Ser.)* 282, pt. 17(7).

Zimmer, J. T. 1936a. Studies of Peruvian birds. No. XXII. Notes on the Pipridae. *Amer. Mus. Novit.* 889: 1–29.

Zimmer, J. T. 1936b. Studies of Peruvian birds. No. XXIII. Notes on *Doliornis, Pipreola, Attila, Laniocera, Rhytipterna,* and *Lipaugus. Amer. Mus. Novit.* 893: 1–15.

Zimmer, J. T. 1936c. Studies of Peruvian birds. No. XXIV. Notes on *Pachyramphus, Platypsaris, Tityra,* and *Pyroderus. Amer. Mus. Novit.* 894: 1–26.

Zimmer, J. T. & Phelps, W. H. 1944. New species and subspecies of birds from Venezuela. I. *Amer. Mus. Novit.* 1270.

Zimmer, K. J. & Hilty, S. L. 1997. Avifauna of a locality in the upper Orinoco drainage of Amazonas, Venezuela. In: Remsen, J. V. (ed.) *Studies in Neotropical Ornithology Honoring Ted Parker. Orn. Monogr.* 48: 865–885.

Zimmer, K. J., Parker, T. A., Isler, M. L. & Isler, P. R. 1997. Survey of a southern Amazonian avifauna: the Alta Floresta region, Mato Grosso, Brazil. In: Remsen, J. V. (ed.) *Studies in Neotropical Ornithology Honoring Ted Parker. Orn. Monogr.* 48: 887–918.

Zink, R. M. 2004. The role of subspecies in obscuring avian biological diversity and misleading conservation policy. *Proc. Roy. Soc. Lond. Ser.* B 271: 561–564.

Zyskowski, K., Mittermeier, J. C., Ottema, O. , Rakovic, M., O'Shea, B. J., Lai, J. E., Hochgraf, S. B., León, J. & Au, K. 2011. Avifauna of the easternmost tepui, Tafelberg in central Suriname. *Bull. Peabody Mus. Nat. Hist.* 52: 153–180.

INDEX

Page numbers in italics refer to the caption text in the colour plate section. Other numbers refer to the first page only of the main entry in the species accounts.